THE MODERN LIBRARY
of the World's Best Books

≫≫≫≫≫≫≫≫≫≫≫≫≫≫≫≫≫≫≫≫≫≫≫≫≫≫≫≫≫≫≫≫≫≫≫

A SUBTREASURY OF
AMERICAN HUMOR

>>>>>>>>>>>>>>>>>>>>>>>>>>>>>>>

The publishers will be pleased to send, upon request, an illustrated folder setting forth the purpose and scope of THE MODERN LIBRARY, *and listing each volume in the series. Every reader will find titles he has been looking for, handsomely printed, in definitive editions, and at an unusually low price.*

>>>>>>>>>>>>>>>>>>>>>>>>>>>>>>>

A Subtreasury of
AMERICAN
HUMOR

EDITED BY

E. B. WHITE & KATHARINE S. WHITE

BRIAR CLIFF COLLEGE
LIBRARY
SIOUX CITY, IOWA

THE MODERN LIBRARY

NEW YORK

COPYRIGHT, 1941, BY E. B. WHITE & KATHARINE S. WHITE

>>>

*All rights reserved. This book, or parts thereof, must
not be reproduced in any form without permission.*

PN
6161
.W5223

THE MODERN LIBRARY

IS PUBLISHED BY

RANDOM HOUSE, INC.

BENNETT A. CERF · DONALD S. KLOPFER · ROBERT K. HAAS

Manufactured in the United States of America
By H. Wolff

ACKNOWLEDGMENTS

THE EDITORS are grateful to the many authors who have allowed their work to be reprinted in this book. Every care has been taken to obtain permission from the owners to reprint material which is in copyright; any errors are unintentional and will be gladly corrected in future printings if notification is sent to the publishers, Coward-McCann, Inc., who wish to acknowledge with thanks the courtesy of the following for permission to reprint as indicated:

George Ade for "The Professor Who Wanted to Be Alone" from his *Fables in Slang*.

George P. Anderson for "Lengthy Symphony" by Persis Greely Anderson.

D. Appleton-Century Company for a selection from *The Casting Away of Mrs. Lecks and Mrs. Aleshine* by Frank R. Stockton, copyright, 1886, 1913 by The Century Company.

Morris Bishop for "A Worm-Chorus" and "Ozymandias Revisited" from *Paramount Poems*.

Roark Bradford for "The Adulteration of Old King David" from his *Ol' Man Adam an' His Chillun*.

Brandt & Brandt, agents, for "Whitey" from *Penrod and Sam* by Booth Tarkington, copyright, 1916 by Booth Tarkington, and "For City Spring" from *Burning City,* copyright, 1935 by Stephen Vincent Benét, and published by Farrar & Rinehart, Inc.

Dodd, Mead & Company for "Death in the Rumble Seat," "Ring Out, Wild Bells," and "Time...Fortune...Life...Luce..." from *A Bed of Neuroses* by Wolcott Gibbs, copyright, 1929-1937 by Wolcott Gibbs; "It's a Wise Parent" from *Dithers and Jitters* by Cornelia Otis Skinner, copyright, 1938 by Cornelia Otis Skinner; and selections from *Dere Mable* by Edward Streeter, copyright, 1918, 1941 by Edward Streeter; "Confessions of a Gallomaniac" by Frank Moore Colby, from *The Margin of Hesitation* by Frank Moore Colby, copyright, 1921, by Dodd, Mead & Company, Inc. Used by permission of Dodd, Mead & Company, Inc.

Doubleday, Doran and Company, Inc. for "The Waist-Band That Was Taut Up to the Moment It Gave Way" and "The Ninny Who Swam Away from the Life Preserver" from *Hand-Made Fables* by George Ade, copyright, 1920; reprinted by permission of Doubleday,

27731

Doran and Company; "Fable of the Iron Dogs" from *The Almost Perfect State,* "the coming of archy," "mehitabel was once cleopatra," "the song of mehitabel," and "the old trouper" from *archy and mehitabel* by Don Marquis, copyright, 1927 by Doubleday, Doran and Company, Inc.; "Sonnets to a Red-Haired Lady" from *Sonnets to a Red-Haired Lady* by Don Marquis, copyright, 1922 by Doubleday, Doran and Company, Inc.; and "The Whisky Rebellion" from *A Parody Outline of History* by Donald Ogden Stewart, copyright, 1921 by Doubleday, Doran and Company, Inc.

Duell, Sloan & Pearce, Inc. for "A Hobby a Day Keeps the Doldrums Away," "Ode to the End of Summer" and "Public Journal" from *A Pocketful of Wry* by Phyllis McGinley. Reprinted by permission of the publishers.

E. P. Dutton & Co., Inc. for "Sea Chill" from *Gaily the Troubadour* by Arthur Guiterman and "Anthologistics" from *Lyric Laughter* by Arthur Guiterman, both volumes published and copyright by E. P. Dutton & Co., Inc., New York.

Irwin Edman and *Harper's Magazine* for "Intermission, Please!"

Farrar & Rinehart, Inc. for "A Fish Fry" from *The Green Pastures* by Marc Connelly, copyright, 1929 and reprinted by permission of Farrar & Rinehart, Inc., Publishers.

Lee Furman, Inc. for "In Mulberry Street" and "Natural History" from *Back Where I Came From* by A. J. Liebling, and "Tanya" from *My Ears Are Bent* by Joseph Mitchell.

Milt Gross for "Ferry-Tail from Keeng Mitas for Nize Baby" from his *Nize Baby.*

Harcourt, Brace and Company, for "Mrs. Heywood Cox Broun" from *The Collected Works of Heywood Broun,* copyright, 1941 by Heywood Hale Broun; "the Cambridge ladies" from *Collected Poems by e. e. cummings,* published by Harcourt Brace & Company. Copyright, 1923, 1925, 1931, 1935, 1938 by E. E. Cummings; copyright, 1926 by Boni & Liveright; a selection from *Babbitt* by Sinclair Lewis; copyright, 1922 by Harcourt, Brace and Company, Inc.; "The Sock Hunt" from *My Sister Eileen,* copyright, 1938 by Ruth McKenney; "The Summer of the Beautiful White Horse" from *My Name is Aram,* copyright, 1940 by William Saroyan; and "A. E. Housman Turns 'Georgey Porgey' Into a Shropshire Lad" from *Selected Poems and Parodies of Louis Untermeyer,* copyright, 1935 by Harcourt, Brace and Company, Inc. All reprints by permission of the publishers.

Harper & Brothers, for the following by Robert Benchley: "Christ-

mas Afternoon" from *Of All Things,* copyright, 1921 by Harper &
Brothers; "Happy Childhood Tales" from *No Poems,* copyright, 1932
by Robert Benchley; "More Songs for Meller" from *The Early Worm,*
copyright, 1927 by Harper & Brothers; "The Blue Sleeve Garter"
from *Pluck and Luck,* copyright, 1925 by Harper & Brothers; "Novels
and Hats," "The Loeb Classics," and "When Nature Lovers Write
Books" from *The Colby Essays* by Frank Moore Colby, copyright,
1926 by Harper & Brothers; "If Grant Had Been Drinking at Appo-
mattox" and "The Greatest Man in the World" from *The Middle-
Aged Man on the Flying Trapeze* by James Thurber, copyright, 1935
by James Thurber; "The Night the Bed Fell" from *My Life and Hard
Times* by James Thurber, copyright, 1933 by James Thurber; "The
Owl Who Was God," "The Shrike and the Chipmunks," "The Moth
and the Star," and "The Unicorn in the Garden" from *Fables for Our
Time* by James Thurber, copyright, 1939 by James Thurber; "A Mississippi Pilot," from *Life on the Mississippi* by Mark Twain; "Feni-
more Cooper's Literary Offenses" from *In Defense of Harriet Shelley
and Other Essays* by Mark Twain, copyright, 1918 by The Mark
Twain Company; "His Grandfather's Old Ram," from *Roughing It*
by Mark Twain; "Huck and Jim Talk about Kings," from *The Adventures of Huckleberry Finn* by Mark Twain; "The Hunting of the
Cow" from *Mark Twain in Eruption* by Mark Twain, edited by Bernard de Voto, copyright, 1940 by The Mark Twain Company; "Dusk
in Fierce Pajamas" and "The Parable of the Family Which Dwelt
Apart" from *Quo Vadimus* by E. B. White, copyright, 1934 by E. B.
White; and "Harper to Mifflin to Chance" from *The Fox of Peapack,*
copyright, 1932 by E. B. White. All titles published by Harper &
Brothers.

Lucien Harris for "Miss Cow Falls a Victim to Mr. Rabbit" from
Uncle Remus by Joel Chandler Harris.

Holiday House, Inc. for "Why There Are No Trees on the Desert"
from *Ol' Paul, the Mighty Logger,* by Glen Rounds.

Houghton Mifflin Company for "Sunthin' in the Pastoral Line"
from *Lowell's Complete Poetical Works;* "Jungle Folk" from *Condensed Novels (Second Series)* by Bret Harte; "The Peterkins Celebrate the Fourth of July" from *The Peterkin Papers* by Lucretia P.
Hale and "Cacoëthes Scribendi" from Holmes' *Complete Poetical
Works.* All selections used by permission of the authorized publishers,
Houghton Mifflin Company.

Alva Johnston and *The Saturday Evening Post* for "How to Become a Great Writer."

Alfred A. Knopf, Inc. for "The Governor" from *Our Government* by James M. Cain; selections from *Thoughts without Words* and illustrations by Clarence Day; "The Noblest Instrument" reprinted from *Life With Father* by Clarence Day; "Going to Bed Before a Young Lady" by "M" contained in *Tall Tales of the Southwest,* edited by Franklin J. Meine; "Brief Gust of Glory" reprinted from *Happy Days* by H. L. Mencken; "The Wedding: A Stage Direction" reprinted from *A Book of Burlesque* by H. L. Mencken and "Back to Methuselah" reprinted from *The Intimate Notebooks of George Jean Nathan.* All selections used by permission of and special arrangement with Alfred A. Knopf, Inc., authorized publishers.

John Lardner for "Sit Still" by Ring Lardner.

Little, Brown & Company for "Doucement, Doucement!" from *The Mott Family in France* by Donald Moffat; "Let's Stay Home and Make Friends" from *Free Wheeling* by Ogden Nash; "The Song of Songs" from *I'm a Stranger Here Myself* by Ogden Nash; "Bankers Are Just Like Anybody Else, Except Richer," "Cat Naps Are Too Good for Cats," "First Families, Move Over!", " 'My Child Is Phlegmatic...' Anxious Parent," "Requiem," "The Strange Case of Mr. Fortague's Disappointment," and "To a Small Boy Standing on My Shoes While I am Wearing Them," from *The Face Is Familiar* by Ogden Nash; and "A Weekend at Lady Astor's" from *A Pearl in Every Oyster* by Frank Sullivan. All selections reprinted by permission of Little, Brown & Company.

Liveright Publishing Corp. for "A Short History of Man" from *How to Tell Your Friends from the Apes* by Will Cuppy; selections from *Poems in Praise of Practically Nothing* by Samuel Hoffenstein; a selection from *Gentlemen Prefer Blondes* by Anita Loos; "In Old Chinatown" from *Dawn Ginsbergh's Revenge* by S. J. Perelman; and "The Vanderbilt Convention" from *Broccoli and Old Lace* by Frank Sullivan. All titles published by Liveright.

Phyllis McGinley for "Song from New Rochelle" from *On the Contrary.*

Paul McPharlin and The Fine Book Circle for "Three Love Letters" by Benjamin Franklin, translated from the French by Paul McPharlin. Selection taken from *Satires and Bagatelles* by Benjamin Franklin, edited by Paul McPharlin, published by The Fine Book Circle, Detroit, 1937.

G. P. Putnam's Sons for "The Disinterested Arbiter," "The Party Over There," "Cat and King," "Revenge," "Officer and Thug," and "Saint and Soul" from *Fantastic Fables* by Ambrose Bierce; "Ain't There at Least One Gen'leman Here?" from *I'm Sorry if I Have Offended and Other Sob Ballads* by C. Knapp; and "Farewell, My Lovely!" from *Farewell to Model T* by Lee Strout White.

Random House, Inc. for "Appreciation of Art" from *Junior Miss* by Sally Benson, copyright, 1941 by Random House, Inc., 1939-1941 by Sally Benson; "Portrait" from *Dead Reckoning* by Kenneth Fearing, copyright, 1938 by Random House, Inc.; "Lady's Room" from *Celibate at Twilight* by John Mosher, copyright, 1940 by Random House, Inc., 1926-1940 by John Mosher; "The Idol's Eye" and "Waiting for Santy" from *Strictly from Hunger* by S. J. Perelman, copyright, 1937 by Random House, Inc., and "Down with the Restoration!" from *Look Who's Talking* by S. J. Perelman. All selections reprinted by permission of Random House, Inc.

Charles Scribner's Sons for "Mr. Dooley on the Education of the Young" from *Mr. Dooley at His Best* by Finley Peter Dunne, edited by Elmer Ellis; "Mr. Dooley on the Power of Music" and "Mr. Dooley on Golf" from *Mr. Dooley on Making a Will and Other Necessary Evils* by Finley Peter Dunne; "The Norris Plan" from *In the Worst Possible Taste,* copyright, 1922 by Corey Ford and published by Charles Scribner's Sons; "The Horse," "The Hen," "The Cow," and "The Gnu" with the accompanying illustrations, from *More Animals* by Oliver Herford; "Large Coffee," "Odd's Bodkins," and "On Conversation" from *First and Last* by Ring Lardner; "Alibi Ike" from *Round Up* by Ring Lardner; "Sonnets to Baedeker" from *Bay Window Ballads* by David McCord; and "Benny and the Bird-Dogs" from *When the Whippoorwill* by Marjorie Kinnan Rawlings.

Simon & Schuster, Inc. for selections from *The Diary of Our Own Samuel Pepys* by Franklin P. Adams, copyright, 1935 by Franklin P. Adams and "Boggains in the Bronx" from *Thunder in the Bronx* by Arthur Kober, copyright, 1935 by Arthur Kober, and published by Simon & Schuster, Inc.

Frederick A. Stokes Company, Inc. for "The Man from Yellowhouse" reprinted by permission of Frederick A. Stokes Company, Inc., from *Wolfville* by Alfred Henry Lewis, copyright, 1897.

Mrs. Bert Leston Taylor for "The Passionate Professor" by Bert Leston Taylor.

The Viking Press, Inc. for "To a Thesaurus," "Advice to Young

Men," and "Lines to Three Boys" from *The Melancholy Flute* by
Franklin P. Adams, copyright, 1936 by Franklin P. Adams; "The
Ballet Visits the Splendide's Magician" from *Hotel Splendide* by
Ludwig Bemelmans, copyright, 1941 by Ludwig Bemelmans; "Glory
in the Daytime" from *Here Lies* by Dorothy Parker; "Little Words,"
"Tombstone for an Actress," and "The Searched Soul" from *Not So
Deep as a Well* by Dorothy Parker, copyright, 1926, 1928, 1931, 1936
and "The Highly Recurrent Mr. Hamilton" and "Re-enter Margot
Asquith" by Dorothy Parker from *The New Yorker;* "Capsule Criticism" from *Shouts and Murmurs* by Alexander Woollcott; and "Manhattan" from *Enchanted Aisles* by Alexander Woollcott. All selections
by permission of The Viking Press, Inc.

The Yale University Press for selections and illustrations from
Scenes from the Mesozoic by Clarence Day.

The following selections were first printed in *The New Yorker*
and "to the best of our knowledge" have not been published since in
book form except in a few cases in *New Yorker* anthologies. The
editors and publishers are grateful to both the magazine and the
authors and artists for allowing them to be used in this volume: Nine
selections from "The Talk of the Town"; "Memoirs of a Master"—
M. R. A.; "La Presse Perverse"—Robert Benchley; drawing of Henry
Luce—Will Cotton; "Woman Out of Taxi"—Angela Cypher (Marjorie Allen Seiffert); two book reviews—Clifton Fadiman; "Limericks
Long After Lear"—Morris Bishop and Richard Taylor; two theater
reviews and "Shakespeare, Here's Your Hat"—Wolcott Gibbs; "Boy
Meets Bullfinch" and "Mother Taft's Chickens"—Geoffrey Hellman;
"Dr. C-dm-n's Daily"—Nunnally Johnson; "At Home with the Pa-
leys"—E. J. Kahn Jr.; "Who Is This King of Glory?"—A. J. Liebling
and St. Clair McKelway; "What Did You Do, Grandfather?"—Rich-
ard Lockridge; "An Affix for Birds"—St. Clair McKelway; "Atheist
Hit by Truck"—John McNulty; "Inflexible Logic"—Russell Maloney;
"The Downfall of Fascism in Black Ankle County"—Joseph Mitchell;
"Savage Homecoming"—Clifford Orr; "The Mesecks"—Kenneth Allan
Robinson; "Christopher K*a*p*l*a*n"—Leonard Q. Ross (Leo C.
Rosten); "A Ride With Ralph"—Francis Steegmuller; "A Garland of
Ibids" and "The Jukes Family"—Frank Sullivan; illustrations for
"Fables for Our Time"—James Thurber; "Owl Man"—Sanderson
Vanderbilt; "Fpafm"—Frances Warfield; "Famous Baths and Bathers"
—Carolyn Wells.

Preface

A COLLECTION, whether of birds' eggs or of funny pieces, is likely to reveal more about the collector than about the subject. I know this to be true, because there was a cabinet of birds' eggs in the attic of the house I lived in as a child, and although I learned very little about birds from this early and fascinating anthology, I caught quite a glimpse of the cousin who had assembled all those eggs under one roof. They were arranged according to a plan which struck me as admirable: they were placed according to size—starting with an ostrich egg and ending with a hummingbird's. I'm sure that even at that date there must have been a more scientific way of grouping birds' eggs, but there was no lovelier. It was a memorable collection. The cousin died in a gun accident before I ever encountered him in the flesh, the only anthologist with whose taste I have been in complete agreement. There was not one egg that was not a perfect work of art.

In this collection of American humor, Katharine S. White (who shall hereafter be known as my wife) and I have tried to select some things we like ourselves, and have made no attempt to throw in anything to please anybody else. This is a subtreasury designed for the safekeeping of our own valuables. Anyone else who wants to pay his way in is at liberty to wander about, criticizing the contents of the vaults and looking for trouble. That is part of your money's worth. There are some well-known pieces in here, and some that are not well known, and two or three old chestnuts for roasting over an open fire these crisp fall nights. One thing you may *not* find in here is your favorite humorist, and we strongly advise you not to look for him, poor fellow. We passed him on the street the other day and he seemed far from well.

However, there is a little more to this book (we hope) than pure prejudice, and there is a little more to it than may be suggested by so sudden a mobilization of funny stuff, as though an emergency had arisen in humor. We have looked up some authors whose works were not familiar to us, and we have gone to some trouble to arrange things sensibly, according to their nature. (I would have arranged them according to size, remembering the ostrich egg, if there hadn't been a steadier hand to lead me.) Parodists are here lined up, with their victims, under the same chapter heading. Story tellers are bunched, and moralists, and critics, and so on. I think you will find this a convenience, and possibly even interesting.

In one sense, any deliberate compilation of reading matter is a dubious project for anyone in his right mind to undertake, and some anthologies I have seen have reminded me strongly of the shell collections of ladies who have just come in from their first day on a Florida beach—a lot of broken-down pectens and some damaged sea worms. This anthology should be more resourceful and prettier than that, if only because our period of collection has been a long one and we have conscientiously discarded many specimens that turned out to be defective or that grew dull after they had lain around.

It will be apparent immediately that the book contains only humor which is, so to speak, "literary"—that is, it has been written down on paper, in words, to be read. The only drawings are drawings which are inseparable from the text. There are no jokes, as such, in the book. There is no unconscious humor, as far as we know. Vast fields of American humor are here untouched—the radio gag, the anecdote, the newsbreak, the after-dinner speech, the pun, the epigram, the humor that ripples in the subway and explodes in the ball park, the quip, the crack, the nifty, the wow, the wonderful stuff that the stenographer with her pad upon her knee tosses to the stockroom boy coming in with a fresh supply of paper clips, the humor of Mickey and Pluto, of blackface minstrels, of newspaper comic strips, of Benny Goodman playing Bach, the coinage of Winchell, the pantomime of Chaplin, the red curls of Harpo, the vast unwritten satires of Ed Wynn and Ethel Merman and Ray Bolger and W. C. Fields and the rest. There is nothing that can be done about them in a book. The melodious and collaborative humor of Merman-Porter is not distributable through the ordinary channels of book publishing, short of a pop-up containing a concealed Victrola. No subtreasury of American humor is complete today without a scene from *Of Thee I Sing* and the night-club parody from *Pal Joey,* but you simply can't present them without all those girls. I never realized how confining a book could be till we got going on this one.

We had our fair share of disillusionment in assembling it. It seemed like a gay idea, to begin with, but it soon began to ride us hard and we developed some nasty saddle sores before we got through. There was quite a period when we entertained the notion that we would include what we fondly called "newspaper humor." We were going to collect a lot of terribly funny stories from the press. We collected them, all right, and some of them were funny, too, but we soon had to keep them in a separate icebox on account of the way the cream was beginning to taste. Old newspaper stories have an odor all their own; they are extremely hard to run down, and after you find them, you wish you hadn't. Something has happened to them in the meantime. Ask any newspaperman to name a funny story that he has written or that he has read, and he will direct you to within about three months of a certain issue of a certain newspaper (except it wasn't the *Times* it was the *Tribune*), and at last you discover the exact date and the very paper and you coax the library into letting you examine this immortal yet crumbling relic, this sere and yellow specimen, and as it trickles into your lap, particle by particle, you read with glassy eyes and set jaw the howlingly funny news story of long ago. It is a bad moment.

This is not said in disparagement of the humor of the press, or of reporters, plenty of whom are first-class humorists and are daily performing a brilliant feat in gathering news and transmitting it somewhat humorously. It simply means that even the perfect newspaper story, by the most expert and gifted reporter, dies like a snake with the setting of the sun. The news goes out of it (though some humor may remain), and when the news goes out of it the heart goes out of it. It doesn't bear reprinting except in a textbook, and this is not a textbook.*

So we ended by deleting from the "Reporters at Work" section of our book all the daily stuff, leaving only the magazine stuff, including a few pieces from "The Talk of the Town" in *The New Yorker*. In a way this seems unjust: the best reporting (including the best humorous reporting) is to be found in newspapers, not in magazines; but an anthologist has to take material which can go into type a second time with some effect, regardless of how good or even distinguished it may have been in its first appearance. The "Talk of the Town" pieces, although they had grown whiskers as timely articles do, stood up a little better, we found, than the daily paper pieces, probably because the prime purpose of a daily story is to acquaint you with the facts, whereas the prime purpose of a *New Yorker* story is to enter-

* *Note to Professors of English: Pay no attention to this sentence.*

tain you with the facts. As far as possible we picked pieces which,
though they were not out of newspapers, at least had been written by
men who had been (or are now) newspaper reporters: Joseph Mitchell,
Alva Johnston, Sanderson Vanderbilt, John McNulty, A. J. Liebling,
St. Clair McKelway.

At any rate, in this section as in all the others, the editors decided
not to include anybody or anything just for the sake of being inclusive
or of getting coverage. We asked simply that we be amused, now in
1941. Our motto throughout was:

> If it be not droll to we,
> What care us how droll it be!

A lot of the humor of fifty to one hundred years ago was dialect
humor. Then was the heyday of the crackerbarrel philosopher, sometimes wise, always wise-seeming, and nowadays rather dreary. We
plunged into this period with willing hearts and open minds, and came
out of it exhausted and not greatly enriched. While I was in there it
occurred to me that a certain basic confusion often exists in the use of
tricky or quaint or illiterate spelling to achieve a humorous effect.
I mean, it is not always clear whether the author intends his character
to be writing or speaking—and I, for one, feel that unless I know at
least this much about what I am reading, I am off to a bad start.
For instance, here are some spellings from the works of Petroleum V.
Nasby: he spells "would" *wood,* "of" *uv,* "you" *yoo,* "hence" *hentz,*
"office" *offis.*

Now, it happens that I pronounce "office" *offis.* And I pronounce
"hence" *hentz,* and I even pronounce "of" *uv.* Therefore, I infer that
Nasby's character is supposed not to be speaking but to be writing.
Yet in either case, justification for this perversion of the language is
lacking; for if the character is speaking, the queer spelling is unnecessary, since the pronunciation is impossible to distinguish from the
natural or ordinary pronunciation, and if the character is writing, the
spelling is most unlikely. Who ever wrote "uv" for "of"? Nobody.
Anyone who knows how to write at all, knows how to spell a simple
word like "of." If you can't spell "of" you wouldn't be able to spell
anything and wouldn't be attempting to set words to paper—much
less words like "solissitood." A person who can't spell "of" is an
illiterate, and the only time such a person attempts to write anything

down is in a great crisis. He doesn't write political essays or diaries or letters or satirical paragraphs.

In *Dere Mabel,* which is patently offered as "written" material, since it is a book of letters, some of the spelling seems highly questionable. All "ing" words are spelled "in" without the "g." This is rare, I think, in real life. Even partially or badly educated persons know the ending "ing." All schoolboys know it. It is one of the first things you learn when you learn to spell in school.

Obviously, some of the pieces by the dialect writers seemed funny to us in spite of the handicap of spelling. In the case of Dooley, the Irish dialect is difficult but worth the effort, and it smooths out after the first hundred miles. Finley Peter Dunne was a sharp and gifted humorist, who wrote no second-rate stuff, and he had the sympathetic feeling for his character which is indispensable. This same sympathy is discernible in Jewish humor—in the work of Gross, Kober, Ross. It is sympathy, not contempt or derision, that makes their characters live. Lardner's ball player was born because the author had a warm feeling for ballplayers, however boyish or goofy. The spelling in all these cases is not a device for gaining a humorous effect, but is a necessary tool for working the material, which is itself inherently humorous.

I suspect that the popularity of all dialect stuff derives in part from flattery of the reader—giving him a pleasant sensation of superiority which he gets from working out the intricacies of misspelling, and the satisfaction of detecting boorishness or illiteracy in someone else. This is not the whole story, but it has some bearing in the matter. Incidentally, I am told by an authority on juvenile literature that dialect is tops with children. They like to study out the words. When they catch on to the thing, they must feel that first fine glow of maturity— the ability to exercise higher intellectual powers than those of the character they are looking at.

Since this book is an arbitrary selection, we do not feel obliged to explain anything or to apologize for anything. The inclusion of any item can be ascribed to the editors' jaundiced taste, the omission of any item to their sheer vindictiveness.

There are some admirable American humorists who are absent from the book through no fault of their own or of ours either. One of them is Harry Leon Wilson, whose stories are too long to reprint in a volume of this sort. We tried breaking off a limb of *Merton* and of *Bunker*

Bean, but they didn't seem to do well, separated from the main trunk.
Another man is Henry Thoreau. There is hardly a paragraph of *Walden* which does not seem humorous to me; but we didn't include any
of it, having no wish to attitudinize, and because it, too, is unsatisfactory when broken up. Nevertheless, Thoreau makes me laugh the inaudible, the enduring laugh. Oliver Wendell Holmes is present in the
book but is inadequately represented; the humor in the *Autocrat* is in
such dilution as to be unsuitable for a concentrated pill.

Tall stories are commonly regarded as the rockbed of American
humor, and we have included a few of them that we liked. We found,
however, that tall stories can be unspeakably boring. It is possible to
be quite tall without being a bit funny. We also found (or rather
we verified the fact) that we had no taste for the Genial School of
humor—a large school with some rather impressive pupils. Geniality
is not, per se, humorous, in spite of the illusion of humor it often
gives, and too often geniality turns out to be long-windedness in sheep's
clothing. Verbosity is an occupational disease in America, and writing
can be as dangerous as painting the luminous dials of watches. Many a
humorist has been stricken fatally at an early age—you will find their
dry bones in the magazines whose principal literary requirement is that
every story be long enough to break over into the back pages among
the advertisements.

Among those absent from this book are the Canadians. We kept
the Canadians out simply because we were getting crowded for space
and the Canadian border made a convenient place to stop. And while
I am on the delicate subject of who is in this book and who isn't, it
will be observed by the more observant readers that there are certain
items in here which I wrote myself. This is an unsavory episode upon
which I shall not dwell.

It will also be observed that quite a large amount of the material in
here was published first in *The New Yorker.* This discovery should
surprise nobody. My wife and I happen to own a complete file of the
bound volumes of *The New Yorker,* and after a long evening with
George Horatio Derby or somebody or other who wrote the best light
verse during the McKinley administration, it would often be our
stealthy custom to pull out a volume at random and dip up a nice
funny piece before going to bed. We could easily have assembled the
whole book from this invaluable shelf of ours, but it would have been
a little tough on Washington Irving and Mark Twain and a few others

who had the misfortune to be doing their work before the magazine got well under way.

A great deal of modern humor has been born and is growing up which would never have seen the light and would still be in the kept-under stage if it had not been for the receptive attitude of *The New Yorker* toward new writers, and for its solid conviction that humor is an art form and not a barber shop fitting. We have a speaking acquaintance with *New Yorker* pieces, a parental feeling about some of them, and a high regard for the magazine and its editor and its contributors. It would be odd indeed if our book didn't show this attachment.

As for the pieces themselves, we do not pretend that they are thoroughly representative of *New Yorker* humor; we have not even included some of our favorite writers, confident that they will endure their horrid fate with characteristic poise. And my wife thinks it would be well to add, also, that where we have used two pieces by one writer and one piece by another writer, it doesn't mean that we think the first man is twice as good as the second. We may think he is only half as good and are trying to cover up.

In the back of the book you will find an alphabetical list of authors, with their dates. An author with *no* birth date can be assumed to be living. It appears that some authors elect to keep the fact of their birth a secret from the world, although it is clear from the color of their jackets that they are alive and hearty.

The same list will help you identify the many authors who used, or use, pseudonyms. There was hardly a writer prior to the Twentieth Century who signed his own name to his stuff. They must all either have been ashamed or in debt.

Analysts have had their go at humor, and I have read some of this interpretative literature, but without being greatly instructed. Humor can be dissected, as a frog can, but the thing dies in the process and the innards are discouraging to any but the pure scientific mind.

A certain type of humor has come to be big business in the United States. The gag factories are as impressive as Allis Chalmers, and will probably soon be taken over for defense purposes. Radio comedians employ their own corps of geniuses, who sit and think and think of something funny to say. It is sometimes rather grim business, this production for the big markets. In a newsreel theater the other day I saw a picture of a man who had developed the soap bubble to a higher point than it had ever before reached. He had become the ace soap bubble blower of America, had perfected the business of blowing bubbles, refined it, doubled it, squared it, and had even worked himself up into a convenient lather. The effect was not pretty. Some of the bubbles were too big to be beautiful, and the blower was always jumping into them or out of them, or playing some sort of unattractive trick with them. It was, if anything, a rather repulsive sight. Humor is a little like that: it won't stand much blowing up, and it won't stand much poking. It has a certain fragility, an evasiveness, which one had best respect. Essentially, it is a complete mystery. A human frame convulsed with laughter, and the laughter becoming hysterical and uncontrollable, is as far out of balance as one shaken with the hiccoughs or in the throes of a sneezing fit.

One of the things commonly said about humorists is that they are really very sad people—clowns with a breaking heart. There is some truth in it, but it is badly stated. It would be more accurate, I think, to say that there is a deep vein of melancholy running through everyone's life and that a humorist, perhaps more sensible of it than some others, compensates for it actively and positively. Practically everyone is a manic depressive of sorts, with his up moments and his down moments, and you certainly don't have to be a humorist to taste the sadness of situation and mood. But, as everyone knows, there is often a rather fine line between laughing and crying, and if a humorous piece of writing brings a person to the point where his emotional responses are untrustworthy and seem likely to break over into the opposite realm, it is because humorous writing, like poetical writing, has an extra content. It plays, like an active child, close to the big hot fire which is Truth. And sometimes the reader feels the heat.

The world likes humor, but it treats it patronizingly. It decorates its serious artists with laurel, and its wags with Brussels sprouts. It feels that if a thing is funny it can be presumed to be something less than great, because if it were truly great it would be wholly serious. Writers know this, and those who take their literary selves with great seriousness are at considerable pains never to associate their name with anything funny or flippant or nonsensical or "light." They suspect it would hurt their reputation, and they are right. Many a poet writing today signs his real name to his serious verse and a pseudonym to his comical verse, being unwilling to have the public discover him in any but a pensive and heavy moment. It is a wise precaution. (It is often a bad poet, too.)

When I was reading over some of the parody diaries of Franklin P. Adams, I came across this entry, for April 28, 1926:

"Read H. Canby's book, *Better Writing,* very excellent. But when he says, 'A sense of humour is worth gold to any writer,' I disagree with him vehemently. For the writers who amass the greatest gold have, it seems to me, no sense of humour; and I think also that if they had, it would be a terrible thing for them, for it would paralyze them so that they would not write at all. For in writing, emotion is more to be treasured than a sense of humour, and the two are often in conflict."

That is a sound observation. The conflict is fundamental. There constantly exists, for a certain sort of person of high emotional content, at work creatively, the danger of coming to a point where something cracks within himself or within the paragraph under construction —cracks and turns into a snicker. Here, then, is the very nub of the conflict: the careful form of art, and the careless shape of life itself. What a man does with this uninvited snicker (which may closely resemble a sob, at that) decides his destiny. If he resists it, conceals it, destroys it, he may keep his architectural scheme intact and save his building, and the world will never know. If he gives in to it, he becomes a humorist, and the sharp brim of the fool's cap leaves a mark forever on his brow.

I'm sure there isn't a humorist alive but can recall the day, in the early stages of his career, when someone he loved and respected took him anxiously into a corner and asked him when he was "going to write something serious." That day is memorable, for it gives a man pause to realize that the bright star he is following is held to be not of the first magnitude.

I think the stature of humor must vary some with the times. The court fool in Shakespeare's day had no social standing and was no better than a lackey, but he did have some artistic standing and was listened to with considerable attention, there being a well-founded belief that he had the truth hidden somewhere about his person. Artistically he stood probably higher than the humorist of today, who has gained social position but not the ear of the mighty. (Think of the trouble the world would save itself if it would pay some attention to nonsense!) A narrative poet at court, singing of great deeds, enjoyed a higher standing than the fool and was allowed to wear fine clothes; yet I suspect that the ballad singer was more often than not a second-rate stooge, flattering his monarch lyrically, while the fool must often have been a first-rate character, giving his monarch good advice in bad puns.

In the British Empire of our time, satirical humor of the Gilbert and Sullivan sort enjoys a solid position in the realm, and *Punch,* which is as British as vegetable marrow, is socially acceptable everywhere an Englishman is to be found. The *Punch* editors not only write the jokes but they help make the laws of England. Here in America we have an immensely humorous people in a land of milk and honey and wit, who cherish the ideal of the "sense" of humor and at the same time are highly suspicious of anything which is nonserious. Whatever else an American believes or disbelieves about himself, he is absolutely sure he has a sense of humor.

Frank Moore Colby, one of the most intelligent humorists operating in this country in the early years of the century, in an essay called "The Pursuit of Humor" described how the American loves and guards his most precious treasure:

"... Now it is the commonest thing in the world to hear people call the absence of a sense of humor the one fatal defect. No matter how owlish a man is, he will tell you that. It is a miserable falsehood, and it does incalculable harm. A life without humor is like a life without legs. You are haunted by a sense of incompleteness, and you cannot go where your friends go. You are also somewhat of a burden. But the only really fatal thing is the shamming of humor when you have it not. There are people whom nature meant to be solemn from their cradle to their grave. They are under bonds to remain so. In so far as they are true to themselves they are safe company for any one; but outside their proper field they are terrible. Solemnity is relatively a blessing, and the man who was born with it should never be encouraged to wrench himself away.

"We have praised humor so much that we have started an insincere cult, and there are many who think they must glorify it when they hate it from the bottom of their hearts. False humor-worship is the deadliest of social sins, and one of the commonest. People without a grain of humor in their composition will eulogize it by the hour. Men will confess to treason, murder, arson, false teeth, or a wig. How many of them will own up to a lack of humor? The courage that could draw this confession from a man would atone for everything."

Relatively few American humorists have become really famous, so

that their name is known to everyone in the land in the way that many
novelists and other solemn literary characters have become famous.
Mark Twain made it. He had, of course, an auspicious start, since he
was essentially a story teller and his humor was an added attraction.
(It was also very, very good.) In this century Ring Lardner is the idol
of professional humorists and of plenty of other people, too; but I
think I am correct in saying that at the height of his career he was not
one of the most widely known literary figures in this country, and the
name Lardner was not known to the millions but only to the thousands.
Even today he has not reached Mr. and Mrs. America and all the clip-
pers at sea, to the extent that Mark Twain reached them, and I doubt
if he ever will. On the whole, the humorists who contribute pleasure
to a wide audience are the ones who create characters and tell tales,
the ones who are story tellers at heart. Lardner told stories and gave
birth to some characters, but I think he was a realist and a parodist
and a satirist first of all, not essentially a writer of fiction. The general
public needs something to get a grip on—a Penrod, a Huck Finn, a
Brer Rabbit, or a Father Day. The subtleties of satire and burlesque
and nonsense and parody and criticism are no dish for the masses;
they are only for the top (or, if you want, for the bottom) layer of
intellect. Clarence Day, for example, was relatively inconspicuous when
he was oozing his incomparable "Thoughts without Words," which
are his best creations; he became generally known and generally loved
only after he had brought Father to life. (Advice to young writers who
want to get ahead without any annoying delays: don't write about
Man, write about *a* man.)

I was interested, in reading DeVoto's *Mark Twain in Eruption,* to
come across some caustic remarks of Mr. Clemens's about an anthology
of humor which his copyright lawyer had sent him and which Mark
described as "a great fat, coarse, offensive volume." He was not amused.
"This book is a cemetery," he wrote.

"In this mortuary volume I find Nasby, Artemus Ward, Yawcob
Strauss, Derby, Burdette, Eli Perkins, the Danbury News Man,
Orpheus C. Kerr, Smith O'Brien, Josh Billings, and a score of others,
maybe two score, whose writings and sayings were once in everybody's
mouth but are now heard of no more and are no longer mentioned.
Seventy-eight seems an incredible crop of well-known humorists for
one forty-year period to have produced, and yet this book has not
harvested the entire crop—far from it. It has no mention of Ike
Partington, once so welcome and so well known; it has no mention

of Doesticks, nor of the Pfaff crowd, nor of Artemus Ward's numerous
and perishable imitators, nor of three very popular Southern humorists
whose names I am not able to recall, nor of a dozen other sparkling
transients whose light shone for a time but has now, years ago, gone
out.

"Why have they perished? Because they were merely humorists.
Humorists of the 'mere' sort cannot survive. Humor is only a fragrance,
a decoration. Often it is merely an odd trick of speech and of spelling,
as in the case of Ward and Billings and Nasby and the 'Disbanded
Volunteer,' and presently the fashion passes and the fame along with
it. There are those who say a novel should be a work of art solely,
and you must not preach in it, you must not teach in it. That may
be true as regards novels but it is not true as regards humor. Humor
must not professedly teach, and it must not professedly preach, but
it must do both if it would live forever. By forever, I mean thirty
years. With all its preaching it is not likely to outlive so long a term
as that. The very things it preaches about, and which are novelties
when it preaches about them, can cease to be novelties and become
commonplaces in thirty years. Then that sermon can thenceforth interest no one.

"I have always preached. That is the reason that I have lasted thirty
years. If the humor came of its own accord and uninvited, I have
allowed it a place in my sermon, but I was not writing the sermon for
the sake of humor. I should have written the sermon just the same,
whether any humor applied for admission or not. I am saying these
vain things in this frank way because I am a dead person speaking
from the grave. Even I would be too modest to say them in life. I
think we never become really and genuinely our entire and honest
selves until we are dead—and not then until we have been dead years
and years. People ought to start dead, and then they would be honest
so much earlier."

Well, I didn't intend to get off onto the broad subject of humor, or
even to let Mark Twain get off onto it. I don't think I agree that humor
must preach in order to live; it need only speak the truth—and I
notice it always does. As for this book, I think the truth is in it. We,
the compilers, hope that there will be spots, here and there, where our
taste will coincide with the taste of the reader, and that enjoyment and
profit will result.

—E. B. W.

CONTENTS

ALL SORTS OF DILEMMAS

HISTORY, POLITICS, AND AFFAIRS OF STATE

PARODIES AND BURLESQUES

FOLKLORE AND TALL STORIES

NONSENSE

THE CRITICS AT WORK

THE REPORTERS AT WORK

VERSE

REMINISCENCE

A SUBTREASURY OF AMERICAN HUMOR

STORIES AND PEOPLE

The first section of this book is a fiction section, but a great deal of fiction will be found elsewhere in the book, too. In classifying material, it was sometimes a toss-up whether a piece fitted more appropriately under one head or under another.

The Frank Stockton contribution to the following group of stories has been slightly tampered with, as explained in a note. Mostly we have done no tampering, and any piece appearing in the Subtreasury may be presumed to be exactly as written by its author, unless otherwise noted.

In general, we have resisted the temptation to use chapters or excerpts from novels or long stories, but there are exceptions and this fictional department happens to contain three notable ones. We didn't, for the sake of sticking to our principles, want to miss such a plum as the first chapter of "Babbitt," which, although a fragment of a novel, stands by itself as a little work of art and is written with good humor as well as with great compassion. We did not want to omit "Mrs. Lecks and Mrs. Aleshine," either, or Miss Loos's lady-like blonde.

Neither Sinclair Lewis nor Marjorie Kinnan Rawlings is classified in the library as a humorist, but if that didn't stop us it needn't stop you.

Marjorie Kinnan Rawlings

BENNY AND THE BIRD-DOGS

You can't change a man, no-ways. By the time his mammy turns him loose and he takes up with some innocent woman and marries her, he's what he is. If it's his nature to set by the hearthfire and scratch hisself, you just as good to let him set and scratch. If it's his nature, like Will Dover, my man, to go to the garage in his Sunday clothes and lay down under some backwoods Cracker's old greasy Ford and tinker with it, you just as good to let him lay and tinker. And if it's his nature, like Uncle Benny, to prowl; if it's his nature to cut the fool; why, it's interfering in the ways of Providence even to stop to quarrel with him about it. Some women is born knowing that. Sometimes a woman, like the Old Hen (Uncle Benny's wife, poor soul!), has to quarrel a lifetime before she learns it. Then when it does come to her, she's like a cow has tried to jump a high fence and has got hung up on it—she's horn-swoggled.

The Old Hen's a mighty fine woman—one of the finest I know. She looks just the way she did when she married Uncle Benny Mathers thirty years ago, except her hair has turned gray, like the feathers on an Irish Gray game hen. She's plump and pretty and kind of pale from thirty years' fretting about Uncle Benny. She has a disposition, by nature, as sweet as new cane syrup. When she settled down for a lifetime's quarrelling at him, it was for the same reason syrup sours—the heat had just been put to her too long.

I can't remember a time when the Old Hen wasn't quarrelling at Uncle Benny. It begun a week after they was married. He went off prowling by hisself, to a frolic or such as that, and didn't come home until four o'clock in the morning. She was setting up waiting for him. When she crawled him about it, he said, "Bless Katy, wife, let's sleep now and quarrel in the morning." So she quarrelled in the morning and just kept it up. For thirty years. Not for meanness—she just kept hoping she could change him.

3

Change him? When he takened notice of the way she was fussing
and clucking and ruffling her feathers, he quit calling her by her given
name and began calling her the Old Hen. That's all I could ever see
she changed him.

Uncle Benny's a sight. He's been constable here at Oak Bluff,
Florida, for twenty years. We figure it keeps him out of worse trouble
to let him be constable. He's the quickest shot in three counties and
the colored folks is all as superstitious of him as if he was the devil
hisself. He's a comical-appearing somebody. He's small and quick and
he don't move—he prances. He has a little bald sun-tanned head with
a rim of white hair around the back of it. Where the hair ends at the
sides of his head, it sticks straight up over his ears in two little white
tufts like goat-horns. He's got bright blue eyes that look at you quick
and wicked, the way a goat looks. That's exactly what he looks and
acts like—a mischievous little old billy-goat. And he's been popping
up under folks' noses and playing tricks on them as long as Oak
Bluff has knowed him. Doc in particular. He loved to torment Doc.

And stay home? Uncle Benny don't know what it is to stay home.
The Old Hen'll cook hot dinner for him and he won't come. She'll
start another fire in the range and warm it up for him about dusk-
dark and he won't come. She'll set up till midnight, times till daybreak, and maybe just about the time the east lightens and the birds
gets to whistling good, he'll come home. Where's he been? He's been
with somebody 'gatoring, or with somebody catching crabs to Salt
Springs; he's been to a square-dance twenty miles away in the flat-
woods; he's been on the highway in that Ford car, just rambling as
long as his gas held out—and them seven pieded bird-dogs setting up
in the back keeping him company.

It was seven years ago, during the Boom, that he bought the Model-T
and begun collecting bird-dogs. Everybody in Florida was rich for a
whiles, selling gopher holes to the Yankees. Now putting an automobile under Uncle Benny was like putting wings on a wild-cat—it just
opened up new territory. Instead of rambling over one county, he
could ramble over ten. And the way he drove—like a bat out of
Torment. He's one of them men just loves to cover the ground. And
that car and all them bird-dogs worked on the Old Hen like a quart
of gasoline on a camp-fire. She really went to raring. I tried to tell her
then 'twasn't no use to pay him no mind, but she wouldn't listen.

I said, "It's just his nature. You can't do a thing about it but take it for your share and go on. You and Uncle Benny is just made different. You want him home and he don't want to be home. You're a barn-yard fowl and he's a wild fowl."

"Mis' Dover," she said, "it's easy for you to talk. Your man runs a garage and comes home nights. You don't know how terrible it is to have a man that prowls."

I said, "Leave him prowl."

She said, "Yes, but when he's on the prowl, I don't no more know where to look for him than somebody's tom-cat."

I said, "If 'twas me, I wouldn't look for him."

She said, "Moonlight nights he's the worst. Just like the varmints."

I said, "Don't that tell you nothing?"

She said, "If he'd content hisself with prowling— But he ain't con-tent until he cuts the fool. He takes that Ford car and them seven bird-dogs and maybe a pint of moonshine, and maybe picks up Doc to prowl with him, and he don't rest until he's done something crazy. What I keep figuring is, he'll kill hisself in that Ford car, cutting the fool."

I said, "You don't need to fret about him and that Ford. What's un-natural for one man is plumb natural for another. And cutting the fool is so natural for Uncle Benny, it's like a bird in the air or a fish in water—there won't no harm come to him from it."

She said, "Mis' Dover, what the devil throws over his back has got to come down under his belly."

I said, "Uncle Benny Mathers is beyond rules and sayings. I know men-folks, and if you'll listen to me, you'll settle down and quit quar-relling and leave him go his way in quiet."

I happened to be in on it this spring, the last time the Old Hen ever quarrelled at Uncle Benny. Me and Doc was both in on it. It was the day of old lady Weller's burying. Doc carried me in his car to the cemetery. My Will couldn't leave the garage, because the trucks hauling the Florida oranges north was bringing in pretty good business. Doc felt obliged to go to the burying. He's a patent-medicine salesman—a big fat fellow with a red face and yellow hair. He sells the Little Giant line of remedies. Old lady Weller had been one of his best customers. She'd taken no nourishment the last week of her life except them remedies, and Doc figured he ought to pay her the proper respect and show everybody he was a man was always grateful to his customers.

Uncle Benny and the Old Hen went to the burying in the Model-T.

And the seven bird-dogs went, setting up in the back seat. They always went to the buryings.

Uncle Benny said, "Walls nor chains won't hold 'em. Better to have 'em go along riding decent and quiet, than to bust loose and foller the Model-T like a daggone pack of bloodhounds."

That was true enough. Those bird-dogs could hear that old Ford crank up and go off in low gear, clear across the town. They'd always hope it was time to go bird-hunting again, and here they'd come, trailing it. So there were the bird-dogs riding along to old lady Weller's burying, with their ears flopping and their noses in the air for quail. As constable, Uncle Benny sort of represented the town, and he was right in behind the hearse. I mean, that car was a pain, to be part of a funeral procession. In the seven years he'd had it, he'd all but drove it to pieces, and it looked like a rusty, mangy razor-back hog. The hood was thin and narrow, like a shoat's nose—you remember the way all Model-T Fords were built. It had no top to it, nor no doors to the front seat, and the back seat rose up in a hump where the bird-dogs had squeezed the excelsior chitlin's out of it.

The Old Hen sat up stiff and proud, not letting on she minded. Doc and I figured she's been quarrelling at Uncle Benny about the bird-dogs, because when one of them put his paws on her shoulders and begun licking around her ears, she turned and smacked the breath out of him.

The funeral procession had just left the Oak Bluff dirt road and turned onto No. 9 Highway, when the garage keeper at the bend ran out.

He hollered, "I just got a 'phone call for Uncle Benny Mathers from the high sheriff!"

So Uncle Benny cut out of the procession and drove over to the pay station by the kerosene tank to take the message. He caught up again in a minute and called to Doc, "A drunken nigger is headed this way in a Chevrolet and the sheriff wants I should stop him."

About that time here comes the Chevrolet and started to pass the procession, wobbling back and forth as if it had the blind staggers. You may well know the nigger was drunk or he wouldn't have passed a funeral. Uncle Benny cut out of line and took out after him. When he saw who was chasing him, the nigger turned around and headed back the way he'd come from. Uncle Benny was gaining on him when they passed the hearse. The bird-dogs begun to take an interest and rared up, barking. What does Uncle Benny do but go to the side of the Chevrolet so the nigger turns around—and then Uncle Benny crowded him so all he could do was to shoot into line in the funeral procession. Uncle Benny cut right in after him and the nigger shot out of line and Uncle Benny crowded him in again.

I'll declare, I was glad old lady Weller wasn't alive to see it. She'd had no use for Uncle Benny, she'd hated a nigger, and she'd despised dogs so to where she kept a shotgun by her door to shoot at them if one so much as crossed her cornfield. And here on the way to her burying, where you'd figure she was entitled to have things the way she liked them, here was Uncle Benny chasing a nigger in and out of line, and seven bird-dogs were going Ki-yippity-yi! Ki-yippity-yi! Ki-yippity-yi! I was mighty proud the corpse was no kin to me.

The Old Hen was plumb mortified. She put her hands over her face and when the Ford would swerve by or cut in ahead of us, Doc and me could see her swaying back and forth and suffering. I don't scarcely need to say Uncle Benny was enjoying hisself. If he'd looked sorrowful-like, as if he was just doing his duty, you could of forgive him. Near a filling-station the Chevrolet shot ahead and stopped and the nigger jumped out and started to run. Uncle Benny stopped and climbed out of the Ford and drew his pistol and called "Stop!" The nigger kept on going.

Now Uncle Benny claims that shooting at niggers in the line of duty is what keeps him in practice for bird-shooting. He dropped a ball to the right of the nigger's heel and he dropped a ball to the left of it. He called "Stop!" and the nigger kept on going. Then Uncle Benny took his pistol in both hands and took a slow aim and he laid the third ball against the nigger's shin-bone. He dropped like a string-haltered mule.

Uncle Benny said to the man that ran the filling-station, "Get your gun. That there nigger is under arrest and I deputize you to keep him that-a-way. The sheriff'll be along to pick him up direckly."

He cut back into the funeral procession between us and the hearse, and we could tell by them wicked blue eyes he didn't know when he'd enjoyed a burying like old lady Weller's. When we got back from the burying, he stopped by Will's garage. The Old Hen was giving him down-the-country.

She said, "That was the most scandalous thing I've ever knowed you to do, chasing that nigger in and out of Mis' Weller's funeral."

Uncle Benny's eyes begun to dance and he said, "I know it, wife, but I couldn't help it. 'Twasn't me done the chasing—it was the Model-T."

Doc got in to it then and sided with the Old Hen. He gets excited, the way fat men do, and he swelled up like a spreading adder.

"Benny," he said, "you shock my modesty. This ain't no occasion for laughing or lying."

Uncle Benny said, "I know it, Doc. I wouldn't think of laughing nor lying. You didn't know I've got that Ford trained? I've got it trained to where it'll do two things. It's helped me chase so many niggers, I've got it to where it just naturally takes out after 'em by itself."

Doc got red in the face and asked, real sarcastic, "And what's the other piece of training?"

Uncle Benny said, "Doc, that Ford has carried me home drunk so many times, I've got it trained to where it'll take care of me and carry me home safe when I ain't fitten."

Doc spit halfway across the road and he said, "You lying old jaybird."

Uncle Benny said, "Doc, I've got a pint of moonshine and if you'll come go camping with me to Salt Springs this evening, I'll prove it."

The Old Hen spoke up and she said, "Benny, Heaven forgive you for I won't, if you go on the prowl again before you've cleared the weeds out of my old pindar field. I'm a month late now, getting it planted."

Doc loves Salt Springs crab and mullet as good as Uncle Benny does, and I could see he was tempted.

But he said, "Benny, you go along home and do what your wife wants, and when you're done—when she says you're done—then we'll go to Salt Springs."

So Uncle Benny and the Old Hen drove off. Doc watched after them.

He said, "Anyways, cutting the fool at a burying had ought to last Benny quite a while."

I said, "You don't know him. Cutting the fool don't last him no time at all."

I was right. I ain't so special wise a woman, but if I once know a man, I can come right close to telling you what he'll do. Uncle Benny hadn't been gone hardly no time, when somebody come by the garage hollering that he'd done set the Old Hen's pindar field on fire.

I said to Doc, "What did I tell you? The last thing in the world was safe for that woman to do, was to turn him loose on them weeds. He figured firing was the quickest way to get shut of them."

Doc said, "Let's go see."

We got in his car and drove out to Uncle Benny's place. Here was smoke rolling up back of the house, and the big live oak in the yard was black with soldier blackbirds the grass fire had drove out of the pindar field. The field hadn't had peanuts in it since fall, but bless Katy, it was full of something else. Uncle Benny's wife had it plumb full of setting guinea-hens. She hadn't told him, because he didn't like guineas.

Far off to the west corner of the field was the Old Hen, trying to run the guineas into a coop. They were flying every which-a-way and hollering *Pod-rac! Pod-rac!* the way guineas holler. All the young uns in the neighborhood were in the middle of the field, beating out the grass fire with palmettos. And setting up on top of the east gate, just as unconcerned, was Uncle Benny, with them two little horns of white hair curling in the heat. Now what do you reckon he was doing? He had all seven of them bird-dogs running back and forth retrieving guinea eggs. He'd say now and again, "Dead—fetch!" and they'd wag their tails and go hunt up another nest and here they'd come, with guinea eggs carried gentle in their mouths. He was putting the eggs in a basket.

When the commotion was over, and the fire out, and everybody gone on but Doc and me, we went to the front porch to set down and rest. The Old Hen was wore out. She admitted it was her fault not letting Uncle Benny know about the setting guinea-hens. She was about to forgive him setting the field a-fire, because him and the bird-dogs had saved the guinea eggs. But when we got to the porch, here lay the bird-dogs in the rocking chairs. There was one to every chair, rocking away and cutting their eyes at her. Their coats and paws were smuttied from the burnt grass—and the Old Hen had put clean sugar-sacking covers on every blessed chair that morning. That settled it. She was stirred up anyway about the way he'd cut the fool at the burying, and she really set in to quarrel at Uncle Benny. And like I say, it turned out to be the last piece of quarrelling she ever done.

She said to him, "You taught them bird-dogs to rock in a rocking-chair just to torment me. Ever' beast or varmint you've brought home, you've learned to cut the fool as bad as you do."

"Now wife, what beast or varmint did I ever learn to cut the fool?"

"You learned the 'coon to screw the tops off my syrup cans. You learned the 'possum to hang upside down in my cupboards, and I'd go for a jar of maybe pepper relish and put my hand on him.... There's been plenty of such as that. I've raised ever'thing in the world for you but a stallion horse."

Doc said, "Give him time, he'll have one of them stabled in the kitchen."

"Bird-dogs is natural to have around," she said. "I was raised to bird-dogs. But it ain't natural for 'em to rock in a rocking-chair. There's so terrible many of them, and when they put in the night on the porch laying in the rocking-chairs and rocking, I don't close my eyes for the fuss."

Uncle Benny said, "You see, Doc? You see, Mis' Dover? She's always quarrelling that me and the dogs ain't never home at night. Then when we do come in, she ain't willing we should all be comf'table.

"We just as good to go on to Salt Springs, Doc. Wait while I go in the house and get my camping outfit and we'll set out."

He went in the house and came out with his camping stuff. She knowed he was gone for nobody knew how long.

We walked on down to the gate and the Old Hen followed, sniffling a little and twisting the corner of her apron.

"Benny," she said, "please don't go to Salt Springs. You always lose your teeth in the Boil."

"I ain't lost 'em but three times," he said, and he cranked up the Model-T and climbed in. "I couldn't help losing 'em the first time. That was when I was laughing at the Yankee casting for bass, and his plug caught me in the open mouth and lifted my teeth out. Nor I couldn't help it the second time, when Doc and me was rassling in the rowboat and he pushed me in."

"Yes," she said, "an how'd you lose 'em the third time?"

His eyes twinkled and he shoved the Ford in low. "Cuttin' the fool," he said.

"That's just it," she said, and the tears begun to roll out of her eyes. "Anybody with false teeth hadn't ought to cut the fool!"

Now I always thought it was right cute, the way Uncle Benny fooled Doc about the trained Ford. You know how the old-timey Fords get the gas—it feeds from the hand-throttle on the wheel. Well, Uncle

Benny had spent the day before old lady Weller's funeral at Will's garage, putting in a foot accelerator. He didn't say a word to anybody, and Will and me was the only ones knowed he had it. Doc and Uncle Benny stayed three-four days camping at Salt Springs. Now the night they decided to come home, they'd both had something to drink, but Uncle Benny let on like he was in worse shape than he was.

Doc said, "Benny, you better leave me drive."

Uncle Benny pretended to rock on his feet and roll his head and he said, "I've got that Model-T trained to carry me home, drunk or sober."

Doc said, "Never mind that lie again. You get up there in the seat and whistle in the dogs. I'm fixing to drive us home."

Well, I'd of give a pretty to of been in the back seat with them bird-dogs that night when Doc drove the Ford back to Oak Bluff. It's a treat, any ways, to see a fat man get excited. The first thing Doc knowed, the Ford was running away with him. The Ford lights were none too good, and Doc just did clear a stump by the roadside, and he run clean over a blackjack sapling. He looked at the hand-throttle on the wheel and here it was where the car had ought to be going about twenty miles an hour and it was going forty-five. That rascal of an Uncle Benny had his foot on the foot accelerator.

Doc shut off the gas altogether and the Ford kept right on going.

He said, "Something's the matter."

Uncle Benny seemed to be dozing and didn't pay no mind. The Ford whipped back and forth in the sand road like a 'gator's tail. Directly they got on to the hard road and the Model-T put on speed. They begun to get near a curve. It was a dark night and the carlights wobbling, but Doc could see it coming. He took a tight holt of the wheel and begun to sweat. He felt for the brakes, but Uncle Benny never did have any.

He said, "We'll all be kilt."

When they started to take the curve, the Model-T was going nearly fifty-five—and then just as they got there, all of a sudden it slowed down as if it knowed what it was doing, and went around the curve as gentle as a day-old kitten. Uncle Benny had eased his foot off the accelerator. Doc drawed a breath again.

It's a wonder to me that trip didn't make Doc a nervous wreck. On every straightaway the Ford would rare back on its haunches and stretch out like a greyhound. Every curve they come to, it would go to it like a jack-rabbit. Then just as the sweat would pour down Doc's face and the drops would splash on the wheel, and he'd gather hisself together ready to jump, the Ford would slow down. It was a hot spring night, but Uncle Benny says Doc's teeth were chattering. The Model-T made the last mile lickety-brindle with the gas at the hand-throttle shut off entirely—and it coasted down in front of Will's garage and of its own free will come to a dead stop.

It was nine o'clock at night. Will was just closing up and I had locked the candy and cigarette counter and was waiting for him. There was a whole bunch of the men and boys around, like always, because the garage is the last place in Oak Bluff to put the lights out. Doc climbed out of the Ford trembling like a dish of custard. Uncle Benny eased out after him and I looked at him and right away I knowed he'd been up to mischief.

Doc said, "I don't know how he done it—but dogged if he wasn't telling the truth when he said he had that blankety-blank Model-T trained to carry him home when he ain't fitten."

Will asked, "How come?" and Doc told us. Will looked at me and begun to chuckle and we knowed what Uncle Benny had done to him. I think maybe I would of let Uncle Benny get away with it, but Will couldn't keep it.

"Come here, Doc," he said. "Here's your training."

I thought the bunch would laugh Doc out of town. He swelled up like a toadfish and he got in his car without a word and drove away.

It's a wonderful thing just to set down and figure out how many different ways there are to be crazy. We never thought of Uncle Benny as being really crazy. We'd say, "Uncle Benny's cutting the fool again," and we'd mean he was just messing around some sort of foolishness like a daggone young un. We figured his was what you might call the bottom kind of craziness. The next would be the half-witted. The next would be the senseless. The next would be what the colored folks call "mindless." And clear up at the top would be what you'd call cold-out crazy. With all his foolishness, we never figured Uncle Benny was cold-out crazy.

Well, we missed Uncle Benny from Oak Bluff a day or two. When I came to ask questions, I found he'd gone on a long prowl and was over on the Withlacoochie River camping with some oyster fishermen. I didn't think much about it, because he was liable to stay off that-a-way. But time rocked on and he didn't show up. I dropped by his house to ask the Old Hen about him. She didn't know a blessed thing.

She said, "Ain't it God's mercy we've got no young uns? The pore things would be as good as fatherless."

And then a few days later Doc came driving up to the garage. He got out and blew his nose and we could see his eyes were red.

He said, "Ain't it awful! I can't hardly bear to think about it."

Will said, "Doc, if you know bad news, you must be carrying it. Ain't nothing sorrowful I know of, except the Prohi's have found Philbin's still."

Doc said, "Don't talk about such little accidents at a time like this. You don't mean you ain't heerd about Benny?"

The bunch was there and they all perked up, interested. They knowed if it was Uncle Benny, they could expect 'most any news.

I said, "We ain't heerd a word since he went off to the west coast."

"You ain't heerd about him going crazy?"

I said, "Doc, you mean being crazy. He's always been that-a-way."

"I mean being crazy and going crazy, pore ol' Benny Mathers has gone really cold-out crazy."

Well, we all just looked at him and we looked at one another. And it came over the whole bunch of us that we weren't surprised. A nigger setting by the free air hose said, "Do, Jesus!" and eased away to tell the others.

Doc blew his nose and wiped his eyes and he said, "I'm sure we all forgive the pore ol' feller all the things he done. He wasn't responsible. I feel mighty bad, to think the hard way I've often spoke to him."

Will asked, "How come it to finally happen?"

Doc said, "He'd been up to some foolishness all night, raring through some of them Gulf coast flat-woods. Him and the fellers he was camping with was setting on the steps of the camp-house after breakfast. All of a sudden Uncle Benny goes to whistling, loud and shrill like a jay-bird. Then he says, 'I'm Sampson,' and he begun to tear down the camp-house."

Will asked, "What'd they do with him?"

Doc said, "You really ain't heerd? I declare, I can't believe the news has come so slow. They had a terrible time holding him and tying him. They got in the doctors and the sheriff and they takened pore ol' Uncle Benny to the lunatic asylum at Chattahoochie."

Doc wiped his eyes and we all begun to sniffle and our eyes to burn. I declare, it was just as if Uncle Benny Mathers had died on us.

I said, "Oh, his pore wife—"

Will said, "We'll have to be good to him and go see him and take him cigarettes and maybe slip him a pint of 'shine now and again."

I said, "The way he loved his freedom—shutting him up in the crazy-house will be like putting a wild-cat in a crocus sack."

Doc said, "Oh, he ain't in the asylum right now. He's broke loose. That's what makes me feel so bad. He's headed this way, and no telling the harm he'll do before he's ketched again."

Everybody jumped up and begun feeling in their hip pockets for their guns.

Doc said, "No use to try to put no guns on him. He's got his'n and they say he's shooting just as accurate as ever."

That was enough for me. I ran back of the counter at the garage and begun locking up.

I said, "Doc, you're a sight. 'Tain't no time to go to feeling sorry for Uncle Benny and our lives and property in danger."

Doc said, "I know, but I knowed him so long and I knowed him so good. I can't help feeling bad about it."

I said, "Do something about it. Don't just set there, and him liable to come shooting his way in any minute."

Doc said, "I know, but what can anybody do to stop him? Pore man, with all them deputies after him."

Will said, "Deputies?"

Doc said, "Why, yes. The sheriff at Ocala asked me would I stop along the road and leave word for all the deputies to try and ketch him. Pore ol' Benny, I'll swear. I hated doing it the worst way."

I scooped the money out of the cash register and I told them, "Now, men, I'm leaving. I've put up with Uncle Benny Mathers when he was drunk and I've put up with him when he was cutting the fool. But the reckless way he drives that Ford and the way he shoots a pistol, I ain't studying on messing up around him and him gone cold-out crazy."

Doc said, "Ain't a thing in the world would stop him when he goes by, and all them deputies after him, but a barricade acrost the road."

I said, "Then for goodness' sake, you sorry, low-down, no-account, varminty white men, tear down the wire fence around my chicken yard and fix Uncle Benny a barricade."

Doc said, "I just hated to suggest it."

Will said, "He'd slow down for the barricade and we could come in from behind and hem him in."

Doc said, "It'll be an awful thing to hem him in and have to see him sent back to Chattahoochie."

Will said, "I'll commence pulling out the posts and you-all can wind up the fencing."

They worked fast and I went out and looked up the road now and again to see if Uncle Benny was coming. Doc had stopped at the Standard filling-station on his way, to leave the news, and we could see the people there stirring around and going out to look, the same as we were doing. When we dragged the roll of wire fencing out into the road we hollered to them so they could see what we were doing and they all cheered and waved their hats. The word had spread, and the young uns begun traipsing barefooted down to the road, until some of their mammies ran down and cuffed them and hurried them back home out of the way of Uncle Benny. The men strung the fencing tight across the road between the garage on one side and our smoke-house on the other. They nailed it firm at both ends.

Doc said, "Leave me drive the last nail, men—it may be the last thing I can do for Benny this side of Chattahoochie."

I talked the men into unloading their guns.

"He'll have to stop when he sees the barricade," I said, "and then you can all go in on him with your guns drawed and capture him. I just can't hear to a loaded gun being drawed on him, for fear of somebody getting excited and shooting him."

Doc wiped the sweat off his forehead and he said, "Men, this is a mighty serious occasion. I'd be mighty proud if you'd all have a little snort on me," and he passed the bottle.

"Here's to Uncle Benny, the way we all knowed him before he went cold-out crazy," he said.

And then we heerd a shouting up the dirt road and young uns whistling and women and girls screaming and chickens scattering.

"Yonder comes Uncle Benny!"

And yonder he came.

The Model-T was swooping down like a bull-bat after a mosquito. The water was boiling up out of the radiator in a foot-high stream. The seven pieded bird-dogs were hanging out of the back seat and trembling as if they craved to tell the things they'd seen. And behind Uncle Benny was a string of deputy sheriffs in Fords and Chevrolets and motorcycles that had gathered together from every town between Oak Bluff and Ocala. And Uncle Benny was hunched over the steering wheel with them two tufts of goat-horn hair sticking up in the breeze —and the minute I laid eyes on him I knowed he wasn't one mite crazier than he ever had been. I knowed right then Doc had laid out to get even with him and had lied on him all the way down the road.

It was too late then. I knowed, whatever happened, there'd be people to the end of his life would always believe it. I knowed there'd be young uns running from him and niggers hiding. And I knowed there wasn't a thing in the world now could keep him out of Chattahoochie for the time being. I knowed he'd fight when he was taken, and all them mad and hot and dusty deputies would get him to the lunatic asylum quicker than a black snake can cross hot ashes. And once a man that has cut the fool all his life, like Uncle Benny, is in the crazy-house, there'll be plenty of folks to say to keep him there.

It was too late. Uncle Benny was bearing down toward the garage and right in front of him was the barricade.

Doc hollered, "Be ready to jump on him when he stops!"

Stop? Uncle Benny stop? He kept right on coming. The sight of that chicken-wire barricade was no more to him than an aggravation. Uncle Benny and the Model-T dived into the barricade like a water-turkey into a pool. The barricade held. And the next thing we knowed, the Ford had somersaulted over the fencing and crumpled up like a paper shoe-box and scattered bird-dogs over ten acres and laid Uncle Benny in a heap over against the wall of the smoke-house. I was raised to use the language of a lady, but I could hold in.

"Doc," I said, "you low-down son of a ——"

He said, "Mis' Dover, the name's too good. I've killed my friend."

Killed him? Killed Uncle Benny? It can't be done until the Almighty Hisself hollers "Sooey!" Uncle Benny was messed up considerable, but him nor none of the bird-dogs was dead.

The doctor took a few stitches in him at the garage before he come to, and tied up his head right pretty in a white bandage. We left Will to quiet the deputies and we put Uncle Benny in Doc's car and carried him home to the Old Hen. Naturally, I figured it would set her to quarrelling. Instead, it just brought out all her sweetness. I can guess a man, but I can't guess another woman.

"The pore ol' feller," she said. "I knowed he had it coming to him. What the devil throws over his back—. I knowed he'd kill hisself in that Ford car, cutting the fool and prowling. The biggest load is off my mind. Now," she said, "now, by God's mercy, when it did come to him, he got out alive."

She begun fanning him with a palmetto fan where he lay on the bed, and Doc poured out a drink of 'shine to have ready for him when he come to. Doc's hand was trembling. Uncle Benny opened his eyes. He eased one hand up to the bandage across his head and he groaned and grunted. He looked at Doc as if he couldn't make up his mind whether or not to reach for his pistol. Doc put the 'shine to his mouth and Uncle Benny swallowed. Them wicked blue eyes begun to dance.

"Doc," he said, "how will I get home when I'm drunk, now you've tore up my trained Ford?"

Doc broke down and cried like a little baby.

"I ain't got the money to replace it," he said, "but I'll give you my car. I'll carry the Little Giant line of remedies on foot."

Uncle Benny said, "I don't want your car. It ain't trained."

Doc said, "Then I'll tote you on my back, anywheres you say."

The Old Hen let in the bird-dogs, some of them limping a little, and they climbed on the bed and beat their tails on the counterpane and licked Uncle Benny. We felt mighty relieved things had come out that way.

Uncle Benny was up and around in a few days, with his head bandaged, and him as pert as a woodpecker. He just about owned Oak Bluff—all except the people that did like I figured, never did get over the idea he'd gone really crazy. Most people figured he'd had a mighty good lesson and it would learn him not to cut the fool. The Old Hen was as happy as a bride. She was so proud to have the Ford torn up, and no money to get another, that she'd even now and again pet one of the bird-dogs. She waited on Uncle Benny hand and foot and couldn't do enough to please him.

She said to me, "The pore ol' feller sure stays home nights now."

Stay home? Uncle Benny stay home? Two weeks after the accident the wreck of the Model-T disappeared from behind the garage where Will had dragged it. The next day the seven bird-dogs disappeared. The day after that Doc and Uncle Benny went to Ocala in Doc's car. Will wouldn't answer me when I asked him questions. The Old Hen stopped by the garage and got a Coca-Cola and she didn't know any more than I did. Then Will pointed down the road.

He said, "Yonder he comes."

And yonder he came. You could tell him way off by the white bandage with the tufts of hair sticking up over it. He was scrooched down behind the wheel of what looked like a brand-new automobile. Doc was following behind him. They swooped into the garage.

Will said, "It's a new second-hand body put on the chassis and around the engine of the old Ford."

Uncle Benny got out and he greeted us.

He said, "Will, it's just possible it was the motor of the Model-T that had takened the training. The motor ain't hurt, and me and Doc are real hopeful."

The Old Hen said, "Benny, where'd you get the money to pay for it?"

He said, "Why, a daggone bootlegger in a truck going from Miami to New York bought the bird-dogs for twenty-five dollars apiece. The low-down rascal knowed good and well they was worth seventy-five."

She brightened some. Getting shut of the bird-dogs was a little progress. She walked over to the car and begun looking around it.

"Benny," she said, and her voice come kind of faintified, "if you sold the bird-dogs, what's this place back here looks like it was fixed for 'em?"

We all looked, and here was a open compartment-like in the back, fixed up with seven crocus sacks stuffed with corn shucks. About that time here come a cloud of dust down the road. It was the seven bird-dogs. They were about give out. Their tongues were hanging out and their feet looked blistered.

Uncle Benny said, "I knowed they'd jump out of that bootlegger's truck. I told him so."

I tell you, what's in a man's nature you can't change. It takened the Old Hen thirty years and all them goings-on to learn it. She went and climbed in the front seat of the car and just sat there waiting for Uncle Benny to drive home for his dinner. He lifted the bird-dogs up and set them down to rest on the corn-shucks cushions, and he brought them a pan of water.

He said, "I figure they busted loose just about Lawtey."

The Old Hen never opened her mouth. She hasn't quarrelled at him from that day to this. She was hornswoggled.

Leonard Q. Ross

CHRISTOPHER K*A*P*L*A*N

Mr. Parkhill considered the beginners' grade as more than a group of scholars eager to master the English language. He took a larger view of his responsibilities; to Mr. Parkhill the American Night Preparatory School for Adults was not merely a place where foreigners could learn the English language—it was an incubator of Americans, a kind of intellectual Ellis Island. To imbue the men and women of a dozen nations with the meaning of America—its past, its traditions, its aspirations—this, to Mr. Parkhill, was the greater work to which he had dedicated himself.

So it was that on the eve of any national holiday, Mr. Parkhill devoted at least half an hour to a foray into the patriotic sentiments of the occasion. One Monday night, therefore, two nights before Columbus Day, Mr. Parkhill opened the class session with these ringing words, "Tonight, let us—er—consider the work of the man whose achievement the world will celebrate Wednesday."

A happy murmur ran through the room.

"To this man," said Mr. Parkhill earnestly, "the United States owes its very existence. For he—"

"Jawdge Vashington!" Miss Fanny Gidwitz promptly guessed.

"No, no, Miss Gidwitz. *Not* George Washington—watch that 'w,' Miss Gidwitz. I'm referring to—"

"Paul Rewere!" cried Oscar Trabish impetuously. Mr. Parkhill adjusted his spectacles. Mr. Trabish had formed some strange psychic union with "Paul Rewere": he had already written two compositions and made one fiery speech on his historical alter ego. The compositions had been called "Paul Revere's Horse Makes History" and "Paul Revere. One by the Land, Two by the Seashore." The title of the speech had been announced by Mr. Trabish as "Paul Rewere! Vhy He Vasn't Prazidant?" He had been quite indignant about it.

But now Mr. Parkhill shook his head. "Not Paul Re*were*—it's a 'v,'

Mr. Trabish. Let's not *guess,* class. What date is next Wednesday?"

"Mine boitday!" an excited voice rang out.

Mr. Parkhill ignored this comment. "Next Wednesday," he continued firmly, "is October twelfth. And on October twelfth, 1492—"

He got no further.

"Det's mine boitday! Mine *boit*day! I should live so! Honist!"

Mr. Parkhill recognized that voice. It was Hyman Kaplan's. Mr. Parkhill took a deep breath, a slow, deep breath, and said cautiously, "Mr. Kaplan, is October twelfth—er—really your birthday?"

Mr. Kaplan's eyes widened with hurt. *"Mister* Pockheel." Mr. Parkhill felt ashamed of himself.

Stanislaus Wilkomirski growled, "Kaplan too old for have bir-day." (Mr. Wilkomirski was a member of the Opposition.)

"October tvalf I'm born; October tvalf I'm tsalebratink!" Mr. Kaplan retorted. "All mine *life* I'm hevink boitdays October tvalf. No haxceptions!"

Mr. Parkhill said, "Well, well, well. That *is* a coincidence. October twelfth. Hmm." He smiled politely. "I'm sure we all wish Mr. Kaplan many happy returns."

Mr. Kaplan beamed, jumped to his feet, bowed, and sat down, beaming.

Miss Mitnick, feeling the occasion called for good will and peace among men, said, "Congratulations."

Mr. Kaplan said, "Denks."

"However," Mr. Parkhill went on resolutely, "the historical anniversary is that of Christopher Columbus. On October twelfth, 1492—"

*"Colom*biss!" Mr. Kaplan's rapture positively exploded.

Excitement seized the beginners' grade. "Colombus!" "Aha!" "Columbia Day!" "Colombos discovert America!"

"On October twelfth, 1492—"

Mr. Trabish dropped a sneer in the general direction of Fanny Gidwitz. "And you sad Jawdge Vashington!"

"You said Paul Rewere!"

"On October twelfth, 1492," persevered Mr. Parkhill.

"By me is avery day in year somthing about Paul Rewere!"

"And by *me* is our foist Prazident vert ten hoss-riders!"

"On October twelfth, 1492"—Mr. Parkhill's voice had risen until it was commanding—"Christopher Columbus discovered a new continent!"

The class quieted down at last, and Mr. Parkhill launched upon the saga of Christopher Columbus. He spoke slowly, impressively, almost with fervor. They listened to him closely, caught by the drama of the great voyage. "The food ran low. Water was scarce. The sailors began to grumble. . . ."

Goldie Pomeranz leaned forward and sighed moistly into Mr. Kaplan's ear, "You soitinly locky, Mr. Kaplan. Born same day Columbus did."

Mr. Kaplan was in a world of dreams. *"Christover Colombiss!"* He kept whispering the name to himself. "My!" He had closed his eyes to be alone with his hero. "October tvalf I'm arrivink in de voild—an' October tvalf Colombiss picks ot for discoverink U.S.! Dastiny."

"Mutiny faced Christopher Columbus," Mr. Parkhill said with feeling.

"My boitday is Motch toity," Miss Pomeranz whispered to Mr. Kaplan with sad envy. "Not iven a soborb vas discovered Motch toity."

Mr. Kaplan gave Miss Pomeranz a modest murmur. "Ufcawss, Colombiss discovert lonk bafore I arrived."

"October twalf is October twalf!" cried Mr. Pinsky, a true-blue Kaplan supporter.

Mr. Kaplan sighed, nodded, and let the mantle of history fall upon his shoulders.

Mr. Parkhill, driven to greater efforts by the Pomeranz-Kaplan-Pinsky symposium, told the class of the geographical boundaries in 1492, of the then current belief that the world was flat, of the mockery to which Columbus had been subjected. He described the singular confluence of events which had led to the new continent's being named after Amerigo Vespucci. ("A *mistake!"* Mr. Kaplan cried indignantly.) Mr. Parkhill outlined the immortal voyage of three tiny ships across an ocean infested in men's minds by monstrous things. When he said, "And because Columbus thought he was really in India, he called the natives Indians," the amazement of the beginners' grade of the American Night Preparatory School for Adults burst its bonds.

"Vun mistake on top de odder!" Mr. Kaplan moaned.

"So dey called Hindyans by *mistake?"* asked Mrs. Moskowitz, wide-eyed. Mrs. Moskowitz could scarcely believe that of history.

"Yes, Mrs. Moskowitz, by mistake," said Mr. Parkhill quietly.

Mr. Kaplan shook his head three times. "Dose poor Hindyans."

Mr. Parkhill hurried on to details about Ferdinand and Isabella

27731

Just before he had completed the absorbing tale, Mr. Kaplan announced, without warning, "Ectual ve ain't Americans!"

Mr. Parkhill paused. "'Actual*ly,* we *are*n't Americans,' Mr. Kaplan. There is no such word as—"

"Ectual ve all Colombians!" Mr. Kaplan cried. A passion for justice flamed in his eyes.

Mr. Parkhill turned the class over to Miss Mitnick for General Discussion. General Discussion, Mr. Parkhill had found, was a particularly fruitful exercise, and he occasionally invited one of the more competent students, like Miss Mitnick, to lead the discussion. It was even better training than the more formal Recitation and Speech periods and aroused fewer anxieties in the breasts of the timid.

Miss Mitnick struck the keynote for the evening with a touching if half-embarrassed eulogy of explorers in general and Columbus in particular. She ended her comments with a deft comparison of Columbus with Admiral Byrd. "Both men fond new places for humanity. Natchelly, in different places."

"Edmiral Boyd?" Mr. Kaplan sniffed at once. It was clear that henceforth anyone drawing comparisons between Columbus and lesser spirits would have to answer to Hyman Kaplan. "Vat kind finder new tings is dis Edmiral Boyd?"

"It's '*Ad*miral *Byrd,*'" Mr. Parkhill suggested from the seat he had taken next to Mr. Studniczka.

"Admiral Byrd is a kind *modern* Columbus," Miss Mitnick said, blushing.

"Vat he discovert should compare Colombiss's vunderful didd?" There was hauteur in Mr. Kaplan's tone.

"Admiral Byrd discovered Sout Pole," Miss Mitnick said. She looked a little frightened.

"Som discoverink!" said Mr. Kaplan, dismissing Antarctica scornfully.

"Sout Pole is important, Mr. Kaplan! It has—"

"It's to leff! Averybody *knew* vas Sot Pole, no? All Edmiral Boyd did vas *go* dere!"

Miss Mitnick turned pale.

"*Ad*miral *Byrd,* Mr. Kaplan," said Mr. Parkhill.

"Admiral Byrd is big *hero,*" Miss Mitnick insisted, wetting her lips. "He went through terrible things for humanity—cold, icebergs, alone, freezings."

"Edmiral Boyd *vent mit all modinn conweniences!*"

Miss Mitnick shot a wild S.O.S. to Mr. Parkhill.

"Er—it's *Ad*miral *Byrd!*" Mr. Parkhill said. No one paid any attention to him.

Miss Caravello plunged into the controversy with a passionate "Is only da one Columbus! No more lak!" It was clear that to Miss Caravello Columbus was a peculiarly Italian phenomenon, unparalleled, incomparable. Admiral Byrd, she said flatly, was a "copying cat." For Columbus, Miss Caravello concluded hotly, nothing short of a thousand *"Viva"*s would do. She proceeded to give three of them: *"Viva! Viva! Viva!"*

Mr. Kaplan broke into furious applause.

Now Mr. Gus Matsoukas demanded the floor. "Colomb' good man, no doubts about," he began magnanimously. Columbus was, indeed, worth all that Mr. Kaplan and Miss Caravello had claimed for him. But after all, Mr. Matsoukas insinuated, should one not regard Columbus as no more than a sort of descendant of the first and *greatest* explorer—Ulysses? Ulysses, it turned out, was born in a town no more than seventeen kilometres from Mr. Matsoukas's birthplace.

"Boit*days* is more important den boit*places!*" Mr. Kaplan said.

Mr. Matsoukas, crestfallen, could think of no answer to this proposition. He fell back into his normal coma.

"Anybody else wants to say few words?" asked Miss Mitnick.

There were vague mumblings. Mr. Kaplan raised his hand.

"Floor is *open,*" Miss Mitnick announced. She kept her eyes away from Mr. Kaplan. *"Any*body can talk."

Mr. Kaplan rose at once, said "Foidinand an' Isabel. Ha!" and sat down.

There was a nervous silence. Miss Mitnick twisted her handkerchief around her fingers. "Mr. Kaplan, please," she stammered. "I didn't catch."

Mr. Kaplan got up again. "Foidinand an' Isabel. Ha!" He sat down.

Miss Mitnick looked to Mr. Parkhill in anguish.

"Er—Mr. Kaplan . . ."

"Axplain, Keplen!" Mr. Plonsky called out.

Mr. Kaplan said nothing.

"Keplen wants to talk or Keplen *not* wants to talk?" Mr. Plonsky asked the elements ironically.

Mr. Parkhill recognized his responsibility and decided to intervene.

"Y-yes, Mr. Kaplan. I do think the class is entitled to some explanation of your brief—er—comment."

"All of a sodden Mr. Kaplan makes fun Foidinand, Isabel!" Mrs. Moskowitz snickered. "Not even sayink 'Axcuse!' he makes 'Ha, ha!' on kinks and quinns!"

This frontal attack stirred the royalists into action.

"Talk, Kaplan!"

"You got the floor, no?"

"Tell awreddy! Tell!"

A more formal dialectician cried, "Give your meanink dose remocks!"

Mr. Kaplan faced his attackers calmly, almost apologetically. "Ladies an gantlemen, Mr. Pockheel—an' chairlady." Miss Mitnick lowered her eyes. "Ve all agreeink Colombiss's joiney vas vun de most movvellous tings in de voild." There were murmurs of affirmation. "*Tink* abot det treep, jost *tink*. Viks an' viks Colombiss vas sailink—tru storm, lighteninks, tonder. Tru vafes high like Ampire State Buildink. Fodder an' fodder Colombiss vent—alone!" Mr. Kaplan paused to let the drama sink home. "Vell, in *vat kind boats* Colombiss made det vunderful voyitch?" Mr. Kaplan's eyes narrowed. "I esk—*in vat kind boats?* Leetle, teentsy sheeps! Chizz boxes! Boats full likks! Boats full doit, joims, vater commink in! *Som* boats for discoverink America! An' det's vy I'm sayink '*Shame* on you, Foidinand an' Isabel!' " Mr. Kaplan's eyes flashed. "Couldn't dey give a man like Colombiss batter transportation?"

Fury broke in the classroom.

"Bravo!" cried Miss Caravello. "Bravo!"

"Crazy talk," muttered Mr. Matsoukas, thinking of the raft of Ulysses.

"Maybe dey should builded in 1492 a S.S. Quinn Marie?" asked Mr. Plonsky sarcastically.

Attacks, defences, taunts filled the scholastic air. Miss Mitnick, charged with the duties of arbitration, kept stammering, "Mr. Kaplan please. Mr. Kaplan please." Her voice shook. "Mr. Kaplan please. The ships Ferdinand and Isabella gave were fine for that *time.*"

"For de *time?* But not for de *man!*"

"But in those days—"

"A man like Colombiss should have averyting fromm de bast!"

Mr. Parkhill got up. It seemed to be the only thing to do. "Well, class, I think—"

"Colombiss desoived more den a Senta Maria, a Nina, an' a Pintele!" Mr. Kaplan, soulmate of Columbus, plunged on in his passion, hacking right and left without mercy in the service of his historical partner. "I say det ven a man stotts ot to discover America—"

"Columbus didn't go to discover a specifical *place*," Miss Mitnick objected.

"He didn't go for axercise!" cried Hyman Kaplan.

Miss Mitnick bit her lip. "I mean Columbus didn't *know* was America. He didn't know was a continent in Atlentic Ocean. Columbus just went out ..."

Mr. Kaplan regarded Miss Mitnick with tolerance. *"Vy* he vent ot, plizz?"

"To—to discover," Miss Mitnick said feebly.

"Vat to discover?"

Tears were in Miss Mitnick's eyes. "Just to *discover.*"

Mr. Kaplan looked from side to side, nodding. "Colombiss vent 'jost to discover,' " he repeated softly. " 'Jost to discover.' " He sighed and shook his head, mourning man's naïveté. And then, his face lit with fervor, he struck. "Som people tink det if a man goes ot to mail a latter he *hopes* he'll find a mailbox!"

And now the battle raged once more—with shouts and cries and accusations; with lusty assaults on Mr. Kaplan's logic, and hot defences of Rose Mitnick.

In the corridors the bell rang, but no one heard it. The bell rang again, loud and long, but no one cared.

Mr. Parkhill said, "That's all for tonight, class." He said it calmly, but he had a worried look. For Mr. Parkhill felt that General Discussion had not been a complete success this evening. If only Columbus had discovered America on October eleventh; if only Hyman Kaplan had been born on October thirteenth.

Frank R. Stockton

THE CASTING AWAY OF MRS. LECKS AND MRS. ALESHINE *

I was on my way from San Francisco to Yokohama, when in a very desultory and gradual manner I became acquainted with Mrs. Lecks and Mrs. Aleshine. The steamer, on which I was making a moderately rapid passage toward the land of the legended fan and the lacquered box, carried a fair complement of passengers, most of whom were Americans; and, among these, my attention was attracted from the very first day of the voyage to two middle-aged women who appeared to me very unlike the ordinary traveler or tourist. At first sight they might have been taken for farmers' wives who, for some unusual reason, had determined to make a voyage across the Pacific; but, on closer observation, one would have been more apt to suppose that they belonged to the families of prosperous tradesmen in some little country town, where, besides the arts of rural housewifery, there would be opportunities of becoming acquainted in some degree with the ways and manners of the outside world. They were not of that order of persons who generally take first-class passages on steamships, but the stateroom occupied by Mrs. Lecks and Mrs. Aleshine was one of the best in the vessel.

Mrs. Lecks was a rather tall woman, large-boned and muscular, and her well-browned countenance gave indications of that conviction of superiority which gradually grows up in the minds of those who for a long time have had absolute control of the destinies of a state, or the multifarious affairs of a country household. Mrs. Aleshine was somewhat younger than her friend, somewhat shorter, and a great deal fatter. She had the same air of reliance upon her individual

---

This is Part I of the Stockton novel "The Casting Away of Mrs. Lecks and Mrs. Aleshine." A few cuts have been made, and a few sentences from Part II have been added—this last for the purpose of getting the ladies into smooth water and within reach of land. It seemed the decent thing to do.

26

worth that characterized Mrs. Lecks, but there was a certain geniality about her which indicated that she would have a good deal of forbearance for those who never had had the opportunity or the ability of becoming the thoroughly good housewife which she was herself.

These two worthy dames spent the greater part of their time on deck, where they always sat together in a place at the stern of the vessel which was well sheltered from wind and weather. As they sat thus they were generally employed in knitting, although this occupation did not prevent them from keeping up what seemed to me, as I passed them in my walks about the deck, a continuous conversation. From a question which Mrs. Lecks once asked me about a distant sail, our acquaintance began. There was no one on board for whose society I particularly cared, and as there was something quaint and odd about these countrywomen on the ocean which interested me, I was glad to vary my solitary promenades by an occasional chat with them. They were not at all backward in giving me information about themselves. They were both widows, and Mrs. Aleshine was going out to Japan to visit a son who had a position there in a mercantile house. Mrs. Lecks had no children, and was accompanying her friend because, as she said, she would not allow Mrs. Aleshine to make such a voyage as that by herself, and because, being quite able to do so, she did not know why she should not see the world as well as other people.

These two friends were not educated women. They made frequent mistakes in their grammar, and a good deal of Middle States provincialism showed itself in their pronunciation and expressions. But although they brought many of their rural ideas to sea with them, they possessed a large share of that common sense which is available anywhere, and they frequently made use of it in a manner which was very amusing to me. I think, also, that they found in me a quarry of information concerning nautical matters, foreign countries, and my own affairs, the working of which helped to make us very good ship friends.

Our steamer touched at the Sandwich Islands; and it was a little more than two days after we left Honolulu that, about nine o'clock in the evening, we had the misfortune to come into collision with an eastern-bound vessel. This vessel, which appeared to be a small steamer, struck us with great force near our bows, and then, backing, disappeared into the fog, and we never saw or heard of her again.

It was soon discovered that our injuries were serious and, indeed, disastrous. The hull of our steamer had been badly shattered on the port bow, and the water came in at a most alarming rate. For nearly two hours the crew and many of the passengers worked at the pumps, and everything possible was done to stop the enormous leak; but all labor to save the vessel was found to be utterly unavailing, and a little before midnight the captain announced that it was impossible to keep the steamer afloat, and that we must all take to the boats. The night was now clear, the stars were bright, and, as there was but little wind, the sea was comparatively smooth. With all these advantages, the captain assured us that there was no reason to apprehend danger, and he thought that by noon of the following day we could easily make a small inhabited island, where we could be sheltered and cared for until we should be taken off by some passing vessel.

There was plenty of time for all necessary preparations, and these were made with much order and subordination. Everybody obeyed the captain's orders, and all prepared themselves for the transfer to the boats. The first officer came among us, and told each of us what boats we were to take, and where we were to place ourselves on deck. I was assigned to a large boat which was to be principally occupied by steerage passengers; and as I came up from my stateroom, where I had gone to secure my money and some portable valuables, I met on the companionway Mrs. Lecks and Mrs. Aleshine, who expressed considerable dissatisfaction when they found that I was not going in the boat with them. They, however, hurried below, and I went on deck, where in about ten minutes I was joined by Mrs. Lecks, who apparently had been looking for me. She told me she had something very particular to say to me, and conducted me toward the stern of the vessel, where, behind one of the deck-houses, we found Mrs. Aleshine.

"Look here," said Mrs. Lecks, leading me to the rail, and pointing downward; "do you see that boat there? It has been let down, and there is nobody in it. The boat on the other side has just gone off, full to the brim. I never saw so many people crowded into a boat. The other ones will be just as packed, I expect. I don't see why we shouldn't take this empty boat, now we've got a chance, instead of squeezin' ourselves into those crowded ones. If any of the other people come afterward, why, we shall have our choice of seats, and that's considerable of a p'int, I should say, in a time like this."

"That's so," said Mrs. Aleshine; "and me and Mrs. Lecks would 'a' got right in when we saw the boat was empty, if we hadn't been afraid to be there without any man, for it might have floated off, and neither of us don't know nothin' about rowin'. And then Mrs. Lecks she thought of you, supposin' a young man who knew so much about the sea would know how to row."

"Oh, yes," said I; "but I cannot imagine why this boat should have been left empty. I see a keg of water in it, and the oars, and some tin cans, and so I suppose it has been made ready for somebody. Will you wait here a minute until I run forward and see how things are going on there?"

Amidships and forward I saw that there was some confusion among the people who were not yet in their boats, and I found that there was to be rather more crowding than at first was expected. People who had supposed that they were to go in a certain boat found there no place, and were hurrying to other boats. It now became plain to me that no time should be lost in getting into the small boat which Mrs. Lecks had pointed out, so I slipped quietly aft, and joined Mrs. Lecks and Mrs. Aleshine.

"We must get in as soon as we can," said I, in a low voice, "for this boat may be discovered, and then there will be a rush for it. I suspect it may have been reserved for the captain and some of the officers, but we have as much right in it as they."

"And more too," replied Mrs. Lecks; "for we had nothin' to do with the steerin' and smashin'."

"But how are we goin' to get down there?" said Mrs. Aleshine. "There's no steps."

"That is true," said I. "I shouldn't wonder if this boat is to be taken forward when the others are filled. We must scramble down as well as we can by the tackle at the bow and stern. I'll get in first and keep her close to the ship's side."

"That's goin' to be a scratchy business," said Mrs. Lecks, "and I'm of the opinion we ought to wait till the ship has sunk a little more, so we'll be nearer to the boat."

"It won't do to wait," said I, "or we shall not get in it at all."

"And goodness gracious!" exclaimed Mrs. Aleshine, "I can't stand here and feel the ship sinkin' cold-blooded under me, till we've got where we can make an easy jump!"

"Very well, then," said Mrs. Lecks, "we won't wait. But the first

BRIAR CLIFF COLLEGE
LIBRARY
SIOUX CITY, IOWA

thing to be done is for each one of us to put on one of these life-preservers. Two of them I brought from Mrs. Aleshine's and my cabin, and the other one I got next door, where the people had gone off and left it on the floor. I thought if anythin' happened on the way to the island, these would give us a chance to look about us; but it seems to me we'll need 'em more gettin' down them ropes than any-where else. I did intend puttin' on two myself to make up for Mrs. Aleshine's fat; but you must wear one of 'em, sir, now that you are goin' to join the party."

As I knew that two life-preservers would not be needed by Mrs. Lecks, and would greatly inconvenience her, I accepted the one offered me, but declined to put it on until it should be necessary, as it would interfere with my movements.

"Very well," said Mrs. Lecks, "if you think you are safe in gettin' down without it. But Mrs. Aleshine and me will put ours on before we begin sailor-scramblin'. We know how to do it, for we tried 'em on soon after we started from San Francisco. And now, Barb'ry Aleshine, are you sure you've got everythin' you want? for it'll be no use thinkin' about anythin' you've forgot after the ship has sunk out of sight."

"There's nothin' else I can think of," said Mrs. Aleshine; "at least, nothin' I can carry; and so I suppose we may as well begin, for your talk of the ship sinkin' under our feet gives me a sort o' feelin' like an oyster creepin' up and down my back."

Mrs. Lecks looked over the side at the boat, into which I had already descended. "I'll go first, Barb'ry Aleshine," said she, "and show you how."

The sea was quiet, and the steamer had already sunk so much that Mrs. Lecks's voice sounded frightfully near me, although she spoke in a low tone.

"Watch me," said she to her companion. "I'm goin' to do just as he did, and you must follow in the same way."

So saying, she stepped on a bench by the rail; then, with one foot on the rail itself, she seized the ropes which hung from one of the davits to the bow of the boat. She looked down for a moment, and then she drew back.

"It's no use," she said. "We must wait until she sinks more, and I can get in easier."

This remark made me feel nervous. I did not know at what moment there might be a rush for this boat, nor when, indeed, the steamer might go down. The boat amidships on our side had rowed away some minutes before, and through the darkness I could distinguish another boat, near the bows, pushing off. It would be too late now for us to try to get into any other boat, and I did not feel that there was time enough for me to take this one to a place where the two women could more easily descend to her. Standing upright, I urged them not to delay.

"You see," said I, "I can reach you as soon as you swing yourself off the ropes, and I'll help you down."

"If you're sure you can keep us from comin' down too sudden, we'll try it," said Mrs. Lecks; "but I'd as soon be drowned as to get to an island with a broken leg. And as to Mrs. Aleshine, if she was to slip she'd go slam through that boat to the bottom of the sea. Now, then, be ready! I'm comin' down."

So saying, she swung herself off, and she was then so near me that I was able to seize her and make the rest of her descent comparatively easy. Mrs. Aleshine proved to be a more difficult subject. Even after I had a firm grasp of her capacious waist she refused to let go the ropes, for fear that she might drop into the ocean instead of the boat. But the reproaches of Mrs. Lecks and the downward weight of myself made her loosen her nervous grip; and, although we came very near going overboard together, I safely placed her on one of the thwarts.

I now unhooked the tackle from the stern; but before casting off at the bow I hesitated, for I did not wish to desert any of those who might be expecting to embark in this boat. But I could hear no approaching footsteps, and from my position, close to the side of the steamer, I could see nothing. Therefore I cast off, and, taking the oars, I pushed away and rowed to a little distance, where I could get whatever view was possible of the deck of the steamer. Seeing no forms moving about, I called out, and, receiving no answer, I shouted again at the top of my voice. I waited for nearly a minute, and, hearing nothing and seeing nothing, I became convinced that no one was left on the vessel.

"They are all gone," said I, "and we will pull after them as fast as we can."

And I began to row toward the bow of the steamer, in the direction which the other boats had taken.

"It's a good thing you can row," said Mrs. Lecks, settling herself comfortably in the stern-sheets, "for what Mrs. Aleshine and me would ha' done with them oars I am sure I don't know."

"I'd never have got into this boat," said Mrs. Aleshine, "if Mr. Craig hadn't been here."

"No, indeed," replied her friend. "You'd ha' gone to the bottom, hangin' for dear life to them ropes."

When I had rounded the bow of the steamer, which appeared to me to be rapidly settling in the water, I perceived at no great distance several lights, which of course belonged to the other boats, and I rowed as hard as I could, hoping to catch up with them, or at least to keep sufficiently near. It might be my duty to take off some of the people who had crowded into the other boats, probably supposing that this one had been loaded and gone. How such a mistake could have taken place I could not divine, and it was not my business to do so. Quite certain that no one was left on the sinking steamer, all I had to do was to row after the other boats, and to overtake them as soon as possible. I thought it would not take me very long to do this, but after rowing for half an hour, Mrs. Aleshine remarked that the lights seemed as far off, if not farther, than when we first started after them. Turning, I saw that this was the case, and was greatly surprised. With only two passengers I ought soon to have come up with those heavily laden boats. But after I had thought over it a little, I considered that as each of them was probably pulled by half a dozen stout sailors, it was not so very strange that they should make as good or better headway than I did.

It was not very long after this that Mrs. Lecks said that she thought that the lights on the other boats must be going out, and that this, most probably, was due to the fact that the sailors had forgotten to fill their lanterns before they started. "That sort of thing often happens," she said, "when people leave a place in a hurry."

But when I turned around, and peered over the dark waters, it was quite plain to me that it was not want of oil, but increased distance, which made those lights so dim. I could now perceive but three of them. We were being left behind, that was certain, and all I could do was to row on as long and as well as I could in the direction which the other boats had taken.

"I don't believe this boat has been emptied out since the last rain," said Mrs. Aleshine, "for my feet are wet, though I didn't notice it before."

At this I shipped my oars, and began to examine the boat. The bottom was covered with a movable floor of slats, and as I put my hand down I could feel the water welling up between the slats. The flooring was in sections, and lifting the one beneath me, I felt under it, and put my hand into six or eight inches of water.

The exact state of the case was now as plain to me as if it had been posted up on a bulletin-board. This boat had been found to be unseaworthy, and its use had been forbidden, all the people having been crowded into the others. This had caused confusion at the last moment, and, of course, we were supposed to be on some one of the other boats.

And now here was I, in the middle of the Pacific Ocean, in a leaky boat, with two middle-aged women!

"Anythin' the matter with the floor?" asked Mrs. Lecks.

I let the section fall back into its place, and looked aft. By the starlight I could see that my two companions had each fixed upon me a steadfast gaze. They evidently felt that something was the matter, and wanted to know what it was. I did not hesitate for a moment to inform them. They appeared to me to be women whom it would be neither advisable nor possible to deceive in a case like this.

"This boat has a leak in it," I said. "There is a lot of water in her already, and that is the reason we have got along so slowly."

"And that is why," said Mrs. Aleshine, "it was left empty. We ought to have known better than to expect to have a whole boat just for three of us. It would have been much more sensible, I think, if we had tried to squeeze into one of the others."

"Now, Barb'ry Aleshine," said Mrs. Lecks, "don't you begin findin' fault with good fortune, when it comes to you. Here we've got a comfortable boat, with room enough to set easy and stretch out if we want to. If the water is comin' in, what we've got to do is to get it out again just as fast as we can. What's the best way to do that, Mr. Craig?"

"We must bail her out, and lose no time about it," said I. "If I can find the leak I may be able to stop it."

I now looked about for something to bail with, and the two women aided actively in the search. I found one leather scoop in the bow; but as it was well that we should all go to work, I took two tin cans that had been put in by some one who had begun to provision the boat, and proceeded to cut the tops from them with my jack-knife.

"Don't lose what's in 'em," said Mrs. Lecks; "that is, if it's anythin' we'd be likely to want to eat. If it's tomatoes, pour it into the sea, for nobody ought to eat tomatoes put up in tins."

I hastily passed the cans to Mrs. Lecks, and I saw her empty the contents of one into the sea, and those of the other on a newspaper which she took from her pocket and placed in the stern.

I pulled up the movable floor and threw it overboard, and then began to bail.

"I thought," said Mrs. Aleshine, "that they always had pumps for leaks."

"Now, Barb'ry Aleshine," said Mrs. Lecks, "just gether yourself up on one of them seats, and go to work. The less talkin' we do, and the more scoopin', the better it'll be for us."

I soon perceived that it would have been difficult to find two more valuable assistants in the bailing of a boat than Mrs. Lecks and Mrs. Aleshine. They were evidently used to work, and were able to accommodate themselves to the unusual circumstances in which they were placed. We threw out the water very rapidly, and every little while I stopped bailing and felt about to see if I could discover where it came in. As these attempts met with no success, I gave them up after a time, and set about bailing with new vigor, believing that if we could get the boat nearly dry I should surely be able to find the leak.

But, after working half an hour more, I found that the job would be a long one; and if we all worked at once we would all be tired out at once, and that might be disastrous. Therefore I proposed that we should take turns in resting, and Mrs. Aleshine was ordered to stop work for a time. After this Mrs. Lecks took a rest, and when she went to work I stopped bailing and began again to search for the leak.

For about two hours we worked in this way, and then I concluded it was useless to continue any longer this vain exertion. With three of us bailing we were able to keep the water at the level we first found it; but with only two at work, it slightly gained upon us, so that now there was more water in the boat than when we first discovered it. The boat was an iron one, the leak in it I could neither find nor remedy, and it was quite plain that the water was now coming in more rapidly than it did at first. We were very tired, and even Mrs. Lecks, who had all along counseled us to keep at work, and not to waste one breath in talking, now admitted that it was of no use to try to get the water out of that boat.

It had been some hours since I had used the oars, but whether we had drifted, or remained where we were when I stopped rowing, of course I could not know; but this mattered very little; our boat was slowly sinking beneath us, and it could make no difference whether we went down in one spot or another. I sat and racked my brain to think what could be done in this fearful emergency. To bail any longer was useless labor, and what else was there that we could do?

"When will it be time," asked Mrs. Lecks, "for us to put on the life-preservers? When the water gets nearly to the seats?"

I answered that we should not wait any longer than that, but in my own mind I could not see any advantage in putting them on at all. Why should we wish to lengthen our lives by a few hours of helpless floating upon the ocean?

"Very good," said Mrs. Lecks; "I'll keep a watch on the water. One of them cans was filled with lobster, which would be more than likely to disagree with us, and I've throwed it out; but the other had baked beans in it, and the best thing we can do is to eat some of these right away. They are mighty nourishin', and will keep up strength as well as anythin', and then, as you said there's a keg of water in the boat, we can all take a drink of that, and it'll make us feel like new cre'tur's. You'll have to take the beans in your hands, for we've got no spoons nor forks."

Mrs. Lecks and Mrs. Aleshine were each curled up out of reach of the water, the first in the stern, and the other on the aft thwart. The day was now beginning to break, and we could see about us very distinctly. Before reaching out her hands to receive her beans, Mrs. Aleshine washed them in the water in the boat, remarking at the same time that she might as well make use of it since it was there. Having then wiped her hands on some part of her apparel, they were filled with beans from the newspaper held by Mrs. Lecks, and these were passed over to me. I was very hungry, and when I had finished my beans I agreed with my companions that although they would have been a great deal better if heated up with butter, pepper, and salt, they were very comforting as they were. One of the empty cans was now passed to me, and after having been asked by Mrs. Lecks to rinse it out very carefully, we all satisfied our taste from the water in the keg.

"Cold baked beans and lukewarm water ain't exactly company vittles," said Mrs. Aleshine, "but there's many a poor wretch would be glad to get 'em."

I could not imagine any poor wretch who would be glad of the food together with the attending circumstances; but I did not say so.

"The water is just one finger from the bottom of the seat," said Mrs. Lecks, who had been stooping over to measure, "and it's time to put on the life-preservers."

"Very good," said Mrs. Aleshine; "hand me mine."

Each of us now buckled on a life-preserver, and as I did so I stood up upon a thwart and looked about me. It was quite light now, and I could see for a long distance over the surface of the ocean, which was gently rolling in wide, smooth swells. As we rose upon the summit of one of these I saw a dark spot upon the water, just on the edge of our near horizon. "Is that the steamer?" I thought; "and has she not yet sunk?"

At this there came to me a glimmering of courageous hope. If the steamer had remained afloat so long, it was probable that on account of water-tight compartments, or for some other reason, her sinking had reached its limit, and that if we could get back to her we might be saved. But, alas, how were we to get back to her? This boat would sink long, long before I could row that distance.

However, I soon proclaimed the news to my companions, whereupon Mrs. Aleshine prepared to stand upon a thwart and see for herself. But Mrs. Lecks restrained her.

"Don't make things worse, Barb'ry Aleshine," said she, "by tumblin' overboard. If we've got to go into the water, let us do it decently and in order. If that's the ship, Mr. Craig, don't you suppose we can float ourselves to it in some way?"

I replied that by the help of a life-preserver a person who could swim might reach the ship.

"But neither of us can swim," said Mrs. Lecks, "for we've lived where the water was never more'n a foot deep, except in time of freshets, when there's no swimmin' for man or beast. But if we see you swim, perhaps we can follow, after a fashion. At any rate, we must do the best we can, and that's all there is to be done."

"The water now," remarked Mrs. Aleshine, "is so near to the bottom of my seat that I've got to stand up, tumble overboard or no."

"All right," remarked Mrs. Lecks; "we'd better all stand up, and let the boat sink under us. That will save our jumpin' overboard, or rollin' out any which way, which might be awkward."

"Goodness gracious me!" exclaimed Mrs. Aleshine. "You set the oysters creepin' over me again! First you talk of the ship sinkin' under us, and now it's the boat goin' to the bottom under our feet. Before any sinkin' 's to be done I'd ruther get out."

"Now, Barb'ry Aleshine," said Mrs. Lecks, "stand up straight, and don't talk so much. It'll be a great deal better to be let down gradual than to flop into the water all of a bunch."

"Very well," said Mrs. Aleshine; "it may be best to get used to it by degrees; but I must say I wish I was home."

As for me, I would have much preferred to jump overboard at once, instead of waiting in this cold-blooded manner; but as my companions had so far preserved their presence of mind, I did not wish to do anything which might throw them into a panic. I believed there would be no danger from the suction caused by the sinking of a small boat like this, and if we took care not to entangle ourselves with it in any way, we might as well follow Mrs. Lecks's advice as not. So we all stood up, Mrs. Lecks in the stern, I in the bow, and Mrs. Aleshine on a thwart between us. The last did not appear to have quite room enough for a steady footing, but, as she remarked, it did not matter very much, as the footing, broad or narrow, would not be there very long.

I am used to swimming, and have never hesitated to take a plunge into river or ocean, but I must admit that it was very trying to my nerves to stand up this way and wait for a boat to sink beneath me. How the two women were affected I do not know. They said nothing, but their faces indicated that something disagreeable was about to happen, and that the less that was said about it the better.

The boat had now sunk so much that the water was around Mrs. Aleshine's feet, her standing-place being rather lower than ours. I made myself certain that there were no ropes nor any other means of entanglement near my companions or myself, and then I waited. There seemed to be a good deal of buoyancy in the bow and stern of the boat, and it was a frightfully long time in sinking. The suspense became so utterly unendurable that I was tempted to put one foot on the edge of the boat, and, by tipping it, put an end to this nerve-rack; but I refrained, for I probably would throw the women off their balance, when they might fall against some part of the boat, and do themselves a hurt. I had just relinquished this intention, when two little waves seemed to rise one on each side of Mrs. Aleshine, and gently flowing over the side of the boat, they flooded her feet with water.

"Hold your breaths!" I shouted. And now I experienced a sensation which must have been very like that which comes to a condemned criminal at the first indication of the pulling of the drop. Then there was a horrible sinking, a gurgle, and a swash, and the ocean over which I had been gazing appeared to rise up and envelop me.

In a moment, however, my head was out of the water, and, looking hastily about me, I saw, close by, the heads and shoulders of Mrs. Lecks and Mrs. Aleshine. The latter was vigorously winking her eyes and blowing from her mouth some sea-water that had got into it; but as soon as her eyes fell upon me she exclaimed: "That was ever so much more suddint than I thought it was goin' to be!"

"Are you both all right?"

"I suppose I am," said Mrs. Aleshine, "but I never thought that a person with a life-preserver on would go clean under the water."

"But since you've come up again, you ought to be satisfied," said Mrs. Lecks. "And now," she added, turning her face toward me, "which way ought we to try to swim? and have we got everythin' we want to take with us?"

"What we haven't got we can't get," remarked Mrs. Aleshine; "and as for swimmin', I expect I'm goin' to make a poor hand at it."

I had a hope, which was not quite strong enough to be a belief, that, supported by their life-preservers, the two women might paddle themselves along; and that, by giving them in turn a helping hand, I might eventually get them to the steamer. There was a strong probability that I would not succeed, but I did not care to think of that.

I now swam in front of my companions, and endeavored to instruct them in the best method of propelling themselves with their arms and their hands. If they succeeded in this, I thought I would give them some further lessons in striking out with their feet. After watching me attentively, Mrs. Lecks did manage to move herself slowly through the smooth water, but poor Mrs. Aleshine could do nothing but splash.

"If there was anythin' to take hold of," she said to me, "I might get along; but I can't get any grip on the water, though you seem to do it well enough. Look there!" she added in a higher voice. "Isn't that an oar floatin' over there? If you can get that for me, I believe I can row myself much better than I can swim."

This seemed an odd idea, but I swam over to the floating oar, and brought it her. I was about to show her how she could best use it, but she declined my advice.

"If I do it at all," she said, "I must do it in my own way." And taking the oar in her strong hands, she began to ply it on the water very much in the way in which she would handle a broom. At first she dipped the blade too deeply, but, correcting this error, she soon began to paddle herself along at a slow but steady rate.

"Capital!" I cried. "You do that admirably!"

"Anybody who's swept as many rooms as I have," she said, "ought to be able to handle anythin' that can be used like a broom."

"Isn't there another oar?" cried Mrs. Lecks, who had now been left a little distance behind us. "If there is, I want one."

Looking about me, I soon discovered another floating oar, and brought it to Mrs. Lecks, who, after holding it in various positions, so as to get "the hang of it," as she said, soon began to use it with as much skill as that shown by her friend. If either of them had been obliged to use an oar in the ordinary way, I fear they would have had a bad time of it; but, considering the implement in the light of a broom, its use immediately became familiar to them, and they got on remarkably well.

I now took a position a little in advance of my companions, and as I swam slowly they were easily able to keep up with me. Mrs. Aleshine, being so stout, floated much higher out of the water than either Mrs. Lecks or I, and this permitted her to use her oar with a great deal of freedom. Sometimes she would give such a vigorous brush to the water that she would turn herself almost entirely around, but after a little practice she learned to avoid undue efforts of this kind.

I was not positively sure that we were going in the right direction, for my position did not allow me to see very far over the water; but I remembered that when I was standing up in the boat, and made my discovery, the sun was just about to rise in front of me, while the dark spot on the ocean lay to my left. Judging, therefore, from the present position of the sun, which was not very high, I concluded that we were moving toward the north, and therefore in the right direction. How far off the steamer might be I had no idea, for I was not accustomed to judging distances at sea; but I believed that if we were careful of our strength, and if the ocean continued as smooth as it now was, we might eventually reach the vessel, provided she were yet afloat.

"After you are fairly in the water," said Mrs. Aleshine, as she swept along, although without the velocity which that phrase usually implies, "it isn't half so bad as I thought it would be. For one thing, it don't feel a bit salt, although I must say it tasted horribly that way when I first went into it."

"You didn't expect to find pickle-brine, did you?" said Mrs. Lecks. "Though, if it was, I suppose we could float on it settin'."

"And as to bein' cold," said Mrs. Aleshine, "the part of me that's in is actually more comfortable than that which is out."

"There's one thing I would have been afraid of," said Mrs. Lecks, "if we hadn't made preparations for it, and that's sharks."

"Preparations!" I exclaimed. "How in the world did you prepare for sharks?"

"Easy enough," said Mrs. Lecks. "When we went down into our room to get ready to go away in the boats we both put on black stockin's. I've read that sharks never bite colored people, although if they see a white man in the water they'll snap him up as quick as lightnin'; and black stockin's was the nearest we could come to it. You see, I thought as like as not we'd have some sort of an upset before we got through."

"It's a great comfort," remarked Mrs. Aleshine, "and I'm very glad you thought of it, Mrs. Lecks. After this I shall make it a rule: Black stockin's for sharks."

"I suppose in your case," said Mrs. Lecks, addressing me, "dark trousers will do as well."

To which I answered that I sincerely hoped they would.

"Another thing I'm thankful for," said Mrs. Aleshine, "is that I thought to put on a flannel skeert."

"And what's the good of it," said Mrs. Lecks, "when it's soppin' wet?"

"Flannel's flannel," replied her friend, "whether it's wet or dry; and if you'd had the rheumatism as much as I have, you'd know it."

To this Mrs. Lecks replied with a sniff, and asked me how soon I thought we would get sight of the ship; for if we were going the wrong way, and had to turn round and go back, it would certainly be very provoking.

I should have been happy indeed to be able to give a satisfactory answer to this question. Every time that we rose upon a swell I threw a rapid glance around the whole circle of the horizon; and at last, not a quarter of an hour after Mrs. Lecks's question, I was rejoiced to see, almost in the direction in which I supposed it ought to be, the dark spot which I had before discovered. I shouted the glad news, and as we rose again my companions strained their eyes in the direction to which I pointed. They both saw it, and were greatly satisfied.

"Now, then," said Mrs. Aleshine, "it seems as if there was somethin' to work for"; and she began to sweep her oar with great vigor.

"If you want to tire yourself out before you get there, Barb'ry Aleshine," said Mrs. Lecks, "you'd better go on in that way. Now what I advise is that we stop rowin' altogether, and have somethin' to eat; for I'm sure we need it to keep up our strength."

"Eat!" I cried. "What are you going to eat? Do you expect to catch fish?"

"And eat 'em raw?" said Mrs. Lecks. "I should think not. But do you suppose, Mr. Craig, that Mrs. Aleshine and me would go off and leave that ship without takin' somethin' to eat by the way? Let's all gether here in a bunch, and see what sort of a meal we can make. And now, Barb'ry Aleshine, if you lay your oar down there on the water, I recommend you to tie it to one of your bonnet-strings, or it'll be floatin' away, and you won't get it again."

As she said this, Mrs. Lecks put her right hand down into the water, and fumbled about, apparently in search of a pocket. I could not but smile as I thought of the condition of food when, for an hour or more, it had been a couple of feet under the surface of the ocean; but my ideas on the subject were entirely changed when I saw Mrs. Lecks hold up in the air two German sausages, and shake the briny drops from their smooth and glittering surfaces.

"There's nothin'," she said, "like sausages for shipwreck and that kind o' thing. They're very sustainin', and bein' covered with a tight skin, water can't get at 'em, no matter how you carry 'em. I wouldn't bring these out in the boat, because, havin' the beans, we might as well eat them. Have you a knife about you, Mr. Craig?"

I produced a dripping jack-knife, and after the open blade had been waved in the air to dry it a little, Mrs. Lecks proceeded to divide one of the sausages, handing the other to me to hold meanwhile.

"Now don't go eatin' sausages without bread, if you don't want 'em to give you dyspepsy," said Mrs. Aleshine, who was tugging at a submarine pocket.

"I'm very much afraid your bread is all soaked," said Mrs. Lecks.

To which her friend replied that that remained to be seen, and forthwith produced, with a splash, a glass preserve-jar with a metal top. "I saw this nearly empty, as I looked into the ship's pantry, and I stuffed into it all the soft biscuits it would hold. There was some sort of jam left at the bottom, so that the one who gets the last biscuit will have somethin' of a little spread on it. And now, Mrs. Lecks," she continued triumphantly, as she unscrewed the top, "that rubber ring has kept 'em as dry as chips. I'm mighty glad of it, for I had trouble enough gettin' this jar into my pocket, and gettin' it out, too, for that matter."

Floating thus, with our hands and shoulders above the water, we made a very good meal from the sausages and soft biscuit.

"Barb'ry Aleshine," said Mrs. Lecks, as her friend proceeded to cut the second sausage, "don't you lay that knife down, when you've done with it, as if 't was an oar; for if you do it'll sink, as like as not, about six miles. I've read that the ocean is as deep as that in some places."

"Goodness gracious me!" exclaimed Mrs. Aleshine, "I hope we are not over one of them deep spots."

"There's no knowin'," said Mrs. Lecks, "but if it's more comfortin' to think it's shallerer, we'll make up our minds that way. Now, then," she continued, "we'll finish off this meal with a little somethin' to drink. I'm not given to takin' spirits, but I never travel without a little whisky, ready mixed with water, to take if it should be needed."

So saying, she produced from one of her pockets a whisky-flask tightly corked, and of its contents we each took a sip, Mrs. Aleshine remarking that, leaving out being chilled or colicky, we were never likely to need it more than now.

Thus refreshed and strengthened, Mrs. Lecks and Mrs. Aleshine took up their oars, while I swam slightly in advance, as before. When, with occasional intermissions of rest, and a good deal of desultory conversation, we had swept and swam for about an hour, Mrs. Lecks suddenly exclaimed: "I can see that thing ever so much plainer now, and I don't believe it's a ship at all. To me it looks like bushes."

"You're mighty long-sighted without your specs," said Mrs. Aleshine, "and I'm not sure but what you're right."

For ten minutes or more I had been puzzling over the shape of the
dark spot, which was now nearly all the time in sight. Its peculiar
form had filled me with a dreadful fear that it was the steamer,
bottom upward, although I knew enough about nautical matters to
have no good reason to suppose that this could be the case. I am not
far-sighted, but when Mrs. Lecks suggested bushes, I gazed at the
distant object with totally different ideas, and soon began to believe
that it was not a ship, either right side up or wrong side up, but
that it might be an island. This belief I proclaimed to my companions, and for some time we all worked with increased energy in
the desire to get near enough to make ourselves certain in regard
to this point.

"As true as I'm standin' here," said Mrs. Lecks, who, although she
could not read without spectacles, had remarkably good sight at long
range, "them is trees and bushes that I see before me, though they do
seem to be growin' right out of the water."

"There's an island under them; you may be sure of that!" I cried.
"Isn't this ever so much better than a sinking ship?"

"I'm not so sure about that," said Mrs. Aleshine. "I'm used to the
ship, and as long as it didn't sink I'd prefer it. There's plenty to
eat on board of it, and good beds to sleep on, which is more than
can be expected on a little bushy place like that ahead of us. But then,
the ship might sink all of a suddint, beds, vittles, and all."

"Do you suppose that is the island the other boats went to?" asked
Mrs. Lecks.

This question I had already asked of myself. I had been told that
the island to which the captain intended to take his boats lay about
thirty miles south of the point where we left the steamer. Now I knew
very well that we had not come thirty miles, and had reason to believe, moreover, that the greater part of the progress we had made
had been toward the north. It was not at all probable that the position of this island was unknown to our captain; and it must, therefore,
have been considered by him as an unsuitable place for the landing
of his passengers. There might be many reasons for this unsuitable-
ness: the island might be totally barren and desolate; it might be the
abode of unpleasant natives; and, more important than anything
else, it was, in all probability, a spot where steamers never touched.

But, whatever its disadvantages, I was most wildly desirous to reach it.

"I do not believe," I said, in answer to Mrs. Lecks, "that that is the island to which the captain would have taken us; but, whatever it is, it is dry land, and we must get there as soon as we can."

"That's true," said Mrs. Aleshine, "for I'd like to have ground nearer to my feet than six miles; and if we don't find anything to eat and any place to sleep when we get there, it's no more than can be said of the place where we are now."

"You're too particular, Barb'ry Aleshine," said Mrs. Lecks, "about your comforts. If you find the ground too hard to sleep on, when you get there, you can put on your life-preserver, and go to bed in the water."

"Very good," said Mrs. Aleshine; "and if these islands are made of coral, as I've heard they are, and if they're as full of small p'ints as some coral I've got at home, you'll be glad to take a berth by me, Mrs. Lecks."

I counseled my companions to follow me as rapidly as possible, and we all pushed vigorously forward. When we had approached near enough to the island to see what sort of place it really was, we perceived that it was a low-lying spot, apparently covered with verdure, and surrounded, as far as we could see as we rose on the swells, by a rocky reef, against which a tolerably high surf was running.

Before us we could see a continuous line of white-capped breakers, and so I led my little party to the right, hoping that we would soon see signs of an opening in the reef.

We swam and paddled, however, for a long time and still the surf rolled menacingly on the rocks before us. At last we perceived, at no great distance, a spot where there seemed to be no breakers; and when we reached it we found, to our unutterable delight, that here was smooth water flowing through a wide opening in the reef.

I swam through into an open lagoon followed closely by Mrs. Lecks and Mrs. Aleshine.

The first thing that arrested our attention was a little wharf or landing-stage, erected upon the narrow beach of the island, almost opposite to us.

"As sure as I stand here," exclaimed Mrs. Lecks, who never seemed to forget her upright position, "somebody lives in this place!"

"And it isn't a stickery coral island, either," cried Mrs. Aleshine, "for that sand's as smooth as any I ever saw."

"Whoever does live here," resumed Mrs. Lecks, "has got to take us in, whether they like it or not, and the sooner we get over there the better."

Anita Loos

GENTLEMEN PREFER BLONDES*

March 16th:

A gentleman friend and I were dining at the Ritz last evening and he said that if I took a pencil and a paper and put down all of my thoughts it would make a book. This almost made me smile as what it would really make would be a whole row of encyclopediacs. I mean I seem to be thinking practically all of the time. I mean it is my favorite recreation and sometimes I sit for hours and do not seem to do anything else but think. So this gentleman said a girl with brains ought to do something else with them besides think. And he said he ought to know brains when he sees them, because he is in the senate and he spends quite a great deal of time in Washington, d. c., and when he comes into contract with brains he always notices it. So it might have all blown over but this morning he sent me a book. And so when my maid brought it to me, I said to her, "Well, Lulu, here is another book and we have not read half the ones we have got yet." But when I opened it and saw that it was all a blank I remembered what my gentleman acquaintance said, and so then I realized that it was a diary. So here I am writing a book instead of reading one.

But now it is the 16th of March and of course it is to late to begin with January, but it does not matter as my gentleman friend, Mr. Eisman, was in town practically all of January and February, and when he is in town one day seems to be practically the same as the next day.

I mean Mr. Eisman is in the wholesale button profession in Chicago and he is the gentleman who is known practically all over Chicago as Gus Eisman the Button King. And he is the gentleman who is interested in educating me, so of course he is always coming down to New York to see how my brains have improved since the last time. But when Mr. Eisman is in New York we always seem to do the

* *This is the first chapter of Anita Loos's novel.*

46

same thing and if I wrote down one day in my diary, all I would have to do would be to put quotation marks for all other days. I mean we always seem to have dinner at the Colony and see a show and go to the Trocadero and then Mr. Eisman shows me to my apartment. So of course when a gentleman is interested in educating a girl, he likes to stay and talk about the topics of the day until quite late, so I am quite fatigued the next day and I do not really get up until it is time to dress for dinner at the Colony.

It would be strange if I turn out to be an authoress. I mean at my home near Little Rock, Arkansas, my family all wanted me to do something about my music. Because all of my friends said I had talent and they all kept after me and kept after me about practising. But some way I never seemed to care so much about practising. I mean I simply could not sit for hours and hours at a time practising just for the sake of a career. So one day I got quite tempermental and threw the old mandolin clear across the room and I have really never touched it since. But writing is different because you do not have to learn or practise and it is more tempermental because practising seems to take all the temperment out of me. So now I really almost have to smile because I have just noticed that I have written clear across two pages onto March 18th, so this will do for today and tomorrow. And it just shows how tempermental I am when I get started.

March 19th:

Well last evening Dorothy called up and Dorothy said she has met a gentleman who gave himself an introduction to her in the lobby of the Ritz. So then they went to luncheon and tea and dinner and then they went to a show and then they went to the Trocadero. So Dorothy said his name was Lord Cooksleigh but what she really calls him is Coocoo. So Dorothy said why don't you and I and Coocoo go to the Follies tonight and bring Gus along if he is in town? So then Dorothy and I had quite a little quarrel because every time that Dorothy mentions the subject of Mr. Eisman she calls Mr. Eisman by his first name, and she does not seem to realize that when a gentleman who is as important as Mr. Eisman, spends quite a lot of money educating a girl, it really does not show reverence to call a gentleman by his first name. I mean I never even think of calling Mr. Eisman by his first name, but if I want to call him anything at all, I call him

"Daddy" and I do not even call him "Daddy" if a place seems to be public. So I told Dorothy that Mr. Eisman would not be in town until day after tomorrow. So then Dorothy and Coocoo came up and we went to the Follies.

So this morning Coocoo called up and he wanted me to luncheon at the Ritz. I mean these foreigners really have quite a nerve. Just because Coocoo is an Englishman and a Lord he thinks a girl can waste hours on him just for a luncheon at the Ritz, when all he does is talk about some exposition he went on to a place called Tibet and after talking for hours I found out that all they were was a lot of Chinamen. So I will be quite glad to see Mr. Eisman when he gets in. Because he always has something quite interesting to talk about, as for instants the last time he was here he presented me with quite a beautiful emerald bracelet. So next week is my birthday and he always has some delightful surprise on holidays.

I did intend to luncheon at the Ritz with Dorothy today and of course Coocoo had to spoil it, as I told him that I could not luncheon with him today, because my brother was in town on business and had the mumps, so I really could not leave him alone. Because of course if I went to the Ritz now I would bump into Coocoo. But I sometimes almost have to smile at my own imagination, because of course I have not got any brother and I have not even thought of the mumps for years. I mean it is no wonder that I can write.

So the reason I thought I would take luncheon at the Ritz was because Mr. Chaplin is at the Ritz and I always like to renew old acquaintances, because I met Mr. Chaplin once when we were both working on the same lot in Hollywood and I am sure he would remember me. Gentlemen always seem to remember blondes. I mean the only career I would like to be besides an authoress is a cinema star and I was doing quite well in the cinema when Mr. Eisman made me give it all up. Because of course when a gentleman takes such a friendly interest in educating a girl as Mr. Eisman does, you like to show that you appreciate it, and he is against a girl being in the cinema because his mother is authrodox.

March 20th:

Mr. Eisman gets in tomorrow to be here in time for my birthday. So I thought it would really be delightful to have at least one good time before Mr. Eisman got in, so last evening I had some literary gentlemen in to spend the evening because Mr. Eisman always likes me to have literary people in and out of the apartment. I mean he is quite anxious for a girl to improve her mind and his greatest interest in me is because I always seem to want to improve my mind and not waste any time. And Mr. Eisman likes me to have what the French people call a "salo" which means that people all get together in the evening and improve their minds. So I invited all of the brainy gentlemen I could think up. So I thought up a gentleman who is the proffessor of all of the economics up at Columbia College, and the editor who is the famous editor of the New York Transcript and another gentleman who is a famous playright who writes very, very famous plays that are all about Life. I mean anybody would recognize his name but it always seems to slip my memory because all of we real friends of his only call him Sam. So Sam asked if he could bring a gentleman who writes novels from England, so I said yes, so he brought him. And then we all got together and I called up Gloria and Dorothy and the gentleman brought their own liquor. So of course the place was a wreck this morning and Lulu and I worked like proverbial dogs to get it cleaned up, but Heaven knows how long it will take to get the chandelier fixed.

March 22nd:

Well my birthday has come and gone but it was really quite depressing. I mean it seems to me a gentleman who has a friendly interest in educating a girl like Gus Eisman, would want her to have the biggest square cut diamond in New York. I mean I must say I was quite disappointed when he came to the apartment with a little thing you could hardly see. So I told him I thought it was quite cute, but I had quite a headache and I had better stay in a dark room all day and I told him I would see him the next day, perhaps. Because even Lulu thought it was quite small and she said, if she was I, she really would do something definite and she said she always believed in the old addage, "Leave them while you're looking good." But he came in at dinner time with really a very very beautiful bracelet of square cut diamonds so I was quite cheered up. So then we had dinner at the Colony and we went to a show and supper at the Trocadero as usual whenever he is in town. But I will give him credit that he realized how small it was. I mean he kept talking about how bad business was and the button profession was full of bolshevicks who make nothing but trouble. Because Mr. Eisman feels that the country is really on the verge of the bolshevicks and I become quite worried. I mean if the bolshevicks do get in, there is only one gentleman who could handle them and that is Mr. D. W. Griffith. Because I will never forget when Mr. Griffith was directing Intolerance. I mean it was my last cinema just before Mr. Eisman made me give up my career and I was playing one of the girls that fainted at the battle when all of the gentlemen fell off the tower. And when I saw how Mr. Griffith handled all of those mobs in Intolerance I realized that he could do anything, and I really think that the government of America ought to tell Mr. Griffith to get all ready if the bolshevicks start to do it.

Well I forgot to mention that the English gentleman who writes novels seems to have taken quite an interest in me, as soon as he found out that I was literary. I mean he has called up every day and I went to tea twice with him. So he has sent me a whole complete set of books for my birthday by a gentleman called Mr. Conrad. They all seem to be about ocean travel although I have not had time to more than glance through them. I have always liked novels about ocean travel ever since I posed for Mr. Christie for the front cover of a novel about ocean travel by McGrath because I always say that a girl never really looks as well as she does on board a steamship, or even a yacht.

So the English gentleman's name is Mr. Gerald Lamson as those who have read his novels would know. And he also sent me some of his own novels and they all seem to be about middle age English gentlemen who live in the country over in London and seem to ride bicycles, which seems quite different from America, except at Palm Beach. So I told Mr. Lamson how I write down all of my thoughts and he said he knew I had something to me from the first minute he saw me and when we become better acquainted I am going to let him read my diary. I mean I even told Mr. Eisman about him and he is quite pleased. Because of course Mr. Lamson is quite famous and it seems Mr. Eisman has read all of his novels going to and fro on the trains and Mr. Eisman is always anxious to meet famous people and take them to the Ritz to dinner on Saturday night. But of course I did not tell Mr. Eisman that I am really getting quite a little crush on Mr. Lamson, which I really believe I am, but Mr. Eisman thinks my interest in him is more literary.

March 30th:

At last Mr. Eisman has left on the 20th Century and I must say I am quite fatigued and a little rest will be quite welcome. I mean I do not mind staying out late every night if I dance, but Mr. Eisman is really not such a good dancer so most of the time we just sit and drink some champagne or have a bite to eat and of course I do not dance with anyone else when I am out with Mr. Eisman. But Mr. Eisman and Gerry, as Mr. Lamson wants me to call him, became quite good friends and we had several evenings, all three together. So now that Mr. Eisman is out of town at last, Gerry and I are going out together this evening and Gerry said not to dress up, because Gerry seems to like me more for my soul. So I really had to tell Gerry that if all the gentlemen were like he seems to be, Madame Frances' whole dress making establishment would have to go out of business. But Gerry does not like a girl to be nothing else but a doll, but he likes her to bring in her husband's slippers every evening and make him forget what he has gone through.

But before Mr. Eisman went to Chicago he told me that he is going to Paris this summer on professional business and I think he intends to present me with a trip to Paris as he says there is nothing so educational as traveling. I mean it did worlds of good to Dorothy when she went abroad last spring and I never get tired of hearing her telling how the merry-go-rounds in Paris have pigs instead of horses. But I really do not know whether to be thrilled or not because, of course, if I go to Paris I will have to leave Gerry and both Gerry and I have made up our minds not to be separated from one another from now on.

March 31st:

Last night Gerry and I had dinner at quite a quaint place where we had roast beef and baked potato. I mean he always wants me to have food which is what he calls "nourishing," which most gentlemen never seem to think about. So then we took a hansom cab and drove for hours around the park because Gerry said the air would be good for me. It is really very sweet to have some one think of all those things that gentlemen hardly ever seem to think about. So then we talked quite a lot. I mean Gerry knows how to draw a girl out and I told him things that I really would not even put in my diary. So when he heard all about my life he became quite depressed and we both had tears in our eyes. Because he said he never dreamed a girl could go through so much as I, and come out so sweet and not made bitter by it all. I mean Gerry thinks that most gentlemen are brutes and hardly ever think about a girl's soul.

So it seems that Gerry has had quite a lot of trouble himself and he can not even get married on account of his wife. He and she have never been in love with each other but she was a suffragette and asked him to marry her, so what could he do? So we rode all around the park until quite late talking and philosophizing quite a lot and I finally told him that I thought, after all, that bird life was the highest form of civilization. So Gerry calls me his little thinker and I really would not be surprised if all of my thoughts will give him quite a few ideas for his novels. Because Gerry says he has never seen a girl of my personal appearance with so many brains. And he had almost given up looking for his ideal when our paths seemed to cross each other and I told him I really thought a thing like that was nearly always the result of fate.

So Gerry says that I remind him quite a lot of Helen of Troy, who was of Greek extraction. But the only Greek I know is a Greek gentleman by the name of Mr. Georgopolis who is really quite wealthy and he is what Dorothy and I call a "Shopper" because you can always call him up at any hour and ask him to go shopping and he is always quite delighted, which very few gentlemen seem to be. And he never seems to care how much anything costs. I mean Mr. Georgopolis is also quite cultured, as I know quite a few gentlemen who can speak to a waiter in French but Mr. Georgopolis can also speak to a waiter in Greek which very few gentlemen seem to be able to do.

April 1st:
I am taking special pains with my diary from now on as I am really writing it for Gerry. I mean he and I are going to read it together some evening in front of the fireplace. But Gerry leaves this evening for Boston as he has to lecture about all of his works at Boston, but he will rush right back as soon as possible. So I am going to spend all of my time improving myself while he is gone. And this afternoon we are both going to a museum on 5th Avenue, because Gerry wants to show me a very very beautiful cup made by an antique jeweler called Mr. Cellini and he wants me to read Mr. Cellini's life which is a very very fine book and not dull while he is in Boston.

So the famous playright friend of mine who is called Sam called up this morning and he wanted me to go to a literary party tonight that he and some other literary gentlemen are giving to Florence Mills in Harlem but Gerry does not want me to go with Sam as Sam always insists on telling riskay stories. But personally I am quite broad minded and I always say that I do not mind a riskay story as long as it is really funny. I mean I have a great sense of humor. But Gerry says Sam does not always select and choose his stories and he just as soon I did not go out with him. So I am going to stay home and read the book by Mr. Cellini instead, because, after all, the only thing I am really interested in, is improving my mind. So I am going to do nothing else but improve my mind while Gerry is in Boston. I mean I just received a cable from Willie Gwynn who arrives from Europe tomorrow, but I am not even going to bother to see him. He is a sweet boy but he never gets anywhere and I am not going to waste my time on such as him, after meeting a gentleman like Gerry.

April 2nd:

I seem to be quite depressed this morning as I always am when there is nothing to put my mind to. Because I decided not to read the book by Mr. Cellini. I mean it was quite amuseing in spots because it was really quite riskay but the spots were not so close together and I never seem to like to always be hunting clear through a book for the spots I am looking for, especially when there are really not so many spots that seem to be so amuseing after all. So I did not waste my time on it but this morning I told Lulu to let all of the house work go and spend the day reading a book entitled "Lord Jim" and then tell me all about it, so that I would improve my mind while Gerry is away. But when I got her the book I nearly made a mistake and gave her a book by the title of "The Nigger of the Narcissus" which really would have hurt her feelings. I mean I do not know why authors cannot say "Negro" instead of "Nigger" as they have their feelings just the same as we have.

Well I just got a telegram from Gerry that he will not be back until tomorrow and also some orchids from Willie Gwynn, so I may as well go to the theatre with Willie tonight to keep from getting depressed, as he really is a sweet boy after all. I mean he never really does anything obnoxious. And it is quite depressing to stay at home and do nothing but read, unless you really have a book that is worth bothering about.

April 3rd:

I was really so depressed this morning that I was even glad to get a letter from Mr. Eisman. Because last night Willie Gwynn came to take me to the Follies, but he was so intoxicated that I had to telephone his club to send around a taxi to take him home. So that left me alone with Lulu at nine o'clock with nothing to do, so I put in a telephone call for Boston to talk to Gerry but it never went through. So Lulu tried to teach me how to play mah jong, but I really could not keep my mind on it because I was so depressed. So today I think I had better go over to Madame Frances and order some new evening gowns to cheer me up.

Well Lulu just brought me a telegram from Gerry that he will be in this afternoon, but I must not meet him at the station on account of all of the reporters who always meet him at the station wherever he comes from. But he says he will come right up to see me as he has something to talk about.

April 4th:

What an evening we had last evening. I mean it seems that Gerry is madly in love with me. Because all of the time he was in Boston lecturing to the womens clubs he said, as he looked over the faces of all those club women in Boston, he never realized I was so beautiful. And he said that there was only one in all the world and that was me. But it seems that Gerry thinks that Mr. Eisman is terrible and that no good can come of our friendship. I mean I was quite surprised, as they both seemed to get along quite well together, but it seems that Gerry never wants me to see Mr. Eisman again. And he wants me to give up everything and study French and he will get a divorce and we will be married. Because Gerry does not seem to like the kind of life all of us lead in New York and he wants me to go home to papa in Arkansas and he will send me books to read so that I will not get lonesome there. And he gave me his uncle's Masonic ring, which came down from the time of Soloman and which he never even lets his wife wear, for our engagement ring, and this afternoon a lady friend of his is going to bring me a new system she thought up of how to learn French. But some way I still seem to be depressed. I mean I could not sleep all night thinking of the terrible things Gerry said about New York and about Mr. Eisman. Of course I can understand Gerry being jealous of any gentleman friend of mine and of course I never really thought that Mr. Eisman was Rudolph Valentino, but Gerry said it made him cringe to think of a sweet girl like I having a friendship with Mr. Eisman. So it really made me feel quite depressed. I mean Gerry likes to talk quite a lot and I always think a lot of talk is depressing and worries your brains with things you never even think of when you are busy. But so long as Gerry does not mind me going out with other gentlemen when they have something to give you mentally, I am going to luncheon with Eddie Goldmark of the Goldmark Films who is always wanting me to sign a contract to go into the cinema. Because Mr. Goldmark is madly in love with Dorothy and Dorothy is always wanting me to go back in the cinema because Dorothy says that she will go if I will go.

April 6th:

Well I finally wrote Mr. Eisman that I was going to get married and it seems that he is coming on at once as he would probably like to give me his advice. Getting married is really quite serious and Gerry talks to me for hours and hours about it. I mean he never seems to get tired of talking and he does not seem to even want to go to shows or dance or do anything else but talk, and if I don't really have something definite to put my mind on soon I will scream.

April 7th:

Well Mr. Eisman arrived this morning and he and I had quite a long talk, and after all I think he is right. Because here is the first real opportunity I have ever really had. I mean to go to Paris and broaden out and improve my writing, and why should I give it up to marry an author, where he is the whole thing and all I would be would be the wife of Gerald Lamson? And on top of that I would have to be dragged into the scandal of a divorce court and get my name smirched. So Mr. Eisman said that opportunities come to seldom in a girls life for me to give up the first one I have really ever had. So I am sailing for France and London on Tuesday and taking Dorothy with me and Mr. Eisman says that he will see us there later. So Dorothy knows all of the ropes and she can get along in Paris just as though she knew French and besides she knows a French gentleman who was born and raised there, and speaks it like a native and knows Paris like a book. And Dorothy says that when we get to London nearly everybody speaks English anyway. So it is quite lucky that Mr. Lamson is out lecturing in Cincinnati and he will not be back until Wednesday and I can send him a letter and tell him that I have to go to Europe now but I will see him later perhaps. So anyway I will be spared listening to any more of his depressing conversation. So Mr. Eisman gave me quite a nice string of pearls and he gave Dorothy a diamond pin and we all went to the Colony for dinner and we all went to a show and supper at the Trocadero and we all spent quite a pleasant evening.

Sinclair Lewis

GEORGE F. BABBITT STARTS THE DAY*

The towers of Zenith aspired above the morning mist; austere towers of steel and cement and limestone, sturdy as cliffs and delicate as silver rods. They were neither citadels nor churches, but frankly and beautifully office-buildings.

The mist took pity on the fretted structures of earlier generations: the Post Office with its shingle-tortured mansard, the red brick minarets of hulking old houses, factories with stingy and sooted windows, wooden tenements colored like mud. The city was full of such grotesqueries, but the clean towers were thrusting them from the business center, and on the farther hills were shining new houses, homes—they seemed—for laughter and tranquillity.

Over a concrete bridge fled a limousine of long sleek hood and noiseless engine. These people in evening clothes were returning from an all-night rehearsal of a Little Theater play, an artistic adventure considerably illuminated by champagne. Below the bridge curved a railroad, a maze of green and crimson lights. The New York Flyer boomed past, and twenty lines of polished steel leaped into the glare.

In one of the skyscrapers the wires of the Associated Press were closing down. The telegraph operators wearily raised their celluloid eye-shades after a night of talking with Paris and Peking. Through the building crawled the scrubwomen, yawning, their old shoes slapping. The dawn mist spun away. Cues of men with lunch-boxes clumped toward the immensity of new factories, sheets of glass and hollow tile, glittering shops where five thousand men worked beneath one roof, pouring out the honest wares that would be sold up the Euphrates and across the veldt. The whistles rolled out in greeting a chorus cheerful as the April dawn; the song of labor in a city built—it seemed—for giants.

This is the first chapter of Sinclair Lewis's novel "Babbitt."

There was nothing of the giant in the aspect of the man who was beginning to awaken on the sleeping-porch of a Dutch Colonial house in that residential district of Zenith known as Floral Heights.

His name was George F. Babbitt. He was forty-six years old now, in April, 1920, and he made nothing in particular, neither butter nor shoes nor poetry, but he was nimble in the calling of selling houses for more than people could afford to pay.

His large head was pink, his brown hair thin and dry. His face was babyish in slumber, despite his wrinkles and the red spectacle-dents on the slopes of his nose. He was not fat but he was exceedingly well fed; his cheeks were pads, and the unroughened hand which lay helpless upon the khaki-colored blanket was slightly puffy. He seemed prosperous, extremely married and unromantic; and altogether unromantic appeared this sleeping-porch, which looked on one sizable elm, two respectable grass-plots, a cement driveway, and a corrugated iron garage. Yet Babbitt was again dreaming of the fairy child, a dream more romantic than scarlet pagodas by a silver sea.

For years the fairy child had come to him. Where others saw but Georgie Babbitt, she discerned gallant youth. She waited for him, in the darkness beyond mysterious groves. When at last he could slip away from the crowded house he darted to her. His wife, his clamoring friends, sought to follow, but he escaped, the girl fleet beside him, and they crouched together on a shadowy hillside. She was so slim, so white, so eager! She cried that he was gay and valiant, that she would wait for him, that they would sail—

Rumble and bang of the milk-truck.

Babbitt moaned, turned over, struggled back toward his dream. He could see only her face now, beyond misty waters. The furnace-man slammed the basement door. A dog barked in the next yard. As Babbitt sank blissfully into a dim warm tide, the paper-carrier went by whistling, and the rolled-up *Advocate* thumped the front door. Babbitt roused, his stomach constricted with alarm. As he relaxed, he was pierced by the familiar and irritating rattle of some one cranking a Ford: snap-ah-ah, snap-ah-ah, snap-ah-ah. Himself a pious motorist, Babbitt cranked with the unseen driver, with him waited through taut hours for the roar of the starting engine, with him agonized as the roar ceased and again began the infernal patient snap-ah-ah—a round, flat sound, a shivering cold-morning sound, a sound infuriating and inescapable. Not till the rising voice of the motor told him that the Ford was moving was he released from the panting tension. He glanced once at his favorite tree, elm twigs against the gold patina of sky, and fumbled for sleep as for a drug. He who had been a boy very credulous of life was no longer greatly interested in the possible and improbable adventures of each new day.

He escaped from reality till the alarm-clock rang, at seven-twenty.

It was the best of nationally advertised and quantitatively produced alarm-clocks, with all modern attachments, including cathedral chime, intermittent alarm, and a phosphorescent dial. Babbitt was proud of being awakened by such a rich device. Socially it was almost as creditable as buying expensive cord tires.

He sulkily admitted now that there was no more escape, but he lay and detested the grind of the real-estate business, and disliked his family, and disliked himself for disliking them. The evening before, he had played poker at Vergil Gunch's till midnight, and after such holidays he was irritable before breakfast. It may have been the tremendous home-brewed beer of the prohibition-era and the cigars to which that beer enticed him; it may have been resentment of return from this fine, bold man-world to a restricted region of wives and stenographers, and of suggestions not to smoke so much.

From the bedroom beside the sleeping-porch, his wife's detestably cheerful "Time to get up, Georgie boy," and the itchy sound, the brisk and scratchy sound, of combing hairs out of a stiff brush.

He grunted; he dragged his thick legs, in faded baby-blue pajamas, from under the khaki blanket; he sat on the edge of the cot, running his fingers through his wild hair, while his plump feet mechanically felt for his slippers. He looked regretfully at the blanket—forever a suggestion to him of freedom and heroism. He had bought it for a camping trip which had never come off. It symbolized gorgeous loafing, gorgeous cursing, virile flannel shirts.

He creaked to his feet, groaning at the waves of pain which passed behind his eyeballs. Though he waited for their scorching recurrence, he looked blurrily out at the yard. It delighted him, as always; it was the neat yard of a successful business man of Zenith, that is, it was perfection, and made him also perfect. He regarded the corrugated iron garage. For the three-hundred-and-sixty-fifth time in a year he reflected, "No class to that tin shack. Have to build me a frame garage. But by golly it's the only thing on the place that isn't up-to-date!" While he stared he thought of a community garage for his acreage development, Glen Oriole. He stopped puffing and jiggling. His arms were akimbo. His petulant, sleep-swollen face was set in harder lines. He suddenly seemed capable, an official, a man to contrive, to direct, to get things done.

On the vigor of his idea he was carried down the hard, clean, unused-looking hall into the bathroom.

Though the house was not large it had, like all houses on Floral Heights, an altogether royal bathroom of porcelain and glazed tile and metal sleek as silver. The towel-rack was a rod of clear glass set in nickel. The tub was long enough for a Prussian Guard, and above the set bowl was a sensational exhibit of tooth-brush holder, shaving-brush holder, soap-dish, sponge-dish, and medicine-cabinet, so glittering and so ingenious that they resembled an electrical instrument-board. But the Babbitt whose god was Modern Appliances was not pleased. The air of the bathroom was thick with the smell of a heathen toothpaste. "Verona been at it again! 'Stead of sticking to Lilidol, like I've re-peat-ed-ly asked her, she's gone and gotten some confounded stinkum stuff that makes you sick!"

The bath-mat was wrinkled and the floor was wet. (His daughter Verona eccentrically took baths in the morning, now and then.) He slipped on the mat, and slid against the tub. He said "Damn!" Furiously he snatched up his tube of shaving-cream, furiously he lathered, with a belligerent slapping of the unctuous brush, furiously he raked his plump cheeks with a safety-razor. It pulled. The blade was dull. He said, "Damn—oh—oh—damn it!"

He hunted through the medicine-cabinet for a packet of new razor-blades (reflecting, as invariably, "Be cheaper to buy one of these dinguses and strop your own blades,") and when he discovered the packet, behind the round box of bicarbonate of soda, he thought ill of his wife for putting it there and very well of himself for not saying "Damn." But he did say it, immediately afterward, when with wet and soap-slippery fingers he tried to remove the horrible little envelope and crisp clinging oiled paper from the new blade.

Then there was the problem, oft-pondered, never solved, of what to do with the old blade, which might imperil the fingers of his young. As usual, he tossed it on top of the medicine-cabinet, with a mental note that some day he must remove the fifty or sixty other blades that were also, temporarily, piled up there. He finished his shaving in a growing testiness increased by his spinning headache and by the emptiness in his stomach. When he was done, his round face smooth and streamy and his eyes stinging from soapy water, he reached for a towel. The family towels were wet, wet and clammy and vile, all of them wet, he found, as he blindly snatched them—his own face-towel, his wife's, Verona's, Ted's, Tinka's, and the lone bath-towel with the huge welt of initial. Then George F. Babbitt did a dismaying thing. He wiped his face on the guest-towel! It was a pansy-embroidered trifle which always hung there to indicate that the Babbitts were in the best Floral Heights society. No one had ever used it. No guest had ever dared to. Guests secretively took a corner of the nearest regular towel.

He was raging, "By golly, here they go and use up all the towels, every doggone one of 'em, and they use 'em and get 'em all wet and sopping, and never put out a dry one for me—of course, I'm the goat!—and then I want one and—I'm the only person in the doggone house that's got the slightest doggone bit of consideration for other people and thoughtfulness and consider there may be others that may want to use the doggone bathroom after me and consider—"

He was pitching the chill abominations into the bath-tub, pleased by the vindictiveness of that desolate flapping sound; and in the midst his wife serenely trotted in, observed serenely, "Why Georgie dear, what are you doing? Are you going to wash out the towels? Why, you needn't wash out the towels. Oh, Georgie, you didn't go and use the guest-towel, did you?"

It is not recorded that he was able to answer.

For the first time in weeks he was sufficiently roused by his wife to look at her.

Myra Babbitt—Mrs. George F. Babbitt—was definitely mature. She had creases from the corners of her mouth to the bottom of her chin, and her plump neck bagged. But the thing that marked her as having passed the line was that she no longer had reticences before her husband, and no longer worried about not having reticences. She was in a petticoat now, and corsets which bulged, and unaware of being seen in bulgy corsets. She had become so dully habituated to married life that in her full matronliness she was as sexless as an anemic nun. She was a good woman, a kind woman, a diligent woman, but no one, save perhaps Tinka her ten-year-old, was at all interested in her or entirely aware that she was alive.

After a rather thorough discussion of all the domestic and social aspects of towels she apologized to Babbitt for his having an alcoholic headache; and he recovered enough to endure the search for a B.V.D. undershirt which had, he pointed out, malevolently been concealed among his clean pajamas.

He was fairly amiable in the conference on the brown suit.

"What do you think, Myra?" He pawed at the clothes hunched on a chair in their bedroom, while she moved about mysteriously adjusting and patting her petticoat and, to his jaundiced eye, never seeming to get on with her dressing. "How about it? Shall I wear the brown suit another day?"

"Well, it looks awfully nice on you."

"I know, but gosh, it needs pressing."

"That's so. Perhaps it does."

"It certainly could stand being pressed, all right."

"Yes, perhaps it wouldn't hurt it to be pressed."

"But gee, the coat doesn't need pressing. No sense in having the whole darn suit pressed, when the coat doesn't need it."

"That's so."

"But the pants certainly need it, all right. Look at them—look at those wrinkles—the pants certainly do need pressing."

"That's so. Oh, Georgie, why couldn't you wear the brown coat with the blue trousers we were wondering what we'd do with them?"

"Good Lord! Did you ever in all my life know me to wear the coat of one suit and the pants of another? What do you think I am? A busted bookkeeper?"

"Well, why don't you put on the dark gray suit to-day, and stop in at the tailor and leave the brown trousers?"

"Well, they certainly need— Now where the devil is that gray suit? Oh, yes, here we are."

He was able to get through the other crises of dressing with comparative resoluteness and calm.

His first adornment was the sleeveless dimity B.V.D. undershirt, in which he resembled a small boy humorlessly wearing a cheese-cloth tabard at a civic pageant. He never put on B.V.D.'s without thanking the God of Progress that he didn't wear tight, long, old-fashioned undergarments, like his father-in-law and partner, Henry Thompson. His second embellishment was combing and slicking back his hair. It gave him a tremendous forehead, arching up two inches beyond the former hair-line. But most wonder-working of all was the donning of his spectacles.

There is character in spectacles—the pretentious tortoise-shell, the meek pince-nez of the school teacher, the twisted silver-framed glasses of the old villager. Babbitt's spectacles had huge, circular, frameless lenses of the very best glass; the ear-pieces were thin bars of gold. In them he was the modern business man; one who gave orders to clerks and drove a car and played occasional golf and was scholarly in regard to Salesmanship. His head suddenly appeared not babyish but weighty, and you noted his heavy, blunt nose, his straight mouth and thick, long upper lip, his chin overfleshy but strong; with respect you beheld him put on the rest of his uniform as a Solid Citizen.

The gray suit was well cut, well made, and completely undistinguished. It was a standard suit. White piping on the V of the vest added a flavor of law and learning. His shoes were black laced boots, good boots, honest boots, standard boots, extraordinarily uninteresting boots. The only frivolity was in his purple knitted scarf. With considerable comment on the matter to Mrs. Babbitt (who, acrobatically fastening the back of her blouse to her skirt with a safety-pin, did not hear a word he said) he chose between the purple scarf and a tapestry effect with stringless brown harps among blown palms, and into it he thrust a snake-head pin with opal eyes.

A sensational event was changing from the brown suit to the gray the contents of his pockets. He was earnest about these objects. They were of eternal importance, like baseball or the Republican Party. They included a fountain pen and a silver pencil (always lacking a supply of new leads) which belonged in the right-hand upper vest pocket. Without them he would have felt naked. On his watch-chain were a gold penknife, silver cigar cutter, seven keys (the use of two of which he had forgotten), and incidentally a good watch. Depending from the chain was a large, yellowish elk's-tooth—proclamation of his membership in the Benevolent and Protective Order of Elks. Most significant of all was his loose-leaf pocket note-book, that modern and efficient note-book which contained the addresses of people whom he had forgotten, prudent memoranda of postal money-orders which had reached their destinations months ago, stamps which had lost their mucilage, clippings of verse by T. Cholmondeley Frink and of the newspaper editorials from which Babbitt got his opinions and his polysyllables, notes to be sure and do things which he did not intend to do, and one curious inscription—D.S.S.D.M.Y.P.D.F.

But he had no cigarette-case. No one had ever happened to give him one, so he hadn't the habit, and people who carried cigarette-cases he regarded as effeminate.

Last, he stuck in his lapel the Boosters' Club button. With the conciseness of great art the button displayed two words: "Boosters—Pep!" It made Babbitt feel loyal and important. It associated him with Good Fellows, with men who were nice and human, and important in business circles. It was his V.C., his Legion of Honor ribbon, his Phi Beta Kappa key.

With the subtleties of dressing ran other complex worries. "I feel kind of punk this morning," he said. "I think I had too much dinner last evening. You oughtn't to serve those heavy banana fritters."

"But you asked me to have some."

"I know, but— I tell you, when a fellow gets past forty he has to look after his digestion. There's a lot of fellows that don't take proper care of themselves. I tell you at forty a man's a fool or his doctor—I mean, his own doctor. Folks don't give enough attention to this matter of dieting. Now I think— Course a man ought to have a good meal after the day's work, but it would be a good thing for both of us if we took lighter lunches."

"But Georgie, here at home I always do have a light lunch."

"Mean to imply I make a hog of myself, eating down-town? Yes, sure! You'd have a swell time if you had to eat the truck that new steward hands out to us at the Athletic Club! But I certainly do feel out of sorts, this morning. Funny, got a pain down here on the left side —but no, that wouldn't be appendicitis, would it? Last night, when I was driving over to Verg Gunch's, I felt a pain in my stomach, too. Right here it was—kind of a sharp shooting pain. I— Where'd that dime go to? Why don't you serve more prunes at breakfast? Of course I eat an apple every evening—an apple a day keeps the doctor away—but still, you ought to have more prunes, and not all these fancy doodads."

"The last time I had prunes you didn't eat them."

"Well, I didn't feel like eating 'em, I suppose. Matter of fact, I think I did eat some of 'em. Anyway— I tell you it's mighty important to—

I was saying to Verg Gunch, just last evening, most people don't take sufficient care of their diges—"

"Shall we have the Gunches for our dinner, next week?"

"Why sure; you bet."

"Now see here, George: I want you to put on your nice dinner-jacket that evening."

"Rats! The rest of 'em won't want to dress."

"Of course they will. You remember when you didn't dress for the Littlefields' supper-party, and all the rest did, and how embarrassed you were."

"Embarrassed, hell! I wasn't embarrassed. Everybody knows I can put on as expensive a Tux. as anybody else, and I should worry if I don't happen to have it on sometimes. All a darn nuisance, anyway. All right for a woman, that stays around the house all the time, but when a fellow's worked like the dickens all day, he doesn't want to go and hustle his head off getting into the soup-and-fish for a lot of folks that he's seen in just reg'lar ordinary clothes that same day."

"You know you enjoy being seen in one. The other evening you admitted you were glad I'd insisted on your dressing. You said you felt a lot better for it. And oh, Georgie, I do wish you wouldn't say 'Tux.' It's 'dinner-jacket.' "

"Rats, what's the odds?"

"Well, it's what all the nice folks say. Suppose Lucile McKelvey heard you calling it a 'Tux.' "

"Well, that's all right now! Lucile McKelvey can't pull anything on me! Her folks are common as mud, even if her husband and her dad are millionaires! I suppose you're trying to rub in *your* exalted social position! Well, let me tell you that your revered paternal ancestor, Henry T., doesn't even call it a 'Tux'! He calls it a 'bob-tail jacket for a ringtail monkey,' and you couldn't get him into one unless you chloroformed him!"

"Now don't be horrid, George."

"Well, I don't want to be horrid, but Lord! you're getting as fussy as Verona. Ever since she got out of college she's been too rambunctious to live with—doesn't know what she wants—well, I know what she wants!—all she wants is to marry a millionaire, and live in Europe, and hold some preacher's hand, and simultaneously at the same time stay right here in Zenith and be some blooming kind of a socialist agitator or boss charity-worker or some damn thing!

Lord, and Ted is just as bad! He wants to go to college, and he doesn't want to go to college. Only one of the three that knows her own mind is Tinka. Simply can't understand how I ever came to have a pair of shillyshallying children like Rone and Ted. I may not be any Rockefeller or James J. Shakespeare, but I certainly do know my own mind, and I do keep right on plugging along in the office and— Do you know the latest? Far as I can figure out, Ted's new bee is he'd like to be a movie actor and— And here I've told him a hundred times, if he'll go to college and law-school and make good, I'll set him up in business and— Verona just exactly as bad. Doesn't know what she wants. Well, well, come on! Aren't you ready yet? The girl rang the bell three minutes ago."

Before he followed his wife, Babbitt stood at the westernmost window of their room. This residential settlement, Floral Heights, was on a rise; and though the center of the city was three miles away— Zenith had between three and four hundred thousand inhabitants now—he could see the top of the Second National Tower, an Indiana limestone building of thirty-five stories.

Its shining walls rose against April sky to a simple cornice like a streak of white fire. Integrity was in the tower, and decision. It bore its strength lightly as a tall soldier. As Babbitt stared, the nervousness was soothed from his face, his slack chin lifted in reverence. All he articulated was "That's one lovely sight!" but he was inspired by the rhythm of the city; his love of it renewed. He beheld the tower as a temple-spire of the religion of business, a faith passionate, exalted, surpassing common men; and as he clumped down to breakfast he whistled the ballad "Oh, by gee, by gosh, by jingo" as though it were a hymn melancholy and noble.

John Mosher

LADY'S ROOM

Cousin Millicent Opal was the immediate cause of Mr. Opal's new room. Cousin Millicent was an elderly maiden lady of independent means and somewhat mystical tastes, and she had several times indicated a curiosity about his Fire Island hideaway. The politest and most tentative woman in the world, she could yet manage to make her whims imperative. Early in the spring, Mr. Opal found himself enclosing what had been an upstairs porch and with discretion furnishing a room which, he decided, would be primarily designed for female guests. It was by no means a large room—only one female guest could be accommodated at a time—and yet, as he went on with his arrangements, he became amazed at the magnitude of this seemingly simple undertaking.

"My approach to the whole problem," he said to his neighbor, Miss Penelope Asia, "is the psychological rather than the decorative. I have a number of lady friends and they are all different. I am trying to adapt this small room to the needs of each one."

Miss Asia's dachshund, Aspiration, was barking madly at the catbirds and she had to shout at him to stop. "Try to get used to the birds," she exclaimed. "God knows, all the rest of us have to."

"I hope you won't say anything like that to Cousin Millicent," said Mr. Opal. "She is a member of the Audubon Society. I want you ladies to keep on good terms down here. After all, we are on an island."

"That's why you have that Audubon print on the wall, I suppose," said Miss Asia. "Well, it's cheerful. And I like the white walls."

"White seemed to me suitable for all women," said Mr. Opal. "A general cool effect. Calming to the nerves. I always dread tantrums."

"It's light," remarked Miss Asia. "Some women like to sleep late. I can imagine your Cousin Millicent will be up at the crack of dawn from what you say, but what about the other types? That little Miss

67

Bailey you like so much—I am sure she doesn't go in for the dawn. At least from the wrong end, so to speak."

Mr. Opal pointed out the heavy dark shades which should, he thought, reconcile even Miss Bailey and her kind to the hardships of beach life. It was obvious that he had made an intensive study of all the peculiarities of the female sex. As he looked about the finished room, he felt confident that he had not overlooked any caprice of his imminent guests. He had, he told Miss Asia, searched all over town for this wicker chair, placed now in the most appropriate corner. It was a rather old-fashioned affair, with a large side pocket built into it, convenient for magazines, books, and knitting. Beside it, for a more sportive character, he had placed a trim little table with a bright-blue top of some modernistic resistant material that wouldn't develop rings.

"I am not unaware," said Mr. Opal, "that one or two of the ladies I know enjoy a little private sip of something."

"Miss Bailey?" said Miss Asia.

Mr. Opal ventured to remark that perhaps Miss Asia was not really devoted to Miss Bailey, but conceded that he could visualize Miss Bailey spread out in the armchair for an afternoon of reflection with a tall glass on the table beside her.

"And after two or three hours of reflection," said Miss Asia, "I can visualize her, too, pulling the dunes down."

Evading useless argument, Mr. Opal pointed to the writing table, which he had placed with care for the lighting. It was the smallest writing table he had been able to unearth in any of the shops, and it was the ideal morsel of furniture for a lady's epistolary needs—the penning of occasional checks, the notations in a diary, the answers to invitations, and the tender notes, on scented paper, of exquisite sentiment. For a letter of condolence it was surely perfect. That some women might demand more he knew and was prepared for. The lady with a portable typewriter and a briefcase could, of course, be accommodated. Such special products could make use of a folding table, concealed at the moment in the closet. Or literary types might prefer to move the mirror off the dressing table and make use of that for their work. Such women were generally husky and re-sourceful, and Mr. Opal felt no great concern about them. "To any woman of enterprise or creative ability," he explained, "I shall just hand over the whole house at once. I might as well do it at the beginning as a bit later."

Even Miss Asia had to concede that he had thought of practically everything and that the room was really rather attractive, too, though decoration had not been his aim. He was, she could see, prepared now for the intellectual woman, the homebody, the flibbertigibbet, the dreamer, the dressy and active type, the young, and those beyond their first youth. She herself could think of nothing that he need add.

Being thus so beautifully ready for guests—or a guest, rather—Mr. Opal suddenly discovered that no one was turning up. Cousin Millicent wrote that she had changed her mind and was going to the mountains; she would come next year; she couldn't possibly manage the beach this summer; she was so disappointed. Mr. Opal made a tentative grab for Miss Bailey, but Miss Bailey was having the time of her life, curiously enough, in the steamy environs of Nyack and couldn't be lured away. For a while it seemed that this studied sanctuary, this room that was a valentine to womanhood itself, would remain unoccupied, unappreciated. Then, all at once, it was Miss Asia who came to Mr. Opal's rescue.

She came running, breathless. "You've got to help me out," she cried. "My house is absolutely crammed. There isn't even a single free couch. And I've just got this telegram, sent up from Ocean Beach —they kept it there overnight—they always do—sleep on them. Cora Wind is coming on the next boat. She'll be here in ten minutes."

Mr. Opal had never heard of Cora Wind, but he said he would be delighted to place his guest room at her disposal, and then he began to sense from a word or two of Miss Asia's that there was something mysterious in the air. The last person on earth, it seemed, that Miss Asia expected to see out here on Fire Island, just at this time, was Mrs. Wind. "The woman must be insane to make such a trip now," Miss Asia said. "But, of course, that is the way some women are affected."

Miss Asia didn't stop to explain but rushed off to meet the boat, promising to bring Mrs. Wind straight back with her from the dock. The whole thing seemed ominous. Mr. Opal hoped his first guest would not be a mental case. With a vague sense of approaching calamity, he went to the room, opened a window or two, saw that it was ready. He was glad the room was far enough from his own so that if Mrs. Wind had an acute melancholia he wouldn't hear her crying all night.

Mrs. Wind was not melancholy. She was, on the other hand, simply beaming with health and good humor, but even to Mr. Opal, a bachelor, no family man at all, it was perfectly apparent why Miss Asia had been amazed to find Mrs. Wind coming to Fire Island. Naturally, Mrs. Wind must know what she is doing, he thought. And, of course, a woman in her condition must have had expert medical advice. People couldn't be certain, though, about such things. Dates got mixed. Wasn't there supposed to be some mental state which accompanied the physical manifestations and led women to all sorts of unreasonable behavior? Like this, for instance? Like coming on this wild trip?

Pale, he threw open the door and showed his guest her room. Somehow they would have to, come what might, get through the night.

"And I thought," Mr. Opal said to himself, "that I was ready for everything."

Edward Streeter

TWO LETTERS FROM A ROOKIE TO HIS GIRL *

Dere Mable:

Having nothin better to do I take up my pen to rite.

We have been here now three weeks. As far as I am concerned I am all ready to go. I told the Captin that I was ready any time. He said yes, but that wed have to wait for the slow ones cause they was all goin together. I says was I to go out to drill with the rest. He said yes more for the example than anything else. Its kind of maddening to be hangin round here when I might be over there helpin the Sammies put a stop to this thing.

In the mean time I been doin guard duty. Seems like I been doin it every night but I know what there up against and I dont say nothin. Guard duty is something like extemperaneus speakin. You got to know everything your goin to say before you start. Its very tecknickle. For instance you walk a post but there aint no post. An you mount guard but you dont really mount nothin. An you turn out the guard but you dont really turn em out. They come out them selves. Just the other night I was walkin along thinkin of you Mable an my feet which was hurtin. It made me awful lonesome. An officer come up and he says why dont you draw your pistol when you here someone comin. An I says I dont wait till the sheep is stole I drew it this afternoon from the Supply sargent. An I showed it to him tucked inside my shirt where noone could get it away from me without some tussel, you bet, Mable. But it seems that you got to keep on drawin it all the time. Then later I here footsteps. I was expectin the relief so I was right on the job. An a man come up and I poked my pistol right in his face and says Halt. Who goes there? And he says Officer of the day. An bein disappointed as who wouldnt be I says Oh hell I thought it was the relief. And he objected to that. The relief, Mable—but whats the use you wouldn't understand it.

* *From "Dere Mable."*

71

Theres some mistake up north Mable about the way were built, Mable. Its kind of depresin to think that you could forget about us so quick. Everyones gettin sweters without sleeves and gloves without fingers. We still got everything we started with Mable. Why not sox without feet and pants without legs. If your makin these things for after the war I think your anticipatin a little. Besides its depresin for the fellos to be reminded all the time. Its like givin a fello a life membership to the Old Soldiers home to cheer him up when he sails. I was sayin the other day that if the fellos at Washington ever get onto this theyll be issuin soleles shoes and shirtles sleves.

Its gettin awful cold. No wonder this is a healthy place. All the germs is froze. I guess there idea of the hardenin proces is to freeze a fello stiff. The Captin said the other day we was gettin in tents of trainin. Thats all right but Id kind of like to see those steam heated barraks. Youve red about those fellos that go swimmin in the ice in winter. I guess thed like our shouer baths. They say Cleanliness is next to Godliness, Mable. I say its next to impossible.

I started this letter almost a weak ago. I just found it in my bakin can. They call it a bakin can but its too small to bake nothin. I keep my soap in it. I got some news for you. The regiment is to be dismantled. The Captin called me over this mornin and asked me where Id like to be transferred. I said home if it was the same to him. So there goin to send me to the artillery. This is a very dangerous and useful limb of the servus, Mable. I dont kno my address. Just write me care of the General.

I got the red muffler that your mother sent me. Give her my love just the same

yours relentlessly,
Bill.

Dere Mable:
I havnt rote for some time I had such sore feet lately. When they broke up our regiment and sent me over to the artillery I thought I was goin to quit usin my feet. That was just another roomor.

Thanks for the box of stuff you sent me. I guess the brakeman must have used it for a chair all the way. It was pretty well baled but that dont matter. And thanks for the fudge too. That was fudge wasnt it, Mable? And the sox. They dont fit but I can use them for somethin. A good soldier never throws nothin away. An thank your mother for the half pair of gloves she sent me. I put them away. Maybe sometime shell get a chance to nit the other half. Or if I ever get all my fingers shot off theyll come in very handy.

The artillerys a little different from the infantry. They make us work harder. At least theres more work on the skedule. I know now what they mean when they say that the "artillerys active on the western front."

They got a drill over here called the standin gun drill. The names misleadin. I guess it was invented by a troop of Jap akrobats. They make you get up and sit on the gun. Before you can get settled comfortable they make you get down again. It looks like they didnt know just what they did want you to do.

I dont like the sargent. I dont like any sargent but this one particular. The first day out he kept sayin "Prepare to mount" and then "Mount." Finally I went up to him and told him that as far as I was concerned he could cut that stuff for I was always prepared to do what I was told even though it was the middle of the night. He said, Fine, then I was probably prepared to scrub pans all day Sunday.

I dont care much for horses. I think they feels the same way about me. Most of them are so big that the only thing there good for is the view of the camp you get when you climb up. They are what they call hors de combat in French. My horse died the other day. I guess it wasnt much effort for him. If it had been he wouldnt have done it.

They got a book they call Drill Regulations Field and Light. Thats about as censible as it is all the way through. For instance they say that when the command for action is given one man jumps for the wheel and another springs for the trail an another leaps for the muzzle. I guess the fellow that rote the regulations thought we was a bunch of grass hoppers.

Well I got to quit now an rite a bunch of other girls. Thanks again for the box although it was so busted that it wasnt much good but that dont matter.

Yours till you here otherwise,
Bill.

Dorothy Parker

GLORY IN THE DAYTIME

Mr. Murdock was one who carried no enthusiasm whatever for
plays and their players, and that was too bad, for they meant so much
to little Mrs. Murdock. Always she had been in a state of devout
excitement over the luminous, free, passionate elect who serve the
theater. And always she had done her wistful worshiping, along with
the multitudes, at the great public altars. It is true that once, when
she was a particularly little girl, love had impelled her to write Miss
Maude Adams a letter beginning "Dearest Peter," and she had received
from Miss Adams a miniature thimble inscribed "A kiss from Peter
Pan." (That was a day!) And once, when her mother had taken her
holiday shopping, a limousine door was held open and there had
passed her, as close as *that,* a wonder of sable and violets and round
red curls that seemed to tinkle on the air; so, forever after, she was as
good as certain that she had been not a foot away from Miss Billie
Burke. But until some three years after her marriage, these had remained her only personal experiences with the people of the lights and
the glory.

Then it turned out that Miss Noyes, new-come to little Mrs. Murdock's own bridge club, knew an actress. She actually knew an
actress; the way you and I know collectors of recipes and members of
garden clubs and amateurs of needlepoint.

The name of the actress was Lily Wynton, and it was famous. She
was tall and slow and silvery; often she appeared in the rôle of a
duchess, or of a Lady Pam or an Honorable Moira. Critics recurrently
referred to her as "that great lady of our stage." Mrs. Murdock had
attended, over years, matinée performances of the Wynton successes.
And she had no more thought that she would one day have opportunity to meet Lily Wynton face to face than she had thought—
well, than she had thought of flying!

Yet it was not astounding that Miss Noyes should walk at ease among the glamorous. Miss Noyes was full of depths and mystery, and she could talk with a cigarette still between her lips. She was always doing something difficult, like designing her own pajamas, or reading Proust, or modeling torsos in plasticine. She played excellent bridge. She liked little Mrs. Murdock. "Tiny one," she called her.

"How's for coming to tea tomorrow, tiny one?" she said, at a therefore memorable meeting of the bridge club. "Lily Wynton's going to drop up. You might like to meet her."

The words fell so easily that she could not have realized their weight. Lily Wynton was coming to tea. Mrs. Murdock might like to meet her. Little Mrs. Murdock walked home through the early dark, and stars sang in the sky above her.

Mr. Murdock was already at home when she arrived. It required but a glance to tell that for him there had been no singing stars that evening in the heavens. He sat with his newspaper opened at the financial page, and bitterness had its way with his soul. It was not the time to cry happily to him of the impending hospitalities of Miss Noyes; not the time, that is, if one anticipated exclamatory sympathy. Mr. Murdock did not like Miss Noyes. When pressed for a reason, he replied that he just plain didn't like her. Occasionally he added, with a sweep that might have commanded a certain admiration, that all those women made him sick. Usually when she told him of the temperate activities of the bridge club meetings, Mrs. Murdock kept any mention of Miss Noyes's name from the accounts. She had found that this omission made for a more agreeable evening. But now she was caught in such a sparkling swirl of excitement that she had scarcely kissed him before she was off on her story.

"Oh, Jim," she cried. "Oh, what do you think! Hallie Noyes asked me to tea tomorrow to meet Lily Wynton!"

"Who's Lily Wynton?" he said.

"Ah, Jim," she said. "Ah, really, Jim. Who's Lily Wynton! Who's Greta Garbo, I suppose!"

"She some actress or something?" he said.

Mrs. Murdock's shoulders sagged. "Yes, Jim," she said. "Yes. Lily Wynton's an actress."

She picked up her purse and started slowly toward the door. But before she had taken three steps, she was again caught up in her sparkling swirl. She turned to him, and her eyes were shining.

"Honestly," she said, "it was the funniest thing you ever heard in your life. We'd just finished the last rubber—oh, I forgot to tell you, I won three dollars, isn't that pretty good for me?—and Hallie Noyes said to me, 'Come on in to tea tomorrow. Lily Wynton's going to drop up,' she said. Just like that, she said it. Just as if it was anybody."

"Drop up?" he said. "How can you drop *up?*"

"Honestly, I don't know what I said when she asked me," Mrs. Murdock said. "I suppose I said I'd love to—I guess I must have. But I was so simply—Well, you know how I've always felt about Lily Wynton. Why, when I was a little girl, I used to collect her pictures. And I've seen her in, oh, everything she's ever been in, I should think, and I've read every word about her, and interviews and all. Really and truly, when I think of *meeting* her—Oh, I'll simply die. What on earth shall I say to her?"

"You might ask her how she'd like to try dropping down, for a change," Mr. Murdock said.

"All right, Jim," Mrs. Murdock said. "If that's the way you want to be."

Wearily she went toward the door, and this time she reached it before she turned to him. There were no lights in her eyes.

"It—it isn't so awfully nice," she said, "to spoil somebody's pleasure in something. I was so thrilled about this. You don't see what it is to me, to meet Lily Wynton. To meet somebody like that, and see what they're like, and hear what they say, and maybe get to know them. People like that mean—well, they mean something different to me. They're not like this. They're not like me. Who do I ever see? What do I ever hear? All my whole life, I've wanted to know—I've almost prayed that some day I could meet—Well. All right, Jim."

She went out, and on to her bedroom.

Mr. Murdock was left with only his newspaper and his bitterness for company. But he spoke aloud.

" 'Drop up!' " he said. " 'Drop *up*,' for God's sake!"

The Murdocks dined, not in silence, but in pronounced quiet. There was something straitened about Mr. Murdock's stillness; but little Mrs. Murdock's was the sweet, far quiet of one given over to dreams. She had forgotten her weary words to her husband, she had passed through her excitement and her disappointment. Luxuriously she floated on innocent visions of days after the morrow. She heard her own voice in future conversations. . . .

I saw Lily Wynton at Hallie's the other day, and she was telling me all about her new play—no, I'm terribly sorry, but it's a secret, I promised her I wouldn't tell anyone the name of it. . . . Lily Wynton dropped up to tea yesterday, and we just got to talking, and she told me the most interesting things about her life; she said she'd never dreamed of telling them to anyone else. . . . Why, I'd love to come, but I promised to have lunch with Lily Wynton. . . . I had a long, long letter from Lily Wynton. . . . Lily Wynton called me up this morning. . . . Whenever I feel blue, I just go and have a talk with Lily Wynton, and then I'm all right again. . . . Lily Wynton told me. . . . Lily Wynton and I . . . "Lily," I said to her . . .

The next morning, Mr. Murdock had left for his office before Mrs. Murdock rose. This had happened several times before, but not often. Mrs. Murdock felt a little queer about it. Then she told herself that it was probably just as well. Then she forgot all about it, and gave her mind to the selection of a costume suitable to the afternoon's event. Deeply she felt that her small wardrobe included no dress adequate to the occasion; for, of course, such an occasion had never before arisen. She finally decided upon a frock of dark blue serge with fluted white muslin about the neck and wrists. It was her style, that was the most she could say for it. And that was all she could say for herself. Blue serge and little white ruffles—that was she.

The very becomingness of the dress lowered her spirits. A nobody's frock, worn by a nobody. She blushed and went hot when she recalled the dreams she had woven the night before, the mad visions of intimacy of equality with Lily Wynton. Timidity turned her heart liquid, and she thought of telephoning Miss Noyes and saying she had a bad cold and could not come. She steadied, when she planned a course of conduct to pursue at teatime. She would not try to say anything; if she stayed silent, she could not sound foolish. She would listen and watch and worship and then come home, stronger, braver, better for an hour she would remember proudly all her life.

Miss Noyes's living-room was done in the early modern period. There were a great many oblique lines and acute angles, zigzags of aluminium and horizontal stretches of mirror. The color scheme was sawdust and steel. No seat was more than twelve inches above the floor, no table was made of wood. It was, as has been said of larger places, all right for a visit.

Little Mrs. Murdock was the first arrival. She was glad of that; no, maybe it would have been better to have come after Lily Wynton;

no, maybe this was right. The maid motioned her toward the living room, and Miss Noyes greeted her in the cool voice and the warm words that were her special combination. She wore black velvet trousers, a red cummerbund, and a white silk shirt, opened at the throat. A cigarette clung to her lower lip, and her eyes, as was her habit, were held narrow against its near smoke.

"Come in, come in, tiny one," she said. "Bless its little heart. Take off its little coat. Good Lord, you look easily eleven years old in that dress. Sit ye doon, here beside of me. There'll be a spot of tea in a jiff."

Mrs. Murdock sat down on the vast, perilously low divan, and, because she was never good at reclining among cushions, held her back straight. There was room for six like her, between herself and her hostess. Miss Noyes lay back, with one ankle flung upon the other knee, and looked at her.

"I'm a wreck," Miss Noyes announced. "I was modeling like a mad thing, all night long. It's taken everything out of me. I was like a thing bewitched."

"Oh, what were you making?" cried Mrs. Murdock.

"Oh, Eve," Miss Noyes said. "I always do Eve. What else is there to do? You must come pose for me some time, tiny one. You'd be nice to do. Ye-es, you'd be very nice to do. My tiny one."

"Why, I—" Mrs. Murdock said, and stopped. "Thank you very much, though," she said.

"I wonder where Lily is," Miss Noyes said. "She said she'd be here early—well, she always says that. You'll adore her, tiny one. She's really rare. She's a real person. And she's been through perfect hell. God, what a time she's had!"

"Ah, what's been the matter?" said Mrs. Murdock.

"Men," Miss Noyes said. "Men. She never had a man that wasn't a louse." Gloomily she stared at the toe of her flat-heeled patent leather pump. "A pack of lice, always. All of them. Leave her for the first little floozie that comes along."

"But—" Mrs. Murdock began. No, she couldn't have heard right. How could it be right? Lily Wynton was a great actress. A great actress meant romance. Romance meant Grand Dukes and Crown Princes and diplomats touched with gray at the temples and lean, bronzed, reckless Younger Sons. It meant pearls and emeralds and chinchilla and rubies red as the blood that was shed for them. It meant a grim-faced boy sitting in the fearful Indian midnight, beneath the dreary whirring of the *punkahs,* writing a letter to the lady he had seen but once; writing his poor heart out, before he turned to the service revolver that lay beside him on the table. It meant a golden-locked poet, floating face downward in the sea, and in his pocket his last great sonnet to the lady of ivory. It meant brave, beautiful men, living and dying for the lady who was the pale bride of art, whose eyes and heart were soft with only compassion for them.

A pack of lice. Crawling after little floozies; whom Mrs. Murdock swiftly and hazily pictured as rather like ants.

"But—" said little Mrs. Murdock.

"She gave them all her money," Miss Noyes said. "She always did. Or if she didn't, they took it anyway. Took every cent she had, and then spat in her face. Well, maybe she's beginning to learn a little sense now. Oh, there's the bell—that'll be Lily. No, sit ye doon, tiny one. You belong there."

Miss Noyes rose and made for the archway that separated the living-room from the hall. As she passed Mrs. Murdock, she stooped suddenly, cupped her guest's round chin, and quickly, lightly kissed her mouth.

"Don't tell Lily," she murmured, very low.

Mrs. Murdock puzzled. Don't tell Lily what? Could Hallie Noyes think that she might babble to the Lily Wynton of these strange confidences about the actress's life? Or did she mean—But she had no more time for puzzling. Lily Wynton stood in the archway. There she stood, one hand resting on the wooden molding and her body swayed toward it, exactly as she stood for her third-act entrance of her latest play, and for a like half-minute.

You would have known her anywhere, Mrs. Murdock thought. Oh, yes, anywhere. Or at least you would have exclaimed, "That woman looks something like Lily Wynton." For she was somehow different in the daylight. Her figure looked heavier, thicker, and her face—there was so much of her face that the surplus sagged from the strong, fine bones. And her eyes, those famous dark, liquid eyes. They were dark, yes, and certainly liquid, but they were set in little hammocks of folded flesh, and seemed to be set but loosely, so readily did they roll. Their whites, that were visible all around the irises, were threaded with tiny scarlet veins.

"I suppose footlights are an awful strain on their eyes," thought little Mrs. Murdock.

Lily Wynton wore, just as she should have, black satin and sables, and long white gloves were wrinkled luxuriously about her wrists. But there were delicate streaks of grime in the folds of her gloves, and down the shining length of her gown there were small, irregularly shaped dull patches; bits of food or drops of drink, or perhaps both, sometime must have slipped their carriers and found brief sanctuary there. Her hat—oh, her hat. It was romance, it was mystery, it was strange, sweet sorrow; it was Lily Wynton's hat, of all the world, and no other could dare it. Black it was, and tilted, and a great, soft plume drooped from it to follow her cheek and curl across her throat. Beneath it, her hair had the various hues of neglected brass. But oh, her hat.

"Darling!" cried Miss Noyes.

"Angel," said Lily Wynton. "My sweet."

It was that voice. It was that deep, soft, glowing voice. "Like purple velvet," someone had written. Mrs. Murdock's heart beat visibly.

Lily Wynton cast herself upon the steep bosom of her hostess, and murmured there. Across Miss Noyes's shoulder she caught sight of little Mrs. Murdock.

"And who is this?" she said. She disengaged herself.

"That's my tiny one," Miss Noyes said. "Mrs. Murdock."

"What a clever little face," said Lily Wynton. "Clever, clever little face. What does she do, sweet Hallie? I'm sure she writes, doesn't she? Yes, I can feel it. She writes beautiful, beautiful words. Don't you, child?"

"Oh, no, really I—" Mrs. Murdock said.

"And you must write me a play," said Lily Wynton. "A beautiful, beautiful play. And I will play in it, over and over the world, until I am a very, very old lady. And then I will die. But I will never be forgotten, because of the years I played in your beautiful, beautiful play."

She moved across the room. There was a slight hesitancy, a seeming insecurity, in her step, and when she would have sunk into a chair, she began to sink two inches, perhaps, to its right. But she swayed just in time in her descent, and was safe.

"To write," she said, smiling sadly at Mrs. Murdock, "to write. And such a little thing, for such a big gift. Oh, the privilege of it. But the anguish of it, too. The agony."

"But, you see, I—" said little Mrs. Murdock.

"Tiny one doesn't write, Lily," Miss Noyes said. She threw herself back upon the divan. "She's a museum piece. She's a devoted wife."

"A wife!" Lily Wynton said. "A wife. Your first marriage, child?"

"Oh, yes," said Mrs. Murdock.

"How sweet," Lily Wynton said. "How sweet, sweet, sweet. Tell me, child, do you love him very, very much?"

"Why, I—" said little Mrs. Murdock, and blushed. "I've known him for ages," she said.

"You love him," Lily Wynton said. "You love him. And is it sweet to go to bed with him?"

"Oh—" said Mrs. Murdock, and blushed till it hurt.

"The first marriage," Lily Wynton said. "Youth, youth. Yes, when I was your age I used to marry, too. Oh, treasure your love, child, guard it, live in it. Laugh and dance in the love of your man. Until you find out what he's really like."

There came a sudden visitation upon her. Her shoulders jerked upward, her cheeks puffed, her eyes sought to start from their hammocks. For a moment she sat thus, then slowly all subsided into place. She lay back in her chair, tenderly patting her chest. She shook her head sadly, and there was grieved wonder in the look with which she held Mrs. Murdock.

"Gas," said Lily Wynton, in the famous voice. "Gas. Nobody knows what I suffer from it."

"Oh, I'm so sorry," Mrs. Murdock said. "Is there anything—"

"Nothing," Lily Wynton said. "There is nothing. There is nothing that can be done for it. I've been everywhere."

"How's for a spot of tea, perhaps?" Miss Noyes said. "It might help." She turned her face toward the archway and lifted up her voice. "Mary! Where the hell's the tea?"

"You don't know," Lily Wynton said, with her grieved eyes fixed on Mrs. Murdock, "you don't know what stomach distress is. You can never, never know, unless you're a stomach sufferer yourself. I've been one for years. Years and years and years."

"I'm terribly sorry," Mrs. Murdock said.

"Nobody knows the anguish," Lily Wynton said. "The agony."

The maid appeared, bearing a triangular tray upon which was set an heroic-sized tea service of bright white china, each piece a hectagon. She set it down on a table within the long reach of Miss Noyes and retired, as she had come, bashfully.

"Sweet Hallie," Lily Wynton said, "my sweet. Tea—I adore it. I worship it. But my distress turns it to gall and wormwood in me. Gall and wormwood. For hours, I should have no peace. Let me have a little, tiny bit of your beautiful, beautiful brandy, instead."

"You really think you should, darling?" Miss Noyes said. "You know—"

"My angel," said Lily Wynton, "it's the only thing for acidity."

"Well," Miss Noyes said. "But do remember you've got a performance tonight." Again she hurled her voice at the archway. "Mary! Bring the brandy and a lot of soda and ice and things."

"Oh, no, my saint," Lily Wynton said. "No, no, sweet Hallie. Soda and ice are rank poison to me. Do you want to freeze my poor, weak stomach? Do you want to kill poor, poor Lily?"

"Mary!" roared Miss Noyes. "Just bring the brandy and a glass." She turned to little Mrs. Murdock. "How's for your tea, tiny one? Cream? Lemon?"

"Cream, if I may, please," Mrs. Murdock said. "And two lumps of sugar, please, if I may."

"Oh, youth, youth," Lily Wynton said. "Youth and love."

The maid returned with an octagonal tray supporting a decanter of brandy and a wide, squat, heavy glass. Her head twisted on her neck in a spasm of diffidence.

"Just pour it for me, will you, my dear?" said Lily Wynton. "Thank you. And leave the pretty, pretty decanter here, on this enchanting little table. Thank you. You're so good to me."

The maid vanished, fluttering. Lily Wynton lay back in her chair, holding in her gloved hand the wide, squat glass, colored brown to the brim. Little Mrs. Murdock lowered her eyes to her teacup, carefully carried it to her lips, sipped, and replaced it on its saucer. When she raised her eyes, Lily Wynton lay back in her chair, holding in her gloved hand the wide, squat, colorless glass.

"My life," Lily Wynton said, slowly, "is a mess. A stinking mess. It always has been, and it always will be. Until I am a very, very old lady. Ah, little Clever-Face, you writers don't know what struggle is."

"But really I'm not—" said Mrs. Murdock.

"To write," Lily Wynton said. "To write. To set one word beautifully beside another word. The privilege of it. The blessed, blessed peace of it. Oh, for quiet, for rest. But do you think those Jew bastards would close that play while it's doing a nickel's worth of business?

Oh, no. Tired as I am, sick as I am, I must drag along. Oh, child, child, guard your precious gift. Give thanks for it. It is the greatest thing of all. It is the only thing. To write."

"Darling, I told you tiny one doesn't write," said Miss Noyes. "How's for making more sense? She's a wife."

"Ah, yes, she told me. She told me she had perfect, passionate love," Lily Wynton said. "Young love. It is the greatest thing. It is the only thing." She grasped the decanter; and again the squat glass was brown to the brim.

"What time did you start today, darling?" said Miss Noyes.

"Oh, don't scold me, sweet love," Lily Wynton said. "Lily hasn't been naughty. Her wuzzunt naughty dirl 't all. I didn't get up until late, late, late. And though I parched, though I burned, I didn't have a drink until after my breakfast. 'It is for Hallie,' I said." She raised the glass to her mouth, tilted it, and brought it away, colorless.

"Good Lord, Lily," Miss Noyes said. "Watch yourself. You've got to walk on that stage tonight, my girl."

"All the world's a stage," said Lily Wynton. "And all the men and women merely players. They have their entrance and their exitses, and each man in his time plays many parts, his act being seven ages. At first, the infant, mewling and puking—"

"How's the play doing?" Miss Noyes said.

"Oh, lousily," Lily Wynton said. "Lousily, lousily, lousily. But what isn't? What isn't, in this terrible, terrible world? Answer me that." She reached for the decanter.

"Lily, listen," said Miss Noyes. "Stop that. Do you hear?"

"Please, sweet Hallie," Lily Wynton said. "Pretty please. Poor, poor Lily."

"Do you want me to do what I had to do last time?" Miss Noyes said. "Do you want me to strike you, in front of tiny one, here?"

Lily Wynton drew herself high. "You do not realize," she said, icily, "what acidity is." She filled the glass and held it, regarding it as though through a lorgnon. Suddenly her manner changed, and she looked up and smiled at little Mrs. Murdock.

"You must let me read it," she said. "You mustn't be so modest."

"Read—" said little Mrs. Murdock.

"Your play," Lily Wynton said. "Your beautiful, beautiful play. Don't think I am too busy. I always have time. I have time for everything. Oh, my God, I have to go to the dentist tomorrow. Oh, the suffering I have gone through with my teeth. Look!" She set down her glass, inserted a gloved forefinger in the corner of her mouth, and dragged it to the side. "Oogh!" she insisted. "Oogh!"

Mrs. Murdock craned her neck shyly, and caught a glimpse of shining gold.

"Oh, I'm so sorry," she said.

"As wah ee id a me ass ime," Lily Wynton said. She took away her forefinger and let her mouth resume its shape. "That's what he did to me last time," she repeated. "The anguish of it. The agony. Do you suffer with your teeth, little Clever-Face?"

"Why, I'm afraid I've been awfully lucky," Mrs. Murdock said. "I—"

"You don't know," Lily Wynton said. "Nobody knows what it is. You writers—you don't know." She took up her glass, sighed over it, and drained it.

"Well," Miss Noyes said. "Go ahead and pass out, then, darling. You'll have time for a sleep before the theater."

"To sleep," Lily Wynton said. "To sleep, perchance to dream. The privilege of it. Oh, Hallie, sweet, sweet Hallie, poor Lily feels so terrible. Rub my head for me, angel. Help me."

"I'll go get the eau de Cologne," Miss Noyes said. She left the room, lightly patting Mrs. Murdock's knee as she passed her. Lily Wynton lay in her chair and closed her famous eyes.

"To sleep," she said. "To sleep, perchance to dream."

"I'm afraid," little Mrs. Murdock began. "I'm afraid," she said, "I really must be going home. I'm afraid I didn't realize how awfully late it was."

"Yes, go, child," Lily Wynton said. She did not open her eyes. "Go to him. Go to him, live in him, love him. Stay with him always. But when he starts bringing them into the house—get out."

"I'm afraid—I'm afraid I didn't quite understand," Mrs. Murdock said.

"When he starts bringing his fancy women into the house," Lily Wynton said. "You must have pride, then. You must go. I always did. But it was always too late then. They'd got all my money. That's all they want, marry them or not. They say it's love, but it isn't. Love is the only thing. Treasure your love, child. Go back to him. Go to bed with him. It's the only thing. And your beautiful, beautiful play."

"Oh, dear," said little Mrs. Murdock. "I—I'm afraid it's really terribly late."

There was only the sound of rhythmic breathing from the chair where Lily Wynton lay. The purple voice rolled along the air no longer.

Little Mrs. Murdock stole to the chair upon which she had left her coat. Carefully she smoothed her white muslin frills, so that they would be fresh beneath the jacket. She felt a tenderness for her frock; she wanted to protect it. Blue serge and little ruffles—they were her own.

When she reached the outer door of Miss Noyes's apartment, she stopped a moment and her manners conquered her. Bravely she called in the direction of Miss Noyes's bedroom.

"Good-by, Miss Noyes," she said. "I've simply got to run. I didn't realize it was so late. I had a lovely time—thank you ever so much."

"Oh, good-by, tiny one," Miss Noyes called. "Sorry Lily went by-by. Don't mind her—she's really a real person. I'll call you up, tiny one. I want to see you. Now where's that damned cologne?"

"Thank you ever so much," Mrs. Murdock said. She let herself out of the apartment.

Little Mrs. Murdock walked homeward, through the clustering dark. Her mind was busy, but not with memories of Lily Wynton. She thought of Jim; Jim, who had left for his office before she had arisen that morning, Jim, whom she had not kissed good-by. Darling Jim. There were no others born like him. Funny Jim, stiff and cross and silent; but only because he knew so much. Only because he knew the silliness of seeking afar for the glamour and beauty and romance of living. When they were right at home all the time, she thought. Like the Blue Bird, thought little Mrs. Murdock.

Darling Jim. Mrs. Murdock turned in her course, and entered an enormous shop where the most delicate and esoteric of foods were sold for heavy sums. Jim liked red caviar. Mrs. Murdock bought a jar of the shiny, glutinous eggs. They would have cocktails that night, though they had no guests, and the red caviar would be served with them for a surprise, and it would be a little, secret party to celebrate her return to contentment with her Jim, a party to mark her happy renunciation of all the glory of the world. She bought, too, a large, foreign cheese. It would give a needed touch to dinner. Mrs. Murdock had not given much attention to ordering dinner, that morning. "Oh, anything you want, Signe," she had said to the maid. She did not want to think of that. She went on home with her packages.

Mr. Murdock was already there when she arrived. He was sitting with his newspaper opened to the financial page. Little Mrs. Murdock ran in to him with her eyes a-light. It is too bad that the light in a person's eyes is only the light in a person's eyes, and you cannot tell at a look what causes it. You do not know if it is excitement about you, or about something else. The evening before, Mrs. Murdock had run in to Mr. Murdock with her eyes a-light.

"Oh, hello," he said to her. He looked back at his paper, and kept his eyes there. "What did you do? Did you drop up to Hank Noyes's?"

Little Mrs. Murdock stopped right where she was.

"You know perfectly well, Jim," she said, "that Hallie Noyes's first name is Hallie."

"It's Hank to me," he said. "Hank or Bill. Did what's-her-name show up? I mean drop up. Pardon me."

"To whom are you referring?" said Mrs. Murdock, perfectly.

"What's-her-name," Mr. Murdock said. "The movie star."

"If you mean Lily Wynton," Mrs. Murdock said, "she is not a movie star. She is an actress. She is a great actress."

"Well, did she drop up?" he said.

Mrs. Murdock's shoulders sagged. "Yes," she said. "Yes, she was there, Jim."

"I suppose you're going on the stage now," he said.

"Ah, Jim," Mrs. Murdock said. "Ah, Jim, please. I'm not sorry at all I went to Hallie Noyes's today. It was—it was a real experience to meet Lily Wynton. Something I'll remember all my life."

"What did she do?" Mr. Murdock said. "Hang by her feet?"

"She did no such thing!" Mrs. Murdock said. "She recited Shakespeare, if you want to know."

"Oh, my God," Mr. Murdock said. "That must have been great."

"All right, Jim," Mrs. Murdock said. "If that's the way you want, to be."

Wearily she left the room and went down the hall. She stopped at the pantry door, pushed it open, and spoke to the pleasant little maid.

"Oh, Signe," she said. "Oh, good evening, Signe. Put these things somewhere, will you? I got them on the way home. I thought we might have them some time."

Wearily little Mrs. Murdock went on down the hall to her bedroom.

Arthur Kober

BOGGAINS IN THE BRONX

Bella looked at her watch, quickly drew her napkin across her mouth, pushed the plate away, and rose. Ma Gross saw her rise and frowned.

"Come on, Pa," said Bella. "Help me clear the table."

Mr. Gross had his newspaper propped up against a sugar bowl and was too deep in a news item to pay any attention to his daughter. The latter now started stacking the dishes.

"Come on, Ma," she said. "I'll wash the dishes and you can dry them."

"Look, look, how she rushes!" Mrs. Gross was obviously suspicious of such eager and unsolicited aid. "So who you rushing to see, Miss Hurry-Shmurry? Maybe you rushing to see Pressident Rosenvelt, he's waiting donnstairs in the hall?"

Mrs. Gross's rasping voice managed to spear her husband. "Awways talk, talk, talk with the tongue," he shouted. "Give the poor tongue a couple minutes' rest!"

"Look who's talking!" Mrs. Gross curled her lip contemptuously as she addressed her husband. "He comes home fomm woik, puts by him the nose in newspaper, and now alluva sudden Mr. Boss, he's talking. Put better back the nose in newspaper, Mr. Boss."

"Aw, please help me with the dishes, will ya?" Bella pleaded. "Kitty Shapiro and her intended, Dr. Rappaport, they're coming here to pick me up. We're gonna take in a pickcha show."

Bella's parents suddenly came to life. Pa dropped the newspaper and began to empty the remains of the evening's dinner into one large platter. Ma carefully folded the napkins and placed them in the top drawer of the bureau.

"So is coming here Kitty's intendit, the docteh?" Mrs. Gross asked with great interest.

"The denttist!" Pa was more explicit.

"Where comes a fine boy like a denttist to Kitty Shapiro?" Ma wanted to know.

"What'sa metta with Kitty Shapiro?" Mr. Gross didn't like or dislike Kitty—he hardly knew her, but because he habitually challenged anything his wife said, he found himself in the position of defending his daughter's friend. "A nice girl, Kitty."

"Eh, she ain't so extra," his wife said, disparagingly. "She got no shape, she got no good looks, and still in all she's engaged. She got luck, that's all."

Bella removed the fruit bowl from the mantelpiece and took it into the kitchen. The bowl was a prize Mrs. Gross had captured on one of her vacations. It bore the inscription, burnt on the surface, "Souvenir of Flugelman Manor, Catskill Mts., Greene Co., N. Y." She found some oranges in the icebox and placed these in the bowl.

Mrs. Gross took advantage of her daughter's momentary absence to ask a question which had long disturbed her and which she asked with annoying regularity. "What is with our Bella? Such a nice girl can't catch a fine, steady boy who knows how to put by a dolleh? She got a good head on her," she added, listing her daughter's virtues. "She's ten times smott like Kitty Shapiro, and still in all Kitty, she can catch a nice boy, a docteh—"

"A denttist-docteh," Pa interrupted.

"Awright, a denttist-docteh, and our Bella can't find a steady boy who makes heavy wages."

"Oh, so you're off on that again!" said Bella, coming out of the kitchen. No subject annoyed her as much as this discussion of a future husband. She felt that there was no hurry about getting married—she was twenty-one; besides, she was waiting until "Mr. Right," as she put it, came along. "Can't you find anything else to talk about?" she exclaimed indignantly.

"Get awready engaged and I'll stop talking," Ma said.

"Don't worry," replied Bella, placing the bowl and its yellow contents in the center of the table, "you'll get rid of me soon enough."

"Sure! To a *schlemiel* like Mexie Fine, a collitch boy he can't even make a living yet!"

Bella turned toward her mother and, assuming a very haughty air, said, "I'll have you unnastann, Ma, that Max Fine and I are not keeping company."

This subject was too familiar to Pa to be of any interest. He gathered his newspaper and wandered out toward the bathroom.

"Max and I," Bella added, "we just happen to be platonic friends."

"Tonic-shmonic! Believe me, all I say is when I see my dutter married, I'll be happy like anything. When—" The doorbell interrupted Mrs. Gross.

Bella admitted Kitty Shapiro and Dr. Rappaport.

"Hello, Kitty." Mrs. Gross's greeting was very warm. "How's the Mamma filling? She's filling good?"

"She's O. K., thank you. Oh, this here is my intended, Dr. Rappaport." She turned to her intended and took his hand. "Come here, Butchkie," she said. "Dr. Rappaport, this here is Mrs. Gross, Billie's mother."

"Pleasta meetchoo, Mrs. Gross." He extended a hand. This surprised Ma Gross, who quickly wiped her hand on her apron before shaking his.

"Likewise," she said. Suddenly her eye was caught by the engagement ring Kitty was wearing. "Say, that's some beyoodyful stone!" Kitty extended her hand so that Mrs. Gross could make a closer examination. "A stone like that must cust heavy money, believe me."

"Dr. Rappaport got it wholesale fomm a patient of his, a jewlerer," Kitty explained. "Dincha, Butchkie?" She gave her fiancé a smile which expressed profound admiration and affection.

Pa Gross came out of the bathroom, his suspenders dangling from his trousers, his newspaper in his hand. "Oh, hello, Kitty," he said, becoming aware of his guests.

"Hello, Mr. Gross. Come here, Butchkie." Again Kitty took her fiancé's hand. "This here is Mr. Gross, Billie's father. Mr. Gross, this here is my intended, Dr. Rappaport."

"Hoddeya do, Mr. Gross?"

"I can't complain, thenks," replied Mr. Gross.

"Pa! Look at you!" Bella's eyes flashed as she pointed to his trailing suspenders.

"Excuse me, Docteh," Pa apologized. "Bella don't like to see by me the pents falling donn. It ain't stylish by her."

"And by you it's stylish?" Mrs. Gross jumped to the defense of her daughter. "Listen to him awready!"

"Gee, Billie." Kitty was now examining Bella's dress. "That's some nifty outfit you got on. Turn arounn." Bella did so. "Very chick, Billie. Very! Is it new?"

"I just got it last week. Max Fine gave me a card to the wholesaler's. Really like it?"

"I should say. It's very chick, Billie. Wear it in good health."

"Thank you."

Pa had sidled up to Dr. Rappaport. He tapped him on the shoulder and said, "Listen, Docteh. If you don't mind, I'd like to esk you something."

"Sure, go ahead."

"I got by me here in mouth a britch—" Pa opened his mouth and pulled his lip up with his finger. Bella turned and looked at her father in dismay.

"Pa!" she cried. "Waddeya doing?"

"Look at him! This is nice! This is refined!" It was Ma who was now indignant.

"What'sa metta?" Pa asked, closing his mouth. "What I done so terrible?"

"The Docteh is here a guest in house," Ma explained. "He didn't come here fa no visits fa two and a half dolless."

"Oh, that's awright," said Dr. Rappaport, generously. "I don't mind."

"Give him one of your cards, Butchkie." Kitty turned to the others. "I better start getting my future hubby some business now."

"What pickcha we seeing?" asked Bella, looking into the bureau mirror as she got into her coat.

"Oh, there's one down the street where Herbert Moshill takes off a doctor. I thought it would be good fa Dr. Rappaport to see it. You know," Kitty explained, "because they got things in common. Well, goodnight."

Goodnights were exchanged. Ma waited until Bella and her friends had gone before she expressed herself.

"You seen the stone Kitty got on?" she asked her husband.

"No," he said.

"Such a stone!" She shrugged her shoulders. "Such stones I don't even wish my worst enemies. In five-and-ten cent stores you get such stones. Believe me, before our Bella wears such a ring, betta she stick single."

"A nice boy, the Docteh," Pa said abstractedly, turning the pages of the newspaper.

"What's so nice? A shrimp! A skinny boy! Comes a good wind and blows him right away. Nice! Before our Bella marries such a shrimp, betta she stick single."

Pa looked up from his newspaper in surprise. "You want Bella to stay single?"

"God fabbid!" Ma quickly replied. "Oney such boggains like that denttist, Kitty Shapiro can kipp!"

Heywood Broun

MRS. HEYWOOD COX BROUN *

Maybe my mother won't like this column, but at least it seemed to me that she suggested it herself. Every once and so often there appears in the letter department of my home town paper a very violent communication about me signed Mrs. Heywood Cox Broun. Mrs. Heywood Cox Broun is my mother, and, unlike her younger son, she never pulls her punches or sneaks up on an adversary.

Although her economic point of view is highly conservative, she expresses it with all the flaming ardor of a revolutionist. I know some radicals who, by dint of hard practice, can actually hiss the words "Wall Street." My mother can do that with "labor union."

If she actually met a labor union face to face I believe her hostility would evaporate. You see, most of her contacts have been made through the editorial page of the New York *Herald Tribune.* I have lent her a few copies of the *New Masses,* but they only served to madden her. I imagine it would have been shrewder tactics to have started with the *New Republic.*

In the beginning Mrs. Heywood Cox Broun did not take "my views" very seriously, but I am happy to say that she no longer tries to dispose of me as a posing pink. Only the other day she admitted in all seriousness that she regarded me as a menace, and I was very proud.

"The trouble with you, Heywood," she told me, "is that you have never been an employer."

To be sure, that is not entirely accurate. For one year I was a minor newspaper executive, and theoretically I had the power to hire and fire. I never fired anybody, but the one writer whom I engaged turned out to be top man in his division. Not only did I pick and choose Bill McGeehan for the sport page of the *Tribune* but I exploited him.

* This portrait first appeared in Broun's daily column, "It Seems to Me." in The World-Telegram.

The bargaining base on which I was empowered to operate was very slim. The managing editor said I could have him if he would come for $50 a week, and if he wouldn't take that I could go as high as $55. Bill was a very shy man all the days of his life, and I was pretty shy myself back in 1916. Besides, I never had hired anybody before. The conference was carried on with each of us looking out the opposite window.

"Mr. McGeehan," I said, "I am empowered to offer you either $50 or $55 a week to come to work. Which would you rather have?"

Bill chose $55, and in a few months he was the best-known sports writer in New York. There is, then, no blot on my escutcheon as an employer. Still, it is probably true that my talents do not lie in that direction, and I have no ambition to try again. The strain of waiting to see which salary he would accept taught me my lesson.

My mother thinks I am a "phony," although I am pretty certain she did not use that word, in the matter of parading and picketing. "It might teach you a good lesson and you would get to bed earlier if somebody did send you to jail for a couple of months," is her dictum.

However, if anything of the martyr complex lurks in me I have a right to assert that it is hereditary. For one afternoon there was no elevator service in the apartment building in which my mother lives, and now it has **been** restored, which makes my mother pretty indignant. The service came back because the landlord signed up with the union. My mother is considering walking up and down the five flights of stairs as a protest.

Individually the elevator boys are all right by her. She furnishes ice cream on Sundays and takes up the Christmas collection from the tenants. I forgot to say that my mother is very executive. She would make an excellent agitator herself, but she doesn't like to see anybody else agitate. I can easily imagine a situation in which she would picket for Eddie and George and Caleb. But they mustn't do it themselves. In some way that isn't fair to Mr. Pease and Mr. Elliman.

I am using them as symbols. She has another landlord. Mrs. Heywood Cox Broun has been in the same building for twenty-five years, and to my certain knowledge she has called that landlord every conceivable name, short of profanity and obscenity, which my mother does not employ, that a gentlewoman can lay her tongue to. But when it's a union fight my mother switches sides. She does not think that anybody else should employ violence.

When the revolution comes it's going to be a tough problem what to do with her. We will either have to shoot her or make her a commissar. In the meantime we still dine together.

Mark Twain

HIS GRANDFATHER'S OLD RAM*

Every now and then, in these days, the boys used to tell me I ought to get one Jim Blaine to tell me the stirring story of his grandfather's old ram—but they always added that I must not mention the matter unless Jim was drunk at the time—just comfortably and sociably drunk. They kept this up until my curiosity was on the rack to hear the story. I got to haunting Blaine; but it was of no use, the boys always found fault with his condition; he was often moderately but never satisfactorily drunk. I never watched a man's condition with such absorbing interest, such anxious solicitude; I never so pined to see a man uncompromisingly drunk before. At last, one evening I hurried to his cabin, for I learned that this time his situation was such that even the most fastidious could find no fault with it—he was tranquilly, serenely, symmetrically drunk—not a hiccup to mar his voice, not a cloud upon his brain thick enough to obscure his memory. As I entered, he was sitting upon an empty powder-keg, with a clay pipe in one hand and the other raised to command silence. His face was round, red, and very serious; his throat was bare and his hair tumbled; in general appearance and costume he was a stalwart miner of the period. On the pine table stood a candle, and its dim light revealed "the boys" sitting here and there on bunks, candle-boxes, powder-kegs, etc. They said:

"Sh—! Don't speak—he's going to commence."

THE STORY OF THE OLD RAM

I found a seat at once, and Blaine said:

"I don't reckon them times will ever come again. There never was a more bullier old ram than what he was. Grandfather fetched him from Illinois—got him of a man by the name of Yates—Bill Yates—maybe

* From "Roughing It."

you might have heard of him; his father was a deacon—Baptist—and he was a rustler, too; a man had to get up ruther early to get the start of old Thankful Yates; it was him that put the Greens up to j'ining teams with my grandfather when he moved west. Seth Green was prob'ly the pick of the flock; he married a Wilkerson—Sarah Wilkerson—good cretur, she was—one of the likeliest heifers that was ever raised in old Stoddard, everybody said that knowed her. She could heft a bar'l of flour as easy as I can flirt a flapjack. And spin? Don't mention it! Independent? Humph! When Sile Hawkins come a-browsing around her, she let him know that for all his tin he couldn't trot in harness alongside of *her*. You see, Sile Hawkins was—no, it warn't Sile Hawkins, after all—it was a galoot by the name of Filkins —I disremember his first name; but he *was* a stump—come into pra'r-meeting drunk, one night, hooraying for Nixon, becuz he thought it was a primary; and old Deacon Ferguson up and scooted him through the window and he lit on old Miss Jefferson's head, poor old filly. She was a good soul—had a glass eye and used to lend it to old Miss Wagner, that hadn't any, to receive company in; it warn't big enough, and when Miss Wagner warn't noticing, it would get twisted around in the socket, and look up, maybe, or out to one side, and every which way, while t'other one was looking as straight ahead as a spy-glass. Grown people didn't mind it, but it 'most always made the children cry, it was so sort of scary. She tried packing it in raw cotton, but it wouldn't work, somehow—the cotton would get loose and stick out and look so kind of awful that the children couldn't stand it no way. She was always dropping it out, and turning up her old deadlight on the company empty, and making them oncomfortable, becuz *she* never could tell when it hopped out, being blind on that side, you see. So somebody would have to hunch her and say, 'Your game eye has fetched loose, Miss Wagner, dear'—and then all of them would have to sit and wait till she jammed it in again—wrong side before, as a general thing, and green as a bird's egg, being a bashful cretur and easy sot back before company. But being wrong side before warn't much difference, anyway, becuz her own eye was sky-blue and the glass one was yaller on the front side, so whichever way she turned it it didn't match nohow. Old Miss Wagner was considerable on the borrow, she was. When she had a quilting, or Dorcas S'iety at her house she gen'ally borrowed Miss Higgins's wooden leg to stump around on; it was considerable shorter than her other pin, but much *she* minded that. She said she couldn't abide crutches when she had company, becuz they were so slow; said when she had company and things had to be done, she wanted to get up and hump herself. She was as bald as a jug, and so she used to borrow Miss Jacops's wig— Miss Jacops was the coffin-peddler's wife—a ratty old buzzard, he was, that used to go roosting around where people was sick, waiting for 'em; and there that old rip would sit all day, in the shade, on a coffin that he judged would fit the can'idate; and if it was a slow customer and kind of uncertain, he'd fetch his rations and a blanket along and sleep in the coffin nights. He was anchored out that way, in frosty weather, for about three weeks, once, before old Robbins's place, waiting for him; and after that, for as much as two years, Jacops was not on speaking terms with the old man, on account of his disapp'inting him. He got one of his feet froze, and lost money, too, becuz old Robbins took a favorable turn and got well. The next time Robbins got sick, Jacops tried to make up with him, and varnished up the same old coffin and fetched it along; but old Robbins was too many for him; he had him in, and 'peared to be powerful weak; he bought the coffin for ten dollars and Jacops was to pay it back and twenty-five more besides if Robbins didn't like the coffin after he'd tried it. And then Robbins died, and at the funeral he bursted off the lid and riz up in his shroud and told the parson to let up on the performances, becuz he could *not* stand such a coffin as that. You see he had been in a trance once before, when he was young, and he took the chances on another, cal'lating that if he made the trip it was money in his pocket, and if he missed fire he couldn't lose a cent. And, by George, he sued Jacops for the rhino and got judgment; and he set up the coffin in his back parlor and said he 'lowed to take his time, now. It was always an aggravation to Jacops, the way that miserable old thing acted. He moved back to Indiany pretty soon—went to Wellsville—Wellsville was the place the Hogadorns was from. Mighty fine family. Old Maryland stock. Old Squire Hogadorn could carry around more mixed licker, and cuss better than 'most any man I ever see. His second wife was the Widder Billings—she that was Becky Martin; her dam was Deacon Dunlap's first wife. Her oldest child, Maria, married a missionary and died in grace—et up by the savages. They et *him,* too, poor feller—biled him. It warn't the custom, so they say, but they explained to friends of his'n that went down there to bring away his things, that they'd tried missionaries every other way and never could get any good out of 'em

—and so it annoyed all his relations to find out that that man's life was fooled away just out of a dern'd experiment, so to speak. But mind you, there ain't anything ever reely lost; everything that people can't understand and don't see the reason of does good if you only hold on and give it a fair shake; Prov'dence don't fire no blank ca'tridges, boys. That there missionary's substance, unbeknowns to himself, actu'ly converted every last one of them heathens that took a chance at the barbecue. Nothing ever fetched them but that. Don't tell *me* it was an accident that he was biled. There ain't no such a thing as an accident. When my Uncle Lem was leaning up agin a scaffolding once, sick, or drunk, or suthin, an Irishman with a hod full of bricks fell on him out of the third story and broke the old man's back in two places. People said it was an accident. Much accident there was about that. He didn't know what he was there for, but he was there for a good object. If he hadn't been there the Irishman would have been killed. Nobody can ever make me believe anything different from that. Uncle Lem's dog was there. Why didn't the Irishman fall on the dog? Becuz the dog would 'a' seen him a-coming and stood from under. That's the reason the dog warn't app'inted. A dog can't be depended on to carry out a special prov'dence. Mark my words, it was a put-up thing. Accidents don't happen, boys. Uncle Lem's dog—I wish you could 'a' seen that dog. He was a reg'lar shepherd—or ruther he was part bull and part shepherd—splendid animal; belonged to Parson Hagar before Uncle Lem got him. Parson Hagar belonged to the Western Reserve Hagars; prime family; his mother was a Watson; one of his sisters married a Wheeler; they settled in Morgan County, and he got nipped by the machinery in a carpet factory and went through in less than a quarter of a minute; his widder bought the piece of carpet that had his remains wove in, and people come a hundred mile to 'tend the funeral. There was fourteen yards in the piece. She wouldn't let them roll him up, but planted him just so—full length. The church was middling small where they preached the funeral, and they had to let one end of the coffin stick out of the window. They didn't bury him—they planted one end, and let him stand up, same as a monument. And they nailed a sign on it and put—put on—put on it—sacred to—the m-e-m-o-r-y—of fourteen y-a-r-d-s—of three-ply—car —— pet—containing all that was—m-o-r-t-a-l—of—of —W-i-l-l-i-a-m—W-h-e—"

Jim Blaine had been growing gradually drowsy and drowsier—his head nodded, once, twice, three times—dropped peacefully upon his breast, and he fell tranquilly asleep. The tears were running down the boys' cheeks—they were suffocating with suppressed laughter—and had been from the start, though I had never noticed it. I perceived that I was "sold." I learned then that Jim Blaine's peculiarity was that whenever he reached a certain stage of intoxication, no human power could keep him from setting out, with impressive unction, to tell about a wonderful adventure which he had once had with his grandfather's old ram—and the mention of the ram in the first sentence was as far as any man had ever heard him get, concerning it. He always maundered off, interminably, from one thing to another, till his whisky got the best of him, and he fell asleep. What the thing was that happened to him and his grandfather's old ram is a dark mystery to this day, for nobody has ever yet found out.

Ring Lardner

ALIBI IKE

His right name was Frank X. Farrell, and I guess the X stood for "Excuse me." Because he never pulled a play, good or bad, on or off the field, without apologizin' for it.

"Alibi Ike" was the name Carey wished on him the first day he reported down South. O' course we all cut out the "Alibi" part of it right away for the fear he would overhear it and bust somebody. But we called him "Ike" right to his face and the rest of it was understood by everybody on the club except Ike himself.

He ast me one time, he says:

"What do you all call me Ike for? I ain't no Yid."

"Carey give you the name," I says. "It's his nickname for everybody he takes a likin' to."

"He mustn't have only a few friends then," says Ike. "I never heard him say 'Ike' to nobody else."

But I was goin' to tell you about Carey namin' him. We'd been workin' out two weeks and the pitchers was showin' somethin' when this bird joined us. His first day out he stood up there so good and took such a reef at the old pill that he had everyone lookin'. Then him and Carey was together in left field, catchin' fungoes, and it was after we was through for the day that Carey told me about him.

"What do you think of Alibi Ike?" ast Carey.

"Who's that?" I says.

"This here Farrell in the outfield," says Carey.

"He looks like he could hit," I says.

"Yes," says Carey, "but he can't hit near as good as he can apologize."

Then Carey went on to tell me what Ike had been pullin' out there. He'd dropped the first fly ball that was hit to him and told Carey his glove wasn't broke in good yet, and Carey says the glove could easy of been Kid Gleason's gran'father. He made a whale of a catch out o' the next one and Carey says "Nice work!" or somethin' like that, but

Ike says he could of caught the ball with his back turned only he slipped when he started after it and, besides that, the air currents fooled him.

"I thought you done well to get to the ball," says Carey.

"I ought to been settin' under it," says Ike.

"What did you hit last year?" Carey ast him.

"I had malaria most o' the season," says Ike. "I wound up with .356."

"Where would I have to go to get malaria?" says Carey, but Ike didn't wise up.

I and Carey and him set at the same table together for supper. It took him half an hour longer'n us to eat because he had to excuse himself every time he lifted his fork.

"Doctor told me I needed starch," he'd say, and then toss a shovelful o' potatoes into him. Or, "They ain't much meat on one o' these chops," he'd tell us, and grab another one. Or he'd say: "Nothin' like onions for a cold," and then he'd dip into the perfumery.

"Better try that apple sauce," says Carey. "It'll help your malaria."

"Whose malaria?" says Ike. He'd forgot already why he didn't only hit .356 last year.

I and Carey begin to lead him on.

"Whereabouts did you say your home was?" I ast him.

"I live with my folks," he says. "We live in Kansas City—not right down in the business part—outside a ways."

"How's that come?" says Carey. "I should think you'd get rooms in the post office."

But Ike was too busy curin' his cold to get that one.

"Are you married?" I ast him.

"No," he says. "I never run round much with girls, except to shows onct in a wile and parties and dances and roller skatin'."

"Never take 'em to the prize fights, eh?" says Carey.

"We don't have no real good bouts," says Ike. "Just bush stuff. And I never figured a boxin' match was a place for the ladies."

Well, after supper he pulled a cigar out and lit it. I was just goin' to ask him what he done it for, but he beat me to it.

"Kind o' rests a man to smoke after a good work-out," he says. "Kind o' settles a man's supper, too."

"Looks like a pretty good cigar," says Carey.

"Yes," says Ike. "A friend o' mine give it to me—a fella in Kansas City that runs a billiard room."

"Do you play billiards?" I ast him.

"I used to play a fair game," he says. "I'm all out o' practice now—can't hardly make a shot."

We coaxed him into a four-handed battle, him and Carey against Jack Mack and I. Say, he couldn't play billiards as good as Willie Hoppe; not quite. But to hear him tell it, he didn't make a good shot all evenin'. I'd leave him an awful-lookin' layout and he'd gather 'em up in one try and then run a couple o' hundred, and between every carom he'd say he'd put too much stuff on the ball, or the English didn't take, or the table wasn't true, or his stick was crooked, or somethin'. And all the time he had the balls actin' like they was Dutch soldiers and him Kaiser William. We started out to play fifty points, but we had to make it a thousand so as I and Jack and Carey could try the table.

The four of us set round the lobby a wile after we was through playin', and when it got along toward bedtime Carey whispered to me and says:

"Ike'd like to go to bed, but he can't think up no excuse."

Carey hadn't hardly finished whisperin' when Ike got up and pulled it:

"Well, good night, boys," he says. "I ain't sleepy, but I got some gravel in my shoes and it's killin' my feet."

We knowed he hadn't never left the hotel since we'd came in from the grounds and changed our clo'es. So Carey says:

"I should think they'd take them gravel pits out o' the billiard room."

But Ike was already on his way to the elevator, limpin'.

"He's got the world beat," says Carey to Jack and I. "I've knew lots o' guys that had an alibi for every mistake they made; I've heard pitchers say that the ball slipped when somebody cracked one off'n 'em; I've heard infielders complain of a sore arm after heavin' one into the stand, and I've saw outfielders tooken sick with a dizzy spell when they've misjudged a fly ball. But this baby can't even go to bed without apologizin', and I bet he excuses himself to the razor when he gets ready to shave."

"And at that," says Jack, "he's goin' to make us a good man."

"Yes," says Carey, "unless rheumatism keeps his battin' average down to .400."

Well, sir, Ike kept whalin' away at the ball all through the trip till everybody knowed he'd won a job. Cap had him in there regular

the last few exhibition games and told the newspaper boys a week
before the season opened that he was goin' to start him in Kane's
place.

"You're there, kid," says Carey to Ike, the night Cap made the
'nnouncement. "They ain't many boys that wins a big league berth
their third year out."

"I'd of been up here a year ago," says Ike, "only I was bent over
all season with lumbago."

It rained down in Cincinnati one day and somebody organized a
little game o' cards. They was shy two men to make six and ast I and
Carey to play.

"I'm with you if you get Ike and make it seven-handed," says Carey.
So they got a hold of Ike and we went up to Smitty's room.

"I pretty near forgot how many you deal," says Ike. "It's been a long
wile since I played."

I and Carey give each other the wink, and sure enough, he was just
as ig'orant about poker as billiards. About the second hand, the pot
was opened two or three ahead of him, and they was three in when
it come his turn. It cost a buck, and he throwed in two.

"It's raised, boys," somebody says.

"Gosh, that's right, I did raise it," says Ike.

"Take out a buck if you didn't mean to tilt her," says Carey.

"No," says Ike, "I'll leave it go."

Well, it was raised back at him and then he made another mistake
and raised again. They was only three left in when the draw come,
Smitty'd opened with a pair o' kings and he didn't help 'em. Ike stood
pat. The guy that'd raised him back was flushin' and he didn't fill.
So Smitty checked and Ike bet and didn't get no call. He tossed his
hand away, but I grabbed it and give it a look. He had king, queen,
jack and two tens. Alibi Ike he must have seen me peekin', for he
leaned over and whispered to me.

"I overlooked my hand," he says. "I thought all the wile it was a
straight."

"Yes," I says, "that's why you raised twice by mistake."

They was another pot that he come into with tens and fours. It
was tilted a couple o' times and two o' the strong fellas drawed ahead
of Ike. They each drawed one. So Ike throwed away his little pair

and come out with four tens. And they was four treys against him.
Carey'd looked at Ike's discards and then he says:

"This lucky bum busted two pair."

"No, no, I didn't," says Ike.

"Yes, yes, you did," says Carey, and showed us the two fours.

"What do you know about that?" says Ike. "I'd of swore one was
a five spot."

Well, we hadn't had no pay day yet, and after a wile everybody
except Ike was goin' shy. I could see him gettin' restless and I was
wonderin' how he'd make the get-away. He tried two or three times.
"I got to buy some collars before supper," he says.

"No hurry," says Smitty. "The stores here keeps open all night in
April."

After a minute he opened up again.

"My uncle out in Nebraska ain't expected to live," he says. "I ought
to send a telegram."

"Would that save him?" says Carey.

"No, it sure wouldn't," says Ike, "but I ought to leave my old man
know where I'm at."

"When did you hear about your uncle?" says Carey.

"Just this mornin'," says Ike.

"Who told you?" ast Carey.

"I got a wire from my old man," says Ike.

"Well," says Carey, "your old man knows you're still here yet this
afternoon if you was here this mornin'. Trains leavin' Cincinnati in
the middle o' the day don't carry no ball clubs."

"Yes," says Ike, "that's true. But he don't know where I'm goin' to
be next week."

"Ain't he got no schedule?" ast Carey.

"I sent him one openin' day," says Ike, "but it takes mail a long
time to get to Idaho."

"I thought your old man lived in Kansas City," says Carey.

"He does when he's home," says Ike.

"But now," says Carey, "I s'pose he's went to Idaho so as he can be
near your sick uncle in Nebraska."

"He's visitin' my other uncle in Idaho."

"Then how does he keep posted about your sick uncle?" ast Carey.

"He don't," says Ike. "He don't even know my other uncle's sick.
That's why I ought to wire and tell him."

"Good night!" says Carey.

"What town in Idaho is your old man at?" I says.

Ike thought it over.

"No town at all," he says. "But he's near a town."

"Near what town?" I says.

"Yuma," says Ike.

Well, by this time he'd lost two or three pots and he was desperate. We was playin' just as fast as we could, because we seen we couldn't hold him much longer. But he was tryin' so hard to frame an escape that he couldn't pay no attention to the cards, and it looked like we'd get his whole pile away from him if we could make him stick.

The telephone saved him. The minute it begun to ring, five of us jumped for it. But Ike was there first.

"Yes," he says, answerin' it. "This is him. I'll come right down."

And he slammed up the receiver and beat it out o' the door without even sayin' good-by.

"Smitty'd ought to locked the door," says Carey.

"What did he win?" ast Carey.

We figured it up—sixty-odd bucks.

"And the next time we ask him to play," says Carey, "his fingers will be so stiff he can't hold the cards."

Well, we set round a wile talkin' it over, and pretty soon the telephone rung again. Smitty answered it. It was a friend of his'n from Hamilton and he wanted to know why Smitty didn't hurry down. He was the one that had called before and Ike had told him he was Smitty.

"Ike'd ought to split with Smitty's friend," says Carey.

"No," I says, "he'll need all he won. It costs money to buy collars and to send telegrams from Cincinnati to your old man in Texas and keep him posted on the health o' your uncle in Cedar Rapids, D. C."

And you ought to heard him out there on that field! They wasn't a day when he didn't pull six or seven, and it didn't make no difference whether he was goin' good or bad. If he popped up in the pinch he should of made a base hit and the reason he didn't was so-and-so. And if he cracked one for three bases he ought to had a home run, only the ball wasn't lively, or the wind brought it back, or he tripped on a lump o' dirt, roundin' first base.

They was one afternoon in New York when he beat all records. Big Marquard was workin' against us and he was good.

In the first innin' Ike hit one clear over that right field stand, but it was a few feet foul. Then he got another foul and then the count come to two and two. Then Rube slipped one acrost on him and he was called out.

"What do you know about that!" he says afterward on the bench. "I lost count. I thought it was three and one, and I took a strike."

"You took a strike all right," says Carey. "Even the umps knowed it was a strike."

"Yes," says Ike, "but you can bet I wouldn't of took it if I'd knew it was the third one. The score board had it wrong."

"That score board ain't for you to look at," says Cap. "It's for you to hit that old pill against."

"Well," says Ike, "I could of hit that one over the score board if I'd knew it was the third."

"Was it a good ball?" I says.

"Well, no, it wasn't," says Ike. "It was inside."

"How far inside?" says Carey.

"Oh, two or three inches or half a foot," says Ike.

"I guess you wouldn't of threatened the score board with it then," says Cap.

"I'd of pulled it down the right foul line if I hadn't thought he'd call it a ball," says Ike.

Well, in New York's part o' the innin' Doyle cracked one and Ike run back a mile and a half and caught it with one hand. We was all sayin' what a whale of a play it was, but he had to apologize just the same as for gettin' struck out.

"That stand's so high," he says, "that a man don't never see a ball till it's right on top o' you."

"Didn't you see that one?" ast Cap.

"Not at first," says Ike; "not till it raised up above the roof o' the stand."

"Then why did you start back as soon as the ball was hit?" says Cap.

"I knowed by the sound that he'd got a good hold of it," says Ike.

"Yes," says Cap, "but how'd you know what direction to run in?"

"Doyle usually hits 'em that way, the way I run," says Ike.

"Why don't you play blindfolded?" says Carey.

"Might as well, with that big high stand to bother a man," says

Ike. "If I could of saw the ball all the time I'd of got it in my hip pocket."

Along in the fifth we was one run to the bad and Ike got on with one out. On the first ball throwed to Smitty, Ike went down. The ball was outside and Meyers throwed Ike out by ten feet.

You could see Ike's lips movin' all the way to the bench and when he got there he had his piece learned.

"Why didn't he swing?" he says.

"Why didn't you wait for his sign?" says Cap.

"He give me his sign," says Ike.

"What is his sign with you?" says Cap.

"Pickin' up some dirt with his right hand," says Ike.

"Well, I didn't see him do it," Cap says.

"He done it all right," says Ike.

Well, Smitty went out and they wasn't no more argument till they come in for the next innin'. Then Cap opened it up.

"You fellas better get your signs straight," he says.

"Do you mean me?" says Smitty.

"Yes," Cap says. "What's your sign with Ike?"

"Slidin' my left hand up to the end o' the bat and back," says Smitty.

"Do you hear that, Ike?" ast Cap.

"What of it?" says Ike.

"You says his sign was pickin' up dirt and he says it's slidin' his hand. Which is right?"

"I'm right," says Smitty. "But if you're arguin' about him goin' last innin', I didn't give him no sign."

"You pulled your cap down with your right hand, didn't you?" ast Ike.

"Well, s'pose I did," says Smitty. "That don't mean nothin'. I never told you to take that for a sign, did I?"

"I thought maybe you meant to tell me and forgot," says Ike.

They couldn't none of us answer that and they wouldn't of been no more said if Ike had of shut up. But wile we was settin' there Carey got on with two out and stole second clean.

"There!" says Ike. "That's what I was tryin' to do and I'd of got away with it if Smitty'd swang and bothered the Indian."

"Oh!" says Smitty. "You was tryin' to steal then, was you? I thought you claimed I give you the hit and run."

"I didn't claim no such a thing," says Ike. "I thought maybe you might of gave me a sign, but I was goin' anyway because I thought I had a good start."

Cap prob'ly would of hit him with a bat, only just about that time Doyle booted one on Hayes and Carey come acrost with the run that tied.

Well, we go into the ninth finally, one and one, and Marquard walks McDonald with nobody out.

"Lay it down," says Cap to Ike.

And Ike goes up there with orders to bunt and cracks the first ball into that right-field stand! It was fair this time, and we're two ahead, but I didn't think about that at the time. I was too busy watchin' Cap's face. First he turned pale and then he got red as fire and then he got blue and purple, and finally he just laid back and busted out laughin'. So we wasn't afraid to laugh ourselfs when we seen him doin' it, and when Ike come in everybody on the bench was in hysterics.

But instead o' takin' advantage, Ike had to try and excuse himself. His play was to shut up and he didn't know how to make it.

"Well," he says, "if I hadn't hit quite so quick at that one I bet it'd of cleared the center-field fence."

Cap stopped laughin'.

"It'll cost you plain fifty," he says.

"What for?" says Ike.

"When I say 'bunt' I mean 'bunt,' " says Cap.

"You didn't say 'bunt,' " says Ike.

"I says 'Lay it down,' " says Cap. "If that don't mean 'bunt,' what does it mean?"

" 'Lay it down' means 'bunt' all right," says Ike, "but I understood you to say 'Lay on it.' "

"All right," says Cap, "and the little misunderstandin' will cost you fifty."

Ike didn't say nothin' for a few minutes. Then he had another bright idear.

"I was just kiddin' about misunderstandin' you," he says. "I knowed you wanted me to bunt."

"Well, then, why didn't you bunt?" ast Cap.

"I was goin' to on the next ball," says Ike. "But I thought if I took a good wallop I'd have 'em all fooled. So I walloped at the first one to fool 'em, and I didn't have no intention o' hittin' it."

"You tried to miss it, did you?" says Cap.

"Yes," says Ike.

"How'd you happen to hit it?" ast Cap.

"Well," Ike says, "I was lookin' for him to throw me a fast one and I was goin' to swing under it. But he come with a hook and I met it right square where I was swingin' to go under the fast one."

"Great!" says Cap. "Boys," he says, "Ike's learned how to hit Marquard's curve. Pretend a fast one's comin' and then try to miss it. It's a good thing to know and Ike'd ought to be willin' to pay for the lesson. So I'm goin' to make it a hundred instead o' fifty."

The game wound up 3 to 1. The fine didn't go, because Ike hit like a wild man all through that trip and we made pretty near a clean-up. The night we went to Philly I got him cornered in the car and I says to him:

"Forget them alibis for a wile and tell me somethin'. What'd you do that for, swing that time against Marquard when you was told to bunt?"

"I'll tell you," he says. "That ball he throwed me looked just like the one I struck out on in the first innin' and I wanted to show Cap what I could of done to that other one if I'd knew it was the third strike."

"But," I says, "the one you struck out on in the first innin' was a fast ball."

"So was the one I cracked in the ninth," says Ike.

You've saw Cap's wife, o' course. Well, her sister's about twict as good-lookin' as her, and that's goin' some.

Cap took his missus down to St. Louis the second trip and the other one come down from St. Joe to visit her. Her name is Dolly, and some doll is right.

Well, Cap was goin' to take the two sisters to a show and he wanted a beau for Dolly. He left it to her and she picked Ike. He'd hit three on the nose that afternoon—off'n Sallee, too.

They fell for each other that first evenin'. Cap told us how it come off. She begin flatterin' Ike for the star game he'd played and o' course he begin excusin' himself for not doin' better. So she thought he was modest and it went strong with her. And she believed everything he said and that made her solid with him—that and her make-up. They was together every mornin' and evenin' for the five days we was

there. In the afternoons Ike played the grandest ball you ever see, hittin'
and runnin' the bases like a fool and catchin' everything that stayed
in the park.

I told Cap, I says: "You'd ought to keep the doll with us and he'd
make Cobb's figures look sick."

But Dolly had to go back to St. Joe and we come home for a long
serious.

Well, for the next three weeks Ike had a letter to read every day
and he'd set in the clubhouse readin' it till mornin' practice was half
over. Cap didn't say nothin' to him, because he was goin' so good.
But I and Carey wasted a lot of our time tryin' to get him to own up
who the letters was from. Fine chanct!

"What are you readin'?" Carey'd say. "A bill?"

"No," Ike'd say, "not exactly a bill. It's a letter from a fella I used
to go to school with."

"High school or college?" I'd ask him.

"College," he'd say.

"What college?" I'd say.

Then he'd stall a wile and then he'd say:

"I didn't go to the college myself, but my friend went there."

"How did it happen you didn't go?" Carey'd ask him.

"Well," he'd say, "they wasn't no colleges near where I lived."

"Didn't you live in Kansas City?" I'd say to him.

One time he'd say he did and another time he didn't. One time he
says he lived in Michigan.

"Where at?" says Carey.

"Near Detroit," he says.

"Well," I says, "Detroit's near Ann Arbor and that's where they
got the university."

"Yes," says Ike, "they got it there now, but they didn't have it there
then."

"I come pretty near goin' to Syracuse," I says, "only they wasn't no
railroads runnin' through there in them days."

"Where'd this friend o' yours go to college?" says Carey.

"I forget now," says Ike.

"Was it Carlisle?" ast Carey.

"No," says Ike, "his folks wasn't very well off."

"That's what barred me from Smith," I says.

"I was goin' to tackle Cornell's," says Carey, "but the doctor told me I'd have hay fever if I didn't stay up North.

"Your friend writes long letters," I says.

"Yes," says Ike; "he's tellin' me about a ball player."

"Where does he play?" ast Carey.

"Down in the Texas League—Fort Wayne," says Ike.

"It looks like a girl's writin'," Carey says.

"A girl wrote it," says Ike. "That's my friend's sister, writin' for him."

"Didn't they teach writin' at this here college where he went?" says Carey.

"Sure," Ike says, "they taught writin', but he got his hand cut off in a railroad wreck."

"How long ago?" I says.

"Right after he got out o' college," says Ike.

"Well," I says, "I should think he'd of learned to write with his left hand by this time."

"It's his left hand that was cut off," says Ike; "and he was left-handed."

"You get a letter every day," says Carey. "They're all the same writin'. Is he tellin' you about a different ball player every time he writes?"

"No," Ike says. "It's the same ball player. He just tells me what he does every day."

"From the size o' the letters, they don't play nothin' but double-headers down there," says Carey.

We figured that Ike spent most of his evenin's answerin' the letters from his "friend's sister," so we kept tryin' to date him up for shows and parties to see how he'd duck out of 'em. He was bugs over spaghetti, so we told him one day that they was goin' to be a big feed of it over to Joe's that night and he was invited.

"How long'll it last?" he says.

"Well," we says, "we're goin' right over there after the game and stay till they close up."

"I can't go," he says, "unless they leave me come home at eight bells."

"Nothin' doin'," says Carey. "Joe'd get sore."

"I can't go then," says Ike.

"Why not?" I ast him.

"Well," he says, "my landlady locks up the house at eight and I left my key home."

"You can come and stay with me," says Carey.

"No," he says, "I can't sleep in a strange bed."

"How do you get along when we're on the road?" says I.

"I don't never sleep the first night anywheres," he says. "After that I'm all right."

"You'll have time to chase home and get your key right after the game," I told him.

"The key ain't home," says Ike. "I lent it to one o' the other fellas and he's went out o' town and took it with him."

"Couldn't you borry another key off'n the landlady?" Carey ast him.

"No," he says, "that's the only one they is."

Well, the day before we started East again, Ike come into the club-house all smiles.

"Your birthday?" I ast him.

"No," he says.

"What do you feel so good about?" I says.

"Got a letter from my old man," he says. "My uncle's goin' to get well."

"Is that the one in Nebraska?" says I.

"Not right in Nebraska," says Ike. "Near there."

But afterwards we got the right dope from Cap. Dolly'd blew in from Missouri and was goin' to make the trip with her sister.

Well, I want to alibi Carey and I for what come off in Boston. If we'd of had any idear what we was doin', we'd never did it. They wasn't nobody outside o' maybe Ike and the dame that felt worse over it than I and Carey.

The first two days we didn't see nothin' of Ike and her except out to the park. The rest o' the time they was sight-seein' over to Cambridge and down to Revere and out to Brook-a-line and all the other places where the rubes go.

But when we come into the beanery after the third game Cap's wife called us over.

"If you want to see somethin' pretty," she says, "look at the third finger on Sis's left hand."

Well, o' course we knowed before we looked that it wasn't goin' to be no hangnail. Nobody was su'prised when Dolly blew into the dinin' room with it—a rock that Ike'd bought off'n Diamond Joe the first trip to New York. Only o' course it'd been set into a lady's-size ring instead o' the automobile tire he'd been wearin'.

Cap and his missus and Ike and Dolly ett supper together, only Ike didn't eat nothin', but just set there blushin' and spillin' things on the table-cloth. I heard him excusin' himself for not havin' no appetite. He says he couldn't never eat when he was clost to the ocean. He'd forgot about them sixty-five oysters he destroyed the first night o' the trip before.

He was goin' to take her to a show, so after supper he went upstairs to change his collar. She had to doll up, too, and o' course Ike was through long before her.

If you remember the hotel in Boston, they's a little parlor where the piano's at and then they's another little parlor openin' off o' that. Well, when Ike come down Smitty was playin' a few chords and I and Carey was harmonizin'. We seen Ike go up to the desk to leave his key and we called him in. He tried to duck away, but we wouldn't stand for it.

We ast him what he was all duded up for and he says he was goin' to the theayter.

"Goin' alone?" says Carey.

"No," he says, "a friend o' mine's goin' with me."

"What do you say if we go along?" says Carey.

"I ain't only got two tickets," he says.

"Well," says Carey, "we can go down there with you and buy our own seats; maybe we can all get together."

"No," says Ike. "They ain't no more seats. They're all sold out."

"We can buy some off'n the scalpers," says Carey.

"I wouldn't if I was you," says Ike. "They say the show's rotten."

"What are you goin' for, then?" I ast.

"I didn't hear about it bein' rotten till I got the tickets," he says.

"Well," I says, "if you don't want to go I'll buy the tickets from you."

"No," says Ike, "I wouldn't want to cheat you. I'm stung and I'll just have to stand for it."

"What are you goin' to do with the girl, leave her here at the hotel?" I says.

"What girl?" says Ike.

"The girl you ett supper with," I says.

"Oh," he says, "we just happened to go into the dinin' room together, that's all. Cap wanted I should set down with 'em."

"I noticed," says Carey, "that she happened to be wearin' that rock you bought off'n Diamond Joe."

"Yes," says Ike. "I lent it to her for a wile."

"Did you lend her the new ring that goes with it?" I says.

"She had that already," says Ike. "She lost the set out of it."

"I wouldn't trust no strange girl with a rock o' mine," says Carey.

"Oh, I guess she's all right," Ike says. "Besides, I was tired o' the stone. When a girl asks you for somethin', what are you goin' to do?"

He started out toward the desk, but we flagged him.

"Wait a minute!" Carey says. "I got a bet with Sam here, and it's up to you to settle it."

"Well," says Ike, "make it snappy. My friend'll be here any minute."

"I bet," says Carey, "that you and that girl was engaged to be married."

"Nothin' to it," says Ike.

"Now look here," says Carey, "this is goin' to cost me real money if I lose. Cut out the alibi stuff and give it to us straight. Cap's wife just as good as told us you was roped."

Ike blushed like a kid.

"Well, boys," he says, "I may as well own up. You win, Carey."

"Yatta boy!" says Carey. "Congratulations!"

"You got a swell girl, Ike," I says.

"She's a peach," says Smitty.

"Well, I guess she's O. K.," says Ike. "I don't know much about girls."

"Didn't you never run round with 'em?" I says.

"Oh, yes, plenty of 'em," says Ike. "But I never seen none I'd fall for."

"That is, till you seen this one," says Carey.

"Well," says Ike, "this one's O. K., but I wasn't thinkin' about gettin' married yet a wile."

"Who done the askin'—her?" says Carey.

"Oh, no," says Ike, "but sometimes a man don't know what he's gettin' into. Take a good-lookin' girl, and a man gen'ally almost always does about what she wants him to."

"They couldn't no girl lasso me unless I wanted to be lassoed," says Smitty.

"Oh, I don't know," says Ike. "When a fella gets to feelin' sorry for one of 'em it's all off."

Well, we left him go after shakin' hands all round. But he didn't take Dolly to no show that night. Some time wile we was talkin' she'd came into that other parlor and she'd stood there and heard us. I don't know how much she heard. But it was enough. Dolly and Cap's missus took the midnight train for New York. And from there Cap's wife sent her on her way back to Missouri.

She'd left the ring and a note for Ike with the clerk. But we didn't ask Ike if the note was from his friend in Fort Wayne, Texas.

When we'd came to Boston Ike was hittin' plain .397. When we got back home he'd fell off to pretty near nothin'. He hadn't drove one out o' the infield in any o' them other Eastern parks, and he didn't even give no excuse for it.

To show you how bad he was, he struck out three times in Brooklyn one day and never opened his trap when Cap ast him what was the matter. Before, if he'd whiffed oncet in a game he'd of wrote a book tellin' why.

Well, we dropped from first place to fifth in four weeks and we was still goin' down. I and Carey was about the only ones in the club that spoke to each other, and all as we did was remind ourself o' what a boner we'd pulled.

"It's goin' to beat us out o' the big money," says Carey.

"Yes," I says. "I don't want to knock my own ball club, but it looks like a one-man team, and when that one man's dauber's down we couldn't trim our whiskers."

"We ought to knew better," says Carey.

"Yes," I says, "but why should a man pull an alibi for bein' engaged to such a bearcat as she was?"

"He shouldn't," says Carey. "But I and you knowed he would or we'd never started talkin' to him about it. He wasn't no more ashamed o' the girl than I am of a regular base hit. But he just can't come clean on no subjec'."

Cap had the whole story, and I and Carey was as pop'lar with him as an umpire.

"What do you want me to do, Cap?" Carey'd say to him before goin' up to hit.

"Use your own judgment," Cap'd tell him. "We want to lose an-other game."

But finally, one night in Pittsburgh, Cap had a letter from his missus and he come to us with it.

"You fellas," he says, "is the ones that put us on the bum, and if you're sorry I think they's a chancet for you to make good. The old lady's out to St. Joe and she's been tryin' her hardest to fix things up. She's explained that Ike don't mean nothin' with his talk; I've wrote and explained that to Dolly, too. But the old lady says that Dolly says that she can't believe it. But Dolly's still stuck on this baby, and she's pinin' away just the same as Ike. And the old lady says she thinks if you two fellas would write to the girl and explain how you was always kiddin' with Ike and leadin' him on, and how the ball club was all shot to pieces since Ike quit hittin', and how he acted like he was goin' to kill himself, and this and that, she'd fall for it and maybe soften down. Dolly, the old lady says, would believe you before she'd believe I and the old lady, because she thinks it's her we're sorry for, and not him."

Well, I and Carey was only too glad to try and see what we could do. But it wasn't no snap. We wrote about eight letters before we got one that looked good. Then we give it to the stenographer and had it wrote out on a typewriter and both of us signed it.

It was Carey's idear that made the letter good. He stuck in some-thin' about the world's serious money that our wives wasn't goin' to spend unless she took pity on a "boy who was so shy and modest that he was afraid to come right out and say that he had asked such a beautiful and handsome girl to become his bride."

That's prob'ly what got her, or maybe she couldn't of held out much longer anyway. It was four days after we sent the letter that Cap heard from his missus again. We was in Cincinnati.

"We've won," he says to us. "The old lady says that Dolly says she'll give him another chance. But the old lady says it won't do no good for Ike to write a letter. He'll have to go out there."

"Send him to-night," says Carey.

"I'll pay half his fare," I says.

"I'll pay the other half," says Carey.

"No," says Cap, "the club'll pay his expenses. I'll send him scoutin'."

"Are you goin' to send him to-night?"

"Sure," says Cap. "But I'm goin' to break the news to him right now. It's time we win a ball game."

So in the clubhouse, just before the game, Cap told him. And I certainly felt sorry for Rube Benton and Red Ames that afternoon! I and Carey was standin' in front o' the hotel that night when Ike come out with his suitcase.

"Sent home?" I says to him.

"No," he says, "I'm goin' scoutin'."

'Where to?" I says. "Fort Wayne?"

"No, not exactly," he says.

"Well," says Carey, "have a good time."

"I ain't lookin' for no good time," says Ike. "I says I was goin' scoutin'."

"Well, then," says Carey, "I hope you see somebody you like."

"And you better have a drink before you go," I says.

"Well," says Ike, "they claim it helps a cold."

FABLES AND OTHER MORAL TALES

Fables teach a little lesson. This section of our book should *and the moral*
prove useful to those who wish to improve their ways, or
minds.

Among the moralists missing here is Kin Hubbard, a good
teacher and a funny one. We fully intended putting him in,
but backed down when we found, after collecting a bagful of
Abe Martin's sayings, that we didn't enjoy reading them
when they were strung together like sausages: they should
be taken, as originally published, one after breakfast in the
morning. It was hard to abandon Kin Hubbard after reading
what he said about a garden. (He said in order to live off a
garden, you practically had to live in it.)

James Thurber

FABLES FOR OUR TIME

THE OWL WHO WAS GOD

Once upon a starless midnight there was an owl who sat on the branch of an oak tree. Two ground moles tried to slip quietly by, unnoticed. "You!" said the owl. "Who?" they quavered, in fear and astonishment, for they could not believe it was possible for anyone to see them in that thick darkness. "You two!" said the owl. The moles hurried away and told the other creatures of the field and forest that the owl was the greatest and wisest of all animals because he could see in the dark and because he could answer any question. "I'll see about that," said a secretary bird, and he called on the owl one night when it was again very dark. "How many claws am I holding up?" said the secretary bird. "Two," said the owl, and that was right. "Can you give me another expression for 'that is to say' or 'namely'?" asked the secretary bird. "To wit," said the owl. "Why does a lover call on his love?" asked the secretary bird. "To woo," said the owl.

The secretary bird hastened back to the other creatures and reported that the owl was indeed the greatest and wisest animal in the world because he could see in the dark and because he could answer any question. "Can he see in the daytime, too?" asked a red fox. "Yes," echoed a dormouse and a French poodle. "Can he see in the daytime, too?" All the other creatures laughed loudly at this silly question, and they set upon the red fox and his friends and drove them out of the region. Then they sent a messenger to the owl and asked him to be their leader.

When the owl appeared among the animals it was high noon and the sun was shining brightly. He walked very slowly, which gave him an appearance of great dignity, and he peered about him with large, staring eyes, which gave him an air of tremendous importance. "He's God!" screamed a Plymouth Rock hen. And the others took up the cry "He's God!" So they followed him wherever he went and when he began to bump into things they began to bump into things, too. Finally he came to a concrete highway and he started up the middle of it and all the other creatures followed him. Presently a hawk, who was acting as outrider, observed a truck coming toward them at fifty miles an hour, and he reported to the secretary bird and the secretary bird reported to the owl. "There's danger ahead," said the secretary bird. "To wit?" said the owl. The secretary bird told him. "Aren't you afraid?" he asked. "Who?" said the owl calmly, for he could not see the truck. "He's God!" cried all the creatures again, and they were still crying "He's God!" when the truck hit them and ran them down. Some of the animals were merely injured, but most of them, including the owl, were killed.

Moral: You can fool too many of the people too much of the time.

THE SHRIKE AND THE CHIPMUNKS

Once upon a time there were two chipmunks, a male and a female. The male chipmunk thought that arranging nuts in artistic patterns was more fun than just piling them up to see how many you could pile up. The female was all for piling up as many as you could. She told her husband that if he gave up making designs with the nuts there would be room in their large cave for a great many more and he would soon become the wealthiest chipmunk in the woods. But he would not let her interfere with his designs, so she flew into a rage and left him. "The shrike will get you," she said, "because you are helpless and cannot look after yourself." To be sure, the female chipmunk had not been gone three nights before the male had to dress for a banquet and could not find his studs or shirt or suspenders. So he couldn't go to the banquet, but that was just as well, because all the chipmunks who did go were attacked and killed by a weasel.

The next day the shrike began hanging around outside the chipmunk's cave, waiting to catch him. The shrike couldn't get in because the doorway was clogged up with soiled laundry and dirty dishes. "He will come out for a walk after breakfast and I will get him then," thought the shrike. But the chipmunk slept all day and did not get up and have breakfast until after dark. Then he came out for a breath of air before beginning work on a new design. The shrike swooped down to snatch up the chipmunk, but could not see very well on account of the dark, so he batted his head against an alder branch and was killed.

A few days later the female chipmunk returned and saw the awful mess the house was in. She went to the bed and shook her husband. "What would you do without me?" she demanded. "Just go on living, I guess," he said. "You wouldn't last five days," she told him. She swept the house and did the dishes and sent out the laundry, and then she made the chipmunk get up and wash and dress. "You can't be healthy if you lie in bed all day and never get any exercise," she told him. So she took him for a walk in the bright sunlight and they were both caught and killed by the shrike's brother, a shrike named Stoop.

Moral: Early to rise and early to bed makes a male healthy and wealthy and dead.

THE MOTH AND THE STAR

A young and impressionable moth once set his heart on a certain star.
He told his mother about this and she counselled him to set his heart
on a bridge lamp instead. "Stars aren't the thing to hang around," she
said; "lamps are the thing to hang around." "You get somewhere that
way," said the moth's father. "You don't get anywhere chasing stars."
But the moth would not heed the words of either parent. Every evening
at dusk when the star came out he would start flying toward it and
every morning at dawn he would crawl back home worn out with his
vain endeavor. One day his father said to him, "You haven't burned a
wing in months, boy, and it looks to me as if you were never going
to. All your brothers have been badly burned flying around street
lamps and all your sisters have been terribly singed flying around house
lamps. Come on, now, get out of here and get yourself scorched! A
big strapping moth like you without a mark on him!"

The moth left his father's house, but he would not fly around street
lamps and he would not fly around house lamps. He went right on
trying to reach the star, which was four and one-third light years, or
twenty-five trillion miles, away. The moth thought it was just caught
in the top branches of an elm. He never did reach the star, but he
went right on trying, night after night, and when he was a very, very
old moth he began to think that he really had reached the star and
he went around saying so. This gave him a deep and lasting pleasure,
and he lived to a great old age. His parents and his brothers and his
sisters had all been burned to death when they were quite young.

*Moral: Who flies afar from the sphere of our sorrow is here today
and here tomorrow.*

It is for this reason that
James Thurber
wrote my
selection

THE UNICORN IN THE GARDEN

Once upon a sunny morning a man who sat in a breakfast nook
looked up from his scrambled eggs to see a white unicorn with a
golden horn quietly cropping roses in the garden. The man went up to
the bedroom where his wife was still asleep and woke her. "There's a
unicorn in the garden," he said. "Eating roses." She opened one un-
friendly eye and looked at him. "The unicorn is a mythical beast,"
she said, and turned her back on him. The man walked slowly downstairs and out into the garden. The unicorn was still there; he was
now browsing among the tulips. "Here, unicorn," said the man, and
he pulled up a lily and gave it to him. The unicorn ate it gravely. With
a high heart, because there was a unicorn in his garden, the man went
upstairs and roused his wife again. "The unicorn ate a lily," he said.
His wife sat up in bed and looked at him coldly. "You are a booby,"
she said, "and I am going to have you put in the booby hatch." The
man, who had never liked the words "booby" and "booby hatch,"
and who liked them even less on a shining morning when there was
a unicorn in the garden, thought for a moment. "We'll see about
that," he said. He walked over to the door. "He has a golden horn in
the middle of his forehead," he told her. Then he went back to the
garden to watch the unicorn, but the unicorn had gone away. The
man sat down among the roses and went to sleep.

As soon as the husband had gone out of the house, the wife got up and dressed as fast as she could. She was very excited and there was a gloat in her eye. She telephoned the police and she telephoned a psychiatrist; she told them to hurry to her house and bring a strait jacket. When the police and the psychiatrist arrived, they sat down in chairs and looked at her with great interest. "My husband," she said, "saw a unicorn this morning." The police looked at the psychiatrist and the psychiatrist looked at the police. "He told me it ate a lily," she said. The psychiatrist looked at the police and the police looked at the psychiatrist. "He told me it had a golden horn in the middle of its forehead," she said. At a solemn signal from the psychiatrist, the police leaped from their chairs and seized the wife. They had a hard time subduing her, for she put up a terrific struggle, but they finally subdued her. Just as they got her into the strait jacket, her husband came back into the house. "Did you tell your wife you saw a unicorn?" asked the psychiatrist. "Of course not," said the husband. "The unicorn is a mythical beast." "That's all I wanted to know," said the psychiatrist. "Take her away. I'm sorry, sir, but your wife is as crazy as a jay bird." So they took her away, cursing and screaming, and shut her up in an institution. The husband lived happily ever after.

Moral: Don't count your boobies until they are hatched.

George Ade

FABLES IN SLANG

THE PROFESSOR WHO WANTED TO BE ALONE

Now it happens that in America a man who goes up hanging to a Balloon is a Professor.

One day a Professor, preparing to make a Grand Ascension, was sorely pestered by Spectators of the Yellow-Hammer Variety, who fell over the Stay-Ropes or crowded up close to the Balloon to ask Fool Questions. They wanted to know how fur up he Calkilated to go and was he Afeerd and how often had he did it. The Professor answered them in the Surly Manner peculiar to Showmen accustomed to meet a Web-Foot Population. On the Q. T. the Prof. had Troubles of his own. He was expected to drop in at a Bank on the following Day and take up a Note for 100 Plunks. The Ascension meant 50 to him, but how to Corral the other 50? That was the Hard One.

This question was in his Mind as he took hold of the Trapeze Bar and signaled the Farm Hands to let go. As he trailed Skyward beneath the buoyant silken Bag he hung by his Knees and waved a glad Adieu to the Mob of Inquisitive Yeomen. A Sense of Relief came to him as he saw the Crowd sink away in the Distance.

Hanging by one Toe, and with his right Palm pressed to his Eyes, he said: "Now that I am Alone, let me Think, let me Think."

There in the Vast Silence He Thought.

Presently he gave a sigh of Relief.

"I will go to my Wife's Brother and make a Quick Touch," he said. "If he refuses to Unbelt I will threaten to tell his Wife of the bracelet he bought in Louisville."

Having reached this Happy Conclusion, he loosened the Parachute and quickly descended to the Earth.

Moral: Avoid Crowds.

THE WAIST-BAND THAT WAS TAUT UP TO THE MOMENT IT GAVE WAY

Once there was a Family consisting of Mr. and Mrs. Stuffer and three little Stuffers.

Mrs. Stuffer had belonged to the Bolt Family back in Fodderville, where she put on Weight before being shipped up to the City.

Her Mother was a Gullep, and Lineal Descendant of a New England Pilgrim named Grubb.

Mr. Stuffer also was well connected, never fear.

His Mother had been one of the Gobbels and his Grandsire on the other Branch of the Tree was often referred to, for he was none other than Phillip Gormann-Deizer, with a Colonial Home near the Gorge at Eatonville.

Their Folks, as far back as Records carried, had regarded America as the Land of Plenty and Then Some.

Also one of the Traditions coming from the grand old Pioneer Stock seemed to be that the Main Tract of the Alimentary System is the Home of the Soul.

The Stuffers could say truly that not one of their previous Relatives ever permitted a Guest to go away Hungry.

Sometimes he was taking Bi-Carb when he departed, but, Thank Edna, he never was craving Nourishment.

So the Family Honour stood safe and intact.

Back in the Country, where the Stuffers received their early Schooling as two-handed Scoopers, no Man could hold up his Head unless he was a bountiful Provider, and no Woman was respected unless she had Apple Butter and two kinds of Pie on the Table.

Those were the Blissful Days when the Deacon with the Throat-Warmers would close his Eyes and ask that this Food be Blessed and Sanctified to our Uses.

And take it from Hortense, when the Deacon made that reasonable Request, there was something piled in front of him waiting to be Sanctified.

No one ever heard of Luxuries during that oleaginous Period.

Anything that could be Et was a Necessity.

The family that wanted a Sunday Dinner away back Yonder did not have to hock the Morris Chairs.

The Barn Lot was swarming with Springers; the Garden had many rows of Sass; Berries could be had for the Picking.

Anything you might think of was Ten Cents.

For one measly Dime, the genial Grocer would let you have a Pound of Butter or a Dozen Eggs or a Peck of Murphys or a hunk of Bacon or an armful of Roasting Ears.

Beans were about as costly as Gravel.

Off in the Pantry, the solid loaves of Salt-Rising Bread were stacked, careless-like, the same as Cord-Wood.

The Humble Toiler who stowed away 14 to 16 Spare-Ribs smothered with Kraut, four or five helpings of Fresh Vegetables, a few light Biscuits inlaid with golden Butter, and possibly a quarter of a mile of Noodles, would trick out his Modest Snack with Spiced Peaches, frosty Doughnuts, and a little quart Bowl of preserved Cherries, to say nothing of Coffee Curdled with heavy Cream, and never suspect that he was living somewhat Snooky.

He was simply getting regular every-day Chow of the Farm-Hand variety.

It was on Sunday, when the Minister and his Wife or Cousin Elam's Family came over, that Mother extended herself and showed Class.

The Family never had Flowers on the Table, because the Space was taken up with Jams and Jells.

At that time, Dinner did not open with *Canapé Scabouche* followed by *Potage à la Bohonque*.

It opened with a Breast and a Second Joint and a couple of Drumsticks and much Gravy, with here and there a Giblet, and enough Mashed Potatoes to plaster a Small Room, and a Million Green Peas that never had been to Market, and an awful mix-up of String Beans, while the Odd Corners were chinked in with Cottage Cheese and Pickled Watermelon Rind and Sweet Peppers.

Butter was not rolled into Marbles during the Seventies.

Well, we should say Not!

It was lifted in half-pound Gobs, and those who smeared it never felt Improvident.

What is now called Service consisted of cleaning up the Trough and going back for another Load.

The Conversation was wholly made up of:

(1) Urgent Appeals for every one to Pack in a little bit more;

(2) Weak Protests from the Packees;

(3) Contrite Apologies from the Cook as to the Quality and Amount of Eatables in sight;

(4) Stereotyped Assurances to perturbed Hostess that everything was Swell, Elegant, and Hunky.

If the Fig Cake was a Triumph and the Jelly Cake held its Shape but the Hickory-Nut Cake went Blah, that called for a lot of Explaining.

There was a Time when every Woman thought that a soggy Cake was a Reflection on her Character. Then, if the Visitors moved slowly from the Dining Room with their Eyes protruding slightly, the Meal was voted a Success.

Not every Parlour sported an upright Piano, and the Citizen who guided a team of Bays from the front Pad of a two-seated Carriage was some Rajah, but the humblest Family waded knee-deep in Vittles.

When Winter came on, each Cellar in the Township was loaded to the Guards with Turnips, Punkins, Bell-Flower Apples, Pop-Corn, Vinegar, Walnuts, Cabbage, Potatoes, Lye Hominy, Side-Meat, Canned Stuff, Hard Cider, Sorghum Molasses, Lard, Honey in the Comb, Rutabagas, Fruit-Jars in Platoons, Jelly-Glasses in Brigades, Sage, Carrots, Navy Beans, Corn Meal, Buckwheat Flour, Onions, and other Medicinal Herbs, with possibly a few chilled Geese and Rabbits for immediate Consumption.

A barbed-wire Entanglement could have been strung around any Domicile in the Autumn, and the imprisoned Family would have come out on May 1st wearing Double Chins.

After the Stuffers landed in Town and had to use pleading Language to get a couple of fibrous Chops, they would become sentimental over Memories of Hog-Killing.

Oh, Elmer!

The Steaming Kettles of Water and the sound of scraping Knives.

Pallid Carcasses suspended in the frosty Air and the gleeful Eviscerators singing "Molly Darling" as they Rummaged.

If a close-figuring Landlady, who tries to set a Table for Seven Per, could have seen the Cans of Lard, the Platters of Tenderloin, the Hams Waiting to be Cured, and the Sausage Meat ready to glide into the Links, she would have declared it was all a Mirage.

It is hard for some People to realize, along in this Stretch of Tribulation, that not long ago, out where Things are Grown, everyone who sat down to a Repast was urged to make a Grand Drive and go as far as he liked.

The mere Thought of any one going light on new-laid Eggs, or laying off on Butter, or messing around with Bran, Excelsior, Saw-dust, Husks, Chop-Feed, and other Substitutes for Something to Eat would have been too Silly for Utterance.

The Practice of Economy was well-nigh Universal, but it did not involve playing a Joke on the Œsophagus.

The Woman of the House was Thrifty, for she fed her Cook-Stove a Splinter at a Time.

When Pa's red Unmentionables with the Glass Buttons became too Intimate and Itchy, they were chopped down for Ulysses or Grover.

Patches were made into Quilts and Rags worked over into Carpets.

A Peach-Basket, treated with a Nickel's Worth of Gold Paint and decked out with Bows of Ribbon, became a Hanging Basket for the Pet Geranium.

All the spare Coppers went into the little Tin Bank.

Only a favoured Few were permitted to walk on the Brussels Carpet.

Any good Citizen of Jasper Township would have assured you that Frugality was his Middle Name.

But Frugality did not mean getting up from the Table unsatiated.

For any one to back away before he felt himself Distended would have been regarded as Evidence of a cowardly Nature.

As soon as a Member of the Family began to fly at the Menu with a lack of wolfish Enthusiasm, he was subject to treatment as an Invalid.

The real Local Gazimbat was the Lad who held the Flapjack Record and was ready to meet all Comers during the Sweet-Corn Season.

A never-failing Appetite for anything that could be carried in and planked on the Table was classed as one of the Christian Virtues.

The Owner was held in Regard as one who had acquired Moral Grandeur and lifted himself above the Weaklings.

He went around blowing that he could Eat Anything, and all the Light Feeders slunk into the Background when he lifted his Bazoo.

Now that you have a Steer on the Pre-Natal Influences and Environ-ment of the Stuffer Family, can you see the Bunch dropped down in a Residence Thoroughfare of a congested Metropolis, three miles from a Cow and six miles from a Hen that could be relied upon to come across every Day?

Although badly separated from the Base of Supplies, they were still true to the honoured Customs of the Grubbs and the Gobbels and the Gulleps.

Mrs. Stuffer often said that she would rather cut off her Right Hand than have an Acquaintance drop in and find one Section of the Dining-Room Table unoccupied by tempting Viands.

She remarked time and again that, Come what Might, she never would Stint her Loved Ones or deny them such simple Essentials as Fresh Eggs, Sure-Enough Butter, Steak cut thick, Leg of Lamb, and submerged Short-Cake.

And there were a Hundred Thousand More like her.

If one is accustomed to the Best—and no real Daughter of a generous Mother ever compromised on Seconds or Culls—one must not Pike when telephoning the Orders.

This elaborate Overture will give you a Rough Idea of what Mr. Stuffer was up against.

He came to the City on a Guarantee.

His Salary looked like the Income of J. P. Morgan until he began to check up the Outgo.

Back in Fodderville, a neat frame Dwelling with a scroll-saw Veranda, a bed of Peonies, and Exposure on four Sides would set you back about $15 per Moon.

Up in the City, you couldn't get a Hat-Rack for any such Money.

It seemed to the Stuffers that everything in Town was sold by the Minute or the Ounce.

It was a grievous Shock to the Missus when they began to weigh the Vegetables on her.

She had got used to having them thrown at her with a Shovel.

The Neighbors no longer brought in Produce at Special inside Prices—Eggs figured by the wear and tear on the Fowl and no Overhead Charge on Honey except the Time put in by the Bees.

The Stuffers suddenly discovered that when you go out to spend a Dollar in the City, you don't have to take a Wheelbarrow along.

But Mr. Stuffer and Mrs. Stuffer and each of the miniature Stuffers had it firmly fixed in the Coke that the Minute you begin letting down on That to which you have been Accustomed you lose Self-Respect and indirectly confess to being in Straitened Circumstances.

It was all right for those living in Huts and Hovels to cheapen the Standards of Living, but the Stuffers could not endure the Thought of giving up any of the old Stand-by Dishes.

Some Persons of a Poetical Turn mark the changing Seasons by the Trailing Arbutus, which precedes the bold Iris; then old-fashioned

Roses, followed by a riotous show of Dahlias; Autumn Leaves tinged Red and Yellow, harbingers of snowy Fields and icy Boughs.

Every Sign of the Zodiac meant a new Item in the Bill of Fare for the practical Stuffers.

With the first warm days of Spring, did they go looking for Wood-Violets?

Not one Look.

They began to sit up and demand Green Onions, Asparagus, Head Lettuce, and Strawberries.

June is the Month of Roses. Also of Fried Chicken and a pleasant gateway to Corn on the Cob.

Autumn Days need not be Melancholy if one is surrounded by Turkey and Mincemeat.

Even Winter has a Charm of its own, if Sausage and Buckwheat Cakes are ever smiling in the Background.

When Prices began to Sizz-Boom-Ah, the old Pay Envelope failed to stand up under the Strain, but can you expect one reared on the Fat of the Land to accept Macaroni as a Compromise?

The Producer would let out a Howl every time the Meat Bill came in, but he would have howled in a higher Key if the Good Woman had failed to throw him his Roast Beef and Mutton Chops.

He wielded a very consistent Knife and Fork and his daily Demand was for something that Sticks to the Ribs.

Of course, both of them saw the Article in the Paper, entitled "How to feed a Family of Five on 80 Cents a Day."

Once, just after the 1st of the Month, while Mr. Stuffer was still Bleeding, his Companion tried out a Sample Menu recommended by Hazel McGinnis Updyke, a famous Tipster weighing between 80 and 90 pounds.

He stirred the watery Soup as if moved by a dull Curiosity as to the grains of Barley hiding at the Bottom, and then he gave Friend Wife a Look—but, Ooey, such a Look!

It seemed to say, "And this is the Woman who promised to Love, Honour, and be of some Help!"

Then came Rice Croquettes, one of the most startling Specimens of Near-Food ever touted by a Lady writing Syndicate Come-Ons and boarding at an Italian Table d'Hôte.

You eat it, but after you get through you are not sure that anything has Happened.

After which, Bread Pudding, said to have broken up more Homes than High White Shoes.

As Mr. Stuffer left the House, his well-meaning Partner felt in her Heart of Hearts that he was going out to a Restaurant to get some Ham and Eggs.

She resolved that never again would she ask him to be Untrue to his Nobler Self.

So, at the next Meal, she jollied him up with Lamb Steak and Kidneys, Mushrooms in Cream, Succotash, Waffles and Maple Syrup, Endive Salad and Sharp Cheese, with a Finale of Blueberry Pie à la Mode.

Experts tell us that Blueberry Pie, showing its bold Colour between the slopes of Vanilla Ice Cream, is practically the Last Word with those who want something to hit the Spot.

It is the Pièce de Résistance, the Dénouement, the Dramatic Climax, the Grand Transformation, Little Eva ascending to Paradise.

Nothing comes after it except the Pepsin Tablet and the Hot-Water Bag.

Mrs. Stuffer watched her Husband as he lighted his Sublima.

He had a Sleepy Look, which is always a Good Sign.

Then he Groaned, and she knew that she had won back his Love.

Any time you get them to Groaning, you are a Jewel of a Housekeeper.

Having set out to defy the Increased Cost and indulge themselves within Reason, the little Family soon found itself riding a troublous Sea with the Breakers just ahead. Man's Chief Enemies, they had been told long ago, are Pride, Lust, Avarice, etc.

Now they learned Different. They came to know that the two principal Destroyers of Happiness are the Middleman and the Cold-Storage Warehouse.

Hemmed in by extortionate Retailers, Food Pirates, and Commission Sharks, they stood Resolute and vowed they would never Surrender.

As they were riding over the Hills to the Poor-House, Mr. Stuffer made the dismal Observation that it was a Blue Finish for a Life of Honest Endeavour.

"That may be true," said Mrs. Stuffer, "but I have this Satisfaction," as she lifted her Head proudly: "I set a scrumptious Table to the very last."

Moral: Cling to your Ideals, such as they are.

———

THE NINNY WHO SWAM AWAY FROM THE LIFE PRESERVER

Once there was a Citizen who put in most of his Time acting as Custodian of a Thirst.

He could inhale through a Straw, bury his Nose in it or leave it flow from the Original Package.

After he had bombarded the Innards with Aqua Fortis for a matter of 20 years, he awoke one Morning suffering from a combination of Pin-Wheels, Moving-Pictures and a General Alarm of Fire.

Doc came in answer to a Hurry-Up and found that he was on the Job about 8 years too late.

The Patient had something like 15 Things the matter with him, ranging from Cirrhosis of the Liver to Water on the Brain, although the latter did not sound Reasonable.

He had six Weeks in which to settle up his Affairs before receiving the Wreaths and Pillows.

During that time he chopped on the Fire-Water because he somewhat blamed the Old Stuff for sending him away at 42 when he might have stuck around to be 87.

His Pals came to see him just before he winked out.

They found him very white and drawn and sort of Aghast at the Record he had established.

After the funeral the Pall-Bearers took off many Dark Gloves and flew at the High Balls.

One of them expressed the Opinion that what killed Jim was cutting out the Stimulants. The Shock was too much for him.

All the other Diagnosticians nodded their heads gravely.

And the Host went to the Cellar for another Load.

Moral: It is absolutely Harmless unless Discontinued.

Don Marquis

FABLE OF THE IRON DOGS

Once there were two iron dogs on the front lawn of a Pennsylvania millionaire.

One of them said, "I do not believe in a future for iron dogs. When I lose another leg, I will go to the scrap heap, and that will be the end of me."

The other one said, "I have the utmost faith in some noble destiny for iron dogs; though I should be broken to bits, yet will I live again somehow, somewhere, somewhen, to some excellent purpose."

The millionaire just then came along and directed a workman to remove the iron dogs, for his daughter had come home from a select school and told him they were a Mistake.

The first iron dog was thrown upon the junk heap as he had predicted, and became rust, doing no one any good.

But the second one, who had believed in his own destiny, was melted down and made into munitions with which to kill Germans.

* * *

MORAL

You don't have to have a soul unless you want one.

Milt Gross

FERRY-TAIL FROM KEENG MITAS FOR
NIZE BABY

Oohoo, nize baby, itt opp all de Cheeken Zoop so mamma'll gonna
tell you a Ferry-Tail from Keeng Mitas. Wance oppon a time was a
werry, werry reech Keeng from de name from Keeng Mitas. Sotch
a welt wot he hed!—wot it would make J. P. Morgan witt Hanry Fudd
witt John D. Rockefeller dey should look like puppers. (Nize baby,
take anodder spoon cheeken zoop—)

So instat from bing setisfite witt contempted—he becrutched yat
averybody helse wot dey possassed, und he was only trying how he
could incriss yat wot he had (mmmm-dot griddy ting). So a whole
time he was hudding opp de moneh witt glutting yat from it like a
miser. So wan day he was wukking opp witt don in de godden so he
was tinking so, "Hm—wot could I do, dot I should hev it ivvin more
yat from wot I got?" (mmm-dot salfish critchure). So he was inter-
ropted by a leedle Ferry wot it was stending in de front from him witt
a Megic Want.

So de Ferry sad, "You Keeng Mitas? ? ?"

So de Keeng sad, "So wot is? ?"

So de Ferry sad, "I'm a Ferry wot I could grent you wot annyting
wot you'll weesh so'll be foolfeeled de weesh! ! !" So de Keeng sad,
"Wot kind bunco-steerage game you call dees, ha? You got maybe
some goot-for-notting Hoil Stocks wot you want to sell it, ha, maybe?
Odder a petent carpet-swipper, odder maybe a phuny Gold mine yat,
ha! ! Try batter by Old Keeng Cole, not by me—Goot hefternoon! !"

So de Ferry sad, "Hm—you a werry septical poison, ha? Soppose
wot you geeve me a hopportunity I should conweence you?"

So de Keeng sad, "Ho K, I weesh wot averyting wot I toch it, it
should toin into gold."

So he was holding in de hand a spectre. so de Ferry gave him a tree times a tep witt de megic want—so he gave a look—so it was by him a solit gold spectre in de hend! !—Noo, noo!—So don't esk! ! !

So de Keeng was dencing witt jomping witt lipping witt bonding witt prencing from joy. You should see wot he was deshing hitter witt titter—opp witt don, high witt low—beck witt futt, to witt frau,—wot he was touching averyting on wheech he put on de hends. So his Wessel sad, "Is goot now?" So de Keeng sad, "Yeh, is good bot look a hincome-tax I'll gonna have und'll be mine lock yat wot I'll gat maybe to-morrow roomateezum in de hends." (MMMmmm—dot apparitious ting.)

So it came gredually deener-time so de Keeng was werry hongry so he set don he should itt opp a hoyster. So so soon wot he toched de hoyster it became solit gold! ! So he said, "Hm—Wott's dees? ?" So he tried he should ketch in queek a potato in de mout no one should see, so so soon wot he stodded he should chew it, it became solit gold wot it broke him two teet witt a cron witt a heff from de breedge—woik yat besites wot it was werry hot so it made him yat a bleesters on de tong! !

So he sad—"Hm!—Is a seerous preposition. It simms wot I'll have to employ stragedy." So he sad to de Wessel, "I'll gonna stend witt de mout open—So you'll put in a binn-shooter a hepple, wot you'll shoot it, it should go in mine mout wot I'll swallow it queeck it shouldn't toch me." So de Wessel compiled gredually witt de requast, bot he was a werry poor mox-man, so instat from de Keeng's mout it went in de had wot it became immiditly gold wot it gave him sotch a knock wot he had almost conclusion from de brain.

So was a werry cricketal situation—wot de Keeng sad, "Hm, so it rimmains wot I'll gonna hev to leeve maybe a whole life on gold-feesh, Ha! !" So it was gredually all kind from trobbles! ! It came de night so he stodded in he should ondrass so it was dere by him a pair from 18 carrot Bivvy Dizz wot de wessels had to ondrass him yat witt a can-uppener. So one day he was wukking opp witt don so it came ronning over to heem his leedle dudder—Hm, deed she was a switt child! ! So he was so epsom minded, dot dope, wot he put on her head de hend he should toch her so she became solit gold. Yi yi yi yi—So you should see a griff from a remuss wot it was by de Keeng—mmm! ! ! Deed he was sowry! ! ! witt meeserable witt don-hotted—witt rependant—wot he was wipping beeterly.

So it gredually appeared in de front from him de Ferry witt de

Megic Want so he sad, "Goot Monnink, Keeng, How is by you de Gold Rosh? ? ?" So de Keeng gave sotch a grun from meesery wot it toched de Ferry's hott—so he sad, "You'll gonna be steengy witt griddy witt salfish anny more?"

So de Keeng sad, "NO."

"You'll gonna dunnate maybe itch year someting to de Meelk Fond?"

"Yeh."

"Wid de Selwation Ommy?"

"Yeh."

"Widd de Uffan's Home?"

"Yeh."

"So you'll gonna refumm, ha?"

"Yeh."

"In odder woids you'll gonna be from now on a deeference indiwijial halltogadder?"

"Cruss mine hott!"

So de Ferry gave him tree times a tep witt de Megic Want so dere it was stending in de front from him de leedle dudder jost like new, wot dey leeved heppily hever hefter.

(Hm—Sotch a dollink baby—ate opp all de cheeken Zoop!)

Ambrose Bierce

FANTASTIC FABLES

THE DISINTERESTED ARBITER

Two Dogs who had been fighting for a bone, without advantage to either, referred their dispute to a Sheep. The Sheep patiently heard their statements, then flung the bone into a pond.

"Why did you do that?" said the Dogs.

"Because," replied the Sheep, "I am a vegetarian."

THE PARTY OVER THERE

A Man in a Hurry, whose watch was at his lawyer's, asked a Grave Person the time of day.

"I heard you ask that Party Over There the same question," said the Grave Person. "What answer did he give you?"

"He said it was about three o'clock," replied the Man in a Hurry; "but he did not look at his watch, and as the sun is nearly down I think it is later."

"The fact that the sun is nearly down," the Grave Person said, "is immaterial, but the fact that he did not consult his timepiece and make answer after due deliberation and consideration is fatal. The answer given," continued the Grave Person, consulting his own timepiece, "is of no effect, invalid, and void."

"What, then," said the Man in a Hurry, eagerly, "is the time of day?"

"The question is remanded to the Party Over There for a new answer," replied the Grave Person, returning his watch to his pocket and moving away with great dignity.

He was a Judge of an Appellate Court.

CAT AND KING

A Cat was looking at a King, as permitted by the proverb.

"Well," said the monarch, observing her inspection of the royal person, "how do you like me?"

"I can imagine a King," said the Cat, "whom I should like better."

"For example?"

"The King of Mice."

The sovereign was so pleased with the wit of the reply that he gave her permission to scratch his Prime Minister's eyes out.

REVENGE

An Insurance Agent was trying to induce a Hard Man to Deal With to take out a policy on his house. After listening to him for an hour, while he painted in vivid colors the extreme danger of fire consuming the house, the Hard Man to Deal With said:

"Do you really think it likely that my house will burn down inside the time that my policy will run?"

"Certainly," replied the Insurance Agent; "have I not been trying all this time to convince you that I do?"

"Then," said the Hard Man to Deal With, "why are you so eager to have your Company bet me money that it will not?"

The Agent was silent and thoughtful for a moment; then he drew the other apart into an infrequented place and whispered in his ear:

"My friend, I will impart to you a dark secret. Years ago the Company betrayed my sweetheart by promise of marriage. Under an assumed name I have wormed myself into its service for revenge; and as there is a heaven above us, I will have its heart's blood."

OFFICER AND THUG

A Chief of Police who had seen an Officer beating a Thug was very indignant, and said he must not do so any more on pain of dismissal.

"Don't be too hard on me," said the Officer, smiling; "I was beating him with a stuffed club."

"Nevertheless," persisted the Chief of Police, "it was a liberty that must have been very disagreeable, though it may not have hurt. Please do not repeat it."

"But," said the Officer, still smiling, "it was a stuffed Thug."

In attempting to express his gratification the Chief of Police thrust out his right hand with such violence that his skin was ruptured at the arm-pit and a stream of sawdust poured from the wound. He was a stuffed Chief of Police.

————

SAINT AND SOUL

St. Peter was sitting at the gate of Heaven when a Soul approached, and, bowing civilly, handed him its card.

"I am very sorry, sir," said St. Peter, after reading the card, "but I really cannot admit you. You will have to go to the Other Place. Sorry, sir, very sorry."

"Don't mention it," said the Soul; "I have been all the month at a watering place, and it will be an agreeable change. I called only to ask if my friend Elihu Root is here."

"No, sir," the Saint replied; "Mr. Root is not dead."

"O, I know that," said the Soul, "I thought he might be visiting God."

E. B. White

THE PARABLE OF THE FAMILY WHICH DWELT APART

On a small, remote island in the lower reaches of Barnetuck Bay there lived a family of fisherfolk by the name of Pruitt. There were seven of them, and they were the sole inhabitants of the place. They subsisted on canned corn, canned tomatoes, pressed duck, whole-wheat bread, terrapin, Rice Krispies, crabs, cheese, queen olives, and home-made wild-grape preserve. Once in a while Pa Pruitt made some whiskey and they all had a drink.

They liked the island and lived there from choice. In winter, when there wasn't much doing, they slept the clock around, like so many bears. In summer they dug clams and set off a few pinwheels and salutes on July 4th. No case of acute appendicitis had ever been known in the Pruitt household, and when a Pruitt had a pain in his side he never even noticed whether it was the right side or the left side, but just hoped it would go away, and it did.

One very severe winter Barnetuck Bay froze over and the Pruitt family was marooned. They couldn't get to the mainland by boat because the ice was too thick, and they couldn't walk ashore because the ice was too treacherous. But inasmuch as no Pruitt had anything to go ashore for, except mail (which was entirely second class), the freeze-up didn't make any difference. They stayed indoors, kept warm, and ate well, and when there was nothing better to do, they played crokinole. The winter would have passed quietly enough had not someone on the mainland remembered that the Pruitts were out there in the frozen bay. The word got passed around the county and finally reached the Superintendent of State Police, who immediately notified Pathé News and the United States Army. The Army got there first, with three bombing planes from Langley Field, which flew low over the island and dropped packages of dried apricots and bouillon cubes,

which the Pruitts didn't like much. The newsreel plane, smaller than
the bombers and equipped with skis, arrived next and landed on a
snow-covered field on the north end of the island. Meanwhile, Major
Bulk, head of the state troopers, acting on a tip that one of the Pruitt
children had appendicitis, arranged for a dog team to be sent by plane
from Laconia, New Hampshire, and also dispatched a squad of troopers to attempt a crossing of the bay. Snow began falling at sundown, and during the night three of the rescuers lost their lives
about half a mile from shore, trying to jump from one ice cake to
another.

The plane carrying the sled dogs was over southern New England
when ice began forming on its wings. As the pilot circled for a forced
landing, a large meat bone which one of the dogs had brought along
got wedged in the socket of the main control stick, and the plane went
into a steep dive and crashed against the side of a powerhouse, instantly killing the pilot and all the dogs, and fatally injuring Walter
Ringstead, 7, of 3452 Garden View Avenue, Stamford, Conn.

Shortly before midnight, the news of the appendicitis reached the
Pruitt house itself, when a chartered autogiro from Hearst's International News Service made a landing in the storm and reporters informed Mr. Pruitt that his oldest boy, Charles, was ill and would have
to be taken to Baltimore for an emergency operation. Mrs. Pruitt
remonstrated, but Charles said his side did hurt a little, and it ended
by his leaving in the giro. Twenty minutes later another plane came in,
bearing a surgeon, two trained nurses, and a man from the National
Broadcasting Company, and the second Pruitt boy, Chester, underwent an exclusive appendectomy in the kitchen of the Pruitt home,
over the Blue Network. This lad died, later, from eating dried apricots
too soon after his illness, but Charles, the other boy, recovered after a
long convalescence and returned to the island in the first warm days of
spring.

He found things much changed. The house was gone, having caught
fire on the third and last night of the rescue when a flare dropped by
one of the departing planes lodged in a bucket of trash on the piazza.
After the fire, Mr. Pruitt had apparently moved his family into the
emergency shed which the radio announcers had thrown up, and
there they had dwelt under rather difficult conditions until the night
the entire family was wiped out by drinking a ten-per-cent solution of

carbolic acid which the surgeon had left behind and which Pa Pruitt had mistaken for grain alcohol.

Barnetuck Bay seemed a different place to Charles. After giving his kin decent burial, he left the island of his nativity and went to dwell on the mainland.

ALL SORTS OF DILEMMAS

Humorists fatten on trouble. They have always made trouble pay. They struggle along with a good will and endure pain cheerfully, knowing how well it will serve them in the sweet by and by. Here in this department you see them wrestling with foreign languages, fighting folding ironing boards and swollen drainpipes, suffering the terrible discomfort of tight boots (or as Josh Billings wittily called them, "tite" boots). They pour out their sorrows profitably, in a form which is not quite fiction nor quite fact either.

The New Yorker *has lately been a handy repository for these literary exaggerations and has even given them a name, for convenience in handling. It calls them "casuals." We need hardly assure the reader, as he dips into the coming section, that beneath the sparkling surface of these comical dilemmas flows the strong tide of human woe.*

Frank Moore Colby

CONFESSIONS OF A GALLOMANIAC

Down to the outbreak of the war I had no more desire to converse with a Frenchman in his own language than with a modern Greek. I thought I understood French well enough for my own purposes, because I had read it off and on for twenty years, but when the war aroused sympathies and sharpened curiosities that I had not felt before, I realized the width of the chasm that cut me off from what I wished to feel. Nor could it be bridged by any of the academic, natural, or commercial methods that I knew of. They were either too slow or they led in directions that I did not wish to go. I tried a phonograph, and after many bouts with it I acquired part of a sermon by Bossuet and real fluency in discussing a quinsy sore throat with a Paris physician, in case I ever went there and had one. I then took fourteen conversation lessons from a Mme. Carnet, and being rather well on in years at the start, I should, if I had kept on diligently, have been able at the age of eighty-five to inquire faultlessly my way to the post-office. I could already ask for butter and sing a song written by Henry IV—when my teacher went to France to take care of her half-brother's children. I will say this for Mme. Carnet. I came to understand perfectly the French for all her personal and family affairs. No human being has ever confided in me so abundantly as she did. No human being has ever so sternly repressed any answering confidences of my own. Her method of instruction, if it was one, was that of jealous, relentless, unbridled soliloquy.

Thrown on the world with no power of sustaining a conversation on any other subject than the members of the Carnet family, I nevertheless resolved to take no more lessons but to hunt down French people and make them talk. What I really needed was a governess to take me to and from my office and into the park at noon, but at my age that was out of the question. Then began a career of hypocritical benevolence. I scraped acquaintance with every Frenchman whom I heard talking English very badly, and I became immensely interested in his welfare. I formed the habit of introducing visiting Frenchmen to French-speaking Americans, and sitting, with open mouth, in the flow of their conversation. Then I fell in with M. Bernou, the commissioner who was over here buying guns, and whose English and my French were so much alike that we agreed to interchange them. We met daily for two weeks and walked for an hour in the park, each tearing at the other's language. Our conversations, as I look back on them, must have run about like this:

"It calls to walk," said he, smiling brilliantly.

"It is good morning," said I, "better than I had extended."

"I was at you yestairday ze morning, but I deed not find."

"I was obliged to leap early," said I, "and I was busy standing up straight all around the forenoon."

"The book I prayed you send, he came, and I thank, but positively are you not deranged?"

"Don't talk," said I. "Never talk again. It was really nothing any-where. I had been very happy, I reassure."

"Pardon, I glide, I glode. There was the hide of a banane. Did I crash you?"

"I noticed no insults," I replied. "You merely gnawed my arm."

Gestures and smiles of perfect understanding.

I do not know whether Bernou, who like myself was middle-aged, felt as I did on these occasions, but by the suppression of every thought that I could not express in my childish vocabulary, I came to feel exactly like a child. They said I ought to think in French and I tried to do so, but thinking in French when there is so little French to think with, divests the mind of its acquisitions of forty years. Experience slips away for there are not words enough to lay hold of it. Knowledge of good and evil does not exist; the sins have no names; and the mind under its linguistic limitations is like a rather defective toy Noah's ark. From the point of view of Bernou's and my vocabulary, Central Park was as the Garden of Eden after six months—new and unnamed things everywhere. A dog, a tree, a statue taxed all our powers of description, and on a complex matter like a policeman our minds could not meet at all. We could only totter together a few steps in any mental direction. Yet there was a real pleasure in this earnest interchange of insipidities and they were highly valued on each side. For my part I shall always like Bernou, and feel toward him as my childhood's friend. I wonder if he noticed that I was an old, battered man, bothered with a tiresome profession. I certainly never suspected that he was. His language utterly failed to give me that impression.

After I lost Bernou I fastened upon an unfrocked priest who had come over here and gone into the shoe trade—a small, foxy man, who regarded me, I think, in the light of an aggressor. He wanted to become completely American and forget France, and as I was trying to reverse the process, I rather got in his way. He could talk of mediæval liturgies and his present occupation, but nothing in between, and as he spoke English very well, his practical mind revolted at the use of a medium of communication in which one of us almost strangled when there was another available in which we were both at ease. I could not pump much French out of him. He would burst into English rather resentfully. Then I took to the streets at lunch-time and tried newsdealers, book-shops, restaurants, invented imaginary errands, bought things that I did not want, and exchanged them for objects even less desirable. That kept a little conversation going day by day, but on the whole it was a dry season. It is a strange thing. There are more than thirty thousand of them in the city of New York, and I had always heard that the French are a clannish folk and hate to learn another language, but most of my overtures in French brought only English upon me. The more pains I took the more desirable it seemed to them that I should be spared the trouble of continuing. I was always diving into French and they were always pulling me out again. They thought they were humane.

French people hate broken French worse than most of us hate broken English. But when dragged out into the light of English I tried to talk just as foolishly in order that they might think it was not really my French that was the matter with me. Sometimes that worked quite well. Finding me just as idiotic in my own language they went back to theirs. It certainly worked well with my friend M. Bartet, a paralytic tobacconist in the West Thirties near the river, to whom my relation was for several months that of a grandchild, though, I believe we were of the same age. He tried to form my character by bringing me up on such praiseworthy episodes of his early life as he thought I was able to grasp.

Now at the end of a long year of these persistent puerilities I am able to report two definite results: In the first place a sense of my incapacity and ignorance infinitely vaster than when I began, and in the second a profound distrust, possibly vindictive in its origin, of all Americans in the city of New York who profess an acquaintance with French culture, including teachers, critics, theater audiences, lecture audiences, and patronesses of visiting Frenchmen.

It was perhaps true, as people said at the time, that a certain French theatrical experiment in New York could not continue for the simple reason that it was too good a thing for the theater-going public to support. It may be that the precise equivalent of the enterprise, even if not hampered by a foreign language, could not have permanently endured. Yet from what I saw of its audiences, critics, enthusiasts, and from what I know of the American Gallophile generally, including myself, I believe the linguistic obstacle to have been more serious than they would have us suppose—serious enough to account for the situation without dragging in our æsthetic incapacity. It was certainly an obstacle that less than one-half of any audience ever succeeded in surmounting.

I do not mean that the rest of the audience got nothing out of it, for so expressive were the players by other means than words, that they often sketched the play out in pantomime. The physical activities of the troupe did not arise, as some of the critics declared, from the vivacity of the Gallic temperament; nor were they assumed, as others believed, because in the seventeenth century French actors had been acrobats. These somewhat exaggerated gestures were occasioned by the perception that the majority of the spectators were beginners in French. They were supplied by these ever-tactful people as a running translation for a large body of self-improving Americans.

I do not blame other Americans for dabbling in French, since I myself am the worst of dabblers, but I see no reason why any of us should pretend that it is anything more than dabbling. The usual way of reading French does not lead even to an acquaintance with French literature. Everybody knows that words in a living language in order to be understood have to be lived with. They are not felt as a part of living literature when you see them pressed out and labeled in a glossary, but only when you hear them fly about. A word is not a definite thing susceptible of dictionary explanation. It is a cluster of associations, reminiscent of the sort of men that used it, suggestive of social class, occupation, mood, dignity or the lack of it,

primness, violences, pedantries, or platitudes. It hardly seems necessary to say that words in a living literature ought to ring in the ear
with the sounds that really belong to them, or that poetry without an
echo cannot be felt.

It may be that there is no way out of it. Perhaps it is inevitable that
the colleges which had so long taught the dead languages as if they
were buried should now teach the living ones as if they were dead.
But there is no need of pretending that this formal acquaintance with
books results in an appreciation of literature. No sense of the intimate
quality of a writer can be founded on a verbal vacuum. His plots, his
place in literature, his central motives, and the opinion of his critics
could all be just as adequately conveyed, if his books were studied in
the language of the deaf and dumb. Of course, one may be drawn to
an author by that process but it would hardly be the artistic attraction
of literature; it is as if one felt drawn to a woman by an interest
exclusively in her bones.

Elementary as these remarks may seem I offer them to Gallophiles
without apology. On the contrary I rather fear that I am writing over
their heads.

St. Clair McKelway

AN AFFIX FOR BIRDS

When I was in Tokio a few years ago, I decided to study the Japanese language. My Japanese teacher, whose name was Watanabe-san, used to ride out to my house every morning on his motorcycle. He wore a gray felt hat turned up at the front, a wing collar with a striped bow tie, a vest with white piping, a short black coat, and long flannel underdrawers. The trousers to his suit he carried rolled and strapped on the parcel rack of his motorcycle in order to keep them from getting muddy when the motorcycle was churning through Tokio's unpaved streets. Promptly at eight o'clock each morning I would hear in front of the house the putt-putting and then the expiring gasps of Watanabe-san's motorcycle, and I would go down and let him in. He would enter the vestibule bowing, and inhaling noisily through his teeth. Then he would put on his pants and we would sit down at the breakfast table. For him to come at this hour was my own idea. I had to get to work at nine, and I thought this plan would save me some time. When I first told him that I would take my breakfast while he gave me the lesson, I had no idea that he would breakfast with me. I thought he would eat his meal at his own home, before he mounted his motorcycle, and since I never had anything but orange juice and coffee, I thought it would be all right for me to sit there and have them while he taught me the language of the country. This was perfectly all right with Watanabe-san, but after the first two mornings he brought his own breakfast with him in a red lacquer box, which he strapped on his parcel-carrier along with his trousers. It was a Japanese breakfast. There were black lacquer dishes and bowls, all intricately fitted into the red lacquer box. On the plates and in the bowls were daubs and pools. The little pieces of pickled fish, the preserved turnip, the bean custard, the chips of cold fried beef, the tepid mauve soup, and the stewed rice would be laid out on my breakfast table, and Watanabe-san would go at them with his chopsticks, which he carried in an upper vest pocket. "This," he would say, holding up a cube of preserved radish, "is *daikon*. We say in Japanese *daikon*. You say after me, *daikon*." "*Daikon*," I would say.

Watanabe-san was a teacher of English in one of the city high schools, an ambitious man, small, round, and full of energy. He had protuberant teeth, like Willie Stevens. Watanabe-san's teeth were so long and so disparate that you felt he ought to be able to cross them, like fingers, if he tried. When he talked animatedly, it was as if he were waving a hand at you. His grin was circular on account of these teeth and was, for the same reason, incessant. Most Japanese I have met have had a nervous laugh, but Watanabe-san's grin was purely physical. He would have had to use force to bring his lips together. He was as patient a man as I have ever seen and he tried hard to teach me how to say Japanese words. He never talked about anything that did not directly concern the lesson I was laboring over. I never heard him express an opinion of any kind. He was affable but detached. His excellent references showed that he had tried to teach many young foreigners the Japanese language.

As the lessons progressed, Watanabe-san's most frequent remark to me got to be, "Wrong affix, I am very sorry. That is the affix for birds." He would start his lips crawling toward one another when he said this, to show me that he was not laughing at me, but I never saw them meet. What was happening to my Japanese lessons was that Watanabe-san had tried to teach me twelve simple affixes for each verb we took up, and the only affixes I ever seemed to remember were the affixes one was supposed to use when speaking of, or to, birds. Perhaps I had better go into this a little way at this point. The idea is something like this: In Japanese, when you say "go" to, or of, a servant, you use one affix, and when you say "go" to, or of, your father, you use another; moreover, you use an entirely different affix when you say "go" to, or of, your mother, and you use still another affix when you say "go" to, or of, birds. There are separate affixes, as well, for horses, soldiers, fish, policemen, dogs, alligators, automobile-drivers, and so on—twelve simple, as they say, affixes and dozens of complex ones for every verb in the language. My parents were not in Japan, and this made it simpler, but for the first two weeks or so, and for some obscure reason that I never want to know the truth about, I would seem to forget all the affixes of all the verbs I learned, except the ones for birds, so that whenever I said anything in Japanese, I would find myself talking to, or of, birds. For instance, I learned, or thought I learned, how to say to a taxi-driver, "Please turn at the next corner and stop at the little stone house on the right." What I said, when I thought I was saying that, was, according to subsequent lessons from Watanabe-san, "Birds, please turn at the next corner and stop flying at the little stone aviary on the right." I used to try it on taxi-drivers, and they always turned around and laughed nervously. Then I would point to the corner at which we were to turn, and when we reached my house, I would lean over and clutch the driver's shoulder, crying "Stoppo! Stoppo!" Most drivers knew this hybrid, but sometimes it was necessary to pretend I was about to jump from the car as it passed the little stone house on the right, or else reach up front and pull back the emergency brake.

I would have fought this tendency to talk only to, or of, birds, and I might have conquered it, but I found out in succeeding weeks that there was a great deal more to the Japanese language than verb affixes. Take the mere arrangement of words, admitting for the sake of the explanation that the things I was studying *were* words. I found that if I got one word in the wrong place, the sentence would change itself materially and the whole paragraph would, in all likelihood, never mean the same thing again. What happens when you do that is a lot worse than the collapse of a house of cards. The sentence doesn't go to pieces, exactly. It takes on new life, all the words revise themselves, the nouns, as likely as not, become verbs, the verbs adjectives, and here and there a word shudders so that it becomes a different thing. I have seen cases in which a word has disappeared altogether. I found that a mere twitch of the lip on my part would fix my sentence about stopping at the little stone house so that I, a dog, would be instructing the policeman in the front seat to throw me under the wheels of the taxicab and let the birds stone me. Almost any foreign language is apt to throw a student off for a while, but Japanese has peculiarities not quite like any other I have ever heard of. When a sentence goes striding away on its own hook this way, not even the Japanese have any sure method of telling what it was you meant to say. A student of English might say something like "stone house stop right," and alert people familiar with the language would know what he was getting at. But when you tell Japanese policemen to let the birds stone you, they think that is what you mean, and from the way you have arranged the words and affixes, there is absolutely no reason for them to think otherwise.

The sensation that comes from starting out to say one thing and then finding that you have said something entirely different is a fascinating one, once you get used to it. One morning, I remember, I tried to say, "The cherry blossoms in Hibiya Park are very beautiful this spring," and Watanabe-san told me afterward that what I had really said was "We cherry-colored birds always fly in Hibiya Park in the spring." This was a good instance of word-disappearance. The word "blossom" had vanished.

"What became of 'blossom'?" I said to Watanabe-san that morning.

"The word 'blossom,'" he said, "became the word 'colored' and, combined with the word 'cherry,' became a descriptive phrase. You see," he added, "you used the affix for birds." Watanabe-san would tell me these things, grinning cheerfully, and I would grin back at him a little across the breakfast table.

I bought, at his suggestion, a large and comprehensive English-Japanese dictionary, and this served to get me even deeper into the thing when Watanabe-san was nowhere around. I would say something to myself in Japanese intended to be fairly simple and direct, and then, by means of the dictionary and its phonetic symbols, I would be able, a few minutes later, to find out what I had said to myself. Once anybody starts something of this kind, he can never know where he will end up. At first I would just find out what I had said and then let it go. For instance, having found that instead of saying, "What an ancient temple bell you are ringing there beside the pond," I had said, "Dogs, keep barking until we have put our mother under water," I would think about it for a while and then try something else. The thing never did get to me, as it well might have, because when I began replying to what I found I had said and then looking up my replies, I carried the dictionary down the street to a bookstore and sold it.

Watanabe-san was as polite and tractable about it all as anybody could possibly have been. I had the feeling that he had been through this sort of thing before, and would go through it again and again in the future. I settled the bill for the lessons the morning after I had disposed of the dictionary, and Watanabe-san said goodbye very gracefully, took off his pants, and departed.

Frederic S. Cozzens

AN INVITATION TO A PARTY*

"We have an invitation to a party," said Mrs. Sparrowgrass, "on Friday next, and I think a party is a very pleasant thing in the country. There is more sociability, more hospitality, warmer welcomes, less dress, and less style than there is in the city." Here Mrs. Sparrowgrass handed me an engraved card of rather formidable dimensions, which I must confess looked anything but *rural*. I took the missive with some misgivings, for I have a natural horror of parties. "I wonder," said I, in the most playful kind of bitter irony, "whether we will meet out here that young lady that never sings herself, but is always so passionately fond of music?" Mrs. Sparrowgrass said she thought not; she said she heard she was married.

"And that gentleman," I continued, "who was a stranger to me that always wanted to be presented to some young lady that I didn't know?"

Mrs. Sparrowgrass said she believed he had gone to California.

"And that lady who prized confectionery above good-breeding, and went home with her pockets well stuffed with mottoes, in defiance of the eighth commandment, and the laws of propriety?"

Mrs. Sparrowgrass said she knew the lady to whom I alluded, but she assured me she was yet in New York, and had not been seen about our village.

"Then," said I, "Mrs. Sparrowgrass, we will go to the party. Put my best shirt, and the white waistcoat in Monday's wash. Never mind expense. Get me a crumb of bread, and bring me my old white gloves. I am going to be gay."

"I think," said Mrs. Sparrowgrass, "that a party in town is nothing but an embarrassment." "True," said I. "Don't you remember," said she, "what a fuss I used to make about getting my hair fixed, and how put out I was that night when you forgot the japonica?" "Certainly."

* *From "The Sparrowgrass Papers," 1856.*

158

"And then, when we were all dressed and ready, how we used to wait for fear of getting there too early, and after we did reach the house, how we always got in a corner, and made happy wall-flowers of ourselves, and some old friends." "Of course I do." "Where nobody took any notice of us." "Exactly." "Then what difference did it make how I was dressed—whether I wore Honiton lace or cotton edging?" "I am afraid," said I, "Mrs. Sparrowgrass, if you had made a point of wearing cotton lace, you would not have been invited." At this palpable *double entendre* I felt that secret satisfaction which every man must feel when he has said a good thing. It was lost upon Mrs. Sparrowgrass. "Here," she continued, "we expect a simple, old-fashioned entertainment." Then I chimed in—"No gas-lights to make your eyes ache—no patent-leather to make your feet ache—no fashionable follies to make your heart ache—and no overheated, ill-ventilated rooms, boned-turkies, game, ice-cream, Charlotte Russe, pâtés, champagne, and chicken-salad, to make your head ache next morning." "There will be oysters and ice-cream," said Mrs. Sparrowgrass, dubiously. "I wish," said I, "there was a prospect of apples and cider instead. The moment I get inside the doors, and breathe the mingled odors of oysters and geraniums, it will carry me back to town, and for one evening, at least, I shall forget that we are living in the country.

>   ———'I could be content
>   To see no other *verdure* than its own;
>   To feel no other breezes than are blown
>   Through its tall woods;'

but we must succumb; we will go like plain, sensible people, won't we?"

"If you were me, what would you wear?" said Mrs. Sparrowgrass.

"Something very plain, my dear."

"Then," said Mrs. Sparrowgrass, "I have nothing very plain, suitable for a party, and to-morrow I must go to town and do a little shopping."

"I am afraid," said I (after the second day's hard shopping in town) "your dress is going to be too plain, my dear. Every hour brings a fresh boy, with a fresh bundle, and a fresh bill, to my office." Mrs. Sparrowgrass said, "that if I thought so, perhaps she had better get something expensive when she went to buy the trimmings." I told her I thought her dress would do without trimming. She said, "it would be ridiculous without gimp or gallon; but perhaps I would prefer velvet ribbon, on account of the flounces?" I told her she had better get the velvet ribbon, and omit the gimp and galloon. Mrs. Sparrowgrass said, "very well," and the next day another boy brought another bundle, and another bill, which convinced me that extras form an important item in rural architecture. Then we had a dressmaker for several days, and the stitching went on by sun-light and lamp-light, and on the last day Mrs. S. discovered that she had nothing for her head, and the new bonnet was taken to pieces to get at the feathers for a coiffure. Then when the night fell, there fell, too, a soaking rain; and I had forgotten the carriage, so I was obliged to go a mile in the mud to order one from the village livery stable. Then I had to walk back, as the man said "it was out;" but he promised to send it for us right straight off. Then I had to get dressed over again. Then Mrs. Sparrowgrass could not find her best handkerchief, and I dropped five spermacetti blotches on the new silk dress looking for it. Then she found the handkerchief. Then our girl said that the new dog had run off with one of my boots. Then I had to go out in the mud in my slippers after the dog. Then I got the boot and put it on so as to make that sure. Then we waited for the carriage. We were all dressed and ready, but no carriage. We exercised all the patience we could muster, on account of the carriage, and listened at the windows to see if we could hear it. Two months have elapsed, and it hasn't come yet. Next day we heard that the party had been an elegant affair. That everybody was there, so we concluded the carriage had not been able to come for us on account of business.

I have bought me another dog. I bought him on account of his fine, long ears, and beautiful silky tail. He is a pup, and much caressed by the young ones. One day he went off to the butcher's and came back with no more tail than a toad. The whole bunch of young Sparrowgrasses began to bawl when he reached the cottage, on account of his tail. I did not know him when I came home, and he could not recognize me—he had lost his organ of recognition. He reminded me of a dog I once heard of, that looked as if he had been where they wanted a tail merely, and had taken his, and thrown the dog away. Of course I took my stick, and went to see the butcher. Butcher said "he supposed I was something of a dog fancier, and would like to see my dog look stylish." I said on the contrary, that I had bought him on account of his handsome silky tail, and that I would give ten dollars to have it replaced. Then the idea of having it replaced seemed so ludicrous that I could not restrain a smile, and then the butcher caught the joke, and said there was no way to do it except with fresh putty. I do love a man who can enjoy a joke, so I took a fancy to that butcher. When I got home and saw the dog, I thought less of the butcher, but put a piece of black court-plaster on the dog, and it improved his appearance at once. So I forgave the butcher, and went to bed at peace with all mankind.

~~~~~

Our neighbor has been making an improvement in his house. He has had a drain made in the kitchen, with a long earthen pipe ending in a cess-pool at the end of his garden. The object of it is to carry off the superfluous water from the house. It was a great convenience, he said, "on wash days." One objection might be urged, and that was, after every heavy rain he found a gully in his garden path, and several cart loads of gravel in his cess-pool. Besides, the pipe was of an equal width, and one obstruction led to another; sometimes it was a silver spoon and a child's frock; sometimes it was a scrubbing-brush, a piece of soap, and a handkerchief. I said that if he had made a square wooden trough, gradually widening from end to end, it would have cleared itself, and then I thought it would be a good thing for me to have such a one myself. Then I had a cess-pool built at the bottom of the wall, under the bank, which is about one hundred and fifty feet from the kitchen, and told my carpenter to make a trough of that length. Carpenter asked me "how big I wanted it?" I told him about eight inches in diameter at the end nearest to the house, and then gradually widening all the way for the whole length. As I said this, my carpenter smiled, and said he never heard of such a thing. I told him no, that the idea was an original one of my own. He asked me how much I would like to have it widened. I thought for a moment, and said, "about half an inch to the foot." He said very well, and the next week he came with two horses, and an edifice in his cart that looked like a truncated shot-tower. I asked him what that was? He said it was the big end of my pipe. When he laid it on the ground on its side I walked through it, and could not touch the upper side with my hand. Then I asked the carpenter what he meant by it, and he said it was made according to directions. I said not at all, that I told him to increase the diameter at the rate of half an inch to the foot, and he had made it about a foot to the foot, as near as I could judge. "Sparrowgrass," said he, a little nettled, "jest take your pencil and put down eight inches." "Well, that's the diameter of the small end, I believe?" I told the carpenter he was right so far. "Now, for every foot there is an increase of half an inch in the width; that's according to directions, too, ain't it?" Yes. "Well, then, put down one hundred and fifty half inches, how much does that make, altogether, in feet?" Six feet eleven inches. "Now," said he, "jest you take my rule, and measure the big end of that 're pipe." "Carpenter," said I, "I see it all; but the next time I build an aqueduct I will be a little more careful in the figures." "Sparrowgrass," said he, pointing to the pipe, "didn't you tell me that that was an original idea of your own?" I answered that I believed I did make a remark of that kind. "Well," said he, with a sort of muffled laugh, "that is the first time that I see an original idea come out at the big end."

Max Adeler

A VERY DANGEROUS INVENTION

A step-ladder is an almost indispensable article to persons who are moving into a new house. Not only do the domestics find it extremely convenient when they undertake to wash the windows, to remove the dust from the door and window-frames, and to perform sundry other household duties, but the lord of the castle will require it when he hangs his pictures, when he fixes the curtains and when he yields to his wife's entreaty for a hanging shelf or two in the cellar. I would, however, warn my fellow-countrymen against the contrivance which is offered to them under the name of the "Patent Combination Step-ladder." I purchased one in the city just before we moved, because the dealer showed me how, by the simple operation of a set of springs, the ladder could be transformed into an ironing-table, and from that into a comfortable settee for the kitchen, and finally back again into a step-ladder, just as the owner desired. It seemed like getting the full worth of the money expended to obtain a trio of such useful articles for a single price, and the temptation to purchase was simply irresistible. But the knowledge gained by a practical experience of the operation of the machine enables me to affirm that there is no genuine economical advantage in the use of this ingenious article.

Upon the day of its arrival, the servant-girl mounted the ladder for the purpose of removing the globes from the chandelier in the parlor, and while she was engaged in the work the weight of her body unexpectedly put the springs in motion, and the machine was suddenly converted into an ironing-table, while the maid-servant was prostrated upon the floor with a sprained ankle and amid the fragments of two shattered globes.

Then we decided that the apparatus should be used exclusively as an ironing-table, and to this purpose it would probably have been devoted permanently if it had suited. On the following Tuesday, however, while half a dozen shirts were lying upon it ready to be ironed, some one knocked against it accidentally. It gave two or three ominous preliminary jerks, ground two shirts into rags, hurled the flat-iron out into the yard, and after a few convulsive movements of the springs, settled into repose in the shape of a step-ladder.

It became evident then that it could be used with greatest safety as a settee, and it was placed in the kitchen in that shape. For a few days it gave much satisfaction. But one night when the servant had company the bench was perhaps overloaded, for it had another and most alarming paroxysm; there was a trembling of the legs, a violent agitation of the back, then a tremendous jump, and one of the visitors was hurled against the range, while the machine turned several somersaults, jammed itself halfway through the window-sash, and appeared once more in the similitude of an ironing-table.

It has now attained to such a degree of sensitiveness that it goes through the entire drill promptly and with celerity if any one comes near it or coughs or sneezes close at hand. We have it stored away in the garret, and sometimes in the middle of the night a rat will jar it, or a current of air will pass through the room, and we can hear it dancing over the floor and getting into service as a ladder, a bench and a table fifteen or twenty times in quick succession.

The machine will be disposed of for a small fraction of the original cost. It might be a valuable addition to the collection of some good museum. I am convinced that it will shine with greater lustre as a curiosity than as a household utensil.

Francis Steegmuller

A RIDE WITH RALPH

At Raton, late one afternoon, we transcontinental passengers were waiting in our places, wondering whether we would approve of the new driver who was to take us on to Santa Fe and Albuquerque, when we suddenly heard the group of drivers lounging outside the bus station burst into a cheer. "Yeah, Ralph!" they cried, and we saw a blond and very boyish giant coming toward us, wearing the company's uniform and a dazzling pair of new cowhide boots. "So long, boys!" he called, looking very handsome and serious, and after climbing on board and examining our tickets, he at once made himself as popular within the bus as he seemed to be without.

"Well, folks," he said earnestly, facing us all, "I'll be with you as far as Albuquerque, and I hope you'll like me as much as I know I'll like you all. I'll do my best to be satisfactory, and I'll do everything in my power to give you a fine ride. It's mighty dandy country through these parts, and I hope you enjoy it. If you have any suggestions or complaints, I'll be glad to have 'em. Let's go!" He swung into his seat, there was an appreciative murmur, and we were off.

Since I rode just beside Ralph in the front seat, we soon fell to talking, and long before we made our first comfort stop—the bus halts considerately every two hours from New York to Los Angeles—he had revealed that a certain subject was very much on his mind. "A pair of boots is quite an investment," he stated. "Have you any idea of what a good pair of boots costs?" I confessed ignorance. "If I was to buy them retail, in a regular swell shoestore in Denver," he informed me, "they'd cost me plenty, and I'd go without. But anybody's foolish to go to those swell stores; what you do is to write to a firm in K.C., give 'em your measurements, and you get a fine pair of boots by mail. It's a sort of wholesale proposition, see, and it certainly is worth while. But would you believe it, even buyin' 'em that way, these boots set me back sixteen bucks; you can see they're quite an investment."

I pointed out that so handsome a pair was worth investing in, but admitted that I was disappointed to hear that they weren't real New Mexican boots, and that they came from Kansas City. "You can buy two kinds of boots in New Mexico," Ralph told me. "You can buy common ordinary boots that ain't worth half what you pay for 'em, and you can buy the best boots in the world—made of imported kangaroo hide—but you've got to be richer than you and me to get *them*. They'll set you back anywhere from fifty to a hundred bucks. But oh, man, they're soft as velvet and sure worth it if you got the dough. Now, these boots are O.K., but you know they're—they're —uh, beginnin' to pinch a little. As a matter of fact, they're—they're beginnin' to hurt me quite a good deal. Isn't that funny?"

I said I thought it was anything but funny, and Ralph agreed. "It ain't funny a heck of a bit," he revealed. "They sure feel pretty bad, and I've got to do something about it pretty quick. I've got a friend up here in Wagon Mound; he'll fix me up. We stop there ten minutes anyway."

"Well, you'd better get to Wagon Mound as fast as you can," I suggested. "You don't want to be in misery."

"That's right," said Ralph. "I don't know whether it's the cowhide beginnin' to bind, or my feet beginnin' to swell, but it's gettin' worse every minute." He took my advice with thrilling literalness, and we rushed over the road at a rate that permitted him to talk no more. I watched the speedometer go from the usual 50 to 55, to 60 and a little over. It was dark by now, and after a breathless half-hour a cluster of lights appeared and we drew up in front of a ramshackle chili joint. "Folks," said Ralph, switching on the lights and turning around to us, "this is Wagon Mound. It ain't much of a place, but you'll find some good chili inside the café and the comfort stations are around to the left. We'll be here ten minutes." He gave me an intent glance. "I'm in torture," he confided in a low voice, and disappeared.

The passengers followed him, but the chili joint struck me as uninviting, and I remained in the bus. After a while they began to drift back, very garrulous and interested. "The driver's certainly having a hell of a time with those new boots," one of them announced. "He's got a Mexican in there trying to pull them off and they won't budge; whenever the Mexican pulls, the driver yells and says he's taking his skin off, and they don't seem to be getting any place. He's afraid he's gonna have to cut 'em off, and he hates to do that. They're brand-new." As the bus filled, everyone talked of Ralph and his boots: we remained in Wagon Mound a good deal longer than ten minutes, but finally Ralph limped in, still wearing his cowhides, and in a bad mood. He made no reply to our sympathetic inquiries, informed us crossly that the next stop would be Las Vegas, switched off the lights, and drove on. "The next stop'll be Las Vegas if I live to get the hell there," I heard him mutter mirthlessly in the darkness, but as I was not sure whether he was addressing me or not, I judged it wiser not to reply.

The ride to Las Vegas, accomplished in considerably less than the scheduled time, made the spurt to Wagon Mound seem stodgy, and after telling us that we had something over half an hour for our supper, Ralph limped away out of sight. Speculation was vociferous as we ate at a long counter, and bets were made as to whether he would reappear with or without his boots. Nobody got into the bus, but all waited near it, to get a good view, and the silence of pity fell over us when Ralph emerged limping, still booted, from the gloom of some nearby buildings. "All aboard," he called, in a voice in which despair had taken the place of surliness. "All aboard, folks. We make no stop between here and Santa Fe." We filed sombrely aboard. I was the last, and could not resist murmuring that it was too bad. "Get in, buddy," said the boy, dully. "If I go nuts, you grab the wheel."

For the sake of all of us, I hoped Ralph wouldn't go nuts, for evidently Santa Fe contained further possibility of aid, and we tore through the darkness like a shell, Ralph's hands now and again straying alarmingly and futilely from the wheel to his boots. After a long stretch of silence he looked around, evidently to see if I was there, and after clearing his throat a few times he asked, in a private, piteous, small voice, *"You* don't happen to know anything about pullin' off boots, do you, buddy?" I replied just as privately that while I had never done it, I should be glad to try, but at this he merely shook his head, and drove on. Unspoken sympathy filled the speeding bus. Ralph's misery seemed to permeate us all, the ride began to seem endless. Then, suddenly, all was changed. Dramatically, far ahead in the darkness on the road we saw a waving light; Ralph shoved on his brakes, which hissed alarmingly, and as we all stared he opened the door to a Mexican, who blew out his lantern, climbed in, and asked for a ticket to Santa Fe. This transaction took a little time, and though I couldn't understand the Spanish, I realized that Ralph and the Mexican were conversing about something other than the ticket. Finally, after the Mexican had uttered several emphatic statements, Ralph abruptly killed the motor and turned to us. "Folks," he announced thrillingly, "I can't go on like this! If you'll have the kindness to put up with a few minutes' delay, I'll sure appreciate it. This friend of mine is going to perform some first aid, and then we'll shoot right along. Is that O.K. with everybody?" We all called out our assent, and preparations began. Ralph left the wheel, sat on the step of the bus, and stretched out one leg; the Mexican turned his back, straddled Ralph's leg, grasped the enormous boot tightly, found a footing, and bent forward; Ralph, holding onto the bus, placed his other foot firmly against the Mexican's posterior, and while one pulled, the other pushed, and both grunted. Everyone crowded to watch. The Mexican manipulated the toe and heel, and Ralph shoved with all the strength of his gigantic self. It appeared hopeless at first; the leather was so tight about Ralph's great calf and foot that it seemed to be almost part of him. That was evidently the way it felt to him, too; he whispered and cursed. Finally, the boot began wonderfully to move, and after a few particularly Herculean efforts, it actually slipped forward and the Mexican fell flat on his face, the boot clutched triumphantly in his hands. The crowd exclaimed with delight; Ralph whispered to himself some more, and stretched out his other leg, the Mexican manipulated as deftly as before, and was rewarded by falling flat on his face once again.

We were all much impressed by the way Ralph sat with his head in his hands for a few moments. "Does that relieve you?" I asked him, when he finally breathed deeply and looked around at us.

"Relieve me!" he cried. "Take it from me, folks, there's one boy that knows what heaven is now!"

Obviously, Ralph couldn't drive us to Santa Fe with only stockings on his feet, so I offered him my slippers, which were in the suitcase on the rack above me; he gingerly slipped his sore toes into them, and after a little experimenting decided he could make them do by wearing them as mules. "All right, folks!" he called, when he had thanked us. "Everything's O.K. now. Let's go to Santa Fe!" Cheers arose, he switched out the lights, and we were off. The Mexican hero grinned himself into a snoring sleep, and for the next hour and a half we tore over the mountains, making up for lost time.

"This is Santa Fe, folks; we'll be here ten minutes!" Ralph called out when we had rolled through the dark streets to the station. "The comfort stations are at the rear of the waiting-room!" I was going to stop over in Santa Fe for the night, so when the passengers dismounted, Ralph handed me my suitcase and bade me farewell, standing beside the bus in my slippers. "It's sure nice of you to let me wear these to Albuquerque," he said earnestly. "I just don't know what I'd do without 'em. Because those boots"—he almost smiled— "those boots, well, I sure couldn't wear *them* to Albuquerque!"

"No," I said. "You'd better send them back to K.C., don't you think?"

He ignored this. "The slippers will be waitin' for you here when you take your bus tomorrow night," he replied. "I sure hope you have a good trip all the way to L.A., and I'm sorry I won't be drivin' you."

I was sorry, too. The drivers between Santa Fe and L.A. were all good fellows, but none of them was quite the boy Ralph was, and his absence was hardly compensated for even by the note which I had found with my slippers in the bus station the next night. "Dear Friend," it said, "I am deeply grateful to you for letting me use your slippers. They came in very handy. On inspection I note they are in rather poor condition and as I know my feet are large if I am responsible for the damage I would be glad to have them sewed if you would leave them together with your address. Yours truly, Ralph L."

James T. Fields

A WATCH THAT "WANTED CLEANING"

I think I never saw a person who needed renewal of garments in a more pronounced degree than the gaunt individual I encountered a few weeks ago in Omaha. We met casually on the upland overlooking Council Bluffs, whither I had gone for a morning walk in that city of newness and hospitality. The man was sitting on the stump of a recently beheaded tree, regarding a watch, which he now and then held up in a kind of hopeless manner, and listened to for a sign of life from its inner apartments. When he saw me approaching he rose up and asked for "the time o' day." As I had only "Boston time," and that was of no use so far "out West," he sighed, again shook the unresponsive article in his hand, and spoke as follows: —"This 'ere watch, stranger, 's a puzzler. Some thing's the matter with 'er. I've seen a good-dle of trouble in my day, but nothin' at all like *this* afore. In my younger days I once had a personal difficulty with a bear, but that was fun compared to this affliction."

Noticing a settled grief on the poor fellow's soiled and sunken countenance, I sat down beside him on the ample resting-place he had chosen, and made inquiry as to the cause of his *untimely* sorrow. After a brief pause he thus unburdened himself:—"Stranger, if you was in the watch line, we'd have nothing to do with one another; but as you ain't, I don't mind givin' you 'er history, which you'll allow is somewhat discouragin'. I bought 'er two months ago in *She*-cargo for sixteen dollars down and five dollars in poultry. I had 'er of a fine-lookin' man who keeps jewillry on the sidewalk down by the Palmer House. He was a perfect gentleman in appearance, wore studs himself, and his conversation was high-toned. He said he was a member in reg'lar standin' of more'n fifty churches in various parts of the United States where he traded. He said he set his life by the watch, but *would* part with 'er if he was shore the man he sold 'er to was a moral man, and would take good care of 'er. He said she was wunst the property of a particular friend o' hisn, one o the craowned heads o' Ure-up, but the king was obleeged to sell 'er on accoaunt of a change in his circumstarnces. He said there was more'n two hundred jewills in 'er which was invisible to the naked eye. Waal, to make a long story short, I negoshated for 'er on the spot, and I 'member just as well as if't was yisterday, he said she wouldn't warnt cleanin' ef I car'd 'er in mur pocket, keerful, for twenty year.

"So, ye see, I took 'er 'long to Rock Island on the Mississippi, where I live, but she seemed to go on the jump all the way daown. Waal, I carried 'er into Jason's one day, and asked *him* to give a look into 'er insides, and tell me, ef he could, what made 'er act so. He screwed *his* old glass into the right eye, and arter a while he laid 'er down on the coaunter, and says he, 'She's a powerful good watch, but she *warnts cleanin'!*" When I heerd that, I was dumbfounded. Says I, 'She was cleaned all over last week.' Says he, 'That may be, but she's full o' dirt naow. It's dusty this fall,' says he, 'and some on it's got into *'er.*' Waal, I thought it all over, and said he might go to work on 'er next day; and he charged me tew dollars and fifty cents for cleanin' on 'er aout. Pooty soon I had to go off to Aurory, and she begun to act quair agin. So I took 'er into a watchmaker's there, and asked him to fling *his* eye round, and see what ailed 'er. Waal, he did, for ez much as five minits, and then says he, 'She's a fust-rate watch, but she warnts cleanin'!' Says I (and I couldn't help gittin' riled then), 'She's bin cleaned aout twice lately, and that's a fact.' 'Waal,' says he, 'I never seed a dirtier, and if she ain't 'tended to, double quick, in twenty-four hours she'll bust of 'er own accord, and fly all to pieces, and never go agin.' This illarmed me, nat'rally, and so I told him to strip 'er and go to work with his toothbrush and things, and I'd pay him what was right. So he did, and he sot down on me for one seventy-five, and one fifty for what he called *inside-entle* expenses. Waal, she went ellygant all the way on to Milwaukee, but the fust night I got thar she begun to hitch and sputter to that extent I run over to a watchmaker, early in the mornin', for assistance. Waal, he turned 'er over three or four times, and kind o' smiled at the rumblin' inside on 'er. Then he looked thoughtful and pried 'er open. Says I, *'Enny thing serious?'* Says he,—and his reply run through me like a fawk,—says he, 'She's a *r*emarkable good timepiece, but she warnts *cleanin'!*' Waal, to make an end to mur story, I had 'er put through *his* mill, and some o' *his* ile slung into 'er. He said 't was such a ugly job (I told him when he took 'er in hand to be careful o' the invisible jewills), that his bill would be four dollars and ten cents, the ten cents bein' for fingerin' careful round the reubies and things. Waal, Sir, she cut up agin last night, and I stept in to Cross & Jones's, and asked their young man to ixamine 'er parts, and pronoaunce upon 'er. Waal, he rubbed in *his* magnifying-glass, and screwtenized 'er, and says he, 'That's the most valuble watch I ever seed inside o' Omaha, but she warnts *cleanin'* most ——y!' When I heerd that, I expressed myself like a *dis*gusted night-hawk, and snatched 'er aout o' *his* hands, and brought 'er raound here to ponder over. What I wish to inquire is, Stranger (and I ask for information), how many times a watch thet's full o' invisible jewills has to be cleaned aout in the course o' two months? I never owned one afore, but if the jewills *nee-sessiates* that expense, as I'm a pore man, hadn't I better have 'em punched aout, don't you think?"

And I advised him to have the "jewills" removed immediately, and sold in Europe for the most they would bring.

Cornelia Otis Skinner

IT'S A WISE PARENT

To one born west of the Alleghenies and reared in a suburban community, the social life of the New York child seems nothing short of amazing. In that remote and happy time known (unless Mrs. Roosevelt has a copyright on the title) as "my day," children met and played together for the simple reason that their mothers were "such good friends." This convention seems to have gone the way of family prayers and afternoon calls, and every year I become increasingly aware that I do not move in those charmed circles in which my son apparently whirls. However, no other New York parent appears to share my antiquated sense of etiquette. Once I ventured to send a shy message to a nebulous mother to the effect that since our offspring were such good buddies it might be nice if she'd come to tea some afternoon—an overture that caused as much bewilderment as if I'd asked her to dinner because we patronized the same osteopath.

Recently, while walking in the Park, my seven-year-old son and I encountered a little girl who was out with her father. The children exchanged a greeting that implied close acquaintanceship. I asked my son who she was and was casually informed she was his "girl friend." Concealing the stab to a mother's heart, I smiled generously and ventured to beam understandingly at the father. He gave me the kind of look Robert Taylor might give an autograph seeker, tipped his hat, and strolled on, the while his child rushed over to whisper into my son's ear that she'd be seeing him Thursday.

Hers, it turned out, had been one of those whimsical "won't-you-come-to-my-party" cards that arrive by post or are brought home, somewhat mangled, from school. My child receives a good many of these. Not that he is especially in demand; it's just that he knows a large number of children who have birthdays and, presumably, parents. Children's parties in New York are fast becoming something that isn't far behind the débutante racket, and it wouldn't surprise me if those society impresarios who arrange the coming-out parties have up their enterprising sleeves a list, purchasable for a consideration, of eligible little boys between the ages of six and ten. These festivities are expensive not only to the parents of the hosts but also to the parents of the gift-bearing guests, and I consider my monthly bill from Schwarz's one more social outrage that should be righteously ignored.

Once, thinking it might be my maternal duty to catch an inside glimpse of the houses to which my son has entrée, I committed the error of calling for him at a residence whose marble exterior and wrought-iron garage door should have forewarned me of the elaborate juvenile goings-on in there. A butler answered the bell. Butlers have an over-refining effect on me and in their presence I hear myself using the broad "a" on words like "hat." I murmured my son's name and the fact that I had come to fetch him. After I had made it plain that I was my child's mother and not his governess, the butler reluctantly led me up a carved stone stairway, opened a period door, and thrust me into a completely dark room. I was greeted by the whoops and catcalls of fifteen small boys and it was some moments before I realized that a moving picture was being shown and that I was standing between the screen and the projection machine. There was nothing to do but drop to a crouching position. My eyes were by now getting focussed—the way they do in the Blue Grotto—and in the dusk I could distinguish, over on a couch across the room, a pair of adults whom I presumed to be the parents of the child host. Fearing to cut off any more breathless moments of "Our Gang," I approached their presence in a crouching shuffle that must have seemed like a definite throwback to the Neanderthal Man. This startled them a good deal, but what startled them much more was my announcement that I was the mother of such-and-such a boy. Even in the gloom I could see their shocked astonishment. It was all very well for the nursemaids, waiting below, to crash the gate, but for a parent! They did manage, though, to utter a few polite phrases and we all three simulated an animated interest in the film, which was blessedly nearing its custard-pie finale. The lights flashed on and the party was pronounced over. My son and I thanked our hosts and departed, I sheepishly, he triumphantly with a considerable quantity of loot in the way of candy, favors, and, I later found out, a few of the birthday gifts of the unsuspecting host.

Only once have I attempted giving a child's party in New York.

Five little boys were invited and, as a refining influence, three little girls. My son supplied the list of names. Knowing practically none of the parents, I felt that along with the invitations I should at least send a few references. But New York parents are a trusting lot. As long as their children attend the same school or their nanas gossip together in the Park, they ask no questions. The invitations were unanimously accepted, and on the day and hour specified the children arrived all at once. I hovered nervously about the front door. Remembering my own recent experience, I wanted to prove, in case some child arrived accompanied by a mother, that here was one New York parent with neighborly instincts. This resulted in my shaking hands, effusively, with a number of nursery governesses who clearly thought me demented but who nonetheless left their charges in my dubious custody.

With the forethought of the Georgia women who buried their silver before the advent of Sherman, I had put away most of my bric-a-brac and sent the plants and the goldfish to spend a quiet day with a friend on another floor of my apartment house. The dog, I figured, could defend himself. Altogether there was little damage done—nothing more serious than a lollipop rammed into the piano strings and a spot on the carpet caused by a displaced butter ball. The entertainment was simple—one or two games and supper. There was no movie and no magician and no one even pinned a tail on a donkey. There was complete bedlam during the games and an equally complete silence during supper, which I understand is proof that the party was a hit. At the end several children said "Aw, do we have to go now?" though one young bounder informed me that at *his* party they had had Charlie McCarthy and a couple of trained seals. The governesses arrived at precisely six-thirty and the unknown children marched off to unknown homes to tell unknown parents that they'd had ice cream. My son retired to bed in a vile humor—another proof the party was a success—and I poured myself a drink fit for a lumberjack. I had hardly taken a sip when the telephone rang and the maid informed me that the mother of one of the children wished to speak with me. I felt sure she was calling to thank me for my kindness to her child and said "Hello" in a voice of honey. Someone with ill-concealed irritation announced she was Cynthia's mother. I remembered Cynthia, and none too pleasantly. I had seen her surreptitiously pouring her soup into the centrepiece and I suspected her of being the vandal who stuck the lollipop in the piano strings. The voice went on to say that Cynthia had returned home without her band.

"Her band?" I asked incredulously.

"Yes," came the voice. "She takes it out when she eats. It must be in your house somewhere. Would you mind looking for it?"

With a shudder I said no, and added that I'd bring it by on my way out to dinner. I'm not good at finding things and Cynthia's band was no exception. I searched with avidity and dread. When my husband came home, he too joined the search. It was the cook who found it, carefully wrapped in a paper napkin and deposited in an empty glass. It was a repellent contraption of wire and silver, vaguely surrealist in aspect. I wrapped it tenderly in cotton and placed it in a box from Cartier's. Cynthia lives on Park Avenue in a penthouse I am never likely to enter, although my child informs me he has been there. I left the box with the doorman, requesting him to see that Cynthia's mother got it immediately. I had it well timed and it seemed probable that she would be at the dinner table when she opened it. At least I hoped so.

Ring Lardner

LARGE COFFEE

Note: Readers of the daily papers will recall a paragraph printed earlier this week to the effect that the body of a Mr. Lardner was found in a New York hotel room by a house officer who had broken in after the chambermaids had reported that they had rapped on the door every day for over a fortnight and had received no response, and were disposed to believe that the occupant of the room would need a clean towel if living, and perhaps two of them if dead. The occupant was in the last-named condition or worse. Dressed as usual in pajamas, he was sprawled out on the floor, his head crushed in by a blow from some blunt instrument, probably another hotel. At the time the item appeared, there was mention of the discovery of a diary. It now develops that one really was unearthed and turned over to the police, who used parts of it as curl papers for Grover Whalen. We have acquired the mechanical rights to the balance and herewith publish extracts from it as a human document of particular interest to men and women who, like the writer thereof, have been battered and broken by an insensate world.

Friday, May 31

Today I registered and was assigned this room, 657, which is to be my home through most of the summer. At a conference of my wife and children, it was decided that I ought to contribute something to their support and they recommended that I do a little writing for the magazines or newspapers. I told them this would be impossible in our hut on Long Island unless they and the neighbors agreed to become hermits so that my mind would not be constantly distracted by the knowledge that other people were having fun. It is my plan to visit the family one day in the middle of each week, not at the week-end when there seems to be a tendency to drink cocktails and expect you to sit by, look on and like it. The hotel is giving me a rate of $4.00 a day, really a bargain because the room has a window.

You can look right into other people's rooms on the courtyard if they don't keep their shades down. O diary, I hope it's a hot summer. (Editors' Note: Did he get his hope?)

Sunday, June 2

I spent so much thought yesterday and this morning on what I would have sent up for breakfast that when I sat down at the type-writer, my mind was too tired to work. I spoke of this over the telephone (my only means of communication with the outside world) to a friend and he advised me to make a selection of a few nourishing and inoffensive victuals, commit them to memory and order them every morning. I then asked him what to do about the coffee problem, which is something of a problem to me. You see, when you drink lots of coffee you can kind of kid yourself into believing it's something else, so for breakfast I always want four cups. What I mean is enough coffee to fill one cup four times. Yesterday morning I said to the order clerk, "Two orders of coffee," and the result was two small pots of coffee, each containing enough for two cups. But the set-up, as I believe they call it, was for two people; there were two cereal dishes, two plates for my bacon and eggs and two cups for my coffee. This lay-out congested the table, leaving no space for my shoe tree. So this morning I said, "Two orders of coffee, but served for one person." The result was a small pot of coffee, containing enough for two cups. Well, my friend said I would have to work this out for myself; the only advice he could give me was ridiculous—that I give up coffee. This evening I will try to think of a solution and also select a permanent breakfast so there will be no more brain fag or waste of time.

Friday, June 7

The breakfast I have picked out for the summer consists of orange juice, corn flakes, medium hard boiled eggs and buttered toast. Boiled eggs are preferable to other kinds because they don't bring you two plates for them even if your coffee order makes them believe you are two people. I selected toast instead of plain rolls or sweet rolls because the sweet ones are too filling and messy, and the plain ones are made in Bethlehem, Pa. The toast is also immune, but you have to say something when the order clerk insists. The coffee situation is just as baffling as a week ago. One morning I said, "I am living alone, but I drink four cups of coffee." I got a large pot of coffee and four cups. Another morning I said, "Double coffee, served for one." I got a large pot of coffee, two cups and two orders of tooth-proof toast. Yesterday I asked the waiter how much a large pot of coffee cost. He said it was sixty cents. So this morning I said to the order clerk, "One orange juice, one corn flakes, one medium hard boiled egg, one buttered toast and sixty cents worth of coffee." "Coffee," she replied, "is only thirty cents a pot." "But I want twice as much as that." "Oh, all right. You want two orders." "Yes, but I'm not two people." I got one small pot of coffee.

Monday, July 8

It is the hottest summer in history. Everybody on our court is free and easy. Formality and modesty have been thrown to the winds, if there are any. A business woman who looks like Tom Heeney and has a red splotch under her left shoulder blade is occupying the room just opposite. She is out all day and goes to bed at eight and reads the Brooklyn telephone directory. The electric light in my bathroom wouldn't work today and I wanted to shave on account of the waiters. I told the floor clerk to send me the electrician. Pretty soon a plumber came and turned on everything but the light. "I don't see anything wrong," he said. "The light won't turn on," I said. "Oh," said he. "You want the electrician." The electrician came. I said, "The light won't turn on in the bathroom and I know the bulb isn't burned out because I tried another bulb and it wouldn't work." So the electrician tried another bulb and found it wouldn't work. "It must be something else," he said. He found the trouble and fixed it. This may have no bearing on the case, but I want to tell all.

I have been getting my large pot of coffee every morning, but never with less than two cups and nearly always with two egg cups, two dishes for cereal and two orders of toast.

Friday, July 12

Double coffee, large coffee, enough coffee for four cups, sixty cents worth of coffee, enough coffee for two people served for one person. I have thought I might ask Percy Hammond to come and room with me, but that would only mean six or eight cups on the same-sized table. An assistant manager called me up at twenty minutes to three this morning and said somebody had just complained that I was using a typewriter. What the hell does Mrs. Heeney think I moved in here for, to be near Gimbel Brothers?

Thursday, August 22

Yesterday morning I got what I wanted and I called right back and asked for the order clerk. "Are you the only order clerk?" "Oh, no." "Well, are you the one that just took the order for 657?" "Yes. Was it wrong?" "No. It was right. Now listen, I'm not trying to start a flirtation, but what is your name?" "If there's any complaint, I'll connect you with the superintendent." "There's no complaint, but I want your name so I can give you my order every morning." "Well, my name is Foley." "Thanks, Miss Foley. And when I call you to-morrow and other mornings, please do as you just did—send me a large pot of coffee and only one cup."

Every day the paper says cooler tomorrow. They ought to put that with the rest of the comics. A mystifying combination of tenants has taken the room across the court. There are two young women and a man. They can't be going to stay in town very long because the women apparently haven't brought anything but nightgowns and when the man isn't in B.V.D.'s he's out of them. I feel as if some time I would almost have to shout at them, "Don't you want a fourth for bridge?"

Monday, September 2

The worst has happened. Miss Foley "isn't here any more." My house was built on sand. I've got to start all over again and work up from the bottom.

And I'm pretty sure that late tonight I will lean out the window and holler, "Hey! Don't you want a fourth for strip bridge?"

Donald Moffat

"DOUCEMENT, DOUCEMENT!"

Those who expect the French to take up any of the idealistic policies which have been offered to the world as insurance against future catastrophes without, so to speak, first carefully reading through all the fine print would spare themselves disillusionment by hearkening to Mr. Mott's experience in buying an automobile.

The actual purchase of the car was simple. He bought it sight unseen before ever he set sail for France, from an American acquaintance named Walters, who had left it in a garage at Nice before coming home for good. The car was of the type known as a touring *camionette,* a word which sounded to Mr. Mott like the name of an affectionate, pretty, and frolicsome girl. He gained further comfort by learning that this pleasant fancy lost nothing in translation, as the equivalent for *camionette,* in the United States, is a small truck with a "pick-up body."

So Mr. Mott gladly paid the agreed price, and received, besides the keys and a walletful of licenses, a receipted bill of sale and a copy of a letter from Mr. Walters to the garage at Nice, containing an account of the sale and a description of Mr. Mott, for identification.

Mr. Mott therefore sailed for France feeling well confirmed in his title to the car, and thought no more about it until a week before he left Paris to take possession, when he wrote to M. Roux, proprietor of the Garage d'Angleterre et de la Méditerranée, saying that he would be in Nice the following Saturday, and hoped to find the car ready. He got no answer until Thursday, on which day M. Roux replied that the *camionette* was well, but that before Mr. Mott could have it he must get authority from the *patron,* M. Meyer, who conducted a transport agency at a certain address in Paris. Mr. Mott was slightly annoyed, because time was short; but he reflected that a day and a half ought to be ample to conclude a mere formality like this.

The next morning he set out in search of M. Meyer, and, after spending an hour marvelling at the taste of small Parisian business-men for hiding their offices behind dark courtyards and misleading stairways, he eventually found him. M. Meyer greeted him with smil-ing politeness, led him to a dim inner office, sat him in a comfortable chair, and faced him across the flat-topped desk—a gracious, round, and ruddy little man with a head completely bald, and a dense, curved mustache, black as a derby hat. M. Meyer leaned forward in his chair, smiled sympathetically, and waited.

Mr. Mott said: "My name is Mott, Monsieur. I am the American who bought Mr. Walters' *camionette*, which is now in the garage at Nice. I have come to ask you for a letter authorizing the *garagiste* to let me have the car. I go to Nice tomorrow."

"Ah," said M. Meyer, "of course. A charming fellow, M. Walters. So you have bought his little car, Monsieur?"

"Yes, before I sailed. Permit me to offer my passport, for identifica-tion."

M. Meyer examined every page of the passport with interest and care. Then he turned to the photograph, held it out at arm's length, and compared it with the original, feature by feature. "Well," he said at length, pleasure and surprise in his voice. "A good likeness. I compliment you. And now?"

"A letter to M. Roux, if you will be so kind." Mr. Mott was con-gratulating himself on M. Meyer's amiability, and the simplicity of the little transaction, when M. Meyer hesitated and fell to drumming on the desk, plunged in profound thought. After a full minute of this, "Monsieur," he said, apologetically, "pardon me; but in an affair of this kind it is not well to move too quickly. For both our sakes, care must be exercised. I shall therefore be so ungracious as to beg of you some further identification—identification, that is to say, as the actual purchaser of the little car. That you are indeed M. Mott is established. But that M. Mott has bought the car of M. Walters?" He stopped, and smiled agreeably.

"Certainly, M. Meyer," replied Mr. Mott. He took out the wallet given him by Mr. Walters, and spread on the desk the keys and the four licenses, besides his own *certificate de domicile* and *carte d'identité* for good measure, acquired since reaching Paris. M. Meyer examined them earnestly, then conceded, with a polite bow, that the defence had scored one point at least.

"Perfect," he said. "Everything in perfect order; *mais*" (Oh! that French *mais*, thought Mr. Mott) "you will forgive me, Monsieur? Papers like these, as you know, may be easily lost and as easily picked up by another, not the true owner. You will also agree that they may easily be stolen, and while I do not, of course, suggest for an instant that such is here the case—a thousand pardons—you will appreciate that it is my unfortunate duty not to neglect such a possibility. Also, Monsieur—"

"I understand perfectly, Monsieur," Mr. Mott interrupted, digging once more into his pocketbook. "As a man of business you could pursue no other course. But here is the copy of a letter Mr. Walters wrote to the *garagiste* telling of the sale. If you will send for the original, which is doubtless in your files, you may compare them and so satisfy your praiseworthy scruples."

M. Meyer rang for a clerk and sent him for the letter. And to Mr. Mott's surprise he was back with it before M. Meyer had finished Chapter I of his recitation on the subject of Paris Weather—Past, Present, and Future. M. Meyer compared the copy with the original word for word, then fitted them together, held them up to the light over his head, and gazed through them for signs of forgery.

Finally he lowered his arms. "The letters," he pronounced, "are identical. I congratulate you, Monsieur.... Yet," he added, after a thoughtful pause, "how easy it would be for a clever man to make up such a letter, and having dispatched it, to keep a copy to produce at the required moment. Of course," he went on, with a jolly laugh, "I know perfectly well that *you* have not been guilty of such villainy; but you see my difficulty: I am compelled to act on that very supposition. You pretend to be M. Mott; your passport confirms the assertion. You pretend to have bought an automobile from M. Walters, and in support of this contention you show me these licenses. But"—here M. Meyer spread his arms wide, as if beseeching Mr. Mott's co-operation and charity—"nothing to show that you have paid for the car except"—shaking his head regretfully, and letting his arms fall—"this letter, which, as I have demonstrated, is technically open to suspicion."

Mr. Mott watched him, fascinated. Then suddenly, cursing himself for his stupidity, he remembered the receipted bill of sale, his trump card. Once more he reached into his pocket, bulging with the accumulation of papers that always seemed mysteriously to fill his clothes after a few days in Paris. He found the bill of sale, unfolded it. "Here, Monsieur," he said, handing it over, "here is Mr. Walters' own receipt for the money, signed by his own hand. Examine it carefully, I beg."

M. Meyer took him at his word; then mournfully shook his head. "It is obviously correct," he said, "but, alas, worthless. *Tenez,* I believe you to be M. Mott; I believe that you actually bought the little car from M. Walters, and paid for it. It is my great desire to help you, to serve you. But this!" Again he shook his head. "As the world knows, Monsieur, a receipted bill is valueless in the eyes of the law unless payment of the sales tax is attested by the affixation of the government stamps, and countersigned by the vendor. On this paper, as you see, there are no stamps whatever. Therefore, alas, the sale is not yet complete. It is unfortunate. . . . I regret, Monsieur, infinitely."

"But, Monsieur," Mr. Mott protested, "the sale occurred in the United States, where the custom of taxing receipted bills has not yet been introduced. How could there be stamps?"

"You argue well, Monsieur. But! We are not now in the United States. That, you will agree, is evident." On this point M. Meyer was polite, but quite firm. "We are in France. The little *camion,* the subject of the transaction, is also in France. Thus you see, Monsieur, there must be stamps. I am sure that you understand the friendliness of my attitude, and that I take these precautions not from any doubt of you, but because such affairs must be concluded in an orderly fashion. Indeed, the fact that the principals in the transaction are both foreigners, Americans, makes my position all the more delicate. Consider the international complications that might arise if I did not take my responsibilities, as intermediary, at the foot of the letter." He paused.

Mr. Mott said slowly: "Yes, I see, Monsieur. . . . But these stamps? Where may they be procured?"

"I do not know. It is not, strictly speaking, my affair. But if I may offer the suggestion, your American consul might be able to help you."

Mr. Mott got up and held out his hand. "Thank you, Monsieur, I will go there directly." He congratulated himself, as M. Meyer showed him to the door, on having kept firm hold of his sense of reality—as well as his temper.

At the consulate, when Mr. Mott looked into the waiting-room, he found it so full of troubled-looking compatriots that he left at once, and went to a café to brood. His brooding brought him an idea, the idea that comes eventually to most Americans who get up against it in France. He went to the office of a lawyer he knew, an American lawyer named Emily. "Emily," he said, "I'm up against it. What shall I do?" and he explained the situation. Emily told him. "What you need," she said, "is seals. Give me that paper." She took the receipted bill and disappeared, and presently came back with a gorgeous seal, fixed to the paper with masses of wax and red ribbon. "What's that?" Mr. Mott asked. "That's a seal," said Emily. "Take it to the consul, tell him I sent you, and have him put on stamps." "What kind?" asked Mr. Mott. "Don't be so fussy," Emily replied. "Goodbye."

The consul was young, bored, and, as soon as Mr. Mott mentioned Emily's name, obliging. He stuck on stamps—what stamps Mr. Mott did not inquire—cancelled them with a flourishing signature, and also gave Mr. Mott a letter to the consul at Nice, in case. It was then too late to go back to M. Meyer.

The next morning he packed and took his baggage to the Gare de Lyon, to be sure of having plenty of time to catch his afternoon train in case M. Meyer had any further ideas. But he had none. His eyes lit up with pleasure when he saw the glorified document. He barely glanced at it. "Perfect," he said. "I am truly delighted. Now I will compose the letter to M. Roux." He wrote. "There, Monsieur, and forgive my precautions; they have been a trouble to you, I know, but a necessary one. I wish you many happy days of touring under our sunny, smiling skies." They parted on the best of terms, with many gallant expressions of mutual admiration and esteem; but as Mr. Mott turned on the stairs to bow a last farewell, he caught M. Meyer gazing inscrutably after him, in his eye still glowing the living embers of doubt—not, Mr. Mott knew, of his personal honesty, but of the completeness and authenticity of his chain of evidence.

At Nice, Mr. Mott went straight to the garage, where M. Roux, huge, greasy, and jolly, greeted him with warmth, and thus dispelled his secret fear that M. Meyer, in the last throes of suspicion, had cancelled the letter by wire.

M. Roux led him to the *camionette*. "*Voilà,* Monsieur, all ready for the *tourisme: essence,* oil, water—everything. A fine little bus."

Mr. Mott thanked him and offered M. Meyer's letter, explaining what it was.

"Oh, that," M. Roux laughed. "Keep it. *I* don't want it. Any friend of M. Walters is a friend of mine, and unquestionably an honest man."

"But you wrote me," Mr. Mott protested, "that you couldn't let me have the car without it. Would you have?"

"But, of course. Those were just the orders of the *patron*; I had to write to you. He's careful, that one. However"—he shrugged—"one must remember that he is not only a man of affairs, but from the North as well. What would you?" M. Roux took the letter and, without reading it, folded it small (the worldwide sign of the peasant), put it in his pocket, and proceeded to think of other things.

HISTORY, POLITICS, AND
AFFAIRS OF STATE

The following is the only section in the book arranged chronologically. We thought it would be easier for our readers to understand history if they took events up in proper sequence.

One of the supposedly humorous American historians was Bill Nye. A chapter from his "History of the United States" might logically have found a place in here if it had been funny (to us), and we wish it had, because Opper's illustrations are so good.

The editors wish to point out to military experts the timeliness of Orpheus C. Kerr's observations on. Civil War artillery. We also refer you, for the history of the Whisky Rebellion, to the parody section.

Washington Irving

THE MOST HORRIBLE BATTLE EVER RECORDED IN POETRY OR PROSE *

Now had the Dutchmen snatched a huge repast, and finding themselves wonderfully encouraged and animated thereby, prepared to take the field. Expectation, says the writer of the Stuyvesant manuscript,—Expectation now stood on stilts. The world forgot to turn around, or rather stood still, that it might witness the affray,—like a round-bellied alderman, watching the combat of two chivalrous flies upon his jerkin. The eyes of all mankind, as usual in such cases, were turned upon Fort Christina. The sun, like a little man in a crowd at a puppet-show, scampered about the heavens, popping his head here and there, and endeavoring to get a peep between the unmannerly clouds that obtruded themselves in his way. The historians filled their inkhorns; the poets went without their dinners, either that they might buy paper and goose-quills, or because they could not get anything to eat. Antiquity scowled sulkily out of its grave, to see itself outdone,—while even Posterity stood mute, gazing in gaping ecstasy of retrospection on the eventful field.

The immortal deities, who whilom had seen service at the "affair" of Troy, now mounted their feather-bed clouds, and sailed over the plain, or mingled among the combatants in different disguises, all itching to have a finger in the pie. Jupiter sent off his thunderbolt to a noted coppersmith, to have it furbished up for the direful occasion. Venus vowed by her chastity to patronize the Swedes, and in semblance of a blear-eyed trull paraded the battlements of Fort Christina, accompanied by Diana, as a sergeant's widow, of cracked reputation. The noted bully, Mars, stuck two horse-pistols into his belt, shouldered a rusty firelock, and gallantly swaggered at their elbow, as a drunken corporal,—while Apollo trudged in their rear, as a bandy-legged fifer, playing most villanously out of tune.

* A chapter from "Knickerbocker's History of New York."

On the other side, the ox-eyed Juno, who had gained a pair of black eyes overnight, in one of her curtain-lectures with old Jupiter, displayed her haughty beauties on a baggage-wagon; Minerva, as a brawny gin-suttler, tucked up her skirts, brandished her fists, and swore most heroically, in exceeding bad Dutch (having but lately studied the language), by way of keeping up the spirits of the soldiers; while Vulcan halted as a club-footed blacksmith, lately promoted to be a captain of militia. All was silent awe, or bustling preparation; war reared his horrid front, gnashed loud his iron fangs, and shook his direful crest of bristling bayonets.

And now the mighty chieftains marshalled out their hosts. Here stood stout Risingh, firm as a thousand rocks,—incrusted with stockades, and intrenched to the chin in mud batteries. His valiant soldiery lined the breastwork in grim array, each having his mustachios fiercely greased, and his hair pomatumed back, and queued so stiffly, that he grinned above the ramparts like a grisly death's-head.

There came on the intrepid Peter,—his brows knit, his teeth set, his fists clenched, almost breathing forth volumes of smoke, so fierce was the fire that raged within his bosom. His faithful squire Van Corlear trudged valiantly at his heels, with his trumpet gorgeously bedecked with red and yellow ribbons, the remembrances of his fair mistresses at the Manhattoes. Then came waddling on the sturdy chivalry of the Hudson. There were the Van Wycks, and the Van Dycks, and the Ten Eycks; the Van Nesses, the Van Tassels, the Van Grolls; the Van Hoesens, the Van Giesons, and the Van Blarcoms; the Van Warts, the Van Winkles, the Van Dams; the Van Pelts, the Van Rippers, and the Van Brunts. There were the Van Hornes, the Van Hooks, the Van Bunschotens; the Van Gelders, the Van Arsdales, and the Van Bummels; the Vander Belts, the Vander Hoofs, the Vander Voorts, the Vander Lyns, the Vander Pools, and the Vander Spiegels;—then came the Hoffmans, the Hooghlands, the Hoppers, the Cloppers, the Ryckmans, the Dyckmans, the Hogebooms, the Rosebooms, the Ooothouts, the Quackenbosses, the Roerbacks, the Garrebrantzes, the Bensons, the Brouwers, the Waldrons, the Onderdonks, the Varra Vangers, the Schermerhorns, the Stoutenburghs, the Brinkerhoffs, the Bontecous, the Knickerbockers, the Hockstrassers, the Ten Breecheses and the Tough Breecheses, with a host more of worthies, whose names are too crabbed to be written, or if they could be written, it would be impossible for man to utter,—

all fortified with a mighty dinner, and, to use the words of a great Dutch poet,

> "Brimful of wrath and cabbage."

For an instant the mighty Peter paused in the midst of his career, and mounting on a stump, addressed his troops in eloquent Low Dutch, exhorting them to fight like *duyvels,* and assuring them that if they conquered, they should get plenty of booty,—if they fell, they should be allowed the satisfaction, while dying, of reflecting that it was in the service of their country, and after they were dead, of seeing their names inscribed in the temple of renown, and handed down, in company with all the other great men of the year, for the admiration of posterity. Finally, he swore to them, on the word of a governor (and they knew him too well to doubt it for a moment), that if he caught any mother's son of them looking pale, or playing craven, he would curry his hide till he made him run out of it like a snake in spring-time. Then lugging out his trusty sabre, he brandished it three times over his head, ordered Van Corlear to sound a charge, and shouting the words "St. Nicholas and the Manhattoes!" courageously dashed forwards. His warlike followers, who had employed the interval in lighting their pipes, instantly stuck them into their mouths, gave a furious puff, and charged gallantly under cover of the smoke.

The Swedish garrison, ordered by the cunning Risingh not to fire until they could distinguish the whites of their assailants' eyes, stood in horrid silence on the covert-way, until the eager Dutchmen had ascended the glacis. Then did they pour into them such a tremendous volley, that the very hills quaked around, and were terrified even unto an incontinence of water, insomuch that certain springs burst forth from their sides, which continue to run unto the present day. Not a Dutchman but would have bitten the dust beneath that dreadful fire, had not the protecting Minerva kindly taken care that the Swedes should, one and all, observe their usual custom of shutting their eyes and turning away their heads at the moment of discharge.

The Swedes followed up their fire by leaping the counterscarp, and falling tooth and nail upon the foe with furious outcries. And now might be seen prodigies of valor, unmatched in history or song. Here was the sturdy Stoffel Brinkerhoff brandishing his quarter-staff, like the giant Blanderon his oak-tree (for he scorned to carry any other weapon), and drumming a horrific tune upon the hard heads of the

Swedish soldiery. There were the Van Kortlandts, posted at a distance, like the Locrian archers of yore, and plying it most potently with the long-bow, for which they were so justly renowned. On a rising knoll were gathered the valiant men of Sing-Sing, assisting marvellously in the fight, by chanting the great song of St. Nicholas; but as to the Gardeniers of Hudson, they were absent on a marauding party, laying waste the neighboring water-melon patches.

In a different part of the field were the Van Grolls of Antony's Nose, struggling to get to the thickest of the fight, but horribly perplexed in a defile between two hills, by reason of the length of their noses. So also the Van Bunschotens of Nyack and Kakiat, so renowned for kicking with the left foot, were brought to a stand for want of wind, in consequence of the hearty dinner they had eaten, and would have been put to utter rout but for the arrival of a gallant corps of voltigeurs, composed of the Hoppers, who advanced nimbly to their assistance on one foot. Nor must I omit to mention the valiant achievements of Antony Van Corlear, who, for a good quarter of an hour, waged stubborn fight with a little pursy Swedish drummer, whose hide he drummed most magnificently, and whom he would infallibly have annihilated on the spot, but that he had come into the battle with no other weapon but his trumpet.

But now the combat thickened. On came the mighty Jacobus Varra Vanger and the fighting-men of the Wallabout; after them thundered the Van Pelts of Esopus, together with the Van Rippers and the Van Brunts, bearing down all before them; then the Suy Dams, and the Van Dams, pressing forward with many a blustering oath, at the head of the warriors of Hell-gate, clad in their thunder-and-lightning gaberdines; and lastly, the standard-bearers and body-guard of Peter Stuyvesant, bearing the great beaver of the Manhattoes.

And now commenced the horrid din, the desperate struggle, the maddening ferocity, the frantic desperation, the confusion and self-abandonment of war. Dutchman and Swede commingled, tugged, panted, and blowed. The heavens were darkened with a tempest of missives. Bang! went the guns; whack! went the broad-swords; thump! went the cudgels; crash! went the musket-stocks; blows, kicks, cuffs, scratches, black eyes and bloody noses swelling the horrors of the scene! Thick thwack, cut and hack, helter-skelter, higgledy-piggledy, hurly-burly, head-over-heels, rough-and-tumble! Dunder and blixum! swore the Dutchmen; splitter and splutter! cried the Swedes. Storm the works! shouted Hardkoppig Peter. Fire the mine! roared stout Risingh. Tanta-rar-ra-ra! twanged the trumpet of Antony Van Corlear;—until all voice and sound became unintelligible,—grunts of pain, yells of fury, and shouts of triumph mingling in one hideous clamor. The earth shook as if struck with a paralytic stroke; trees shrunk aghast, and withered at the sight; rocks burrowed in the ground like rabbits; and even Christina creek turned from its course, and ran up a hill in breathless terror!

Long hung the contest doubtful; for though a heavy shower of rain, sent by the "cloud-compelling Jove," in some measure cooled their ardor, as doth a bucket of water thrown on a group of fighting mastiffs, yet did they but pause for a moment, to return with tenfold fury to the charge. Just at this juncture a vast and dense column of smoke was seen slowly rolling toward the scene of battle. The combatants paused for a moment, gazing in mute astonishment, until the wind, dispelling the murky cloud, revealed the flaunting banner of Michael Paw, the Patroon of Communipaw. That valiant chieftain came fearlessly on at the head of a phalanx of oyster-fed Pavonians and a *corps de reserve* of the Van Arsdales and Van Bummels, who had remained behind to digest the enormous dinner they had eaten. These now trudged manfully forward, smoking their pipes with outrageous vigor, so as to raise the awful cloud that has been mentioned, but marching exceedingly slow, being short of leg, and of great rotundity in the belt.

And now the deities who watched over the fortunes of the Nederlanders having unthinkingly left the field, and stepped into a neighboring tavern to refresh themselves with a pot of beer, a direful catastrophe had wellnigh ensued. Scarce had the myrmidons of Michael Paw attained the front of battle, when the Swedes, instructed by the cunning Risingh, levelled a shower of blows full at their tobacco-pipes. Astounded at this assault, and dismayed at the havoc of their pipes, these ponderous warriors gave way, and like a drove of frightened elephants broke through the ranks of their own army. The little Hoppers were borne down in the surge; the sacred banner emblazoned with the gigantic oyster of Communipaw was trampled in the dirt; on blundered and thundered the heavy-sterned fugitives, the Swedes pressing on their rear and applying their feet *a parte poste* of the Van Arsdales and the Van Bummels with a vigor that prodigiously accelerated their movements; nor did the renowned Michael Paw himself fail to receive divers grievous and dishonorable visitations of shoe-leather.

But what, oh Muse! was the rage of Peter Stuyvesant, when from afar he saw his army giving way! In the transports of his wrath he sent forth a roar, enough to shake the very hills. The men of the Manhattoes plucked up new courage at the sound, or, rather, they rallied at the voice of their leader, of whom they stood more in awe than of all the Swedes in Christendom. Without waiting for their aid, the daring Peter dashed, sword in hand, into the thickest of the foe. Then might be seen achievements worthy of the days of the giants. Wherever he went, the enemy shrank before him; the Swedes fled to right and left, or were driven, like dogs, into their own ditch; but as he pushed forward singly with headlong courage, the foe closed behind and hung upon his rear. One aimed a blow full at his heart; but the protecting power which watches over the great and good turned aside the hostile blade and directed it to a side-pocket, where reposed an enormous iron tobacco-box, endowed, like the shield of Achilles, with supernatural powers, doubtless from bearing the portrait of the blessed St. Nicholas. Peter Stuyvesant turned like an angry bear upon the foe, and seizing him, as he fled, by an immeasureable queue, "Ah, whoreson caterpillar," roared he, "here's what shall make worms' meat of thee!" So saying, he whirled his sword, and dealt a blow that would have decapitated the varlet, but that the pitying steel struck short and shaved the queue forever from his crown. At this moment an arquebusier levelled his piece from a neighboring mound, with deadly aim; but the watchful Minerva, who had just stopped to tie up her garter, seeing the peril of her favorite hero, sent old Boreas with his bellows, who, as the match descended to the pan, gave a blast that blew the priming from the touch-hole.

Thus waged the fight, when the stout Risingh, surveying the field from the top of a little ravelin, perceived his troops banged, beaten, and kicked by the invincible Peter. Drawing his falchion and uttering a thousand anathemas, he strode down to the scene of combat with some such thundering strides as Jupiter is said by Hesiod to have taken when he strode down the spheres to hurl his thunder-bolts at the Titans.

When the rival heroes came face to face, each made a prodigious start in the style of a veteran stage-champion. Then did they regard each other for a moment with the bitter aspect of two furious ram-

cats on the point of a clapper-clawing. Then did they throw themselves
into one attitude, then into another, striking their swords on the
ground, first on the right side, then on the left; at last at it they went,
with incredible ferocity. Words cannot tell the prodigies of strength
and valor displayed in this direful encounter,—an encounter compared to which the far-famed battles of Ajax with Hector, of Aeneas
with Turnus, Orlando with Rodomont, Guy of Warwick with Col-
brand the Dane, or of that renowned Welsh knight, Sir Owen of the
Mountains, with the giant Guylon, were all gentle sports and holiday
recreations. At length the valiant Peter, watching his opportunity,
aimed a blow, enough to cleave his adversary to the very chine; but
Risingh, nimbly raising his sword, warded it off so narrowly, that,
glancing on one side, it shaved away a huge canteen in which he carried his liquor,—thence pursuing its trenchant course, it severed off a
deep coat-pocket, stored with bread and cheese,—which provant rolling among the armies, occasioned a fearful scrambling between the
Swedes and Dutchmen, and made the general battle to wax more furious than ever.

Enraged to see his military stores laid waste, the stout Risingh,
collecting all his forces, aimed a mighty blow full at the hero's crest.
In vain did his fierce little cocked hat oppose its course. The biting
steel clove through the stubborn ram beaver, and would have cracked
the crown of any one not endowed with supernatural hardness of
head; but the brittle weapon shivered in pieces on the skull of Hardkoppig Piet, shedding a thousand sparks, like beams of glory, round
his grizzly visage.

The good Peter reeled with the blow, and turning up his eyes
beheld a thousand suns, besides moons and stars, dancing about the
firmament; at length, missing his footing, by reason of his wooden
leg, down he came on his seat of honor with a crash which shook the
surrounding hills, and might have wrecked his frame, had he not been
received into a cushion softer than velvet, which Providence, or
Minerva, or St. Nicholas, or some cow, had benevolently prepared for
his reception.

The furious Risingh, in despite of the maxim, cherished by all true
knights, that "fair play is a jewel," hastened to take advantage of the
hero's fall; but, as he stooped to give a fatal blow, Peter Stuyvesant
dealt him a thwack over the sconce with his wooden leg, which set
a chime of bells ringing triple bob-majors in his cerebellum. The

bewildered Swede staggered with the blow, and the wary Peter seizing a pocket-pistol, which lay hard by, discharged it full at the head of the reeling Risingh. Let not my reader mistake; it was not a murderous weapon loaded with powder and ball, but a little sturdy stone pottle charged to the muzzle with a double dram of true Dutch courage, which the knowing Antony Van Corlear carried about him by way of replenishing his valor, and which had dropped from his wallet during his furious encounter with the drummer. The hideous weapon sang through the air, and true to its course as was the fragment of a rock discharged at Hector by bully Ajax, encountered the head of the gigantic Swede with matchless violence.

This heaven-directed blow decided the battle. The ponderous pericranium of General Jan Risingh sank upon his breast; his knees tottered under him; a deathlike torpor seized upon his frame, and he tumbled to the earth with such violence, that old Pluto started with affright, lest he should have broken through the roof of his infernal palace.

His fall was the signal of defeat and victory: the Swedes gave way, the Dutch pressed forward; the former took to their heels, the latter hotly pursued. Some entered with them, pell-mell, through the sally-port; others stormed the bastion, and others scrambled over the curtain. Thus in a little while the fortress of Fort Christina, which, like another Troy, had stood a siege of full ten hours, was carried by assault, without the loss of a single man on either side. Victory, in the likeness of a gigantic ox-fly, sat perched upon the cocked hat of the gallant Stuyvesant; and it was declared, by all the writers whom he hired to write the history of his expedition, that on this memorable day he gained a sufficient quantity of glory to immortalize a dozen of the greatest heroes in Christendom!

Orpheus C. Kerr

THE LATEST IMPROVEMENTS IN ARTILLERY

Washington, D. C., August —, 1861.
By invitation of a well-known official, I visited the Navy-Yard yesterday, and witnessed the trial of some newly-invented rifled cannon. The trial was of short duration, and the jury brought in a verdict of "innocent of any intent to kill."

The first gun tried was similar to those used in the Revolution, except that it had a larger touch-hole, and the carriage was painted green, instead of blue. This novel and ingenious weapon was pointed at a target about sixty yards distant. It didn't hit it, and as nobody saw any ball, there was much perplexity expressed. A midshipman did say that he thought the ball must have run out of the touch-hole when they loaded up—for which he was instantly expelled from the service. After a long search without finding the ball, there was some thought of summoning the Naval Retiring Board to decide on the matter, when somebody happened to look into the mouth of the cannon, and discovered that the ball hadn't gone out at all. The inventor said this would happen sometimes, especially if you didn't put a brick over the touch-hole when you fired the gun. The Government was so pleased with this explanation, that it ordered forty of the guns on the spot, at two hundred thousand dollars apiece. The guns to be furnished as soon as the war is over.

The next weapon tried was Jink's double back-action revolving cannon for ferry-boats. It consists of a heavy bronze tube, revolving on a pivot, with both ends open, and a touch-hole in the middle. While one gunner puts a load in at one end, another puts in a load at the other end, and one touch-hole serves for both. Upon applying the match, the gun is whirled swiftly round on a pivot, and both balls fly out in circles, causing great slaughter on both sides. This terrible engine was aimed at the target with great accuracy; but as the gunner has a large family dependent on him for support, he refused to apply the match. The Government was satisfied without firing, and ordered six of the guns at a million dollars apiece. The guns to be furnished in time for our next war.

The last weapon subjected to trial was a mountain howitzer of a new pattern. The inventor explained that its great advantage was, that it required no powder. In battle it is placed on the top of a high mountain, and a ball slipped loosely into it. As the enemy passes the foot of the mountain, the gunner in charge tips over the howitzer, and the ball rolls down the side of the mountain into the midst of the doomed foe. The range of this terrible weapon depends greatly on the height of the mountain and the distance to its base. The Government ordered forty of these mountain howitzers at a hundred thousand dollars apiece, to be planted on the first mountains discovered in the enemy's country.

These are great times for gunsmiths, my boy; and if you find any old cannon around the junk-shops, just send them along.

There is much sensation in nautical circles arising from the immoral conduct of the rebel privateers; but public feeling has been somewhat easier since the invention of a craft for capturing the pirates, by an ingenious Connecticut chap. Yesterday he exhibited a small model of it at a cabinet meeting, and explained it thus:

"You will perceive," says he to the President, "that the machine itself will only be four times the size of the Great Eastern, and need not cost over a few millions of dollars. I have only got to discover one thing before I can make it perfect. You will observe that it has a steam-engine on board. This engine works a pair of immense iron clamps, which are let down into the water from the extreme end of a very lengthy horizontal spar. Upon approaching the pirate, the captain orders the engineer to put on steam. Instantly the clamps descend from the end of the spar and clutch the privateer athwartships. Then the engine is reversed, the privateer is lifted bodily out of the water, the spar swings around over the deck, and the pirate ship is let down into the hold by the run. Then shut your hatches, and you have ship and pirates safe and sound."

The President's gothic features lighted up beautifully at the words of the great inventor; but in a moment they assumed an expression of doubt, and says he:

"But how are you going to manage, if the privateer fires upon you while you are doing this?"

"My dear sir," says the inventor, "I told you I had only one thing to discover before I could make the machine perfect, and that's it."

So you see, my boy, there's a prospect of our doing something on the ocean next century, and there's only one thing in the way of our taking in pirates by the cargo.

Last evening a new brigadier-general, aged ninety-four years, made a speech to Regiment Five, Mackerel Brigade, and then furnished each man with a lead-pencil. He said that, as the Government was disappointed about receiving some provisions it had ordered for the troops, those pencils were intended to enable them to draw their rations as usual. I got a very big pencil, my boy, and have lived on a sheet of paper ever since.

Yours, pensively,

ORPHEUS C. KERR.

James Russell Lowell

SUNTHIN' IN THE PASTORAL LINE *

Jaalam, 17th May, 1862

To the Editors of The Atlantic Monthly

GENTLEMEN,—At the special request of Mr. Biglow, I intended to inclose, together with his own contribution, (into which, at my suggestion, he has thrown a little more of pastoral sentiment than usual,) some passages from my sermon on the day of the National Fast, from the text, "Remember them that are in bonds, as bound with them," Heb. xiii. 3. But I have not leisure sufficient at present for the copying of them, even were I altogether satisfied with the production as it stands. I should prefer, I confess, to contribute the entire discourse to the pages of your respectable miscellany, if it should be found acceptable upon perusal, especially as I find the difficulty in selection of greater magnitude than I had anticipated. What passes without challenge in the fervour of oral delivery, cannot always stand the colder criticism of the closet. I am not so great an enemy of Eloquence as my friend Mr. Biglow would appear to be from some passages in his contribution for the current month. I would not, indeed, hastily suspect him of covertly glancing at myself in his somewhat caustick animadversions, albeit some of the phrases he girds at are not entire strangers to my lips. I am a more hearty admirer of the Puritans than seems now to be the fashion, and believe, that, if they Hebraized a little too much in their speech, they showed remarkable practical sagacity as statesmen and founders. But such phenomena as Puritanism are the results rather of great religious than of merely social convulsions, and do not long survive them. So soon as an earnest conviction has cooled into a phrase, its work is over, and the best that can be done with it is to bury it. *Ite, missa est.* I am inclined to agree with Mr. Biglow that we cannot settle the great political questions which are now presenting themselves to the nation by the opinions of Jere-

* *From "The Biglow Papers—Second Series."*

miah or Ezekiel as to the wants and duties of the Jews in their time,
nor do I believe that an entire community with their feelings and
views would be practicable or even agreeable at the present day. At
the same time I could wish that their habit of subordinating the
actual to the moral, the flesh to the spirit, and this world to the other,
were more common. They had found out, at least, the great military
secret that soul weighs more than body.—But I am suddenly called to
a sick-bed in the household of a valued parishioner.

With esteem and respect,

Your obedient servant,

HOMER WILBUR.

Once git a smell o' musk into a draw,
An' it clings hold like precerdents in law:
Your gra'ma'am put it there,—when, goodness knows,—
To jes' this-worldify her Sunday-clo'es;
But the old chist wun't sarve her gran'son's wife,
(For, 'thout new funnitoor, wut good in life?)
An' so ole clawfoot, from the precinks dread
O' the spare chamber, slinks into the shed,
Where, dim with dust, it fust or last subsides
To holdin' seeds an' fifty things besides;
But better days stick fast in heart an' husk,
An' all you keep in 't gits a scent o' musk.

Jes' so with poets: wut they 've airly read
Gits kind o' worked into their heart an' head,
So 's 't they can't seem to write but jest on sheers
With furrin countries or played-out ideers,
Nor hev a feelin', ef it doos n't smack
O' wut some critter chose to feel 'way back:
This makes 'em talk o' daisies, larks, an' things,
Ez though we'd nothin' here that blows an' sings,—
(Why, I'd give more for one live bobolink
Than a square mile o' larks in printer's ink,)—
This makes 'em think our fust o' May is May,
Which 't ain't, for all the almanicks can say.

O little city-gals, don't never go it
Blind on the word o' noospaper or poet!

They 're apt to puff, an' May-day seldom looks
Up in the country ez it doos in books;
They 're no more like than hornets'-nests an' hives,
Or printed sarmons be to holy lives.
I, with my trouses perched on cowhide boots,
Tuggin' my foundered feet out by the roots,
Hev seen ye come to fling on April's hearse
Your muslin nosegays from the milliner's,
Puzzlin' to find dry ground your queen to choose,
An' dance your throats sore in morocker shoes:
I've seen ye an' felt proud, thet, come wut would,
Our Pilgrim stock wuz pethed with hardihood.
Pleasure doos make us Yankees kind o' winch,
Ez though 't wuz sunthin' paid for by the inch;
But yit we du contrive to worry thru,
Ef Dooty tells us thet the thing 's to du,
An' kerry a hollerday, ef we set out,
Ez stiddily ez though 't wuz a redoubt.

I, country-born an' bred, know where to find
Some blooms thet make the season suit the mind,
An' seem to metch the doubtin' bluebird's notes,—
Half-vent'rin' liverworts in furry coats,
Bloodroots, whose rolled-up leaves ef you oncurl,
Each on 'em 's cradle to a baby-pearl,—
But these are jes' Spring's pickets; sure ez sin,
The rebble frosts 'll try to drive 'em in;
For half our May's so awfully like May n't,
't would rile a Shaker or an evrige saint;
Though I own up I like our back'ard springs
Thet kind o' haggle with their greens an' things,
An' when you 'most give up, 'uthout more words
Toss the fields full o' blossoms, leaves, an' birds;
Thet's Northun natur', slow an' apt to doubt,
But when it *doos* git stirred, ther' 's no gin-out!

Fust come the blackbirds clatt'rin' in tall trees,
An' settlin' things in windy Congresses,—
Queer politicians, though, for I'll be skinned
Ef all on 'em don't head aginst the wind.

'fore long the trees begin to show belief,—
The maple crimsons to a coral-reef,
Then saffern swarms swing off from all the willers
So plump they look like yaller caterpillars,
Then gray hossches'nuts leetle hands unfold
Softer 'n a baby's be at three days old:
Thet 's robin-redbreast's almanick; he knows
Thet arter this ther' 's only blossom-snows;
So, choosin' out a handy crotch an' spouse,
He goes to plast'rin' his adobe house.

Then seems to come a hitch,—things lag behind,
Till some fine mornin' Spring makes up her mind,
An' ez, when snow-swelled rivers cresh their dams
Heaped-up with ice thet dovetails in an' jams,
A leak comes spirtin' thru some pin-hole cleft,
Grows stronger, fercer, tears out right an' left,
Then all the waters bow themselves an' come,
Suddin' in one gret slope o' shedderin' foam,
Jes' so our Spring gits everythin' in tune
An' gives one leap from Aperl into June:
Then all comes crowdin' in; afore you think,
Young oak-leaves mist the side-hill woods with pink;
The catbird in the laylock-bush is loud;
The orchards turn to heaps o' rosy cloud;
Red-cedars blossom tu, though few folks know it,
An' look all dipt in sunshine like a poet;
The lime-trees pile their solid stacks o' shade
An' drows'ly simmer with the bees' sweet trade;
In eilum-shrouds the flashin' hangbird clings
An' for the summer vy'ge his hammock slings;
All down the loose-walled lanes in archin' bowers
The barb'ry droops its strings o' golden flowers,
Whose shrinkin' hearts the school-gals love to try
With pins,—they'll worry yourn so, boys, bimeby!
But I don't love your cat'logue style,—do you?—
Ez ef to sell off Natur' by vendoo;
One word with blood in 't 's twice ez good ez two:

'nuff sed, June's bridesman, poet o' the year,
Gladness on wings, the bobolink, is here;
Half-hid in tip-top apple-blooms he swings,
Or climbs aginst the breeze with quiverin' wings,
Or, givin' way to 't in a mock despair,
Runs down, a brook o' laughter, thru the air.

I ollus feel the sap start in my veins
In Spring, with curus heats an' prickly pains,
Thet drive me, when I git a chance, to walk
Off by myself to hev a privit talk
With a queer critter thet can't seem to 'gree
Along o' me like most folks,—Mister Me.
Ther' 's times when I'm unsoshle ez a stone,
An' sort o' suffercate to be alone,—
I'm crowded jes' to think thet folks are nigh,
An' can't bear nothin' closer than the sky;
Now the wind's full ez shifty in the mind
Ez wut it is ou'-doors, ef I ain't blind,
An' sometimes, in the fairest sou'west weather,
My innard vane pints east for weeks together,
My natur' gits all goose-flesh, an' my sins
Come drizzlin' on my conscience sharp ez pins:
Wal, et sech times I jes' slip out o' sight
An' take it out in a fair stan'-up fight
With the one cuss I can't lay on the shelf,
The crook'dest stick in all the heap,—Myself.

'T wuz so las' Sabbath arter meetin'-time:
Findin' my feelin's would n't noways rhyme
With nobody's, but off the hendle flew
An' took things from an east-wind pint o' view,
I started off to lose me in the hills
Where the pines be, up back o' 'Siah's Mills:
Pines, ef you 're blue, are the best friends I know,
They mope an' sigh an' sheer your feelin's so,—
They hesh the ground beneath so, tu, I swan,
You half-forgit you've gut a body on.

Ther' 's a small school'us' there where four roads meet,
The door-steps hollered out by little feet,
An' side-posts carved with names whose owners grew
To gret men, some on 'em, an' deacons, tu;
't ain't used no longer, coz the town hez gut
A high-school, where they teach the Lord knows wut:
Three-story larnin' 's pop'lar now; I guess
We thriv' ez wal on jes' two stories less,
For it strikes me ther' 's sech a thing ez sinnin'
By overloadin' children's underpinnin':
Wal, here it wuz I larned my A B C,
An' it 's a kind o' favorite spot with me.

We're curus critters: Now ain't jes' the minute
Thet ever fits us easy while we're in it;
Long ez 't wuz futur', 't would be perfect bliss,—
Soon ez it's past, *thet* time's wuth ten o' this;
An' yit there ain't a man thet need be told
Thet Now's the only bird lays eggs o' gold.
A knee-high lad, I used to plot an' plan
An' think 't wuz life's cap-sheaf to be a man;
Now, gittin' gray, there's nothin' I enjoy
Like dreamin' back along into a boy:
So the ole school'us' is a place I choose
Afore all others, ef I want to muse;
I set down where I used to set, an' git
My boyhood back, an' better things with it,—
Faith, Hope, an' sunthin', ef it is n't Cherrity,
It's want o' guile, an' thet's ez gret a rerrity,—
While Fancy's cushin', free to Prince and Clown,
Makes the hard bench ez soft ez milk-weed-down.

Now, 'fore I knowed, thet Sabbath arternoon
When I sot out to tramp myself in tune,
I found me in the school'us' on my seat,
Drummin' the march to No-wheres with my feet.
Thinkin' o' nothin', I've heerd ole folks say,
Is a hard kind o' dooty in its way:

It's thinkin' everythin' you ever knew,
Or ever hearn, to make your feelin's blue.
I sot there tryin' thet on for a spell:
I thought o' the Rebellion, then o' Hell,
Which some folks tell ye now is jest a metterfor
(A the'ry, p'raps, it wun't *feel* none the better for);
I thought o' Reconstruction, wut we'd win
Patchin' our patent self-blow-up agin:
I thought ef this 'ere milkin' o' the wits,
So much a month, warn't givin' Natur' fits,—
Ef folks warn't druv, findin' their own milk fail,
To work the cow thet hez an iron tail,
An' ef idees 'thout ripenin' in the pan
Would send up cream to humor ary man:
From this to thet I let my worryin' creep,
Till finally I must ha' fell asleep.

Our lives in sleep are some like streams thet glide
'twixt flesh an' sperrit boundin' on each side,
Where both shores' shadders kind o' mix an' mingle
In sunthin' thet ain't jes' like either single;
An' when you cast off moorin's from To-day,
An' down towards To-morrer drift away,
The imiges thet tengle on the stream
Make a new upside-down'ard world o' dream:
Sometimes they seem like sunrise-streaks an' warnin's
O' wut 'll be in Heaven on Sabbath-mornin's,
An', mixed right in ez ef jest out o' spite,
Sunthin' thet says your supper ain't gone right.
I'm gret on dreams, an' often when I wake,
I've lived so much it makes my mem'ry ache,
An' can't skurce take a cat-nap in my cheer
'thout hevin' 'em, some good, some bad, all queer.

Now I wuz settin' where I'd ben, it seemed,
An' ain't sure yit whether I r'ally dreamed,
Nor, ef I did, how long I might ha' slep',
When I hearn some un stompin' up the step,

An' lookin' round, ef two an' two make four,
I see a Pilgrim Father in the door.
He wore a steeple-hat, tall boots, an' spurs
With rowels to 'em big ez ches'nut-burrs,
An' his gret sword behind him sloped away
Long 'z a man's speech thet dunno wut to say.—
"Ef your name 's Biglow, an' your given-name
Hosee," sez he, "it's arter you I came;
I 'm your gret-gran'ther multiplied by three."—
"My *wut?*" sez I.—"Your gret-gret-gret," sez he:
"You would n't ha' never ben here but for me.
Two hundred an' three year ago this May
The ship I come in sailed up Boston Bay;
I'd been a cunnle in our Civil War,—
But wut on airth hev *you* gut up one for?
Coz we du things in England, 't ain't for you
To git a notion you can du 'em tu:
I 'm told you write in public prints: ef true,
It 's nateral you should know a thing or two."—
"Thet air 's an argymunt I can't endorse,—
't would prove, coz you wear spurs, you kep' a horse:
For brains," sez I, "wutever you may think,
Ain't boun' to cash the drafs o' pen-an'-ink,—
Though mos' folks write ez ef they hoped jes' quickenin'
The churn would argoo skim-milk into thickenin';
But skim-milk ain't a thing to change its view
O' wut it's meant for more 'n a smoky flue.
But du pray tell me, 'fore we furder go,
How in all Natur' did you come to know
'bout our affairs," sez I, "in Kingdom-Come?"—
"Wal, I worked round at sperrit-rappin' some,
An' danced the tables till their legs wuz gone,
In hopes o' larnin' wut wuz goin' on,"
Sez he, "but mejums lie so like all-split
Thet I concluded it wuz best to quit.
But, come now, ef you wun't confess to knowin',
You 've some conjectures how the thing 's a-goin'."—
Gran'ther," sez I, "a vane warn't never known
Jor asked to hev a jedgment of its own;

An' yit, ef 't ain't gut rusty in the jints,
It's safe to trust its say on certin pints:
It knows the wind's opinions to a T,
An' the wind settles wut the weather'll be."
"I never thought a scion of our stock
Could grow the wood to make a weather-cock;
When I wuz younger 'n you, skurce more 'n a shaver,
No airthly wind," sez he, "could make me waver!"
(Ez he said this, he clinched his jaw an' forehead,
Hitchin' his belt to bring his sword-hilt forrard.)—
"Jes' so it wuz with me," sez I, "I swow,
When *I* wuz younger 'n wut you see me now,—
Nothin' from Adam's fall to Huldy's bonnet,
Thet I warn't full-cocked with my jedgment on it;
But now I'm gittin' on in life, I find
It 's a sight harder to make up my mind,—
Nor I don't often try tu, when events
Will du it for me free of all expense.
The moral question 's ollus plain enough,—
It's jes' the human-natur' side thet's tough;
Wut's best to think may n't puzzle me nor you,—
The pinch comes in decidin' wut to *du;*
Ef you *read* History, all runs smooth ez grease,
Coz there the men ain't nothin' more 'n idees,—
But come to *make* it, ez we must to-day,
Th' idees hev arms an' legs an' stop the way:
It's easy fixin' things in facts an' figgers,—
They can't resist, nor warn't brought up with niggers;
But come to try your the'ry on,—why, then
Your facts an' figgers change to ign'ant men
Actin' ez ugly—" —"Smite 'em hip an' thigh!"
Sez gran'ther, "and let every man-child die!
Oh for three weeks o' Crommle an' the Lord!
Up, Isr'el, to your tents an' grind the sword!"—
"Thet kind o' thing worked wal in ole Judee,
But you forgit how long it's ben A.D.;
You think thet 's ellerkence,—I call it shoddy,
A thing," sez I, "wun't cover soul nor body;

I like the plain all-wool o' common-sense,
Thet warms ye now, an' will a twelvemonth hence.
You took to follerin' where the Prophets beckoned,
An', fust you knowed on, back come Charles the Second;
Now wut I want 's to hev all we gain stick,
An' not to start Millennium too quick;
We hain't to punish only, but to keep,
An' the cure 's gut to go a cent'ry deep."
"Wall, milk-an'-water ain't the best o' glue,"
Sez he, "an' so you'll find afore you're thru;
Ef reshness venters sunthin'," shilly-shally
Loses ez often wut 's ten times the vally.
Thet exe of ourn, when Charles's neck gut split,
Opened a gap thet ain't bridged over yit:
Slav'ry 's your Charles, the Lord hez gin the exe"—
"Our Charles," sez I, "hez gut eight million necks.
The hardest question ain't the black man's right,
The trouble is to 'mancipate the white;
One 's chained in body an' can be sot free,
But t' other's chained in soul to an idee:
It's a long job, but we shall worry thru it;
Ef bagnets fail, the spellin'-book must du it."
"Hosee," sez he, "I think you're goin' to fail:
The rettlesnake ain't dangerous in the tail;
This 'ere rebellion 's nothin' but the rettle,—
You 'll stomp on thet an' think you've won the bettle;
It's Slavery thet's the fangs an' thinkin' head,
An' ef you want selvation, cresh it dead,—
An' cresh it suddin, or you'll larn by waitin'
Thet Chance wun't stop to listen to debatin'!"—
"God's truth!" sez I,—"an' ef I held the club,
An' knowed jes' where to strike,—but there's the rub!"—
"Strike soon," sez he, "or you'll be deadly ailin',—
Folks thet's afeared to fail are sure o' failin';
God hates your sneakin' creturs thet believe
He'll settle things they run away an' leave!"
He brought his foot down fercely, ez he spoke,
An' give me sech a startle thet I woke.

Petroleum V. Nasby

THE GREAT PRESIDENTIAL EXCURSION

The Great Presidential Excursion to the Tomb of Douglas.—An Account of the Ride of the Modern John Gilpin, who went a Pleasuring and came Home with nothing but the Necks of His Bottles: by His Chaplain.—From Washington to Detroit.

AT THE BIDDLE HOUSE
(wich is in Detroit, Michigan),
September the 4th, 1866.

Step by step I am assendin the ladder uv fame; step by step I am climbin to a proud eminence. Three weeks ago I wuz summoned to Washinton by that eminently grate and good man, Androo Johnson, to attend a consultation ez to the proposed Western tour, wich wuz to be undertaken for the purpose uv arousin the masses uv the West to a sence uv the danger wich wuz threatnin uv em in case they per-sisted in centralizin the power uv the Government into the hands uv a Congress, instid uv diffusin it throughout the hands uv one man, wich is Johnson. I got there too late to take part in the first uv the discussion. When I arrove they hed everything settled cepting the appintment uv a Chaplain for the excursion. The President insisted upon my fillin that position, but Seward objected. He wanted Beecher, but Johnson wuz inflexibly agin him. "I am determined," sez he, "to carry out my policy, but I hev some bowels left. Beecher hez done enuff already, considerin the pay he got. No, no! he shel be spared this trip; indeed he shel."

"Very good," said Seward; "but at least find some clergyman who endorses us without hevin P. M. to his honored name. It wood look better."

"I know it wood," replied Johnson; "but where kin we find sich a one? I hev swung around the entire circle, and hevn't ez yet seen him. Nasby it must be."

There wuz then a lively discussion ez to the propriety, before the

procession started, of removin all the Federal offis-holders on the proposed route, and appintin men who beleeved in us (Johnson, Beecher,
and Me), that we might be shoor uv a sootable recepshun at each
pint at wich we wuz to stop. The Annointed wuz in favor uv it. Sez
he, "Them ez won't support my polisy shan't eat my bread and butter."
Randall and Doolittle chimed in, for it's got to be a part of their
religion to assent to whatever the President sez, but I mildly protested. I owe a duty to the party, and I am determined to do it.

"Most High," sez I, "a settin hen wich is lazy makes no fuss; cut
its head off, and it flops about, for a while, lively. Lincoln's offis-
holders are settin hens. They don't like yoo nor yoor policy, but while
they are on their nests, they will keep moderitly quiet. Cut off their
heads, and they will spurt their blood in your face. Ez to bein en-
shoord of a reception at each point, you need fear nothin. Calkerlatin
moderately, there are at least twenty-five or thirty patriots who feel a
call for every offis in your disposal. So long, Yoor Highnis, ez them
offisis is held just where they kin see em, and they don't know wich
is to git em, yoo may depend upon the entire enthoosiasm uv each,
individyooally and collectively. In short, ef there's 4 offises in a town,
and yoo make the appointments, yoo hev sekoored 4 supporters;
till yoo make the appointments yoo hev the hundred who expect to
get em."

The President agreed with me that until after the trip the gullotine
shood stop.

Secretary Seward sejested that a clean shirt wood improve my personal appearance, and akkordingly a cirkular wuz sent to the clerks
in the Departments, assessin em for that purpose. Sich uv em ez re-
foosed to contribute their quota wuz instantly dismissed for disloyalty.

At last we started, and I must say we wuz got up in a highly conciliatory style. Every wun of the civilians uv the party wore buzzum
pins, et settry, wich wuz presented to em by the Southern delegates to
the Philadelphia convention, wich wuz made uv the bones uv Federal soldiers wich hed fallen at various battles. Sum uv em were par-
tiklerly valuable ez anteeks, hevin bin made from the bones uv the
fust soldiers who fell at Bull Run.

The Noo York recepshun wuz a gay affair. I never saw His Imperial Highness in better spirits, and he delivered his speech to better
advantage than I ever heard him do it before, and I bleeve I've heard
it a hundred times. We left Noo York sadly. Even now, ez I write,

the remembrance uv that perceshun, the recollection uv that banquet, lingers around me, and the taste uv them wines is still in my mouth. But we hed to go. We hed a mishn to perform, and we put ourselves on a steamboat and started.

ALBANY.—There wuz a immense crowd, but the Czar uv all the Amerikas didn't get orf his speech here. The Governor welcomed him, but he welcomed him ez the Cheef Magistrate uv the nashen, and happened to drop in Lincoln's name. That struck a chill over the party, and the President got out uv it ez soon ez possible. Bein reseeved ez Cheef Magistrate, and not ez the great Pacificator, ain't His Eggslency's best holt. It wuz unkind uv Governor Fenton to do it. If he takes the papers, he must know that His Mightiness ain't got but one speech, and he ought to hev made sich a reception ez wood hev enabled him to hev got it off. We shook the dust off uv our feet, and left Albany in disgust.

SKENACTADY.—The people uv this delightfull little village wuz awake when the Imperial train arrived. The changes hadn't bin made in the offises here, and consekently there wuz a splendid recepshun. I didn't suppose there wuz so many patriots along the Mohawk. I wuz pinted out by sum one ez the President's private adviser—a sort uv private Secretary uv State; and after the train started, I found jest 211 petitions for the Post Offis in Skenactedy in my side coat pocket, wich the patriots who hed hurrahed so vocifferously hed dexterously deposited there. The incident wuz a movin one. "Thank God!" thought I. "So long ez we hev the post offises to give, we kin alluz hev a party." The Sultan swung around the cirkle wunst here, and leavin the Constoo-shun in their hands, the train moved off.

UTICA.—The President spoke here with greater warmth, and jerked more originality than I hed before observed. He introdoost here the remark that he didn't come to make a speech; that he wuz goin to shed a tear over the tomb uv Douglas; that, in swingin around the cirkle, he hed fought traitors on all sides uv it, but that he felt safe. He shood leave the Constooshun in their hands, and ef a martyr wuz wanted, he wuz ready to die with neetnees and dispatch.

ROME.—Here we hed a splendid recepshun, and I never heard His Majesty speek more felicitously. He menshuned to the audience that he had swung around the Southern side uv the cirkle, and wuz now swingin around the Northern side uv it, and that he wuz fightin traitors on all sides. He left the Constitooshun in their hands, and bid em good bye. I reseeved at this pint only 130 petitions for the post offis, wich I took ez a bad omen for the comin election.

LOCKPORT.—The President is improvin wonderfully. He rises with the occasion. At this pint he mentioned that he wuz sot on savin the country wich hed honored him. Ez for himself, his ambishn wuz more than satisfied. He hed bin Alderman, Member uv the Legislacher, Congressman, Senator, Military Governor, Vice President, and President. He hed swung around the entire cirkle uv offises, and all he wanted now wuz to heal the wounds uv the nashen. He felt safe in leavin the Constooshn in their hands. Ez he swung around the cirkle—

At this pint I interrupted him. I told him that he hed swung around the cirkle wunst in this town, and ez useful ez the phrase wuz, it might spile by too much yoose.

At Cleveland we begun to get into hot water. Here is the post to which the devil uv Ablishnism is chained, and his chain is long enough to let him rage over neerly the whole state. I am pained to state that the President wuzn't treated here with the respeck due his station. He commenst deliverin his speech, but wuz made the subjeck uv ribald laffture. Skasely hed he got to the pint uv swingin around the cirkle, when a foul-mouthed nigger-lover yelled "Veto!" and another vociferated "Noo Orleens!" and another remarked "Memphis!" and one after another interruption occurred until His Highness wuz completely turned off the track, and got wild. He forgot his speech, and struck out crazy, but the starch wuz out uv him, and he wuz worsted. Grant, wich we hed taken along to draw the crowds, played dirt on us here, and stepped onto a boat for Detroit, leavin us only Farragut ez a attraction, who tried twice to git away ditto, but wuz timely prevented. The President recovered his ekanimity, and swung around the cirkle wunst, and leavin the Constooshun in their hands, retired.

At the next pint we wuz astounded at seein but one man at the station. He wuz dressed with a sash over his shoulder, and wuz wavin a flag with wun hand, firin a saloot with a revolver with the other, and playin "Hail to the Chief!" on a mouth organ, all to wunst.

"Who are you, my gentle friend?" sez I.

"I'm the newly-appinted Postmaster, sir," sez he. "I'm a perceshun a waitin here to do honor to our Cheef Magistrate, all alone, sir. There wuz twenty Johnsonians in this hamlet, sir; but when the commishn came for me, the other nineteen wuz soured, and sed they didn't care a d—n for him nor his policy, sir. Where is the President?"

Androo wuz a goin to swing around the cirkle for this one man, and leave the Constooshn in his hands, but Seward checked him.

At Fremont we hed a handsome recepshun, for the offises hevn't bin changed there, but Toledo didn't do so well. The crowd didn't cheer Androo much, but when Farragut was trotted out they gave him a rouser, wich wuz anything but pleasin to the Cheef Magistrate uv this nashen, who bleeves in bein respected.

Finally we reeched Detroit. This bein a Democratic city, the President wuz hisself agin. His speech here wuz wun uv rare merit. He gathered together in one quiver all the sparklin arrows he had used from Washington to this point, and shot em one by one. He swung around the cirkle; he didn't come to make a speech; he hed bin Alderman uv his native town; he might hev been Dicktater, but woodent; and ended with a poetickal cotashun wich I coodent ketch, but wich, ez neer ez I cood understand, wuz,

> "Kum wun, kum all; this rock shel fly
> From its firm base—in a pig's eye."

Here we repose for the nite. To-morrow we start onward, and shel continue swingin around the cirkle till we reach Chicago.

PETROLEUM V. NASBY, P. M.

(wich is Postmaster),

and likewise Chaplin to the expedishn.

Mark Twain

THE HUNTING OF THE COW *

(*October 18, 1907*). Two colossal historical incidents took place yesterday, incidents which must go echoing down the corridors of time for ages, incidents which can never be forgotten while histories shall continue to be written. Yesterday, for the first time, business was opened to commerce by the Marconi Company and wireless messages sent entirely across the Atlantic, straight from shore to shore; and on that same day the President of the United States for the fourteenth time came within three miles of flushing a bear. As usual he was far away, nobody knew where, when the bear burst upon the multitude of dogs and hunters and equerries and chamberlains in waiting, and sutlers and cooks and scullions, and Rough Riders and infantry and artillery, and had his customary swim to the other side of a pond and disappeared in the woods. While half the multitude watched the place where he vanished, the other half galloped off, with horns blowing, to scour the State of Louisiana in search of the great hunter. Why don't they stop hunting the bear altogether and hunt the President? He is the only one of the pair that can't be found when he is wanted.

By and by the President was found and laid upon the track and he and the dogs followed it several miles through the woods, then gave it up, because Rev. Dr. Long, the "nature fakir," came along and explained that it was a cow track. This is a sorrowful ending to a mighty enterprise. His Excellency leaves for Washington today, to interest himself further in his scheme of provoking a war with Japan with his battleships. . . .

(*October 21, 1907*). Alas, the President has got that cow after all! If it was a cow. Some say it was a bear—a real bear. These were eyewitnesses, but they were all White House domestics; they are all under wages to the great hunter, and when a witness is in that condition it makes his testimony doubtful. The fact that the President himself

---

* *From Mark Twain's memoirs. The entry for October 18 has been cut.*

thinks it was a bear does not diminish the doubt but enlarges it. He was once a reasonably modest man, but his judgment has been out of focus so long now that he imagines that everything he does, little or big, is colossal.

I am sure he honestly thinks it was a bear, but the circumstantial evidence that it was a cow is overwhelming. It acted just as a cow would act; in every detail from the beginning to the end it acted precisely as a cow would act when in trouble; it even left a cow track behind, which is what a cow would do when in distress, or indeed at any other time if it knew a President of the United States was after it —hoping to move his pity, you see; thinking maybe he would spare her life on account of her sex, her helpless situation, and her notorious harmlessness. In her flight she acted just as a cow would have done when in a frenzy of fright, with a President of the United States and a squadron of bellowing dogs chasing after her; when her strength was exhausted, and she could drag herself no further, she did as any other despairing cow would have done—she stopped in an open spot, fifty feet wide, and humbly faced the President of the United States with the tears running down her cheeks, and said to him with the mute eloquence of surrender: "Have pity, sir, and spare me. I am alone, you are many; I have no weapon but my helplessness, you are a walking arsenal; I am in awful peril, you are as safe as you would be in a Sunday school; have pity, sir—there is no heroism in killing an exhausted cow."

Here are the scareheads that introduce the wonderful dime-novel performance:

ROOSEVELT TELLS OF HUNTING TRIP

Ate All the Game, Except a Wildcat, and That
Had a Narrow Escape.

Swam Despite Alligators.

Charged Into the Canebrake After Bear and
Hugged the Guides After the Kill.

There it is—he hugged the guides after the kill. It is the President all over; he is still only fourteen years old after living half a century; he takes a boy's delight in showing off; he is always hugging something or somebody—when there is a crowd around to see the hugging and envy the hugged. A grown person would have milked the cow and let her go; but no, nothing would do this lad but he must kill her and be a hero. The account says: "The bear slain by the President was killed Thursday, and the killing was witnessed by one of the McKenzies and by Alex Ennolds."

These names will go down in history forever, in the company of an exploit which will take a good deal of the shine out of the twelve labors of Hercules. Testimony of the witnesses: "They say that the President's bearing was extremely sportsmanlike."

Very likely. Everybody knows what mere sportsmanlike bearing is, unqualified by an adverb, but none of us knows quite what it is when it is extremely sportsmanlike, because we have never encountered that inflamed form of the thing before. The probabilities are that the sportsmanlike bearing was not any more extremely sportsmanlike than was that of Hercules; it is quite likely that the adverb is merely emotional and has the hope of a raise of wages back of it. The chase of the frightened creature lasted three hours and reads like a hectic chapter in a dime novel—and this time it is a chapter of pathetically humble heroics.

In the outcome the credit is all with the cow, none of it is with the President. When the poor hunted thing could go no further it turned, in fine and picturesque defiance, and gallantly faced its enemies and its assassin. From a safe distance Hercules sent a bullet to the sources of its life; then, dying, it made fight—so there *was* a hero present after all. Another bullet closed the tragedy, and Hercules was so carried away with admiration of himself that he hugged his domestics and bought a compliment from one of them for twenty dollars. But this résumé of mine is pale; let us send it down to history with the colors all in it:

The bear slain by the President was killed Thursday, and the killing was witnessed by one of the McKenzies and by Alex Ennolds. They say that the President's bearing was extremely sportsmanlike. The animal had been chased by the dogs for three hours, the President following all the time. When at last they came within hearing distance the President dismounted, threw off his coat and dashed into the canebrake, going to within twenty paces of the beast. The dogs were coming up rapidly, with the President's favorite, Rowdy, in the lead.

The bear had stopped to bid defiance to the canines when the President sent a fatal bullet from his rifle through the animal's vitals. With the little life left in it the bear turned on the dogs. The President then lodged a second bullet between the bear's shoulders, breaking the creature's neck.

Other members of the party soon came up, and the President was so re-joiced over his success that he embraced each of his companions. Ennolds said: "Mr. President, you are no tenderfoot."

Mr. Roosevelt responded by giving Ennolds a $20 note.

There was little hunting yesterday, because the dogs encountered a drove of wild hogs, more ferocious than bears. One of the best dogs was killed by a boar.

There were daily swims in the lake by members of the party, including the President.

"The water was fine," he said, "and I did not have the fear of alligators that some seem to have."

Whatever Hercules does is to him remarkable; when other people are neglectful and fail to notice a detail, here and there, proper for admiration and comment, he supplies the omission himself. Mr. Ennolds lost a chance; if he had been judiciously on watch he could have done the alligator compliment himself, and got another twenty for it.

Finley Peter Dunne

MR. DOOLEY ON THE POWER OF MUSIC

"I always told ye," said Mr. Dooley, "that 'twas as a vocal entertainer that I preferred me frind Willum Jennings Bryan, an' glad I am we're goin' to hear his meelojous voice on th' concert platform again. Whin th' good Lord has give a man th' power iv speech in a volyum onknown in ancyent or modhren times, it's a shame f'r him to hide th' gift in a speechless job. To go an' make this gr-reat barytone Sicrety iv State was like turnin' a nightingale into a hod carrier. It was conthry to nature. All a Sicrety iv State has to do is to think. It's a kind iv a menial job, beneath a man that has a harp in his throat with a hurricane behind it, so that whin he aven breathes a faint melody purrs fr'm his lips an' whin he utthers so much as a how-d'ye-do, 'tis as though a mighty hand had slammed th' sthrings iv a joynt guitar. There ar-re plenty iv thinkers in th' world, poor fellows, with squeaky voices. They have to do something to arne a livin'. So they think, an' a hard livin' it is. But there's niver enough music to go around, an' why shud a gr-reat orkesthry iv sthring an' wind an' wood an' brass be asked to pondher? Is th' slide thrombone, is th' organ at th' audjiotoroom, is th' harp that wanst through Tara's halls, expicted to think? Does Adeliny Patti cook, or Melba sew, or Caruso dhrive a dhray? Ye bet they don't.

"Those who see Willum Jennings in those tur-rble days whin he was discussin' th' thrivyal dee-tails iv foolish threaties with th' bunco steerers that have been sintinced be their governments to come over here as ambassadures, were shocked at th' appearance iv th' popylar favrite. His pictures looked thoughtful. Gazin' fearlessly into th' camera, with a quill pen in his hand an' his brow knitted, he was th' livin' image iv a gr-reat mind in th' midst iv a large an' gloomy think an' caught off his guard be a shameless phottygrafter who had come upon him onobsarved. But those who knew him well saw a faraway look in his dhreamy eyes that seemed to say: 'Oh, that I were out iv this prison again an' tastin' th' glad, free life iv th' concert platform, with a sea iv upturned faces lookin' at me through their spectacles, an' th' little handkerchiefs iv th' ladies flutterin' th' Chat-talky salute at me, an' me voice flyin' out an' meltin' th' hearts iv th' aujience an' returnin' to nestle in th' pouches iv me own happy ears.'

"He was well-threated. Th' vouchers f'r his pay were cashed without a kick be Bill McAdoo. He was inthrojooced to sivral prom'nent ambassadures be th' lawyer iv th' departmint. An' as often as wanst a week th' good, kind, onselfish ol' gintleman in th' White House ast him over an' pointed out where he was to sign a docymint that had been thoughtfully prepared f'r him. Still he was not happy. Nobody iver ast him to oblige with a melody. Th' people around him bumped him in th' hall. Ivrybody he met seemed indiff'rent to music. Week afther week he set alone hummin' snatches iv old orations till wan day he cud stand it no longer. He up an' quit.

"Th' partin' between th' two ol' frinds was pathetic. 'Must ye be goin' so soon?' says the Prisidint. 'Why, ye've on'y been here three years, an' I've har'ly seen annything iv ye,' he says, openin' a letter. 'I must,' says th' Sicrety iv State. 'Well, Gawd bless ye, Willum. Tumulty, tell th' gintleman that's waitin' I won't keep him a minyit. Well, Gawd bless ye, Willum.' 'Gawd bless ye, Dock.' Th' two great men seized each other be both hands, but prompt interference be th' polis previnted anny actual vilence.

"So our hero bust th' bars iv his gilded cage, flew out into th' air, lit on th' bough iv a three, an' poored forth his bursting heart to th' stars. An' there he is now, like th' lark that Hogan writes about whin he has too much. Though singin' he's always sore an' while sore is iver singin'. Day afther day he serenades his former boss an' pupil with a melody that sounds like 'Come into th' garden, Dock, an' I'll dhrop a brick on ye.'

"What does he sing about? He's set th' Bible to music. He's arrangin' th' articles iv war f'r th' piccolo. But his principal songs ar-re songs iv love. I r-read a head line in th' pa-aper an' it says: 'Misther Bryan discusses internaytional complications.' 'Well,' says I, 'I guess I can affoord to miss this wan. But no,' thinks I, 'I will read it if on'y to see to what extint this heer bricklayin' job has damaged a gr-reat artist.' Well, sir, wud ye believe it, he's come out absolutely oninjured. There ain't a crack in his voice or a blot on his beautiful ideels. There was niver a word in this ballad about threaties, or agreements, th' Hague conference, or torpedoes, or Bilgium. It was just a sweet song. It was all about love. 'Ye wish to hear me on th' subjick iv war an' our foreign situations,' he says. 'Very well, Proffissor, th' key iv G, if ye plaze. Are ye ready? Let her go! Love, love, love. All th' wurruld is love. Soft an' sweet an' sticky it covers th' globe. It is heerd fr'm th' throats iv th' little sparrows in th' sthreets, in th' flight iv th' wind through th' pines, in th' swash iv th' waves that break on th' shores iv Lake Chattalky (where I appear week endin' July fifteen), in th' cry iv th' shrapnel whirlin' over th' threnches, in th' cooin' iv th' pnoomatic guns squirtin' their wealth iv green an' goolden gas. I love ivry-body. I love th' Kaiser, th' Mikado iv Japan, th' Sultan iv Turkey, Tom Ryan, Champ Clark, th' reptile press, an' th' infamious conspiracy iv Wall Sthreet criminals that has skinned me out iv th' prisidincy three times runnin'.'

"Well, sir, whin I heard this magnificint an' statesmanlike appeal to th' American people, who had just took off their coats an' were squarin' away, th' tears came to me eyes an' I felt like grabbin' Gin'ral von Hindenburg around th' waist an' waltzin' out into th' consarvatory with him. Th' effect iv this pow'rful utthrance was instantanyous. Lord Kitchener tilly-grafted to Charlie Schwab: 'I've been so affected be th' wurruds iv ye'er peerless leader Thomas J. O'Brien (if our papers gets th' name right) that I've made up me mind this hijous war must be ended at wanst. So plaze cancel th' order f'r two millyon sixteen-inch shells. Make it five millyon eighteen-inch an' be sure ye fill them full iv th' juice.' Th' German Impror announced that th' message iv Willum Jennings Bryan had melted his heart. He was sorry he hadn't been more neighborly iv late with his English cousins an' he'd ordhered a fleet iv Zeppelins to call on thim an' pay his respicts. An' all th' other nations iv Europe that hadn't got into th' riot, now saw that their attichood might be mistook an' voted to make th' war unanimous. Such is th' effect iv th' human voice on th' human heart.

"Mind ye, I don't want ye to go away with th' idee that I don't think Willum Jennings Bryan is a thoughtful man. Haven't I voted f'r him more times thin I've voted f'r annywan but Carther Haitch? I voted f'r him whin votin' f'r him was wan way iv proclaimin' to th' wurruld that I cudden't pay me room rint. I voted f'r him whin 'twas th' same as tellin' th' groceryman that he gave me credit at his peril. There is plenty iv room f'r all th' thoughts in th' wurruld under that splendid dome. If he doesn't care to exercise thim it's his own business.

He entertains thim an' sings thim to sleep. Wanst in a while he lets wan out f'r a romp. Th' little crather comes thrippin' into th' wurruld where rough people knock it down an' stamp on it an' thin he calls it back an' it creeps into its little cot in th' organ loft an' is niver seen or heerd again. He let loose a thought on silver that had an excitin' time while it was out, but long ago he hauled it in an' tucked it away. Thin I remimber he released a thought about th' govermint ownin' th' railroads. It was chased back to th' consarvatory iv music be th' Ku Klux an' hasn't aven showed its face at th' window since. Th' other day he let out a pretty little idee. I hope no harm will come to it. 'Tis nawthin' less thin startin' a polis foorce to prevint war. Yes, sir, an internaytional organization iv coppers to keep th' peace in th' rowdy neighborhood iv th' wurruld. How'll they be ar-rmed? What a foolish question. They'll be ar-rmed with love, iv coorse. Who'll pay thim? That's a financyal deetail that can be arranged later on. What'll happen if wan iv th' roughnecks reaches f'r a gun? Don't bother me with thrifles.

"Th' gin'ral idee as him an' me see it is this: All is quiet at th' headquarters iv th' internaytional peace polis at Chat-talky. Th' chief iv polis is settin' in a bower iv roses playin' a mandolin whin a snow-white pigeon flutthers through th' window. There is a pink ribbon around its neck. Th' chief onties it an' finds a message that reads: 'Pancho Villa is on th' loose agin. He has filled himself up with paint an' is out with a Winchester shootin' up th' bordher.' Th' chief calls th' resarves. Th' peace bulls in unyforms iv crame-colored pongee silk an' carryin' bunches iv f'rget-me-nots, turn out an' throt to th' scene iv th' disturbance at a double-quick. They find Pancho, but instead iv slammin' the desprit patriot over th' head with a walnut log an' dhraggin' him be wan ankle to th' wagon, which is th' custom iv some peace agents I know, they shower him with petals fr'm their bokays. Th' sergeant disarms him with a melting look, whispers something soothing in his ear, smooths his hair, fixes his tie, an' maybe kisses him on th' forehead. An' that's th' end iv th' throuble.

"It sounds all right to me. It ain't th' way I've seen polis business thransacted, but a little more tinderness in dealin' with th' rough an' petulant might not be out iv place. Th' worst that cud happen wud be more polismen wud be kilt.

"An' there ye ar-re. I don't know whether 'twill succeed or not. I hope so. But there's wan thing I am afraid iv, Hinnissy. Ye see, me boy, th' wurruld is a pretty old hunk of mud an' wickedness, an' I've been here a long time an' I've obsarved this sad thruth. Ye don't have to lend a man money. Ye don't have to amuse him; ye don't have to take care iv him if he's sick; ye don't have to do annything f'r him but wan thing."

"An' what's that?" asked Mr. Hennessy.

"If he wants to fight ye, ye've got to accommodate him," said Mr. Dooley.

James M. Cain

THE GOVERNOR

THE GOVERNOR'S *office, about two o'clock in the afternoon. Ranged about the table, talking in whispers, are a petitioner for a pardon, dressed in ordinary clothes, but having a pasty pallor, a singularly close haircut, and a habit of starting nervously whenever he is addressed; two guards, carrying guns on their hips in holsters; a witness, a prosecutor, and counsel for the petitioner.* THE GOVERNOR *enters, accompanied by a woman secretary, and they all stand up until he has sat down and donned his glasses. In a moment a lovely aroma begins to perfume the air. It is such an aroma as pervades a bonded distillery, and unmistakably it comes from the head of the table, where* THE GOVERNOR *has taken his place.*

THE GOVERNOR. Gen'lemen, y' may p'ceed.

COUNSEL FOR THE PETITIONER. Yes, Yexcellency.

THE GOVERNOR. 'N I'll ashk y' t' be's brief's y' can, c'se busy af'noon w' me. Gi' me th' facksh, that's all I w'nt know. 'M plain, blunt man, got no time f' detailsh. Gi' me facksh, 'n 'y won't have t' worry 'bout fair trea'm'nt f'm me.

COUNSEL. I think I speak for everybody here, Yexcellency, when I say we're all anxious to save Yexcellency's time, and—

THE GOVERNOR. 'Preciate 'at.

COUNSEL. And so I imagine the best way would be for me to sketch in for Yexcellency, briefly of course, the history of this case, I may say this very unusual case—

THE PROSECUTOR. So unusual, Yexcellency, that the Parole Board threw up its hands and refused to have anything to do with it whatsoever, and that is why Yexcellency's valuable time—

THE GOVERNOR. Nev' min' Parole Board. Is 't mer'tor's case, tha's all want know.

224

THE PROSECUTOR. I understand that, Yexcellency. I only wanted to say that the prawscution regards this case as abslutely prepawstrous.

THE GOVERNOR. A' right. Y' said it.

COUNSEL. Now, Yexcellency, this young man Greenfield Farms, this young man you see here—

THE GOVERNOR. One mom'nt. When's ex'cution take plashe?

COUNSEL. I'm glad Yexcellency reminded me of that, because praps I ought to have explained it sooner. Fact of the matter, Yexcellency, this is not a capital case—

THE GOVERNOR. Gi' me facksh, gi' me facksh! I got no time f' detailsh. When's ex'cution take plashe, I said.

COUNSEL. Yes, Yexcellency. I was only telling Yexcellency that there won't be any execution, because—

THE GOVERNOR. Wha's 'at?

COUNSEL. Because this young man Farms wasn't sentenced to death; he was sentenced to the penitentiary.

THE GOVERNOR. Oh!

COUNSEL. On a ten-year term, ten years in prison, for participation in the armed march we had some years ago, when the miners made all that trouble. Or, as it's never been clear in my mind that Farms had any idea what he was doing at that time—

THE PETITIONER. Never did. I hope my die I just went out there to see what was going on—

A GUARD. Hey! Sh!

COUNSEL. Praps I should have said alleged participation.

THE PROSECUTOR. And another thing praps you should have said was that of his ten years in prison he has already served three and he'll get two more off for good behavior and that leaves five and five is a little different from ten.

THE GOVERNOR. C'me on, c'me on!

THE PROSECUTOR. I'm only—

THE GOVERNOR. Y' only pett'fogg'n. Shu' up.

COUNSEL. Now, Yexcellency will recall that as a result of that uprising, six defendants, of which Farms was one, were convicted of treason to the State and the rest were allowed to plead guilty of unlawful assemblage—

THE GOVERNOR. Don't was' m' time talk'n 'bout 'at upris'n. I know all 'bout it. I's right there 'n saw fi' thous'n of 'm march by m' own front ya'd. Get on 'th facksh.

COUNSEL. Then if Yexcellency is familiar with that, we're ready now for this witness, and after he has told his story I can outline briefly to Yexcellency the peculiar bearing it has on this case, and—

THE GOVERNOR. Is 'at witness?

THE WITNESS. Yes, sir.

THE GOVERNOR. Sit over here where I c'n see y' better. 'N don't shtan' 'n awe 'f me. Washa name?

THE WITNESS. Ote Bailey, sir.

THE GOVERNOR. Shpeak right out, Bailey. 'M plain, blunt man 'n y' needn't shtan' 'n awe 'f me.

COUNSEL. Now, Bailey, if you'll tell the Governor in your own words what you told the Parole Board—

THE WITNESS. Well, it was like this. I was coming down the street on the milk-wagon early in the morning, right down Center Street in Coal City, and it was cold and there was a thin skim of ice on the street. And the mare was a-slipping and sliding pretty near every step, because she was old and the cheap dairy company hadn't shoed her right for cold weather. And—

THE GOVERNOR. Wha's 'at? Milk-wagon?

COUNSEL. Just a moment, Yexcellency. Now, Bailey, you forgot to tell the Governor when this was.

THE WITNESS. This here was twenty-three year ago come next January.

COUNSEL. All right, now go ahead and—

THE GOVERNOR. Hol' on, Bailey, hol' on. (*To* COUNSEL) Young man, I got worl' o' patience. 'M plain, blunt man, al's will'n t' help people 'n distress, p'ticularly when—p'ticularly—p'ticularly—h'm—p'ticularly. But wha's twen'-three yea's 'go got t' do 'th 'is ex'cution? Tell me that.

COUNSEL. Well, Yexcellency, I thought it would save time if we let Bailey tell his story first, and then I can outline the bearing it has on this case. But if Yexcellency prefers, I'll be glad to—

THE GOVERNOR. Young man, 're you trifl'n 'th me?

COUNSEL. Not at all, Yexcellency, I—

THE GOVERNOR. I warn y' ri' now I won't shtan' f' trifl'n. Facksh, facksh, tha's what I want!

COUNSEL. Yes, Yexcellency.

THE GOVERNOR. A' right, Bailey, g' on 'th it. I'll see 'f I c'n get facksh m'self.

THE WITNESS. So pretty soon, the mare went down. She went right down in the shafts, and I seen I would have to unhook her to get her up.

THE GOVERNOR. Y' right, y' qui' right. Y' can't get 'm up 'thout y' unhook 'm. No use try'n. G' on.

THE WITNESS. So then I got down offen the wagon and commence unhooking her. And I just got one breeching unwrapped, 'cause they didn't have snap breechings then, when I hearded something

THE GOVERNOR. Whasha hear?

THE WITNESS. I hearded a mewling.

THE GOVERNOR. Mewl'n?

THE WITNESS. That's right. First off, sound like a cat, but then it didn't sound like no cat. Sound funny.

THE GOVERNOR. What sound like?

THE WITNESS. Sound like a child.

THE GOVERNOR. Y' sure?

THE WITNESS. Yes, sir.

THE GOVERNOR. Sound' like child. Thank God, now 'm gett'n some facksh. G' on. What 'en?

THE WITNESS. So I left the mare, left her laying right where she was, and commence looking around to see where it was coming from.

THE GOVERNOR. Where *what* was com'n f'm?

THE WITNESS. This here mewling.

THE GOVERNOR. Oh, yes. Mewl'n. F'got f' mom'nt. G' on, Bailey. Shpeak right out. Don't shtan' 'n awe 'f me. What 'en?

THE WITNESS. So pretty soon I figured it must be coming from the sewer, what run right down under Center Street, and I went over to the manhole and listened and sure enough that was where it was coming from.

THE GOVERNOR. Shew'r?

THE WITNESS. Yes, sir.

THE GOVERNOR. Keep right on, Bailey. Y' g' me more facksh 'n fi' minutes 'n whole pack' lawyersh g' me 'n week.

COUNSEL. I assure Yexcellency—

THE GOVERNOR. Keep out o' this, young man. Y' tried m' patience 'nough already. 'M after facksh 'n 'm gett'n 'm. G' on, Bailey.

THE WITNESS. So I tried to get the cover offen the manhole, but I couldn't lift it. I tried hard as I could, but I couldn't budge it.

THE GOVERNOR. Busha tried?

THE WITNESS. Yes, sir.

THE GOVERNOR. Thasha shtuff! G' on.

THE WITNESS. So then I figured the best thing was to get some help and I run all the way up and down the street looking for a cop. And pretty soon I found a couple of them. And first off they didn't believe it, but then when they come to the manhole and heared this here mewling, they tried to lift the cover with me, and all three of us couldn't move it, and why we couldn't move it was it was froze to the rim.

THE GOVERNOR. F'oze?

THE WITNESS. Yes, sir.

THE GOVERNOR. F'oze. G'on.

THE WITNESS. So then we figured the best thing to do would be to put in a alarm. We figured if we got the fire company down there, maybe they would have something to move it with.

THE GOVERNOR. G'on. Keep right on till I tell y' to shtop, Bailey.

THE WITNESS. So we went to the box and put in a alarm. And pretty soon here come the hook-and-ladder galloping down the street. And five fellows what was members of the Coal City Volunteer Fire Department was on it, because they was still setting in the fire-house playing a poker game what they had started the night before after supper.

THE GOVERNOR. The Coal City Vol'teer Fi' D'pa'ment?

THE WITNESS. Yes, sir. So then—

THE GOVERNOR. Wait minute. Wait minute, Bailey. Y' touch m' heart now. The ol' Coal City Vol'teer Fi' D'pa'ment, wha' y' know 'bout 'at? I was mem' that m'self. I was mem' that—le's see, mus' been thirty yea's 'go.

COUNSEL. I hear it was a wonderful company in those days, Yexcellency.

THE GOVERNOR. Won'ful 'n 'en some. We won State ca'nival three times runn'n. C'n y' 'magine 'at?

COUNSEL. You don't mean it, Yexcellency!

THE GOVERNOR. Well, well! Y' touch m' heart now, Bailey, y' cert'ny have. 'S goin' be ha'd f' me t' send y' t' chair 'f y' was mem' old Coal City Vol'teer Fi' D'pa'ment. G' on. What en?

THE WITNESS. —?

COUNSEL. Don't sit there with your mouth hanging open like that, Bailey. The Governor was thinking of something else, of course.

THE WITNESS. Oh! So then them fellows pulled in their horses and goᵗ down offen the hook-and-ladder and commence hollering where was the fire. So we told them it wasn't no fire, but a child down the sewer, and then they got sore, because they claim we broke up their poker game and it was roodles.

THE GOVERNOR. What 'en?

THE WITNESS. So we ast them to help us get the cover off, and they wasn't going to do it. But just then this here mewling come again, just a little bit. It had kind of died off, but now it started up again, and them fellows, soon as they heard it, they got busy. 'Cause this here mewling, it give you the shivers right up and down your back.

THE GOVERNOR. What 'en?

THE WITNESS. So then we put the blade of one of them axes next to the cover, between it and the rim, and beat on it with another ax. And that broke it loose and we got it off.

THE GOVERNOR. What 'en?

THE WITNESS. So then them fireman put a belt on me, what they use to hook on the hose when they shove it up on them ladders, and let me down in the sewer. And I struck a match and sure enough there was the child, all wrapped up in a bunch of rags, laying out on the sewer water. And why it hadn't sunk was that the sewer water was froze and a good thing we didn't shove no ladder down there because if we had the ice would of got broke and the child would of fell in.

THE GOVERNOR. What 'en?

THE WITNESS. So I grabbed the child, and them fellows pulled me up, and then we all got on the hook-and-ladder and whipped up them horses for the Coal City Hospital, 'cause it looked like to me that child was half froze to death, but when we give it in to the hospital we found out that being in the sewer hadn't hurt it none and it was all right.

THE GOVERNOR. So y' saved child?

THE WITNESS. Yes, sir.

THE GOVERNOR. Tha's good! ... Well, Bailey, y' made good case f' y'self. I don't min' say'n, 'm 'pressed.

COUNSEL. But this witness isn't quite finished with his testimony, Yex-cellency.

THE GOVERNOR. Wha's 'at? He saved child, didn' he? 'A's all wan' know. Facksh, facksh, tha's what I go on!

COUNSEL. But Yexcellency—

THE GOVERNOR. A' right, a'right. G' on, Bailey, what 'en?

THE WITNESS. So then, when I got back to the milk-wagon and unwrapped the other breeching and unslipped the traces, the old mare couldn't get up nohow. She was stiff from cold, and I had to get them cops again and shoot her. So the dairy company was pretty sore. The old mare, she weren't worth more'n twenty-five dollars, but them company men let on I was hired to take care of the company property and not pull no babies outen the sewer.

THE GOVERNOR. What 'en?

THE WITNESS. So we had it pretty hot for a while, and then later on that day I went down to the hospital for to look at the baby and got them nurses there to name him Greenfield Farms, what was the name of the dairy company, so when they put it in the Coal City *News* about the baby being found, the company would get a free ad outen it, anyway twenty-five dollars' worth, what was the worth of the mare, and they did and we was square.

THE GOVERNOR. What 'en?

THE WITNESS. Well, I reckon that's all. 'Cepting I picked up the paper about six months ago, and I seen where a fellow name of Greenfield Farms had spoke a piece at a entertainment what they had in the penitentiary, and I got to wondering if it was the same one, and I asked one or two people about it, and they sent me to this gentleman here, and come to find out it was.

COUNSEL. So Yexcellency can see that this young man here, this young man Greenfield Farms, is one and the same with the child this witness pulled out of the sewer twenty-three years ago.

THE GOVERNOR. 'N 'a's all?

THE WITNESS. Yes, sir.

THE GOVERNOR. Well Bailey, don' min' say'n y' touch m' heart. The ol' Coal City Vol'teer Fi' D'pa'ment, wha' y' know 'bout 'at?

COUNSEL. Now, Yexcellency, you've heard the story of this witness, I may say the truly remarkable story of this witness, which I think Yexcellency will agree had the stamp of truth all over it—

THE GOVERNOR. The ol' Coal City Vol'teer Fi' D'pa'ment . . .!

COUNSEL. A story, praps I should add, that we are prepared to substantiate in every particular from the hospital records, which we will leave with Yexcellency, and I may call Yexcellency's attention to this certificate in particular, which states that the child was at least a month old when it was admitted, and—

THE GOVERNOR. Now wha's all 'is got t' do 'th pa'don f' Bailey?

COUNSEL. Farms, Yexcellency.

THE GOVERNOR. Farmsh, 'en?

COUNSEL. I'm coming to that, Yexcellency. Now the salient point about this evidence, Yexcellency, is that it establishes beyond any reasonable doubt in my mind that there is nowhere in existing records any proof of Farms's citizenship. He was, I remind Yexcellency, a month old when admitted to the Coal City Hospital. And what does that prove? It proves, Yexcellency, that he *might* have been born almost anywhere on the whole face of the earth. He *might* have been born anywhere from Greenland's icy mountains to India's coral strand. He is, so far as documentary proof to the contrary goes, Yexcellency that *most* unfortunate being, I may say that *pitiable* being, who can claim *no* land as his own, being *nothing* more or less, Yexcellency, as the fellow says, a man without a country!

THE GOVERNOR. Well, well, well, I ashk y' f' facksh, 'n now y' begin shpout'n poetry at me. Man 'thout country, hunh? Tha's in'st'n.

COUNSEL. Now I remind Yexcellency once more that the crime of which Farms stands convicted is treason. And treason is unique among crimes, Yexcellency, in that before any man can be *convicted* of it, his *citizenship* must be established, beyond all *shadow* of doubt, because TREASON, Yexcellency, as all the AUTHORITIES agree—

THE GOVERNOR. Shtop yell'n!

COUNSEL. Yes, Yexcellency—implies a ALLEGIANCE—a allegiance to the State against which it is alleged to have been committed. And under the law—

THE GOVERNOR. Law? Law? Y' talk'n t' me 'bout law?

COUNSEL. Yes, Yexcellency, and—

THE GOVERNOR. Washa com'n t' me 'bout law for? Why 'nsha go t' court 'bout law?

COUNSEL. We've been to court, Yexcellency. We applied to the Supreme Court two months ago for a new trial, on the basis of the evidence which Yexcellency has just listened to, and which, praps I should

have explained sooner, was not presented at the original trial because Farms had no idea at that time of the importance of his
citizenship and neglected to inform me of the peculiar circumstances attending his birth. And the court denied the application,
on the ground that while this evidence, if it *had* been presented
at the trial, *might* have resulted in the granting of a motion to
dismiss, it could not properly be regarded as *new* evidence, as it
is essentially evidence of *lack* of evidence on the part of the State,
rather than *direct* evidence of innocence.

THE PROSECUTOR. In other words, Yexcellency is being asked to certify
that if the dog hadn't stopped to scratch fleas he would have caught
the rabbit.

COUNSEL. Not in the least, Yexcellency—

THE GOVERNOR. Y' know what? Y' both pair pett-fogg'n lawyersh. Y'
'sgrace t' bar. Farmsh! C'me here. I'll do this m'self. Sit there,
where c'n see y'.

THE PETITIONER. Yes, sir. Thank you, sir, Governor.

THE GOVERNOR. A' right, Farmsh, shpeak right up now. Y' needn't
shtan' 'n awe 'f me. 'M plain, blunt man 'n got heart 's big 's all
outdoorsh. Washa got say f' y'self?

THE PETITIONER. Governor, all I got to say is I went out there when
them miners was gathering by the creek forks just to see what was
going on—

THE GOVERNOR. Thasha shtuff! Facksh! Motivesh! Tha's wha' want.
G' on, Farmsh. What 'en?

THE PETITIONER. And then when they marched down the road, I went
along with them just for fun, and then two months afterwards,
when they come and arrested me, I didn't have no more idea what
they meant than the man in the moon, and—

THE GOVERNOR. Now we com'n. G'on.

THE PETITIONER. And then they sent me up. And—and . . .

THE GOVERNOR. Farmsh, now I ask y' some'n. If I was t' set y' free, what
would y' do 'th y' lib'ty?

THE PETITIONER. If you was to set me free, Governor, the first thing I
would do would be to go to the judge and get my citizenship
fixed up—

THE PROSECUTOR. That's great! I'll say that's great! There you are,
Yexcellency, right out of their own mouths! First this man isn't

guilty because maybe the prawscution couldn't have proved his citizenship. And the first thing he's going to do if he gets a pardon is to get his citizenship fixed up! If that doesn't—

COUNSEL. Not at all, Yexcellency. In fact, I resent the imputation of—

THE GOVERNOR. Shtop! F' God's sake shtop! (*To the Secretary*) C'mute 'sen'ce 'mpris'nment f' life!

THE PETITIONER. What? Oh my God!

THE PROSECUTOR. Hunh?

COUNSEL. But, Yexcellency—

THE GOVERNOR. No more! 'M not g'n lis'n 'nother word! 'S comp'mise. 'S comp'mise, I know it's comp'mise. But 's bes' c'n do. Who y' think y' are, tak'n up my time way y' have? Don' min' f' m'self. 'M plain, blunt man 'n give y' shirt off m' back 'f y' need it. But my time b'longsh t' people. Y' und'shtan' 'at? My time b'longsh t' people, 'n wha' y' do with it? I ashk y' f' facksh 'n y' come in here 'th noth'n but tech'calitiesh! Tech'calitiesh I said! Pett'fogg'n! Trifl'n detailsh! Dog! Fleash! Rabbit! Poetry! 'M done with it! 'M not g'n lis'n 'nother word!

COUNSEL. But really, Yexcellency—

THE PETITIONER. Yeah, a fine lawyer you was. First you git me sent up for ten year and now you git me sent up for life—

THE WITNESS. Yeah, and a fine thing the Coal City Volunteer Fire Department done for the country when they pulled you out of the sewer—

THE GOVERNOR. Wha's 'at? Wha's at?

COUNSEL. I'm just trying to tell Yexcellency—

THE GOVERNOR. Jus' minute, jus' minute! ... The ol' Coal City Vol'teer Fi' D'pa'ment! Wha' y' know 'bout 'at? So Farmsh, y' were memb' ol' Coal City Vol'teer Fi' D'pa'ment?

THE PETITIONER. Well ... I reckon I was, in a way, Governor. I reckon I was, ha ha! I reckon I was kind of born to it, ha ha ha! I reckon I must be pretty near the only person in the world that was ever born to a fire department, ha ha, ha ha!

THE GOVERNOR. Farmsh, 'm g'n ask y' some'n. Look m' 'n eye, Farmsh. Farmsh, y' guilty 'r y' not guilty?

THE PETITIONER. Governor, I hope my die I ain't no more guilty than you are.

THE GOVERNOR. Farmsh, I believe y' tell'n' me truth. Farmsh, y' free man.

THE PETITIONER. Oh my Gawd, Governor, thank you sir, thank—!

THE GOVERNOR. The o' Coal City Vol'teer Fi' D'pa'ment. Wha' y' know 'bout 'at? Wha' y' know 'bout 'at? . . .

(*While the Secretary makes out a pardon and the* GOVERNOR *signs it, the group breaks up in a round of hand-shaking, the lawyers to go out and have a drink together, the petitioner to go back to the penitentiary for the last formalities. When they have all gone, the* GOVERNOR *still sits nodding to himself, and presently falls amiably asleep.*)

Frank Sullivan

A WEEKEND AT LADY ASTOR'S *

For years I had been saying to myself, "Now I must go down to Cliveden and spend a weekend with Lady Astor," but you know how those things are. Weekends are such a bore. I kept putting it off and putting it off and—well—putting it *off* until I read in the newspapers that Nancy and the Cliveden Set were running the Chamberlain Government, and I decided that was something definitely not to be missed. So the following Saturday I threw a few things into a bag, caught the 4:45 tram from Piccadilly Circus, and arrived at Cliveden just as the cuckoos were beginning their evening serenade.

Naturally, my heart beat a little faster as I neared Cliveden. Somewhere in that castle, I thought, is the little woman who rose from a humble beginning as a member of one of the First Families of Virginia to a place in the front rank of the British peerage. I should have counted myself a poor sort of American had I not felt some pride in this doughty little fellow-countrywoman who held the destiny of the British Empire in her small hands; who, by a discreet whisper behind a potted palm or a fan, could probably cause Australia to be abolished or a law passed forbidding Englishmen to dress for dinner.

I thought of the many times my heart had swelled with pride as I sat in the visitors' gallery of the House of Commons and heard the House roar an affectionate greeting to Nancy Astor, rising to a man as she entered and hollering "Shut up!," "Sit down!," or "Go on back to Ameddica, where you came from," even before she had opened her trap.

Cliveden was lovely. The yews were in full bloom and cast blue-black shadows on the silver perukes of the liveried footmen. Scores of beautiful women strolled on the terrace, influencing the decisions of monocled British statesmen by their charm and wit.

"Is the Lady of the House in?" I asked the butler who took my bag.

* *It was in the spring of 1938.*

"Lady Astor is upstairs at the moment, rewriting the *Court Circular* for Monday's *Times*," said the butler. "Are you expected, sir?"

"Well, not exactly. I'm just a fellow-countryman of Lady Astor. I can't really say I know her."

"Ah, you'll like her," smiled the butler. "She's a holy terror. Always on the go. And a mind like a steel trap. Click!" The butler imitated a mind like a steel trap.

"She'll be delighted to see you, sir. Now you'd better run upstairs and police yourself up. Dinner's at nine. White tie."

I was agog at the prospect of being present at one of those famous dinners of the British ruling class I had always read about so much, at which from time immemorial clever girls like Lily Langtry, Margot Asquith, Boadicea, and Nancy Astor have influenced the course of empire by their brilliance and charm. And the Cliveden Set particularly! The Cliveden Set rules the British ruling class at the moment. When you rule the ruling class of England, boy, I'm telling you, you're *ruling!*

It was indeed a brilliant assemblage that gathered in the dining room at nine. There were no cocktails, as Lady Astor is a teetotaller, but fortunately the second assistant gamekeeper ran a speakeasy in one of the haunted rooms of the castle and those of us who had been tipped off, or whose noses had been rendered sufficiently keen by thirst, fortified ourselves there prior to dinner.

We were a company of a hundred and forty-six, twenty-nine being absent. The Honourable Ursula Godolphin-Potts was forced to remain in her room with a headache, the result of overinfluencing a British statesman on the terrace that afternoon. The German Ambassador was also upstairs nursing an injury. While giving Lord Halifax the Nazi salute that afternoon, he had struck his hand a rather nasty bang on a low-hanging branch of an oak, lacerating it severely. Twenty-seven of the guests had left for home just before dinner on receipt of telegrams announcing the serious illnesses of their grandmothers.

The women wore two ostrich plumes, as Lady Astor is only a viscountess. She is ten thousand four hundred and twentieth in direct line of succession to the British Crown, or four thousand two hundred and thirty-eight behind Lady Peel (Beatrice Lillie) and eight hundred and sixty-five and sixty-six, respectively, ahead of Dame May Whitty and Sir Cedric Hardwicke—Noel Coward, of course, being still a commoner.

All the men wore knee breeches and silk stockings except me. As a virile, patriotic Yankee I refused to kowtow to British flummery in this respect, but as a concession to international good will I did roll my trousers up to my knees. The men wore their decorations. Mine consisted of my Junior Order of Birdmen jewel, my gold badge as former honorary police commissioner of Long Beach, Long Island, my insignia of the St. Aloysius Sodality of St. Peter's Church, Saratoga Springs, and my blue ribbon as healthiest American boy in the national 4-H Contest of 1932. We were a brilliant throng and Lady Astor never looked lovelier as she sat on the woolsack at the head of the table, with Neville Chamberlain on her right and Lord Lothian on her left. Of course there was "one vacant chair," as the saying goes. Good old Joe Ribbentrop was missing from his usual place, having been transferred to his home office.

After a deal of good-natured roughhouse over who should precede whom, during which some of the older duchesses got banged about quite a bit, we all reached our correct seats and Lady Astor motioned for silence.

"Welcome to Cliveden, ladies and gentlemen," she said.

"Oh, shut your mouth," said one of the guests.

Nancy Astor was on her feet in an instant.

"If the honourable gentleman from Upper Tooting," she snapped, "thinks that telling me to shut my mouth is any solution of the vital problem which confronts this assemblage at this momentous and solemn hour—I refer to the problem of getting the soup served before it gets cold—then all I can say to the honourable . . ."

"Oh, go sit on a tack!" shouted the honourable gentleman from Upper Tooting.

Would Nancy Astor stand for that? Would the famed mistress of Parliamentary repartee parry this clever thrust or would she allow it to floor her? The dinner table held its breath. Then she let him have it.

"Go sit on one yourself and see how you like it," she snapped.

A murmur of admiration swept the dining room.

"Gad, I wish I'd said that," said Geoffrey Dawson, editor of the *Times,* an Astor paper.

"Isn't she in ripping form tonight, though?" said J. L. Garvin, editor of the *Observer,* another Astor paper.

"I thought she gave him Hail Columbia—if you'll pardon the Americanism," said Lord Lothian.

The Archbishop of Canterbury also seemed pleased.

"Who is the lad who asked our hostess to sit on the tack?" I said to my dinner partner, Lady Feather Barksdale-Wotton.

"Oh, he's a spy from His Majesty's Opposition," said Lady Feather. "He's here every weekend. Rather nice chap."

The dinner proceeded smoothly. Lady Astor, skilled hostess that she is, had assembled a truly stimulating group, representing every shade of political thought, from conservatives who felt that Hitler should be given only Czechoslovakia, Memel, the Ukraine, the Polish Corridor, and Denmark, to extreme radicals who felt he should also be given France and England.

The conversation sparkled. I heard a chap up the table a piece from me say, "Now don't misunderstand me. Some of my best friends are Jews."

"Gad, I wish I'd said that," I exclaimed to Lady Gwydd Stensitty-Wowdle, who sat on my left. "Who's he?"

"That's Lord Londonderry," said Lady Gwydd. "You know—he wrote that amusing book in praise of Hitler."

"Oh, is *he* the one?"

I leaned over and called to him.

"Lord Londonderry."

"Yes, my good man."

"How's tricks? Everything according to *Heil?*"

But he muffed it. The British are so slow at getting a joke.

I caught another fragment of conversation.

"You know," I heard a peer named Lord Featherstonehaugh (pronounced Fuff) say, "sometimes I think Nancy Astor has got herself slightly confused with the British Empire."

Instantly every guest produced a notebook and started writing.

"What are they doing?" I asked the Honourable Hebe Quart, who sat next Lord Fuff.

"Jotting down notes for their memoirs," said Lady Hebe, who was hard at it herself. "We'll all claim we said that instead of Fuff."

I must say that it seemed to me, from what discreet peeking I could do, that not all of them were good reporters. Some of the older peers who were hard of hearing had not quite caught Fuff's mot and other peers who were hard of artery had caught it all right but could not remember it long enough to record it, so that many inaccurate versions got jotted down, such as "Sometimes I think Nancy Astor has got the British Empire slightly confused" or "Sometimes I think Nancy Astor has got herself slightly confused."

This was all very well, but I wanted to see some action.

"When is Lady Astor going to start influencing the British Government?" I asked Lady Feather. "It's four minutes past ten now and I haven't seen anything."

"Silly," admonished Lady Feather. "You have, too. You are seeing the entire Cliveden Set in action. Scarcely a remark has been passed at this table tonight—except by you, of course—that has not been fraught with significance."

"You mean?"

"I mean that we are not so gauche as to come right out and influence the British Empire directly. It's not so much what we say, it's the way we say it. With us, the most commonplace remark, uttered with just the right flicker of an eye, takes on a significance that can cause repercussions in the farthest-flung outposts of the Empire."

Well, that put a different light on things. Here I had been kicking because I thought the dinner conversation was lagging and apparently hell had been popping right in front of me all the time, and I never knew it.

After that I had a grand time. It was fun to hear somebody like Lord Halifax say something about foxhunting and then try to figure out whether that remark meant that Britain would or would not go to the aid of France if France went to the aid of Czechoslovakia when Hitler started his *Putsch* there.

Then Lady Astor asked Neville Chamberlain if he would have another helping of asparagus. It sounded innocent enough, but everybody at the table knew that it really meant: Would Neville get a place in the Cabinet for General Franco? It was done so neatly that even the old seasoned diplomats at the table could not repress enthusiastic gurgles of admiration.

"By gad," said Lord Lothian, "I wouldn't be a bit surprised if sooner or later Nancy Astor succeeded in changing the map of Europe."

"Or vice-versa," heckled the spy from His Majesty's Opposition.

That crack at our gallant little hostess seemed scarcely cricket to me and I rather burned.

"See here," I drawled, "I'm jest a plain, red-blooded American and

I s'pose I ain't up to the ways of you Bridish, but by gum, I'm durned ef I'm a-goin' to set here and listen to y'all cast aspersions on a little woman from Virginia, the Mother of Presidents, that ain't done y'all a mite o' harm. Now get this, you ornery passel o' furriners. George III got England away from the United States but by jiminy, Nancy Astor has got it back. Yip-e-e-e-e!"

"Yip-e-e-e-e! Hear! Hear!" shouted the gentleman from His Majesty's Opposition.

Lady Astor gave me a smile of gratitude.

"Why don't you play that on your bazooka?" sneered Lady Feather.

"You want to make something of it?" I ra'red.

"Sure do, pardner," said Lady Feather, rising.

"Keep your shirt on, honey," I advised. "I never hit a woman with a tiara on yet, and now ain't no time to start."

"I'll take it off," said Lady Feather, taking it off. "Now you take your glasses off."

For a minute it looked as though Lady Feather and I might mix it, but Neville Chamberlain stepped between us and fixed things up. He conceded his watch and chain to me and gave Lady Feather a half-interest in Spain.

After that the ladies retired and when we fellows were left alone over the port and nuts, Bernard Shaw talked most interestingly for an hour or two on why it was all right for Hitler to burke Austria. Then we fellows joined the ladies in the drawing room—all except Bernard, who stayed on alone in the dining room because he still had an hour or so talking to do.

The dinner conversations were resumed in the drawing room, but you couldn't fool me now. I knew that when Nancy Astor asked Neville if he took sugar in his demitasse it could mean anything from the transfer of a British diplomat in Hong Kong to a new alliance with Mussolini.

It set me up no end to be in the know like this, for a while anyhow. Then the idea struck me that if I hung around Cliveden much longer I might start saying things fraught with significance. My common sense told me it was unlikely, but you can't be too careful. What would the folks back home think if they heard I was helping the Cliveden Set influence the course of empire? I got pretty uneasy.

I wanted to leave but didn't have any good excuse, because I hadn't thought to arrange to have one of those telegrams sent about my grandmother being sick.

Then something happened that spurred me to action. I saw Lord Londonderry approaching with a copy of his book on Hitler. He was heading straight for me.

I felt like some wild thing about to be trapped.

Londonderry came on ... on ... on.

I had to act quickly. There wasn't a second to lose. Already he was saying, "Now don't misunderstand me ..."

A footman happened to pass with a tray heaped with telegrams.

With a wit born of desperation I seized one and ripped it open. It was for Neville Chamberlain. It read, "Return home immediately. Grandmother ill. Urgent."

Darting between Lord Londonderry's legs, I escaped to Lady Astor, pretended the telegram was for me, made my apologies, expressed my thanks for her hospitality, caught the 1:20 goods train back to Waterloo, and was on my old bench on the Embankment in an hour. And never did home seem so sweet.

PARODIES AND BURLESQUES

Good parody should be funny in itself, whether or not one has read the book or author parodied. Nevertheless, we have tried to choose only parodies or burlesques in which the literary —or unliterary—source will still be reasonably familiar to present-day readers.

Parody is an easy form of humorous writing, in its lesser manifestations; but a really good parody is rare, and is only performed by a person with high intelligence and a good ear. Some of the items which follow are not true parody but are burlesque, a literary form in which the author takes a healthy swipe at a manner of writing or a habit of mind.

We have made little effort to collect parody verse, because there have been anthologies of such material. What few verse parodies appear in this book will be found in the verse section.

Eugene Field

THE TRIBUNE PRIMER *

THE EDITOR'S HOME

Here is a Castle. It is the Home of an Editor. It has stained Glass windows and Mahogany stairways. In front of the Castle is a Park. Is it not Sweet? The lady in the Park is the editor's wife. She wears a Costly robe of Velvet trimmed with Gold Lace, and there are Pearls and Rubies in her Hair. The editor sits on the front Stoop smoking an Havana Cigar. His little Children are playing with diamond Marbles on the Tesselated Floor. The editor can afford to Live in Style. He gets Seventy-Five Dollars a month Wages.

THE BAD MAN

Here is a Man who has just Stopped his Paper. What a Miserable looking Creature he is. He looks as if he had been stealing Sheep. How will he Know what is going on, now that he has Stopped his Paper? He will Borrow his Neighbor's Paper. One of these Days he will Break his leg, or be a Candidate for Office, and then the Paper will Say Nothing about it. That will be treating him just Right, will it not, little Children?

THE OYSTER

Here we have an Oyster. It is going to a Church Fair. When it Gets to the Fair, it will Swim around in a big Kettle of Warm Water. A Lady will Stir it with a Spoon, and sell the Warm Water for Forty Cents a pint. Then the Oyster will move on to the next Fair. In this Way, the Oyster will visit all the Church Fairs in Town, and Bring a great many Dollars into the Church Treasury. The Oyster goes a great Way in a Good Cause.

* *Excerpts from a parody primer, which appeared first in the Denver Tribune (1882) and were later published in book form. This was Field's first book.*

THE UNFORTUNATE MOUSIE

Poor little Mouse! He got into the Flour Barrel and Made Himself Dead. The Cook baked him in a Loaf of Bread, and here he lies on the Table cut in two by the Sharp bread Knife. But we will not Eat poor Mouse. We will eat the Bread, but we will Take the Mousie and Put him in the Cistern.

THE COAL HOD

Oh, how nice and Black the Coal-Hod is! Run, children, Run quick and put your Little Fat hands in it. Mercy me, your Hands are as Black as the Coal-Hod now! Hark! Mamma is Coming. She will spank you when she Finds your Hands so Dirty. Better go and Rub the Black Dirt off on the Wall Paper before she Comes.

MAMMA'S SCISSORS

These are Mamma's Scissors. They do not Seem to be in good Health. Well, they are a little Aged. They have considerable Work to Do. Mamma uses them to Chop Kindling, cut Stove Pipe, pull Tacks, drive Nails, cut the children's Hair, punch new Holes in the Calendar, slice Bar soap, pound beef Steak, open tomatoe Cans, Shear the New Foundland dog and cut out her New silk Dress. Why doesn't Papa get Mamma a new Pair of Scissors? You should not Ask such a Naughty question. Papa cannot Afford to Play Billiards and Indulge his Extravagant Family in the Luxuries of Life.

THE BOTTLE

This is a Bottle. What is in the Bottle? Very bad Whiskey. It has been Sent to the Local Editor. He did not Buy it. If he had Bought it the Whiskey would have been Poorer than it is. Little children, you Must never Drink Bad Whiskey.

THE HASH

Is this a Chignon? No, it is a Plate of Hash. But where are the Brush and Comb. We cannot serve the Hash unless we have a Brush and Comb. The Comb is in the Butter, and the Baby has put the Brush in the Coffee-Pot. Don't cry, Children, we will Give you some nice Molasses with Pretty, green Flies in it.

THE MUD

The Mud is in the Street. The Lady has on a pair of Red Stockings. She is Trying to Cross the Street. Let us all give Three cheers for the Mud.

THE WASP

See the Wasp. He has pretty yellow Stripes around his Body, and a Darning Needle in his Tail. If you Will Pat the Wasp upon the Tail, we will Give You a Nice Picture Book.

THE BUSINESS MANAGER

Here we Have a Business Manager. He is Blowing about the Circulation of the Paper. He is Saying the Paper has Entered upon an Era of Unprecedented Prosperity. In a Minute he will Go up Stairs and Chide the Editor for leaving his Gas Burning while he Went out for a Drink of Water, and he will dock a Reporter Four Dollars because a Subscriber has Licked him and he cannot Work. Little Children, if we Believed Business Managers went to Heaven, we would Give up our Pew in Church.

THE CONCENTRATED LYE

What a Pretty Can it is. What do you Suppose is in the Can? Open it and see. Goodness me, it is Concentrated Lye! How Nice! Are you not Glad? Let us eat it. Taste it and See how Warm it is. If you will Eat it you will not Want anything More to Eat For a Long Time.

Robert C. Benchley

CHRISTMAS AFTERNOON

(*Done in the Manner, if Not the Spirit, of Dickens*)

What an afternoon! Mr. Gummidge said that, in his estimation, there never had *been* such an afternoon since the world began, a sentiment which was heartily endorsed by Mrs. Gummidge and all the little Gummidges, not to mention the relatives who had come over from Jersey for the day.

In the first place, there was the *ennui*. And such *ennui* as it was! A heavy, overpowering *ennui,* such as results from a participation in eight courses of steaming, gravied food, topping off with salted nuts which the little old spinster Gummidge from Oak Hill said she never knew when to stop eating—and true enough she didn't—a dragging, devitalizing *ennui,* which left its victims strewn about the living-room in various attitudes of prostration suggestive of those of the petrified occupants in a newly unearthed Pompeiian dwelling; an *ennui* which carried with it a retinue of yawns, snarls and thinly veiled insults, and which ended in ruptures in the clan spirit serious enough to last throughout the glad new year.

Then there were the toys! Three and a quarter dozen toys to be divided among seven children. Surely enough, you or I might say, to satisfy the little tots. But that would be because we didn't know the tots. In came Baby Lester Gummidge, Lillian's boy, dragging an electric grain-elevator which happened to be the only toy in the entire collection which appealed to little Norman, five-year-old son of Luther, who lived in Rahway. In came curly-headed Effie in frantic and throaty disputation with Arthur, Jr., over the possession of an articulated zebra. In came Everett, bearing a mechanical negro which would no longer dance, owing to a previous forcible feeding by the baby of a marshmallow into its only available aperture. In came Fonlansbee, teeth buried in the hand of little Ormond, which bore a popular but battered remnant of what had once been the proud false-bosom of a hussar's uniform. In they all came, one after another, some crying, some snapping, some pulling, some pushing—all appealing to their respective parents for aid in their intra-mural warfare.

And the cigar smoke! Mrs. Gummidge said that she didn't mind the smoke from a good cigarette, but would they mind if she opened the windows for just a minute in order to clear the room of the heavy aroma of used cigars? Mr. Gummidge stoutly maintained that they were good cigars. His brother, George Gummidge, said that he, likewise, would say that they were. At which colloquial sally both the Gummidge brothers laughed testily, thereby breaking the laughter record for the afternoon.

Aunt Libbie, who lived with George, remarked from the dark corner of the room that it seemed just like Sunday to her. An amendment was offered to this statement by the cousin, who was in the insurance business, stating that it was worse than Sunday. Murmurings indicative of as hearty agreement with this sentiment as their lethargy would allow came from the other members of the family circle, causing Mr. Gummidge to suggest a walk in the air to settle their dinner.

And then arose such a chorus of protestations as has seldom been heard. It was too cloudy to walk. It was too raw. It looked like snow. It looked like rain. Luther Gummidge said that he must be starting along home soon, anyway, bringing forth the acid query from Mrs. Gummidge as to whether or not he was bored. Lillian said that she felt a cold coming on, and added that something they had had for dinner must have been undercooked. And so it went, back and forth, forth and back, up and down, and in and out, until Mr. Gummidge's suggestion of a walk in the air was reduced to a tattered impossibility and the entire company glowed with ill-feeling.

In the meantime, we must not forget the children. No one else could. Aunt Libbie said that she didn't think there was anything like children to make a Christmas; to which Uncle Ray, the one with the Masonic fob, said, "No, thank God!" Although Christmas is supposed to be the season of good cheer, you (or I, for that matter) couldn't have told, from listening to the little ones, but what it was the children's Armageddon season, when Nature had decreed that only the fittest should survive, in order that the race might be carried on by the strongest, the most predatory and those possessing the best protective coloring. Although there were constant admonitions to Fonlansbee to "Let Ormond have that now; it's his," and to Arthur, Jr., not to be selfish, but to "give the kiddie-car to Effie; she's smaller than you are," the net result was always that Fonlansbee kept the whistle and Arthur, Jr., rode in permanent, albeit disputed, possession of the kiddie-car. Oh, that we mortals should set ourselves up against the inscrutable workings of Nature!

Hallo! A great deal of commotion! That was Uncle George stumbling over the electric train, which had early in the afternoon ceased to function and which had been left directly across the threshold. A great deal of crying! That was Arthur, Jr., bewailing the destruction of his already useless train, about which he had forgotten until the present moment. A great deal of recrimination! That was Arthur, Sr., and George fixing it up. And finally a great crashing! That was Baby Lester pulling over the tree on top of himself, necessitating the bringing to bear of all of Uncle Ray's knowledge of forestry to extricate him from the wreckage.

And finally Mrs. Gummidge passed the Christmas candy around. Mr. Gummidge afterward admitted that this was a tactical error on the part of his spouse. I no more believe that Mrs. Gummidge thought they wanted that Christmas candy than I believe that she thought they wanted the cold turkey which she later suggested. My opinion is that she wanted to drive them home. At any rate, that is what she succeeded in doing. Such cries as there were of "Ugh! Don't let me see another thing to eat!" and "Take it away!" Then came hurried scramblings in the coat-closet for overshoes. There were the rasping sounds made by cross parents when putting wraps on children. There were insincere exhortations to "come and see us soon" and to "get together for lunch some time." And, finally, there were slammings of doors and the silence of utter exhaustion, while Mrs. Gummidge went about picking up stray sheets of wrapping paper.

And, as Tiny Tim might say in speaking of Christmas afternoon as an institution, "God help us, every one."

HAPPY CHILDHOOD TALES

We have had so many stories lately dealing with the sordid facts of life, about kitchen sinks and lynchings and young girls thrown out into the streets by mean old farmers who live in horsehair trunks, to say nothing of incidental subjects, such as gin and cold oatmeal and unfortunate people who have only one glove apiece, that a reaction is taking place in the mind of the reading public and a demand is going up for some of the fanciful happy tales of our youth.

"Enough of these stories of crime and unhappiness!" the people are crying. "Tell us again some of the ancient myths of an older day, the gay little legends on which we were brought up before the world grew grim and sordid."

And so, my little readers, I am going to try to recall to you some of the charming fairy tales, or, at any rate, to make up some like them, and I hope that after this little trip back into the Never-Never Land of our youth, those little cheeks of yours will be blooming again and that you will shut your traps. For, after all, there must be *some* good in the world, else why were erasers put on the ends of lead pencils?

ENDREMIA AND LIASON

(From the Greek Mythology)

Endremia was the daughter of Polygaminous, the God of Ensilage, and Reba, the Goddess of Licorice. She was the child of a most unhappy union, it later turned out, for when she was a tiny child her father struck her mother with an anvil and turned himself into a lily pad to avoid the vengeance of Jove. But Jove was too sly for Polygaminous and struck him with a bolt of lightning the size of the Merchants Bank Building which threw him completely off his balance so that he toppled over into a chasm and was dashed to death.

In the meantime, Little Endremia found herself alone in the world with nobody but Endrocine, the Goddess of Lettuce, and her son Bilax, the God of Gum Arabic, to look after her. But, as Polygaminous (her father; have you forgotten so soon, you dope?) had turned Endremia into a mushroom before he turned himself into a lily pad, neither of her guardians knew who she was, so their protection did her no good.

But Jove had not so soon forgotten the daughter of his favorite (Reba), and appeared to her one night in the shape of a mushroom gatherer. He asked her how she would like to get off that tree (she was one of those mushrooms which grow on trees) and get into his basket. Endremia, not knowing that it was Jove who was asking her, said not much. Whereupon Jove unloosed his mighty wrath and struck down the whole tree with a bolt of lightning which he had brought with him in case Endremia wouldn't listen to reason.

This is why it is never safe to eat the mushrooms which grow on trees, or to refuse to get into Jove's basket.

————

MILGRIG AND THE TREE WILFS

(Something like Hans Christian Andersen)

Once upon a time there was a little girl named Milgrig, believe it or not. She lived in the middle of a deep dark forest with her three ugly sisters and their husbands, who were charcoal burners. Every night the three ugly sisters used to take little Milgrig and pull out a strand of her golden hair, so that by the time she was thirteen years old she looked something awful. And after the three sisters had pulled out her hair, their three husbands (I forgot to tell you that the three husbands were even uglier than the three sisters and much nastier) would stick pins into little Milgrig until she looked like a war map.

One night, when little Milgrig was so full of pins that she couldn't see straight, a fairy prince came riding up to the door of the charcoal burners' hut and asked if he had lost his way.

"How should I know?" replied the oldest sister, who was uglier than all the rest. "What was your way?"

"My way was to the king's castle," replied the prince, "and I must get there before midnight, for my father is torturing my mother with red-hot irons."

"Your father sounds like a good egg," replied the oldest husband, who was uglier than all the rest. "We must ask him down some night."

The prince, however, did not think that this was very funny and asked if little Milgrig might not be allowed to show him the way to the castle.

The ugly husbands and sisters, thinking that Milgrig would not know the way and would get the prince lost in the forest, agreed heartily to this suggestion, and the pins were pulled out of Milgrig to make it possible for her to walk.

"Good luck and a happy landing!" they all called out after the two young people as they set forth on their perilous journey.

But the prince was no fool, and knew his way through the forest as well as you or I do (better, I'll wager), and he took little Milgrig to the palace just as fast as his palfrey would carry him.

She wasn't particularly crazy about going, but a prince is a prince, and she knew enough to keep her mouth shut.

When they reached the palace and the prince found that his father had already killed his mother, he turned to little Milgrig and said: "Now you are the queen."

At this, little Milgrig was very pleased and immediately dispatched messengers to the charcoal burners' hut, where the three ugly sisters and three still uglier brothers-in-law were burned alive in a slow fire. Little Milgrig and the prince, happy in this termination to their little affair, lived happily ever after.

And so now, my readers, you must toddle off to bed, for we have had an evening with the happy, happy story-tellers of an earlier day and have had a vacation, for one night at least, from the drab, unpleasant sordidness of present-day writing.

THE BLUE SLEEVE GARTER

(Sex and Political Economy as blended by Mr. Galsworthy)

I

PROSCENIUM

In the rich gloom of the Board Room, surrounded by charts showing the Unemployment Situation and the old Corn Laws, Lister Hoag, seventeenth baronet, reviewed in his well dressed mind the situation which confronted his heart. There was, of course, Melisse. Tomorrow! Seventh anniversary of their wedding day! Seven years of what? He broke a lead pencil. Seven years of Melisse. Poor Melisse! And yet—in a way—poor Trevor! Sentiment was tip. Unquestionably sentiment was tip. Still, Lister felt a strange ache when he thought of it all. What good in thinking? What good in tying one's tie? No—by Gad!

Old Breamley was speaking. To sell these ships now would mean a clear profit of thirty thousand pounds. Thirty thousand Melisses! Fifteen minutes—half an hour—what difference did it make? He would soon be with Melisse. He would take her in his arms and tell her that everything was tup. And that would be no lie. Everything *was* tup. Silly old guff! Would Rodney Granish mind? And if he did, would Maxton Sixby blorrow? Jolly—if young Sixby blorrowed! What a mess! And now about these ships. The Germans wanted them. And England needed them. Reconstruction. Well, perhaps. But Melisse's neck was whiter than Reconstruction. And her eyes deeper. What a jolly old mup it all was! Everything! Or—perhaps—nothing! Lister shut his eyes and marked "Three hundred pounds" on his pad. No use to have a heart. Or a liver either, for that matter.

II

CODA

It was warm in bed. Heavy brocade shut out the smart breeze which blew in the long windows from the Free Trade Club across Cavendish Square. Lister Hoag ran his bare arm along the soft mountain ranges of the coverlet. Nice.

Melisse was asleep beside him. At any rate, Melisse was beside him. The curve from her chin to her shoulder reminded Lister of the curve on the chart showing the Unemployment Situation. It was a long, gentle curve and yet to him it cried out that the Government was wrong, all wrong. What right had one man to have a job when another hadn't? What right had they to tax wheat when Bleeker and Tony Napin and Thornlip and all those other poor devils were eating ha'penny rolls? Political principles—he mused—were tip. Absolutely tip. And yet if one had no political principles one was likely to have no principles at all. If, as a member of the community, as an Englishman—and he certainly was an Englishman—he accepted the challenge, what was left but revolution? No, by George! England was there, and since England was there, there she must stay.

Melisse stirred softly at his side. She wanted to speak. She said: "What time is it, dear?"

Automatically, Lister looked at his wrist watch. It was the watch that had been given him by the governors of the Liberal Union. A rum crowd, the Union. No spines. No convictions. Like the Board. Seven per cent preference—nine per cent ordinary. What whip! And, since it *was* whip, why bother? But somehow the War had changed all that. The War had changed everything. Nobody was sure now. A chap didn't know in the morning what the Prime would be by night, and the Prime didn't know at night what a chap would be in the morning. England was twill. But she was England, nevertheless.

"It's a quarter to eight, dear."

But Melisse was asleep again, with a faint curl of disgust on her fifteenth century lips.

III

TEATIME AT BLEEMS

Nine hours later Trevor Ramsty stood facing the tea table across which Melisse Hoag was stretching a white arm. England was still England.

"Draw up. Cream, Trevor? Go away, Whang! You've had your tea. Don't tell me, Trevor, that you are going out for the Socialists? That's sugar you're taking, you know, ducky, not opium."

"Not so much going out for Socialists as going in for talking, empress."

Melisse looked at him. Very nicely put! Trevor *would* be nice to have with one on a canal boat.

" 'Ware shoals, Melisse!" said Ramsty.

"Budney, my dear, sheer budney!"

Trevor bit his lip thoughtfully.

"You stweem a bit—for you."

"That will do, Cherry! And please someone take Whang downstairs. He has become intolerable since the Free Trade Club gave him that new leash."

Whang placed his paws on Lister's spats and said:

"Put me out if you will, but remember, I can vote at the next General Election."

Lister was incalculable—did such odd things! To be sure, he was nice. Very nice. But incalculable.

"I'm sorry, Melisse, if I have made a gaff."

"Not a bit; jolly good tib. The thing about England today is that we are too English. Whang here knows better. He eats anything."

Trevor smiled queerly.

"Are you quite, quite sure?" asked Melisse.

"Rather! And, by the way, is it full fig tonight?"

"Just as you like. Meemie will be there."

"Full fig, then."

"I thought so."

"I thought you would think so."

"It *was* good of you to get me Rennie Cleenist, though. I do hope he'll behave and not be full of Debt Refunding. I'm putting him between Lillie Omster and Neyla Brann. Seven. You know them all.

Oh, and you mustn't mind if Old Wadney talks Merchant Marine. He loves it so. Did you read Willie's story about him? Oh, too frightfully amusing—clearly meant for H. K. V. Whang, put that hat down! Whose hat is it?"

"Mine," said Lister, as he entered the room, "but never mind. We sold those ships."

IV

NAPIN REFULGENT

The Board Room was no brighter than it had ever been. In fact, as Lister sat and poked holes in the map of Solvent Europe, the room seemed full of four per cents. Napin had been caught. Why quibble about that? Caught red handed, stealing the rudders off the ships which the company had sold to the Germans. But as Lister looked at the pale face of the young man, he saw on beyond Tony Napin and into the system which engulfed him. Capital. Labour. Tripe! It was man against man. Bug against bug. Oxford against Cambridge. And Napin had stolen rudders.

"See here, Napin! Come home with me and have a drink. You'll jolly well need one."

Tony said nothing but put on someone's hat and coat which were hanging on the wall and waited for Lister to lead the way.

"Napin, old bean," said Lister, "you're about done in. How can a man funk it when the world is as it is today? Look at the Liberals. Fed up on Liability Insurance. Look at the Labour Party. Eating Enfranchisement pap. Look at the Hangnail Prevention League. Nothing but—"

"I beg pardon, Mr. Hoag," said Napin. "You were saying something about a drink. I haven't all night, you know, sir. I'm due at jail at seven sharp."

V

MELISSE

Tony Napin had been in the room with Melisse just fifteen minutes when he asked her to run away with him. The afternoon sun was slanting in through the stained glass windows on which old Manton Hoag, sixteenth baronet, had had lettered in old English the complete text of the Reform Act. To speak perfectly frankly, Melisse was quite impressed with the twelfth century directness of Napin's proposition. Her brown eye rested on the silver tea service, her blue eye following suit.

Of course, there was Lister. Poor, dear Lister. He would be cut up no end. But really, Lister was frightfully civic. For seven years Lister had made love to her by explaining the principles of Public Ownership of Metropolitan Utilities. Their baby had been conceived in Single Tax and had run away from home at the age of four rather than hear more about Redistribution of Unearned Capital. It was harsh to think, but dear Lister was suffering from hardening of the Trade Arteries.

Then there was Trevor. Trevor was a sweet lover. Melisse could not deny that. But he *did* talk of Socialism when he should have been talking ways and means. Funny! That Trevor had—and here Melisse upset the sugar bowl—oh, well! Trevor *had,* that was all. Thinking was tosh. Tosh—and rather dreadful.

And now Napin. He had walked into the room, said how-do-you-do, and had asked her to run away with him. Nothing about Germany's debt. Nothing about the Merchant Marine. Nothing about taxation. Simply, "Pack your things!" It was stupendous. And terribly exciting. Why not? Or perhaps rather—why?

The telephone was over there. Melisse took her hand out of the hot tea and went to it.

"Can I speak to Mr. Hoag, please? ... In the Board Room ... Mrs. Hoag speaking ... Lister, dear ... How is the Bill of Rights coming on? ... Bully! ... And the Swedish Disenfranchisement? ... Sweet! ... And do you still feel the same way about taxing indeterminate inheritances? ... Ducky! ... Well, then, Lister dear, please do something for me.... Take them all, the Bill of Rights, the Swedish Disenfranchisement, and the Inheritance Tax and roll them up in one big bundle.... Have you done that? ... Righto ... What are you to do with them now? ... You know very well, my dear.... I'm off for Innsbruck with young Napin.... Yes. N-a-p-i-n. Care of General Delivery, Innsbruck ... Cheerio ..."

Whang climbed up on the tea table and pushed his nose into the sugar bowl. At last he was alone.

MORE SONGS FOR MELLER

As Señorita Raquel Meller sings entirely in Spanish, it is again explained, the management prints little synopses of the songs on the program, telling what each is all about and why she is behaving the way she is. They make delightful reading during those periods when Señorita Meller is changing mantillas, and, in case she should run out of songs before she runs out of mantillas, we offer a few new synopses for her repertoire.

(1) ¿ VOY BIEN?
(Am I Going in the Right Direction?)

When the acorns begin dropping in Spain there is an old legend that for every acorn which drops there is a baby born in Valencia. This is so silly that no one pays any attention to it now, not even the game-keeper's daughter, who would pay attention to anything. She goes from house to house, ringing doorbells and then running away. She hopes that some day she will ring the right doorbell and will trip and fall, so that Prince Charming will catch her. So far, no one has even come to the door. Poor Pepita! if that is her name.

(2) CAMISETAS DE FLANELA
(Flannel Vests)

Princess Rosamonda goes nightly to the Puerta del Sol to see if the early morning edition of the papers is out yet. If it isn't she hangs around humming to herself. If it is, she hangs around humming just the same. One night she encounters a young matador who is returning from dancing school. The finches are singing and there is Love in the air. Princess Rosamonda ends up in the Police Station.

(3) LA GUIA
(The Time-Table)

It is the day of the bull fight in Madrid. Everyone is cock-eyed. The bull has slipped out by the back entrance to the arena and has gone home, disgusted. Nobody notices that the bull has gone except Nina, a peasant girl who has come to town that day to sell her father. She looks with horror at the place in the Royal Box where the bull ought to be sitting and sees there instead her algebra teacher whom she had told that she was staying at home on account of a sick headache. You can imagine her feelings!

(4) NO PUEDO COMER ESO
(I Can Not Eat That!)

A merry song of the Alhambra—of the Alhambra in the moonlight —of a girl who danced over the wall and sprained her ankle. Lititia is the ward of grouchy old Pampino, President of the First National Banco. She has never been allowed further away than the edge of the piazza because she teases people so. Her lover has come to see her and finds that she is fast asleep. He considers that for once he has the breaks, and tiptoes away without waking her up. Along about eleven o'clock she awakes, and is sore as all get-out.

(5) LA LAVANDERA
(The Laundryman)

A coquette, pretending to be very angry, bites off the hand of her lover up to the wrist. Ah, naughty Cirinda! Such antics! However does she think she can do her lessons if she gives up all her time to love-making? But Cirinda does not care. Heedless, heedless Cirinda!

(6) ABRA VD. ESA VENTANA
(Open That Window)

The lament of a mother whose oldest son is too young to vote. She walks the streets singing: "My son can not vote! My son is not old enough!" There seems to be nothing that can be done about it.

Ring Lardner

ODD'S BODKINS

AUTHOR'S NOTE:
Each morn when the neighbors are through with our papers
And stealthily slide them beneath our front door,
I grab the *American*, knowing that there I can
Find O. O. McIntyre's column of lore.
You ask what it's like? I've no copy right here,
But p'rhaps I can give you some sort of idear.

Diary of a Modern New Yorker: Up and out five hours before dawn, and by scooter to the Hermitage Hotel, where the big Seminole Indian chef, Gwladys, cooked me a flagon of my favorite breakfast dish, beet root and wrestlers' knees. Hallooed to Lily Langtry and we fell to arguing over the origin of the word "breakfast," she contending that it was a combination of "break" and "fast," derived from a horse's instructions to a starter in a six-furlong race, and I maintaining that it was five furlongs. We decided to leave it to Percy Hammond, the philatelist, but his nurse told us he was out shoplifting.

Home for a moment to slit my mail and found invitations from Mussolini, Joan Blondell, Joan Crawford, Joan of Arc, President Buchanan, Joe Walcott, and Louisa M. Alcott. Then answered a pleasant long-distance call from Gwladys, the little French chef in the Café des Trois Outfielders in Sydney, her voice as plain as if she were in Melbourne. She had heard I had a cold, she said, and was worried. It was gratifying to hear her whimpers of relief when I assured her the crisis was past.

Breaking bread in the evening at the office of J. P. Morgan & Company and sat between Bernie Shaw, H. J. Wells, Charlie Dickens, Lizzie Barrett, Will Thackeray, Lottie Brontë, Paul Whiteman, and Bill Klem. Chatted for a moment after dinner with *Who's Who* and, finding a heavy rainstorm outside, dismissed my driver, Gwladys, and pirouetted to the lower West Side, where I sat on the New York

Central tracks till dawn, watching the operations of a switch engine. I have always been a sucker for a New York Central switch engine in a heavy rainstorm.

Thingumabobs: I once motored around Vienna for two weeks thinking it was Vienna. When I chided the native jehu, Gwladys, he chirped: "Why, Massa, Ah done thought you knowed it was Vienna all de time."...If they did not wear identical hats, Jack Dempsey and Connie Bennett could easily pass for sisters....Ellsworth Vines, the golf pro, is a dead ringer for Frank Crowninshield....One-word description of Franklin Delano Roosevelt—President....Otto Kahn always wears a union suit at first nights....There is something about the name Babe Ruth that suggests rare old Dresden filigree work.... Mayor O'Brien is the image of Joan Crawford....One of my favorite people—Senator Long....Tallulah Bankhead and Jimmy Durante have profiles exactly alike....Few ladies with as little money can act as grampous as Bernie Baruch....Two of my favorite people—Senator Long.

Thoughts While Strolling: Damon Runyon's feet. Kate Smith, a small-town girl who became nation-wide in a big city. Rosamond Pinchot and Theodore Dreiser could pass for twins. How did I get to thinking about "The Song of the Shirt"? Oh, yes; it started at tea when Fannie Hurst brought up Arthur Brisbane's quaint method of writing. His syndicated column averages close to 130,000 words a day, yet he writes it all in longhand on his shirt bosom, then forgets it and sends his shirt to the laundry. Damon Runyon's feet.

Mention of the name Rex Cole invariably reminds me of the Mother Goose rhyme, "Old King Cole," etc., and I never can figure out why. The surnames of two successful *Saturday Evening Post* writers, Samuel Blythe and Charles Francis Coe, begin with the second and third letters of the alphabet. Damon Runyon's feet. Personal nomination for the most thrilling of the summer's detective yarns—"Dracula." If you saw only the left side of Theodore Dreiser's face, you would swear it was the right side of Ruth Etting's. Rube Goldberg, cover-designer for *Spalding's Base Ball Guide,* never wears a hat to bed. Damon Runyon's feet. One-word description of the Vice-President— Garner.

Insomniacs: While writing a novel "Red" (Socker) Lewis never eats anything but alphabet soup.... Irvin S. Cobb cannot eat before, dur-

ing, or after 5 A.M. . . . Theodore Dreiser always dresses according to
the time of day he happens to be writing about. Thus, if an incident
in one of his novels takes place in the morning, he puts on a morning
coat; if at noon, a noon coat, etc. . . . There is a striking resemblance
between Damon Runyon's feet and Ethel Merman. . . . Theodore
Dreiser often arises at 2 A.M. and walks for two hours steadily. I once
knew a fellow in Gallipolis who often arose at 6 P.M., and at 2 A.M.
walked for two hours unsteadily. No dog as cunning as the Cubanola
Glide.

Frank Sullivan

A GARLAND OF IBIDS

I have just finished reading a book[1] which struck me as being one of the finest books I have read since I read "The Flowering of New England," by the same author.[2] But there is a fly in the ointment. I have been rendered cockeyed by the footnotes. There seem to be too many of them, even for a book largely about Boston.[3] I do not know why the author had to have so many footnotes. Maybe he had a reason for each one, but I suspect the footnote habit has crept up on him, for I got out his book on Emerson,[4] published in 1932, and he used practically no footnotes in it.

You read along in "New England: Indian Summer," interested to the hilt in what Van Wyck Brooks is telling you about Longfellow,[5]

[1] "New England: Indian Summer."
[2] Van Wyck Brooks, author of "New England: Indian Summer," "The Flowering of New England," "The Life of Emerson," "The Ordeal of Mark Twain," and other books.
[3] Sometimes referred to as The Hub. Capital and chief city of Massachusetts. Scene of the Boston Tea Party and the arrest of Henry L. Mencken. Bostonians are traditionally noted for their civic pride, or, as an envious New York critic once termed it, their parochial outlook. It is related that on an occasion when Saltonstall Boylston learned that his friend L. Cabot Lowell was leaving for a trip around the world, he inquired of Lowell, "Which route shall you take, L.C.?" "Oh, I shall go by way of Dedham, of course," replied Mr. Lowell. On another occasion, the old Back Bay aristocrat Ralph Waldo Mulcahy said to Oliver Wendell Rooney, "By the way, Rooney, did your ancestors come over on the Mayflower?" "Oh, no," replied Mr. Rooney. "They arrived on the next boat. They sent the servants over on the Mayflower."
[4] Ralph Waldo Emerson, Sage of Concord and famous transcendentalist philosopher, not to be confused with Ralph McAllister Ingersoll, editor of *PM*.
[5] Henry Wadsworth Longfellow, Good Gray Poet. Longfellow was no footnote addict. He preferred foot*prints*. Cf. his "Psalm of Life":

> And, departing, leave behind us
> Footprints on the sands of time.

Thoreau,[6] Phillips,[7] James,[8] Alcott,[9] Lowell,[10] Adams,[11] and other great figures of the Periclean Age of The Hub,[12] when suddenly there is a footnote.

[6] Henry David Thoreau, philosopher who lived at Walden Pond for two years on carrots, twigs, nuts, minnows, creek water, and, as Margaret Fuller suspected (booming it out at Brook Farm in that full, rich voice of hers, to the dismay of William Ellery Channing, Henry Wadsworth Longfellow, Edward Everett Hale, John Lothrop Motley, Charles Eliot Norton, and William Lloyd Garrison), sirloin steaks and creamery butter smuggled to him by Emerson. Suffering as he did from a vitamin deficiency, the result of too much moss in his diet, Thoreau became somewhat of a misanthrope and would often creep up behind members of the Saturday Club and shout "Boo!," or, as some authorities maintain, "Pooh!" The matter is not clarified very much, one must admit, by a letter Mrs. Harriet Beecher Stowe wrote to her son, Harriet Beecher Stowe, Jr. (not to be confused with Herbert Bayard Swope), on June 7, 1854, in which she states: "Not much to write home about, as the saying goes. Dave Thoreau here for supper last nite [sic.] He got into an argument with John Greenleaf Whittier, the Good Gray Poet, as to whether snow is really ermine too dear for an earl, and Greenleaf called him a Communist. Dave then crept up behind Greenleaf and shouted either 'Boo!' [sic] or 'Pooh!' [sic], I couldn't make out wich [sic]. All well here except F. Marion Crawford, Sarah Orne Jewett, Charles Dudley Warner, Thomas Wentworth Higginson, and William Dean Howells, who complain of feeling sic [sic]. Your aff. mother, H. B. Stowe, Sr."

[7] Wendell Phillips. He was about the only Bostonian of his time who wore no middle name and he was therefore considered half naked. Even Mark Twain, when he went to visit Howells in Boston, registered as Samuel Langhorne Clemens.

[8] Probably not Jesse James. Probably is either William James, deviser of Pragmatic Sanctions, or his brother Henry, the novelist. It was about this time that Henry James was going through his transition period, and could not make up his mind whether he was in England living in America or in America living in England.

[9] Amos Bronson Alcott, educator and bad provider. The Mr. Micawber of his day. Not to be confused with Novelist Bus Bronson of Yale or Mrs. Chauncey Olcott.

[10] James Russell Lowell, poet, essayist, and kinfolk of late rotund, cigar-smoking Back Bay Poetess Amy Lowell, no rhymester she.

[11] Henry Adams, author of "The Education of Henry Adams," by Henry Adams. Not to be confused with Henry Adams, Samuel Adams, John Adams, John Quincy Adams, Abigail Adams, Charles Edward Adams (not to be confused with Charles Francis Adams, Charles Henry Adams, or Henry Adams), Maude Adams, Franklin Pierce Adams, Samuel Hopkins Adams, Bristow Adams, George Matthew Adams, James Truslow Adams, Adams Express, Adams & Flanagan, Horace Flanagan, or Louis Adamic.

[12] Sometimes referred to as Boston. One is reminded of the famous quatrain:

> Here's to the City of Boston,
> The home of Filene and the Card.,
> Where the Rileys speak only to Cabots
> And the Cabots speak only to God!

The text is in fine, clear type. The footnotes are in small type. So it is quite a chore to keep focussing up and down the page, especially if you have old eyes or a touch of astigmatism.[13] By and by you say to yourself, "I be damn if I look down at any more footnotes!," but you do, because the book is so interesting you don't want to miss even the footnotes.[14]

When you get to the footnote at the bottom of the page, like as not all you find is *ibid*. *Ibid* is a great favorite of footnote-mad authors.[15] It was a great favorite with Gibbon.[16] How come writers of fiction do not need footnotes? Take Edna Ferber.[17] She doesn't use footnotes. Suppose Edna Herford [18] took to writing her novels in this manner:

[13] In this connection, it is interesting to note that Louisa May Alcott had a touch of astigmatism, if we are to accept the word of Charles Eliot Norton. Edward Everett Hale states in his Letters, Vol. XV, Ch. 8, pp. 297 *et seq.,* that William Cullen Bryant told Oliver Wendell Holmes that on one occasion when the fun was running high at Thomas Wentworth Higginson's home and all barriers were down, Thomas Bailey Aldrich had put the question bluntly to Charles Eliot Norton, saying, "Now listen, has Louisa May Alcott got astigmatism or hasn't she?" Charles Eliot Norton answered, perhaps unwisely, "Yes." Cf. the famous dictum of General William Tecumseh Sherman, sometimes erroneously ascribed to General Ulysses Simpson Grant: "Never bring up a lady's name in the mess."

[14] Ah there, Van Wyck!

[15] So is cf.

[16] Edward Gibbon, English historian, not to be confused with Cedric Gibbons, Hollywood art director. Edward Gibbon was a great hand for footnotes, especially if they gave him a chance to show off his Latin. He would come sniffing up to a nice, spicy morsel of scandal about the Romans and then, just as the reader expected him to dish the dirt, he'd go into his Latin routine, somewhat as follows: "In those days vice reached depths not plumbed since the reign of Caligula and it was an open secret that the notorious Empress Theodoro *in tres partes divisa erat* and that she was also addicted to the *argumentum ad hominem!*" Gibbon, prissy little fat man that he was, did that just to tease readers who had flunked Caesar.

[17] Edna Cabot Ferber, contemporary New England novelist. It is related of Edna Ferber that she once met Oliver Herford in Gramercy Park and recoiled at the sight of an extremely loud necktie he was wearing. "Heavens above, Oliver Herford!" exclaimed Miss Ferber, never one not to speak her mind. "That is a terrible cravat. Why do you wear it?" "Because it is my wife's whim that I wear it," explained Oliver Herford. "Well, land sakes alive, before I'd wear a tie like that just on account of a wife's whim!" jeered Miss Ferber. "You don't know my wife," said Oliver Herford. "She's got a whim of iron." Miss Ferber later made this incident the basis for the dramatic battle between the husband and wife in her novel "The Cravat."

[18] No, no, no, not Edna Herford! Edna *Ferber!* Edna Herford is the fellow who had the wife with the iron whim.

"Cicely Ticklepaw* sat at her dressing table in a brown study. She had 'a very strange feeling she'd ne'er felt before, a kind of a grind of depression.'† Could it be love?‡ If so, why had she sent him§ away? She sighed, and a soft cry of 'Aye me!'‖ escaped her. Seizing a nail file desperately, she commenced hacking away at her fingernails, when a voice behind her said, 'O! that I were a glove upon that hand, that I might touch that cheek!'$ Cicely reddened, turned. It was Cleon Bel Murphy! Softly, she told him, 'What man art thou, that, thus bescreen'd in night, so stumblest on my counsel?'"&

What would Van Wyck Brooks say if Edna Ferber wrote like that?[19] Yes. Exactly. Now, where were we?[20] No, I was not. I know what I was saying. You keep out of this. You're a footnote.[21] Yeah? Well, just for that, no more footnotes. Out you go![22] I am, that's who.[23] See what I mean, Van Wyck? Give a footnote an inch and it'll take a foot.[24] I give up. They got me. And they'll get you too in the end, Van Wyck. You may think you're strong enough to keep 'em under control; you may think you can take a footnote or leave it. All I say is, remember Dr. Jekyll! Lay off 'em, Van. I'm telling you for your own good.

—UNEASY BROOKS FAN [25]

* Blonde, lovely, and twenty-one.
† See "I'm Falling in Love with Someone"—Victor Herbert.
‡ Sure.
§ Cleon Bel Murphy, the man she loves.
‖ "Romeo and Juliet," Act. II, Scene 2.
$ *Ibid*.
& *Ibid*.
[19] And what would Edna Ferber say if Edna Ferber wrote like that?
[20] You were saying Louisa May Alcott had astigmatism.
[21] Yeah? And how far would you have got in this article without footnotes?
[22] Who's gonna put me out?
[23] Yeah? You and who else?
[24] Yoo-hoo! Footnote!
[25] Frank Saltonstall Sullivan.

Donald Ogden Stewart

THE WHISKY REBELLION

(In the Bedtime Story Manner of Thornton W. Burgess)

"Just the *day* for a Whisky Rebellion," said Aunt Polly and off she ran, lipperty-lipperty-lip, to get a few shooting rifles.

"Oh goody goody," cried little Emily. "Now we can all shoot at those horrid Revenue Officers," for the collectors of internal revenue were far from popular with these kindly Pennsylvania folk and Aunt Polly Pinkwood had often promised the children that if they were good some day they would be allowed to take a shot at a Revenue Officer.

Soon she returned, bearing in her arms a number of bright shiny new guns. The children crowded around in glee and soon all were supplied with weapons except little Frank who of course was too young to use a gun and was given a two-gallon jug of nice, old whisky to carry. Jed hitched up old Taylor, the faithful farm horse, and as quick as you could say Jack Robinson the little ones had piled into the old carryall. Round Mr. Sun was just peeping over the Purple Hills when the merry little party started on its way, singing and laughing at the prospect of the day's sport.

"I bet I kill five Revenue Officers," said little Edgar.

"Ha Ha Ha—you boaster, you," laughed Aunt Polly. "You will be lucky if you kill two, for I fear they will be hard to find today."

"Oh do you think so, Aunt Polly?" said little Elinor and she began to cry, for Elinor dearly loved to shoot.

"Hush dear," said Miss Pinkwood with a kindly pat, for she loved her little charges and it hurt her to see them unhappy. "I was only joking. And now children I will tell you a story."

"Oh goody goody," cried they all. "Tell us a true story."

"All right," said Aunt Polly. "I shall tell you a true story," and she began.

"Once there was a brave handsome man—"

"Mr. Welsbach," cried the children with one voice, for it was well known in the neighborhood that Aunt Polly had long been sweet on

Julius Welsbach, the popular superintendent of the Sabbath School and the best whisky maker for miles around.

"Hush children," said Aunt Polly blushing in vexation. "Of course not. And if you interrupt me I shall not tell my story at all." But she was not really angry.

"And one day this brave handsome man was out making whisky and he had just sampled some when he looked up and what do you suppose he saw?"

"Snakes," cried little Elmer whose father had often had delirium tremens, greatly to the delight of his children.

"No, Elmer," said Miss Pinkwood, "not snakes."

"Pink lizards," cried little Esther, Elmer's sister.

"No," said Aunt Polly, with a hearty laugh, "he saw a—stranger. And what do you suppose the stranger had?"

"A snoot full," chorused the Schultz twins. "He was pie-eyed."

"No," replied Miss Pinkwood laughing merrily. "It was before noon. Guess again children. What did the stranger have?"

"Blind staggers," suggested little Faith whose mother had recently been adjudged insane.

"Come children," replied Aunt Polly. "You are not very wide awake this morning. The stranger had a gun. And when the brave handsome man offered the stranger a drink what do you suppose the stranger said?"

"I know," cried little Prudence eagerly. "He said, 'Why yes I don't care if I do.' That's what they all say."

"No, Prudence," replied Miss Pinkwood. "The stranger refused a drink."

"Oh come now, Aunt Polly," chorused the boys and girls. "You said you were going to tell us a true story." And their little faces fell.

"Children," said Miss Polly, "the stranger refused the drink because he was a Revenue Officer. And he pointed his gun at the brave handsome man and said he would have to go to jail because he had not paid the tax on his whisky. And the brave handsome man would have had to have gone to jail, too; but fortunately his brother came up just at the right time and—"

"Shot the Revenuer dead," cried the children in glee.

"Yes children," said Miss Polly. "He shot the Revenue Officer dead."

"Oh goody goody," cried all. "Now tell us another story. Tell us about the time your father killed a Revenue Officer with an ax."

"Oh you don't want to hear that again, do you children?" said Aunt Polly.

"Oh yes—yes—please," they cried, and Aunt Polly was just going to begin when Jed the driver stopped his horses and said:

"This hilltop is as good a place to shoot from as I know of, Miss Pinkwood. You can see both roads, and nobody can see you."

"Thank you, Jed," said Aunt Polly giving him a kindly smile, and without more ado the children clambered out of the carryall and filled their guns with powder and bullets.

"I get first shot," proudly announced Robert, the oldest boy, and somewhat of a bully.

"Robert!" said Aunt Polly severely, and she looked almost ready to cry, for Aunt Polly had tried hard to teach the boys to be true knights of chivalry and it hurt her to have Robert wish to shoot a Revenue Officer before the girls had had a chance. Robert had not meant to hurt Aunt Polly's feelings but had only been thoughtless, and soon all was sunshine again as little Ellen the youngest made ready to fire the first shot.

The children waited patiently and soon they were rewarded by the sight of a Revenue Officer riding on horseback in the distant valley, as pretty a target as one could wish.

"Now do be careful, dear," whispered Miss Pinkwood, "for if you miss, he may take alarm and be off." But little Ellen did not miss. "Bang" went her gun and the little Merry Breezes echoed back and forth, "She got him. She got him," and old Mother West Wind smiled down at the happy sport. Sure enough, when old Mr. Smoke had cleared away there was a nice dead Revenue Officer lying in the road. "Well done, Ellen," said Miss Pinkwood, patting her little charge affectionately which caused the happy girl to coo with childish delight.

Mary had next shot and soon all were popping away in great glee. All the merry wood folk gathered near to watch the children at their sport. There was Johnny Chuck and Reddy Fox and Jimmy Skunk and Bobby Coon and oh everybody.

Soon round Mr. Sun was high in the Blue Sky and the children began to tire somewhat of their sport. "I'm as hungry as a bear," said little Dick. "I'm as hungry as two bears," said Emily. "Ha Ha

Ha," laughed Miss Pinkwood, "I know what will fix that," and soon she had spread out a delicious repast.

"Now children," said Miss Pinkwood when all had washed their faces and hands, "while you were busy washing I prepared a surprise for you," and from a large jug, before their delighted gaze, she poured out—what do you think? "Bronxes," cried little Harriet. "Oh goody goody." And sure enough Aunt Polly had prepared a jug of delicious Bronx cocktails which all pronounced excellent.

And after that there were sandwiches and olives and pie and good three year old whisky, too.

"That's awfully smooth rye, Aunt Polly," said little Prudence smacking her two red lips. "I think I'll have another shot."

"No dear," said Miss Pinkwood, pleased by the compliment, but firm withal. "Not now. Perhaps on the way home, if there is any left," for Aunt Polly knew that too much alcohol in the middle of the day is bad for growing children, and she had seen many a promising child spoiled by over-indulgent parents.

After lunch those children who could stand helped Aunt Polly to clear away the dishes and then all went sound asleep, as is the custom in Pennsylvania.

When they awoke round Mr. Sun was just sinking behind the Purple Hills and so, after taking a few more scattered shots at Revenue Officers, they piled once more into the carryall and drove back to town. And as they passed Mrs. Oliphant's house (Aunt Polly's sister) Aunt Flo Oliphant came out on the porch and waved her handkerchief at the merry party.

"Let's give her a cheer," said Fred.

"Agreed," cried they all, and so twelve little throats united in three lusty "huzzahs" which made Auntie Flo very happy you may be sure.

And as they drove up before the Pinkwoods' modest home twelve tired but happy children with one accord voted the Whisky Rebellion capital fun and Aunt Polly a brick.

E. B. White

DUSK IN FIERCE PAJAMAS

Ravaged by pink eye, I lay for a week scarce caring whether I lived or died. Only Wamba, my toothless old black nurse, bothered to bring me food and quinine. Then one day my strength began to return, and with it came Wamba to my bedside with a copy of *Harper's Bazaar* and a copy of *Vogue*. "Ah brought you couple magazines," she said proudly, her red gums clashing.

In the days that followed (happy days of renewed vigor and re-awakened interest), I studied the magazines and lived, in their pages, the gracious lives of the characters in the ever-moving drama of society and fashion. In them I found surcease from the world's ugliness, from disarray, from all unattractive things. Through them I escaped into a world in which there was no awkwardness of gesture, no unsuitability of line, no people of no importance. It was an enriching experience. I realize now that my own life is by contrast an unlovely thing, with its disease, its banalities, its uncertainties, its toil, its single-breasted suits, and its wine from lesser years. I am aware of a life all around me of graciousness and beauty, in which every moment is a tiny pearl of good taste, and in which every acquaintance has the common decency to possess a good background.

Lying here in these fierce pajamas, I dream of the *Harper's Bazaar* world, the *Vogue* life; dream of being a part of it. In fancy I am in Mrs. Cecil Baker's pine-panelled drawing-room. It is dusk. (It is almost always dusk in the fashion magazines.) I have on a Gantner & Mattern knit jersey bathing suit with a flat-striped bow and an all-white buck shoe with a floppy tongue. No, that's wrong. I am in chiffon, for it is the magic hour after bridge. Suddenly a Chippendale mahogany hors-d'œuvre table is brought in. In its original old blue-and-white Spode compartments there sparkle olives, celery, hard-boiled eggs, radishes—evidently put there by somebody in the employ of Mrs. Baker. Or perhaps my fancy wanders away from the

drawing-room: I am in Mrs. Baker's dining-room, mingling unostenta-
tiously with the other guests, my elbows resting lightly on the dark
polished oak of the Jacobean table, my fingers twiddling with the
early Georgian silver. Or perhaps I am not at Mrs. Baker's oak table
in chiffon at all—perhaps instead I am at Mrs. Jay Gould's teakwood
table in a hand-knitted Anny Blatt ensemble in diluted tri-colors and
an off-the-face hat.

It is dusk. I am dining with Rose Hobart at the Waldorf. We have
lifted our champagne glasses. "To sentiment!" I say. And the haunting
dusk is shattered by the clean glint of jewels by Cartier.

It is dusk. I am seated on a Bruce Buttfield pouf, for it is dusk.

Ah, magazine dreams! How dear to me now are the four evenings
in the life of Mrs. Allan Ryan, Junior. I have studied them one by
one, and I feel that I know them. They are perfect little crystals of
being—static, precious. There is the evening when she stands, motionless, in a magnificent sable cape, her left arm hanging gracefully
at her side. She is ready to go out to dinner. What will this, her
first of four evenings, bring of romance, or even of food? Then there
is the evening when she just sits on the edge of a settee from the
Modernage Galleries, the hard bright gleam of gold lamé topping
a slim, straight, almost Empire skirt. I see her there (the smoke from
a cigarette rising), sitting, sitting, waiting. Or the third evening—the
evening with books. Mrs. Ryan is in chiffon; the books are in morocco.
Or the fourth evening, standing with her dachshund, herself in profile,
the dog in full face.

So I live the lives of other people in my fancy: the life of the
daughter of Lord Curzon of Kedleston, who has been visiting the
Harold Talbotts on Long Island. All I know of her is that she appeared one night at dinner, her beauty set off by the lustre of artificial
satin and the watery fire of aquamarine. It is all I know, yet it is
enough; for it is her one perfect moment in time and space, and I
know about it, and it is mine.

It is dusk. I am with Owen Johnson over his chafing dish. It is
dusk. I am with Prince Matchabelli over his vodka. Or I am with
the Countess de Forceville over her bridge tables. She and I have
just pushed the tables against the wall and taken a big bite of gaspacho.
Or I am with the Marquis de Polignac over his Pommery.

How barren my actual life seems, when fancy fails me, here with
Wamba over my quinine. Why am I not to be found at dusk, slicing

black bread very thin, as William Powell does, to toast it and sprinkle it with salt? Why does not twilight find me (as it finds Mrs. Chester Burden) covering a table with salmon-pink linens on which I place only white objects, even to a white salt shaker? Why don't I learn to simplify my entertaining, like the young pinch-penny in *Vogue*, who has all his friends in before the theatre and simply gives them champagne cocktails, caviar, and one hot dish, then takes them to the show? Why do I never give parties after the opera, as Mr. Paul Cravath does, at which I have the prettiest women in New York? Come to think of it, why don't the prettiest women in New York ever come down to my place, other than that pretty little Mrs. Fazaenzi, whom Wamba won't let in? Why haven't I a butler named Fish, who makes a cocktail of three parts gin to one part lime juice, honey, vermouth, and apricot brandy in equal portions—a cocktail so delicious that people like Mrs. Harrison Williams and Mrs. Goodhue Livingston seek him out to get the formula? And if I *did* have a butler named Fish, wouldn't I kid the pants off him?

All over the world it is dusk! It is dusk at Armando's on East Fifty-fifth Street. Armando has taken up his accordion; he is dreaming over the keys. A girl comes in, attracted by the accordion, which she mistakes for Cecil Beaton's camera. She is in stiff green satin, and over it she wears a silver fox cape which she can pull around her shoulders later in the evening if she gets feeling like pulling a cape around her shoulders. It is dusk on the Harold Castles' ranch in Hawaii. I have risen early to shoot a goat, which is the smart thing to do in Hawaii. And now I am walking silently through hedges of gardenias, past the flaming ginger flowers, for I have just shot a goat. I have on nothing but red sandals and a Martex bath towel. It is dusk in the Laurentians. I am in ski togs. I feel warm and safe, knowing that the most dangerous pitfall for skiers is *color,* knowing that although a touch of brilliance against the snow is effective, too much of it is the sure sign of the amateur. It is the magic hour before cocktails. I am in the modern penthouse of Monsieur Charles de Beistegui. The staircase is entirely of cement, spreading at the hemline and trimmed with padded satin tubing caught at the neck with a bar of milk chocolate. It is dusk in Chicago. I am standing beside Mrs. Howard Linn, formerly Consuelo Vanderbilt, formerly Sophie M. Gay, formerly Ellen Glendinning, formerly Saks-Fifth Avenue. It is dusk! A pheasant has Julian Street down and is pouring a magnificent old red Burgundy down his neck. Dreams, I'm afraid. It is really dusk in my own apartment. I am down on my knees in front of an airbound radiator, trying to fix it by sticking pins in the vent. Dusk in these fierce pajamas. Kneeling here, I can't help wondering where Nancy Yuille is, in her blue wool pants and reefer and her bright red mittens. For it is dusk. I said *dusk*, Wamba! Bring the quinine!

Franklin P. Adams

THE DIARY OF OUR OWN SAMUEL PEPYS *

Friday, November 30, 1923

Up, and by subway to my office, and I spied in the subway the most lovely lady ever I saw in my life, and she was carrying a rose, which I looked at, and just before I made to get off the car she gave it to me, and I wore it in my buttonhole, but at the office I took it off and put it into a drawer. And I deemed it as pleasant and warming a thing as ever had happened to me. So to do my stint, and thence to Gerald Brooks, for some frivolity.

Monday, December 31, 1923

So to see "The Song and Dance Man," and found most of it amusing, but nothing so much as the song and dance Mr. Cohan performed between acts, about My Maggie May, or some such trumpery. So home and had a bath and did on my black suit, and so to Ruth Hale's, where a great crowd was gathered, and Miss Edna Ferber said I looked as though I had just been confirmed. I am a confirmed admirer of you, quoth I, which was a quick and chivalrous thing to say, true though it was. So all the evening in songs and merrymaking, and as happy an eve of a New Year as ever I had. So ends the year, in which I have had the joyousest content of any year, and the lowest times, too. Cast up my accounts, and am the solventest ever I have been, all of which gives me the highest hope for the New Year ever I had. So end two years under my present employer, and so pleasant they were never would I work anywhere else, and so dreamed of a headline in 1974, World Man, Ninety-Two, Dies at Desk as Year Begins.

* *Selections from the weekly chronicles of New York City and of his own life which Franklin P. Adams has been writing for various newspapers since 1911.*

Monday, February 25, 1924

Early up and to my office, and read how M. Alonso beat Will Tilden yesterday at indoor tennis, and read some matters about the taxes, but I have the feeling that the taxes are built on such political foundations, and more destined to placate voters than to be equable. To Beatrice Kaufman's for dinner, and she asked me questions about H. Ross's tobogganing, the noise of it having been bruited about for a radius of thirty miles. And did he look funny tobogganing? she asked. Well, quoth I, you know how he looks *not* tobogganing, which seems to answer her.

Monday, May 5, 1924

To the office, and pretty hard at work all day, and thence to Neysa's, and met Mary Brandon, who told me how she had made Rob Sherwood laugh by telling him she thought the Riviera was a street in Paris, and he said You do not really think so, do you? And she said, No, I know it is a big store. Whereat Neysa laughed sympathetically, for it is not so long ago that she took ship for Antwerp and felt deeply aggrieved to learn on arrival that it was not in Italy. So to Kate Spaeth's for dinner and thence to see "Peg o' My Dreams," and save for a pair of gracile girl dancers, and one remark of Mr. Huntley's, when, upon somebody saying he had not visited the Aquarium, said, Well, what do you *do* all day?, I found it a dull piece.

Thursday, May 8, 1924

At my desk all the morning, merrily enough, and thence to A. Bachrach's, who gave me a fine yellow tye, and had me help him solve a cross-word puzzle, and so home by omnibuss, on the roof of one and in the rain, and there was a lady behind me who called "George!" to somebody on the Avenue, and he mounted the stage and sate beside her, and she said, "Of all things!" And when the conductor came for the fare, she said to him, "Think of meeting your husband like that," as who should say, "Don't get the idea that I am roguish." So home, and D. Taylor and Ethel Kelley to dinner, and she told me a limerick Brian Hooker told her:

> *There was an old fellow named Sidney*
> *Who drank till he ruined a kidney.*
> *It shriveled and shrank*
> *As he sat there and drank*
> *But he had a good time of it, didney?*

Sunday, March 22, 1925

So to catch up H. Harrison and Dorothy Parker, and we were for driving Miss Edna Ferber with us, but she ill in bed, but not so ill that she did not look lovely, with, quoth Dorothy, the pink maribou flowing like water. Thence to the country, and I and all to lunch at an inn, very gay and merry, and thence to the city again, and to Mistress Ruth Fleischmann's to dinner, and very late to bed.

Monday, March 23, 1925

Read this morning a highly amusing story by Anita Loos, in Harper's Bazaar, called "Gentlemen Prefer Blondes," and I had no notion Miss Loos had so much writing humour and insight, and I hope she will write other stories. And I read a fine story of R. Lardner's, too, in Liberty, called "Haircut." Mr. Ramsay MacDonald is concerned over the state of society, and asks whither it is going, but I doubt that things are in a bad way. Ignorance and bigotry and greed are with us, but they do grow a little less every few centuries. In the evening to see "The Little Minister," and I thought it a tenuous play and tedious, and Miss Chatterton acted with a charm that seemed to me unspontaneous and synthetick. But even in 1898, when I took my grandmother to see that play, I did not care for it, and the part I enjoyed the most was being let go to the theatre in the evening.

Saturday, March 28, 1925

Very betimes up, and read in a copy of Lord Byron's Poems, and was struck with how tedious the long ones were; and I wondered, if some of the long poems that Keats and Shelley and Tennyson and Byron used to write were printed to-day, would anybody read them? I doubt that anybody reads them to-day, for that matter. Read in the publick prints that the income taxes for the State are to be smaller, which pleased me, but I do find any taxpaying very irksome, having to work so hard for the money I earn. For when I am writing I feel that there is no sum of money great enough to pay me for the travail I go through, yet when I do get my weekly pay, I do feel that nobody, let alone myself, could write so well or so amusingly or so profoundly as to merit such a huge guerdon. I always have felt so, regardless of the worth of my writings or the size of the reward for them. News from Albany that the school teachers are to have an increase in their pay, which I am glad to hear, for teaching seemeth to me the hardes:

work there is, and the most thankless. So to see Mistress Neysa for a little, and played my piece on the pianoforte, "Sleep, Baby, Sleep," but R. Ives said I played it so loud that it would wake up the inmates of a maternity home a mile off, which was not true. So to Miss Ruth Hale's, and caught up H. Broun; and with him to a picture show, and he bought a picture of Arthur Dove's, with no title, and it seemed to me it might be called "Now is the Time to Paint That Barn: Order by Number," the picture being some samples of various colors of paint. But B. thought it had great beauty, but all the others could say was that it was very interesting, which is a great thing to say about any work of art or any persons nowadays. For there is no argument against that, for the describer, if pressed, will say that it is interesting because of its dulness, or its lack of interest. All of which is too complex for me.

Thursday, April 23, 1925

Very betimes up, and read of the fight that is raging between the Governor and the Mayor, and whether this means that Mr. Hylan will not be elected Mayor again I can not tell, but those who are deep in the city's politicks say so. A fine, warm day, but I at my stint all the day, and so uptown and met Nell Wylie the poet, and said, "Guess whose birthday this is," and she said "Yours?" and I said, "No, but you are getting warm." "Shakespeare's" she said. Which was the prettiest compliment I had had all day. So to Miss E. Root's, and she played me all the score of "Princess Ida," as melodick and full of sweetness as anything Sullivan ever wrote, and I vowed to hear the opera as soon as I might. So took Will Benét home with me, and early to bed.

Wolcott Gibbs

SHAKESPEARE, HERE'S YOUR HAT

(A New Play by Mr. William Saroyan, in Book Form, with the Customary Prefatory Notes by the Author)

I

This play is a masterpiece. It is young, gusty, comical, tragic, beautiful, heroic, and as real as a slaughterhouse or some dame fixing her hair. It could only have been written in America, by an Armenian boy who is an artist and a lover and a dreamer. All at once. All mixed up. It could only have been written by Saroyan.

Other people write plays, but they are no good. I go to them and I sit there and think, "My God, this is lousy! It was written by a man in an English suit of clothes who makes fifty thousand dollars a year, but it is not alive. It is dead. It stinks." A man making fifty thousand dollars a year doesn't write about Life; he writes about other people who make fifty thousand dollars a year; he writes about a bunch of rich corpses and, generally speaking, he is a rich corpse himself. Not me, though. Not Saroyan. This play is lyric and simple and alive. It says just exactly what it means. When the boy in this play dynamites his grandmother because he needs some money to get gin, that is something real. When he puts a nickel in the piano for music, that is real, too. When he meets the society girl and says "How's chances, sister?" and she answers "O.K., Mac," that is a real, lovely, and heartbreaking thing.

In the plays about the rich corpses, it takes three acts and about sixty thousand dollars' worth of scenery to get around to a beautiful and natural request like that, and half the time nothing comes of it, either.

II

I am a warm, rich, and passionate human being and very few things are too much for me. Not even dramatic criticism. When a man writes in a newspaper or a magazine that he doesn't understand this play

or is bored by it, that is all right with me. It is hard to imagine anybody not liking something that is as eloquent and native and true as
a child running after a butterfly or a colored man scratching himself,
but I do not get sore. I am just sorry for the crazy bastard.

III

The following are excerpts from some of the reviews published in
the New York press:

RICHARD WATTS, JR., *Herald Tribune:* It is a darling play . . . but we
must not ignore the Chinese.

BROOKS ATKINSON, *Times:* Lit with the same ineluctable fire that once
informed the witches and the cauldron on the heath.

JOHN MASON BROWN, *Post:* Challenges the best of Aristophanes, Gogol,
Pirandello, Racine, and the Song of Solomon.

SIDNEY B. WHIPPLE, *World-Telegram:* Either Saroyan is crazy ... or I
am. A child has done this horrid thing.

IV

This play was written in an hour and a half with a quill pen I
generally keep in a little bowl of bird shot. For a man like me, an
original, talented, profound, sensitive, and humorous Armenian, a
typewriter is an artificial barrier standing between the living brain
and the clean paper. It is not for me, as the airbrush was not for
Michelangelo and the adding machine was not for Euclid.

At that time I was working in Hollywood, where all authors use
typewriters. "The greatest play in the world is right there on those
keys, if you can only figure out how to hit them in the right order,"
one of them said to me. He was a man who made forty, fifty, a
hundred thousand dollars a year, and he went around with a falcon
on his wrist. I would rather use the quill pen. Me, personally.

V

Generally speaking, the American theatre is the aspirin of the
middle classes. People go to a play because they want to get in out
of the rain. Or because they have a date with some rabbit in it later
on. Or just because they happen to know the press agent and don't
have to pay. It is not that way with me. I go because I love Life.

That is an important statement and I want to repeat it: *William Saroyan loves Life.*

In the theatre today, except in this play of mine, what you see is not Life. It is a drawing-room compromise with Life arrived at by a man who has never had to sleep in a silo or eat birch bark or trap mice to make himself a hat or any of the other brave, haunting, and sometimes foolish things people do when they don't happen to have been born on Park Avenue or in Newport, Rhode Island.

The cure for the American theatre is more plays like this one. More plays by Saroyan.

THE TIME OF <u>WHOSE</u> LIFE?

(*A dormitory at Groton, just before vespers. Three of the boys— Jones Minor, Ferris Major, and Tilden Elliott III—are changing from their rugger togs into their vespers togs. They are breathless and wondering, enchanted with a sweet world that also holds things like ginger beer and scones and "Esquire" magazine. Ferguson Nicholson, the housemaster, a tall, thin man, noble because of the pain in his heart, is sitting in one corner, reading "Variety" and drinking a dry Martini. In another corner an old graduate, mad and very dirty, is throwing cards into a hat. A scrubwoman comes in. A lifetime of toil, including six years with the Shuberts, has not quenched her brimming and precious spirit.*)

SCRUBWOMAN (*compassionate, supernatural; the Earth Mother*): How about sweeping up around here, gents? Get some of the fug out of the joint.

JONES MINOR: Sweep. You won't sweep the torture and despair of Life from the heart with a broom....

FERRIS MAJOR: Or the beauty of it either.

OLD GRADUATE (*lost in his eternal dream of the past*): Dissolute and damned. Both the student body and the faculty.

HOUSEMASTER: Elliott.

ELLIOTT: Yes, sir?

HOUSEMASTER: Go down to the Greek's and get me two ham sandwiches and a billiard ball.

ELLIOTT (*uneasily*): What for?

HOUSEMASTER (*watching the scrubwoman; fascinated by the unique, all-female, and mysterious experiences once enjoyed somewhere in the world by this scrubwoman*): Ham on white. British mustard.

ELLIOTT (*still puzzled, but going out dutifully*): A cue ball?

HOUSEMASTER: No, the red one. (*To the scrubwoman; waving the cocktail-shaker*) Martini?

SCRUBWOMAN: No thanks, pal. The Head don't like us to drink on duty.

HOUSEMASTER: You're missing a lot. *I'm* always drunk. The days and nights are whittling me away, and—(*he breaks off as the Headmaster, a quiet, grave man, carrying a bridle, comes into the cubicle.*) Were you looking for something, sir?

HEADMASTER (*genially*): Ah, Nicholson. Fried again, I see. (*With a change of mood, sternly*) Ferris Major!

FERRIS MAJOR (*springing up, dynamic, translated*): Sir?

HEADMASTER: Is there a polo pony in this room?

FERRIS MAJOR: A what, sir?

HEADMASTER (*going to a closet, opening it, and discovering a polo pony*): As I thought. You know the rules, I believe, Ferris. No polo ponies or young women in dorm after four o'clock.

FERRIS MAJOR (*in a low voice, accepting his doom*): Yes, sir.

HEADMASTER: This means a birching, of course. (*He goes out, leading the polo pony; fatal, inexorable, the Scourge of God.*)

OLD GRADUATE (*throwing the ace of spades at the hat*): Dissolute and damned. Both the student body and the faculty.

HOUSEMASTER (*still preoccupied by the scrubwoman; the strange, illicit, bygone adventures of the scrubwoman*): I drink to your unconquerable spirit, Mrs. Le Bogan.

SCRUBWOMAN: My name ain't Mrs. Le Bogan.

HOUSEMASTER: Then Guinevere or Héloïse. In any case, I drink. To your ancient sins, Faustine.

SCRUBWOMAN: Listen, what the hell you talking about?

HOUSEMASTER (*wearily*): I don't know. What do any of us talk about? Love. Happiness. Towering injustice everywhere. The game with St. Paul's. (*Furiously, draining the Martini*) How the hell do I know? What do *you* talk about?

SCRUBWOMAN (*sly, roguish, Salome, old but not regenerate*): Jeez, I dunno, mister. Harry K. Thaw. The time we burned up the city of Chicago. Shooting Garfield. All like that.

HOUSEMASTER: Life! The terror and the wonder and the beauty of it. (*Gathering momentum*) Life! *Life!* LIFE!

(*As he goes on, Elliott reënters with the sandwiches and the billiard ball; the scrubwoman wrings out her mop and starts to wipe up the floor; the old graduate opens another pack of cards and begins throwing them at the hat; Jones Minor and Ferris Major gather up their hymnals and prayer books; the polo pony trots in through the door and back into the closet. Life has come full circle.*)

OLD GRADUATE (*sombre, triumphant; his opinion of everything borne out*): Dissolute and damned. Both the student body and the faculty.

(*From the courtyard the bell for vespers sounds, very wonderful and sad. The curtain falls.*)

DEATH IN THE RUMBLE SEAT

(*With the Usual Apologies to Ernest Hemingway*)

Most people don't like the pedestrian part, and it is best not to look at that if you can help it. But if you can't help seeing them, long-legged and their faces white, and then the shock and the car lifting up a little on one side, then it is best to think of it as something very unimportant but beautiful and necessary artistically. It is unimportant because the people who are pedestrians are not very important, and if they were not being *cogido* by automobiles it would just be something else. And it is beautiful and necessary because, without the possibility of somebody getting *cogido*, driving a car would be just like anything else. It would be like reading "Thanatopsis," which is neither beautiful nor necessary, but hogwash. If you drive a car, and don't like the pedestrian part, then you are one of two kinds of people. Either you haven't very much vitality and you ought to do something about it, or else you are yellow and there is nothing to be done about it at all.

If you don't know anything about driving cars you are apt to think a driver is good just because he goes fast. This may be very exciting at first, but afterwards there is a bad taste in the mouth and the feeling of dishonesty. Ann Bender, the American, drove as fast on the Merrick Road as anybody I have ever seen, but when cars came the other way she always worked out of their terrain and over in the ditch so that you never had the hard, clean feeling of danger, but only bumping up and down in the ditch, and sometimes hitting your head on the top of the car. Good drivers go fast too, but it is always down the middle of the road, so that cars coming the other way are dominated, and have to go in the ditch themselves. There are a great many ways of getting the effect of danger, such as staying in the middle of the road till the last minute and then swerving out of the pure line, but they are all tricks, and afterwards you know they were tricks, and there is nothing left but disgust.

The cook: I am a little tired of cars, sir. Do you know any stories?

I know a great many stories, but I'm not sure that they're suitable.

The cook: The hell with that.

Then I will tell you the story about God and Adam and naming the animals. You see, God was very tired after he got through making the world. He felt good about it, but he was tired so he asked Adam if he'd mind making up names for the animals.

"What animals?" Adam said.

"Those," God said.

"Do they have to have names?" Adam said.

"You've got a name, haven't you?" God said.

I could see—

The cook: How do *you* get into this?

Some people always write in the first person, and if you do it's very hard to write any other way, even when it doesn't altogether fit into the context. If you want to hear this story, don't keep interrupting.

The cook: O.K.

I could see that Adam thought God was crazy, but he didn't say anything. He went over to where the animals were, and after a while he came back with the list of names.

"Here you are," he said.

God read the list, and nodded.

"They're pretty good," he said. "They're all pretty good except that last one."

"That's a good name," Adam said. "What's the matter with it?"

"What do you want to call it an elephant for?" God said.

Adam looked at God.

"It looks like an elephant to me," he said.

The cook: Well?

That's all.

The cook: It is a very strange story, sir.

It is a strange world, and if a man and a woman love each other, that is strange too, and what is more, it always turns out badly.

In the golden age of car-driving, which was about 1910, the sense of impending disaster, which is a very lovely thing and almost non-existent, was kept alive in a number of ways. For one thing, there was always real glass in the windshield so that if a driver hit anything, he was very definitely and beautifully *cogido*. The tires weren't much good either, and often they'd blow out before you'd gone ten miles. Really, the whole car was built that way. It was made not only so that it would precipitate accidents but so that when the accidents came it was honestly vulnerable, and it would fall apart, killing all the people with a passion that was very fine to watch. Then they began building the cars so that they would go much faster, but the glass and the tires were all made so that if anything happened it wasn't real danger, but only the false sense of it. You could do all kinds of things with the new cars, but it was no good because it was all planned in advance. Mickey Finn, the German, always worked very far into the other car's terrain so that the two cars always seemed to be one. Driving that way he often got the *faender,* or the clicking when two cars touch each other in passing, but because you knew that nothing was really at stake it was just an empty classicism, without any value because the insecurity was all gone and there was nothing left but a kind of mechanical agility. It is the same way when any art gets into its decadence. It is the same way about s-x—

The cook: I like it very much better when you talk about s-x, sir, and I wish you would do it more often.

I have talked a lot about s-x before, and now I thought I would talk about something else.

The cook: I think that is very unfortunate, sir, because you are at your best with s-x, but when you talk about automobiles you are just a nuisance.

Corey Ford

THE NORRIS PLAN *

Aroused by the frank discussion of Birth Control in Mr. Charles G. Norris's tract, entitled "Seed," as well as by the mention of the same subject in Mrs. Kathleen Norris's "Passion Flower" and other novels, the young and impressionable Mr. Riddell attempted in the following to try his own hand at the all-important theme of limiting our excess productivity in America. It is of added interest to note that the influence of the Norris style was so strong that young Riddell, perhaps unconsciously framed his treatise in the respective manners of the Norrises themselves.

When this was written, Mrs. Kathleen Norris was already the author of thirty-three novels.†

It was early in the summer that Kathy told him that Edgar Wallace was going to have another novel.

It was a heavenly warm bright shiny clear happy Sunday morning, and the broad green velvety smooth flat rolling croquet field in the middle of Central Park was filled with gay yellow warm sunlight. She and Charles were moving idly among the wickets, swinging their mallets at the smooth fat shiny round balls. Charles had tried for the stake and missed it, and now he sat on his up-ended mallet, his smooth fat shiny round face puckered into a frown.

"Edgar thinks he's going to have another novel, Charlie."

"Gosh, that's tough!" Charlie commented absently. He was trying to remember whether he was dead on her.

"He's been typing his eyes out," Kathy continued in a rather faint voice. "He says the first ten novels aren't so bad, or even the first twenty," she pursued. "But when you get to write the fiftieth novel or so, it's terrible."

* *This parody book review was first published in somewhat longer form over the signature John Riddell.*

† Thirty-four at the time of going to press. J. R.
286

Charlie extended his toe, slyly moved his ball over an inch or two in front of the wicket, and faced her with a great wholesome happy cheerful laugh.

"What's terrible, honey?" he asked.

"The novel, of course!" she conceded honestly. "Charlie," she went on suddenly, deliberately, not looking at him as she knocked her ball into position for the center wicket, "I wonder how you'd feel if I were going to have another novel?"

"I know how I'd feel," Charlie said promptly; "I'd take it out into a vacant lot somewhere and burn it!"

"Oh, Charlie, why?" Kathy asked, widening her big dark round bright eyes reproachfully. "Everybody writes them." Her cheeks were suddenly red, and her eyes full of tears. "Look at Faith Baldwin, or Hugh Walpole, or Mary Roberts Rinehart, or Mazo de la Roche, or Margaret Ayer Barnes—they deliver one every year. Sometimes they even have twins."

"Well, if I was in Edgar's place," Charlie said, as he judged his distance and then rapped the stake smartly, "I'd go to my publishers and have them decide that the public couldn't stand another novel just now, that they'd have to save his reputation by—well, cutting it out."

"Oh, but Charlie! Isn't that a terribly wrong thing to do?"

"What's wrong with it?"

"Well—well—" She stopped, puzzled and a little sick. "It seems so unfair to the novel. It—it ought to have its little chance."

"Don't you think the public ought to have a chance, too?"

"But—but there seems to be something so *humiliating* about it," Kathy faltered, her cheeks burning. "To have a whole season go by without being on the best-seller lists! To have to give up the first-serial rights—and the second-serial rights—and the movie rights—and the foreign rights—"

"It isn't half as bad, I should think, as writing it," Charlie argued.

"Oh, no, Charlie, that's natural!"

"I don't know about that," Charlie began, laying his mallet down and pointing an argumentative forefinger at the woman before him. "I've been doing a lot of thinking about this whole subject of book-control. Of course, my publishers don't agree with me. They believe that the practice of Literary Contraception profanes the sacrament of Inspiration, and is a frustration of the creative instinct in Art. It is my opinion, however, that reckless breeding should be checked for the sake of the author's reputation. It unquestionably takes the lives of thousands of writers annually, ruins the careers of as many more, and in addition brings hundreds of thousands of diseased, crippled and deformed novels into the world that should never have been written. Some of them die, many linger on in dire poverty, shivering in their paper jackets, while others roam at large, doubtless interbreeding in the movies and producing a weak and imbecile line of sequels that threatens to lower the whole stock of American literature.

"Several authors that you and I know are—or were—examples of such reckless breeding. You may recall, Kathy, an author by the name of John Erskine?"

"Very well."

"His history came to my attention very forcibly the other day in a Liggett's window. He's confined now in the dollar reprints; but before he was put where he couldn't do any further harm, he had brought a weak and helpless novel into the world named *Unfinished Business,* which was totally unable to exist alone, and was forced to depend on its older sister Helen and its brother Galahad for its entire support. Thus the future happiness of two healthy novels was threatened by this imbecile brother; and the poor author—whose health had been none too good after having *Adam and Eve* and *Uncle Sam*—went into a serious decline."

He shook his head.

"The saddest case is that of Emil Ludwig. After writing the life of everyone else, the poor fellow has now produced a biography of himself!"

"Uncle Emil! *Himself?*"

"Pitiful case. A fine talent gone to pot-boiling. He had a publisher in New York, and he bore him one volume after another. After Emil had delivered six or seven books in rapid succession, however, the public grew tired of him, disappeared at intervals, rejected a couple. You wouldn't know him today; he's beaten in spirit, in substance, in artistic integrity. The biography-racket has crushed him body and soul. You can't deny it, legal book-control undoubtedly would have been a blessing to Uncle Emil."

Kathy leaned weakly on her mallet. The warm bright sunny cheerful Park swam before her, the croquet-wickets, stakes, balls, and idle spectators seemed blurred before her eyes.

"You look kind of white yourself, Kathy," interrupted Charles curiously.

"I don't know—I'm all right, I guess."

"You've been having too many novels in the last few years," he said solicitously. "Every three months or so. It weakens you, honey. *Passion Flower* was too much for you—let alone *Margaret Yorke*."

The very title made waves of nausea sweep over her. She clutched her mallet and swung listlessly at the croquet-ball before her. It went short of the wicket.

"A lot of other American authors present interesting phases of this same problem," continued Charlie, hitting his ball deftly between two wickets, and rapping the stake. "Take the late James Branch Cabell, for instance. He was undoubtedly one of the outstanding figures of our era; but he did not know the meaning of book-control. Overproduction weakened him, and he died in giving birth to his last novel. If he had practiced literary contraception, he might have been alive today. Let me see—are you still for the middle wicket?"

Kathy shook her head vaguely. She was thinking again of her panic-stricken visit to her publisher this very morning and her face burned, and her hands were dry. A business-like man; it was nothing to him. No, there was no question about Mrs. Norris's condition; she was scheduled for his fall lists. He was sorry, but he did not know any way out of it now. It would be extremely expensive to remove it at this date. He never advised it.

It was like a nightmare. Her publisher had removed her last doubt. This was no longer fear: it was terrible certainty.

"I'm going to have a novel. In October."

No, she did not have the courage to tell Charlie. She dragged herself across the court, and swung dizzily again at the ball. Charlie smiled as it wired itself behind the wicket, and he took his turn, grasping the mallet firmly as he elaborated further on his favorite theme: "There is one thing more I'd like to bring up about this question, and I'm done. It requires approximately three novels a year to sustain our present-day novelists, if they depend on royalties alone. The average number of novels born of literate stock is 2.8; while those of men and women from the pulpwoods is 97.2. You can clearly see where book-control is being practiced. In order to save the decent novelists from bringing about a complete suicide of American literature, not only must they publish more, but the fecundity of the illiterate writers must be curtailed. It must be obvious to anyone who stops to consider the situation at all that our intellectual class of writers is dying out, and the cheaper novelists and less mentally fit are on the increase; it must necessarily follow that our standard of national literature will decline and continue to decline."

He paused and drew out a sheaf of notes from his hip pocket. Kathy saw the scene rapidly growing black before her eyes; she felt herself swaying guiltily as Charlie read the climax of his argument aloud.

"The crux of the whole situation is simply this: our intelligent writers are not producing, and our ignorant, inferior ones are. Unless book-control is stopped among the upper classes, and its use legalized among the lower classes, the best part of our literature will die off, and the country will be over-run by incompetents and morons—"

There was a little moan, and then a faint thud behind him. Kathy had fainted.

"Kathy! Kathy!"

She found herself stretched upon the wooden bench at the side of the croquet field. Her teeth chattered, and Charlie, who was fumbling about vaguely, pale with concern and sympathy, held her hands.

"You're freezing!"

"Don't look so scared, Charlie!"

She laughed frantically, her teeth still chattering. He stared at her sympathetically.

"Anything I could do for you, Kath?" He was not thinking of what he was saying. Her heart beat fast, and she regarded him steadily, not moving a muscle. Suddenly, in an odd tone, he began, "Kathy—"

She looked at him, turning over to lie on her back, her face flushed, her hands icy, and her head rocking.

"Kath," he said, clearing his throat. "Have you thought—you know, this might be—"

Kath swallowed with a dry throat and patted his hand.

"It is, Charlie," she whispered, with a little effort.

"How d'you know?" he asked quickly.

"I asked a publisher. Our publisher."

"And he said—?"

"—Said there was no mistake about it. It is due some time in October."

"He—What do you know about that?" Charlie stammered, his face lighted with bewilderment and surprise. "You poor kid," he added awkwardly.

Kathy's cold fingers continued to cling tightly to his hand; she watched him anxiously.

"Isn't there some way to—get out of it, Kath?" Charlie asked presently, a little doubtfully. "You've had thirty-three, you see. I just thought maybe—well, remember, you're not as strong as you were—you see, the last ten or twelve you've had have all died—"

Her pale face grew whiter, and gripping his hand, with sudden fear and entreaty in her voice, she said:

"Charlie, I won't. It means—no, I couldn't do that. Getting rid of your own novel! That's—that's *badder,* to me, than not writing a novel at all. Think of it, dear—not to have the name of Norris on the best-seller lists this fall—"

"Well, now, I don't know about that," said Charlie in a queer strained voice.

"Charlie!" She looked up at him in sudden comprehension. "You don't mean that *you*—"

Suddenly she was sitting up, her arm tightly about him, her wet cheek pressed against his. He spoke after a long pause, his eyes lowered guiltily.

"It's true, Kathy. My publisher told me today. *I'm going to have a novel in October myself."*

She was laughing joyfully, exultantly.

"Then all this that you were saying about literary contraception, and book-control, and our country being over-run by incompetents and morons—you don't mean a word of it?"

"Of course I mean it," he affirmed stoutly. "I'm strongly in favor of book-control—"

She stared at him in bewilderment.

"—for everybody else," he concluded hastily.

The Norrises embraced together in perfect understanding.

James Thurber

IF GRANT HAD BEEN DRINKING AT APPOMATTOX

(*"Scribner's"* magazine is publishing a series of three articles: *"If Booth Had Missed Lincoln," "If Lee Had Not Won the Battle of Gettysburg,"* and *"If Napoleon Had Escaped to America."* This is the fourth.)

The morning of the ninth of April, 1865, dawned beautifully. General Meade was up with the first streaks of crimson in the eastern sky. General Hooker and General Burnside were up, and had breakfasted, by a quarter after eight. The day continued beautiful. It drew on toward eleven o'clock. General Ulysses S. Grant was still not up. He was asleep in his famous old navy hammock, swung high above the floor of his headquarters' bedroom. Headquarters was distressingly disarranged: papers were strewn on the floor; confidential notes from spies scurried here and there in the breeze from an open window; the dregs of an overturned bottle of wine flowed pinkly across an important military map.

Corporal Shultz, of the Sixty-fifth Ohio Volunteer Infantry, aide to General Grant, came into the outer room, looked around him, and sighed. He entered the bedroom and shook the General's hammock roughly. General Ulysses S. Grant opened one eye.

"Pardon, sir," said Corporal Shultz, "but this is the day of surrender. You ought to be up, sir."

"Don't swing me," said Grant, sharply, for his aide was making the hammock sway gently. "I feel terrible," he added, and he turned over and closed his eye again.

"General Lee will be here any minute now," said the Corporal firmly, swinging the hammock again.

"Will you cut that out?" roared Grant. "D'ya want to make me sick, or what?" Shultz clicked his heels and saluted. "What's he coming here for?" asked the General.

"This is the day of surrender, sir," said Shultz. Grant grunted bitterly.

"Three hundred and fifty generals in the Northern armies," said Grant, "and he has to come to *me* about this. What time is it?"

"You're the Commander-in-Chief, that's why," said Corporal Shultz. "It's eleven twenty-five, sir."

"Don't be crazy," said Grant. "Lincoln is the Commander-in-Chief. Nobody in the history of the world ever surrendered before lunch. Doesn't he know that an army surrenders on its stomach?" He pulled a blanket up over his head and settled himself again.

"The generals of the Confederacy will be here any minute now," said the Corporal. "You really ought to be up, sir."

Grant stretched his arms above his head and yawned.

"All right, all right," he said. He rose to a sitting position and stared about the room. "This place looks awful," he growled.

"You must have had quite a time of it last night, sir," ventured Shultz.

"Yeh," said General Grant, looking around for his clothes. "I was wrassling some general. Some general with a beard."

Shultz helped the commander of the Northern armies in the field to find his clothes.

"Where's my other sock?" demanded Grant. Shultz began to look around for it. The General walked uncertainly to a table and poured a drink from a bottle.

"I don't think it wise to drink, sir," said Shultz.

"Nev' mind about me," said Grant, helping himself to a second, "I can take it or let it alone. Didn' ya ever hear the story about the fella went to Lincoln to complain about me drinking too much? 'So-and-So says Grant drinks too much,' this fella said. 'So-and-So is a fool,' said Lincoln. So this fella went to What's-His-Name and told him what Lincoln said and he came roarin' to Lincoln about it. 'Did you tell So-and-So I was a fool?' he said. 'No,' said Lincoln, 'I thought he knew it.' " The General smiled, reminiscently, and had another drink. "*That's* how I stand with Lincoln," he said, proudly.

The soft thudding sound of horses' hooves came through the open window. Shultz hurriedly walked over and looked out.

"Hoof steps," said Grant, with a curious chortle.

"It is General Lee and his staff," said Shultz.

"Show him in," said the General, taking another drink. "And see what the boys in the back room will have."

Shultz walked smartly over to the door, opened it, saluted, and stood aside. General Lee, dignified against the blue of the April sky, magnificent in his dress uniform, stood for a moment framed in the doorway. He walked in, followed by his staff. They bowed, and stood silent. General Grant stared at them. He only had one boot on and his jacket was unbuttoned.

"I know who you are," said Grant. "You're Robert Browning, the poet."

"This is General Robert E. Lee," said one of his staff, coldly.

"Oh," said Grant. "I thought he was Robert Browning. He certainly looks like Robert Browning. There was a poet for you, Lee: Browning. Did ja ever read 'How They Brought the Good News from Ghent to Aix'? 'Up Derek, to saddle, up Derek, away; up Dunder, up Blitzen, up Prancer, up Dancer, up Bouncer, up Vixen, up—' "

"Shall we proceed at once to the matter in hand?" asked General Lee, his eyes disdainfully taking in the disordered room.

"Some of the boys was wrassling here last night," explained Grant. "I threw Sherman, or some general a whole lot like Sherman. It was pretty dark." He handed a bottle of Scotch to the commanding officer of the Southern armies, who stood holding it, in amazement and discomfiture. "Get a glass, somebody," said Grant, looking straight at General Longstreet. "Didn't I meet you at Cold Harbor?" he asked. General Longstreet did not answer.

"I should like to have this over with as soon as possible," said Lee. Grant looked vaguely at Shultz, who walked up close to him, frowning.

"The surrender, sir, the surrender," said Corporal Shultz in a whisper.

"Oh sure, sure," said Grant. He took another drink. "All right," he said. "Here we go." Slowly, sadly, he unbuckled his sword. Then he handed it to the astonished Lee. "There you are, General," said Grant. "We dam' near licked you. If I'd been feeling better we *would* of licked you."

Nunnally Johnson

DR. C-DM-N'S DAILY

(Overset matter which failed to get into one of our local newspapers)

What is the broadest definition of religion?
Love is *all*.
I have eczema in the worst way. Is there any certain cure?
Live from day to day that love may grow in thy heart and may there be blessings on thy eczema.
What is Mussolini's first name?
Benito.
Where was he born?
A pure heart is richer by far than a pure heart. Honor thy father and thy mother.
Bound the Club Alabam.
Sin is fleeting but love stayeth in the heart and enriches him that giveth and him that receiveth.
What day of the week did July 3, 1887 fall on?
Blessed be he that standeth by love and charity for education will prevail and self control is the definition of birth control.
Where is the Metropolitan Museum of Art?
The Metropolitan Museum of Art is on Fifth Avenue at—well, love conquereth all and a heart full of sweetness and goodfellowship bringeth fair days and long.
Where did you say the Metropolitan Museum of Art is?
Love is *all*.
I am about to be married. Now what do you think of that?
Huxley said, "Let love be in thy heart," while Aristotle said, "Let love be in thy heart," but Burton said, "Let love be in thy heart."
I wonder where my baby is tonight?
After the storm cometh calm and if love be in thy heart then love be in thy heart.

Bret Harte

JUNGLE FOLK *

By R-dy-d K-pl-g

It was high noon of a warm summer's day when Moo Kow came
down to the watering-place. Miaow, otherwise known as "Puskat"—
the warmth-loving one—was crouching on a limb that overhung the
pool, sunning herself. Brer Rabbit—but that is Another Story by Another Person.

Three or four Gee Gees, already at the pool, moved away on the
approach of Moo Kow.

"Why do ye stand aside?" said the Moo Kow.

"Why do you say 'ye'?" said the Gee Gees together.

"Because it's more impressive than 'you.' Don't you know that all
animals talk that way in English?" said the Moo Kow.

"And they also say 'thou,' and don't you forget it!" interrupted
Miaow from the tree. "I learnt that from a Man Cub."

The animals were silent. They did not like Miaow's slang, and were
jealous of her occasionally sitting on a Man Cub's lap. Once Dun-kee,
a poor relation of the Gee Gees, had tried it on, disastrously—but that
is also Another and a more Aged Story.

"We are ridden by The English—please to observe the Capital letters," said Pi Böl, the leader of the Gee Gees, proudly. "They are a
mighty race who ride anything and everybody. D'ye mind that—I
mean, look ye well to it!"

"What should they know of England who only England know?"
said Miaow.

"Is that a conundrum?" asked the Moo Kow.

"No; it's poetry," said the Miaow.

"I know England," said Pi Böl prancingly. "I used to go from the

* This is one of three sections of a Kipling parody called "Stories Three," from
Bret Harte's second book of "Condensed Novels."

Bank to Islington three times a day—I mean," he added hurriedly, "before I became a screw—I should say, a screw-gun horse."

"And I," said the Moo Kow, "am terrible. When the young women and children in the village see me approach they fly shriekingly. My presence alone has scattered their sacred festival—The Sundés Kool Piknik. I strike terror to their inmost souls, and am more feared by them than even Kreep-mows, the insidious! And yet, behold! I have taken the place of the mothers of men, and I have nourished the mighty ones of the earth! But that," said the Moo Kow, turning her head away bashfully, "that is Anudder Story."

A dead silence fell on the pool.

"And I," said Miaow, lifting up her voice, "I am the horror and haunter of the night season. When I pass like the night wind over the roofs of the houses men shudder in their beds and tremble. When they hear my voice as I creep stealthily along their balconies they cry to their gods for succor. They arise, and from their windows they offer me their priceless household treasures—the sacred vessels dedicated to their great god Shiv—which they call 'Shivin Mugs'—the Kloes Brösh, the Boo-jak, urging me to fly them! And yet," said Miaow mournfully, "it is but my love song! Think ye what they would do if I were on the war-path."

Another dead silence fell on the pool. Then arose that strange, mysterious, indefinable Thing, known as "The Scent." The animals sniffed.

"It heralds the approach of the Stalkies—the most famous of British Skool Boaz," said the Moo Kow. "They have just placed a decaying guinea-pig, two white mice in an advanced state of decomposition, and a single slice of Limburger cheese in the bed of their tutor. They had previously skillfully diverted the drains so that they emptied into the drawing-room of the head-master. They have just burned down his house in an access of noble zeal, and are fighting among themselves for the spoil. Hark! do ye hear them?"

A wild medley of shrieks and howls had arisen, and an irregular mob of strange creatures swept out of the distance toward the pool. Some were like pygmies, some had bloody noses. Their talk consisted of feverish, breathless ejaculations,—a gibberish in which the words "rot," "oach," and "giddy" were preëminent. Some were exciting themselves by chewing a kind of "bhang" made from the plant called pappahmint; others had their faces streaked with djam.

"But who is this they are ducking in the pool?" asked Pi Böl.

"It is one who has foolishly and wantonly conceived that his parents have sent him here to study," said the Moo Kow; "but that is against the rules of the Stalkies, who accept study only as a punishment."

"Then these be surely the 'Bander Log'—the monkey folk—of whom the good Rhuddyidd has told us," said a Gee Gee—"the ones who have no purpose—and forget everything."

"Fool!" said the Moo Kow. "Know ye not that the great Rhuddyidd has said that the Stalkies become Major-Generals, V.C.'s, and C.B.'s of the English? Truly, they are great. Look now; ye shall see one of the greatest traits of the English Stalky."

One of the pygmy Stalkies was offering a bun to a larger one, who hesitated, but took it coldly.

"Behold! it is one of the greatest traits of this mighty race not to show any emotion. He *would* take the bun—he *has* taken it! He is pleased—but he may not show it. Observe him eat."

The taller Stalky, after eating the bun, quietly kicked the giver, knocked off his hat, and turned away with a calm, immovable face.

"Good!" said the Moo Kow. "Ye would not dream that he was absolutely choking with grateful emotion?"

"We would not," said the animals.

"But why are they all running back the way they came?" asked Pi Böl.

"They are going back to punishment. Great is its power. Have ye not heard the gospel of Rhuddyidd the mighty? 'Force is everything! Gentleness won't wash, courtesy is deceitful. Politeness is foreign. Be ye beaten that ye may beat. Pass the kick on!'"

But here he was interrupted by the appearance of three soldiers who were approaching the watering-place.

"Ye are now," said the Moo Kow, "with the main guard. The first is Bleareyed, who carries a raven in a cage, which he has stolen from the wife of a deputy commissioner. He will paint the bird snow white and sell it as a dove to the same lady. The second is Otherwise, who is dragging a small garden engine, of which he has despoiled a native gardener, whom he has felled with a single blow. The third is Mulled-winey, swinging a cut-glass decanter of sherry which he has just snatched from the table of his colonel. Mulledwiney and Otherwise will play the engine upon Bleareyed, who is suffering from heat apoplexy and djim-djams."

The three soldiers seated themselves in the pool.

"They are going to tell awful war stories now," said the Moo Kow, "stories that are large and strong! Some people are shocked—others like 'em."

Then he that was called Mulledwiney told a story. In the middle of it Miaow got up from the limb of the tree, coughed slightly, and put her paw delicately over her mouth. "You must excuse me," she said faintly. "I am taken this way sometimes—and I have left my salts at home. Thanks! I can get down myself!" The next moment she had disappeared, but was heard coughing in the distance.

Mulledwiney winked at his companions and continued his story:—

"Wid that we wor in the thick av the foight. Whin I say 'thick' I mane it, sorr! We wor that jammed together, divil a bit cud we shoot or cut! At furrest, I had lashed two mushkits together wid the baynits out so, like a hay fork, and getting the haymaker's lift on thim, I just lifted two Paythians out—one an aych baynit—and passed 'em, aisy-like, over me head to the rear rank for them to finish. But what wid the blud gettin' into me ois, I was blinded, and the pressure kept in-craysin' until me arrums was thrussed like a fowl to me sides, and sorra a bit cud I move but me jaws!"

"And bloomin' well you knew how to use them," said Otherwise.

"Thrue for you—though ye don't mane it!" said Mulledwiney, playfully tapping Otherwise on the head with a decanter till the cut glass slowly shivered. "So, begorra! there wor nothing left for me to do but to *ate* thim! Wirra! but it was the crooel worruk."

"Excuse me, my lord," interrupted the gasping voice of Pi Böl as he began to back from the pool, "I am but a horse, I know, and being built in that way—naturally have the stomach of one—yet, really, my lord, this—er"— And his voice was gone.

The next moment he had disappeared. Mulledwiney looked around with affected concern.

"Save us! But we've cleaned out the Jungle! Sure, there's not a baste left but ourselves!"

It was true. The watering-place was empty. Moo Kow, Miaow, and the Gee Gees had disappeared. Presently there was a booming crash and a long, deep rumbling among the distant hills. Then they knew they were near the old Moulmein Pagoda, and the dawn had come up like thunder out of China 'cross the bay. It always came up that way there. The strain was too great, and day was actually breaking.

S. J. Perelman

WAITING FOR SANTY

A CHRISTMAS PLAYLET

(WITH A BOW TO MR. CLIFFORD ODETS)

Scene: The sweatshop of S. Claus, a manufacturer of children's toys, on North Pole Street. Time: The night before Christmas.

At rise, seven gnomes, Rankin, Panken, Rivkin, Riskin, Ruskin, Briskin, and Praskin, are discovered working furiously to fill orders piling up on stage right. The whir of lathes, the hum of motors, and the hiss of drying lacquer are so deafening that at times the dialogue cannot be heard, which is very vexing if you vex easily. (Note: The parts of Rankin, Panken, Rivkin, Riskin, Ruskin, Briskin, and Praskin are interchangeable, and may be secured directly from your dealer or the factory.)

RISKIN (*filing a Meccano girder, bitterly*). A parasite, a leech, a blood-sucker—altogether a five-star no goodnick! Starvation wages we get so he can ride around in a red team with reindeers!

RUSKIN (*jeering*). Hey, Karl Marx, whyn'tcha hire a hall?

RISKIN (*sneering*). Scab! Stool pigeon! Company spy! (*They tangle and rain blows on each other. While waiting for these to dry, each returns to his respective task.*)

BRISKIN (*sadly, to Panken*). All day long I'm painting "Snow Queen" on these Flexible Flyers and my little Irving lays in a cold tenement with the gout.

PANKEN. You said before it was the mumps.

BRISKIN (*with a fatalistic shrug*). The mumps—the gout—go argue with City Hall.

PANKEN (*kindly, passing him a bowl*). Here, take a piece fruit.

BRISKIN (*chewing*). It ain't bad, for wax fruit.

PANKEN (*with pride*). I painted it myself.

BRISKIN (*rejecting the fruit*). Ptoo! Slave psychology!

RIVKIN (*suddenly, half to himself, half to the Party*). I got a belly full of stars, baby. You make me feel like I swallowed a Roman candle

PRASKIN (*curiously*). What's wrong with the kid?

RISKIN. What's wrong with all of us? The system! Two years he and Claus's daughter's been making goo-goo eyes behind the old man's back.

PRASKIN. So what?

RISKIN (*scornfully*). So what? Economic determinism! What do you think the kid's name is—J. Pierpont Rivkin? He ain't even got for a bottle Dr. Brown's Celery Tonic. I tell you, it's like gall in my mouth two young people shouldn't have a room where they could make great music.

RANKIN (*warningly*). Shhh! Here she comes now! (*Stella Claus enters, carrying a portable gramophone. She and Rivkin embrace, place a record on the turntable, and begin a very slow waltz, unmindful that the gramophone is playing "Cohen on the Telephone."*)

STELLA (*dreamily*). Love me, sugar?

RIVKIN. I can't sleep, I can't eat, that's how I love you. You're a double malted with two scoops of whipped cream; you're the moon rising over Mosholu Parkway; you're a two weeks' vacation at Camp Nitgedaiget! I'd pull down the Chrysler Building to make a bobbie pin for your hair!

STELLA. I've got a stomach full of anguish. Oh, Rivvy, what'll we do?

PANKEN (*sympathetically*). Here, try a piece fruit.

RIVKIN (*fiercely*). Wax fruit—that's been my whole life! Imitations! Substitutes! Well, I'm through! Stella, tonight I'm telling your old man. He can't play mumblety-peg with two human beings! (*The tinkle of sleigh bells is heard offstage, followed by a voice shouting, "Whoa, Dasher! Whoa, Dancer!" A moment later S. Claus enters in a gust of mock snow. He is a pompous bourgeois of sixty-five who affects a white beard and a false air of benevolence. But to-night the ruddy color is missing from his cheeks, his step falters, and he moves heavily. The gnomes hastily replace the marzipan they have been filching.*)

STELLA (*anxiously*). Papa! What did the specialist say?

CLAUS (*brokenly*). The biggest professor in the country...the best cardiac man that money could buy....I tell you I was like a wild man.

STELLA. Pull yourself together, Sam!

CLAUS. It's no use. Adhesions, diabetes, sleeping sickness, decalcomania
—oh, my God! I got to cut out climbing in chimneys, he says—
me, Sanford Claus, the biggest toy concern in the world!

STELLA (*soothingly*). After all, it's only one man's opinion.

CLAUS. No, no, he cooked my goose. I'm like a broken uke after a
Yosian picnic. Rivkin!

RIVKIN. Yes, Sam.

CLAUS. My boy, I had my eye on you for a long time. You and Stella
thought you were too foxy for an old man, didn't you? Well, let
bygones be bygones. Stella, do you love this gnome?

STELLA (*simply*). He's the whole stage show at the Music Hall, Papa;
he's Toscanini conducting Beethoven's Fifth; he's—

CLAUS (*curtly*). Enough already. Take him. From now on he's a partner in the firm. (*As all exclaim, Claus holds up his hand for
silence.*) And tonight he can take my route and make the deliv-
eries. It's the least I could do for my own flesh and blood. (*As the
happy couple kiss, Claus wipes away a suspicious moisture and
turns to the other gnomes.*) Boys, do you know what day tomorrow is?

GNOMES (*crowding around expectantly*). Christmas!

CLAUS. Correct. When you look in your envelopes tonight, you'll find a
little present from me—a forty-per-cent pay cut. And the first one
who opens his trap—gets this. (*As he holds up a tear-gas bomb
and beams at them, the gnomes utter cries of joy, join hands, and
dance around him, shouting exultantly. All except Riskin and
Briskin, that is, who exchange a quick glance and go underground.*)

FOR (OR AGAINST) CHILDREN

Our first idea was to collect a section of humor from books written for children. We gave it up because, except for "The Peterkin Papers" and "Uncle Remus," we did not find much humor in early juvenile literature, and the humor in modern books for children is for the most part picture-book humor. So this turned into a section quite as much about *children as* for *them. Incidentally, it also has a good deal to say about parents.*

Cross reference: A number of stories about real children will be found in this book under "Reminiscence."

Lucretia P. Hale

THE PETERKINS CELEBRATE THE FOURTH OF JULY

The day began early.

A compact had been made with the little boys the evening before.

They were to be allowed to usher in the glorious day by the blowing of horns exactly at sunrise. But they were to blow them for precisely five minutes only, and no sound of the horns should be heard afterward till the family were downstairs.

It was thought that a peace might thus be bought by a short, though crowded, period of noise.

The morning came. Even before the morning, at half-past three o'clock, a terrible blast of the horns aroused the whole family.

Mrs. Peterkin clasped her hands to her head and exclaimed: "I am thankful the lady from Philadelphia is not here!" For she had been invited to stay a week, but had declined to come before the Fourth of July, as she was not well, and her doctor had prescribed quiet.

And the number of the horns was most remarkable! It was as though every cow in the place had arisen and was blowing through both her own horns!

"How many little boys are there? How many have we?" exclaimed Mr. Peterkin, going over their names one by one mechanically, thinking he would do it, as he might count imaginary sheep jumping over a fence, to put himself to sleep. Alas! the counting could not put him to sleep now, in such a din.

And how unexpectedly long the five minutes seemed! Elizabeth Eliza was to take out her watch and give the signal for the end of the five minutes, and the ceasing of the horns. Why did not the signal come? Why did not Elizabeth Eliza stop them?

And certainly it was long before sunrise; there was no dawn to be seen!

"We will not try this plan again," said Mrs. Peterkin.

"If we live to another Fourth," added Mr. Peterkin, hastening to the door to inquire into the state of affairs.

Alas! Amanda, by mistake, had waked up the little boys an hour too early. And by another mistake the little boys had invited three or four of their friends to spend the night with them. Mrs. Peterkin had given them permission to have the boys for the whole day, and they understood the day as beginning when they went to bed the night before. This accounted for the number of horns.

It would have been impossible to hear any explanation; but the five minutes were over, and the horns had ceased, and there remained only the noise of a singular leaping of feet, explained perhaps by a possible pillow-fight, that kept the family below partially awake until the bells and cannon made known the dawning of the glorious day,—the sunrise, or "the rising of the sons," as Mr. Peterkin jocosely called it when they heard the little boys and their friends clattering down the stairs to begin the outside festivities.

They were bound first for the swamp, for Elizabeth Eliza, at the suggestion of the lady from Philadelphia, had advised them to hang some flags around the pillars of the piazza. Now the little boys knew of a place in the swamp where they had been in the habit of digging for "flag-root," and where they might find plenty of flag flowers. They did bring away all they could, but they were a little out of bloom. The boys were in the midst of nailing up all they had on the pillars of the piazza, when the procession of the Antiques and Horribles passed along. As the procession saw the festive arrangements on the piazza, and the crowd of boys, who cheered them loudly, it stopped to salute the house with some especial strains of greeting.

Poor Mrs. Peterkin! They were directly under her windows! In a few moments of quiet, during the boys' absence from the house on their visit to the swamp, she had been trying to find out whether she had a sick-headache, or whether it was all the noise, and she was just deciding it was the sick-headache, but was falling into a light slumber, when the fresh noise outside began.

There were the imitations of the crowing of cocks, and braying of donkeys, and the sound of horns, encored and increased by the cheers of the boys. Then began the torpedoes, and the Antiques and Horribles had Chinese crackers also.

And, in despair of sleep, the family came down to breakfast.

Mrs. Peterkin had always been much afraid of fireworks, and had never allowed the boys to bring gunpowder into the house. She was even afraid of torpedoes; they looked so much like sugar-plums she was sure some of the children would swallow them, and explode before anybody knew it.

She was very timid about other things. She was not sure even about pea-nuts. Everybody exclaimed over this: "Surely there was no danger in pea-nuts!" But Mrs. Peterkin declared she had been very much alarmed at the Centennial Exhibition, and in the crowded corners of the streets in Boston, at the pea-nut stands, where they had machines to roast the pea-nuts. She did not think it was safe. They might go off any time, in the midst of a crowd of people, too!

Mr. Peterkin thought there actually was no danger, and he should be sorry to give up the pea-nut. He thought it an American institution, something really belonging to the Fourth of July. He even confessed to a quiet pleasure in crushing the empty shells with his feet on the sidewalks as he went along the streets.

Agamemnon thought it a simple joy.

In consideration, however, of the fact that they had had no real celebration of the Fourth the last year, Mrs. Peterkin had consented to give over the day, this year, to the amusement of the family as a Centennial celebration. She would prepare herself for a terrible noise, —only she did not want any gunpowder brought into the house.

The little boys had begun by firing some torpedoes a few days beforehand, that their mother might be used to the sound, and had selected their horns some weeks before.

Solomon John had been very busy in inventing some fireworks. As Mrs. Peterkin objected to the use of gunpowder, he found out from the dictionary what the different parts of gunpowder are,— saltpetre, charcoal, and sulphur. Charcoal, he discovered, they had in the wood-house; saltpetre they would find in the cellar, in the beef barrel; and sulphur they could buy at the apothecary's. He explained to his mother that these materials had never yet exploded in the house, and she was quieted.

Agamemnon, meanwhile, remembered a recipe he had read somewhere for making a "fulminating paste" of iron-filings and powder of brimstone. He had written it down on a piece of paper in his pocket-book. But the iron filings must be finely powdered. This they began upon a day or two before, and the very afternoon before laid out some of the paste on the piazza.

Pin-wheels and rockets were contributed by Mr. Peterkin for the evening. According to a programme drawn up by Agamemnon and Solomon John, the reading of the Declaration of Independence was to take place in the morning, on the piazza, under the flags.

The Bromwicks brought over their flag to hang over the door.

"That is what the lady from Philadelphia meant," explained Elizabeth Eliza.

"She said the flags of our country," said the little boys. "We thought she meant 'in the country.'"

Quite a company assembled; but it seemed nobody had a copy of the Declaration of Independence.

Elizabeth Eliza said she could say one line, if they each could add as much. But it proved they all knew the same line that she did, as they began:—

"When, in the course of—when, in the course of—when, in the course of human—when in the course of human events—when, in the course of human events, it becomes—when, in the course of human events, it becomes necessary—when, in the course of human events, it becomes necessary for one people"—

They could not get any farther. Some of the party decided that "one people" was a good place to stop, and the little boys sent off some fresh torpedoes in honor of the people. But Mr. Peterkin was not satisfied. He invited the assembled party to stay until sunset, and meanwhile he would find a copy, and torpedoes were to be saved to be fired off at the close of every sentence.

And now the noon bells rang and the noon bells ceased.

Mrs. Peterkin wanted to ask everybody to dinner. She should have some cold beef. She had let Amanda go, because it was the Fourth, and everybody ought to be free that one day; so she could not have much of a dinner. But when she went to cut her beef she found Solomon had taken it to soak, on account of the saltpetre, for the fireworks!

Well, they had a pig; so she took a ham, and the boys had bought tamarinds and buns and a cocoa-nut. So the company stayed on, and when the Antiques and Horribles passed again they were treated to pea-nuts and lemonade.

They sung patriotic songs, they told stories, they fired torpedoes, they frightened the cats with them. It was a warm afternoon; the red poppies were out wide, and the hot sun poured down on the alley.

ways in the garden. There was a seething sound of a hot day in the buzzing of insects, in the steaming heat that came up from the ground. Some neighboring boys were firing a toy cannon. Every time it went off Mrs. Peterkin started, and looked to see if one of the little boys was gone. Mr. Peterkin had set out to find a copy of the "Declaration." Agamemnon had disappeared. She had not a moment to decide about her headache. She asked Ann Maria if she were not anxious about the fireworks, and if rockets were not dangerous. They went up, but you were never sure where they came down.

And then came a fresh tumult! All the fire-engines in town rushed toward them clanging with bells, men and boys yelling! They were out for a practice, and for a Fourth-of-July show.

Mrs. Peterkin thought the house was on fire, and so did some of the guests. There was a great rushing hither and thither. Some thought they would better go home; some thought they would better stay. Mrs. Peterkin hastened into the house to save herself, or see what she could save. Elizabeth Eliza followed her, first proceeding to collect all the pokers and tongs she could find, because they could be thrown out of the window without breaking. She had read of people who had flung looking-glasses out of the window by mistake, in the excitement of the house being on fire, and had carried the pokers and tongs carefully into the garden. There was nothing like being prepared. She had always determined to do the reverse. So with calmness she told Solomon John to take down the looking-glasses. But she met with a difficulty,—there were no pokers and tongs, as they did not use them. They had no open fires; Mrs. Peterkin had been afraid of them. So Elizabeth Eliza took all the pots and kettles up to the upper windows, ready to be thrown out.

But where was Mrs. Peterkin? Solomon John found she had fled to the attic in terror. He persuaded her to come down, assuring her it was the most unsafe place; but she insisted upon stopping to collect some bags of old pieces, that nobody would think of saving from the general wreck, she said, unless she did. Alas! this was the result of fireworks on Fourth of July! As they came downstairs they heard the voices of all the company declaring there was no fire; the danger was past. It was long before Mrs. Peterkin could believe it. They told her the fire company was only out for show, and to celebrate the Fourth of July. She thought it already too much celebrated.

Elizabeth Eliza's kettles and pans had come down through the windows with a crash, that had only added to the festivities, the little boys thought.

Mr. Peterkin had been roaming about all this time in search of a copy of the Declaration of Independence. The public library was shut, and he had to go from house to house; but now, as the sunset bells and cannon began, he returned with a copy, and read it, to the pealing of the bells and sounding of the cannon. Torpedoes and crackers were fired at every pause. Some sweet-marjoram pots, tin cans filled with crackers which were lighted, went off with great explosions.

At the most exciting moment, near the close of the reading, Agamemnon, with an expression of terror, pulled Solomon John aside.

"I have suddenly remembered where I read about the 'fulminating paste' we made. It was in the preface to 'Woodstock,' and I have been round to borrow the book, to read the directions over again, because I was afraid about the 'paste' going off. READ THIS QUICKLY! and tell me, *Where is the fulminating paste?*"

Solomon John was busy winding some covers of paper over a little parcel. It contained chlorate of potash and sulphur mixed. A friend had told him of the composition. The more thicknesses of paper you put round it the louder it would go off. You must pound it with a hammer. Solomon John felt it must be perfectly safe, as his mother had taken potash for a medicine.

He still held the parcel as he read from Agamemnon's book: "This paste, when it has lain together about twenty-six hours, will *of itself* take fire, and burn all the sulphur away with a blue flame and a bad smell."

"Where is the paste?" repeated Solomon John, in terror.

"We made it just twenty-six hours ago," said Agamemnon.

"We put it on the piazza," exclaimed Solomon John, rapidly recalling the facts, "and it is in front of our mother's feet!"

He hastened to snatch the paste away before it should take fire, flinging aside the packet in his hurry. Agamemnon, jumping upon the piazza at the same moment, trod upon the paper parcel, which exploded at once with the shock, and he fell to the ground, while at the same moment the paste "fulminated" into a blue flame directly in front of Mrs. Peterkin!

It was a moment of great confusion. There were cries and screams. The bells were still ringing, the cannon firing, and Mr. Peterkin had just reached the closing words: "Our lives, our fortunes, and our sacred honor."

"We are all blown up, as I feared we should be," Mrs. Peterkin at length ventured to say, finding herself in a lilac-bush by the side of the piazza. She scarcely dared to open her eyes to see the scattered limbs about her.

It was so with all. Even Ann Maria Bromwick clutched a pillar of the piazza, with closed eyes.

At length Mr. Peterkin said, calmly, "Is anybody killed?"

There was no reply. Nobody could tell whether it was because everybody was killed, or because they were too wounded to answer. It was a great while before Mrs. Peterkin ventured to move.

But the little boys soon shouted with joy, and cheered the success of Solomon John's fireworks, and hoped he had some more. One of them had his face blackened by an unexpected cracker, and Elizabeth Eliza's muslin dress was burned here and there. But no one was hurt; no one had lost any limbs, though Mrs. Peterkin was sure she had seen some flying in the air. Nobody could understand how, as she had kept her eyes firmly shut.

No greater accident had occurred than the singeing of the tip of Solomon John's nose. But there was an unpleasant and terrible odor from the "fulminating paste."

Mrs. Peterkin was extricated from the lilac-bush. No one knew how she got there. Indeed, the thundering noise had stunned everybody. It had roused the neighborhood even more than before. Answering explosions came on every side, and, though the sunset light had not faded away, the little boys hastened to send off rockets under cover of the confusion. Solomon John's other fireworks would not go. But all felt he had done enough.

Mrs. Peterkin retreated into the parlor, deciding she really did have a headache. At times she had to come out when a rocket went off, to see if it was one of the little boys. She was exhausted by the adventures of the day, and almost thought it could not have been worse if the boys had been allowed gunpowder. The distracted lady was thankful there was likely to be but one Centennial Fourth in her lifetime, and declared she should never more keep anything in the house as dangerous as saltpetred beef, and she should never venture to take another spoonful of potash.

Sally Benson

APPRECIATION OF ART

The auditorium of the Carlton School was crowded and noisy. The children from the lower grades had marched in and were seated in the front rows, where they twisted and uttered unintelligible, piercing cries. Occasionally Miss Moffatt, who taught American history, walked down the aisle and frowned at them, putting her finger to her lips. For a few minutes they would be still. Then they would begin to move and rustle again, and pull and shove at one another.

The performance of "The Tempest" given by the girls of the Junior School was scheduled to begin at eight-thirty, and at a quarter past eight almost every seat was filled. Lois Graves, who was usher in Aisle 3, had put her coat across two of the best seats in the twelfth row, so that when her parents arrived, fashionably late, she was ready for the emergency. She met them at the door and smiled at them politely. She wore a powder-blue taffeta evening dress that swept the floor, and stretched diagonally over one shoulder was a dark-green satin ribbon on which the word "Usher" was printed in large gold letters. In one hand she carried a flashlight and in the other she held some programs.

"Well, dear," Mrs. Graves said. She looked quickly at the other ushers to see if Lois's dress was quite suitable, and sighed with relief as she noted other taffeta dresses in pink, turquoise blue, and pale green. She noticed that little Mildred Farney's dress pulled too tightly across her breasts, and that Jane Turner had on an unbecoming shade of blue. "Well, dear," she repeated.

Lois turned away, brisk and professional, and led the way down the aisle. She walked neatly in her high heels, and when she reached the seats over which she had thrown her coat, she pressed the button of her flashlight and focussed the beam on the floor.

"Say," Mr. Graves said appreciatively, "this is great!"

Lois leaned over them. "You'd better hold my coat so that people won't—you know."

The woman in the adjoining seat stared at them and muttered, "Well, I *must* say!"

"Oh," Mrs. Graves said. "Do you think you should have, Lois?"

"Nuts," Lois whispered. "Don't pay any attention to that old gorilla. She's just mad because she wanted to sit on the aisle and I told her these seats were taken."

With a whirl of her skirts and a rustle of silk, she was gone.

Mrs. Graves put her hand on her husband's sleeve. "It was thoughtful of her just the same."

Mr. Graves opened his program and fished in his pocket for his glasses. "I don't believe I've ever seen 'The Tempest.' What's it about?"

"I'm sure I don't know," Mrs. Graves answered. "I've never even read it. Judy's playing Stephano. It's a boy's part." She held her program two feet away from her eyes and frowned. "Here it is. Here's her name. Judith Graves."

Mr. Graves adjusted his glasses. "Stephano, a drunken Butler," he read aloud.

"Well!" Mrs. Graves exclaimed. "Well!"

A sharp memory of a talk he had had with Judy a week before flashed into Mr. Graves' mind. "Daddy," she had asked, "how many drinks do you have to have before you get drunk?" And he had answered, "It all depends. A person might get drunk on one drink, and then again it might take twenty." "I suppose," Judy had persisted, "if you were used to it, it would take twenty." He had said he imagined it would. And Judy seemed satisfied.

Mrs. Graves looked at him anxiously. "I suppose they know what they're doing. Giving a part like that to a little girl, I mean."

"Oh, sure," he said.

She glanced at her program thoughtfully. "I think it would have been nice if they had decided to give 'The Mikado.' They planned to at first. Except there weren't enough girls who could sing. Here's Fuffy Adams' name. She's going to be Trinculo, a Jester."

"I saw Pete Adams when we came in. He's putting on weight."

"They rented the costumes. Even the wigs."

"Have you seen Judy's costume?" Mr. Graves asked.

"No," she answered. "They only got them yesterday, in time for dress rehearsal. I haven't even heard her lines. She said them for Hilda, but it was the night we played bridge with the Conovers. I heard her in the kitchen, though, and she seemed to be shouting."

"I wouldn't worry."

"Oh, I'm not worrying. After all, Miss Lucy Smith is coaching them, and she must know what she's doing."

There were signs of excitement among the children in the first rows, and at a signal from a slender, faded, blonde woman who appeared from a door at the left, fifteen of them arose and marched up the stairs onto the stage. They stood there swallowing nervously, their arms hanging limply at their sides. Their dresses had become mussed and their eyes were glassy. The blonde woman, a Miss Avery, sat down at the piano and struck an opening chord.

"It's the school song," Mrs. Graves whispered. "I suppose we ought to stand."

According to the program, the words to the school song had been written by a Miss Dorothy Brewer, '09, but the tune was "Flow Gently, Sweet Afton."

Mrs. Graves watched the young faces of the Junior Glee Club tenderly, and her heart melted within her. They started to sing slightly off key, but the sound of their own voices gave them reassurance, and the words rang out clear and sweet:

> The mem'ries of school days will never grow old,
> So raise high the colors, the green and the gold.

For no reason at all, her eyes smarted, and she fumbled in her evening bag for a handkerchief.

> Our dear Alma Mater, our own Carlton School,
> May she evermore flourish and over us rule.

As the song ended there was a burst of applause, which stopped abruptly as Miss Avery swung into the opening bars of "The Star-Spangled Banner." The audience joined enthusiastically in the singing.

"I imagine the play will begin now," Mrs. Graves said, rearranging her evening wrap on the back of the seat. "I wonder when Judy comes on. It would be funny if we didn't recognize her, wouldn't it?"

"We'll know her all right," Mr. Graves said.

The girls of the Junior Glee Club marched back to their places and the lights grew dim. The curtains parted, showing a black backdrop. There was a flash of lightning from above and the sound of tinny thunder. The play had begun.

"They've got the stage awfully dark," Mrs. Graves whispered. "Can you see Judy?"

"I think this crowd are supposed to be sailors. They look as though they're pulling at ropes."

The voices of the girls were lost in the rolls of thunder, and the curtain fell.

"Well, that was short, anyway," Mr. Graves said. "The next scene is on an island."

The curtain rose again; the backdrop had been lifted and the stage was larger. In the direct centre at the rear was an opening surrounded by unbleached muslin that had been dyed gray with green spots to represent a rocky entrance to a cave, and to the right of this stood a small spruce tree in a tub. From the wings came two figures, both strictly feminine, although one of them wore a long, gray, matted beard, a shaggy white wig, black tights, and a doublet. "Prospero," Mrs. Graves said. "And that's Miranda with him. The Burchell child."

Miranda had on a black wig bound with a fillet. It was made of the blackest hair Mrs. Graves had ever seen, and from under it Polly Burchell's face peered, small and round. She walked with the slow, forlorn gait of an overworked chambermaid in a second-rate hotel, but as she began to speak she came to life and gestured with her arms. When she finished her lines, she lapsed into a coma and stared out into the audience during the time Prospero took up the plot. The scene was long, and Mrs. Graves was glad when Ariel danced from the wings. Ariel's tunic was embarrassingly short, and she seemed to be suffering from an acute form of St. Vitus's dance.

"What's the matter with her?" Mr. Graves asked.

"I imagine Miss Smith told her to keep moving, the poor little thing. She's a sprite, you see."

The play dragged on. As each character appeared for the first time, there was a burst of applause from relatives and school friends. Mrs. Graves sat tensely, waiting for Judy's entrance. But Act I ended and there had been no sign of her.

"She probably has just a small part," Mrs. Graves said when the lights went up. "The girls *do* mutter, don't they?" She clapped half-heartedly. "I don't see how Judy can be a *drunken* butler. After all, it's supposed to be an almost deserted island, and there couldn't very well be any liquor on it. At least, I don't see where it would come from. The ship is wrecked. Besides, I don't think Judy would know how to act drunk. As far as I know, she's never even seen anyone very drunk."

"Of course she hasn't," Mr. Graves said. "A little high, maybe, but not boiled."

They waited for her entrance until Act II, Scene 2. A small, fat Caliban, dressed in what looked to be a fur union suit, and Fuffy Adams as Trinculo were talking together when Mrs. Graves heard a voice singing in the wings. It was the first completely audible voice in the performance, and it was Judy's. She reeled onto the stage, a bottle in her hand. Her smooth, dark-brown hair was covered with a straw-colored wig, the tip of her nose was painted a bright red. Her clothes were awry and she looked as tight as an owl.

"This is a very scurvy tune to sing at a man's funeral. Well, here's my comfort," she shouted, and, lifting the bottle to her lips, she took a healthy swig.

The children in the audience broke into delighted laughter, and Judy, hearing them, lifted the bottle again and staggered across the stage, throwing a heavy arm around Fuffy Adams, who giggled with abandon.

The force of Judy's entrance took Caliban off guard and struck her dumb. She forgot her rôle of savage and deformed slave and stood by as quietly as a baby panda in her furry suit, watching Judy's antics. Each time Judy lifted the bottle to her lips the laughter from the lower grades got louder. Over the noise, Judy's voice rang out, blurred with drink, loud and insinuating. She spun around, crying, "Prithee, do not turn me about. My stomach is not constant." And as an added touch, she put her hand on her small, firm stomach and hiccoughed.

When the curtain fell, the applause was deafening. It continued until Judy stood alone on the stage. She lifted the bottle to her lips and reeled again.

Mr. and Mrs. Graves were silent as the lights went on. Finally, Mrs. Graves spoke. "I can't believe it. I can't imagine what's got into her." She looked at her husband and saw that he was smiling.

"You could hear her, anyway," he said.

"Oh, you could hear her all right."

They sat through the next three acts and watched Judy faithfully portray various stages of intoxication; she fought, she laughed senselessly, she was sad, she lapsed into self-pity, and her last line, spoken in a maudlin whine—"O! touch me not. I am not Stephano, but a cramp"—brought down the house.

She gave a superb performance. She took four curtain calls and her cheeks were flushed and her eyes bright. The flowers that Mr. Graves had sent were delivered over the footlights, and she stood holding them in one hand while she clutched the bottle with the other.

Mrs. Graves slipped her wrap over her shoulders. "I wonder where Lois is. I hope she isn't minding too much."

"Judy was good," Mr. Graves said. "She was damned good."

They walked up the aisle. At the door, Pete Adams stopped them and clapped Mr. Graves on the shoulders. "Best thing I ever saw, the act your daughter put on!" he cried. "Reminded me of you, Harry." He wiped the tears from his eyes and coughed convulsively. "Congratulations, Grace! Congratulations!"

Mrs. Graves caught sight of Miss Lucy Smith and glanced hastily away. But Miss Smith bore down on them. She was a plump, white-haired woman, and she was smiling. "Wasn't Judy marvellous?" she said. "I had no idea she had it in her. She didn't act at all like that at rehearsals. To tell you the truth"—she lowered her voice—"I thought she made the other girls seem a trifle *wooden*."

The door to the basement opened and the members of the cast streamed out. In the centre of the group was Judy. She had taken off her wig and her soft hair fell to her shoulders. She carried the property bottle in one hand and her face was streaked with makeup. In her eyes shone a look of utter joy and pride. With her, holding tightly to her arm, was Lois, who caught sight of her father and mother. "Here she is!" she called. "Here's Judy! Talk about your Moscow Art Theatre for real swell acting!"

Judy ran toward them and Mrs. Graves caught her in her arms. She smelled of grease paint, perspiration, and moth balls, and she was trembling.

For an instant she buried her face against her mother, and Mrs. Graves knew that she was close to tears. "You were lovely, Judy darling," she whispered.

"You were great!" Mr. Graves said, and patted her head roughly. Children crowded around them and teachers and parents stopped to congratulate them. Judy seemed to be living in a dream. She leaned closer to her mother and then shook herself free. "Here," she said, and handed the bottle to her father. "Miss Smith says I can keep this for a souvenir. Hold it for me, will you, while I change my clothes?"

Mr. Graves took the bottle, which was made of papier-mâché, and tucked it proudly under his arm. "You run along," he said. "We'll wait here for you. And take your time. There's no hurry."

Booth Tarkington

WHITEY *

Penrod and Sam made a gloomy discovery one morning in mid-October. All the week had seen amiable breezes and fair skies until Saturday, when, about breakfast-time, the dome of heaven filled solidly with gray vapour and began to drip. The boys' discovery was that there is no justice about the weather.

They sat in the carriage-house of the Schofields' empty stable; the doors upon the alley were open, and Sam and Penrod stared torpidly at the thin but implacable drizzle which was the more irritating because there was barely enough of it to interfere with a number of things they had planned to do.

"Yes; this is *nice!*" Sam said, in a tone of plaintive sarcasm. "This is a *perty* way to do!" (He was alluding to the personal spitefulness of the elements.) "I'd like to know what's the sense of it—ole sun pourin' down every day in the week when nobody needs it, then cloud up and rain all Saturday! My father said it's goin' to be a three days' rain."

"Well, nobody with any sense cares if it rains Sunday and Monday," said Penrod. "I wouldn't care if it rained every Sunday as long I lived; but I just like to know what's the reason it had to go and rain to-day. Got all the days o' the week to choose from and goes and picks on Saturday. That's a fine biz'nuss!"

"Well, in vacation——" Sam began, but at a sound from a source invisible to him he paused. "What's that?" he said, somewhat startled.

It was a curious sound, loud and hollow and unhuman, yet it seemed to be a cough. Both boys rose, and Penrod asked uneasily:

"Where'd that noise come from?"

"It's in the alley," said Sam.

* *Three chapters from "Penrod and Sam."*

Perhaps if the day had been bright, both of them would have stepped immediately to the alley doors to investigate; but their actual procedure was to move a little distance in the opposite direction. The strange cough sounded again.

"*Say!*" Penrod quavered. "What *is* that?"

Then both boys uttered smothered exclamations and jumped, for the long, gaunt head which appeared in the doorway was entirely unexpected. It was the cavernous and melancholy head of an incredibly thin, old, whitish horse. This head waggled slowly from side to side; the nostrils vibrated; the mouth opened, and the hollow cough sounded again.

Recovering themselves, Penrod and Sam underwent the customary human reaction from alarm to indignation.

"What you want, you ole horse, you?" Penrod shouted. "Don't you come coughin' around *me!*"

And Sam, seizing a stick, hurled it at the intruder.

"Get out o' here!" he roared.

The aged horse nervously withdrew his head, turned tail, and made a rickety flight up the alley, while Sam and Penrod, perfectly obedient to inherited impulse, ran out into the drizzle and uproariously pursued. They were but automatons of instinct, meaning no evil. Certainly they did not know the singular and pathetic history of the old horse who had wandered into the alley and ventured to look through the open door.

This horse, about twice the age of either Penrod or Sam, had lived to find himself in a unique position. He was nude, possessing neither harness nor halter; all he had was a name, Whitey, and he would have answered to it by a slight change of expression if any one had thus properly addressed him. So forlorn was Whitey's case, he was actually an independent horse; he had not even an owner. For two days and a half he had been his own master.

Previous to that period he had been the property of one Abalene Morris, a person of colour, who would have explained himself as engaged in the hauling business. On the contrary, the hauling business was an insignificant side line with Mr. Morris, for he had long ago given himself, as utterly as fortune permitted, to that talent which, early in youth, he had recognized as the greatest of all those surging in his bosom. In his waking thoughts and in his dreams, in health and in sickness, Abalene Morris was the dashing and emotional prac-

titioner of an art probably more than Roman in antiquity. Abalene
was a crap-shooter. The hauling business was a disguise.

A concentration of events had brought it about that, at one and
the same time, Abalene, after a dazzling run of the dice, found the
hauling business an actual danger to the preservation of his liberty.
He won seventeen dollars and sixty cents, and within the hour
found himself in trouble with an officer of the Humane Society on
account of an altercation with Whitey. Abalene had been offered four
dollars for Whitey some ten days earlier; wherefore he at once drove
to the shop of the junk-dealer who had made the offer and announced
his acquiescence in the sacrifice.

"*No,* suh!" said the junk-dealer, with emphasis. "I awready done
got me a good mule fer my deliv'ry hoss, 'n'at ole Whitey hoss ain'
wuff no fo' dollah nohow! I 'uz a fool when I talk 'bout th'owin'
money roun' that a-way. *I* know what *you* up to, Abalene. Man
come by here li'l bit ago tole me all 'bout white man try to 'rest
you, ovah on the avvynoo. Yessuh; he say white man goin' to git
you yit an' th'ow you in jail 'count o' Whitey. White man tryin'
to fine out who you *is.* He say, nemmine, he'll know Whitey ag'in,
even if he don' know you! He say he ketch you by the hoss; so
you come roun' tryin' fix me up with Whitey so white man grab me,
th'ow *me* in 'at jail. G'on 'way f'um hyuh, you Abalene! You cain'
sell an' you cain' give Whitey to no cullud man 'n 'is town. You go
an' drowned 'at ole hoss, 'cause you sutny goin' to jail if you git
ketched drivin' him."

The substance of this advice seemed good to Abalene, especially as
the seventeen dollars and sixty cents in his pocket lent sweet colours
to life out of jail at this time. At dusk he led Whitey to a broad common at the edge of town, and spoke to him finally.

"G'on, 'bout you biz'nis," said Abalene; "you ain' *my* hoss. Don'
look roun' at me, 'cause *I* ain' got no 'quaintance wif you. I'm a man
o' money, an' I got my own frien's; I'm a-lookin' fer bigger cities,
hoss. You got you' biz'nis an' I got mine. Mista' Hoss, good-night!"

Whitey found a little frosted grass upon the common and remained
there all night. In the morning he sought the shed where Abalene
had kept him, but that was across the large and busy town, and
Whitey was hopelessly lost. He had but one eye, a feeble one, and
his legs were not to be depended upon; but he managed to cover a
great deal of ground, to have many painful little adventures, and to

get monstrously hungry and thirsty before he happened to look in upon Penrod and Sam.

When the two boys chased him up the alley they had no intention to cause pain; they had no intention at all. They were no more cruel than Duke, Penrod's little old dog, who followed his own instincts, and, making his appearance hastily through a hole in the back fence, joined the pursuit with sound and fury. A boy will nearly always run after anything that is running, and his first impulse is to throw a stone at it. This is a survival of primeval man, who must take every chance to get his dinner. So, when Penrod and Sam drove the hapless Whitey up the alley, they were really responding to an impulse thousands and thousands of years old—an impulse founded upon the primordial observation that whatever runs is likely to prove edible. Penrod and Sam were not "bad"; they were never that. They were something which was not their fault; they were historic.

At the next corner Whitey turned to the right into the cross-street; thence, turning to the right again and still warmly pursued, he zig-zagged down a main thoroughfare until he reached another cross-street, which ran alongside the Schofields' yard and brought him to the foot of the alley he had left behind in his flight. He entered the alley, and there his dim eye fell upon the open door he had previously investigated. No memory of it remained, but the place had a look associated in his mind with hay, and as Sam and Penrod turned the corner of the alley in panting yet still vociferous pursuit, Whitey stumbled up the inclined platform before the open doors, staggered thunderously across the carriage-house and through another open door into a stall, an apartment vacant since the occupancy of Mr. Schofield's last horse, now several years deceased.

The two boys shrieked with excitement as they beheld the coincidence of this strange return. They burst into the stable, making almost as much noise as Duke, who had become frantic at the invasion. Sam laid hands upon a rake.

"You get out o' there, you ole horse, you!" he bellowed. "I ain't afraid to drive him out. I——"

"*Wait* a minute!" shouted Penrod. "Wait till I——"

Sam was manfully preparing to enter the stall.

"You hold the doors open," he commanded, "so's they won't blow shut and keep him in here. I'm goin' to hit him with——"

"Quee-*yut!*" Penrod shouted, grasping the handle of the rake so that Sam could not use it. "Wait a *minute,* can't you " He turned with ferocious voice and gestures upon Duke. *"Duke!"* And Duke, in spite of his excitement, was so impressed that he prostrated himself in silence, and then unobtrusively withdrew from the stable. Penrod ran to the alley doors and closed them.

"My gracious!" Sam protested. "What you goin' to do?"

"I'm goin' to keep this horse," said Penrod, whose face showed the strain of a great idea.

"What *for?*"

"For the reward," said Penrod simply.

Sam sat down in the wheelbarrow and stared at his friend almost with awe.

"My gracious," he said, "I never thought o' that. How—how much do you think we'll get, Penrod?"

Sam's thus admitting himself to a full partnership in the enterprise met no objection from Penrod, who was absorbed in the contemplation of Whitey.

"Well," he said judicially, "we might get more and we might get less."

Sam rose and joined his friend in the doorway opening upon the two stalls. Whitey had preëmpted the nearer, and was hungrily nuzzling the old frayed hollows in the manger.

"Maybe a hundred dollars—or sumpthing?" Sam asked in a low voice.

Penrod maintained his composure and repeated the new-found expression which had sounded well to him a moment before. He recognized it as a symbol of the non-committal attitude that makes people looked up to. "Well"—he made it slow, and frowned—"we might get more and we might get less."

"More'n a hundred *dollars?*" Sam gasped.

"Well," said Penrod, "we might get more and we might get less." This time, however, he felt the need of adding something. He put a question in an indulgent tone, as though he were inquiring, not to add to his own information but to discover the extent of Sam's. "How much do you think horses are worth, anyway?"

"I don't know," said Sam frankly, and unconsciously, he added, "They might be more and they might be less."

"Well, when our ole horse died," said Penrod, "papa said he wouldn't take five hundred dollars for him. That's how much *horses* are worth!"

"My gracious!" Sam exclaimed. Then he had a practical after-thought. "But maybe he was a better horse than this'n. What colour was he?"

"He was bay. Looky here, Sam"—and now Penrod's manner changed, from the superior to the eager—"you look what kind of horses they have in a circus, and you bet a circus has the *best* horses, don't it? Well, what kind of horses do they have in a circus? They have some black and white ones, but the best they have are white all over. Well, what kind of a horse is this we got here? He's perty near white right now, and I bet if we washed him off and got him fixed up nice he *would* be white. Well, a bay horse is worth five hundred dollars, because that's what papa said, and this horse——"

Sam interrupted rather timidly.

"He—he's awful bony, Penrod. You don't guess that'd make any—"

Penrod laughed contemptuously.

"Bony! All he needs is a little food and he'll fill right up and look good as ever. You don't know much about horses, Sam, I expect. Why, *our* ole horse—"

"Do you expect he's hungry now?" asked Sam, staring at Whitey.

"Let's try him," said Penrod. "Horses like hay and oats the best, but they'll eat most anything."

"I guess they will. He's tryin' to eat that manger up right now, and I bet it ain't good for him."

"Come on," said Penrod, closing the door that gave entrance to the stalls. "We got to get this horse some drinkin'-water and some good food."

They tried Whitey's appetite first with an autumnal branch which they wrenched from a hardy maple in the yard. They had seen horses nibble leaves, and they expected Whitey to nibble the leaves of this branch, but his ravenous condition did not allow him time for cool discriminations. Sam poked the branch at him from the passageway, and Whitey, after one backward movement of alarm, seized it venomously.

"Here! You stop that!" Sam shouted. "You stop that, you ole horse, you!"

"What's the matter?" called Penrod from the hydrant, where he was filling a bucket. "What's he doin' now?"

"Doin'! He's eatin' the wood part, too! He's chewin' up sticks as big as baseball bats! He's crazy!"

Penrod rushed to see this sight, and stood aghast.

"Take it away from him, Sam!" he commanded sharply.

"Go on, take it away from him yourself!" was the prompt retort of his comrade.

"You had no biz'nuss to give it to him," said Penrod. "Anybody with any sense ought to know it'd make him sick. What'd you want to go and give it to him for?"

"Well, you didn't say not to."

"Well, what if I didn't? I never said I did, did I? You go on in that stall and take it away from him."

"*Yes,* I will!" Sam returned bitterly. Then, as Whitey had dragged the remains of the branch from the manger to the floor of the stall, Sam scrambled to the top of the manger and looked over. "There ain't much left to *take* away! He's swallered it all except some splinters. Better give him the water to try and wash it down with." And, as Penrod complied, "My gracious, look at that horse *drink!*"

They gave Whitey four buckets of water, and then debated the question of nourishment. Obviously, this horse could not be trusted with branches, and, after getting their knees black and their backs sodden, they gave up trying to pull enough grass to sustain him. Then Penrod remembered that horses like apples, both "cooking-apples" and "eating-apples," and Sam mentioned the fact that every autumn his father received a barrel of "cooking-apples" from a cousin who owned a farm. That barrel was in the Williams' cellar now, and the cellar was providentially supplied with "outside doors," so that it could be visited without going through the house. Sam and Penrod set forth for the cellar.

They returned to the stable bulging, and, after a discussion of Whitey's digestion (Sam claiming that eating the core and seeds, as Whitey did, would grow trees in his inside), they went back to the cellar for supplies again—and again. They made six trips, carrying each time a capacity cargo of apples, and still Whitey ate in a famished manner. They were afraid to take more apples from the barrel, which began to show conspicuously the result of their raids, wherefore Penrod made an unostentatious visit to the cellar of his own house. From the inside he opened a window and passed vegetables out to Sam, who placed them in a bucket and carried them hurriedly to the stable, while Penrod returned in a casual manner through the house. Of his *sang-froid* under a great strain it is sufficient to relate that, in the kitchen, he said suddenly to Della, the cook, "Oh, look behind you!" and by the time Della discovered that there was nothing unusual behind her, Penrod was gone, and a loaf of bread from the kitchen table was gone with him.

Whitey now ate nine turnips, two heads of lettuce, one cabbage, eleven raw potatoes, and the loaf of bread. He ate the loaf of bread last and he was a long time about it; so the boys came to a not unreasonable conclusion.

"Well, sir, I guess we got him filled up at last!" said Penrod. "I bet he wouldn't eat a saucer of ice-cream now, if we'd give it to him!"

"He looks better to me," said Sam, staring critically at Whitey. "I think he's kind of begun to fill out some. I expect he must like us, Penrod; we been doin' a good deal for this horse."

"Well, we got to keep it up," Penrod insisted rather pompously. "Long as *I* got charge o' this horse, he's goin' to get good treatment."

"What we better do now, Penrod?"

Penrod took on the outward signs of deep thought.

"Well, there's plenty to *do,* all right. I got to think."

Sam made several suggestions, which Penrod—maintaining his air of preoccupation—dismissed with mere gestures.

"Oh, *I* know!" Sam cried finally. "We ought to wash him so's he'll look whiter'n what he does now. We can turn the hose on him acrost the manger."

"No; not yet," said Penrod. "It's too soon after his meal. You ought to know that yourself. What we got to do is to make up a bed for him—if he wants to lay down or anything."

"Make up a what for him?" Sam echoed, dumfounded. "What you talkin' about? How can—"

"Sawdust," said Penrod. "That's the way the horse we used to have used to have it. We'll make this horse's bed in the other stall, and then he can go in there and lay down whenever he wants to."

"How we goin' to do it?"

"Look, Sam; there's the hole into the sawdust-box! All you got to do is walk in there with the shovel, stick the shovel in the hole till it gets full of sawdust, and then sprinkle it around on the empty stall."

"All *I* got to do!" Sam cried. "What are you goin' to do?"

"I'm goin' to be right here," Penrod answered reassuringly. "He won't kick or anything, and it isn't goin' to take you half a second to slip around behind him to the other stall."

"What makes you think he won't kick?"

"Well, I *know* he won't, and, besides, you could hit him with the shovel if he tried to. Anyhow, I'll be right here, won't I?"

"I don't care where you are," Sam said earnestly. "What difference would that make if he ki—"

"Why, you were goin' right in the stall," Penrod reminded him. "When he first came in, you were goin' to take the rake and—"

"I don't care if I was," Sam declared. "I was excited then."

"Well, you can get excited now, can't you?" his friend urged. "You can just as easy get—"

He was interrupted by a shout from Sam, who was keeping his eye upon Whitey throughout the discussion.

"Look! Looky there!" And undoubtedly renewing his excitement, Sam pointed at the long, gaunt head beyond the manger. It was disappearing from view. "Look!" Sam shouted. "He's layin' down!"

"Well, then," said Penrod, "I guess he's goin' to take a nap. If he wants to lay down without waitin' for us to get the sawdust fixed for him, that's his lookout, not ours."

On the contrary, Sam perceived a favourable opportunity for action.

"I just as soon go and make his bed up while he's layin' down," he volunteered. "You climb up on the manger and watch him, Penrod, and I'll sneak in the other stall and fix it all up nice for him, so's he can go in there any time when he wakes up, and lay down again, or anything; and if he starts to get up, you holler and I'll jump out over the other manger."

Accordingly, Penrod established himself in a position to observe the recumbent figure. Whitey's breathing was rather laboured but regular, and, as Sam remarked, he looked "better," even in his slumber. It is not to be doubted that, although Whitey was suffering from a light attack of colic, his feelings were in the main those of contentment. After trouble, he was solaced; after exposure, he was sheltered; after hunger and thirst, he was fed and watered. He slept.

The noon whistles blew before Sam's task was finished, but by the time he departed for lunch there was made a bed of such quality that Whitey must needs have been a born faultfinder if he complained of

it. The friends parted, each urging the other to be prompt in returning, but Penrod got into threatening difficulties as soon as he entered
the house.

"Penrod," said his mother, "what did you do with that loaf of bread
Della says you took from the table?"

"Ma'am? *What* loaf o' bread?"

"I believe I can't let you go outdoors this afternoon," Mrs. Schofield
said severely. "If you were hungry, you know perfectly well all you
had to do was to—"

"But I wasn't hungry; I—"

"You can explain later," said Mrs. Schofield. "You'll have all afternoon."

Penrod's heart grew cold.

"I *can't* stay in," he protested. "I've asked Sam Williams to come
over."

"I'll telephone Mrs. Williams."

"Mamma!" Penrod's voice became agonized. "I *had* to give that
bread to a—to a poor ole man. He was starving and so were his children and his wife. They were all just *starving*—and they couldn't wait
while I took time to come and ask you, mamma. I *got* to go outdoors
this afternoon. I *got* to! Sam's—"

She relented.

In the carriage-house, half an hour later, Penrod gave an account of
the episode.

"Where'd we been, I'd just like to know," he concluded, "if I
hadn't got out here this afternoon?"

"Well, I guess I could managed him all right," said Sam. "I was in
the passageway, a minute ago, takin' a look at him. He's standin' up
again. I expect he wants more to eat."

"Well, we got to fix about that," said Penrod. "But what I mean—
if I'd had to stay in the house, where would we been about the most
important thing in the whole biz'nuss?"

"What you talkin' about?"

"Well, why can't you wait till I tell you?" Penrod's tone had become
peevish. For that matter, so had Sam's; they were developing one of
the little differences, or quarrels, that composed the very texture of
their friendship.

"Well, why don't you tell me, then?"

"Well, how can I?" Penrod demanded. "You keep talkin' every minute."

"I'm not talkin' *now*, am I?" Sam protested. "You can tell me *now*, can't you? I'm not talk—"

"You are, too!" shouted Penrod. "You talk all the time! You—"

He was interrupted by Whitey's peculiar cough. Both boys jumped and forgot their argument.

"He means he wants some more to eat, I bet," said Sam.

"Well, if he does, he's got to wait," Penrod declared. "We got to get the most important thing of all fixed up first."

"What's that, Penrod?"

"The reward," said Penrod mildly. "That's what I was tryin' to tell you about, Sam, if you'd ever give me half a chance."

"Well, I *did* give you a chance. I kept *tellin'* you to tell me, but—"

"You never! You kept sayin'—"

They renewed this discussion, protracting it indefinitely; but as each persisted in clinging to his own interpretation of the facts, the question still remained unsettled. It was abandoned, or rather, it merged into another during the later stages of the debate, this other being concerned with which of the debaters had the least "sense." Each made the plain statement that if he were more deficient than his opponent in that regard, self-destruction would be his only refuge. Each declared that he would "rather die than be talked to death"; and then, as the two approached a point bluntly recriminative, Whitey coughed again, whereupon they were miraculously silent, and went into the passageway in a perfectly amiable manner.

"I got to have a good look at him, for once," said Penrod, as he stared frowningly at Whitey. "We got to fix up about that reward."

"I want to take a good ole look at him myself," said Sam.

After supplying Whitey with another bucket of water, they returned to the carriage-house and seated themselves thoughtfully. In truth, they were something a shade more than thoughtful; the adventure to which they had committed themselves was beginning to be a little overpowering. If Whitey had been a dog, a goat, a fowl, or even a stray calf, they would have felt equal to him; but now that the earlier glow of their wild daring had disappeared, vague apprehensions stirred. Their "good look" at Whitey had not reassured them—he seemed large, Gothic, and unusual.

Whisperings within them began to urge that for boys to undertake an enterprise connected with so huge an animal as an actual horse was perilous. Beneath the surface of their musings, dim but ominous prophecies moved; both boys began to have the feeling that, somehow, this affair was going to get beyond them and that they would be in heavy trouble before it was over—they knew not why. They knew why no more than they knew why they felt it imperative to keep the fact of Whitey's presence in the stable a secret from their respective families, but they did begin to realize that keeping a secret of that size was going to be attended with some difficulty. In brief, their sensations were becoming comparable to those of the man who stole a house.

Nevertheless, after a short period given to unspoken misgivings, they returned to the subject of the reward. The money-value of bay horses, as compared to white, was again discussed, and each announced his certainty that nothing less than "a good ole hunderd dollars" would be offered for the return of Whitey.

But immediately after so speaking they fell into another silence, due to sinking feelings. They had spoken loudly and confidently, and yet they knew, somehow, that such things were not to be. According to their knowledge, it was perfectly reasonable to suppose that they would receive this fortune, but they frightened themselves in speaking of it; they knew that they *could* not have a hundred dollars for their own. An oppression, as from something awful and criminal, descended upon them at intervals.

Presently, however, they were warmed to a little cheerfulness again by Penrod's suggestion that they should put a notice in the paper. Neither of them had the slightest idea how to get it there, but such details as that were beyond the horizon; they occupied themselves with the question of what their advertisement ought to "say." Finding that they differed irreconcilably, Penrod went to a cache of his in the sawdust-box and brought two pencils and a supply of paper. He gave one of the pencils and several sheets to Sam; then both boys bent themselves in silence to the labour of practical composition. Penrod produced the briefer paragraph. (See Fig. I.) Sam's was more ample. (See Fig. II.)

Neither Sam nor Penrod showed any interest in what the other had written, but both felt that something praiseworthy had been accomplished. Penrod exhaled a sigh, as of relief, and, in a manner he had observed his father use sometimes, he said·

FIG I

Reward.

White horse in Schofields ally finders got him in Schofieldsy stable and will let him taken away by by ~~payi~~ paying for good food he has aten while ~~wat un~~ while ~~wat~~ waiting and

Reward of ~~$400~~ ~~$20~~ ~~$15~~ ~~$5~~ $10

FIG II

FOND

Horse on Saterday moring onwer can get him by ~~the~~ applyeng at stable bhind Mr Schofield ● You will have to proov he is your horse he is whit with kind of brown ~~spot~~ speks and worout ~~fat~~ tall he is geting good care and food reword ~~$15~~ ~~$10~~ seventy five conts each one or we will keep him lock up ●

"Thank goodness, *that's* off my mind, anyway!"

"What we goin' do next, Penrod?" Sam asked deferentially, the borrowed manner having some effect upon him.

"I don't know what *you're* goin' to do," Penrod returned, picking up the old cigarbox which had contained the paper and pencils. *"I'm* goin' to put mine in here, so's it'll come in handy when I haf to get at it."

"Well, I guess I'll keep mine there, too," said Sam. Thereupon he deposited his scribbled slip beside Penrod's in the cigarbox, and the box was solemnly returned to the secret place whence it had been taken.

"There, *that's* 'tended to!" said Sam, and, unconsciously imitating his friend's imitation, he gave forth audibly a breath of satisfaction and relief. Both boys felt that the financial side of their great affair had been conscientiously looked to, that the question of the reward was settled, and that everything was proceeding in a businesslike manner. Therefore, they were able to turn their attention to another matter.

This was the question of Whitey's next meal. After their exploits of the morning, and the consequent imperilment of Penrod, they decided that nothing more was to be done in apples, vegetables, or bread; it was evident that Whitey must be fed from the bosom of nature.

"We couldn't pull enough o' that frostbit ole grass in the yard to feed him," Penrod said gloomily. "We could work a week and not get enough to make him swaller more'n about twice. All we got this morning, he blew most of it away. He'd try to scoop it in toward his teeth with his lip, and then he'd haf to kind of blow out his breath, and after that all the grass that'd be left was just some wet pieces stickin' to the outsides of his face. Well, and you know how he acted about that maple branch. We can't trust him with branches."

Sam jumped up.

"*I* know!" he cried. "There's lots of leaves left on the branches. We can give them to him."

"I just said—"

"I don't mean the branches," Sam explained. "We'll leave the branches on the trees, but just pull the leaves off the branches and put 'em in the bucket and feed 'em to him out the bucket."

Penrod thought this plan worth trying, and for three-quarters of an hour the two boys were busy with the lower branches of various trees in the yard. Thus they managed to supply Whitey with a fair quantity of wet leaves, which he ate in a perfunctory way, displaying little of his earlier enthusiasm. And the work of his purveyors might have been more tedious if it had been less damp, for a boy is seldom bored by anything that involves his staying-out in the rain without protection. The drizzle had thickened; the leaves were heavy with water, and at every jerk the branches sent fat drops over the two collectors. They attained a noteworthy state of sogginess.

Finally, they were brought to the attention of the authorities indoors, and Della appeared upon the back porch.

"Musther Penrod," she called, "y'r mamma says ye'll c'm in the house this minute an' change y'r shoes an' stockin's an' everythun' else ye got on! D'ye hear me?"

Penrod, taken by surprise and unpleasantly alarmed, darted away from the tree he was depleting and ran for the stable.

"You tell her I'm dry as toast!" he shouted over his shoulder.

Della withdrew, wearing the air of a person gratuitously insulted; and a moment later she issued from the kitchen, carrying an umbrella. She opened it and walked resolutely to the stable.

"She says I'm to bring ye in the house," said Della, "an' I'm goin' to bring ye!"

Sam had joined Penrod in the carriage-house, and, with the beginnings of an unnamed terror, the two beheld this grim advance. But they did not stay for its culmination. Without a word to each other they hurriedly tiptoed up the stairs to the gloomy loft, and there they paused, listening.

They heard Della's steps upon the carriage-house floor.

"Ah, there's plenty places t'hide in," they heard her say; "but I'll show ye! She tole me to bring ye, and I'm—"

She was interrupted by a peculiar sound—loud, chilling, dismal, and unmistakably not of human origin. The boys knew it for Whitey's cough, but Della had not their experience. A smothered shriek reached their ears; there was a scurrying noise, and then, with horror, they heard Della's footsteps in the passageway that ran by Whitey's manger. Immediately there came a louder shriek, and even in the anguish of knowing their secret discovered, they were shocked to hear distinctly the words, "O Lard in hivvin!" in the well-known voice of Della. She shrieked again, and they heard the rush of her footfalls across the carriage-house floor. Wild words came from the outer air, and the kitchen door slammed violently. It was all over. She had gone to "tell."

Penrod and Sam plunged down the stairs and out of the stable. They climbed the back fence and fled up the alley. They turned into Sam's yard, and, without consultation, headed for the cellar doors, nor paused till they found themselves in the farthest, darkest, and gloomiest recess of the cellar. There, perspiring, stricken with fear, they sank down upon the earthen floor, with their moist backs against the stone wall.

Thus with boys. The vague apprehensions that had been creeping upon Penrod and Sam all afternoon had become monstrous; the unknown was before them. How great their crime would turn out to be (now that it was in the hands of grown people), they did not know, but, since it concerned a horse, it would undoubtedly be considered of terrible dimensions.

Their plans for a reward, and all the things that had seemed both innocent and practical in the morning, now staggered their minds as manifestations of criminal folly. A new and terrible light seemed to play upon the day's exploits; they had chased a horse belonging to strangers, and it would be said that they deliberately drove him into the stable and there concealed him. They had, in truth, virtually stolen him, and they had stolen food for him. The waning light through the small window above them warned Penrod that his inroads upon the vegetables in his own cellar must soon be discovered. Della, that Nemesis, would seek them in order to prepare them for dinner, and she would find them not. But she would recall his excursion to the cellar, for she had seen him when he came up; and also the truth would be known concerning the loaf of bread. Altogether, Penrod felt that his case was worse than Sam's—until Sam offered a suggestion which roused such horrible possibilities concerning the principal item of their offense that all thought of the smaller indictments disappeared.

"Listen, Penrod," Sam quavered: "What—what if that—what if that ole horse maybe b'longed to a—policeman!" Sam's imagination was not of the comforting kind. "What'd they—do to us, Penrod, if it turned out he was some policeman's horse?"

Penrod was able only to shake his head. He did not reply in words, but both boys thenceforth considered it almost inevitable that Whitey *had* belonged to a policeman, and in their sense of so ultimate a disaster, they ceased for a time to brood upon what their parents would probably do to them. The penalty for stealing a policeman's horse would be only a step short of capital, they were sure. They would not be hanged; but vague, looming sketches of something called the penitentiary began to flicker before them.

It grew darker in the cellar, so that finally they could not see each other.

"I guess they're huntin' for us by now," Sam said huskily. "I don't —I don't like it much down here, Penrod."

Penrod's hoarse whisper came from the profound gloom:

"Well, who ever said you did?"

"Well—" Sam paused; then he said plaintively, "I wish we'd never *seen* that dern ole horse."

"It was every bit his fault," said Penrod. *"We* didn't do anything. If he hadn't come stickin' his ole head in our stable, it'd never happened at all. Ole fool!" He rose. "I'm goin' to get out of here; I guess I've stood about enough for one day."

"Where—where you goin', Penrod? You aren't goin' *home,* are you?"

"No; I'm not! What you take me for? You think I'm crazy?"

"Well, where *can* we go?"

How far Penrod's desperation actually would have led him is doubtful, but he made this statement:

"I don't know where *you're* goin', but *I'm* goin' to walk straight out in the country till I come to a farmhouse and say my name's George and live there!"

"I'll do it, too," Sam whispered eagerly. "I'll say my name's Henry."

"Well, we better get started," said the executive Penrod. "We got to get away from here, anyway."

But when they came to ascend the steps leading to the "outside doors," they found that those doors had been closed and locked for the night.

"It's no use," Sam lamented, "and we can't bust 'em, 'cause I tried to, once before. Fanny always locks 'em about five o'clock—I forgot. We got to go up the stairway and try to sneak out through the house."

They tiptoed back, and up the inner stairs. They paused at the top, then breathlessly stepped out into a hall which was entirely dark. Sam touched Penrod's sleeve in warning, and bent to listen at a door.

Immediately that door opened, revealing the bright library, where sat Penrod's mother and Sam's father.

It was Sam's mother who had opened the door.

"Come into the library, boys," she said. "Mrs. Schofield is just telling us about it."

And as the two comrades moved dumbly into the lighted room, Penrod's mother rose, and, taking him by the shoulder, urged him close to the fire.

"You stand there and try to dry off a little, while I finish telling Mr. and Mrs. Williams about you and Sam," she said. "You'd better make Sam keep near the fire, too, Mrs. Williams, because they both got wringing wet. Think of their running off just when most people would have wanted to stay! Well, I'll go on with the story, then. Della told me all about it, and what the cook next door said *she'd* seen, how they'd been trying to pull grass and leaves for the poor old thing all day—and all about the apples they carried from *your* cellar, and getting wet and working in the rain as hard as they could—and they'd given him a loaf of bread! Shame on you, Penrod!" She paused to laugh, but there was a little moisture round her eyes, even before she laughed. "And they'd fed him on potatoes and lettuce and cabbage and turnips out of *our* cellar! And I wish you'd see the sawdust bed they made for him! Well, when I'd telephoned, and the Humane Society man got there, he said it was the most touching thing he ever knew. It seems he *knew* this horse, and had been looking for him. He said ninety-nine boys out of a hundred would have chased the poor old thing away, and he was going to see to it that this case didn't go unnoticed, because the local branch of the society gives little silver medals for special acts like this. And the last thing he said before he led the poor old horse away was that he was sure Penrod and Sam each would be awarded one at the meeting of the society next Thursday night."

... On the following Saturday morning a yodel sounded from the sunny sidewalk in front of the Schofields' house, and Penrod, issuing forth, beheld the familiar figure of Samuel Williams in waiting.

Upon Sam's breast there glittered a round bit of silver suspended by a white ribbon from a bar of the same metal. Upon the breast of Penrod was a decoration precisely similar.

" 'Lo, Penrod," said Sam. "What you goin' to do?"

"Nothin'."

"I got mine on," said Sam.

"I have, too," said Penrod. "I wouldn't take a hunderd dollars for mine."

"I wouldn't take two hunderd for mine," said Sam.

Each glanced pleasantly at the other's medal. They faced each other without shame. Neither had the slightest sense of hypocrisy either in himself or in his comrade. On the contrary!

Penrod's eyes went from Sam's medal back to his own; thence they wandered, with perhaps a little disappointment, to the lifeless street

and to the empty yards and spectatorless windows of the neighbour-
hood. Then he looked southward toward the busy heart of the town,
where multitudes were.

"Let's go down and see what time it is by the court-house clock,"
said Penrod.

Mark Twain

HUCK AND JIM TALK ABOUT KINGS *

By and by, when we got up, we turned over the truck the gang had
stole off of the wreck, and found boots, and blankets, and clothes, and
all sorts of other things, and a lot of books, and a spy-glass, and three
boxes of seegars. We hadn't ever been this rich before in neither of
our lives. The seegars was prime. We laid off all the afternoon in the
woods talking, and me reading the books, and having a general good
time. I told Jim all about what happened inside the wreck and at the
ferryboat, and I said these kinds of things was adventures; but he said
he didn't want no more adventures. He said that when I went in the
texas and he crawled back to get on the raft and found her gone he
nearly died, because he judged it was all up with *him* anyway it could
be fixed; for if he didn't get saved he would get drownded; and if he
did get saved, whoever saved him would send him back home so as
to get the reward, and then Miss Watson would sell him South, sure.
Well, he was right; he was most always right; he had an uncommon
level head for a nigger.

I read considerable to Jim about kings and dukes and earls and
such, and how gaudy they dressed, and how much style they put on,
and called each other your majesty, and your grace, and your lord-
ship, and so on, 'stead of mister; and Jim's eyes bugged out, and he
was interested. He says:

"I didn' know dey was so many un um. I hain't hearn 'bout none
un um, skasely, but ole King Sollermun, onless you counts dem kings
dat's in a pack er k'yards. How much do a king git?"

"Get?" I says; "why, they get a thousand dollars a month if they
want it; they can have just as much as they want; everything belongs
to them."

* *This conversation takes place when Huck and Jim are hiding out on an
island in the Mississippi. It is Chapter 14 of "The Adventures of Huckleberry
Finn."*

"*Ain'* dat gay? En what dey got to do, Huck?"

"*They* don't do nothing! Why, how you talk! They just set around."

"No; is dat so?"

"Of course it is. They just set around—except, maybe, when there's a war; then they go to the war. But other times they just lazy around; or go hawking—just hawking and sp— Sh!—d'you hear a noise?"

We skipped out and looked; but it warn't nothing but the flutter of a steamboat's wheel away down, coming around the point; so we come back.

"Yes," says I, "and other times, when things is dull, they fuss with the parlyment; and if everybody don't go just so he whacks their heads off. But mostly they hang round the harem."

"Roun' de which?"

"Harem."

"What's de harem?"

"The place where he keeps his wives. Don't you know about the harem? Solomon had one; he had about a million wives."

"Why, yes, dat's so; I—I'd done forgot it. A harem's a bo'd'n-house, I reck'n. Mos' likely dey has rackety times in de nussery. En I reck'n de wives quarrels considable; en dat 'crease de racket. Yit dey say Sollermun de wises' man dat ever live'. I doan' take no stock in dat. Bekase why: would a wise man want to live in de mids' er sich a blim-blammin' all de time? No—'deed he wouldn't. A wise man 'ud take en buil' a biler-factry; en den he could shet *down* de biler-factry when he want to res'."

"Well, but he *was* the wisest man, anyway; because the widow she told me so, her own self."

"I doan' k'yer what de widder say, he *warn't* no wise man nuther. He had some er de dad-fetchedes' ways I ever see. Does you know 'bout dat chile dat he 'uz gwyne to chop in two?"

"Yes, the widow told me all about it."

"*Well,* den! Warn' dat de beatenes' notion in de worl'? You jes' take en look at it a minute. Dah's de stump, dah—dat's one er de women; heah's you—dat's de yuther one; I's Sollermun; en dish yer dollar bill's de chile. Bofe un you claims it. What does I do? Does I shin aroun' mongs' de neighbors en fine out which un you de bill *do* b'long to, en han' it over to de right one, all safe en soun', de way dat anybody dat had any gumption would? No; I take en whack de bill in *two,* en give half un it to you, en de yuther half to de yuther

woman. Dat's de way Sollermun was gwyne to do wid de chile. Now
I want to ast you: what's de use er dat half a bill?—can't buy noth'n
wid it. En what use is a half a chile? I wouldn' give a dern for a million un um."

"But hang it, Jim, you've clean missed the point—blame it, you've
missed it a thousand mile."

"Who? Me? Go 'long. Doan' talk to *me* 'bout yo' pints. I reck'n I
knows sense when I sees it; en dey ain' no sense in sich doin's as dat.
De 'spute warn't 'bout a half a chile, de 'spute was 'bout a whole chile;
en de man dat think he kin settle a 'spute 'bout a whole chile wid a
half a chile doan' know enough to come in out'n de rain. Doan' talk to
me 'bout Sollermun, Huck, I knows him by de back."

"But I tell you you don't get the point."

"Blame de pint! I reck'n I knows what I knows. En mine you, de
real pint is down furder—it's down deeper. It lays in de way Sollermun
was raised. You take a man dat's got on'y one or two chillen; is dat
man gwyne to be waseful o' chillen? No, he ain't; he can't 'ford it.
He know how to value 'em. But you take a man dat's got 'bout five
million chillen runnin' roun' de house, en it's diffunt. *He* as soon
chop a chile in two as a cat. Dey's plenty mo'. A chile er two, mo' er
less, warn't no consekens to Sollermun, dad fetch him!"

I never see such a nigger. If he got a notion in his head once, there
warn't no getting it out again. He was the most down on Solomon
of any nigger I ever see. So I went to talking about other kings, and
let Solomon slide. I told about Louis Sixteenth that got his head cut
off in France long time ago; and about his little boy the dolphin, that
would 'a' been a king, but they took and shut him up in jail, and
some say he died there.

"Po' little chap."

"But some says he got out and got away, and come to America."

"Dat's good! But he'll be pooty lonesome—dey ain' no kings here,
is dey, Huck?"

"No."

"Den he cain't git no situation. What he gwyne to do?"

"Well, I don't know. Some of them gets on the police, and some of
them learns people how to talk French."

"Why, Huck, doan' de French people talk de same way we does?"

"*No*, Jim; you couldn't understand a word they said—not a single
word."

"Well, now, I be ding-busted! How do dat come?"

"*I* don't know; but it's so. I got some of their jabber out of a book. S'pose a man was to come to you and say Polly-voo-franzy—what would you think?"

"I wouldn' think nuffn; I'd take en bust him over de head—dat is, if he warn't white. I wouldn't 'low no nigger to call me dat."

"Shucks, it ain't calling you anything. It's only saying, do you know how to talk French?"

"Well, den, why couldn't he say it?"

"Why, he *is* a-saying it. That's a Frenchman's *way* of saying it."

"Well, it's a blame ridicklous way, en I doan' want to hear no mo' 'bout it. Dey ain' no sense in it."

"Looky here, Jim; does a cat talk like we do?"

"No, a cat don't."

"Well, does a cow?"

"No, a cow don't, nuther."

"Does a cat talk like a cow, or a cow talk like a cat?"

"No, dey don't."

"It's natural and right for 'em to talk different from each other, ain't it?"

"Course."

"And ain't it natural and right for a cat and a cow to talk different from *us?*"

"Why, mos' sholy it is."

"Well, then, why ain't it natural and right for a *Frenchman* to talk different from us? You answer me that."

"Is a cat a man, Huck?"

"No."

"Well, den, dey ain't no sense in a cat talkin' like a man. Is a cow a man?—er is a cow a cat?"

"No, she ain't either of them."

"Well, den, she ain't got no business to talk like either one er the yuther of 'em. Is a Frenchman a man?"

"Yes."

"*Well,* den! Dad blame it, why doan' he *talk* like a man? You answer me *dat!*"

I see it warn't no use wasting words—you can't learn a nigger to argue. So I quit.

Ogden Nash

TO A SMALL BOY STANDING ON MY SHOES WHILE I AM WEARING THEM

Let's straighten this out, my little man,
And reach an agreement if we can.
I entered your door as an honored guest.
My shoes are shined and my trousers are pressed,
And I won't stretch out and read you the funnies
And I won't pretend that we're Easter bunnies.
If you must get somebody down on the floor,
What in the hell are your parents for?
I do not like the things that you say
And I hate the games that you want to play.
No matter how frightfully hard you try,
We've little in common, you and I.
The interest I take in my neighbor's nursery
Would have to grow, to be even cursory,
And I would that performing sons and nephews
Were carted away with the daily refuse,
And I hold that frolicsome daughters and nieces
Are ample excuse for breaking leases.
You may take a sock at your daddy's tummy
Or climb all over your doting mummy,
But keep your attentions to me in check
Or, sonny boy, I will wring your neck.
A happier man today I'd be
Had someone wrung it ahead of me.

Clifford Orr

SAVAGE HOMECOMING

Frieda came back last week from her first summer at Camp Conomo, and her mother isn't sure whether it will be quite wise to send her another year. She's different somehow, her mother says.

First of all, right in the station, there was that little incident about the berries. She came down the platform followed by a porter with her bags, still shining new, and let her mother kiss her with what seemed to be a bit of sufferance.

"How are you, darling?" her mother cried.

"*Mokka-lo-cakki,*" said Frieda. At least, that's what her mother *thought* she said.

"What, darling?" asked her mother.

"That means 'The-health-spirit-is-smiling,'" said Frieda. "It's Indian. It's what you say when someone says '*Wo-manni-no?*' to you."

"I see," said her mother.

"That means 'How-sits-your-stomach?'"

"Hush, darling!" said her mother.

"It's all right," said Frieda. "It's Indian. Miss McClintock says it. She used to yell it right across the lake. Sound carries on the water."

"Well," said her mother, "you're certainly looking well. You're brown as a berry."

"Name one," said Frieda.

"What, dear?" her mother asked.

"Berries," said Frieda, "are red, blue, black, white, and green. They're seldom or never brown, and if you say that anything is brown as a berry, you could never be an Eagle in Elementary Nature. You'd be lucky if you even got to be a Nuthatch."

"I see, dear," said her mother.

Nothing really untoward happened during dinner. Frieda talked, her mother said, in a rather strange sort of jargon, but her mother

343

refrained from any leading questions. She did, however, notice the frequency with which Miss McClintock's name came into the conversation, and finally she got up sufficient courage to ask about her.

"Miss McClintock is Head Counselor of the Otters. Those are the girls who live between the basketball court and the Grand Canyon. The girls on the other side, over near Yosemite and the cookhouse, are Beavers. The Otters are much the best. I wouldn't be a Beaver for anything. The Beavers haven't won Woodcraft for three years."

Her mother clucked, disparagingly.

"Miss McClintock goes to Wellesley," Frieda continued. "I've decided to go to Wellesley."

"But Frieda, dear," said her mother, "you always wanted to go to Vassar, and Father and I registered you when you were just a little thing. Mother would like to have you go where she went."

"Wellesley is best," said Frieda. "Miss McClintock can chin herself nineteen times."

"I'm sure that Miss McClintock is very nice," said her mother, "but we shouldn't let things like—"

"There's a Vassar girl who's one of the counselors of the Beavers," Frieda interrupted. "Miss Fellows. She teaches Basketry."

"Well, she's nice, isn't she?" her mother asked, a trifle timidly.

"She can't clean fish," said Frieda.

Somehow, her mother thought, Frieda's standards had changed. So, it became apparent at bedtime, had her habits. It had always before been a bit of an ordeal to get her upstairs at the appropriate hour, but tonight she discovered that it was eight-thirty all by herself.

"*Kama-bo,*" she said, standing in the doorway.

Her mother guessed that this meant "Good night," so she said it herself, "*Kama-bo!,*" and was rewarded by a smile of understanding as Frieda lifted three outstretched fingers in what was evidently a gesture of benison. She disappeared, but in a moment she was at the door again.

"Mother," she asked, "in case you need anything in the night, do you know the Cry of Distress?"

"I'm sure I shan't need anything, Frieda. Thank you just the same."

"Well, this is it, anyway," said Frieda. "If you cry '*Conomo!*' just once, why that's just a greeting or to let people know you're in the neighborhood, and friendly, see?"

"Yes, dear."

"If you do it twice—'*Conomo! Conomo!*'—that means that you've found a new Specimen or have located the next Cairn, and the others should try to come where you are. Is that clear?"

"Perfectly, dear, but I doubt very much if tonight—"

"But if you cry it three times, with a note of alarm," Frieda went on, "like this—'*Conomo! Conomo! Conomo!*'—that's the Cry of Distress, and I'll come at double-time with a first-aid kit and, if possible, a hand axe and a piece of rope."

"I see, dear," her mother said. "I'll try to remember, and I'm sure you'll be of great help if Mother calls."

"The rope, of course," said Frieda, rather ominously, "is in case of Quicksand."

It was eleven o'clock when Frieda's mother went up to bed. It was after twelve-thirty when she woke up with a dry throat, a tickling in her nostrils, and a slowly reached conviction that she was smelling smoke. In less than a minute, after rushing from her room and half-way down the stairs, sniffing, she had thrown open Frieda's door and had been greeted by a cloud of it rolling out.

"Frieda! Frieda!" she called. "Frieda!"

"Tent Number Eight," said Frieda's sleepy voice from the bed. "All present."

Pawing her way through the smoke and finding the light switch, her mother eventually discovered that there was a small and sullen blaze in the fireplace, and that was all. The fire had been laid and unused all summer and the chimney draught evidently kept closed. But the smoke was almost unbearable. By practically main force, she dragged Frieda from the room and closed the door behind them. She would wake Annie and send her in to open the draught. Frieda was coughing and choking a bit, too, if sleepily. She was coherent enough, though, when her mother had put her into her father's bed and opened the windows wide.

"I was making a smudge," said Frieda.

"You certainly were," said her mother. "What on earth did you light the fire for, and why didn't you open the draught?"

"I felt a mosquito," said Frieda, "so I closed the draught and made a smudge."

"But Frieda, dear, there couldn't have been any mosquitoes. We haven't had any all summer. The screens are brand-new."

"I opened the screens," said Frieda. "Screens are symbols of civilization."

Her mother sat there, pondering this for a while, and finally Frieda spoke again.

"I used a match to light the fire, though," she said, more slowly and more faintly. "I didn't have any tinder. I might have scraped the furniture, only it's maple. Ash is best for tinder."

Her mother sat for another moment, and then rose and switched off the light.

"Good night, Frieda," she said.

There was a long pause.

"*Kama-bo*, Miss McClintock," said Frieda.

SATIRE—BROAD AND OTHERWISE

To satirize is to comment upon something with some keen-ness and imagination, perhaps in a rather roundabout or in-direct fashion, sometimes savagely. Almost all humor is, roughly, satire. Obviously this section of the book could have been swelled to enormous proportions if there had been room. Some of our readers may quibble about the presence of the Franklin letters under this heading, since it appears (accord-ing to Mr. Carl Van Doren, anyway) that the old fellow actu-ally wanted to marry the lady. But even in love, Franklin was a master of satiric persiflage.

The piece called "Mother Taft's Chickens" is simply an oddity—a bit of deadpan research, the sort of thing The New Yorker has done with good effect many times.

Artemus Ward

THE SHAKERS

The Shakers is the strangest religious sex I ever met. I'd hearn tell of
'em and I'd seen 'em, with their broad brim'd hats and long wastid
coats; but I'd never cum into immejit contack with 'em, and I'd sot
'em down as lackin intelleck, as I'd never seen 'em to my Show—least-
ways, if they cum they was disgised in white peple's close, so I didn't
know 'em.

But in the Spring of 18—, I got swampt in the exterior of New York
State, one dark and stormy night, when the winds Blue pityusly, and
I was forced to tie up with the Shakers.

I was toilin threw the mud, when in the dim vister of the futer I
obsarved the gleams of a taller candle. Tiein a hornet's nest to my off
hoss's tail to kinder encourage him, I soon reached the place. I knockt
at the door, which it was opened unto me by a tall, slick-faced, solum
lookin individooal, who turn'd out to be a Elder.

"Mr. Shaker," sed I, "you see before you a Babe in the Woods, so
to speak, and he axes shelter of you."

"Yay," sed the Shaker, and he led the way into the house, another
Shaker bein sent to put my hosses and waggin under kiver.

A solum female, lookin sumwhat like a last year's bean-pole stuck
into a long meal-bag, cum in and axed me was I athurst and did I
hunger, to which I urbanely anserd "a few." She went orf and I en-
deverd to open a conversashun with the old man.

"Elder, I spect?" sed I.

"Yay," he sed.

"Helth's good, I reckon?"

"Yay."

"What's the wages of a Elder, when he understans his bizness—or
do you devote your sarvices gratooitus?"

"Yay."

"Stormy night, sir."

"Yay."

"If the storm continners there'll be a mess underfoot, hay?"

"Yay."

"It's onpleasant when there's a mess underfoot."

"Yay."

"If I may be so bold, kind sir, what's the price of that pecooler kind of weskit you wear, incloodin trimmins?"

"Yay."

I pawsd a minit, and then, thinkin I'd be faseshus with him and see how that would go, I slapt him on the shoulder, bust into a harty larf, and told him that as a *yayer* he had no livin ekal.

He jumpt up as if Bilin water had bin squirted into his ears, groaned, rolled his eyes up tords the sealin and sed: "You're a man of sin!" He then walkt out of the room.

Jest then the female in the meal-bag stuck her hed into the room and statid that refreshments awaited the weary traveler, and I sed if it was vittles she ment the weary traveler was agreeable, and I follered her into the next room.

I sot down to the table and the female in the meal-bag pored out sum tea. She sed nothin, and for five minutes the only live thing in that room was a old wooden clock, which tickt in a subdood and bashful manner in the corner. This dethly stillness made me oneasy, and I determined to talk to the female or bust. So sez I, "Marrige is agin your rules, I bleeve, marm?"

"Yay."

"The sexes liv strickly apart, I spect?"

"Yay."

"It's kinder singler," sez I, puttin on my most sweetest look and speakin in a winnin voice, "that so fair a made as thou never got hitched to some likely feller." [N.B.—She was upards of 40 and homely as a stump fence, but I thawt I'd tickil her.]

"I don't like men!" she sed, very short.

"Wall, I dunno," sez I, "they're a rayther important part of the populashun. I don't scarcely see how we could git along without 'em."

"Us poor wimin folks would git along a grate deal better if there was no men!"

"You'll excoos me, marm, but I don't think that air would work. It wouldn't be regler."

"I'm fraid of men!" she sed.

"That's onnecessary, marm, *You* ain't in no danger. Don't fret your-self on that pint."

"Here we're shot out from the sinful world. Here all is peas. Here we air brothers and sisters. We don't marry and consekently we have no domestic difficulties. Husbans don't abooze their wives—wives don't worrit their husbans. There's no children here to worrit us. Nothin to worrit us here. No wicked matrimony here. Would thow like to be a Shaker?"

"No," sez I, "it ain't my stile."

I had now histed in as big a load of pervishuns as I could carry comfortable, and, leanin back in my cheer, commenst pickin my teeth with a fork. The female went out, leavin me all alone with the clock. I hadn't sot thar long before the Elder poked his hed in at the door. "You're a man of sin!" he sed, and groaned and went away.

Direckly thar cum in two young Shakeresses, as putty and slick lookin gals as I ever met. It is troo they was drest in meal-bags like the old one I'd met previsly, and their shiny, silky har was hid from sight by long white caps, sich as I spose female Josts wear; but their eyes sparkled like diminds, their cheeks was like roses, and they was charming enuff to make a man throw stuns at his granmother, if they axed him to. They commenst clearin away the dishes, castin shy glances at me all the time. I got excited. I forgot Betsy Jane in my rapter, and sez I, "My pretty dears, how air you?"

"We air well," they solumly sed.

"Whar's the old man?" sed I, in a soft voice.

"Of whom dost thow speak—Brother Uriah?"

"I mean the gay and festiv cuss who calls me a man of sin. Shouldn't wonder if his name was Uriah."

"He has retired."

"Wall, my pretty dears," sez I, "let's hav sum fun. Let's play Puss in the corner. What say?"

"Air you a Shaker, sir?" they axed.

"Wall, my pretty dears, I haven't arrayed my proud form in a long weskit yit, but if they was all like you perhaps I'd jine 'em. As it is, I'm a Shaker pro-temporary."

They was full of fun. I seed that at fust, only they was a leetle skeery. I tawt 'em Puss in the corner and sich like plase, and we had a nice time, keepin quiet of course so the old man shouldn't hear.

When we broke up, sez I, "My pretty dears, ear I go you hav no objections, hav you, to a innersent kiss at partin?"

"Yay," thay sed, and I *yay'd*.

I went up stairs to bed. I spose I'd bin snoozin half a hour when I was woke up by a noise at the door. I sot up in bed, leanin on my elbers and rubbin my eyes, and I saw the follerin picter: The Elder stood in the doorway, with a taller candle in his hand. He hadn't no wearin appeerel on except his night close, which fluttered in the breeze like a Seseshun flag. He sed, "You're a man of sin!" then groaned and went away.

I went to sleep agin, and drempt of runnin orf with the pretty little Shakeresses, mounted on my Californy Bar. I thawt the Bar insisted on steerin strate for my dooryard in Baldinsville, and that Betsy Jane cum out and giv us a warm recepshun with a panful of Bilin water. I was woke up arly by the Elder. He sed refreshments was reddy for me down stairs. Then sayin I was a man of sin, he went groanin away.

As I was goin threw the entry to the room where the vittles was, I cum across the Elder and the old female I'd met the night before, and what d'ye spose they was up to? Huggin and kissin like young lovers in their gushingist state. Sez I, "My Shaker friends, I reckon you'd better suspend the rules, and git marrid!"

"You must excoos Brother Uriah," sed the female; "he's subjeck to fits, and hain't got no command over hisself when he's into 'em."

"Sartinly," sez I; "I've bin took that way myself frequent."

"You're a man of sin!" said the Elder.

Arter breakfust my little Shaker frends cum in agin to clear away the dishes.

"My pretty dears," sez I, "shall we *yay* agin?"

"Nay," they sed, and I *nay'd*.

The Shakers axed me to go to their meetin, as they was to hav sarvices that mornin, so I put on a clean biled rag and went. The meetin house was as neat as a pin. The floor was white as chalk and smooth as glass. The Shakers was all on hand, in clean weskits and meal-bags, ranged on the floor like milingtery companies, the mails on one side of the room and the females on tother. They commenst clappin their hands and singin and dancin. They danced kinder slow at fust, but as they got warmed up they shaved it down very brisk, I tell you. Elder Uriah, in particler, exhiberted a right smart chance of spryness in his legs, considerin his time of life, and as he cum a dubble shuffle near where I sot, I rewarded him with a approvin smile, and sed: "Hunky boy! Go it, my gay and festiv cuss!"

"You're a man of sin!" he sed, continnerin his shuffle.

The Sperret, as they called it, then moved a short fat Shaker to say a few remarks. He sed they was Shakers and all was ekal. They was the purest and seleckest peple on the yearth. Other peple was sinful as they could be, but Shakers was all right. Shakers was all goin kerslap to the Promist Land, and nobody wa'nt goin to stand at the gate to bar 'em out; if they did they'd git run over.

The Shakers then danced and sung agin, and arter thay was threw, one of 'em axed me what I thawt of it.

Sez I, "What duz it siggerfy?"

"What?" sez he.

"Why this jumpin up and singin? This long-weskit bizniss, and this anty-matrimony idee? My frends, you air neat and tidy. Your lands is flowin with milk and honey. Your brooms is fine, and your apple sass is honest. When a man buys a kag of apple sass of you he don't find a grate many shavins under a few layers of sass—a little Game I'm sorry to say sum of my New Englan ancesters used to practiss. Your garding seeds is fine, and if I should sow 'em on the rock of Gibralter probly I should raise a good mess of garding sass. You air honest in your dealins. You air quiet and don't distarb nobody. For all this I givs you credit. But your religion is small pertaters, I must say. You mope away your lives here in single retchidness, and as you air all by yourselves nothing ever conflicks with your pecooler idees, except when Human Nater busts out among you, as I understan she sumtimes do. (I give Uriah a sly wink here, which made the old feller squirm like a speared Eel.) You wear long weskits and long faces, and lead a gloomy life indeed. No children's prattle is ever hearn around your harthstuns—you air in a dreary fog all the time, and you treat the jolly sunshine of life as tho' it was a thief, drivin it from your doors by them weskits, and meal-bags, and pecooler noshuns of yourn. The gals among you, sum of which air as slick pieces of caliker as I ever sot eyes on, air syin to place their heds agin weskits which kiver honest, manly harts, while you old heds fool yerselves with the idee that they air fulfillin their mishun here, and air contented. Here you air, all pend up by yerselves, talkin about the sins of a world you don't know nothin of. Meanwhile said world continners to resolve round on her own axeltree onct in every 24 hours, subjeck to the Constitution of the United States, and is a very plesant place of residence. It's a unnatral, onreasonable and dismal life you're leadin here. So it strikes me. My Shaker frends, I now bid you a welcome adoo. You hav treated me exceedin well. Thank you kindly, one and all."

"A base exhibiter of depraved monkeys and onprincipled wax works!" sed Uriah.

"Hello, Uriah," sez I, "I'd most forgot you. Wall, look out for them fits of yourn, and don't catch cold and die in the flour of your youth and beauty."

And I resoomed my jerney.

James Thurber

THE GREATEST MAN IN THE WORLD *

Looking back on it now, from the vantage point of 1940, one can only marvel that it hadn't happened long before it did. The United States of America had been, ever since Kitty Hawk, blindly constructing the elaborate petard by which, sooner or later, it must be hoist. It was inevitable that some day there would come roaring out of the skies a national hero of insufficient intelligence, background, and character successfully to endure the mounting orgies of glory prepared for aviators who stayed up a long time or flew a great distance. Both Lindbergh and Byrd, fortunately for national decorum and international amity, had been gentlemen; so had our other famous aviators. They wore their laurels gracefully, withstood the awful weather of publicity, married excellent women, usually of fine family, and quietly retired to private life and the enjoyment of their varying fortunes. No untoward incidents, on a worldwide scale, marred the perfection of their conduct on the perilous heights of fame. The exception to the rule was, however, bound to occur and it did, in July, 1935, when Jack ("Pal") Smurch, erstwhile mechanic's helper in a small garage in Westfield, Iowa, flew a second-hand, single-motored Bresthaven Dragon-Fly III monoplane all the way around the world, without stopping.

Never before in the history of aviation had such a flight as Smurch's ever been dreamed of. No one had even taken seriously the weird floating auxiliary gas tanks, invention of the mad New Hampshire professor of astronomy, Dr. Charles Lewis Gresham, upon which Smurch placed full reliance. When the garage worker, a slightly built, surly, unprepossessing young man of twenty-two, appeared at Roosevelt Field early in July, 1935, slowly chewing a great quid of scrap tobacco, and announced "Nobody ain't seen no flyin' yet," the news-

* This satiric prophecy was written in 1931, up to which date our national heroes had been well behaved.

papers touched briefly and satirically upon his projected twenty-five-thousand-mile flight. Aëronautical and automotive experts dismissed the idea curtly, implying that it was a hoax, a publicity stunt. The rusty, battered, second-hand plane wouldn't go. The Gresham auxiliary tanks wouldn't work. It was simply a cheap joke.

Smurch, however, after calling on a girl in Brooklyn who worked in the flap-folding department of a large paper-box factory, a girl whom he later described as his "sweet patootie," climbed nonchalantly into his ridiculous plane at dawn of the memorable seventh of July, 1935, spit a curve of tobacco juice into the still air, and took off, carrying with him only a gallon of bootleg gin and six pounds of salami.

When the garage boy thundered out over the ocean the papers were forced to record, in all seriousness, that a mad, unknown young man—his name was variously misspelled—had actually set out upon a preposterous attempt to span the world in a rickety, one-engined contraption, trusting to the long-distance refuelling device of a crazy schoolmaster. When, nine days later, without having stopped once, the tiny plane appeared above San Francisco Bay, headed for New York, spluttering and choking, to be sure, but still magnificently and miraculously aloft, the headlines, which long since had crowded everything else off the front page—even the shooting of the Governor of Illinois by the Capone gang—swelled to unprecedented size, and the news stories began to run to twenty-five and thirty columns. It was noticeable, however, that the accounts of the epoch-making flight touched rather lightly upon the aviator himself. This was not because facts about the hero as a man were too meagre, but because they were too complete.

Reporters, who had been rushed out to Iowa when Smurch's plane was first sighted over the little French coast town of Serly-le-Mer, to dig up the story of the great man's life, had promptly discovered that the story of his life could not be printed. His mother, a sullen short-order cook in a shack restaurant on the edge of a tourists' camping ground near Westfield, met all inquiries as to her son with an angry "Ah, the hell with him; I hope he drowns." His father appeared to be in jail somewhere for stealing spotlights and laprobes from tourists' automobiles; his young brother, a weakminded lad, had but recently escaped from the Preston, Iowa, Reformatory and was already wanted in several Western towns for the theft of money-order blanks from post offices. These alarming discoveries were still piling up at the very time that Pal Smurch, the greatest hero of the twentieth century, blear-eyed, dead for sleep, half-starved, was piloting his crazy junkheap high above the region in which the lamentable story of his private life was being unearthed, headed for New York and a greater glory than any man of his time had ever known.

The necessity for printing some account in the papers of the young man's career and personality had led to a remarkable predicament. It was of course impossible to reveal the facts, for a tremendous popular feeling in favor of the young hero had sprung up, like a grass fire, when he was halfway across Europe on his flight around the globe. He was, therefore, described as a modest chap, taciturn, blond, popular with his friends, popular with girls. The only available snapshot of Smurch, taken at the wheel of a phony automobile in a cheap photo studio at an amusement park, was touched up so that the little vulgarian looked quite handsome. His twisted leer was smoothed into a pleasant smile. The truth was, in this way, kept from the youth's ecstatic compatriots; they did not dream that the Smurch family was despised and feared by its neighbors in the obscure Iowa town, nor that the hero himself, because of numerous unsavory exploits, had come to be regarded in Westfield as a nuisance and a menace. He had, the reporters discovered, once knifed the principal of his high school—not mortally, to be sure, but he had knifed him; and on another occasion, surprised in the act of stealing an altarcloth from a church, he had bashed the sacristan over the head with a pot of Easter lilies; for each of these offences he had served a sentence in the reformatory.

Inwardly, the authorities, both in New York and in Washington, prayed that an understanding Providence might, however awful such a thing seemed, bring disaster to the rusty, battered plane and its illustrious pilot, whose unheard-of flight had aroused the civilized world to hosannas of hysterical praise. The authorities were convinced that the character of the renowned aviator was such that the limelight of adulation was bound to reveal him, to all the world, as a congenital hooligan mentally and morally unequipped to cope with his own prodigious fame. "I trust," said the Secretary of State, at one of many secret Cabinet meetings called to consider the national dilemma, "I trust that his mother's prayer will be answered," by which he referred to Mrs. Emma Smurch's wish that her son might be drowned. It was, however, too late for that—Smurch had leaped the Atlantic and then the Pacific as if they were millponds. At three minutes after two o'clock on the afternoon of July 17, 1935, the garage boy brought his idiotic plane into Roosevelt Field for a perfect three-point landing.

It had, of course, been out of the question to arrange a modest little reception for the greatest flier in the history of the world. He was received at Roosevelt Field with such elaborate and pretentious ceremonies as rocked the world. Fortunately, however, the worn and spent hero promptly swooned, had to be removed bodily from his plane, and was spirited from the field without having opened his mouth once. Thus he did not jeopardize the dignity of this first reception, a reception illumined by the presence of the Secretaries of War and the Navy, Mayor Michael J. Moriarity of New York, the Premier of Canada, Governors Fanniman, Groves, McFeely, and Critchfield, and a brilliant array of European diplomats. Smurch did not, in fact, come to in time to take part in the gigantic hullabaloo arranged at City Hall for the next day. He was rushed to a secluded nursing home and confined in bed. It was nine days before he was able to get up, or to be more exact, before he was permitted to get up. Meanwhile the greatest minds in the country, in solemn assembly, had arranged a secret conference of city, state, and government officials, which Smurch was to attend for the purpose of being instructed in the ethics and behavior of heroism.

On the day that the little mechanic was finally allowed to get up and dress and, for the first time in two weeks, took a great chew of tobacco, he was permitted to receive the newspapermen—this by way of testing him out. Smurch did not wait for questions. "Youse guys," he said—and the *Times* man winced—"youse guys can tell the cockeyed world dat I put it over on Lindbergh, see? Yeh—an' made an ass o' them two frogs." The "two frogs" was a reference to a pair of gallant French fliers who, in attempting a flight only halfway round the world, had, two weeks before, unhappily been lost at sea. The *Times* man was bold enough, at this point, to sketch out for Smurch the accepted formula for interviews in cases of this kind; he explained that there should be no arrogant statements belittling the achievements of other heroes, particularly heroes of foreign nations. "Ah, the hell with that," said Smurch. "I did it, see? I did it, an' I'm talkin' about it." And he did talk about it.

None of this extraordinary interview was, of course, printed. On the contrary, the newspapers, already under the disciplined direction of a secret directorate created for the occasion and composed of statesmen and editors, gave out to a panting and restless world that "Jacky," as he had been arbitrarily nicknamed, would consent to say only that he was very happy and that anyone could have done what he did. "My achievement has been, I fear, slightly exaggerated," the *Times* man's article had him protest, with a modest smile. These newspaper stories were kept from the hero, a restriction which did not serve to abate the rising malevolence of his temper. The situation was, indeed, extremely grave, for Pal Smurch was, as he kept insisting, "rarin' to go." He could not much longer be kept from a nation clamorous to lionize him. It was the most desperate crisis the United States of America had faced since the sinking of the Lusitania.

On the afternoon of the twenty-seventh of July, Smurch was spirited away to a conference-room in which were gathered mayors, governors, government officials, behaviorist psychologists, and editors. He gave them each a limp, moist paw and a brief unlovely grin. "Hah ya?" he said. When Smurch was seated, the Mayor of New York arose and, with obvious pessimism, attempted to explain what he must say and how he must act when presented to the world, ending his talk with a high tribute to the hero's courage and integrity. The Mayor was followed by Governor Fanniman of New York, who, after a touching declaration of faith, introduced Cameron Spottiswood, Second Secretary of the American Embassy in Paris, the gentleman selected to coach Smurch in the amenities of public ceremonies. Sitting in a chair, with a soiled yellow tie in his hand and his shirt open at the throat, unshaved, smoking a rolled cigarette, Jack Smurch listened with a leer on his lips. "I get ya, I get ya," he cut in, nastily. "Ya want me to ack like a softy, huh? Ya want me to ack like that — —— baby-face Lindbergh, huh? Well, nuts to that, see?" Everyone took in his breath sharply; it was a sigh and a hiss. "Mr. Lindbergh," began a United States Senator, purple with rage, "and Mr. Byrd—" Smurch, who was paring his nails with a jackknife, cut in again. "Byrd!" he exclaimed. "Aw fa God's sake, *dat* big—" Somebody shut off his blasphemies with a sharp word. A newcomer had entered the room. Everyone stood up, except Smurch, who, still busy with his nails, did not even glance up. "Mr. Smurch," said someone, sternly, "the President of the United States!" It had been thought that the presence of the Chief Executive might have a chastening effect upon the young hero, and the former had been, thanks to the remarkable coöperation of the press, secretly brought to the obscure conference-room.

A great, painful silence fell. Smurch looked up, waved a hand at the President. "How ya comin'?" he asked, and began rolling a fresh cigarette. The silence deepened. Someone coughed in a strained way. "Geez, it's hot, ain't it?" said Smurch. He loosened two more shirt buttons, revealing a hairy chest and the tattooed word "Sadie" enclosed in a stencilled heart. The great and important men in the room, faced by the most serious crisis in recent American history, exchanged worried frowns. Nobody seemed to know how to proceed. "Come awn, come awn," said Smurch. "Let's get the hell out of here! When do I start cuttin' in on de parties, huh? And what's they goin' to be *in* it?" He rubbed a thumb and forefinger together meaningly. "Money!" exclaimed a state senator, shocked, pale. "Yeh, money," said Pal, flipping his cigarette out of a window. "An' big money." He began rolling a fresh cigarette. "Big money," he repeated, frowning over the rice paper. He tilted back in his chair, and leered at each gentleman, separately, the leer of an animal that knows its power, the leer of a leopard loose in a bird-and-dog shop. "Aw fa God's sake, let's get some place where it's cooler," he said. "I been cooped up plenty for three weeks!"

Smurch stood up and walked over to an open window, where he stood staring down into the street, nine floors below. The faint shouting of newsboys floated up to him. He made out his name. "Hot dog!" he cried, grinning, ecstatic. He leaned out over the sill. "You tell 'em, babies!" he shouted down. "Hot diggity dog!" In the tense little knot of men standing behind him, a quick, mad impulse flared up. An unspoken word of appeal, of command, seemed to ring through the room. Yet it was deadly silent. Charles K. L. Brand, secretary to the Mayor of New York City, happened to be standing nearest Smurch; he looked inquiringly at the President of the United States. The President, pale, grim, nodded shortly. Brand, a tall, powerfully built man, once a tackle at Rutgers, stepped forward, seized the greatest man in the world by his left shoulder and the seat of his pants, and pushed him out the window.

"My God, he's fallen out the window!" cried a quick-witted editor

"Get me out of here!" cried the President. Several men sprang to his side and he was hurriedly escorted out of a door toward a side-entrance of the building. The editor of the Associated Press took charge, being used to such things. Crisply he ordered certain men to leave, others to stay; quickly he outlined a story which all the papers were to agree on, sent two men to the street to handle that end of the tragedy, commanded a Senator to sob and two Congressmen to go to pieces nervously. In a word, he skillfully set the stage for the gigantic task that was to follow, the task of breaking to a grief-stricken world the sad story of the untimely, accidental death of its most illustrious and spectacular figure.

The funeral was, as you know, the most elaborate, the finest, the solemnest, and the saddest ever held in the United States of America. The monument in Arlington Cemetery, with its clean white shaft of marble and the simple device of a tiny plane carved on its base, is a place for pilgrims, in deep reverence, to visit. The nations of the world paid lofty tributes to little Jacky Smurch, America's greatest hero. At a given hour there were two minutes of silence throughout the nation. Even the inhabitants of the small, bewildered town of Westfield, Iowa, observed this touching ceremony; agents of the Department of Justice saw to that. One of them was especially assigned to stand grimly in the doorway of a little shack restaurant on the edge of the tourists' camping ground just outside the town. There, under his stern scrutiny, Mrs. Emma Smurch bowed her head above two hamburger steaks sizzling on her grill—bowed her head and turned away, so that the Secret Service man could not see the twisted, strangely familiar, leer on her lips.

Benjamin Franklin

THREE LOVE LETTERS *

(From Franklin to Madame Helvétius)

I

Mr. Franklin is sorry to have caused the least harm to that beautiful hair, which he always admires with so much Pleasure. If that Lady likes to pass her Days with him, he in turn would like to pass his Nights with her; & as he has already given her many of his days, though he has so few left to give, she appears ungrateful never to have given him a single one of her nights, which steadily pass as a pure loss, without giving happiness to anyone, except Poupon. He nevertheless embraces her heartily, for he loves her infinitely in spite of all her faults.

II

Mr. Franklin having risen, washed, shaved, combed and beautified himself as much as possible, all dressed and on the point of going out, with his head full of the 4 Mesdames Helvétius, & of the sweet kisses which he planned to get from her, is much mortified to find the Possibility of this Felicity put off till next Sunday. However, he will bear up with what Patience he can, hoping to see one of these Ladies at M. de Chaumont's on Wednesday. He will be there early, to see her enter with that Grace & Dignity which so charmed him seven Weeks ago in the same place. He even plans to stop her there & to keep her at his house for life. Her three other selves remaining at Auteil will suffice for the Canary-birds & the Abbés.

* The originals are in French, and are here translated by Paul McPharlin. The first was dated Passy, Sept. 19, 1779; the third letter was printed by Franklin at his Passy press. When he wrote them he was United States Minister to France. Madame Helvétius was the attractive widow of a French philosopher.

III

Nettled by your barbarous Resolution, so emphatically stated yesterday evening, to remain single for life in honour of your dear husband, I returned home, fell upon my Bed thinking myself dead, and found myself in the Elysian Fields.

I was asked whether I wished to see any People in particular. 'Take me to the Philosophers.' 'There are two who live near here in this Garden: they are very good Neighbours and Friends to each other.' 'Who are they?' 'Socrates and Helvétius.' 'I hold them both in tremendous Esteem; but let me first see Helvétius, for I understand a little French and not a Word of Greek.' He received me with great Courtesy, having known me, he said, by Reputation for some time. He asked me a thousand things about the War, and the present state of Religion, of Liberty, and of Government in France. 'You do not inquire about your dear one Madame Helvétius; though she however still loves you exceedingly, and it was not an hour ago that I was with her. 'Ah!' said he, 'you stir the Memory of my old Happiness. But that must be forgotten in order to be content here. For several years at first, I thought only of her. But at length I was consoled. I took another Wife. The most like her that I could find. She is not, 'tis true, altogether so beautiful, but she has as much good Sense, a little more Humour, and she loves me without End. She is forever studying to please me; and she has just gone out to find the best Nectar and Ambrosia to regale me this evening; stay with me and you shall see.' 'I perceive,' said I, 'that your old Companion is more faithful than you, for several good Matches have been offered her, all of which she has refused. I confess that I myself have loved her madly; but she has been adamant to my Attentions, and has definitely rejected me because of her love for you.'

'I take Pity,' said he, 'on your Plight, for she is truly a good and beautiful Woman and very lovable. But do not the Abbé de la Roche and the Abbé Morellet still come to her house occasionally? To be sure they do; for she has not lost a single one of our Friends. Had you won over the Abbé Morellet (with Coffee and Cream) to speak for you, perhaps you would have succeeded; for he is a Reasoner as subtle as Duns Scotus or St. Thomas; he puts his Arguments in such good Order that they become almost irresistable. Or if the Abbé de la Roche had been won over (by some pretty Edition of an old Classic to speak against you, that would have been even better: for I have always observed, that when he advised one thing, she had a strong Inclination to do the opposite.'

At these Words there entered the new Madame Helvétius with the Nectar: instantly I recognised her to be Mistress Franklin, my old American Helpmate. I would have owned her. But she said coldly, 'I was your good Wife forty-nine years and four Months, almost half a century; be content with that. Here I have formed a new Bond, which will last for Eternity.'

Displeased with this Refusal by my Euridice, I straightway made up my Mind to quit those ungrateful Shades, to come back to this good World, again to see the Sun and you. Here I am! Let us be avenged.

H. L. Mencken

THE WEDDING: A STAGE DIRECTION

The scene is a church in an American city of about half a million population, and the time is about eleven o'clock of a fine morning in early spring. The neighborhood is well-to-do, but not quite fashionable. That is to say, most of the families of the vicinage keep two servants (alas, more or less intermittently!), and eat dinner at half-past six, and about one in every four boasts a colored butler (who attends to the fires, washes windows and helps with the sweeping), and a last year's automobile. The heads of these families are merchandise brokers; jobbers in notions, hardware and drugs; manufacturers of candy, hats, badges, office furniture, blank books, picture frames, wire goods and patent medicines; managers of steamboat lines; district agents of insurance companies; owners of commercial printing offices, and other such business men of substance—and the prosperous lawyers and popular family doctors who keep them out of trouble. In one block live a Congressman and two college professors, one of whom has written an unimportant textbook and got himself into "Who's Who in America." In the block above lives a man who once ran for Mayor of the city, and came near being elected.

The wives of these householders wear good clothes and have a liking for a reasonable gayety, but very few of them can pretend to what is vaguely called social standing, and, to do them justice, not many of them waste any time lamenting it. They have, taking one with another, about three children apiece, and are good mothers. A few of them belong to women's clubs or flirt with the suffragettes, but the majority can get all of the intellectual stimulation they crave in the Ladies' Home Journal and the Saturday Evening Post, with Vogue added for its fashions. Most of them, deep down in their hearts, suspect their husbands of secret frivolity, and about ten per cent. have the proofs, but it is rare for them to make rows about it, and the divorce rate among them is thus very low. Themselves indifferent *cooks, they are unable to teach their servants the art, and so the food they set before their husbands and children is often such as would make a Frenchman cut his throat. But they are diligent housewives otherwise; they see to it that the windows are washed, that no one tracks mud into the hall, that the servants do not waste coal, sugar, soap and gas, and that the family buttons are always sewed on. In religion these estimable wives are pious in habit but somewhat nebulous in faith. That is to say, they regard any person who specifically refuses to go to church as a heathen, but they themselves are by no means regular in attendance, and not one in ten of them could tell you whether transubstantiation is a Roman Catholic or a Dunkard doctrine. About two per cent. have dallied more or less gingerly with Christian Science, their average period of belief being one year.*

The church we are in is like the neighborhood and its people: well-to-do but not fashionable. It is Protestant in faith and probably Episcopalian. The pews are of thick, yellow-brown oak, severe in pattern and hideous in color. In each there is a long, removable cushion of a dark, purplish, dirty hue, with here and there some of its hair stuffing showing. The stained-glass windows, which were all bought ready-made and depict scenes from the New Testament, commemorate the virtues of departed worthies of the neighborhood, whose names appear, in illegible black letters, in the lower panels. The floor is covered with a carpet of some tough, fibrous material, apparently a sort of grass, and along the center aisle it is much worn. The normal smell of the place is rather less unpleasant than that of most other halls, for on the one day when it is regularly crowded practically all of the persons gathered together have been very recently bathed.

On this fine morning, however, it is full of heavy, mortuary perfumes, for a couple of florist's men have just finished decorating the chancel with flowers and potted palms. Just behind the chancel rail, facing the center aisle, there is a prie-dieu, and to either side of it are great banks of lilies, carnations, gardenias and roses. Three or four feet behind the prie-dieu and completely concealing the high altar, there is a dense jungle of palms. Those in the front rank are authentically growing in pots, but behind them the florist's men have artfully placed some more durable, and hence more profitable, sophistications. Anon the rev. clergyman, emerging from the vestry-room to the right, will pass along the front of this jungle to the prie-dieu, and so, framed in flowers, face the congregation with his saponaceous smile.

The florist's men, having completed their labors, are preparing to depart. The older of the two, a man in the fifties, shows the ease of an experienced hand by taking out a large plug of tobacco and gnawing off a substantial chew. The desire to spit seizing him shortly, he proceeds to gratify it by a trick long practised by gasfitters, musicians, caterer's helpers, piano movers and other such alien invaders of the domestic hearth. That is to say, he hunts for a place where the carpet is loose along the chancel rail, finds it where two lengths join, deftly turns up a flap, spits upon the bare floor, and then lets the flap fall back, finally giving it a pat with the sole of his foot. This done, he and his assistant leave the church to the sexton, who has been sweeping the vestibule, and, after passing the time of day with the two men who are putting up a striped awning from the door to the curb, disappear into a nearby saloon, there to wait and refresh themselves until the wedding is over, and it is time to take away their lilies, their carnations and their synthetic palms.

It is now a quarter past eleven, and two flappers of the neighborhood, giggling and arm-in-arm, approach the sexton and inquire of him if they may enter. He asks them if they have tickets and when they say they haven't, he tells them that he ain't got no right to let them in, and don't know nothing about what the rule is going to be. At some weddings, he goes on, hardly nobody ain't allowed in, but then again, sometimes they don't scarcely look at the tickets at all. The two flappers retire abashed, and as the sexton finishes his sweeping, there enters the organist.

The organist is a tall, thin man of melancholy, uræmic aspect, wearing a black slouch hat with a wide brim and a yellow overcoat that barely reaches to his knees. A pupil, in his youth, of a man who had once studied (irregularly and briefly) with Charles-Marie Widor, he acquired thereby the artistic temperament, and with it a vast fondness for malt liquor. His mood this morning is acidulous and depressed, for he spent yesterday evening in a Pilsner ausschank with two former members of the Boston Symphony Orchestra, and it was 3 A.M. before they finally agreed that Johann Sebastian Bach, all things considered, was a greater man than Beethoven, and so parted amicably. Sourness is the precise sensation that wells within him. He feels vinegary; his blood runs cold; he wishes he could immerse himself in bicarbonate of soda. But the call of his art is more potent

than the protest of his poisoned and quaking liver, and so he man-
fully climbs the spiral stairway to his organ-loft.

Once there, he takes off his hat and overcoat, stoops down to blow
the dust off the organ keys, throws the electrical switch which sets
the bellows going, and then proceeds to take off his shoes. This done,
he takes his seat, reaches for the pedals with his stockinged feet, tries
an experimental 32-foot CCC, and then wanders gently into a Bach
toccata. It is his limbering-up piece: he always plays it as a prelude to
a wedding job. It thus goes very smoothly and even brilliantly, but
when he comes to the end of it and tackles the ensuing fugue he is
quickly in difficulties, and after four or five stumbling repetitions of
the subject he hurriedly improvises a crude coda and has done.
Peering down into the church to see if his flounderings have had
an audience, he sees two old maids enter, the one very tall and
thin and the other somewhat brisk and bunchy.

They constitute the vanguard of the nuptial throng, and as they
proceed hesitatingly up the center aisle, eager for good seats but
afraid to go too far, the organist wipes his palms upon his trousers
legs, squares his shoulders, and plunges into the program that he
has played at all weddings for fifteen years past. It begins with
Mendelssohn's Spring Song, pianissimo. Then comes Rubinstein's
Melody in F, with a touch of forte toward the close, and then Nevin's
"Oh, That We Two Were Maying," and then the Chopin waltz in
A flat, Opus 69, No. 1, and then the Spring Song again, and then
a free fantasia upon "The Rosary" and then a Moszkowski mazurka,
and then the Dvořák Humoresque (with its heart-rending cry in the
middle), and then some vague and turbulent thing (apparently the
disjecta membra of another fugue), and then Tschaikowsky's
"Autumn," and then Elgar's "Salut d'Amour," and then the Spring
Song a third time, and then something or other from one of the Peer
Gynt suites, and then an hurrah or two from the Hallelujah chorus,
and then Chopin again, and Nevin, and Elgar, and—

But meanwhile, there is a growing activity below. First comes a
closed automobile bearing the six ushers and soon after it another
automobile bearing the bridegroom and his best man. The bridegroom
and the best man disembark before the side entrance of the church
and make their way into the vestryroom, where they remove their
hats and coats, and proceed to struggle with their cravats and collars
before a mirror which hangs on the wall. The room is very dingy. A

baize-covered table is in the center of it, and around the table stand six or eight chairs of assorted designs. One wall is completely covered by a bookcase, through the glass doors of which one may discern piles of cheap Bibles, hymn-books and back numbers of the parish magazine. In one corner is a small washstand. The best man takes a flat flask of whiskey from his pocket, looks about him for a glass, finds it on the washstand, rinses it at the tap, fills it with a policeman's drink, and hands it to the bridegroom. The latter downs it at a gulp. Then the best man pours out one for himself.

The ushers, reaching the vestibule of the church, have handed their silk hats to the sexton, and entered the sacred edifice. There was a rehearsal of the wedding last night, but after it was over the bride ordered certain incomprehensible changes in the plan, and the ushers are now completely at sea. All they know clearly is that the relatives of the bride are to be seated on one side and the relatives of the bridegroom on the other. But which side for one and which for the other? They discuss it heatedly for three minutes and then find that they stand three for putting the bride's relatives on the left side and three for putting them on the right side. The debate, though instructive, is interrupted by the sudden entrance of seven women in a group. They are headed by a truculent old battleship, possibly an aunt or something of the sort, who fixes the nearest usher with a knowing, suspicious glance, and motions to him to show her the way.

He offers her his right arm and they start up the center aisle, with the six other women following in irregular order, and the five other ushers scattered among the women. The leading usher is tortured damnably by doubts as to where the party should go. If they are aunts, to which house do they belong, and on which side are the members of that house to be seated? What if they are not aunts, but merely neighbors? Or perhaps an association of former cooks, parlor maids, nurse girls? Or strangers? The sufferings of the usher are relieved by the battleship, who halts majestically about twenty feet from the altar, and motions her followers into a pew to the left. They file in silently and she seats herself next the aisle. All seven settle back and wriggle for room. It is a tight fit.

(Who, in point of fact, are these ladies? Don't ask the question! The ushers never find out. No one ever finds out. They remain a joint mystery for all time. In the end they become a sort of tradition, and years hence, when two of the ushers meet, they will cackle over

old dreadnaught and her six cruisers. The bride, grown old and fat, will tell the tale to her daughter, and then to her granddaughter. It will grow more and more strange, marvelous, incredible. Variorum versions will spring up. It will be adapted to other weddings. The dreadnaught will become an apparition, a witch, the Devil in skirts. And as the years pass, the date of the episode will be pushed back. By 2017 it will be dated 1150. By 2475 it will take on a sort of sacred character, and there will be a footnote referring to it in the latest Revised Version of the New Testament.

It is now a quarter to twelve, and of a sudden the vestibule fills with wedding guests. Nine-tenths of them, perhaps even nineteen-twentieths, are women, and most of them are beyond thirty-five. Scattered among them, hanging on to their skirts, are about a dozen little girls—one of them a youngster of eight or thereabout, with spindle shanks and shining morning face, entranced by her first wedding. Here and there lurks a man. Usually he wears a hurried, unwilling, protesting look. He has been dragged from his office on a busy morning, forced to rush home and get into his cutaway coat, and then marched to the church by his wife. One of these men, much hustled, has forgotten to have his shoes shined. He is intensely conscious of them, and tries to hide them behind his wife's skirt as they walk up the aisle. Accidentally he steps upon it, and gets a look over the shoulder which lifts his diaphragm an inch and turns his liver to water. This man will be court-martialed when he reaches home, and he knows it. He wishes that some foreign power would invade the United States and burn down all the churches in the country, and that the bride, the bridegroom and all the other persons interested in the present wedding were dead and in hell.

The ushers do their best to seat these wedding guests in some sort of order, but after a few minutes the crowd at the doors becomes so large that they have to give it up, and thereafter all they can do is to hold out their right arms ingratiatingly and trust to luck. One of them steps on a fat woman's skirt, tearing it very badly, and she has to be helped back to the vestibule. There she seeks refuge in a corner, under a stairway leading up to the steeple, and essays to repair the damage with pins produced from various nooks and crevices of her person. Meanwhile the guilty usher stands in front of her, mumbling apologies and trying to look helpful. When she finishes her work and emerges from her improvised drydock, he again offers her his arm, but she sweeps past him without noticing him, and proceeds grandly to a seat far forward. She is a cousin to the bride's mother, and will make a report to every branch of the family that all six ushers disgraced the ceremony by appearing at it far gone in liquor.

Fifteen minutes are consumed by such episodes and divertisements. By the time the clock in the steeple strikes twelve the church is well filled. The music of the organist, who has now reached Mendelssohn's Spring Song for the third and last time, is accompanied by a huge buzz of whispers, and there is much craning of necks and long-distance nodding and smiling. Here and there an unusually gorgeous hat is the target of many converging glances, and of as many more or less satirical criticisms. To the damp funeral smell of the flowers at the altar, there has been added the cacodorous scents of forty or fifty different brands of talcum and rice powder. It begins to grow warm in the church, and a number of women open their vanity bags and duck down for stealthy dabs at their noses. Others, more reverent, suffer the agony of augmenting shines. One, a trickster, has concealed powder in her pocket handkerchief, and applies it dexterously while pretending to blow her nose.

The bridegroom in the vestry-room, entering upon the second year (or is it the third?) of his long and ghastly wait, grows increasingly nervous, and when he hears the organist pass from the Spring Song into some more sonorous and stately thing he mistakes it for the wedding march from "Lohengrin," and is hot for marching upon the altar at once. The best man, an old hand, restrains him gently, and administers another sedative from the bottle. The bridegroom's thoughts turn to gloomy things. He remembers sadly that he will never be able to laugh at benedicts again; that his days of low, rabelaisian wit and care-free scoffing are over; that he is now the very thing he mocked so gaily but yesteryear. Like a drowning man, he passes his whole life in review—not, however, that part which is past, but that part which is to come. Odd fancies throng upon him. He wonders what his honeymoon will cost him, what there will be to drink at the wedding breakfast, what a certain girl in Chicago will say when she hears of his marriage. Will there be any children? He rather hopes not, for all those he knows appear so greasy and noisy, but he decides that he might conceivably compromise on a boy. But how is he going to make sure that it will not be a girl? The thing, as yet, is a medical impossibility—but medicine is making rapid strides. Why not wait until the secret is discovered? This sapient compromise pleases the bridegroom, and he proceeds to a consideration of various problems of finance. And then, of a sudden, the organist swings unmistakably into "Lohengrin" and the best man grabs him by the arm.

There is now great excitement in the church. The bride's mother, two sisters, three brothers and three sisters-in-law have just marched up the center aisle and taken seats in the front pew, and all the women in the place are craning their necks toward the door. The usual electrical delay ensues. There is something the matter with the bride's train, and the two bridesmaids have a deuce of a time fixing it. Meanwhile the bride's father, in tight pantaloons and tighter gloves, fidgets and fumes in the vestibule, the six ushers crowd about him inanely, and the sexton rushes to and fro like a rat in a trap. Finally, all being ready, with the ushers formed two abreast, the sexton pushes a button, a small buzzer sounds in the organ loft, and the organist, as has been said, plunges magnificently into the fanfare of the "Lohengrin" march. Simultaneously the sexton opens the door at the bottom of the main aisle, and the wedding procession gets under weigh.

The bride and her father march first. Their step is so slow (about one beat to two measures) that the father has some difficulty in maintaining his equilibrium, but the bride herself moves steadily and erectly, almost seeming to float. Her face is thickly encrusted with talcum in its various forms, so that she is almost a dead white. She keeps her eyelids lowered modestly, but is still acutely aware of every glance fastened upon her—not in the mass, but every glance individually. For example, she sees clearly, even through her eyelids, the still, cold smile of a girl in Pew 8 R—a girl who once made an unwomanly attempt upon the bridegroom's affections, and was routed and put to flight by superior strategy. And her ears are open, too: she hears every "How sweet!" and "Oh, lovely!" and "Ain't she pale!" from the latitude of the last pew to the very glacis of the altar of God.

While she has thus made her progress up the hymeneal chute, the bridegroom and his best man have emerged from the vestryroom and begun the short march to the prie-dieu. They walk haltingly, clumsily, uncertainly, stealing occasional glances at the advancing bridal party. The bridegroom feels of his lower right-hand waistcoat pocket; the ring is still there. The best man wriggles his cuffs. No one, however, pays any heed to them. They are not even seen, indeed, until the bride and her father reach the open space in front of the altar. There the bride and the bridegroom find themselves standing side by side, but not a word is exchanged between them, nor even a look of recognition. They stand motionless, contemplating the ornate cushion at their feet, until the bride's father and the bridesmaids file to the left of the bride and the ushers, now wholly disorganized and imbecile, drape themselves in an irregular file along the altar rail. Then, the music having died down to a faint murmur and a hush having fallen upon the assemblage, they look up.

Before them, framed by foliage, stands the reverend gentleman of God who will presently link them in indissoluble chains—the estimable rector of the parish. He has got there just in time; it was, indeed, a close shave. But no trace of haste or of anything else of a disturbing character is now visible upon his smooth, glistening, somewhat feverish face. That face is wholly occupied by his official smile, a thing of oil and honey all compact, a balmy, unctuous illumination—the secret of his success in life. Slowly his cheeks puff out, gleaming like soap-bubbles. Slowly he lifts his prayer-book from the prie-dieu and holds it droopingly. Slowly his soft caressing eyes engage it. There is an almost imperceptible stiffening of his frame. His mouth opens with a faint click. He begins to read.

The Ceremony of Marriage has begun.

Clarence Day

THOUGHTS WITHOUT WORDS

I

Down in the Pits of Feeling
  The Female lies, bedeck'd,
Till Man arrives, revealing
  The Light of Intellect.

II

Oh who that ever lived and loved
Can look upon an egg unmoved?
The egg it is the source of all.
'Tis everyone's ancestral hall.
The bravest chief that ever fought,
The lowest thief that e'er was caught,
The harlot's lip, the maiden's leg,
They each and all came from an egg.

The rocks that once by ocean's surge
Beheld the first of eggs emerge—
Obscure, defenseless, small and cold—
They little knew what eggs could hold.
The gifts the reverent Magi gave,
Pandora's box, Aladdin's cave,
Wars, loves, and kingdoms, heaven and hell
All lay within that tiny shell.

Oh, join me gentlemen, I beg,
In honoring our friend, the egg.

III

Who drags the fiery artist down?
What keeps the pioneer in town?
Who hates to let the seaman roam?
It is the wife, it is the home.

IV

The story of his life.

V

Here's Bishop Briskoe Pettifogg.
Is he in—or on—the hands of God?

VI

When eras die, their legacies
    Are left to strange police.
Professors in New England guard
    The glory that was Greece.

Kenneth Fearing

PORTRAIT

The clear brown eyes, kindly and alert, with 20-20 vision,
give confident regard to the passing world through R. K.
Lampert & Company lenses framed in gold
> his soul, however, is all his own
>> Arndt Brothers necktie and hat (with feather)
>> supply a touch of youth

With his soul his own, he drives, drives, chats and drives
> the second and third bicuspids, lower right, replaced
> by bridgework, while two incisors have porcelain
> crowns

(Render unto federal, state, and city Caesar, but not
unto time
> render nothing unto time until Amalgamated Death
> serves final notice, in proper form

The vault is ready
> the will has been drawn by Clagget, Clagget, Clag-
> get & Brown
>> the policies are adequate, Confidential's best,
>> reimbursing for disability, partial or complete,
>> with double indemnity should the end be a
>> pure and simple accident)

Nothing unto time
> nothing unto change
>> nothing unto fate
>>> nothing unto you, and nothing unto me,
>>> or to any other known or unknown party
>>> or parties, living or deceased

380

But Mercury shoes, with special arch supports, take
much of the wear and tear
    on the course, a custombuilt driver corrects a tend-
    ency to slice
        love's ravages have been repaired (it was a text-
        book case) by Drs. Schultz, Lightner, Mann-
        heim, and Goode
            while all of it is enclosed in excellent
            tweed, with Mr. Baumer's personal atten-
            tion to the shoulders and the waist

And all of it now roving, chatting amiably through space
in a Plymouth 6
    with his soul (his own) at peace, soothed by Walter
    Lippmann, and sustained by Haig & Haig.

e. e. cummings

the Cambridge ladies

the Cambridge ladies who live in furnished souls
are unbeautiful and have comfortable minds
(also, with the church's protestant blessings
daughters, unscented shapeless spirited)
they believe in Christ and Longfellow, both dead,
are invariably interested in so many things—
at the present writing one still finds
delighted fingers knitting for the is it Poles?
perhaps. While permanent faces coyly bandy
scandal of Mrs. N and Professor D
....the Cambridge ladies do not care, above
Cambridge if sometimes in its box of
sky lavender and cornerless, the
moon rattles like a fragment of angry candy

Ogden Nash

BANKERS ARE JUST LIKE ANYBODY ELSE, EXCEPT RICHER

This is a song to celebrate banks,
Because they are full of money and you go into them
    and all you hear is clinks and clanks,
Or maybe a sound like the wind in the trees on the hills,
Which is the rustling of the thousand-dollar bills.
Most bankers dwell in marble halls,
Which they get to dwell in because they encourage
    deposits and discourage withdralls,
And particularly because they all observe one rule which
    woe betides the banker who fails to heed it,
Which is you must never lend any money to anybody
    unless they don't need it.
I know you, you cautious conservative banks!
If people are worried about their rent it is your duty to
    deny them the loan of one nickel, yes, even one
    copper engraving of the martyred son of the late
    Nancy Hanks;
Yes, if they request fifty dollars to pay for a baby you
    must look at them like Tarzan looking at an uppity
    ape in the jungle,
And tell them what do they think a bank is, anyhow,
    they had better go get the money from their wife's
    aunt or ungle.
But suppose people come in and they have a million
    and they want another million to pile on top of it,
Why, you brim with the milk of human kindness and
    you urge them to accept every drop of it,
And you lend them the million so then they have two
    million and this gives them the idea that they
    would be better off with four,

So they already have two million as security so you have
    no hesitation in lending them two more,
And all the vice-presidents nod their heads in rhythm,
And the only question asked is do the borrowers want
    the money sent or do they want to take it withm.
But please do not think that I am not fond of banks,
Because I think they deserve our appreciation and
    thanks,
Because they perform a valuable public service in elimi-
    nating the jackasses who go around saying that health
    and happiness are everything and money isn't essential,
Because as soon as they have to borrow some unimportant
    money to maintain their health and happiness they starve
    to death so they can't go around any more sneering at
    good old money, which is nothing short of providential.

FIRST FAMILIES, MOVE OVER!

Carry me back to Ole Virginny,
And there I'll meet a lot of people from New York,
There the Ole Marsa of the Hounds is from Smithtown or
    Peapack or Millbrook,
And the mocking bird makes music in the sunshine accompanied
    by the rattling shaker and the popping cork.

All up and down the old plantation
Socialites are riding hell-for-leather like witches and war-
    locks,
And there is only one thing that keeps the squirearchy from
    being a genuine reproduction,
Which is that the peasantry's hair is kinky so they
    haven't any forelocks so they can't tug their
    forelocks.

In the evening by the bright light you can hear those
    darkies singing,
How the white folks do enjoy it and call the attention

of their friends from Piping Rock to the natural
musical talent of the dusky proletariat.

You can hear those banjos ringing because the hands
have been ordered to exchange their saxophones
for banjos,

And they wish they were singing Lookie lookie lookie,
here comes Cookie, but their instructions are to
sing Swing Low Sweet Chariot.

Oh what is more beautiful and more Southern than a
Southern beauty from Philadelphia or Rumson,

And indeed where was Southern beauty before the
advent of Schiaparelli and Elizabeth Arden?

And what is more gracious than a hostess calling you
you-all in the singular and plural indiscriminately,

And what has more local color than a lovely girl in
jodhpurs telling you about her gyarrrden?

Oh the long happy days spent huntin' or shootin' or
fishin',

Or in any other sport provided it's lackin' in g's!

Oh the long happy evenings spent sniffing jasmine and
poring over the shiny new family Bible,

And figuring out that after all this is really your home
because great-grandmother Wilkins was a Filkins
and the Filkinses were related by marriage to the
Randolphs or the Lees!

So please somebody carry me back to Ole Virginny,

Where gentlemen are gentlemen and a lady is known by
the product she endorses,

Where the atmosphere is as Southern as an advertisement
for a medium-priced rye whiskey,

And where the Virginians from Virginia have to ride automobiles because the Virginians from Long Island are the
only ones who can afford to ride horses.

Russell Maloney

INFLEXIBLE LOGIC

When the six chimpanzees came into his life, Mr. Bainbridge was
thirty-eight years old. He was a bachelor and lived comfortably in
a remote part of Connecticut, in a large old house with a carriage
drive, a conservatory, a tennis court, and a well-selected library. His
income was derived from impeccably situated real estate in New
York City, and he spent it soberly, in a manner which could give
offence to nobody. Once a year, late in April, his tennis court was
resurfaced, and after that anybody in the neighborhood was welcome
to use it; his monthly statement from Brentano's seldom ran below
seventy-five dollars; every third year, in November, he turned in his
old Cadillac coupé for a new one; he ordered his cigars, which were
mild and rather moderately priced, in shipments of one thousand,
from a tobacconist in Havana; because of the international situation
he had cancelled arrangements to travel abroad, and after due thought
had decided to spend his travelling allowance on wines, which seemed
likely to get scarcer and more expensive if the war lasted. On the
whole, Mr. Bainbridge's life was deliberately, and not too unsuccessfully, modelled after that of an English country gentleman of the late
eighteenth century, a gentleman interested in the arts and in the
expansion of science, and so sure of himself that he didn't care if
some people thought him eccentric.

Mr. Bainbridge had many friends in New York, and he spent
several days of the month in the city, staying at his club and looking
around. Sometimes he called up a girl and took her out to a theatre
and a night club. Sometimes he and a couple of classmates got a little
tight and went to a prizefight. Mr. Bainbridge also looked in now
and then at some of the conservative art galleries, and liked occasionally
to go to a concert. And he liked cocktail parties, too, because of the
fine footling conversation and the extraordinary number of pretty
girls who had nothing else to do with the rest of their evening. It

was at a New York cocktail party, however, that Mr. Bainbridge kept his preliminary appointment with doom. At one of the parties given by Hobie Packard, the stockbroker, he learned about the theory of the six chimpanzees.

It was almost six-forty. The people who had intended to have one drink and go had already gone, and the people who intended to stay were fortifying themselves with slightly dried canapés and talking animatedly. A group of stage and radio people had coagulated in one corner, near Packard's Capehart, and were wrangling about various methods of cheating the Collector of Internal Revenue. In another corner was a group of stockbrokers, talking about the greatest stockbroker of them all, Gauguin. Little Marcia Lupton was sitting with a young man, saying earnestly, "Do you really want to know what my greatest ambition is? I want to be myself," and Mr. Bainbridge smiled gently, thinking of the time Marcia had said that to him. Then he heard the voice of Bernard Weiss, the critic, saying, "Of course he wrote one good novel. It's not surprising. After all, we know that if six chimpanzees were set to work pounding six typewriters at random, they would, in a million years, write all the books in the British Museum."

Mr. Bainbridge drifted over to Weiss and was introduced to Weiss's companion, a Mr. Noble. "What's this about a million chimpanzees, Weiss?" he asked.

"Six chimpanzees," Mr. Weiss said. "It's an old cliché of the mathematicians. I thought everybody was told about it in school. Law of averages, you know, or maybe it's permutation and combination. The six chimps, just pounding away at the typewriter keys, would be bound to copy out all the books ever written by man. There are only so many possible combinations of letters and numerals, and they'd produce all of them—see? Of course they'd also turn out a mountain of gibberish, but they'd work the books in, too. All the books in the British Museum."

Mr. Bainbridge was delighted; this was the sort of talk he liked to hear when he came to New York. "Well, but look here," he said, just to keep up his part in the foolish conversation, "what if one of the chimpanzees finally did duplicate a book, right down to the last period, but left that off? Would that count?"

"I suppose not. Probably the chimpanzee would get around to doing the book again, and put the period in."

"What nonsense!" Mr. Noble cried.

"It may be nonsense, but Sir James Jeans believes it," Mr. Weiss said, huffily. "Jeans or Lancelot Hogben. I know I ran across it quite recently."

Mr. Bainbridge was impressed. He read quite a bit of popular science, and both Jeans and Hogben were in his library. "Is that so?" he murmured, no longer feeling frivolous. "Wonder if it has ever actually been tried? I mean, has anybody ever put six chimpanzees in a room with six typewriters and a lot of paper?"

Mr. Weiss glanced at Mr. Bainbridge's empty cocktail glass and said drily, "Probably not."

Nine weeks later, on a winter evening, Mr. Bainbridge was sitting in his study with his friend James Mallard, an assistant professor of mathematics at New Haven. He was plainly nervous as he poured himself a drink and said, "Mallard, I've asked you to come here— Brandy? Cigar?—for a particular reason. You remember that I wrote you some time ago, asking your opinion of ... of a certain mathematical hypothesis or supposition."

"Yes," Professor Mallard said, briskly. "I remember perfectly. About the six chimpanzees and the British Museum. And I told you it was a perfectly sound popularization of a principle known to every schoolboy who had studied the science of probabilities."

"Precisely," Mr. Bainbridge said. "Well, Mallard, I made up my mind ... It was not difficult for me, because I have, in spite of that fellow in the White House, been able to give something every year to the Museum of Natural History, and they were naturally glad to oblige me.... And after all, the only contribution a layman can make to the progress of science is to assist with the drudgery of experiment.... In short, I—"

"I suppose you're trying to tell me that you have procured six chimpanzees and set them to work at typewriters in order to see whether they will eventually write all the books in the British Museum. Is that it?"

"Yes, that's it," Mr. Bainbridge said. "What a mind you have, Mallard. Six fine young males, in perfect condition. I had a—I suppose you'd call it a dormitory—built out in back of the stable. The typewriters are in the conservatory. It's light and airy in there, and I moved most of the plants out. Mr. North, the man who owns the circus, very obligingly let me engage one of his best animal men. Really, it was no trouble at all."

Professor Mallard smiled indulgently. "After all, such a thing is not unheard of," he said. "I seem to remember that a man at some university put his graduate students to work flipping coins, to see if heads and tails came up an equal number of times. Of course they did."

Mr. Bainbridge looked at his friend very queerly. "Then you believe that any such principle of the science of probabilities will stand up under an actual test?"

"Certainly."

"You had better see for yourself." Mr. Bainbridge led Professor Mallard downstairs, along a corridor, through a disused music room, and into a large conservatory. The middle of the floor had been cleared of plants and was occupied by a row of six typewriter tables, each one supporting a hooded machine. At the left of each typewriter was a neat stack of yellow copy paper. Empty wastebaskets were under each table. The chairs were the unpadded, spring-backed kind favored by experienced stenographers. A large bunch of ripe bananas was hanging in one corner, and in another stood a Great Bear water-cooler and a rack of Lily cups. Six piles of typescript, each about a foot high, were ranged along the wall on an improvised shelf. Mr. Bainbridge picked up one of the piles, which he could just conveniently lift, and set it on a table before Professor Mallard. "The output to date of Chimpanzee A, known as Bill," he said simply.

"'"Oliver Twist," by Charles Dickens,'" Professor Mallard read out. He read the first and second pages of the manuscript, then feverishly leafed through to the end. "You mean to tell me," he said, "that this chimpanzee has written—"

"Word for word and comma for comma," said Mr. Bainbridge. "Young, my butler, and I took turns comparing it with the edition I own. Having finished 'Oliver Twist,' Bill is, as you see, starting the sociological works of Vilfredo Pareto, in Italian. At the rate he has been going, it should keep him busy for the rest of the month."

"And all the chimpanzees"—Professor Mallard was pale, and enunciated with difficulty—"they aren't all—"

"Oh, yes, all writing books which I have every reason to believe are in the British Museum. The prose of John Donne, some Anatole France, Conan Doyle, Galen, the collected plays of Somerset Maugham, Marcel Proust, the memoirs of the late Marie of Rumania, and a monograph by a Dr. Wiley on the marsh grasses of Maine and Massachusetts. I can sum it up for you, Mallard, by telling you that since I started this experiment, four weeks and some days ago, none of the chimpanzees has spoiled a single sheet of paper."

Professor Mallard straightened up, passed his handkerchief across his brow, and took a deep breath. "I apologize for my weakness," he said. "It was simply the sudden shock. No, looking at the thing scientifically—and I hope I am at least as capable of that as the next man —there is nothing marvellous about the situation. These chimpanzees, or a succession of similar teams of chimpanzees, would in a million years write all the books in the British Museum. I told you some time ago that I believed that statement. Why should my belief be altered by the fact that they produced some of the books at the very outset? After all, I should not be very much surprised if I tossed a coin a hundred times and it came up heads every time. I know that if I kept at it long enough, the ratio would reduce itself to an exact fifty per cent. Rest assured, these chimpanzees will begin to compose gibberish quite soon. It is bound to happen. Science tells us so. Meanwhile, I advise you to keep this experiment secret. Uninformed people might create a sensation if they knew."

"I will, indeed," Mr. Bainbridge said. "And I'm very grateful for your rational analysis. It reassures me. And now, before you go, you must hear the new Schnabel records that arrived today."

During the succeeding three months, Professor Mallard got into the habit of telephoning Mr. Bainbridge every Friday afternoon at five-thirty, immediately after leaving his seminar room. The Professor would say, "Well?," and Mr. Bainbridge would reply, "They're still at it, Mallard. Haven't spoiled a sheet of paper yet." If Mr. Bainbridge had to go out on Friday afternoon, he would leave a written message with his butler, who would read it to Professor Mallard: "Mr. Bainbridge says we now have Trevelyan's 'Life of Macaulay,' the Confessions of St. Augustine, 'Vanity Fair,' part of Irving's 'Life of George Washington,' the Book of the Dead, and some speeches delivered in Parliament in opposition to the Corn Laws, sir." Professor Mallard would reply, with a hint of a snarl in his voice, "Tell him to remember what I predicted," and hang up with a clash.

The eleventh Friday that Professor Mallard telephoned, Mr. Bainbridge said, "No change. I have had to store the bulk of the manuscript in the cellar. I would have burned it, except that it probably has some scientific value."

"How dare you talk of scientific value?" The voice from New Haven roared faintly in the receiver. "Scientific value! You—you—chimpanzee!" There were further inarticulate sputterings, and Mr. Bainbridge hung up with a disturbed expression. "I am afraid Mallard is overtaxing himself," he murmured.

Next day, however, he was pleasantly surprised. He was leafing through a manuscript that had been completed the previous day by Chimpanzee D, Corky. It was the complete diary of Samuel Pepys, and Mr. Bainbridge was chuckling over the naughty passages, which were omitted in his own edition, when Professor Mallard was shown into the room. "I have come to apologize for my outrageous conduct on the telephone yesterday," the Professor said.

"Please don't think of it any more. I know you have many things on your mind," Mr. Bainbridge said. "Would you like a drink?"

"A large whiskey, straight, please," Professor Mallard said. "I got rather cold driving down. No change, I presume?"

"No, none. Chimpanzee F, Dinty, is just finishing John Florio's translation of Montaigne's essays, but there is no other news of interest."

Professor Mallard squared his shoulders and tossed off his drink in one astonishing gulp. "I should like to see them at work," he said. "Would I disturb them, do you think?"

"Not at all. As a matter of fact, I usually look in on them around this time of day. Dinty may have finished his Montaigne by now, and it is always interesting to see them start a new work. I would have thought that they would continue on the same sheet of paper, but they don't, you know. Always a fresh sheet, and the title in capitals."

Professor Mallard, without apology, poured another drink and slugged it down. "Lead on," he said.

It was dusk in the conservatory, and the chimpanzees were typing by the light of student lamps clamped to their desks. The keeper lounged in a corner, eating a banana and reading *Billboard*. "You might as well take an hour or so off," Mr. Bainbridge said. The man left.

Professor Mallard, who had not taken off his overcoat, stood with his hands in his pockets, looking at the busy chimpanzees. "I wonder if you know, Bainbridge, that the science of probabilities takes everything into account," he said, in a queer, tight voice. "It is certainly almost beyond the bounds of credibility that these chimpanzees should write books without a single error, but that abnormality may be corrected by—*these!*" He took his hands from his pockets, and each one held a .38 revolver. "Stand back out of harm's way!" he shouted.

"Mallard! Stop it!" The revolvers barked, first the right hand, then the left, then the right. Two chimpanzees fell, and a third reeled into a corner. Mr. Bainbridge seized his friend's arm and wrested one of the weapons from him.

"Now I am armed, too, Mallard, and I advise you to stop!" he cried. Professor Mallard's answer was to draw a bead on Chimpanzee E and shoot him dead. Mr. Bainbridge made a rush, and Professor Mallard fired at him. Mr. Bainbridge, in his quick death agony, tightened his finger on the trigger of his revolver. It went off, and Professor Mallard went down. On his hands and knees he fired at the two chimpanzees which were still unhurt, and then collapsed.

There was nobody to hear his last words. "The human equation ... always the enemy of science ..." he panted. "This time ... vice versa ... I, a mere mortal ... savior of science ... deserve a Nobel ..."

When the old butler came running into the conservatory to investigate the noises, his eyes were met by a truly appalling sight. The student lamps were shattered, but a newly risen moon shone in through the conservatory windows on the corpses of the two gentlemen, each clutching a smoking revolver. Five of the chimpanzees were dead. The sixth was Chimpanzee F. His right arm disabled, obviously bleeding to death, he was slumped before his typewriter. Painfully, with his left hand, he took from the machine the completed last page of Florio's Montaigne. Groping for a fresh sheet, he inserted it, and typed with one finger, "UNCLE TOM's CABIN, by Harriet Beecher Stowe. Chapte ..." Then he, too, was dead.

Finley Peter Dunne

MR. DOOLEY ON THE EDUCATION OF THE YOUNG

"If ye had a boy wud ye sind him to colledge?" asked Mr. Hennessy. "Well," said Mr. Dooley, "at th' age whin a boy is fit to be in colledge I wudden't have him around th' house."

*　　*　　*

The troubled Mr. Hennessy had been telling Mr. Dooley about the difficulty of making a choice of schools for Packy Hennessy, who at the age of six was at the point where the family must decide his career.

" 'Tis a big question," said Mr. Dooley, "an' wan that seems to be worryin' th' people more thin it used to whin ivry boy was designed f'r th' priesthood, with a full undherstandin' be his parents that th' chances was in favor iv a brick yard. Nowadays they talk about th' edycation iv th' child befure they choose th' name. 'Tis: 'Th' kid talks in his sleep. 'Tis th' fine lawyer he'll make.' Or, 'Did ye notice him admirin' that photygraph? He'll be a gr-reat journalist.' Or, 'Look at him fishin' in Uncle Tim's watch pocket. We must thrain him f'r a banker.' Or, 'I'm afraid he'll niver be sthrong enough to wurruk. He must go into th' church.' Befure he's baptized too, d'ye mind. 'Twill not be long befure th' time comes whin th' soggarth'll christen th' infant: 'Judge Pathrick Aloysius Hinnissy, iv th' Northern District iv Illinye,' or 'Profissor P. Aloysius Hinnissy, LL.D., S.T.D., P.G.N., iv th' faculty iv Northre Dame.' Th' innocent child in his cradle, wondherin' what ails th' mist iv him an' where he got such funny lookin' parents fr'm, has thim to blame that brought him into the wurruld if he dayvilops into a sicond story man befure he's twinty-wan an' is took up be th' polis. Why don't you lade Packy down to th' occulist an' have him fitted with a pair iv eye-glasses? Why don't ye put goloshes on him, give him a blue umbrelly an' call him a doctor at wanst an' be done with it?

"To my mind, Hinnissy, we're wastin' too much time thinkin' iv th' future iv our young, an' thryin' to larn thim early what they oughtn' to know till they've growed up. We sind th' childher to school as if 'twas a summer garden where they go to be amused instead iv a pinitinchry where they're sint f'r th' original sin. Whin I was a la-ad I was put at me ah-bee abs, th' first day I set fut in th' school behind th' hedge an' me head was sore inside an' out befure I wint home. Now th' first thing we larn th' future Mark Hannas an' Jawn D. Gateses iv our naytion is waltzin', singin', an' cuttin' pitchers out iv a book. We'd be much betther teachin' thim th' sthrangle hold, f'r that's what they need in life.

"I know what'll happen. Ye'll sind Packy to what th' Germans call a Kindygarten, an' 'tis a good thing f'r Germany, because all a German knows is what some wan tells him, and his grajation papers is a certyficate that he don't need to think annymore. But we've inthrajooced it into this counthry, an' whin I was down seein' if I cud injooce Rafferty, th' Janitor iv th' Isaac Muggs Grammar School, f'r to vote f'r Riordan—an' he's goin' to—I dhropped in on Cassidy's daughter, Mary Ellen, an' see her kindygartnin'. Th' childher was settin' ar-round on th' flure an' some was moldin' dachshunds out iv mud an' wipin' their hands on their hair, an' some was carvin' figures iv a goat out iv paste-board an' some was singin' an some was sleepin' an' a few was dancin' an' wan la-ad was pullin' another la-ad's hair. 'Why don't ye take th' coal shovel to that little barbaryan, Mary Ellen?' says I. 'We don't believe in corporeal punishment,' says she. 'School shud be made pleasant f'r th' childher,' she says. 'Th' child who's hair is bein' pulled is larnin' patience,' she says, 'an' th' child that's pullin' th' hair is discoverin' th' footility iv human indeavor,' says she. 'Well, oh, well,' says I, 'times has changed since I was a boy,' I says. 'Put thim through their exercises,' says I. 'Tommy,' says I, 'spell cat,' I says. 'Go to th' divvle,' says th' cheerub. 'Very smartly answered,' says Mary Ellen. 'Ye shud not ask thim to spell,' she says. 'They don't larn that till they get to colledge,' she says, 'an',' she says, 'sometimes not even thin,' she says. 'An' what do they larn?' says I. 'Rompin',' she says, 'an' dancin',' she says, 'an' indepindance iv speech, an' beauty songs, an' sweet thoughts, an' how to make home home-like,' she says. 'Well,' says I, 'I didn't take anny iv thim things at colledge, so ye needn't unblanket thim,' I says. 'I won't put thim through anny exercise to-day,' I says. 'But whisper, Mary Ellen,' says I, 'Don't ye niver feel like bastin' the seeraphims?' 'Th' teachin's iv Freebull and Pitzotly is conthrary to that,' she says. 'But I'm goin' to be marrid an' lave th' school on

Choosdah, th' twinty-sicond iv Janooary,' she says, 'an' on Mondah, th' twinty-first, I'm goin' to ask a few iv th' little darlin's to th' house an',' she says, 'stew thim over a slow fire,' she says. Mary Ellen is not a German, Hinnissy.

"Well, afther they have larned in school what they ar're licked f'r larnin' in th' back yard—that is squashin' mud with their hands—they're conducted up through a channel iv free an' beautiful thought till they're r-ready f'r colledge. Mamma packs a few doylies an' tidies into son's bag, an' some silver to be used in case iv throuble with th' landlord, an' th' la-ad throts off to th' siminary. If he's not sthrong enough to look f'r high honors as a middleweight pugilist he goes into th' thought departmint. Th' prisidint takes him into a Turkish room, gives him a cigareet an' says: 'Me dear boy, what special branch iv larnin' wud ye like to have studied f'r ye be our compitint professors? We have a chair iv Beauty an' wan iv Puns an' wan iv Pothry on th' Changin' Hues iv th' Settin' Sun, an' wan on Platonic Love, an' wan on Non-sense Rhymes, an' wan on Sweet Thoughts, an' wan on How Green Grows th' Grass, an' wan on th' Relation iv Ice to th' Greek Idee iv God,' he says. 'This is all ye'll need to equip ye f'r th' perfect life, onless,' he says, 'ye intind bein' a dintist, in which case,' he says, 'we won't think much iv ye, but we have a good school where ye can larn that disgraceful thrade,' he says. An' th' la-ad makes his choice, an' ivry mornin' whin he's up in time he takes a whiff iv hasheesh an' goes off to hear Professor Maryanna tell him that 'if th' dates iv human knowledge must be rejicted as subjictive, how much more must they be subjicted as rejictive if, as I think, we keep our thoughts fixed upon th' inanity iv th' finite in comparison with th' onthinkable truth with th' ondivided an' onimaginable reality. Boys, ar-re ye with me?' . . ."

"I don't undherstand a wurrud iv what ye'r sayin'," said Mr. Hennessy.

"No more do I," said Mr. Dooley. "But I believe 'tis as Father Kelly says: 'Childher shuddn't be sint to school to larn, but to larn how to larn. I don't care what ye larn thim so long as 'tis onpleasant to thim.' 'Tis thrainin' they need, Hinnissy. That's all. I niver cud make use iv what I larned in colledge about thrigojoomethry an'—an'—grammar an' th' welts I got on th' skull fr'm th' schoolmasther's cane I have niver been able to turn to anny account in th' business, but 'twas th' bein' there an' havin' to get things to heart without askin' th' meanin' iv thim an' goin' to school cold an' comin' home hungry, that made th' man iv me ye see befure ye."

"That's why th' good woman's throubled about Packy," said Hennessy.

"Go home," said Mr. Dooley.

MR. DOOLEY ON GOLF

"Well, sir," said Mr. Dooley, "I don't want to say annything that wud hurt a frind, but I do think th' authorities ar-re very lax in lavin' Hogan at large, as they ar-re doin'."

"An' what ails Hogan?" Mr. Hennessy asked.

"He's got what th' dock calls a fixed deelusion," said Mr. Dooley. "He thinks he's a goluf player. No, he don't play th' game. Nobody does that. They wurruk at it. But Hogan he slaves at it. He don't think iv annything else. He takes it down to th' wather-office with him in th' mornin', an' he carries it home with him at night an' sleeps with it. If ye go over to his house at this minyit ye'll find him in th' front parlor swingin' a poker an' tellin' the good woman how he played th' eighth hole. There's nawthin' more excitin' to th' mother iv siven at th' end of a complete wash-day thin to listen to an account iv a bum goluf game fr'm th' lips iv her lifemate. 'Tis almost as absorbin' as th' invintory iv a grocery store. I was over there th' other night, an' he broke three panes iv glass showin' me what he calls a mashie shot, an' he near took an ear off his aunt Bridget practisin' with a war-club that he calls a nibbelick. I wudden't be harsh with him, but a few months or aven years in a well upholstered cell with a ball an' chain on his leg, might restore him to himself an' make him again th' safe an' bashful husband an' father he wanst was.

"But 'tis a gr-reat game, a gr-rand, jolly, hail-fellow-well-met spoort. With th' exciption maybe iv th' theery iv infant damnation, Scotland has given nawthin' more cheerful to th' wurruld thin th' game iv goluf. Whin 'twas first smuggled into this counthry, I cudden't make out what 'twas like. I thought whin I first read about it that it was intinded f'r people with a hackin' cough, an' that no wan who was robust enough to play 'Twinty Questions' in a wheel-chair, wud engage in it without a blush. I had it in me mind that 'twas played iv a rainy afthernoon in th' front parlor. Th' two athletes got out their needles an' their embroidery canvas, give a shout iv glee an' flew at it. Th' results was submitted to th' 'Ladies Home Journal,' an' me frind Eddie Bok decided who was champeen, an' give him a goold thimble f'r a prize.

"But I know betther now. 'Tis a rough an' angry game, full of ondacint remarks an' other manly charackteristics, d'ye mind. An' whin 'tis over it laves as much bad blood as a German submarine. At th' end iv ivry goluf match th' player loathes himsilf, is not on speakin' terms with th' fellow he played agin, cud kill his own caddy an' his opponent's, an' hates th' criminal that laid out th' coorse, th' game itsilf, th' Jook iv Argyll, each wan iv his clubs, th' little bur-rd that twittered whin he was shootin', th' pretty wild flowers on th' margin iv th' links, an' each separate spear iv grass on th' puttin'-green. If that Dutch pote that wrote th' 'Hymn iv Hate' wants to write an-other on th' same subjeck with a rale punch in it he ought to larn goluf. 'Twuld help him.

"How's it played, says ye? I don't exactly know. I niver studied law. But ye can get th' rules iv th' game in th' public library, in siven volumes edited be th' Lord Chief Justice iv Scotland. If ye have a dispute over th' rules, th' quickest way to get a decision is to hire a lawyer, make a test case, an' carry it to th' supreem coort. In a gin'ral way, all I can say about it is that it's a kind iv a game iv ball that ye play with ye'er own worst inimy which is ye'ersilf, an' a man ye don't like goes around with ye an' gloats over ye, an' a little boy follows ye to carry th' clubs an' hide th' ball afther ye've hit it. Th' ball is small, made iv injy rubber an' filled with a pizinous substance, an' if ye hit it a good smash it busts an' puts out ye'er eye. Ye're supposed to smash this little grenade fr'm place to place an' here an' there an' up an' down an' hither an' yon with an enormous insthrument iv wood or iron, ontill in due time ye get to what is called a puttin'-green. There's a little hole with a tin can in it in th' middle iv this place, an' whin ye're within a fut or two iv this hole ye take a small hammer out iv th' bag, an' ye hit th' ball four or five times till it tumbles into th' hole. Thin ye wipe th' cold sweat fr'm ye'er brow, write down '5' on a little card, an' walk away a few feet an' do it all over again.

"So far so good. But that ain't nearly all. Ye've got along pretty well, pokin th' ball down th' pretty grass, whin wan day ye see a dark, evil-lookin' man watchin' ye. Ye mark him at wanst as ye'er inimy, an' well it is ye do, f'r he's th' expert that is layin' out the coorse. He marks the spot where ye'er best shot goes, an' says he, with a scowl, 'I'll fix that crokey-playin' plumber.' An' he digs a hole five feet deep an' dumps a wagon iv soft coal ashes into it. Thin he picks out th' other places where ye loved to land, an' he puts in railroad ties, barbed wire, ditches, mounds, pizen-ivy, blackberry bushes, thrailin'-arbutus, a swamp, an' a field iv thistles, tears down a hill an' builds a mountain, gashes th' fair face iv nature with gapin' caverns an' chasms filled with gravel, cigaret stumps, brick-bats, sardine cans, hairpins, an' futprints, calls thim bunkers, an' goes his way. This pro-fissyonal torturer is what is known as a goluf archytect. If ye left a thurly good goluf archytect in th' garden iv Eden f'r an hour he'd make it look like Bilgium afther th' war.

"Well, ye play wanst through this jungle that a wire-haired tarryer cudden't get into, an' ye're told be a frind that ye ought to take a lesson. So ye pick out a bright-faced Scotch lad with a head shaped like a alligator pear an' who can hit th' ball a mile blindfolded an' ye give him what change ye have an' ask him to pint out ye'er faults. He pints out all ye'er wife has told ye about an' manny dark wans besides. I see Hogan takin' a goluf lesson wanst, an' how he iver dared to lift his head again is more thin I cud undherstand. Afther th' profissyonal has recited th' catalog iv ye'er sins an' vices, an' ye've made an act iv conthrition, he tells ye how to hit th' ball. Ye'd think that ought to be aisy. Just go up an' give it a cuff.

"But it ain't annything like as soft as that. There ar-re forty different things ye have to think iv with each shot, an' if ye do wan iv thim wrong, ye're a lost soul. When ye'er idjication is completed ye go out an' do all th' things he told ye, but nineteen, an' th' ball skips lightly into a pit. Now is ye'er time to escape. If ye lave it lie there, turn ye'er back on it, run to th' parish-house an' ask f'r th' prayers iv th' congregation, it may not be too late. Ye may be saved. Fly, weak an' wretched man, while ye have th' strenth! But if ye delay, if ye step but wan fut into th' thrap, ye're doomed an' on'y th' kindly hand iv death will release ye fr'm a life iv shame.

"Oh, 'tis th' jolly game, th' jolly ol' Scotch game. No wondher it's played all over th' counthry. Th' next pleasantest feelin' in the wurruld to bein' perfectly happy is bein' perfectly cross. That's why it's took up be middle-aged gintlemen. They want a chanst to go into a towerin' rage in th' open an' undher th' blue sky. To a goluf player, Hinnissy, th' spreadin' ellum three, a bloomin' rose bush, or a purlin' brook ar-re not what they seem to us. He don't use what ye call figures of speech about thim. No, sir, he uses a nibblelick or a fish-net.

"Another gr-reat injoocement to men to spind their Sundays on th' goluf-coorse is th' prisince iv th' fair sect. Hogan tells me there's nawthin' so pleasant to a tired player as to come up on a tee an' find in front iv him four beautiful ladies. Niver excipt in a sleepin'-car in th' mornin' ar-re ladies so atthractive as whin ye see thim fr'm a tee, with their lovely hair out iv curl, their tender faces tanned a lively pink or vermilion, an' a lumber jack's boots on their dainty feet, while they dab pitcheresquely at th' herbage or stand in graceful attichoods on th' puttin'-green correctin' each other's scoors. Their presence lights up th' whole landscape an' gives th' men players a chanst to rest an' gnash their teeth.

"Yes, sir, th' bravest an' th' best an' th' fairest can be seen, east or west, or north or south, beltin' away winter an' summer at this noble game or hallucynation or rite or whativer ye call it—sinitors, judges, congressmen, gr-reat iditors, preachers, th' prisidint himsilf. Whin a reporter wants to see Dock Wilson he don't look f'r him in th' White House. No, sir. But ye r-read: A riprisintative iv th' 'Daily Gloom' found th' prisidint on th' eighteenth green. He seemed in very good spirits. Whin told that Count von Bernstorff had set fire to th' threasury departmint, Ambassador Gerard had been pizened be th' Kaiser, an' American battleship had been sunk be Cap Boy-Ed in th' North River, an' Dernburg was ladin' a charge iv th' turn-d'ye-mind armed with dumb-bells an' bowlin'-pins on Governor's Island, he laughed good naturedly an' said: 'We mustn't get too excited about this kind iv play-fulness. I'll write thim a little letter th' first time we have a rainy day. By th' way, me boy, whin ye go down to ye'er office, I'd like ye to turn in this scoor an' tell th' spoortin' editor I missed a short putt f'r an eight at th' sixteenth. Otherwise I niver played betther.'

"Did I iver see th' game played? Faith, I did. Th' other mornin' I see Hogan go out with his kit iv tools. In other games wan bat is enough, but in goluf ye have to own twinty. All th' money that used to go f'r shoes in Hogan's fam'ly now goes f'r goluf-clubs. If he manages to hit th' ball with a club, he tells ye he wudden't part with that club f'r a hundherd dollars an' asts ye to feel it an' say ain't that a nice club. Whin he misses it he says th' club has gone back on him an' he buys a new wan. He has as manny implymints iv this new thrade iv his as a tinker. He has a hammer to beat th' ball into th' ground with, an' a pick to get it out, an' a little shovel to scrape it fr'm th' sand, an' a little hatchet to knock it into th' hole whin he gets near it. 'Where ar-re ye goin' with th' hardware?' says I. 'Is it to open a safe or build a battleship?' says I. 'I'm goin' to play goluf,' says he angrily. 'This is th' day I hang Larkin's hide on th' fence,' he says.

"So I followed him out to Douglas Park, an' there we met Larkin, who had a bag iv akel size. Hogan used to be champeen caber tosser iv th' ward an' Larkin was a sthructural ir'n-wurruker befure his health give out an' he become a horseshoer, but they groaned undher their burdens. Fortchnitly at that moment two bright little boys iv about eight years stepped up an' relieved thim iv their burden. 'What are these pigmies goin' to do with this here year's output iv th' Gary mills?' says I. 'They're goin' to carry thim,' says Larkin. 'They're caddies,' he says. 'Well,' says I, ' 'tis very nice iv th' little toddlers. Th' young cannot start too arly in helpin' th' aged. But,' I says, 'why don't ye get up on their backs an' have thim carry ye around? A little more weight wudden't make much difference,' says I. 'Hush up,' says Hogan.

"Th' poor fellow was standin' on what they call th' tee, which is where ye take th' first lick at th' ball. He had a pole in his hand an' was swingin' it at a dandeline an' missin'. Ivinchooly he stepped up to where th' ball roosted on a little pile iv sand, stood with his legs apart like th' statue he calls th' Goloshes iv Rhodes, waggled th' stick in th' air, p'inted it tords th' pole, cried out, 'Stand away, Larkin, get round behind me, Martin, stop shufflin' there, boy,' an' screamed 'Fore' at a fat old gintleman that was at wurruk in a thrench three city blocks ahead. Thin he hauled off with th' bat, muttherin' to himsilf: 'Eye on th' ball, slow back, keep th' lift arm sthraight, pivot on th' right foot, folly through.' Up crept th' dhread insthrument slow an' cautious an' down it came with a blow that wud've foorced th' Dardanelles. I expicted to see th' ball splintered into a thousan' pieces or disappear into space. But it didn't. It left th' tee ridin' on a piece iv turf th' size iv ye'er hat, floated lazily off to wan side, dhropped, bounced twice, an' nestled in a bush. 'Watch it, boy,' yells Hogan. 'Watch it. Go right to it. Oh,' says he, 'what did I do that was wrong, what *did* I do?' says he, wringin' his hands. 'Ye dhropped ye're right shouldher,' says Larkin. 'Took ye're eye off it,' says Larkin's caddy. 'Toed it,' says ar innocint bystander. 'Ye made a mistake thryin' to hit at all. Ye shud've kicked it,' says I. Hogan stood by, his face convulsed with mortyfication ontil Larkin, a man whose Sunday mornin' recreation used to be raisin' a kag iv beer over his head fifty times, give a lunge at th' ball, done a complete spin an' missed it altogether. Thin a wan smile come to Hogan's lips. 'What ar-re ye haw-hawin' about?' says Larkin. They niver spoke again. Most iv th' time they weren't in speakin' distance iv each other. Fr'm time to time they wud meet be chanst on a puttin'-green an' Hogan wud say to himsilf: 'I'm down in twelve,' an' Larkin wud kick his ball over to th' next tee. So they wint rollickin' on. Hogan spoke to me wanst. He said: 'Dammit, stop coughin'.' Whin I left thim at th' sivinth hole th' excitement was at its hite. Larkin' was lookin' f'r his ball in a geeranyum bush, an' Hogan was choppin' down an evergreen three with wan iv his little axes. 'Where ar-re ye goin'?' says he. 'I don't know,' says I, 'but I may dhrop in at th' morgue an' listen to an inquest,' says I. 'I've got to spend me holiday someway,' says I.

"I see Hogan th' next day an' asked him why he played. 'Why,' says I, 'd'ye make a joke iv ye'ersilf at ye'er time iv life, an' ye a man with a family?' says I. 'That's just it,' says he. 'I do it because iv me time iv life an' me fam'ly cares,' says he. 'I defy anny man in th' wurruld to get a bad lie in a bunker an' think iv annything else. He's that mad all his other sorrows, his debts, his sins, an' his future, disappears,' he says, 'like a summer cloud in a hur'cane. I'm that onhappy nawthin' bothers me. If a man come up an' told me me house was afire I'd not hear him. I don't know what it is,' says he, 'onless,' he says, 'it's th' feelin' that ye're bein' persecuted. It's ye'er sinse iv injustice that's stirred up in ye, that makes ye injye a round,' says he."

"Is th' Prisidint a good goluf player, d'ye know, at all?" asked Mr. Hennessy after a moment of judicial silence.

"As a goluf player he cud give Lincoln a sthroke a hole," said Mr. Dooley.

Geoffrey Hellman

MOTHER TAFT'S CHICKENS

Quite a few people have told me, and I have often seen it in print, that the main object of formal education is not so much to inculcate certain facts and dates as to teach you where to go to find out things you want to know. I can find out practically anything I want to know by calling up the *Times,* the Public Library's information desk, the British Library of Information, the French Information Center, or by asking my sister, and I have never precisely understood the connection between this easy ability of mine and the years I spent on algebra, geometry, geology, corrective posture, and Greek. Several months ago I asked the Public Library's information people just what they supposed the connection was, and they said they had no idea offhand but would call me back. I haven't heard from them yet.

My suspicion that the dissection of a frog teaches you, at best, how to dissect a frog, and not a thing more, received a regrettable boost the other day when I came across a printed list, headed "Lost Alumni," sent out by the Taft School, of Watertown, Connecticut, to several hundred of its graduates and ex-students. Taft, as anyone up on educational affairs knows, is one of the best-regarded prep schools in the country, with a student body recruited largely from thoughtful, substantial families and with an admirably low college-entrance-examination mortality record. Its annual algebra contests with Hotchkiss, discontinued a few years ago because of the terrible feeling they engendered, were at one time a lively feature of the Eastern scholastic scene. The list of lost Taft alumni which I have been studying contains four hundred and eleven names, ranging from William Tatlock, class of 1891, to John Ordway, of the class of 1939, who seems to have dropped out of sight like a plummet. The list is accompanied by a statement which reads in part, "You will help us by sending in addresses of any of those listed on the enclosure."

Well, I have every sympathy with Taft's inability to put its finger on Linson E. Tsao, 1914, and I don't suppose that John L. Lewis, 1907, can be the man I keep reading about in the papers, but some of the other lost characters strike me as being surprisingly accessible. Lawrence H. Nott, 1923, for example, is living at 108 East Eighty-second Street, New York, New York; Frederick B. Gleason, Jr., 1927, is at 315 East Sixty-eighth Street; and Alexis C. Coudert, 1931, is at 103 East Eighty-sixth Street. Horace H. Work, Jr., 1936, has an office at 535 Fifth Avenue, and I imagine that the whereabouts of Manfred W. Ehrich, Jr., one of the fifteen missing members of the class of 1933, could be ascertained by sending a postcard to his father at 20 Exchange Place. I am in a position to give this information about Taft's stormy petrels as a result of having spent a few minutes with the New York telephone book, without stirring from my desk.

Comparatively few Taft men come from New York, and perhaps for this reason a number of alumni have managed to conceal themselves right on Park Avenue. Thus, William H. Symington, 1908, listed as lost, is at 1021 Park, while Stockton Green and William S. Begg, Taft 1925 and Yale 1929 both of them, are living with their families at 1120 and 1192 Park, respectively. Leonard Cox, 1911, in what seems a more likely effort to throw the school off his trail, is hiding out in the Village, at 63 East Eleventh Street. Richard C. Plater, Jr., a Watertown classmate of Mr. Green and Mr. Begg and similarly listed as lost, is at 301 Nehoiden Avenue, Needham, Massachusetts, and at least two missing alumni are safe and sound in Connecticut—Warner Bishop, 1912, at 301 Park Place, Bridgeport, and John H. Lynch, Jr., 1921, at his place, Mountain Greenery, in Ridgefield. Another 1921 man-wanted, Mark H. Haight, is at 179-58 Selover Road, St. Albans, Long Island. I can't keep this up much longer, as J. Edgar Hoover is waiting in the reception room to take me out to lunch, but as an indication that my powers of raising the lost aren't confined to Greater New York and New England, I would like to reveal that William H. Woodin, son of the late Secretary of the Treasury and one of twenty missing members of the Taft class of 1919, is at Wilmot Road, Tucson, Arizona, while Spelman Prentice, 1929, a grandson of the late John D. Rockefeller whom Taft is unable to locate, is receiving mail, if not his class notices, at Wolf Pen Road, Prospect, Kentucky. The addresses of Messrs. Woodin and Prentice, and those of all the other lost alumni listed in this paragraph, appear in the current issue of the New York *Social Register,* a copy of which, along with the telephone book, is surely available in Watertown.

I haven't looked up Ambrose Bierce, but if he isn't in one of them, it's only because he didn't go to Taft.

Frank Sullivan

THE JUKES FAMILY

The air is so cluttered with homely little radio programs recounting the daily heartaches and joys of a multitude of families—"The Green Family," "The Brown Family," "This Man's Family," "That Man's Family," and so on—that I have decided to climb on the band wagon with my own program, "The Jukes Family." It will recount, from day to day, the joys and sorrows of an average, homey, not-quite-bright family of the lower lower class.

The matriarch is Ma Jukes, a friendly old party of forty-five who has brought fifteen or twenty children into the world and has learned to take things as they come. She does the best she can to manage her unruly brood, each of whom has some characteristic that sets him or her apart from the herd. For instance, it has long been a subject of frank discussion in the family whether the ears on Laddie, the seventh boy, extend above the top of his head or whether the plateau of his head simply fails to rise to the top of his ears.

The fourth child, Slim, age twenty-two, has a penchant for bigamy which frequently brings upon him the good-natured raillery of the rest of the family. Another of the boys, Timmy, is doing a stretch in Sing Sing, and Mayzetta, the third girl, is in her sophomore year at the Dobbville Home for Delinquent Females. But the glamour girl of the Jukes Family is Babs—tall, striking, with dark, flashing eyes and a head of hair five and a half feet long. And every single strand of it a natural emerald green! Ma Jukes' family (she was a Cabot) all had hair of vivid yellow. Pa's folks' hair had been Alice blue. Nature's alchemy had combined the two colors happily in Babs.

Now then, as our first program opens, we find Ma Jukes setting a kettle of water to boil. A dozen or so of the youngsters, among them her first-born, Jeddie, a fine-looking chap of thirty with white hair and pink eyes, romp boisterously under her feet as she putters about the stove. There is a scuffle among the bairns. Ma intervenes.

"Monongahela!" she admonishes a strapping girl of about ten. "You give Jeddie back his doll. Ain't you ashamed to be playin' with dolls, a big gal like you.... Tarnation take it, git out from under my feet afore ye git scalded. Oh, it's you, Chub."

Chub is an attractive child of nineteen, always hanging around the stove because he *likes* to be scalded. Ma goodnaturedly ladles a teaspoonful of hot water on him.

"Now, thar, that's enough. Git along an' quit pesterin' yer pore ole ma."

Chub scampers off with a happy scream of agony.

"I declar'," says Ma, philosophizing in the manner of all the Mas on the family radio programs, "I don't know what the younger generation's a-comin' to. When I was a young un we hung around our ma to git the scrapin's from the cake bowl, not to git hot water thrun on us. Now, whatever's a-keepin' yer pa?"

"I'm hongry," cries Eglantine Jukes, a comely sprite of fifteen without a chin.

Here the voice of Chuckles Gladsome, the announcer, is heard. Ma winces. In the cheery voice of the typical family-program announcer, Chuckles says that if little Eglantine is "hongry," she had just better get herself a good, big, heapin' ole dish of rich, creamy, juicy, delicious, nourishing Dwerps, the Sweetheart of Breakfast Foods. "So go to your corner grocery store tonight, or at the very latest tomorrow morning, etc., etc.," concludes Chuckles.

"I'm still hongry," says Eglantine.

"Well, yer pa oughta be here any minnit now with the chicken," says Ma. "Wonder what's a-keepin' him? Oh, here he is!"

Pa Jukes enters. He is a jovial soul who takes the responsibilities of a large family in his stride. His face, if you can call it a face, is unlined by the years, and its frank, open expression is enhanced rather than marred by an almost complete absence of chin.

"Howdy, Pa," says Ma. "Where's the chicken? You said you was a-goin' to snag us a chicken fer supper."

"Shucks, Ma, there ain't none," apologizes Pa. "Dad rat it, I was lucky I got out of Ole Man Eddy's hencoop 'thout gettin' a hideful o' buckshot."

Ma's face falls at this news, but only for an instant. She quickly hides her disappointment and presents a brave front to the children.

All mothers on family programs are constantly presenting brave fronts in the face of domestic problems. "Tarnation take the ornery ole cuss!" she says. "Can't even leave a neighbor have a measly ole chicken. An' after the way we all pitched in an' helped, the night his barn took fire."

"Now, Ma," says Pa, "you know we wa'n't doin' no mor'n our plain duty in helpin' put that fire out. You know 's well 's I do, 'twas our Buster set that barn afire."

Buster is the firebug of the Jukes family, a gay, irresponsible Puck of thirteen with the typical Jukes no-chin, and regarded by the neighbors as quite a tease because of his habit of setting buildings afire every so often.

"Well," says Ma, "I kind o' had my face fixed fer chicken, but I guess we c'n manage. Here, Lump, you run down to Perkins' grocery and fetch up a few cans salmon an' any other vittles ye think might tech the spot."

"Not me," Lump says. "Jedge tole me ef I got caught swipin' any more stuff out'n stores, he'd send me to state's prison sure 'nough."

"That so, young Mister High-an'-Mighty!" snaps Pa Jukes. "Well, lemme tell you one thing, you young whippersnapper, ef state's prison's good enough fer yer brother Timmy, it's plenty good enough fer you."

"Now, Pa," says Ma, soothingly.

"Well, dad rat it, Ma, jest don't let him git so uppity, that's all. I don't know what's got into the younger generation lately. Why, there ain't a nicer crowd o' boys you'd want to meet than the boys at Sing Sing. Leastwise, 'twas so in my day thar."

"Pa, mebbe one o' the children that ain't never been pinched better go," advises Ma. "It'll look better."

There are shouts from the kiddies of "Me, Ma! Let me go! I wanna go, Ma!"

At this point the door bursts open and in comes Wash Jukes, an attractive, coffee-colored lad of fourteen.

"Guess what, Ma!" Wash exults. "The jedge jes' pernounced me a ju-vile delinquent!"

Wash's brothers and sisters are agog with admiration and Ma glows with maternal pride, but Brother Lump is in the clutch of the green-eyed monster.

"Shucks!" says Lump. "I was a ju-vile delinquent when I was ten year old, wa'n't I, Ma?"

"Go on, po' white trash," sneers Wash.

"Wash Jukes!" Ma rebukes. "You lemme hear you call yer brother po' white trash again an' I'll slap ye down. Now git along to the store and fetch back some vittles." She sighs.

"What's wrong, Ma?" asks Pa.

"Pa, I'm a-worrit about Babs. I wa'n't fixin' to tell ye, because I didn't aim to fret ye none, but she ain't been hum now fer two days and two nights."

"Shucks, Ma, she prob'ly stopped off at some gal friend's house on her way hum from school."

"She hadn't oughta gone an' done it 'thout lettin' me know. I declar', I don't know what the younger generation's a-comin' to. When I was a gal Babs' age, ef I stayed away from hum fer more'n one night a-runnin', I got Hail Columbia from the matron."

"Don't ye fret none about Babs, Ma. She's jest young an' full o' fun. Leave her have her fling. She'll be old soon enough."

"Mebbe yer right, Pa, but it seems to me the young uns don't pay no heed to their elders nowadays nohow. Mebbe I'm a-gettin' old-fashioned, but I kind o' like to know whar my children is o' nights. Say, that reminds me, I got a letter from Timmy today."

"Ye did? Then he's out o' solitary. They don't let ye write no letters when yer in solitary. Leastwise, they didn't in my day at Sing Sing. What's he say?"

"Tarnation take it, how do I know? That's why I'm a-waitin' for Babs to come hum, so's she can read it to me. Buster!"

"Yes, Ma!"

"Quit settin' fire to Chub!"

"But he ast me to set him afire, Ma," Buster says.

"Sure I did, Ma," says Chub.

"Makes no difference," says Ma, sternly. " 'Tain't good fer ye. Ye want to grow up all charred?"

"Yes," says Chub, eagerly.

"Well, I swan to glory, I don't know what the younger generation's a-comin' to. Pa, put out Chub, will ye?"

With a good-natured chuckle, Pa throws a pail of water over Chub just as Wash returns from his trip to Perkins' store. The hungry brood crowds around him eagerly.

"Any luck, Wash?" says Ma.

"Naw," says Wash. "Ole Perkins was a-watchin' me all the time. All I could git was this." He takes a ham from beneath his blouse.

"Well," says Ma, " 'tain't much, but it's somethin'."

"And this." Wash produces another package.

"A flitch o' bacon," says Ma. "Now, that's real nice." Ma's tone is cheery. She is presenting a brave front.

"And these," says Wash, and he unloads from various crannies of his person a quantity of canned goods, fresh vegetables, assorted table delicacies, a watermelon, and a case of soft drinks.

"That all ye got?" asks Ma, striving to keep the disappointment from her voice. "Well, ye done the best ye could. We'll manage somehow."

Now the door opens and who bursts in but Babs, her handsome eyes flashing and her green hair flying in the wind.

"Ma," cries Babs, "guess what!"

"Babs Jukes, whar you been?" says Ma, severely. "Go tidy up yer hair. Look at ye!"

"Ma!" cries Babs. "I got a job!"

Pa winces at the sound of the ugly three-letter word.

"Whar's the job?" Ma inquires, coldly, after a pause.

"In the circus! Lady Godiva!"

An artistic career! Well, that's different. Not quite to be classed as work. The alarm subsides, and the family is agog to hear about Babs' job.

"My sakes!" says Ma. "To think we got a real, gen-wine actress in the family!"

"Babs, c'n I have yer autograph?" asks little Monongahela.

Ma is thinking happily how she will come it over her neighbor up the alley, Mrs. Kallikak, who has been insufferable ever since her son got the hot squat for the axe murder of seven.

"Reason I ain't been hum," says Babs, "is I had to go to New York right away an' sign up. Guess they was afraid some other circus might grab me."

"I allus knew Babs'd go places," says Pa, with pride.

"Gee Whittaker, I'm tired," says Babs. "I set up on that train from New York the hull night."

"Set down, child," urges Ma. "I'll git ye a cup o' tea."

Babs sinks into a chair and the youngsters crowd around their distinguished sister, beseeching her for details of her new career and entreating her to get them jobs as freaks in the sideshow.

Suddenly, above the childish babble, there is heard a shriek, then a sinister crackling noise, and cries of alarm as the children scurry to safety.

"Buster! You quit that!" Ma shouts, as is her wont whenever she hears crackling, but it is too late. This time Buster's prank has succeeded all too well. By the time rescue measures have been taken, Babs' once-glorious mane is a smoldering ruin, naught of it remaining save a charred stubble.

Babs is inconsolable.

"Don't you fret none, dearie," Ma attempts to comfort her. "It'll grow in again in no time at all. Onct, when I had the type-ford fever—"

But here the voice of Chuckles Gladsome interrupts Ma.

"Well, folks," says he, "all I can say is, if Babs Jukes wants that hair to grow again in time for her to join the circus, she had just better go tonight, or tomorrow morning at the very latest, to the nearest drugstore and get a bottle of Stickney's Famous Hair Restorer. Ladies, if your hair bothers you, if it is dull, dry, and hard to manage—"

A shot rings out.

When the smoke clears, Ma Jukes is standing over poor Chuckles with Pa's shotgun in her right hand.

"Got him, by cracky!" she announces, with grim pleasure.

"Ma," Pa says. "Ye hadn't ought to o' gone an' done that. The law says 'tain't legal to shoot a buck announcer out o' season. Now ye've let ye'se'f in fer a good fine, and whar ye're a-goin' to raise the dough, I don't know."

Well, what will happen to Ma? Will any jury convict? Will any Fish and Game Commission slap a fine on her for shooting an announcer, in season or out? Is Ma on her way to the clink? And how about Babs' hair? Will it grow back in time for her to join the circus? Follow the adventures of that happy-go-lucky, madcap, lovable, charming, irresponsible bunch, the Jukes Family! Tune in on this station tomorrow afternoon at this same hour and find out what happened to Ma Jukes. Your announcer is Paul Parks, substituting for Chuckles Gladsome. Bi-ing, ba-ang, bo-ong!

THE VANDERBILT CONVENTION

Undoubtedly, the Vanderbilts constitute one of the most interesting families this country has produced. Intertwined as they are with the industrial development of the country they have, in addition, a romantic interest that intrigues the great mass of their newspaper-reading countrymen.

Some Vanderbilt, somewhere, is always doing something that arouses the curiosity of his fellow-Americans. One roams the oceans in search of rare specimens of deep-sea fauna. Another drives an old-fashioned coach and four at Newport. One is at the Rota, in Rome, pleading for an annulment of her marriage. One flouts tradition to enter trade as a newspaper-publisher. But whatever the Vanderbilts do, they are, as a newspaper chap I know would put it, "good copy."

There is one difficulty. The descendants of the doughty old Commodore have grown to be almost as numerous as the proverbial sands of the sea. Indeed, he who attempts to explain which Vanderbilt is which is tackling a man-sized problem. Who married whom? When were they divorced and who got the custody of what? How many Willie K.'s are there? Is it Cornelia or Muriel who rides horseback astride? Is Harold married? When did Mrs. Belmont cease being Mrs. Vanderbilt? They are, in truth, a complicated group.

What follows here is an attempt to explain the Vanderbilt family tree simply and briefly. I shall not go into the more remote branches; that would indeed be a Herculean task. My aim, rather, will be to explain and identify the various Vanderbilts who have figured, more or less, in the public eye.

The Commodore, the original Cornelius Vanderbilt, married, first, Sophia Johnson, and, second, Frances Crawford. His son, William Henry Vanderbilt, inheritor of the bulk of the doughty Commodore's fortune, married Maria Louisa Kissam. They had issue as follows: four sons, Cornelius, Frederick, William Kissam, and George, and four daughters, who became Mrs. Elliot Shepard, Mrs. Henry White, Mrs. Hamilton McKay Twombly, and Mrs. William Seward Webb.

William Kissam married, first, an Alabama girl from an old family named Smith. She later married O. H. P. Belmont. William Kissam then married Mrs. Anne Rutherford Harriman Sands. No. Mrs. Anne Sands Harriman Rutherford. No, that's not right either; let's get this straight. He married, secondly, Mrs. *Anne Harriman Sands Ruth-erford*. She then became, by a process of elimination, Mrs. Anne Harriman Sands Rutherford Vanderbilt.

Cornelius Vanderbilt married Alice Gwynne. That is, not the *first* Cornelius. The first Cornelius was the Commodore and he married, first, Frances Crawford, and, second, Sophia Johnson. No, it's the other way round; he married, first, Sophia Johnson, and, second, Frances Crawford. And his grandson, William Kissam, married Anne Harriman Sands Rutherford.

Now then. The Cornelius Vanderbilt who married Alice Gwynne was not the Cornelius whose yacht recently blew up in the East River. No. The Cornelius whose yacht blew up in the East River is the Cornelius who married Grace Wilson, and they had issue as follows: Cornelius Vanderbilt, Jr., and Grace Vanderbilt (Mrs. Henry Gassaway Davis III). Cornelius Vanderbilt, Jr., son of the Cornelius whose yacht blew up, is the Cornelius whose newspapers blew up. His grandfather, Cornelius Vanderbilt, is the Cornelius who married Alice Gwynne. There is no record of anything belonging to this Cornelius ever having blown up.

Now then. Cornelius and Alice Gwynne Vanderbilt had issue as follows: Cornelius, Alfred Gwynne (named after his mother), Reginald, Gertrude, and Gladys.

Gertrude married a Hungarian nobleman, Count Lâszló Széchényi. No, it couldn't have been Gertrude who married the Count. Gertrude is the sculptor, isn't she? Well then, if she's the sculptor, she's the one who married Payne Whitney, because that one is the one who's the sculptor. I remember distinctly reading *that*. No, that's not right, either. It wasn't Payne Whitney that Gladys—I mean Gertrude—married; it was *Harry* Payne Whitney. You see, *Payne* Whitney and *Harry* Payne Whitney—well, maybe it would be better to clear up the Vanderbilts today and leave the Whitneys for some other day.

Now then. It was Birdie Vanderbilt who married the Hungarian Count. No, Birdie is the sculptor. No, it's Gladys who's the sculptor; what am I thinking of! Her statue blew up. No, it was her yacht that blew up.

No, it was Cornelius' yacht that blew up. Birdie married William K. Not the William K. that married, first, Mrs. O. H. P. Belmont, *née* Smith, and, second, Mrs. Anne Harriman Sands Rutherford. Not that one. Birdie married the William K. who married, first, Virginia

Fair. Cathleen is their daughter. No, Cathleen is Reginald's daughter. Reginald married, first, Ellen French, and, second, Margaret Emerson McKim Mead and White. No, that wasn't Reginald.

Suppose we start *all* over again and get this thing straight. Let's begin once more with the doughty old Commodore. He married, first, Sophia Johnson, and, second, Frances Crawford. William Henry Vanderbilt was their son. Not the William Henry Vanderbilt who gives all the clambakes; the other one, the one who married Maria Louisa Kissam.

Now, if William Henry and Maria Louisa Kissam, after getting married, had let it go at that, things wouldn't have become so complicated. But they didn't. They had issue: eight children. These eight children had children and these children in turn had children, so that in the due course of time there came to be so many Vanderbilts that the family became known as the Vanderbilt Convention. And the doughty old Commodore had started practically on a shoestring!

Now then. What I am trying to do here is simply to give an explanation of which Vanderbilt is which, so that the reader who is interested may be able to distinguish them.

Damn it all, why the hell should people want to distinguish the Vanderbilts, anyhow? This country is supposed to be a democracy, isn't it? When our forefathers gathered at Boston—no, it wasn't Boston. It was Philadelphia. Well, it was either New York or Philadelphia. I don't *care* which one it was. It was on some Sub-Treasury steps, and our forefathers, when they gathered to free the Vanderbilts from the tyranny of George II—no, George III—stipulated, didn't they, that each person in the new nation should be conceived in liberty and dedicated to the proposition that all men are entitled to the pursuit of life, liberty, and the pursuit of happiness.

All right then, why harry the poor Vanderbilts this way? Why not let them alone once in a while? Whose business is it which of them is which? The trouble with this country is that there are a lot of morons in this country who can't mind their own business. They have to be always reading intimate details about the lives of other people. They want everything explained to them. What business is it of theirs which Vanderbilt is which? It's the sensational tabloids, and these physical-culture magazines, that encourage all this morbid curiosity. Why can't the Vanderbilts come and go in peace, same as any other citizen? Who do they think they are, anyhow? Why, for that matter, the old man, the doughty old Commodore, who married Sophia Johnson, first, and Frances Crawford, second, was in trade. He ran a ferry between Staten Island and Manhattan!

His son was William Henry Vanderbilt, who married William Kissam—no, Louisa Maria Kissam, and they had issue (eight children) and then somewhere down the line someone of them married Count László Széchényi. They have five children and he fought a duel. But Reginald Vanderbilt married Cathleen Neilson and their daughter, Cathleen, married Henry Gassaway Davis III.

No. It wasn't Cathleen who married Henry Gassaway Davis III. Cathleen married Harry C. Cushing III. It was Grace, daughter of the Cornelius whose yacht blew up, who married Henry Gassaway Cushing III.

If only each Vanderbilt would arrange to have something of his, some little bit of personal property, easily distinguishable, blown up, it would be so much easier to tell them apart. "Ah, there goes Phyllis Vanderbilt. Which one is she, you ask? Why, she's the one whose first husband blew up."

It seems to me that somewhere, some time, some Vanderbilt married Irving Berlin III. On second thought, I guess not. I guess I'm thinking either of Cornelia, daughter of Mrs. George W. Vanderbilt (Mrs. Peter Goelet Gerry) who married the Hon. John Francis Amherst Cecil, or of Mary Cadogan, who married the Marquis of Blandford, son of the Duchess of Marlborough who was Consuelo Vanderbilt (Mrs. Jacques Balsan), daughter of the William Kissam Vanderbilt who married Mrs. O. H. P. Belmont and, later, Mrs. Anne Harriman Sands Rutherford Vanderbilt.

Consuelo, erstwhile Duchess of Marlborough (Mrs. Jacques Balsan), would therefore be the aunt of the Consuelo who married Earl E. T. Smith.

Now, there was a time when the Smiths outnumbered the Vanderbilts by two to one, but that era is passing. The Vanderbilts are beginning to absorb the Smiths, although as yet no Vanderbilt has overtly married a Jones. Still, you never can tell. The descendants of the doughty old Commodore are an impulsive and passionate race and if one of them ever chanced upon an unusually comely Jones there is no telling what might ensue.

I trust I have made everything clear.

—CHOLLY SULLIVAN

Ring Lardner

ON CONVERSATION

The other night I happened to be comeing back from Wilmington, Del. to wherever I was going and was setting in the smokeing compartment or whatever they now call the wash room and overheard a conversation between two fellows who we will call Mr. Butler and Mr. Hawkes. Both of them seemed to be from the same town and I only wished I could repeat the conversation verbatim but the best I can do is report it from memory. The fellows evidently had not met for some three to fifteen years as the judges say.

"Well," said Mr. Hawkes, "if this isn't Dick Butler!"

"Well," said Mr. Butler, "if it isn't Dale Hawkes."

"Well, Dick," said Hawkes, "I never expected to meet you on this train."

"No," replied Butler. "I genally always take Number 28. I just took this train this evening because I had to be in Wilmington today."

"Where are you headed for?" asked Hawkes.

"Well, I am going to the big town," said Butler.

"So am I, and I am certainly glad we happened to be in the same car."

"I am glad too, but it is funny we happened to be in the same car."

It seemed funny to both of them but they successfully concealed it so far as facial expression was conserned. After a pause Hawkes spoke again:

"How long since you been back in Lansing?"

"Me?" replied Butler. "I ain't been back there for 12 years."

"I ain't been back there either myself for ten years. How long since you been back there?"

"I ain't been back there for twelve years."

"I ain't been back there myself for ten years. Where are you headed for?"

416

"New York," replied Butler. "I have got to get there about once
a year. Where are you going?"

"Me?" asked Hawkes. "I am going to New York too. I have got
to go down there every little wile for the firm."

"Do you have to go there very often?"

"Me? Every little while. How often do you have to go there?"

"About once a year. How often do you get back to Lansing?"

"Last time I was there was ten years ago. How long since you was
back?"

"About twelve years ago. Lot of changes there since we left there."

"That's the way I figured it. It makes a man seem kind of old to
go back there and not see nobody you know."

"You said something. I go along the streets there now and don't
see nobody I know."

"How long since you was there?"

"Me?" said Hawkes. "I only get back there about once every ten
years. By the way what become of old man Kelsey?"

"Who do you mean, Kelsey?"

"Yes, what become of him?"

"Old Kelsey? Why he has been dead for ten years."

"Oh, I didn't know that. And what become of his daughter? I
mean Eleanor."

"Why Eleanor married a man named Forster or Jennings or something like that from Flint."

"Yes, but I mean the other daughter, Louise."

"Oh, she's married."

"Where are you going now?"

"I am headed for New York on business for the firm."

"I have to go there about once a year myself—for the firm."

"Do you get back to Lansing very often?"

"About once in ten or twelve years. I hardly know anybody there
now. It seems funny to go down the street and not know nobody."

"That's the way I always feel. It seems like it was not my old home
town at all. I go up and down the street and don't know anybody
and nobody speaks to you. I guess I know more people in New York
now than I do in Lansing."

"Do you get to New York often?"

"Only about once a year. I have to go there for the firm."

"New York isn't the same town it used to be neither."

"No, it is changeing all the time. Just like Lansing. I guess they all change."

"I don't know much about Lansing any more. I only get there about once in ten or twelve years."

"What are you reading there?"

"Oh, it is just a little article in Asia. They's a good many interesting articles in Asia."

"I only seen a couple copies of it. This thing I am reading is a little article on 'Application' in the American."

"Well, go ahead and read and don't let me disturb you."

"Well, I just wanted to finish it up. Go ahead and finish what you're reading yourself."

"All right. We will talk things over later. It is funny we happened to get on the same car."

FOLKLORE AND TALL STORIES

Folklore and tall stories, accumulating from generation to generation, are our humorous heritage from the early unsophisticated America. There have been many scholarly analyses of this source material of our national humor. And there have been good collections of regional stuff—Negro, cowboy, early New England, early Southern. For example, we first encountered M's "Going to Bed Before a Young Lady" in Franklin J. Meine's "Tall Tales of the Southwest."

Since it has been so well covered, we are presenting only a moderate amount of folk humor, in proportion to the amount available. Also, we found that a good many of the tales were merely quaint, not funny. There is a tendency in this whole field to confuse quaintness with humor—the two are not interchangeable. Some of the great legendary figures, real or mythical, such as David Crockett, Mike Fink, Pecos Bill— the rangy swashbucklers—are genuinely interesting to read about, but it takes lots of space to account for all the bears Davy Crockett could shoot in a week.

It should be noted that the Paul Bunyan story printed here was written for children. For some reason, the simple-minded editors of this anthology found it better reading than the adult versions of the Bunyan legends.

Marc Connelly

A FISH FRY*

In the darkness many voices are heard singing "Rise, Shine, Give God The Glory." They sing it gayly and rapidly. The lights go up as the second verse ends. The chorus is being sung diminuendo by a mixed company of angels. That is they are angels in that they wear brightly colored robes and have wings protruding from their backs. Otherwise they look and act like a company of happy Negroes at a fish fry. The scene itself is a pre-Creation Heaven with compromises. In the distance is an unbroken stretch of blue sky. Companionable vari-colored clouds billow down to the floor of the stage and roll overhead to the branches of a live oak tree which is up left. The tree is leafy and dripping with Spanish moss, and with the clouds makes a frame for the scene. In the cool shade of the tree are the usual appurtenances of a fish fry; a large kettle of hot fat set on two small parallel logs, with a fire going underneath, and a large rustic table formed by driving four stakes into the ground and placing planks on top of the small connecting boards. On the table are piles of biscuits and corn bread and the cooked fish in dish pans. There are one or two fairly large cedar or crock "churns" containing boiled custard, which looks like milk. There is a gourd dipper beside the churns and several glasses and cups of various sizes and shapes from which the custard is drunk.

The principal singers are marching two by two in a small area at the right of the stage. Two MAMMY ANGELS *are attending to the frying*

* This is Part I, Scene 2, of "The Green Pastures." In an author's note Marc Connelly says: "'The Green Pastures' is an attempt to present certain aspects of a living religion in the terms of its believers. The religion is that of thousands of Negroes in the deep South. With terrific spiritual hunger and the greatest humility these untutored black Christians—many of whom cannot even read the book which is the treasure house of their faith—have adapted the contents of the Bible to the consistencies of their everyday lives.... The author is indebted to Mr. Roark Bradford, whose retelling of several of the Old Testament stories in 'Ol' Man Adam an' His Chillun' first stimulated his interest in this point of view."

beside the kettle. Behind the table a MAN ANGEL *is skinning fish and passing them to the cooks. Another is ladling out the custard. A* MAMMY ANGEL, *is putting fish on bread for a brood of cherubs, and during the first scene they seat themselves on a grassy bank upstage. Another* MAMMY ANGEL *is clapping her hands disapprovingly and beckoning a laughing* BOY CHERUB *down from a cloud a little out of her reach. Another* MAMMY ANGEL *is solicitously slapping the back of a girl cherub who has a large fish sandwich in her hand and a bone in her throat. There is much movement about the table, and during the first few minutes several individuals go up to the table to help themselves to the food and drink. Many of the women angels wear hats and a few of the men are smoking cigars. A large boxful is on the table. There is much laughter and chatter as the music softens, but continues, during the early part of the action. The following short scenes are played almost simultaneously.*

FIRST COOK (*at kettle; calling off*). Hurry up, Cajey. Dis yere fat's cryin' fo' mo' feesh.

A VOICE (*off stage*). We comin', fas' we kin. Dey got to be ketched, ain't dey? We cain't say, "C'm'on little fish. C'm'on an' git fried," kin we?

SECOND COOK (*at table*). De trouble is de mens is all worm fishin'.

FIRST MAN ANGEL (*at table*). Whut dif'runce do it make? Yo' all de time got to make out like somebody's doin' somethin' de wrong way.

SECOND COOK (*near table*). I s'pose you got de perfec' way fo' makin' bait.

FIRST MAN ANGEL. I ain't sayin' dat. I is sayin' what's wrong wid worm fishin'.

SECOND COOK. Whut's wrong wid worm fishin'? Ever'thing, dat's all. Dey's only one good way fo' catfishin', an' dats minny fishin'. Anybody know dat.

FIRST MAN ANGEL. Well, it jest so happen dat minny fishin' is de doggondest fool way of fishin' dey is. You kin try minny fishin' to de cows come home an' all you catch'll be de backache. De trouble wid you, sister, is you jest got minny fishin' on de brain.

SECOND COOK. Go right on, loud mouf. You tell me de news. My, my! You jest de wisest person in de worl'. First you, den de Lawd God.

FIRST MAN ANGEL (*to the custard ladler*). You cain't tell dem nothin'. (*Walks away to the custard churn.*) Does you try to 'splain some simple fac' dey git man-deaf.

FIRST MAMMY ANGEL (*to* CHERUB *on the cloud*). Now, you heerd me. (*The* CHERUB *assumes several mocking poses, as she speaks.*) You fly down yere. You wanter be put down in de sin book? (*She goes to the table, gets a drink for herself and points out the* CHERUB *to one of the men behind the table.*) Dat baby must got imp blood in him he so vexin'. (*She returns to her position under the cloud.*) You want me to fly up dere an' slap you down? Now, I tol' you. (*The* CHERUB *starts to come down.*)

STOUT ANGEL (*to the* CHERUB *with a bone in her throat*). I tol' you you was too little fo' catfish. What you wanter git a bone in you' froat fo'? (*She slaps the* CHERUB'S *back.*)

SLENDER ANGEL (*leisurely eating a sandwich as she watches the back-slapping*). What de trouble wid Leonetta?

STOUT ANGEL. She got a catfish bone down her froat. (*To the* CHERUB.) Doggone, I tol' you to eat grinnel instead.

SLENDER ANGEL. Ef'n she do git all dat et, she gonter have de bellyache.

STOUT ANGEL. Ain't I tol' her dat? (*To* CHERUB). Come on now; let go dat bone. (*She slaps* CHERUB'S *back again. The bone is dislodged and the* CHERUB *grins her relief.*) Dat's good.

SLENDER ANGEL (*comfortingly.*) Now she all right.

STOUT ANGEL. Go on an' play wid yo' cousins. (*The* CHERUB *joins the* CHERUBS *sitting on the embankment. The concurrency of scenes ends here.*) I ain't see you lately, Lily. How you been?

SLENDER ANGEL. Me, I'm fine. I been visitin' my mammy. She waitin' on de welcome table over by de throne of grace.

STOUT ANGEL. She always was pretty holy.

SLENDER ANGEL. Yes, ma'am. She like it dere. I guess de Lawd's took quite a fancy to her.

STOUT ANGEL. Well, dat's natural. I declare yo' mammy one of de finest lady angels I know.

SLENDER ANGEL. She claim you de best one she know.

STOUT ANGEL. Well, when you come right down to it, I suppose we is all pretty near perfec'.

SLENDER ANGEL. Yes, ma'am. Why is dat, Mis' Jenny?

STOUT ANGEL. I s'pose it's caize de Lawd he don' 'low us 'sociatin' wid de devil any mo' so dat dey cain' be no mo' sinnin'.

SLENDER ANGEL. Po' ol' Satan. Whutevah become of him?

STOUT ANGEL. De Lawd put him some place I s'pose.

SLENDER ANGEL. But dey ain't any place but Heaven, is dey?

STOUT ANGEL. De Lawd could make a place, couldn't he?

SLENDER ANGEL. Dat's de truth. Dey's one thing confuses me though.

STOUT ANGEL. What's dat?

SLENDER ANGEL. I do a great deal of travelin' an' I ain't never come across any place but Heaven anywhere. So if de Lawd kick Satan out of Heaven jest whereat did he go? Dat's my question.

STOUT ANGEL. You bettah let de Lawd keep his own secrets, Lily. De way things is goin' now dey ain't been no sinnin' since dey give dat scamp a kick in de pants. Nowadays Heaven's free of sin an' if a lady wants a little constitutional she kin fly till she wing-weary widout gittin' insulted.

SLENDER ANGEL. I was jest a baby when Satan lef'. I don't even 'member what he look like.

STOUT ANGEL. He was jest right fo' a devil. (*An* ARCHANGEL *enters. He is older than the others and wears a white beard. His clothing is much darker than that of the others and his wings a trifle more imposing.*) Good mo'nin', Archangel.

(*Others say good morning.*)

ARCHANGEL. Good mo'nin', folks. I wonder kin I interrup' de fish fry an' give out de Sunday school cyards? (*Cries of "Suttingly!" "Mah goodness, yes"—etc. The marching* CHOIR *stops.*) You kin keep singin' if you want to. Why don' you sing "When de Saints Come Marchin' In"? Seem to me I ain' heard dat lately. (*The* CHOIR *begins "When the Saints Come Marching In," rather softly, but does not resume marching. The* ARCHANGEL *looks off left.*) All right, bring 'em yere. (*A prim-looking* WOMAN TEACHER-ANGEL *enters, shepherding ten* BOY *and* GIRL CHERUBS. *The* TEACHER *carries ten beribbonned diplomas, which she gives to the* ARCHANGEL. *The* CHERUBS *are dressed in stiffly starched white suits and dresses, the little girls having enormous ribbons at the backs of their dresses and smaller ones in their hair and on the tips of their wings. They line up in front of the* ARCHANGEL *and receive the attention of the rest of the company. The* CHOIR *sings through the ceremony.*) Now den cherubs, why is you yere?

CHILDREN. Because we so good.

ARCHANGEL. Dat's right. Now who de big boss?

CHILDREN. Our dear Lawd.

ARCHANGEL. Dat's right. When you all grow up what you gonter be?

CHILDREN. Holy angels at de throne of grace.

ARCHANGEL. Dat's right, Now, you passed yo' 'xaminations and it gives me great pleasure to hand out de cyards for de whole class. Gineeva Chaproe. (*The* FIRST GIRL CHERUB *goes to him and gets her diploma. The* CHOIR *sings loudly and resumes marching, as the* ARCHANGEL *calls out another name—and presents diplomas.*) Corey Moulter. (SECOND GIRL CHERUB *gets her diploma.*) Nootzie Winebush. (THIRD GIRL CHERUB.) Harriet Prancy. (FOURTH GIRL CHERUB.) I guess you is Brozain Stew't. (*He gives the* FIFTH GIRL CHERUB *the paper. Each of the presentations has been accompanied by handclapping from the bystanders.*) Now you boys know yo' own names. Suppose you come yere and help me git dese 'sorted right?

(BOY CHERUBS *gather about him and receive their diplomas. The little* GIRLS *have scattered about the stage, joining groups of the adult angels. The angel* GABRIEL *enters. He is bigger and more elaborately winged than even the* ARCHANGEL, *but he is also much younger and beardless. His costume is less conventional than that of the other men, resembling more the Gabriel of the Doré drawings. His appearance causes a flutter among the others. They stop their chattering with the children. The* CHOIR *stops as three or four audible whispers of "Gabriel!" are heard. In a moment the heavenly company is all attention.*)

GABRIEL (*lifting his hand.*) Gangway! Gangway for de Lawd God Jehovah! (*There is a reverent hush as* GOD *enters. He is the tallest and biggest of them all. He wears a white shirt with a white bow tie, a long Prince Albert coat of black alpaca, black trousers and congress gaiters. He looks at the assemblage. There is a pause. He speaks in a rich, bass voice.*)

GOD. Is you been baptized?

OTHERS (*chanting*). Certainly, Lawd.

GOD. Is you been baptized?

OTHERS. Certainly, Lawd.

GOD (*with the beginning of musical notation*). Is you been baptized?

OTHERS (*now half-singing*). Certainly, Lawd. Certainly, certainly, certainly, Lawd. (*They sing the last two verses with equivalent part division.*)

Is you been redeemed?
Certainly, Lawd.
Is you been redeemed?
Certainly, Lawd.
Is you been redeemed?
Certainly, Lawd. Certainly, certainly, certainly, Lawd.

Do you bow mighty low?
Certainly, Lawd.
Do you bow mighty low?
Certainly, Lawd.
Do you bow mighty low?
Certainly, Lawd. Certainly, certainly, certainly, Lawd.

(*As the last response ends all heads are bowed.* GOD *looks at them for a moment; then lifts His hand.*)

GOD. Let de fish fry proceed.

(EVERYONE *rises. The* ANGELS *relax and resume their inaudible conversations. The activity behind the table and about the cauldron is resumed. Some of the* CHOIR *members cross to the table and get sandwiches and cups of the boiled custard. Three or four of the* CHILDREN *in the Sunday School class and the* LITTLE GIRL *who had the bone in her throat affectionately group themselves about* GOD *as He speaks with the* ARCHANGEL. *He pats their heads, they hang to His coat-tails, etc.*)

ARCHANGEL. Good mo'nin', Lawd.

GOD. Good mo'nin', Deacon. You lookin' pretty spry.

ARCHANGEL. I cain' complain. We jest been givin' our cyards to de chillun.

GOD. Dat's good.

(*A small* CHERUB, *his feet braced against one of* GOD's *shoes, is using* GOD's *coat-tail as a trapeze. One of the* COOKS *offers a fish sandwich which* GOD *politely declines.*)

FIRST MAMMY ANGEL. Now, you leave go de Lawd's coat, Herman. You heah me?

GOD. Dat's all right, sister. He jest playin'.

FIRST MAMMY ANGEL.—He playin' too rough. (GOD *picks up the* CHERUB *and spanks him good-naturedly. The* CHERUB *squeals with delight and runs to his mother.* GABRIEL *advances to* GOD *with a glass of the custard.*)

GABRIEL. Little b'iled custud, Lawd?

GOD. Thank you very kindly. Dis looks nice.

CUSTARD MAKER (*offering a box*). Ten cent seegar, Lawd?

GOD (*taking it*). Thank you, thank you. How de fish fry goin'? (*Ad lib. cries of "O. K., Lawd," "Fine an' dandy, Lawd," "De best one yit, Lawd," etc. To the* CHOIR.) How you shouters gittin' on?

CHOIR LEADER. We been marchin' and singin' de whole mo'nin'.

GOD. I heerd you. You gettin' better all de time. You gittin' as good as de one at de throne. Why don' you give us one dem ol' time jump-ups?

CHOIR LEADER. Anythin' you say, Lawd. (*To the others.*) "So High!" (*The* CHOIR *begins to sing "So High You Can't Get Over It." They sing softly, but do not march. An* ANGEL *offers his cigar to* GOD *from which He can light His own.*)

GOD. No, thanks. I'm gonter save dis a bit. (*He puts the cigar in his pocket and listens to the singers a moment. Then he sips his custard. After a second sip, a look of displeasure comes on his face.*)

GABRIEL. What's de matter, Lawd?

GOD (*sipping again.*) I ain't jest sure, yit. Dey's something 'bout dis custard. (*Takes another sip.*)

CUSTARD MAKER. Ain't it all right, Lawd?

GOD. It don't seem seasoned jest right. You make it?

CUSTARD MAKER. Yes, Lawd, I put everythin' in it like I allus do. It's supposed to be perfec'.

GOD. Yeah. I kin taste de eggs and de cream and de sugar. (*Suddenly.*) I know what it is. It needs jest a little bit mo' firmament.

CUSTARD MAKER. Dey's firmament in it, Lawd.

GOD. Maybe, but it ain' enough.

CUSTARD MAKER. It's all we had, Lawd. Dey ain't a drap in de jug.

GOD. Dat's all right. I'll jest r'ar back an' pass a miracle. (CHOIR *stops singing.*) Let it be some firmament! An' when I say let it be some firmament, I don't want jest a little bitty dab o' firmament caize I'm sick an' tired of runnin' out of it when we need it. Let it be a whole mess of firmament! (*The stage has become misty until* GOD *and the heavenly company are obscured. As he finishes the speech there is a burst of thunder. As the stage grows darker.*) Dat's de way I like it.

(*Murmurs from the others: "Dat's a lot of firmament." "My, dat is firmament!" "Look to me like he's created rain," etc.*)

FIRST MAMMY ANGEL (*when the stage is dark.*) Now, look Lawd, dat's too much firmament. De cherubs is gettin' all wet.

SECOND MAMMY ANGEL. Look at my Carlotta, Lawd. She's soaked to de skin. Dat's *plenty* too much firmament.

GOD. Well, 'co'se we don't want de chillun to ketch cold. Can't you dreen it off?

GABRIEL. Dey's no place to dreen it, Lawd.

FIRST MAMMY ANGEL. Why don't we jest take de babies home, Lawd?

GOD. No, I don' wanta bust up de fish fry. You angels keep quiet an' I'll pass another miracle. Dat's always de trouble wid miracles. When you pass one you always gotta r'ar back an' pass another. (*There is a hush.*) Let dere be a place to dreen off this firmament. Let dere be mountains and valleys an' let dere be oceans an' lakes. An' let dere be rivers and bayous to dreen it off in, too. As a matter of fac' let dere be de earth. An' when dat's done let dere be de sun, an' let it come out and dry my cherubs' wings.

(*The lights go up until the stage is bathed in sunlight. On the embankment upstage there is now a waist-high wrought-iron railing such as one sees on the galleries of houses in the French quarter of New Orleans. The* CHERUBS *are being examined by their parents and there is an ad lib. murmur of, "You all right, honey?" "You feel better now, Albert?" "Now you all dry, Vangy?" until the* ARCHANGEL, *who has been gazing in awe at the railing, drowns them out.*)

ARCHANGEL. Look yere!

(*There is a rush to the embankment accompanied by exclamations, "My goodness!" "What's dis?" "I declah!" etc.* GABRIEL *towers above the group on the middle of the embankment.* GOD *is wrapped in thought, facing the audience. The* CHOIR *resumes singing "So High You Can't Get Over It" softly. The babbling at the balustrade dies away as the people lean over the railing.* GABRIEL *turns and faces* GOD *indicating the earth below the railing with his left hand.*)

GABRIEL. Do you see it, Lawd?

GOD (*quietly, without turning his head upstage*). Yes, Gabriel.

GABRIEL. Looks mighty nice, Lawd.

GOD. Yes.

(GABRIEL *turns and looks over the railing.*)

GABRIEL (*gazing down*). Yes. suh. Dat'd make mighty nice farming

country. Jest look at dat South forty over dere. You ain't going
to let dat go to waste is you Lawd? Dat would be a pity an' a
shame.

GOD (*not turning*). It's good earth. (GOD *turns, room is made for him
beside* GABRIEL *on the embankment.*) Yes. I ought to have somebody to enjoy it. (*He turns, facing the audience. The others, save
for the* CHOIR *who are lined up in two rows of six on an angle
up right, continue to look over the embankment.*) Gabriel! (GOD
steps down from the embankment two paces.)

GABRIEL (*joining him.*) Yes, Lawd.

GOD. Gabriel, I'm goin' down dere.

GABRIEL. Yes, Lawd.

GOD. I want you to be my working boss yere while I'm gone.

GABRIEL. Yes, Lawd.

GOD. You know dat matter of dem two stars?

GABRIEL. Yes, Lawd.

GOD. Git dat fixed up! You know dat sparrow dat fell a little while
ago? 'Tend to dat, too.

GABRIEL. Yes, Lawd.

GOD. I guess dat's about all. I'll be back Saddy. (*To the choir.*) Quiet,
angels. (*The* CHOIR *stops singing. Those on the embankment
circle down stage.* GOD *goes to embankment. Turns and faces the
company.*) I'm gonter pass one more miracle. You all gonter help
me an' not make a soun' caize it's one of de most impo'tant
miracles of all. (*Nobody moves.* GOD *turns, facing the sky and
raises His arms above his head.*) Let there be man.

(*There is growing roll of thunder as stage grows dark. The* CHOIR
*bursts into "Hallelujah," and continues until the lights go up on
the next scene.*)

Mark Twain

A MISSISSIPPI PILOT*

There used to be an excellent pilot on the river, a Mr. X., who was
a somnambulist. It was said that if his mind was troubled about a
bad piece of river, he was pretty sure to get up and walk in his sleep
and do strange things. He was once fellow-pilot for a trip or two
with George Ealer, on a great New Orleans passenger packet. During
a considerable part of the first trip George was uneasy, but got over
it by and by, as X. seemed content to stay in his bed when asleep.
Late one night the boat was approaching Helena, Ark.; the water
was low, and the crossing above the town in a very blind and tangled
condition. X. had seen the crossing since Ealer had, and as the night
was particularly drizzly, sullen, and dark, Ealer was considering
whether he had not better have X. called to assist in running the
place, when the door opened and X. walked in. Now, on very dark
nights, light is a deadly enemy to piloting; you are aware that if you
stand in a lighted room, on such a night, you cannot see things in
the street to any purpose; but if you put out the lights and stand in
the gloom you can make out objects in the street pretty well. So,
on very dark nights, pilots do not smoke; they allow no fire in the
pilot-house stove, if there is a crack which can allow the least ray
to escape; they order the furnaces to be curtained with huge tarpaulins
and the skylights to be closely blinded. Then no light whatever issues
from the boat. The undefinable shape that now entered the pilot-
house had Mr. X.'s voice. This said:

"Let me take her, George; I've seen this place since you have,
and it is so crooked that I reckon I can run it myself easier than
I could tell you how to do it."

"It is kind of you, and I swear *I* am willing. I haven't got another
drop of perspiration left in me. I have been spinning around and

* *This tall story was told as fact in "Life on the Mississippi." Maybe it was
fact.*

around the wheel like a squirrel. It is so dark I can't tell which way she is swinging till she is coming around like a whirligig."

So Ealer took a seat on the bench, panting and breathless. The black phantom assumed the wheel without saying anything, steadied the waltzing steamer with a turn or two, and then stood at ease, coaxing her a little to this side and then to that, as gently and as sweetly as if the time had been noonday. When Ealer observed this marvel of steering, he wished he had not confessed! He stared, and wondered, and finally said:

"Well, I thought I knew how to steer a steamboat, but that was another mistake of mine."

X. said nothing, but went serenely on with his work. He rang for the leads; he rang to slow down the steam; he worked the boat carefully and neatly into invisible marks, then stood at the center of the wheel and peered blandly out into the blackness, fore and aft, to verify his position; as the leads shoaled more and more, he stopped the engines entirely, and the dead silence and suspense of "drifting" followed; when the shoalest water was struck, he cracked on the steam, carried her handsomely over, and then began to work her warily into the next system of shoal-marks; the same patient, heedful use of leads and engines followed, the boat slipped through without touching bottom, and entered upon the third and last intricacy of the crossing; imperceptibly she moved through the gloom, crept by inches into her marks, drifted tediously till the shoalest water was cried, and then, under a tremendous head of steam, went swinging over the reef and away into deep water and safety!

Ealer let his long-pent breath pour in a great relieving sigh, and said:

"That's the sweetest piece of piloting that was ever done on the Mississippi River! I wouldn't believe it could be done, if I hadn't seen it."

There was no reply, and he added:

"Just hold her five minutes longer, partner, and let me run down and get a cup of coffee."

A minute later Ealer was biting into a pie, down in the "texas," and comforting himself with coffee. Just then the night watchman happened in, and was about to happen out again, when he noticed Ealer and exclaimed:

"Who is at the wheel, sir?"

"X."

"Dart for the pilot-house, quicker than lightning!"

The next moment both men were flying up the pilot-house companion-way, three steps at a jump! Nobody there! The great steamer was whistling down the middle of the river at her own sweet will! The watchman shot out of the place again; Ealer seized the wheel, set an engine back with power, and held his breath while the boat reluctantly swung away from a "towhead," which she was about to knock into the middle of the Gulf of Mexico!

By and by the watchman came back and said:

"Didn't that lunatic tell you he was asleep, when he first came up here?"

"No."

"Well, he was. I found him walking along on top of the railings, just as unconcerned as another man would walk a pavement; and I put him to bed; now just this minute there he was again, away astern, going through that sort of tight-rope deviltry the same as before."

"Well, I think I'll stay by next time he has one of those fits. But I hope he'll have them often. You just ought to have seen him take this boat through Helena crossing. *I* never saw anything so gaudy before. And if he can do such gold-leaf, kid-glove, diamond-breastpin piloting when he is sound asleep, what *couldn't* he do if he was dead!"

Joel Chandler Harris

MISS COW FALLS A VICTIM TO MR. RABBIT

"Uncle Remus," said the little boy, "what became of the Rabbit after he fooled the Buzzard, and got out of the hollow tree?"

"Who? Brer Rabbit? Bless yo' soul, honey, Brer Rabbit went skippin' 'long home, he did, des ez sassy ez a jay-bird at a sparrer's nes'. He went gallopin' 'long, he did, but he feel mighty tired out, en stiff in his jints, en he wuz mighty nigh dead for sumpin fer ter drink, en bimeby, w'en he got mos' home, he spied ole Miss Cow feedin' roun' in a fiel', he did, en he 'termin' fer ter try his han' wid 'er. Brer Rabbit know mighty well dat Miss Cow won't give 'im no milk, kaze she done 'fuse 'im mo'n once, en w'en his ole 'oman wuz sick, at dat. But never mind dat. Brer Rabbit sorter dance up 'long side er de fence, he did, en holler out:

" 'Howdy, Sis Cow,' sez Brer Rabbit, sezee.

" 'W'y, howdy, Brer Rabbit,' sez Miss Cow, sez she.

" 'How you fine yo'se'f deze days, Sis Cow?' sez Brer Rabbit, sezee.

" 'I'm sorter toler'ble, Brer Rabbit; how you come on?' sez Miss Cow, sez she.

" 'Oh, I'm des toler'ble myse'f, Sis Cow; sorter linger'n' twix' a bauk en a break-down,' sez Brer Rabbit, sezee.

" 'How yo' fokes, Brer Rabbit?' sez Miss Cow, sez she.

" 'Dey er des middlin', Sis Cow; how Brer Bull gittin' on?' sez Brer Rabbit, sezee.

" 'Sorter so-so', sez Miss Cow, sez she.

" 'Dey er some mighty nice 'simmons up dis tree, Sis Cow,' sez Brer Rabbit, sezee, 'en I'd like mighty well fer ter have some un um,' sezee.

" 'How you gwineter git um, Brer Rabbit?' sez she.

" 'I 'low'd maybe dat I might ax you fer ter butt 'gin de tree, en shake some down, Sis Cow,' sez Brer Rabbit, sezee.

"C'ose Miss Cow don't wanter diskommerdate Brer Rabbit, en she

march up ter de 'simmon tree, she did, en hit it a rap wid'er horns—
blam! Now, den," continued Uncle Remus, tearing off the corner of
a plug of tobacco and cramming it into his mouth—"now, den, dem
'simmons wuz green ez grass, en na'er one never drap. Den Miss
Cow butt de tree—blim! Na'er 'simmon drap. Den Miss Cow sorter
back off little, en run agin de tree—blip! No 'simmons never drap.
Den Miss Cow back off little fudder, she did, en hi'st her tail on 'er back,
en come agin de tree, kerblam! en she come so fas', en she come so
hard, twel one 'er her horns went spang thoo de tree, en dar she
wuz. She can't go forreds, en she can't go backerds. Dis zackly w'at
Brer Rabbit waitin' fer, en he no sooner seed ole Miss Cow all
fas'en'd up dan he jump up, he did, en cut de pidjin-wing.

"'Come he'p me out, Brer Rabbit,' sez Miss Cow, sez she.

"'I can't clime, Sis Cow,' sez Brer Rabbit, sezee, 'but I'll run'n
tell Brer Bull,' sezee; en wid dat Brer Rabbit put out fer home, en
'twan't long 'fo here he come wid his ole 'oman en all his chilluns,
en de las' one er de fambly wuz totin' a pail. De big uns had big
pails, en de little uns had little pails. En dey all s'roundid ole Miss
Cow, dey did, en you hear me, honey, dey milk't 'er dry. De ole
uns milk't en de young uns milk't, en den w'en dey done got nuff,
Brer Rabbit, he up'n say, sezee:

"'I wish you mighty well, Sis Cow. I 'low'd bein's how dat you'd
hatter sorter camp out all night dat I'd better come en swaje yo'
bag,' sezee."

"Do which, Uncle Remus?" asked the little boy.

"Go 'long, honey! Swaje 'er bag. W'en cows don't git milk't, der bag
swells, en youk'n hear um a moanin' en a beller'n des like dey wuz
gittin' hurtid. Dat's w'at Brer Rabbit done. He 'sembled his family,
he did, en he swaje ole Miss Cow's bag.

"Miss Cow, she stood dar, she did, en she study en study, en
strive fer ter break loose, but de horn done bin jam in de tree so
tight dat twuz way 'fo day in de mornin' 'fo' she loose it. Anyhow
hit wuz endurin' er de night, en atter she git loose she sorter graze
'roun', she did, fer ter jestify 'er stummuck. She 'low'd, ole Miss
Cow did, dat Brer Rabbit be hoppin' 'long dat way fer ter see how
she gittin' on, en she tuck'n lay er trap fer 'im; en des 'bout sunrise
wat'd ole Miss Cow do but march up ter de 'simmon tree en stick
er horn back in de hole? But, bless yo' soul, honey, w'ile she wuz
croppin' de grass, she tuck one moufull too menny, kaze w'en she

hitch on ter de 'simmon tree agin, Brer Rabbit wuz settin' in de fence cornder a watchin' un 'er. Den Brer Rabbit he say ter hisse'f:

" 'Heyo,' sezee, 'w'at dis yer gwine on now? Hole yo' hosses, Sis Cow, twel you hear me comin',' sezee.

"En den he crope off down de fence, Brer Rabbit did, en bimeby here he come—lippity-clippity, clippity-lippity—des a sailin' down de big road.

" 'Mornin', Sis Cow,' sez Brer Rabbit, sezee, 'how you come on dis mornin'?' sezee.

" 'Po'ly, Brer Rabbit, po'ly,' sez Miss Cow, sez she. 'I ain't had no res' all night,' sez she. 'I can't pull loose,' sez she, 'but ef you'll come en ketch holt er my tail, Brer Rabbit,' sez she, 'I reckin may be I kin fetch my horn out,' sez she. Den Brer Rabbit, he come up little closer, but he ain't gittin' too close.

" 'I speck I'm nigh nuff, Sis Cow,' sez Brer Rabbit, sezee. 'I'm a mighty puny man, en I might git trompled,' sezee. 'You do de pullin', Sis Cow,' sezee, 'en I'll do de gruntin',' sezee.

"Den Miss Cow, she pull out 'er horn, she did, en tuck atter Brer Rabbit, en down de big road dey had it, Brer Rabbit wid his years laid back, en Miss Cow wid 'er head down en 'er tail curl. Brer Rabbit kep' on gainin', en bimeby he dart in a brier-patch, en by de time Miss Cow come 'long he had his head stickin' out, en his eyes look big ez Miss Sally's chany sassers.

" 'Heyo, Sis Cow! Whar you gwine?' sez Brer Rabbit, sezee.

" 'Howdy, Brer Big-Eyes,' sez Miss Cow, sez she. 'Is you seed Brer Rabbit go by?'

" 'He des minit pass,' sez Brer Rabbit, sezee, 'en he look mighty sick,' sezee.

"En wid dat, Miss Cow tuck down de road like de dogs wuz atter 'er, en Brer Rabbit, he des lay down dar in de brier-patch en roll en laugh twel his sides hurtid 'im. He bleedzd ter laff. Fox atter 'im, Buzzard atter 'im, en Cow atter 'im, en dey ain't kotch 'im yit."

"M"

GOING TO BED BEFORE A YOUNG LADY*

As I was saying, ten years ago, Judge Douglass, of Illinois, was a beardless youth of twenty years of age, freshly come amongst the people of the "Sucker State," with an air about him suspiciously redolent of Yankeeland. A mere youthful adventurer amongst those "square" Suckers—one would deem the position embarrassing. Not so with the judge; he had come on business. A political fortune was to be made, and no time lost. He was about launching on the sea of popular favour, and he commenced a general coast survey the day he arrived. He soon made himself District Attorney, member of the Legislature, Register of the U. S. Land Office, Secretary of State, and Judge of the Supreme Court.

"How do you adapt yourself," said I, "Judge, to the people? How did you 'naturalize' yourself, as it were?"

"Oh, nothing easier; you see I like it. It's democratic. But it did come awkward at first. You know I am, or rather was, bashful to rather a painful degree. Well, now, nine-tenths of my constituents despise luxuries, and have no such thing as a second room in their houses. In beating up votes, I live with my constituents, eat with my constituents, drink with them, lodge with them, pray with them, laugh, hunt, dance and work with them; I eat their corn dodgers and fried bacon, and sleep two in a bed with them. Among my first acquaintances were the L———s, down under the Bluffs. Fine fellows, the L———s,—by the way, I am sure of five votes there. Well, you perceive, I had to live there: and I did live there. But, sir, I was frightened the first night I slept there. I own it; yes, sir, I acknowledge the corn. An ice in August is something: but I was done to

---

* This sketch was reprinted in The Spirit of the Times (1845) and was credited to a New York paper—The Evening Mirror. The author is not known. The "Judge Douglass" of the story was, presumably, Stephen A. Douglas.

an icicle; had periodical chills for ten days. Did you ever see a Venus
in linsey-woolsey?"

"No!"

"Then you shall see Serena L———s. They call her the 'White
Plover'; seventeen:—plump as a pigeon, and smooth as a persimmon.
How the devil, said I to myself, soliloquizing the first night I slept
there, am I to go to bed before this young lady? I do believe my heart
was topsyturvied, for the idea of pulling off my boots before the
girl was death. And as to doffing my other fixtures, I would sooner
have my leg taken off with a wood-saw. The crisis was tremendous.
It was nearly midnight, and the family had been hours in bed. Miss
Serena alone remained. Bright as the sun, the merry minx talked on.
It was portentously obvious to me at last, that she had determined to
outsit me. By repeated spasmodic efforts, my coat, waistcoat, cravat,
boots and socks were brought off. During the process, my beautiful
neighbor talked to me with unaverted eyes, and with that peculiar
kind of placidity employed by painters to imbody their idea of the
virgin. I dumped myself down in a chair, in a cold perspiration. A
distressing thought occurred to me. Does not the damsel stand on a
point of local etiquette? It may be the fashion of these people to see
strangers in bed before retiring themselves. May I not have kept
those beautiful eyes open, from ignorance of what these people deem
good breeding? Neither the lady's eyes nor tongue had indeed betrayed fatigue. Those large jet eyes seemed to dilate and grow brighter
as the blaze of the wood fire died away; but doubtless this was from
kind consideration for the strange wakefulness of her guest. The thing
was clear. I determined to retire, and without delay. I arose with
firmness, unloosed my suspenders, and in a voice not altogether steady,
said:

" 'Miss Serena, I think I will retire.'

" 'Certainly, sir,' she quietly observed, 'you will lodge there, sir';
inclining her beautiful head towards a bed standing a few yards from
where she was sitting. I proceeded to uncase; entrenching myself
behind a chair the while, fondly imagining the position offered some
security. It is simply plain to a man in his senses, that a chair of the
fashion of the one I had thrown between myself and 'the enemy,' as
a military man would say, offered almost no security at all. No more,
in fact, than standing up behind a ladder—nothing in the way of the
artillery of bright eyes, as a poet would say, sweeping one down by

platoons. Then I had a dead open space of ten feet between me and the bed; a sort of Bridge of Lodi passage which I was forced to make, exposed to a cruel raking fire fore and aft. Although I say it, who should not say it, an emergency never arose for which I had not a resource. I had one for this. The plan was the work of a moment, I de—"

"Ah! I see, you stormed the battery and s—"

"Bah! don't interrupt me. No; I determined, by a bold ruse de guerre, to throw her attention out of the window, clear the perilous passage, and fortify myself under the counterpane before she recovered her surprise. The plan failed. You see I am a small man, physically speaking. Body, limbs, and head, setting up business on one hundred and seven and a half pounds, all told, of flesh, blood, and bones, cannot, individually or collectively, set up any very ostentatious pretensions. I believe the young lady must have been settling in her mind some philosophical point on that head. Perhaps her sense of justice wished to assure itself of a perfectly fair distribution of the respective motives. Perhaps she did not feel easy until she knew that a kind Providence had not added to general poverty individual wrong. Certain it was, she seemed rather pleased with her speculations; for when I arose from a stooping posture finally, wholly disencumbered of cloth, I noticed mischievous shadows playing about the corners of her mouth. It was the moment I had determined to direct her eye to some astonishing circumstance out of the window. But the young lady spoke at the critical moment.

" 'Mr. Douglass,' she observed, 'you have got a mighty small chance of legs there.'

"Men seldom have any notice of their own powers, I never made any pretensions to skill in ground and lofty tumbling; but it is strictly true, I cleared, at one bound, the open space, planted myself on the centre of the bed, and was buried in the blankets in a twinkling."

"I congratulate you, my boy," said I, poising a cube of the crimson core of the melon on the point of my knife; "a lucky escape truly! But was the young lady modest?"

"Modest, sir!—there is not in Illinois a more modest, or more sensible girl. It's habit—all habit. I think nothing of it now. Why, it's only last week I was at a fine wedding party, and a large and fine assembly of both sexes lodged in the same room, with only three feet or so of neutral territory between them."

"You astonish me, Mr. Douglass."

"Fact, sir, upon my honour. You see these people are the very soul of hospitality, and never allow a fine social party to turn out at twelve o'clock at night to go long distances home. All that is more cleverly managed here. An Illinois bed has a power of elongation or expansion perfectly enigmatical to strangers. One bed four feet wide, will, on occasion, flank one whole side of the house, and is called a field-bed, and large parties will range themselves on opposite sides of the house as economically as candles in a box."

"But, my dear fellow, this is drouthy prose, introduce yourself to that little fellow in the corner, and pass him over; and now tell me all about old Canandaigua."

Glen Rounds

WHY THERE ARE NO TREES
ON THE DESERT *

For many years in his spare time Ol' Paul had fooled around cross-breeding plants in a small way. At first he tried to cross an apple tree, a yellow pine, and a sawmill to get a tree that would keep the best features of all three. The idea was that if he could have a tree that would grow lumber already cut, the boards hanging like apples, he could get rid of all his loggers and hire apple or apricot pickers instead. Which of course would be a big saving, as everyone knows that fruit pickers work cheaper than lumberjacks, and feed themselves, which in itself is no small item. Besides that, he could deal direct with the consumer, as the Plankavos, as he hoped to call them, would do away with the sawmills, except for the few needed to provide sawdust for butcher shops and saloons.

I don't know exactly what ever happened to the Plankavo, but while he was fooling around he somehow accidentally crossed a Douglas fir, a California redwood, and a desert cactus. The tree he got was as tall as a redwood, the wood couldn't be told from fir, and it grew well in the dryest desert. The main trouble was the fact that it had thorns seventy feet long, instead of branches. This made Ol' Paul sore, so he didn't breed any more trees. However, a great many years later these trees had grown to a great size, covering the desert with a deep forest.

One day Ol' Paul gets a letter from the Government telling him he'll have to log the desert off. It seems that the Tired Eastern Business Women going out there for their vacations, were complaining that they couldn't see the desert because of the trees, and the cowboys on the dude ranches were all the time coming home with their clothes snagged up by the thorns. Along with the letter is a hand-painted

* A Paul Bunyan story as told for children by Glen Rounds.

picture, showing him what the Government thinks a desert should look like.

As soon as Paul gets the letter he hitches Babe to the south end of the section of land the camp is on, and hauls it down to Nevada. He often moved camp this way as it was quicker than any other, and besides, the men never got homesick for the old camp.

Next morning he takes a look at the timber and knows he's in for plenty of trouble for sure, on account of those seventy-foot thorns. At first they try to tunnel under the thorns and cut the trees off at the roots, but the thorns keep the trees from falling over even after they're cut off.

Then he decides to dynamite, and what a job that is! First they dig out a powder chamber under the roots, then carry in four thousand five hundred and four cases of dynamite and two thousand and four cans of giant powder. The idea is to blast off a township at a time. All the time the heat is affecting the men something fierce, so they can only work in four-hour shifts. Even working shifts day and night and holidays, it takes three weeks and nine days to get the giant blast ready. The last case of dynamite is packed, the percussion caps are wired, and the men all move back out of danger. Ol' Paul looks around and hollers: "Let her go!"

Well sir, the shock throws every man in camp flat on his back, knocks the cupolas off three barns in Iowa, and the smoke and dust go up in a column thirty-four miles high. When the air clears somewhat the men see there's nothing left but the holes. The trees've been blown clean out of sight. As it's nearly supper time, Ol' Paul says they might as well knock off for the day, but first he reaches up and feels around on top of the smoke column, which is still standing. He finds half a wagon load of wild ducks up there.

It seems that a big flock had been flying over when the blast went off. It has shot the air full of sand the exact size of bird shot and killed them all instantly, except one drake who was flying well in the lead. The sand missed him, but the force of the blast put a curl in his tail feathers that has never come out.

That night the men go to bed with their stomachs full of roast duck, and naturally very well satisfied. But the next morning when they go out, they find the trees fallen back to the ground, right side up and in the holes where they were before!

There seems to be nothing for Paul to do but give the men a day off and figure what to do. The trees couldn't be cut down. They couldn't be blasted down. They had been fire-proofed the Year of the Dry Rains, and couldn't be burned down. Ol' Paul chews his nails down to the quick and still can't figure what to do. He thinks and thinks. He thinks standing up, then he thinks sitting down, but this isn't so good as the ground is too hot. So he goes and sits down in the shade of the blacksmith shop and starts whittling.

He whittles a full-rigged clipper ship, full size, and tries all afternoon to get it inside a beer bottle, like the old sailors do. He gets so interested in this business that he forgets about his real problem until near supper time, and never does get the blamed thing into the bottle. So the next morning he gives the men another day off and goes into his office and thinks without whittling. Even so, it is three days before he comes tearing out with his arms full of blueprints, hollering for the straw bosses to get the men together. He's going to make a speech.

"Boys," he says, "the Gov'ment's dependin' on us. If we fail, them plans is blowed higher'n Gilroy's kite. We'll build the biggest piledriver ever seen. And by the Great Ringtailed Catamount, we'll drive them trees down like tent pegs!"

You see, this idea would make a story to be told in every camp this side of Mexico. Ol' Paul liked to do a job like that occasionally, even if there was no profit in it, just to remind folks he was no ordinary logger.

For thirty-nine weeks they work on the great pile-driver. It stands so high that the clouds going by are all the time knocking the upper half off, so he puts a hinge in the middle and lets the upper half down when he sees a cloud coming. For a weight he uses one of the Rocky Mountain peaks. (When he gets done he tosses it up into Colorado, where it sets to this day, right behind Colorado Springs.)

When everything is ready, they set the machine up over a thorn tree, and Babe, grunting mightily, hauls the weight to the top. It comes down and strikes with a crash that is heard for one hundred and three miles. The tree is driven clear to bed rock, its top being sixteen feet below the ground.

Ol' Paul reckons that'll do, and they go to work in real earnest. The noise and dust are terrific, as they drive a tree every three minutes, and Babe is sweating from every pore. The sweat pours down off his sides and down his legs and runs in streams across the desert. It washes big gullies in the soft soil that can be seen to this day. These streams running every which way hinder the work, so Paul grabs a shovel and digs a ditch for them to drain into. This is now known as the Grand Canyon. After Paul left the country the Government ran the Colorado River through it.

As soon as he gets the pile-driver crew working smoothly, Paul goes back to camp to catch up with a number of smaller problems that've piled up while he's busy with the cactus trees. On account of the heat, the men want ice tea every meal, and the cooks need ice to keep the meat from spoiling. But there's no ice to be had.

Suddenly Ol' Paul remembers something. That, by the way was one of the secrets of his success, that habit of remembering things even when they didn't seem worth remembering at the time.

It seems that while they had been building the pile-driver, Babe had been allowed to run loose, and had come back from Alaska with a small snowstorm snagged on one horn. Paul had taken it off, and having no use for a snowstorm round camp at the time, had put it in an old sheep pen in a dry lake-bed a few miles from camp, and forgotten it completely.

So now he decides to go and see how it's getting along. He sort of expects to find it pretty much wilted from the heat, but instead he finds the dry lake frozen from bank to bank. In the center of it the snowstorm's dug a burrow, and is as happy as a clam. Paul breaks off a piece of the ice and finds that it's much colder than ordinary ice, and when it melts it leaves a dry spot. This puzzles him for a bit, then he sees that it's dry ice. Naturally, if you freeze a dry lake you can get nothing but dry ice from it—it stands to reason. So Paul keeps the snowstorm there all the time he's logging off the desert, and the cooks never have to worry about the icebox pans running over.

A. J. Liebling

NATURAL HISTORY

"Fish is brain food," Fritz Strohschneider, a waiter and a friend of mine told me, "but around cities they is brainier. It is just like people, the city fish is more slicker as the country fish.

"I don't go fishing more," he went on without encouragement, "since they exploded Heinrich Heine.

"In the old days it was so nice on Sunday to fish for tommys from the docks. Tommys and eelses. On 96th Street dock we used to sit, me and my friend Jack Poppberger, with a case of beer and our clarinets. It was the most convenient fishing.

"Each one would have four, five lines. The lines are tied to wires and on each wire there is a bell. When a fish bites, the bell rings, like an elevator. You pull him up and it is sport.

"So one Sunday we was sitting on the dock, and we had eight lines out. Suddenly, along comes Heinrich Heine.

"It seems between those bells was musical gradations, by chance of the length of the wires, and as I am sitting tuning my clarinet, so I hear played wonder good on the bells the scale. 'Do, re, mi, fa, sol,' and the rest of it. 'My God, Jake,' I says, 'what is this for a fish?'

"Back it comes the other way the scale—being a fish the scale was its specialty—and then 'dingle, dingle,'—it was trying to pick out 'Annie Laurie.'

"Jake wanted to pull up the line, but I said, 'What, you would murder a musician?'

"We looked down it shouldn't be boys in a boat under the pier, but there was nothing. The next Sunday we came to the same spot. We set the lines and soon it gave 'Ich Weiss Nicht Was Soll Es Bedeuten.' Then I named the fish Heinrich Heine. So we played on our clarinets and Heinrich Heine would accompany us.

"Every Sunday new tunes we were teaching him, and sometimes he even offered for us original compositions. So nice it was in the sunset to sit there with a case of empty beer bottles and play 'Love's Old Sweet Song.' "

Fritz sighed. He flicked listlessly at an imaginary speck of dust with his towel.

"I never saw Heinrich Heine," he said. "I don't know whether he was a tommy or whether an eel. But in a way I helped kill him. Among the tunes we taught him was 'Die Wacht Am Rhein.' We didn't mean no harm. It was before America went in the war. Scotchers, Englishers, Irishers used to come down to the pier. It made them mad to hear the fish play so nice the German antler.

"But when this country went in the war a battleship came in the river. A bright Sunday morning Heinrich Heine commenced to play. 'Ta-tum-tee-um-tee-um-Die Wacht Am Rhein.' The battleship shot a torpedo and exploded Heinrich Heine. Since then I go no more fishing."

George W. Harris

MRS. YARDLEY'S QUILTING *

"Thar's one durn'd nasty muddy job, an' I is jis' glad enuf tu take a ho'n ur two, on the straingth ove hit."

"What have you been doing, Sut?"

"Helpin tu salt ole Missis Yardley down."

"What do you mean by that?"

"Fixin her fur rotten cumfurtably, kiverin her up wif sile, tu keep the buzzards frum cheatin the wurms."

"Oh, you have been helping to bury a woman."

"That's hit, by golly! Now why the devil can't I 'splain mysef like yu? I ladles out my words at random, like a calf kickin at yaller-jackids; yu jis' rolls em out tu the pint, like a feller a-layin bricks— every one fits. How is it that bricks fits so clost enyhow? Rocks won't ni du hit."

"Becaze they'se all ove a size," ventured a man with a wen over his eye.

"The devil yu say, hon'ey-head! haint reapin-mersheens ove a size? I'd like tu see two ove em fit clost. You wait ontil yu sprouts tuther ho'n, afore yu venters tu 'splain mix'd questions. George, did yu know ole Missis Yardley?"

"No."

"Well, she wer a curious 'oman in her way, an' she wore shiney specks. Now jis' listen: Whenever yu see a ole 'oman ahine a par ove *shiney* specks, yu keep yer eye skinn'd; they am dang'rus in the extreme. Thar is jis' no knowin what they ken du. I hed one a-stradil ove me onst, fur kissin her gal. She went fur my har, an' she went fur my skin, ontil I tho't she ment tu kill me, an' wud a-dun hit, ef my hollerin hadent fotch ole Dave Jordan, a *bacheler,* tu my aid. He, like a durn'd fool, cotch her by the laig, an' drug her back'ards ofen me. She jis' kivered him, an' I run, by golly! The nex time I seed him he

* A "Sut Lovingood" varn.

wer bald headed, an' his face looked like he'd been a-fitin wild-cats.

"Ole Missis Yardley wer a great noticer ove littil things, that nobody else ever seed. She'd say right in the middil ove sumbody's serious talk: 'Law sakes! thar goes that yàller slut ove a hen, a-flingin straws over her shoulder; she' arter settin now, an' haint laid but seven aigs. I'll disapint *her,* see ef I don't; I'll put a punkin in her nes', an' a feather in her nose. An' bless my soul! jis' look at that cow wif the wilted ho'n, a-flingin up dirt an' a-smellin the place whar hit cum frum, wif the rale ginuine still-wurim twis' in her tail, too; what upon the face ove the yeath kin she be arter now, the ole fool? watch her, Sally. An' sakes alive! jis' look at that ole sow; she's a-gwine in a fas' trot, wif her empty bag a-floppin agin her sides. Thar, she hes stop't, an's a-listenin! Massy on us! what a long yearnis' grunt she gin; hit cum frum way back ove her kidneys. Thar she goes agin; she's arter no good, sich kerryin on means no good.'

"An' so she wud gabble, no odds who wer a-listenin. She looked like she mout been made at fust 'bout four foot long, an' the common thickness ove wimen when they's at tharsefs, an' then had her har tied tu a stump, a par ove steers hitched to her heels, an' then straiched out a-mos' two foot more—mos' ove the straichin cumin outen her laigs an' naik. Her stockins, a-hangin on the clothes-line tu dry, looked like a par ove sabre scabbards, an' her naik looked like a dry beef shank smoked, an' mout been ni ontu es tough. I never felt hit mysef, I didn't, I jis' jedges by looks. Her darter Sal wer bilt at fust 'bout the laingth ove her mam, but wer never straiched eny by a par ove steers, an' she wer fat enuf tu kill; she wer taller lyin down than she wer a-standin up. Hit wer her who gin me the 'hump shoulder.' Jis' look at me; haint I'se got a tech ove the dromedary back thar bad? haint I humpy? Well, a-stoopin tu kiss that squatty lard-stan ove a gal is what dun hit tu me. She wer the fairest-lookin gal I ever seed. She allers wore thick woolin stockins 'bout six inches too long fur her laig; they rolled down over her garters, lookin like a par ove life presarvers up thar. I tell yu she wer a tarin gal enyhow. Luved kissin, wrastlin, an' biled cabbige, an' hated tite clothes, hot weather, an' suckit-riders. B'leved strong in married folk's ways, cradles, an' the remishun ove sins, an' didn't b'leve in corsets, fleas, peaners, nur the fashun plates."

"What caused the death of Mrs. Yardley, Sut?"

"Nuffin, only her heart stop't beatin 'bout losing a nine dimunt quilt.

True, she got a skeer'd hoss tu run over her, but she'd a-got over that ef a quilt hadn't been mix'd up in the catastrophy. Yu see quilts wer wun ove her speshul gifts; she run strong on the bed-kiver question. Irish chain, star ove Texas, sun-flower, nine dimunt, saw teeth, checker board, an' shell quilts; blue, an' white, an' yaller an' black coverlids; an' callickercumfurts reigned triumphan' 'bout her hous'. They wer packed in drawers, layin in shelfs full, wer hung four dubbil on lines in the lof, packed in chists, piled on cheers, an' wer everywhar, even ontu the beds, an' wer changed every bed-makin. She told everybody she cud git tu listen tu hit that she ment tu give every durn'd one ove them tu Sal when she got married. Oh, lordy! what es fat a gal es Sal Yardley cud ever du wif half ove em, an' sleeping wif a husbun at that, is more nor I ever cud see through. Jis' think ove her onder twenty layer ove quilts in July, an' you in thar too. Gewhillikins! George, look how I is sweatin' now, an' this is December. I'd 'bout es lief be shet up in a steam biler wif a three hundred pound bag ove lard, es tu make a bisiness ove sleepin wif that gal—'twould kill a glass-blower.

"Well, tu cum to the serious part ove this conversashun, that is how the old quilt-mersheen an' coverlidloom cum tu stop operashuns on this yeath. She hed narrated hit thru the neighborhood that nex Saterday she'd gin a quiltin—three quilts an' one cumfurt tu tie. 'Goblers, fiddils, gals, an' whisky,' wer the words she sent tu the men-folk, an' more tetchin ur wakenin words never drap't ofen an 'oman's tongue. She sed tu the gals, 'Sweet toddy, huggin, dancin, an' huggers in 'bundance.' Them words struck the gals rite in the pit ove the stumick, an' spread a ticklin sensashun bof ways, ontil they scratched thar heads wif one han, an' thar heels wif tuther.

"Everybody, he an' she, what were baptized b'levers in the righteousnes ove quiltins wer thar, an' hit jis' so happen'd that everybody in them parts, frum fifteen summers tu fifty winters, wer unannamus b'levers. Strange, warn't hit? Hit wer the bigges' quiltin ever Missis Yardley hilt, an' she hed hilt hundreds; everybody wer thar, 'scept the constibil an' suckit-rider, two dam easily-spared pussons; the numbers ni ontu even too; jis' a few more boys nur gals; that made hit more exhitin, fur hit gin the gals a chance tu kick an' squeal a littil, wifout runnin eny risk ove not gittin kissed at all, an' hit gin reasonabil grouns fur a few scrimmages amung the he's. Now es kissin an' fitin am the pepper an' salt ove all soshul getherins, so hit wer more espishully wif this ove ours. Es I swung my eyes over the crowd, George, I thought quiltins, managed in a morril an' sensibil way, truly am good things—good fur free drinkin, good fur free eatin, good fur free huggin, good fur free dancin, good fur free fitin, an' goodest ove all fur poperlatin a country fas'.

"Thar am a fur-seein wisdum in quiltins, ef they has proper trim-mins: 'vittils, fiddils, an' sperrits in 'bundance.' One holesum quiltin am wuf three old pray'rmeetins on the poperlashun pint, purtickerly ef hits hilt in the dark ove the moon, an' runs intu the night a few hours, an' April ur May am the time chosen. The moon don't suit quiltins whar everybody is well acquainted an' already fur along in courtin. She dus help pow'ful tu begin a courtin match onder, but when hit draws ni ontu a head, nobody wants a moon but the old mammys.

"The mornin cum, still, saft, sunshiney; cocks crowin, hens singin, birds chirpin, tuckeys gobblin—jis' the day tu sun quilts, kick, kiss, squeal, an' make love.

"All the plow-lines an' clothes-lines were straiched tu every post an' tree. Quilts purvailed. Durn my gizzard ef two acres roun that ar house warn't jis' one solid quilt, all out a-sunnin, an' tu be seed. They dazzled the eyes, skeered the hosses, gin wimen the heart-burn, an' perdominated.

"To'ards sundown the he's begun tu drap in. Yearnis' needil-drivin cummenced tu lose ground; threads broke ofen, thimbils got los', an' quilts needed anuther roll. Gigglin, winkin, whisperin, smoofin ove har, an' gals a-ticklin one anuther, wer a-gainin every inch ove groun what the needils los'. Did yu ever notis, George, at all soshul getherins, when the he's begin tu gather, that the young she's begin tu tickil one anuther an' the ole maids swell thar tails, roach up thar backs, an' sharpen thar nails ontu the bed-posts an' door jams, an' spit an' groan sorter like cats a-courtin? Dus hit mean *rale* rath, ur is hit a dare tu the he's, sorter kivered up wif the outside signs ove danger? I honestly b'leve that the young she's ticklin means, 'Cum an' take this job ofen our hans.' But that swellin I jis' don't onderstan; dus yu? Hit looks skeery, an' I never tetch one ove em when they am in the swellin way. I may be mistaken'd 'bout the ticklin bisiness too; hit may be dun like a feller chaws poplar bark when he haint got any terbacker, a-sorter better nur nun make-shif. I dus know one thing tu a certainty: that is, when the he's take hold the ticklin quits, an' ef yu gits one ove the old maids out tu hersef, then she subsides an' is the smoofes, sleekes, saft thing yu ever seed, an' dam ef yu can't hear her purr, jes' es plain!

"But then, George, gals an' ole maids haint the things tu fool time away on. Hits widders, by golly, what am the rale sensibil, steady-goin, never-skeerin, never-kickin, willin, sperrited, smoof pacers. They cum clost up tu the hoss-block, standin still wif thar purty silky years playin, an' the naik-veins a-throbbin, an' waits fur the words, which ove course yu gives, arter yu finds yer feet well in the stirrup, an' away they moves like a cradil on cushioned rockers, ur a spring buggy runnin in damp san'. A tetch ove the bridil, an' they know yu wants em tu turn, an' they dus hit es willin es ef the idear wer thar own. I be dod rabbited ef a man can't 'propriate happiness by the skinful ef he is in contack wif sumbody's widder, an' is smart. Gin me a willin widder, the yeath over: what they don't know, haint worth larnin. They hes all been tu Jamakey an' larnt how sugar's made, an' know how tu sweeten wif hit; an' by golly, they is always ready to use hit. All yu hes tu du is tu find the spoon, an' then drink cumfort till yer blind. Nex tu good sperrits an' my laigs, I likes a twenty-five year old widder, wif roun ankils, an' bright eyes, honestly an' squarly lookin intu yurn, an' sayin es plainly es a partrige sez 'Bob White,' 'Don't be afraid ove me; I hes been thar; yu know hit ef yu hes eny sense, an' thar's no use in eny humbug, ole feller—cum ahead!'

"Ef yu onderstands widder nater, they ken save yu a power ove troubil, onsartinty, an' time, an' ef yu is interprisin yu ʒits mons'rous well paid fur hit. The very soun ove thar littil shoe-heels speak full trainin, an' hes a knowin click as they tap the floor; an' the rustil ove thar dress sez, 'I dar yu tu ax me.'

"When yu hes made up yer mind tu court one, jis' go at hit like hit wer a job ove rail-maulin. Ware yer workin close, use yer common, everyday moshuns an' words, an' abuv all, fling away yer cinamint ile vial an' burn all yer love songs. No use in tryin tu fool em, fur they sees plum thru yu, a durn'd sight plainer than they dus thru thar veils. No use in a pasted shut; she's been thar. No use in borrowin a cavortin fat hoss; she's been thar. No use in har-dye; she's been thar. No use in cloves, tu kill whisky breff; she's been thar. No use in buying clost curtains fur yer bed, fur she has been thar. Widders am a speshul means, George, fur ripenin green men, killin off weak ones, an makin 'ternally happy the soun ones.

"Well, es I sed afore, I flew the track an' got ontu the widders. The fellers begun tu ride up an' walk up, sorter slow, like they warn't in a hurry, the durn'd 'saitful raskils, hitchin thar critters tu enything they cud find. One red-comb'd, long-spurr'd, dominecker feller, frum town, in a red an' white grid-iron jackid an' patent leather gaiters, hitched his hoss, a wild, skeery, wall-eyed devil, inside the yard palins, tu a cherry tree lim'. Thinks I, that hoss hes a skeer intu him big enuf tu run intu town, an' perhaps beyant hit, ef I kin only tetch hit off; so I sot intu thinkin.

"One aind ove a long clothes-line, wif nine dimunt quilts ontu hit, wer tied tu the same cherry tree that the hoss wer. I tuck my knife and socked hit thru every quilt, 'bout the middil, an' jis' below the rope, an' tied them thar wif bark, so they cudent slip. Then I went tu the back aind, an' ontied hit frum the pos', knottin in a hoe-handil, by the middil, tu keep the quilts frum slippin off ef my bark strings failed, an' laid hit on the groun. Then I went tu the tuther aind: thar wer 'bout ten foot tu spar, a-lyin on the groun arter tyin tu the tree. I tuck hit atwix Wall-eye's hine laigs, an' tied hit fas' tu bof stirrups, an' then cut the cherry tree lim' betwix his bridil an' the tree, almos' off. Now, mine yu thar were two ur three uther ropes full ove quilts atween me an' the hous', so I were purty well hid frum thar. I jis' tore off a palin frum the fence, an' tuck hit in bof hans, an' arter raisin hit 'way up yander, I fotch hit down, es hard es I cud, flatsided to'ards the groun, an' hit acksidentally happen'd tu hit Wall-eye, 'bout nine inches ahead ove the root ove his tail. Hit landed so hard that hit made my hans tingle, an' then busted intu splinters. The first things I did, wer tu feel ove mysef, on the same spot whar hit hed hit the hoss. I cudent help duin hit tu save my life, an' I swar I felt sum ove Wall-eye's sensashun, jis' es plain. The fust thing he did, wer tu tare down the lim' wif a twenty-foot jump, his head to'ards the hous'. Thinks I, now yu hev dun hit, yu durn'd wall-eyed fool! tarin down that lim' wer the beginin ove all the troubil, an' the hoss did hit hissef; my conshuns felt clar es a mountin spring, an' I wer in a frame ove mine tu observe things es they happen'd, an' they soon begun tu happen purty clost arter one anuther rite then, an' thar, an' tharabouts, clean ontu town, thru hit, an' still were a-happenin, in the woods beyant thar ni ontu eleven mile from ole man Yardley's gate, an' four beyant town.

"The fust line ove quilts he tried tu jump, but broke hit down; the nex one he ran onder; the rope cotch ontu the ho'n ove the saddil, broke at bof ainds, an' went along wif the hoss, the cherry tree lim' an' the fust line ove quilts, what I hed proverdensally tied fas' tu the rope. That's what I calls foresight, George. Right furnint the frunt door he cum in contack wif old Missis Yardley hersef, an' anuther ole 'oman; they wer a-holdin a nine dimunt quilt spread out, a-'zaminin hit, an' a-praisin hits perfeckshuns. The durn'd onmanerly, wall-eyed fool run plum over Missis Yardley, frum ahine, stompt one hine foot through the quilt, takin hit along, a-kicken ontil he made hits corners snap like a whip. The gals screamed, the men hollered wo! an' the ole 'oman wer toted intu the hous' limber es a wet string, an' every word she sed wer, 'Oh, my preshus nine dimunt quilt!'

"Wall-eye busted thru the palins, an' Dominicker sed 'im, made a mortal rush fur his bitts, wer too late fur them, but in good time fur the strings ove flying quilts, got tangled amung em, an' the gridiron jackid patren wer los' tu my sight amung star an' Irish chain quilts; he went frum that quiltin at the rate ove thuty miles tu the hour. Nuffin lef on the lot ove the hole consarn, but a nine biler hat, a par ove gloves, an' the jack ove hearts.

"What a onmanerly, suddin way ove leavin places sum folks hev got, enyhow.

"Thinks I, well, that fool hoss, tarin down that cherry tree lim', hes dun sum good, enyhow; hit hes put the ole 'oman outen the way fur the balance ove the quiltin, an' tuck Dominicker outen the way an' outen danger, fur that gridiron jackid wud a-bred a scab on his nose afore midnite; hit wer morrily boun tu du hit.

"Two months arterwards, I tracked the route that hoss tuck in his kalamatus skeer, by quilt rags, tufts ove cotton, bunches ove har (human an' hoss), an' scraps ove a gridiron jackid stickin ontu the bushes, an' plum at the aind ove hit. whar all signs gin out, I foun a piece ove watch chain an' a hosses head. The places what know'd Dominicker, know'd im no more.

"Well, arter they'd tuck the ole 'oman up stairs an' camfired her tu sleep, things begun tu work agin. The widders broke the ice, an' arter a littil gigilin, goblin, an' gabblin, the kissin begun. *Smack!*—'Thar, now,' a widder sed that. *Pop!*—'Oh, don't!' *Pfip!*—'Oh, yu quit!' *Plosh!*—'Go *way* yu awkerd critter, yu kissed me in the eye!' anuther widder sed that. *Bop!* 'Now yu ar satisfied, I recon, big mouf!' *Vip!*—'That haint fair!' *Spat!*—'Oh, lordy! May, cum pull Bill away; he's a-tanglin my har'. *Thut!*—'I jis' d-a-r-e yu tu du that agin!' a widder sed that, too. Hit sounded all 'roun that room like poppin co'n in a hot skillet, and wer pow'ful sujestif.

"Hit kep on ontil I be durn'd ef *my* bristils didn't begin tu rise, an' sumthin like a cold buckshot wud run down the marrow in my back-bone 'bout every ten secons, an' then run up agin, tolerabil hot. I kep a swallerin wif nuthin tu swaller, an' my face felt swell'd; an' yet I wer fear'd tu make a bulge. Thinks I, I'll ketch one out tu hersef torreckly, an' then I guess we'll rastil. Purty soon Sal Yardley started fur the smoke-'ous, so I jis' gin my head a few short shakes, let down one ove my wings a-trailin, an' sirkiled roun her wif a side twis' in my naik, steppin side-wise, an' a-fetchin up my hinemos' foot wif a sorter jerkin slide at every step. Sez I, 'Too coo-took a-too.' She onderstood hit, an stopt, sorter spreadin her shoulders. An' jis' es I hed pouch'd out my mouf, an' wer a-reachin forrid wif hit, fur the article hitsef, sunthin interfared wif me, hit did. George, wer yu ever ontu yer hans an' knees, an' let a hell-tarin big, mad ram, wif a ten-yard run, but yu yearnis'ly, jis onst, right squar ontu the pint ove yer back-bone?"

"No, you fool; why do you ask?"

"Kaze I wanted tu know ef yu cud hev a realizin' noshun ove my shock. Hits scarcely worth while tu try to make yu onderstan the case by words only, onles yu hev been tetched in that way. Gr-eat golly! the fust thing I felt, I tuck hit tu be a back-ackshun yeath-quake; an' the fust thing I seed wer my chaw'r terbacker a-flying over Sal's head like a skeer'd bat. My mouf wer pouch'd out, ready fur the article hitsef, yu know, an' hit went outen the roun hole like the wad outen a pop-gun—thug! an' the fust think I know'd, I wer a flying over Sal's head too, an' a-gainin on the chaw'r terbacker fast. I wer strait-ened out strait, toes hinemos', middil finger-nails foremos', an' the fust thing I hearn wer, 'Yu dam Shanghi!' Great Jerus-a-lam! I lit ontu my all fours jis' in time tu but the yard gate ofen hits hinges, an' skeer loose sum more hosses—kep on in a four-footed gallop, clean acrost the lane afore I cud straiten up, an' yere I cotch up wif my chaw'r ter-backer, stickin flat agin a fence-rail. I hed got so good a start that I thot hit a pity tu spile hit, so I jis' jump'd the fence an' tuck thru the orchurd. I tell yu I dusted these yere close, fur I tho't hit wer arter me.

"Arter running a spell, I ventered tu feel roun back thar, fur sum signs ove what hed happened tu me. George, arter two pow'ful hard-tugs, I pull'd out the vamp an' sole ove one ove ole man Yardley's big brogans, what he hed los' amung my coat-tails. Dre'ful! dre'ful! Arter

I got hit away frum thar, my flesh went fas' asleep, frum abuv my kidneys tu my knees; about now, fur the fust time, the idear struck me, what hit wer that hed interfar'd wif me, an' los' me the kiss. Hit wer ole Yardley hed kicked me. I walked fur a month like I were straddlin a thorn hedge. Sich a shock, at sich a time, an' on sich a place —jis' think ove hit! hit am tremenjus, haint hit? The place feels num, right now."

"Well, Sut, how did the quilting come out?"

"How the hell du yu 'speck me tu know? I warn't thar eny more."

Alfred Henry Lewis

THE MAN FROM YELLOWHOUSE

"That's straight, son; you shorely should have seen Jack Moore," continued the Old Cattleman, after a brief pause, as he hitched his chair into a comfortable position; "not seein' Jack is what any gent might call deeprivation.

"Back in the old days," he went on, "Jack Moore, as I relates, is kettle-tender an' does the rope work of the Stranglers. Whatever is the Stranglers? Which you asks some late. I mentions this assembly a heap frequent yeretofore. Well, some folks calls 'em the 'vig'lance committee'; but that's long for a name, so in Wolfville we allers allooded to 'em as 'Stranglers.' This yere is brief, an' likewise sheds some light.

"This Jack Moore—which I'm proud to say he's my friend—I reckons is the most *pro bono publico* gent in the Southwest. He's out to do anythin' from fight to fiddle at a dance, so's it's a public play.

"An' then his idees about his dooties is wide. He jest scouts far an' near, an' don't pay no more heed to distance an' fatigue than a steer does to cobwebs.

"'A offishul,' says Jack, 'who don't diffuse himse'f 'round none, an' confines his endeavors to his own bailiwick, is reestricted an' oneffectooal, an' couldn't keep down crime in a village of prairie-dogs.' An' then he'd cinch on his saddle, an' mebby go curvin' off as far north as the Flint Hills, or east to the Turkey-track.

"That's right; when it comes to bein' active, Jack is what you might call an all-round seelection. An' clean strain? Game as hornets. Never knowed him to quit anythin' in his life—not even whiskey. I says to him myse'f one time: 'Jack; whyever don't you renig on whiskey? Looks like it's sorter gettin' behind you some, ain't it? Some day mebby it outholds you when you can't stand to lose.'

"'Sometimes I thinks I'll pass it up, myse'f,' says Jack, 'but don't you know, I can't do it. I'm too sperited, that a-way, an' chivalrous. That's whatever! I'm too chivalrous.' An' I shore reckons he was.

"But as for doin' his dooty! Which the same is simply relaxation to Jack Moore. I recalls one instance speshul. One day thar comes trailin' along into Wolfville a party from down 'round Yallerhouse some'ers. This yere Yallerhouse gent looks disperited an' off color as to health. But of course we-alls don't refer none to it; for whether this stranger's sick or well is his business, not ours; leastwise in its first stages. This yere's before Doc Peets inhabits Wolfville or he'd informed us touchin' this party's that a-way.

"Which the Yallerhouse gent tracks along into the Red Light, an' tells the barkeep to set out the nose-paint. He drinks alone, not invitin' of the pop'lace, whereby we knows for shore he's offen his feed.

"Well, after he corrals his forty drops, this invalid camps down in one corner of the stage station, an' next mornin' he wakes up outen his head an' plumb locoed.

" 'This yere Yallerhouse man,' says Dan Boggs, comin' along into the Red Light about first-drink time the same mornin', an' speakin' general, 'is what conserv'tive opinion might call "some sick." I stops a minute ago an' asks him how he's stackin' up like, but it ain't no use. He's plumb off his mental reservation, an' crazy as a woman's watch.'

" 'Whatever do you allow is the matter of him, Boggs?' asks Old Man Enright.

" 'Smallpox,' says Boggs, mighty confident.

" 'Smallpox!' repeats Enright; 'be you shore?'

" 'That's what I says,' answers Boggs; 'an' you can gamble my long suit is pickin' out smallpox every time. I knows the signal smoke like my own campfire.'

" 'Well, see yere,' says Dave Tutt, who's come in, 'I jest now rounds up them symptoms of this Yallerhouse gent; an' talkin' of smallpox, I offers a hundred dollars even he ain't got no smallpox. Bein' out solely for legit'mate sport,' continues Tutt, 'an' not aimin' to offend Boggs none, I willin'ly calls it fifty to one hundred he ain't got nothin'.'

" 'Which I takes both bets,' says Boggs, 'an' deems 'em easy. Which both is like robbin' a bird's-nest. Yere's the circ'latin' medium. Thar; cover it an' file it away with the barkeep to wait results.' So Tutt an' Boggs makes their bets mighty eager, an' the barkeep holds the stakes.

"As soon as it gets blown through Wolfville this Yallerhouse party has smallpox, everybody comes canterin' over to the Red Light, gets a drink, an' wants to hold a mass meetin' over it. By partic'lar request Enright takes the chair an' calls 'em to order.

" 'This yere meetin',' says Enright, meanwhile beatin' with the butt of his six-shooter on the poker-table, 'is some sudden an' permiscus; but the objects is easy an' plain. We-alls convenes ourse'fs to consider the physical condition of this party from Yallerhouse, which report says is locoed an' can't talk none for himself. To make this inquiry a success, we-alls oughter see this Yallerhouse gent; an' as thar is fewer of him than of us, I app'ints Jack Moore, Dan Boggs, an' Short Creek Dave, a committee, of three, to bring him before us in a body. Pendin' the return of the committee the meetin' will take a drink with the chair.'

"In about no time back comes the outfit, packin' the Yallerhouse man all easy enough in a blanket, an' spreads him out on the floor. He looks sorter red 'round in spots, like somethin's being stingin' of him, but it's evident, as Boggs says, he's locoed. He lays thar, rollin' his eyes an' carryin' on to himse'f, but he don't address the chair or offer to take no part in the meetin'. Enright quaffs his drink all slow an' dignified, an' gazes at the Yallerhouse man on the floor.

" 'Well, gents,' says Enright at last, settin' down his glass, an' givin' the poker-table a little tap with his gun, 'yere's the party, an' the question is now: "What's he got?" Do I hear any remarks?'

" 'Bein' in the lines, Mister Pres'dent,' says Boggs, 'of previous assertion, an' for the purpose of bringin' the question squar' before this house, I now moves you this yere Yallerhouse party has the smallpox. I ain't aimin' herein at playin' it low on Tutt, an' su'gests that the chair, in puttin' the question, also informs the meetin' as to them wagers; which the money tharof is now in the war-bags of the barkeep. I believes in givin' every gent all necessary light wherein to make up his mind; an', as I says, to open the game all logical, I ag'in moves this Yallerhouse man has the smallpox.'

" 'Yo tambien,' yells a Mexican over near the door.

" 'Put that Greaser out!' shouts Enright, at the same time bangin' the table. 'This ain't no international incident at all, an' nothin' but the clean-strain American wolf is eligible to howl.'

"The Greaser goes out on his saddle-colored head, an' Enright puts Boggs's motion.

" 'Every gent,' says Enright, 'in favor of this Yallerhouse man havin' the smallpox, say "Aye"; contrary "No." '

"Everybody shouts 'Aye!'

" 'Which the "Ayes" has it unanimous,' says Enright. 'The Yallerhouse party has the smallpox, an' the next chicken on the parliamentary roost is the question: "Whatever is to be done to make this yere malady a success?" Is thar any su'gestions?'

" 'Mister Pres'dent,' says Texas Thompson, risin' in his place, 'I've done took no hand in these proceedin's so far, through ignorance of the purposes of this yere convocation. Said purposes bein' now for the first time lined out all right in my mind, an' the question bein', "What's to be done with our captive?" I asks your indulgence. My first idee is that our dooty an' our path is plain; the same bein' simply to take a lariat an' hang this Yallerhouse person to the dance-hall windmill; but this course, on second thought, seems prematoor an' the offsprings of nacheral impulse. Still, somethin' must be done; an' while my mind is by no means cl'ar, I su'gests we turn the gent over to Jack Moore, which is the marshal hereof, to ride herd on him till further orders; an' I makes a motion to that effect.'

" 'Seconds the motion!' says Short Creek Dave.

" 'You don't have to put that motion, Mister Pres'dent,' says Jack; 'I've been circlin' the idee some myse'f, an' I reckons it's my dooty to take charge of this Yallerhouse gent. You can bet anythin' which gets sawed onto me as my dooty goes, an' don't make no doubt about it. Yere's how I trails out on this: If it ain't my dooty to take care of this person, whose dooty is it? 'Tain't nobody's. Tharfore I plays the hand.'

" 'Which the same bein' eminent satisfactory,' says Dave Tutt, risin', as if he thinks of somethin' speshul, 'I now inquires whether this yere is held decisive of them bets I makes with Boggs. I holdin', meanwhile, contrary views emphatic.'

" 'This bein' a question of priv'lege,' says Enright, 'the chair will answer it. These proceedin's decides your bets with Boggs, an' the barkeep pays Boggs the *dinero*. This is a gov'ment of the people, for the people, by the people, an' founded on a *vox populi* bluff. The voice of the majority goes. You tharfore lose your bets to Boggs; drinks on Boggs, of course. Thar is another matter,' continues Enright, 'a bet we overlooks. Takin' care of this Yallerhouse gent will cost a stack or two, an' means must be provided. I tharfore makes as an order that yereafter thar's to be a rake on tens-up or better, showed, to make a fund to back this play; said rake to go ontil Mister Moore reports said Yallerhouse gent as safe or ceased to be.'

"Jack takes this Yallerhouse party over to the calaboose an' lays him away on some blankets. The calaboose is dry, an' what you-alls might call, commodious. It's a slam-up camp; yes indeed! Never has but Steve Stevenson in it. Puts Steve in one night when he's dead-drunk. The calaboose is new then, an' we-alls is that proud an' anxious to try it an' put it to some use, we couldn't resist, so in Steve goes.

"About four hours later Steve comes back up to the Red Light, hotter'n a burnt boot. Seems like he comes to, an' is that outraged an' indignant about bein' corralled that a-way, he busts the corner outen the calaboose an' issues forth a whole lot to find who does it.

"When he comes into the Red Light he revives himse'f with a drink, an' then inquires whether it's humorous, or do we mean it? Seein' how speshul low Steve takes it, we-alls allows it's a joke! an' Steve, while he evident feels some fretted, concloods to let it go at that.

"But on account of the hole through which Steve emerges, an' which he makes liberal an' big, the calaboose is a mighty commodious place. So Jack beds down the Yallerhouse man all right an' starts in to bringin' him through. The rest of us don't crowd 'round none to watch the play, don't hover over it that a-way, 'cause we ain't aimin' to acquire nothin' ourse'fs.

"Jack has a heap of trouble an' worry. Never sees no smallpox, do you? Folks locoed most usual,—clean off up in the air an' pitchin' on their ropes. Of course the Yallerhouse gent has all he needs. That rake on tens-up them days would have took care of a fam'ly. But he keeps Jack herdin' him all the time. Otherwise, not bein' watched, an' crazy that a-way, he's liable to come stampedin' over to the Red Light, or some'ers else, any time, an' skeer us up some.

"'He's a world-beater,' says Jack one day, when he comes over for a drink. 'He's shorely four kings an' an ace. You can't ride him with buckin'-straps an' a Spanish bit. It's got so now—his disease bein' at a crisis like—that I simply has to be with this Yallerhouse party day an' night. He'd shorely lay waste this camp if I didn't.'

"At last the Yallerhouse party an' Jack somehow beats the smallpox, but Yallerhouse comes out shy an eye. The smallpox gouges it out one of them times when Jack ain't lookin' out his game sharp. It's his pistol eye, too; which makes him feel the loss more keen, an' creates general sympathy. The Yallerhouse man gets some morose over it, which ain't, after all, onnacheral. A gent ain't got so many eyes he can afford to go short one on every little game he plays. So he finds fault with Jack a lot, an' allows if he has him back in the States he'd sue him for neglect of dooty.

" 'Which, I shorely likes that!' says Jack to the Yallerhouse party, gettin' peevish over his fault-findin'. 'Don't you know it's merely owin' to the mercy of hell an' my watchful care, you-all ain't bustin' your harp-strings an' raisin' all 'round discord among the heavenly hosts on high right now, instead of bein' safe an' well yere in Wolfville? You don't act like a gent who saveys when he makes a winnin'. S'pose you be an eye out; you're still lookin' at things terrestrial with the other. You talks of gross neglect of dooty! Now let me inform you of some-thin': You come pesterin' 'round me some more an' I'll bend a gun over your head.'

" 'Which if it ain't my six-shooter eye which's out,' says the Yaller-house party, mighty ugly, 'do you know what I'd do? Well, this yere would be the basis of a first-class gun-play. You can gamble thar wouldn't be no jim-crow marshal go pirootin' 'round, losin' no eye of mine an' gettin' away with it, an' then talk of bendin' guns on me; none whatever.'

"But it all preys on Jack. An' a-seein' of this Yallerhouse gent 'round camp a-lookin' at him in a fault-findin' way outen his one eye sorter aggravates Jack like it's a nightmare.

" 'I wouldn't mind it so much,' says Jack to me, confidential, 'if this Yallerhouse gent quits a laig or an arm behind, 'cause in which event we pieces him out with wood, easy. But about eyes, it's different. An eye out is an eye out; an' that settles it.'

"One day Jack can't b'ar it no longer, an', resolvin' to end it, he walks up to the Yallerhouse party in the Red Light, all brisk an' brief.

" 'It's a rough deal on a one-eyed gent,' says Jack, 'an' I shore asks pardon an' states regrets in advance. But things has got to a show-down. I'm slowly becomin' onfit for public dooty. Now yere's an offer, an' you can have either end. You-all can get a hoss an' a hundred dollars of me, an' pull your freight; or you can fix yourse'f with a gun an' have a mighty stirrin' an' eventful time with me right yere. As an outcome of the last, the public will have one of us to plant, an' mebby a vacancy to fill in the post of kettle-tender. Which is it, an' what do you say?'

" 'What for a hoss is she?' asked the Yallerhouse party.

" 'Which she's a *pinto*,' says Jack; 'as excellent a paint pony as ever is roped.'

" 'Does this yere threat you-all makes incloode a saddle an' spurs?' asks the Yallerhouse party.

" 'It shorely does,' replies Jack. 'Is it a go?'

" 'Well,' says the Yallerhouse man, after ponderin' it up one way an' down the other, 'this idee of settlin' for eyes for a hoss an' a hundred dollars is far from bein' usual with me. If I has my eye ag'in, I'd shorely stay an' shoot it out, an' admire to be present. But now sech thoughts is vanity. So round up your money an' your pony at the Red Light in fifteen minutes by the watch, an' as soon as I gets a bottle filled I'm ready to go. I shorely should not regret leavin' an outfit which puts folks in jail for bein' sick, an' connives by reckless an' criminal neglect of dooty at their bein' blinded for life.' "

Roark Bradford

THE ADULTERATION OF OLD KING DAVID *

Ole King David made a mighty king. He always had his armies out fightin' for de Lawd, and he was always busy at home, holdin' cou't and keepin' de women-folks straightened out.

Well, one day ole King David was settin' on de front po'ch, jest settin' back, smokin' a cigar and lettin' his dinner settle. He was a mighty king, but he acted jest like a natchal man, too.

So purty soon a messenger rid up and bowed down to de ground and say, "Yo' Majesty King David, de enemies er de Lawd is done whupped."

"Who say de enemies er de Lawd is whupped, messenger?" say David.

"De General say dey's whupped," says de messenger.

"Well, I don't b'lieve hit," say ole King David. "Dem enemies er de Lawd is a awful pack of liars, and I speck they git de General to say they's whupped jest so's our boys won't fly in and give 'em a sho-'nuff whuppin'. So you jest up and ride back and tell our boys to light into de enemies ag'in and stay lit to dey hollers, 'Calf rope.' "

So de messenger went ridin' off and ole King David r'ared back ag'in, smokin' his cigar and settlin' his dinner.

Well, David was a king and a mighty king. But David was a man, jest like any yuther man. And whar you see a man, hit's bound to be a woman hangin' round somewheres close by. So right across de road was de house of a woman named Miz Uriah.

Miz Uriah was one er deseyar married womens which is good-lookin' and don't keer who knows hit. She's jest de kind dat's always waitin' for her husband to git outer de house so's she kin start messin' round.

Her husband was in de armies er de Lawd, fightin' de enemies, and

* From "Ol' Man Adam an' His Chillun," Roark Bradford's book of Negro Bible stories.

he left her home to look after de chickens and things while he gone. But dat gal ain' studdin' no chickens. She's got her mind on de menfolks.

And while ole King David is tawkin' to de messenger, she's hidin' behind de window blinds, a-watchin'. And soon as she see de messenger leave, she runs back and put on her Sunday dress and goes over to whar ole King David is settin'.

"Good mawnin', King David, Yo' Majesty," she say, sweetenin' up her voice.

"Good mawnin', sister," say ole King David. "What can I do for you dis mawnin'?"

"Well," say Miz Uriah, casual-like, "I comed over to ax you does you yar somethin' 'bout my husband. He ain't much husband, but he better'n no husband a-tall. I guess he's about all a ugly ole gal like me kin git, anyway. I wish I was a good-lookin' gal."

"You don't look so bad, gal," say ole King David.

"Aw, hysh up, Yo' Majesty," says Miz Uriah. "You know I ain't no good-lookin' gal. Jest look at 'at ole ugly laig. Look at 'at flat chest—" and she started twistin' herse'f round, showin' off.

But David is a good man and he know what she's up to, so he say: "Git on back home, gal, befo' I puts you in jail for tryin' to adulterate My Majesty. Git home! You yar me?"

Well, Miz Uriah got on back 'cross de road and ole King David sets down and writes a psa'm 'bout how he resisted temptation. But dat woman ain't started on him yit. She goes on 'cross de road and back in de house, and den de fust thing ole King David know, he sees her draggin' a big washtub out on de front po'ch and start pourin' water in hit.

"Gonter do some washin' today, Sister Uriah?" say ole King David.

"Some, Yo' Majesty," she say.

"I thought you washed yo' clothes on Monday," say de king.

"I does, Yo' Majesty," say Miz Uriah.

"Today's Sadday," say ole King David.

"I ain't said I was gonter wash no clothes today, Yo' Majesty," say Miz Uriah. "Dis is my bath day." And dat gal starts undressin' right out on de front po'ch, right in front er ole King David.

"Whyn't you git back in dat house to git naked, gal?" say ole King David. "You ain't got a lick er sense. S'pose somebody come down de road and sees you?"

"S'pose'n they does," says Miz Uriah. "They won't see nothin' but ole ugly me." And she went right on takin' off her clothes.

Ole King David set and watched her to de last stitch fell off and she stepped in de tub.

"Gal!" say ole King David, "ain't you got no shame? Whyn't you git back in dat house? Standin' out yar naked as a jay bird! Somebody comin' down dat road and see you, fust thing you know."

So Miz Uriah says, kinder baby-like: "Maybe you's right, Yo' Majesty, and I'm is mighty ashame'. But I can't tote dis tub back in de house all by myse'f. Efn Yo' Majesty'll he'p me tote hit in, I'll git back in de house."

Well, yar was ole King David tryin' to keep de kingdom f'm gittin' scandalized by dis fool gal takin' a bath on de front po'ch, and so hit wa'n't nothin' for him to do but go on and he'p her tote de tub back in de house. So he gits up and goes over to he'p her tote de tub back in de house, and dat's de last anybody seed of ole King David to Monday mawnin', when de Lawd come wawkin' up and seed him settin' out on his own front po'ch ag'in, lookin' mighty sad and sinful.

"Heyho, King David!" say de Lawd. "Been writin' any mo' psa'ms since I been round yar?"

"I writ one," say ole King David, "all 'bout how I was resistin' temptation f'm a fool woman."

"Dat sounds good," say de Lawd. "Wait'll I git settled down in dis cheer, and I wants you to read it at me."

"Can't," say ole King David. "I done tored hit up."

So de Lawd and ole King David sot on de po'ch, jest leanin' back and sayin' nothin', to finally yar come Miz Uriah draggin' her washtub out on de front po'ch ag'in, and pourin' water in hit.

Ole King David spotted her and he tried to signal to her to git back in de house, 'cause de Lawd was dar, but she didn't pay him no mind. She jest kept right on pourin' water in de tub. Den when she got de water in de tub, she brought out a bundle er clothes and started washin' 'em.

"Gonter do some washin', sister?" say de Lawd.

"Yes, Lawd. Monday's my regular washday," she say.

Den de Lawd turn to ole King David and say, "Dat's a mighty fine-lookin' neighbor you got over yonder. What's her name?"

"Dat's Uriah's wife," say King David.

"You mean hit's Uriah's widder," say de Lawd.

"Uriah's which?" say de king.

"Widder," say de Lawd. "Ole Uriah got mixed up wid one er my enemies, and when they got done wid him they had to haul him off in a sack."

"Naw?" say ole King David. "So she's a widder woman! Well I be doggone!" So he got up and started back in de house.

"Whar you goin' now, King David?" say de Lawd.

"To git my pencil and paper," say ole King David. "I'm gonter write another psa'm."

NONSENSE

When nonsense is good, it is divine. When it is bad, it is awful. Nonsense that doesn't quite come off is the dreariest stuff in the world. Many writers think they can write nonsense by omitting sense. They are victims of a terrible delusion.

Don Marquis satirized human beings by writing poems about a bug and a cat. The archy and mehitabel pieces included here are perhaps nearer to satire than to pure nonsense; yet they are nonsensical, too, and have been brought into this section, where we found it convenient to stable most of our animals. Josh Billings' notes on the poodle and the mule are not precisely nonsense, either, but they seemed to belong alongside Oliver Herford's verses.

S. J. Perelman, current headman of the zanies, who produces a rich yearly crop of nonsense, is here represented by two of his earlier and (we presume) less well-known pieces.

S. J. Perelman

IN OLD CHINATOWN

The dinner dishes had been cleared away, and Benson and I were comfortably ensconced before a glowing can of Sterno. Jitters, Benson's man, was preparing our whiskies and soda, the kettle was steaming on the hob, and hobstairs and houtside the wind was whistling.

"Benson," I said, lazily puffing on my Trichinopoly cheroot, "they call you the most eminent surgeon in the world. Tell me about your most unusual case."

"That is a poser," laughed Benson. Benson is somewhat of a joker, although he looks more like the nine of clubs or one of the low face-cards. "Well, I should say that the Philip Forceps affair was the most peculiar." And closing his eyes and going to sleep, he told me the following story:

Philip Forceps was a young pair of pliers in the employ of John Greenblatt Whittier, author of "Snowbloom." He was an honest and upright pair of pincers whose duties were few; he would extract tacks and glass which had become imbedded in his master's legs and every fortnight he would trim Whittier's luxurious orange beard. But time passed and John Greenblatt Whittier fell on evil days. He was forced to trade Philip to one Leon Error for a handful of glass beads and Manhattan Island.

Error was at that time a dancer and Forceps used to stand in the wings and enviously watch Error's twinkling legs collapse to the applause of the multitude. One night he returned to his modest hall bedroom on Evans Street. He was about to leap into bed when he happened to spy himself in the full-length mirror. He was astounded. His legs, which had always been straight as an arrow, were now curved like a bow. He rushed to the theater to confront Error with

469

the facts and found him out in the barn milking his cow, a Holbein.

Error offered to take Forceps into his act. "If I can't do it any other way, I'll have to use that brute Forceps," he admitted. The distraught young pair of pliers accepted and LEON ERROR & FORCEPS PHILIP opened, spotted next to the trained leopards. From the first they were a wow. When they played the Palace the waiting line stretched to Bedloe's Island and the Garden held the overflow. Flowers, jewels, beautiful women and rain rained in on the young pincers.

How Philip Forceps' legs were straightened

And then, at a musicale at Libby's baths, Forceps met Anne Margoulies. She was a young dental pincers in the first flush of radiant womanhood, alive, impressionable, dainty. Philip showered her with Lancias, orchids, and telephone calls. He took her to Chinatown, through the Holland Tunnel, through the great red network of sewers. He wined her, dined her, and shined her with steel wool. But she would have none of him, for his legs, curved, like parentheses they were curved, annoyed her. Frantic, Forceps took his problem to Error.

"Why don't you give her a booking?" suggested Error.

"She already has a booking," groaned Forceps with a groan.

His unrequited love was maddening him when, on the verge of insanity, a friend advised that he see Benson, the renowned physician. Benson, or Bensdorp, as he was then called, for he was in the cocoa racket, as we have already shown, was sympathetic, but held out little hope. He consented to do what he could, however, and prescribed a diet for Philip. He must eat no more horseshoes in between meals and he was forbidden to look at croquet wickets. He must not ride horseback and he must eschew arch glances. For this he was given a small pocket eschewer and ordered to eschew each arch glance thirty-two times.

Slowly, painfully, under Benson's tender care, he was won back. It was a hard and desperate fight, for his legs curled outward like hoops on the slightest provocation. But by degrees his ankles became less bowed and one sunny May morning Benson pronounced him normal again. Philip and Anne were married next day in the Little Church Around the Corner. The blushing bride carried a bouquet of magnets and the happy couple left for the Horseshoe Falls.

The Sterno embers were dying out with an eerie glow as the story ended. I awoke Benson.

"Yes," he murmured as we drank each other's health from a slipper. "It was another scalpel to hang at my beltel." And from the next room we heard the quaint cracked notes of Benson's well-tempered clavicle tinkling out the theme song from Olive Hasholem's opera:

> "Marriage by contract, I love you,
> Marriage by contract, you thrill me thro' and thro',
> Dreaming in the gloaming, bringing in the loam,
> Mammy and her gigolos, my old Kaintucky home."

THE IDOL'S EYE

I had been week-ending with Gabriel Snubbers at his villa in Cheyne-Stokes, on the edge of the Downs. Gabriel isn't seen about as much as he used to be; one hears that an eccentric aunt left him a tidy little sum and the lazy beggar refuses to leave his native haunts. Four of us had cycled down from London together: Gossip Gabril-owitsch, the Polish pianist; Downey Couch, the Irish tenor; Frank

Falcovsky, the Jewish prowler; and myself, Clay Modelling. Snubbers, his face beaming, met us at the keeper's lodge. His eyes were set in deep rolls of fat for our arrival, and I couldn't help thinking how well they looked. I wondered whether it was because his daring farce, "Mrs. Stebbins' Step-Ins," had been doing so well at the Haymarket.

"Deuced decent of you chaps to make this filthy trip," he told us, leading us up the great avenue of two stately alms toward the house. "Rum place, this." A surprise awaited us when we reached the house, for the entire left wing had just burned down. Snubbers, poor fellow, stared at it a bit ruefully, I thought.

"Just as well, it was only a plague-spot," sympathized Falcovsky. Snubbers was thoughtful.

"D'ye know, you chaps," he said suddenly, "I could swear an aunt of mine was staying in that wing." Falcovsky stirred the ashes with his stick and uncovered a pair of knitting needles and a half-charred corset.

"No, it must have been the other wing," dismissed Snubbers. "How about a spot of whisky and soda?" We entered and Littlejohn, Snubbers' man, brought in a spot of whisky on a piece of paper which we all examined with interest. A splendid fire was already roaring in the middle of the floor to drive out the warmth.

"Soda?" offered Snubbers. I took it to please him, for Gabriel's cellar was reputedly excellent. A second later I wished that I had drunk the cellar instead. Baking soda is hardly the thing after a three-hour bicycle trip.

"You drank that like a little soldier," he complimented, his little button eyes fastened on me. I was about to remark that I had never drunk a little soldier, when I noticed Littlejohn hovering in the doorway.

"Yes, that will be all," Snubbers waved, "and, oh, by the way, send up to London tomorrow for a new wing, will you?" Littlejohn bowed and left, silently, sleekly Oriental.

"Queer cove, Littlejohn," commented Snubbers. "Shall I tell you a story?" He did, and it was one of the dullest I have ever heard. At the end of it Falcovsky grunted. Snubbers surveyed him suspiciously.

"Why, what's up, old man?" he queried.

"What's up? Nothing's up," snarled Falcovsky. "Can't a man grunt in front of an open fire if he wants to?"

"But ..." began Snubbers.

"But nothing," Falcovsky ground. "You haven't lived till you've grunted in front of an open fire. Just for that—grunt, grunt, grunt," and he grunted several times out of sheer spite. None of us dared remonstrate, for Falcovsky was reputedly the owner of great natural beds of Eskimo pies and would pay through the nose to keep his name free from scandal. The last was no idle boast—Falcovsky's was the only nose in England I have ever seen large enough to pay through, and had the Bank of England ever needed him, he could have made his fortune as a cashier's wicket.

"It's a funny thing," brooded Snubbers.

"Oh, it is, is it?" flared Falcovsky, throwing himself on Snubbers. We tore them apart and only ended the dispute by measuring the former's nose against Snubbers'. Of course Falcovsky won hands down—that is, hands down on his nose—and we resumed our drinking. The baking soda was beginning to tell on Snubbers.

"Remarkable thing happened the other day," he began. "I was pottering about in the garden ..."

"Why must one always potter around in a garden?" demanded Couch. "Can't you potter around in an armchair just as well?"

"I did once," confessed Snubbers moodily, revealing a whitish scar on his chin. "Gad, sir, what a tigress she was!" He chewed his wad of carbon paper reminiscently. "Oh, well, never mind. But as I was saying—I was going through some of my great-grandfather's things the other day ..."

"What things?" demanded Falcovsky, whose nose was beginning to heal.

"His bones, if you must know," Snubbers said coldly. "You know, Great-grandfather died under strange circumstances. He opened a vein in his bath."

"I never knew baths had veins," protested Gabrilowitsch.

"I never knew his great-grandfather had a ba—" began Falcovsky derisively. With a shout Snubbers threw himself on Falcovsky. It was the signal for Pandemonium, the upstairs girl, to enter and throw herself with a shout on Couch. The outcome of the necking bee was as follows: Canadians 12, Visitors 9. Krebs and Vronsky played footie, subbing for Gerber and Weinwald, who were disabled by flying antipasto.

We were silent after Snubbers had spoken; men who have wandered in far places have an innate delicacy about their great-grand-fathers' bones. Snubbers' face was a mask, his voice a harsh whip of pain in the stillness when he spoke again.

"I fancy none of you knew my great-grandfather," he said slowly. "Before your time, I daresay. A rare giant of a man with quizzical eyes and a great shock of wiry red hair, he had come through the Peninsular Wars without a scratch. Women loved this impetual Irish adventurer who would rather fight than eat and vice versa. The wars over, he turned toward cookery, planning to devote his failing years to the perfection of the welsh rarebit, a dish he loved. One night he was chaffing at The Bit, a tavern in Portsmouth, when he overheard a chance remark from a brawny gunner's mate in his cups. In Calcutta the man had heard native tales of a mysterious idol, whose single eye was a flawless ruby.

" 'Topscuttle my bamberger, it's the size of a bloomin' pigeon's egg!' spat the salt, shifting his quid to his other cheek. 'A bloomin' rajah's ransom and ye may lay to that, mateys!'

"The following morning the *Maid of Hull*, a frigate of the line mounting thirty-six guns, out of Bath and into bed in a twinkling, dropped downstream on the tide, bound out for Bombay, object matrimony. On her as passenger went my great-grandfather, an extra pair of nankeen pants his only baggage and a dirk in his throat ready for use. Fifty-three days later in Poona, he was heading for the interior of one of the Northern states. Living almost entirely on cameo brooches and the few ptarmigan which fell to the ptrigger of his pfowlingpiece, he at last sighted the towers of Ishpeming, the Holy City of the Surds and Cosines, fanatic Mohammedan warrior sects. He disguised himself as a beggar and entered the gates.

"For weeks my great-grandfather awaited his chance to enter the temple of the idol. They were changing the guard one evening when he saw it. One of the native janissaries dropped his knife. My great-grandfather leaped forward with cringing servility and returned it to him, in the small of his back. Donning the soldier's turban, he quickly slipped into his place. Midnight found him within ten feet of his prize. Now came the final test. He furtively drew from the folds of his robes a plate of curry, a dish much prized by Indians, and set it in a far corner. The guards rushed upon it with bulging squeals of delight. A twist of his wrist and the gem was his. With an elaborately stifled yawn, my great-grandfather left under pretense of going out for a glass of water. The soldiers winked slyly but when he did not return after two hours, their suspicions were aroused. They hastily made a canvass of the places where water was served and their worst fears were realized. The ruby in his burnoose, Great-grandfather was escaping by fast elephant over the Khyber Pass. Dockside loungers in Yarmouth forty days later stared curiously at a mammoth of a man with flaming red hair striding abstractedly toward the Bull and Bloater Tavern. Under his belt lay the Ruby Eye.

"Ten years to that night had passed, and my great-grandfather, in seclusion under this very roof, had almost forgotten his daring escapade. Smoking by the fireplace, he listened to the roar of the wind and reviewed his campaigns. Suddenly he leaped to his feet—a dark face had vanished from the window. Too late my great-grandfather snatched up powder and ball and sent a charge of grape from his dueling-pistol hurtling into the night. The note pinned to the window drained the blood from his face.

"It was the first of a series. Overnight his hair turned from rose-red to snow-white. And finally, when it seemed as though madness were to rob them of their revenge, *they came*."

Snubbers stopped, his eyes those of a man who had looked beyond life and had seen things best left hidden from mortal orbs. Falcovsky's hand was trembling as he pressed a pinch of snuff against his gums.

"You—you mean?" he quavelled.

"Yes." Snubbers' voice had sunk to a whisper. "He fought with the strength of nine devils, but the movers took away his piano. You see," he added very gently, "Great-grandfather had missed the last four instalments." Gabrilowitsch sighed deeply and arose, his eyes fixed intently on Snubbers.

"And—and the ruby?" he asked softly, his delicate fingers closing around the fire-tongs.

"Oh, *that*," shrugged Snubbers, "I just threw that in to make it interesting."

We bashed in the top of his conk and left him to the vultures.

Frances Warfield

FPAFM

I ordered ham and eggs, as I always do on the diner, and then, as I always do, looked around for pamphlets. There was one handy. "Echoes from Colonial Days," it was called, "being a little fouvenir iffued from time to time for the benefit of the guefts of The Baltimore & Ohio Railroad Company as a reminder of pleafant moments fpent ...." Involuntarily, my lips began to move. I reached for a pencil. But the man across from me already had his pencil out. He had written:

"Oh, fay can you fee?"

I said: "Fing Fomething Fimple."

"Filly, ifn't it?" he said, and kept on writing.

I wrote: "Fing a Fong of Fixpence."

"Oh, ftop the fongs," he said. "Too eafy." He wrote: "The Court-fhip of Miles Ftandifh," "I fee a fquirrel," "I undereftimate ftatefman-fhip," "My fifter feems fuperfenfitive," and seeing that I did not appreciate the last one, which he evidently thought very fine, he wrote: "Forry to fee you fo ftupid."

I ate my lunch grouchily. How could I help it if he was in practice and I was not? He had probably taken this train before.

"Pafs the falt," I said.

"Pleafe pafs the falt," he triumphed.

I paid no attention. "Waiter!" I said. The waiter did not budge.

"You muft fpeak the language," said the man opposite me. He called out: "Fay! Fteward!"

The waiter jumped to attention. "Fir?" he said.

"Pleafe fill the faltcellar."

"The falt-fhaker fhall be replenifhed inftantly," replied the waiter, with a superior gleam in his eyes.

I smiled and my companion unbent a little.

"Let's try for hard ones," he invited.

"Fure," I said.

476

"Farcafm," he said.

"Fubftance."

"Fubfiftence," he scored.

"Fcythe."

"S's inside now," he ruled.

"Perfuafive," I said instantly.

"Languifh."

"Bafilifk."

"Quiefcent."

"Nonfenfe," I finished. "Fon of a fpeckled fea monfter."

"Ftep-fon of a poifonous fnake!" he cried.

"You don't fay fo!" I retored.

"I do fo fay fo!" he replied, getting up and leaving the diner.

"Fool!" I called after him, fniffling.

Morris Bishop

LIMERICKS LONG AFTER LEAR

[PICTURES BY RICHARD TAYLOR]

Said a fervent young lady of Hammels,
"I object to humanity's trammels!
　　I want to be free!
　　Like a bird! Like a bee!
Oh, why am I classed with the mammals?"

A youth who afflicts Essex Fells
Can yell university yells,
  From Abilene's hail
  To the frog call of Yale;
He also puts poison in wells.

A man who smokes hams in Shrub Oak
Hangs his wife in the smokehouse to smoke;
  "It's only to render
    Her tempting and tender,"
He says to censorious folk.

A joker who haunts Monticello
Is really a terrible fellow;
  In the midst of caresses
  He fills ladies' dresses
With garter snakes, ice cubes, and Jell-O.

When a lady returned from Big Moose,
Her husband exclaimed, "What the deuce!
    I am quite reconciled
    To the call of the wild,
But where did you get the papoose?"

A ghoulish old fellow in Kent
Encrusted his wife in cement;
    He said, with a sneer,
    "I was careful, my dear,
To follow your natural bent."

There's a girl out in Center Moriches
Who keeps all the neighbors in stitches;
  She swims down to Islip
  And borrows a dry slip,
And bicycles home without breeches.

A lady who rules Fort Montgomery
Says the wearing of clothes is mere mummery;
   She has frequently tea'd in
   The costume of Eden,
Appearing delightfully summery.

Ring Lardner

SIT STILL

One morning I was walking down Fifth Avenue alongside of the Park and I stopped with the rest of the southbound traffic at Seventy-second Street to allow the crosstown traffic to move, though God knows what good it did them because it is a two-way street and there were just as many going one way as the other, but during the wait I happened to glance at the curb and saw a taxicab that I had never seen before so I got in and the first thing I noticed was an autographed picture of a man named Nathan Schwartz. The driver must have heard me slam the door, for pretty soon he turned around and opened the sliding window that separated his compartment from mine and said where to.

"Where were you headed for?" I retorted.

"Nowhere a special," he said.

"Well," I said, "I figured we might as well ride together as long as we were headed in the same direction. How did Mr. Schwartz come to send you one of his pictures? Do you know him?"

"I'm one of his fans," said the driver. "What I'd appreciate now, though, is where you want me to take you."

"You'll be one of the first people I'll tell as soon as I find out. Just drive along a ways and if I hear anything I'll get in touch with you."

"All right," said the driver, "and maybe you'd better rap twice on the window so I'll know it's you. That will be the signal. Have you got it?"

"Two raps," I said.

"You pick things up quickly, but whether you remember them is the question. Perhaps it will help you if you connect it in your mind with some common fact, like how many legs on a man, or how many rear wheels on a car."

"Or how many times I've been abroad," I chuckled.

"You've got it," said the driver.

486

The policeman jingled his bell and we were on our way. I was about to doze off when I observed a newspaper that had been left on the back seat by the people who had moved out. I picked it up and read an item about Jackie Coogan. He was in New York and staying at the Ritz (Forty-sixth and Madison). I rapped three times on the window, but the driver paid no attention. Then I remembered—"How many legs on a man?"—and rapped twice. The driver opened the window.

"Well?" he said.

"Take me to the Hotel Astor," I ordered, wondering why I had not thought of it before because I had wanted to see the Astor ever since moving to New York.

"That's on the Lincoln Highway, isn't it?" said the driver. "It's either on it or just off it. I'll find it anyhow; there must be plenty of signs."

We continued down the Avenue until we came to Forty-fifth Street.

"We could lose a little distance, by going to Forty-third Street," said the driver, "but Forty-fifth's worse at this time of the day, so I imagine it evens up in the end."

I was pretty hungry when we got to the Astor as I had gone without my lunch.

"Goodbye," I said to the driver.

"Goodbye," he said. "And don't forget—two legs to a man."

The car door was opened by a tall fellow who spoke to me, but I could not place him. I walked up the steps and into the hotel's front lobby, which seemed to be quite crowded, so crowded that I might never have been able to reach the desk without my training as a coxcomb at Yale.

"Have you got a room?" I said to a clerk, thinking of course they were filled up or why would there be such a crush in the lobby?

"Yes, sir. Kindly register and I'll fix you up," he replied.

There was nothing for me to do but write down my name and address. I was afraid to use the only other name I could think of, Nathan Schwartz; the clerk might be one of his fans, too, and know me for an impostor.

The clerk called a bellboy and gave him a key and the bellboy asked where I had left my baggage. I feigned temporary deafness and asked him in turn why, if the hotel had vacant rooms, there was such a crush in the lobby.

"Oh," he said, "that's just our waiting list."

"But why do they have to wait if I didn't?"

"They're not waiting for rooms. They're waiting to sit down," he said.

This statement interested me to such an extent that I spent the next few hours investigating, and I learned the following facts, which may or may not lessen the difficulty:

The lobby has four pillars or columns, which were originally placed there to keep the ceiling from bouncing up and down on the floor. ("Four men to a male quartette.") There are three chairs to each pillar, or twelve chairs in all. ("Twelve horsemen in the Notre Dame backfield.") The occupants of these chairs have been in them continuously for periods ranging from eight to sixty-six years. The man who has been sitting in his chair the shortest while (eight years) is a Mr. J. N. Purdy, but the others refer to him as "The Junior Partner" or "The Kid." He paid one hundred and twenty-five thousand dollars for his seat, a record price at the time, buying it from a Mr. Louis Bolton, who, after an occupancy of only four years and two months, yielded to a life-long ambition to take up window-shopping.

The oldest settler is the man who sits on the desk side of the pillar nearest the entrance to the florist's. No one knows his real name, but they call him "General Grant" because he sat down in 1864 and announced that he would sit it out in that chair if it took all century.

At the same pillar is Mr. Lyman Bates, who used to be an inveterate smoker. He had to give it up fourteen years ago when he ran out of cigars and money, and the bellboys refused to extend him credit. The other tenant of this pillar is a woman, Lucy Pond, who came into the hotel in 1887, expecting to meet a Harvard man and take lunch with him. She got tired standing after three months and, as there were no vacancies at the time, sat down in Mr. Bates' lap. In 1893, it was discovered that a Mr. Levings, who shared the pillar with Bates and "General Grant" at that time, had died quite a while previously. Bates made the discovery and managed to push Levings out of his chair. Miss Pond then moved into it, much to the relief of Bates, whose foot was asleep.

The only other woman squatter is Margaret Vesey. She has a chair at the pillar opposite the newsstand. They say she was quite an attractive girl when she sat down, in 1900, and that Barney Diehl, who had a seat at that column, showed an inclination to flirt with her. He was not rebuffed, but she insisted on his looking at her while he talked and he had to quit on account of stiff neck.

In the early days of Astor squatting it was necessary to put into effect a rule prohibiting standees from attempting to eject the settlers by physical means. The latter were in no condition to put up a battle and the thing was too unfair. But there was no law against the use of strategy and many tricks were employed successfully before it was overdone. For example, one of the standees would bribe a bellboy to shout, "Mr. Gordon is wanted on the telephone by Lily Langtry." Gordon, unable to resist the temptation, would jump out of his chair and the trickster would slip into it. Another effective ruse was starting a cry of "Fire!" The hotel people soon put a stop to that.

It is now understood that when a squatter has occupied one of the chairs for twenty-five years, it becomes his homestead and he is privileged to get up and move around without jeopardizing his rights. He is privileged to get up and move around, but he can't. Because he can't.

One of the bellboys told me of a remark recently made by Mr. Bates. He had overheard a standee speaking of Prof. Goozlequirt, a champion flagpole-sitter who had just come down off a flagpole in Madison Square Garden after sitting there for eighteen days and five hours.

"What makes those Danes so restless?" said Mr. Bates.

N. P. Willis

MISS ALBINA McLUSH

I have a passion for fat women. If there is anything I hate in life it is what dainty people call a *spirituelle*. Motion—rapid motion—a smart, quick, squirrel-like step, a pert, voluble tone—in short, a lively girl—is my exquisite horror! I would as lief have a *diable petit* dancing his infernal hornpipe on my cerebellum as to be in the room with one. I have tried before now to school myself into liking these parched peas of humanity. I have followed them with my eyes, and attended to their rattle till I was as crazy as a fly in a drum. I have danced with them, and romped with them in the country, and periled the salvation of my "white tights" by sitting near them at supper. I swear off from this moment. I do. I won't—no—hang me if ever I show another small, lively, *spry* woman a civility.

Albina McLush is divine. She is like the description of the Persian beauty by Hafiz: "Her heart is full of passion and her eyes are full of sleep." She is the sister of Lurly McLush, my old college chum, who, as early as his sophomore year, was chosen president of the *Dolce far niente* Society—no member of which was ever known to be surprised at anything (the college law of rising before breakfast excepted). Lurly introduced me to his sister one day, as he was lying upon a heap of turnips, leaning on his elbow with his head in his hand, in a green lane in the suburbs. He had driven over a stump, and been tossed out of his gig, and I came up just as he was wondering how in the d——l's name he got there! Albina sat quietly in the gig, and when I was presented, requested me, with a delicious drawl, to say nothing about the adventure—it would be so troublesome to relate it to everybody! I loved her from that moment. Miss McLush was tall, and her shape, of its kind, was perfect. It was not a *fleshy* one exactly, but she was large and full. Her skin was clear, fine-grained and transparent; her temples and forehead perfectly rounded and polished, and her lips and chin swelling into a ripe and tempting pout,

490

like the cleft of a bursted apricot. And then her eyes—large, liquid and sleepy—they languished beneath their long black fringes as if they had no business with daylight—like two magnificent dreams, surprised in their jet embryos by some bird-nesting cherub. Oh! it was lovely to look into them!

She sat, usually, upon a *fauteuil,* with her large, full arm embedded in the cushion, sometimes for hours without stirring. I have seen the wind lift the masses of dark hair from her shoulders when it seemed like the coming to life of a marble Hebe—she had been motionless so long. She was a model for a goddess of sleep as she sat with her eyes half-closed, lifting up their superb lids slowly as you spoke to her, and dropping them again with the deliberate motion of a cloud, when she had murmured out her syllable of assent. Her figure, in a sitting posture, presented a gentle declivity from the curve of her neck to the instep of the small round foot lying on its side upon the ottoman. I remember a fellow's bringing her a plate of fruit one evening. He was one of your lively men—a horrid monster, all right angles and activity. Having never been accustomed to hold her own plate, she had not well extricated her whole fingers from her handkerchief before he set it down in her lap. As it began to slide slowly toward her feet, her hand relapsed into the muslin folds, and she fixed her eye upon it with a kind of indolent surprise, drooping her lids gradually till, as the fruit scattered over the ottoman, they closed entirely, and a liquid jet line was alone visible through the heavy lashes. There was an imperial indifference in it worthy of Juno.

Miss McLush rarely walks. When she does, it is with the deliberate majesty of a Dido. Her small, plump feet melt to the ground like snowflakes; and her figure sways to the indolent motion of her limbs with a glorious grace and yieldingness quite indescribable. She was idling slowly up the Mall one evening just at twilight, with a servant at a short distance behind her, who, to while away the time between his steps, was employing himself in throwing stones at the cows feeding upon the Common. A gentleman, with a natural admiration for her splendid person, addressed her. He might have done a more eccentric thing. Without troubling herself to look at him, she turned to her servant and requested him, with a yawn of desperate ennui, to knock that fellow down! John obeyed his orders; and, as his mistress resumed her lounge, picked up a new handful of pebbles, and tossing one at the nearest cow, loitered lazily after.

Such supreme indolence was irresistible. I gave in—I—who never before could summon energy to sigh—I—to whom a declaration was but a synonym for perspiration—I—who had only thought of love as a nervous complaint, and of women but to pray for a good deliverance —I—yes—I—knocked under. Albina McLush! Thou were too exquisitely lazy. Human sensibilities cannot hold out forever.

I found her one morning sipping her coffee at twelve, with her eyes wide open. She was just from the bath, and her complexion had a soft, dewy transparency, like the cheek of Venus rising from the sea. It was the hour, Lurly had told me, when she would be at the trouble of thinking. She put away with her dimpled forefinger, as I entered, a cluster of rich curls that had fallen over her face, and nodded to me like a waterlily swaying to the wind when its cup is full of rain.

"Lady Albina," said I, in my softest tone, "how are you?"

"Bettina," said she, addressing her maid in a voice as clouded and rich as the south wind on an Aeolian, "how am I today?"

The conversation fell into short sentences. The dialogue became a monologue. I entered upon my declaration. With the assistance of Bettina, who supplied her mistress with cologne, I kept her attention alive through the incipient circumstances. Symptoms were soon told. I came to the avowal. Her hand lay reposing on the arm of the sofa, half-buried in a muslin *foulard*. I took it up and pressed the cool soft fingers to my lips—unforbidden. I rose and looked into her eyes for confirmation. Delicious creature—she was asleep!

I never have had courage to renew the subject. Miss McLush seems to have forgotten it altogether. Upon reflection, too, I'm convinced she would not survive the excitement of the ceremony—unless, indeed, she should sleep between the responses and the prayer. I am still devoted, however, and if there should come a war or an earthquake, or if the millennium should commence, as is expected in 18—, or if anything happens that can keep her waking so long, I shall deliver a declaration, abbreviated for me by a scholar-friend of mine, which, he warrants, may be articulated in fifteen minutes—without fatigue.

Josh Billings

ANIMATED NATUR

THE POODLE

The poodle iz a small dog, with sore eyes, and hid amungst a good deal ov promiskuss hair.

They are sumtimes white for color, and their hair iz tangled all over them, like the hed ov a yung darkey.

They are kept az pets, and, like all other pets, are az stubborn az a setting hen.

A poodle iz a woman's pet, and that makes them kind ov sakred, for whatever a woman luvs she worships.

I hav seen poodles that i almost wanted tew swop places with, but the owners ov them didn't akt to me az tho they wanted tew trade for enny thing.

Thare iz but phew things on the face ov this earth more utterly worthless than a poodle, and yet i am glad thare iz poodles, for if thare wasn't thare iz some people who wouldn't hav enny objekt in living, and hav nothing tew luv.

Thare iz nothing in this world made in vain, and poodles are good for fleas.

Fleas are also good for poodles, for they keep their minds employed scratching, and almost every boddy else's too about the house.

I never knew a man tew keep a poodle. Man's natur iz too koarse for poodles. A poodle would soon fade and die if a man waz tew nuss him.

I don't expekt enny poodle, but if enny boddy duz giv me one he must make up his mind tew be tied onto a long stick every Saturday, and be used for washing the windows on the outside.

This kind of nussing would probably make the poodle mad, and probably he would quit, but i kant help it.

If i hav got to keep a poodle, he haz got tew help wash the windows every Saturday. I am solid on this pint.

Bully for me.

THE MULE

The mule is haf hoss and haf Jackass, and then kums tu a full stop, natur diskovering her mistake.

Tha weigh more, akordin tu their heft, than enny other kreetur, except a crow-bar.

Tha kant hear enny quicker, nor further than the hoss, yet their ears are big enuff for snow shoes.

You kan trust them with enny one whose life aint worth enny more than the mules. The only wa tu keep the mules into a paster, is tu turn them into a medder jineing, and let them jump out.

Tha are reddy for use, just as soon as they will du tu abuse.

Tha haint got enny friends, and will live on huckle berry brush, with an ockasional chanse at Kanada thistels.

Tha are a modern invenshun, i dont think the Bible deludes tu them at tall.

Tha sel for more money than enny other domestik animile. You kant tell their age by looking into their mouth, enny more than you could a Mexican cannons. Tha never have no dissease that a good club wont heal.

If tha ever die tha must kum rite tu life agin, for i never herd noboddy sa "ded mule."

Tha are like sum men, verry korrupt at harte; ive known them tu be good mules for 6 months, just tu git a good chanse to kick sumbody.

I never owned one, nor never mean to, unless thare is a United Staits law passed, requiring it.

The only reason why tha are pashunt, is bekause tha are ashamed ov themselfs.

I have seen eddikated mules in a sirkus.

Tha kould kick, and bite, tremenjis. I would not sa what I am forced tu sa again the mule, if his birth want an outrage, and man want tu blame for it.

Enny man who is willing tu drive a mule, ought to be exempt by law from running for the legislatur.

Tha are the strongest creeturs on earth, and heaviest ackording tu their sise; I herd tell ov one who fell oph from the tow path, on the Eri kanawl, and sunk as soon as he touched bottom, but he kept rite on towing the boat tu the nex stashun, breathing thru his ears, which stuck out ov the water about 2 feet 6 inches; i did'nt see this did, but an auctioneer told me ov it, and i never knew an auctioneer tu lie unless it was absolutely convenient.

Oliver Herford

MORE ANIMALS

THE COW

The Cow is too well known, I fear,
   To need an introduction here.
   If she should vanish from earth's face
It would be hard to fill her place;
For with the Cow would disappear
So much that every one holds Dear.
Oh, think of all the Boots and Shoes,
Milk Punches, Gladstone Bags and Stews,
And Things too numerous to count,
Of which, my child, she is the Fount.
Let's hope, at least, the Fount may last
Until *our* Generation's past.

A Cow

THE GNU

Beware, My Dear, if ever you
Should chance to come across a Gnu!
You may be Fair, and Tall, and Svelte,
But do not hope the Gnu to melt.
You may be Gentle, Kind, and True,
These things mean nothing to the Gnu.
You may love Beasts, both Great and Small,
That won't affect the Gnu at all.
You may be Generous, you may
Subscribe to the S.P.C.A.,
All this of no avail will be,
The Only Thing's to Climb a Tree.
And if there *is* no Tree to Climb,
Don't say you were not warned in Time!

A Gnu.

THE HEN

Alas! my Child, where is the Pen
   That can do Justice to the Hen?
   Like Royalty, She goes her way,
Laying foundations every day,
Though not for Public Buildings, yet
For Custard, Cake and Omelette.
Or if too Old for such a use
They have their Fling at some Abuse,
As when to Censure Plays Unfit
Upon the Stage they make a Hit,
Or at elections Seal the Fate
Of an Obnoxious Candidate
No wonder, Child, we prize the Hen,
Whose Egg is Mightier than the Pen.

THE HORSE

This noble Beast—
  But, why discourse
Upon the Virtues of the Horse?
They are too numerous to tell
Save when you have a Horse to Sell.
No Beast has done so much as He
To elevate Society.
How *could* Society Get On
(Or off), my Child, if He were gone?
We Owe him Much, yet who can say
He ever asked us to Repay?
Ah, Child! How Bright the World would be,
If Creditors were All as He.

A Horse.

Ogden Nash

THE STRANGE CASE OF MR. FORTAGUE'S DISAPPOINTMENT

Once upon a time there was a man name Mr. Lionel Fortague.

He didn't have very much to talk about.

In summer he used to ask people if it was hot enough for them.

It always was.

In winter he used to ask people if it was cold enough for them.

It always was.

Mr. Lionel Fortague got pretty sick of people it was hot enough for.

He got pretty sick of people it was cold enough for, too.

He decided he would arise and go now.

He decided he would go to Innisfree.

The people of Innisfree are different, thought Mr. Lionel Fortague.

As soon as he got to Innisfree he asked the people if it was cold enough for them.

They asked him What? Was what cold enough for who?

Mr. Lionel Fortague was delighted.

~~~

I knew Innisfree would be different, he said to himself.

~~~

He could hardly wait for summer to verify his conclusion.

~~~

As soon as summer came he asked everybody if it was hot enough
for them.

~~~

Everybody said the question was familiar but they couldn't remember
the answer.

~~~

Mr. Lionel Fortague said he would settle down on Innisfree, the home
of iridescent chitchat.

~~~

He said he would a small cabin build there, of clay and wattles made.

~~~

Everybody said did he mean he would build a small cabin there,
made of clay and wattles?

~~~

Mr. Lionel Fortague said yes, but his way of putting it was more
poetic.

~~~

Everybody said maybe, but they were all out of wattles.

~~~

Mr. Lionel Fortague grew very angry at the people of Innisfree.

~~~

He a small cabin built there, of clay and beaverboard made.

~~~

He a fierce-looking dog at an annual clearance sale bought, and it the
people of Innisfree one by one to bite he instructed.

~~~

My, he was disappointed.

~~~

He had forgotten that a bargain dog never bites.

~~~

REQUIEM

There was a young belle of old Natchez
Whose garments were always in patchez.
When comment arose
On the state of her clothes,
She drawled, When Ah itchez, Ah scratchez!

Will Cuppy

A SHORT HISTORY OF MAN

THE JAVA MAN

The Java Man lived in Java five hundred thousand or one million or two million years ago and was lower than we are. He was Lower Pleistocene and Lower Quaternary and knock-kneed. He was called *Pithecanthropus* ("Ape-Man") *erectus* because he walked with a slight stoop. He consisted of a calvarium, three teeth, and a femur. Professor Dubois made him a face which proves that he was dolichocephalic, or long-headed, instead of brachycephalic, or square-headed, and that he was 5 feet, 6½ inches high. The Java Man had immense supraorbital ridges of solid bone and was conscious in spots. Does that remind you of anyone? His Broca's area was low. He could say that the evenings were drawing in and times were hard and his feet hurt. The spiritual life of the Java Man was low because he was only a beginner. He was just a child at heart and was perfectly satisfied with his polygamy, polygyny, polyandry, endogamy, exogamy, and totemism. How he ever became extinct is beyond me. The Java Man has been called the Missing Link by those who should know.

THE PEKIN MAN

The Pekin Man shows that people were living in Asia long, long ago, as most of us knew already. He was discovered near Pekin, or Peiping, and was named *Sinanthropus pekinensis* to keep certain persons from calling him Peiping Tom. *Sin* means China, although the Chinese are no worse than other foreigners. The glabella was prominent, so he was probably a young male. The brain shows that the calvarium, or brain-case, was good. The skull was in perfect condition because the Pekin Man took better care of his skull than some of us. He had begun to think, or whatever the Chinese do. The prefrontal region resembles that found in some parts of the Middle West. The right horizontal ramus shows a tendency to do everything backward. The Pekin Man is lovable because he left no culture. He knew nothing about the Ming Dynasty and the Ch'ing Dynasty and the Sung Dynasty and he wrote no short poems stating that he got drunk and went out in a canoe and fell in. He had no imports and exports but he had fauna and flora. The Pekin Man was fond of overpopulation. We do not know whether he was religious or promiscuous or both.

The Piltdown Man

The Piltdown Man was called the Dawn Man, or Barmy Ned, because he was found in Great Britain. He was a great help because he left crude flint implements. These were used for making still cruder flint implements. The Piltdown Man had little to do. His skull is in small pieces which can be fitted together in various ways after choosing sides. This is called Badminton. The Piltdown Man had aspidistras, delphiniums, and sinus trouble. Already he was aiming at the stars and missing them. The manubrium indicates self-control but very little to control. The Piltdown Man had no chin and was rather toothy. It seems incredible that he had a private life, but those are just the ones who do. The young took after their parents. Anthropologists say that the Piltdown Man was stupider than any person of today. Anthropologists are people who are in museums. They lead sheltered lives. The Early Irish left few skulls. The Early Scotch left no skulls.

The Modern Man

The Modern Man, or Nervous Wreck, is the highest of all Mammals because anyone can see that he is. There are about two billion Modern Men, or too many. The Modern Man's highly developed brain has made him what he is and you know what he is. The development of his brain is caused by his upright or bipedal position, as in the Penguin, the Dinosaur, and other extinct Reptiles. Modern Man has been called the Talking Animal because he talks more than any other three animals chosen at random. He has also been called the Reasoning Animal, but there may be a catch in this. The fissure of Sylvius and the fissure of Rolando enable him to argue in circles. His main pursuits in the order named are murder, robbery, kidnapping, body-snatching, barratry, nepotism, arson, and mayhem. This is known as the Good, the True, and the Beautiful. They mature slowly but make up for it later, generally from July 1 to June 30, inclusive. The females carry nickels and pins in their mouths. They are fond of glittering objects, bits of ribbon, and olives. All Modern Men are descended from a Wormlike Creature, but it shows more on some people. Modern Man will never become extinct if the Democrats can help it.

Don Marquis

ARCHY AND MEHITABEL

i the coming of archy

Dobbs Ferry possesses a rat which slips out of his lair at night and runs a typewriting machine in a garage. Unfortunately, he has always been interrupted by the watchman before he could produce a complete story.

It was at first thought that the power which made the typewriter run was a ghost, instead of a rat. It seems likely to us that it was both a ghost and a rat. Mme. Blavatsky's ego went into a white horse after she passed over, and someone's personality has undoubtedly gone into this rat. It is an era of belief in communications from the spirit land.

And since this matter had been reported in the public prints and seriously received we are no longer afraid of being ridiculed, and we do not mind making a statement of something that happened to our own typewriter only a couple of weeks ago.

We came into our room earlier than usual in the morning, and discovered a gigantic cockroach jumping about upon the keys.

He did not see us, and we watched him. He would climb painfully upon the framework of the machine and cast himself with all his force upon a key, head downward, and his weight and the impact of the blow were just sufficient to operate the machine, one slow letter after another. He could not work the capital letters, and he had a great deal of difficulty operating the mechanism that shifts the paper so that a fresh line may be started. We never saw a cockroach work so hard or perspire so freely in all our lives before. After about an hour of this frightfully difficult literary labor he fell to the floor exhausted, and we saw him creep feebly into a nest of the poems which are always there in profusion.

Congratulating ourself that we had left a sheet of paper in the ma-

chine the night before so that all this work had not been in vain, we
made an examination, and this is what we found:

expression is the need of my soul
i was once a vers libre bard
but i died and my soul went into the body of a cockroach
it has given me a new outlook upon life
i see things from the under side now
thank you for the apple peelings in the wastepaper basket
but your paste is getting so stale i cant eat it
there is a cat here called mehitabel i wish you would have
removed she nearly ate me the other night why dont she
catch rats that is what she is supposed to be for
there is a rat here she should get without delay

most of these rats here are just rats
but this rat is like me he has a human soul in him
he used to be a poet himself
night after night i have written poetry for you
on your typewriter
and this big brute of a rat who used to be a poet
comes out of his hole when it is done
and reads it and sniffs at it
he is jealous of my poetry
he used to make fun of it when we were both human
he was a punk poet himself
and after he has read it he sneers
and then he eats it

i wish you would have mehitabel kill that rat
or get a cat that is onto her job
and i will write you a series of poems showing how things look
to a cockroach
that rats name is freddy
the next time freddy dies i hope he wont be a rat
but something smaller i hope i will be a rat
in the next transmigration and freddy a cockroach
i will teach him to sneer at my poetry then

dont you ever eat any sandwiches in your office
i havent had a crumb of bread for i dont know how long
or a piece of ham or anything but apple parings
and paste leave a piece of paper in your machine
every night you can call me archy

ii   mehitabel was once cleopatra

boss i am disappointed in
some of your readers they
are always asking how does
archy work the shift so as to get a
new line or how does archy do
this or do that they
are always interested in technical
details when the main question is
whether the stuff is
literature or not
i wish you would leave
that book of george moores on
the floor

mehitabel the cat and i want to
read it i have discovered that
mehitabel s soul formerly inhabited a
human also at least that
is what mehitabel is claiming these
days it may be she got jealous of
my prestige anyhow she and
i have been talking it over in a
friendly way who were you
mehitabel i asked her i was
cleopatra once she said well i said i
suppose you lived in a palace you bet
she said and what lovely fish dinners
we used to have and licked her chops

mehitabel would sell her soul for
a plate of fish any day i told her i thought
you were going to say you were

the favorite wife of the emperor
valerian he was some cat nip eh
mehitabel but she did not get me
                                        archy

  iii the song of mehitabel

this is the song of mehitabel
of mehitabel the alley cat
as i wrote you before boss
mehitabel is a believer
in the pythagorean
theory of the transmigration
of the soul and she claims
that formerly her spirit
was incarnated in the body
of cleopatra
that was a long time ago
and one must not be
surprised if mehitabel
has forgotten some of her
more regal manners

i have had my ups and downs
but wotthehell wotthehell
yesterday sceptres and crowns
fried oysters and velvet gowns
and today i herd with bums
but wotthehell wotthehell
i wake the world from sleep
as i caper and sing and leap
when i sing my wild free tune
wotthehell wotthehell
under the blear eyed moon
i am pelted with cast off shoon
but wotthehell wotthehell

do you think that i would change
my present freedom to range
for a castle or moated grange

wotthehell wotthehell
cage me and i d go frantic
my life is so romantic
capricious and corybantic
and i m toujours gai toujours gai

i know that i am bound
for a journey down the sound
in the midst of a refuse mound
but wotthehell wotthehell
oh i should worry and fret
death and i will coquette
there s a dance in the old dame yet
toujours gai toujours gai

i once was an innocent kit
wotthehell wotthehell
with a ribbon my neck to fit
and bells tied onto it
o wotthehell wotthehell
but a maltese cat came by
with a come hither look in his eye
and a song that soared to the sky
and wotthehell wotthehell
and i followed adown the street
the pad of his rhythmical feet
o permit me again to repeat
wotthehell wotthehell

my youth i shall never forget
but there s nothing i really regret
wotthehell wotthehell
there s a dance in the old dame yet
toujours gai toujours gai

the things that i had not ought to
i do because i ve gotto
wotthehell wotthehell
and i end with my favorite motto
toujours gai toujours gai

boss sometimes i think
that our friend mehitabel
is a trifle too gay

iv   the old trouper

i ran onto mehitabel again
last evening
she is inhabiting
a decayed trunk
which lies in an alley
in greenwich village
in company with the
most villainous tom cat
i have ever seen
but there is nothing
wrong about the association
archy she told me
it is merely a plutonic
attachment
and the thing can be
believed for the tom
looks like one of pluto s demons
it is a theatre trunk
archy mehitabel told me
and tom is an old theatre cat
he has given his life
to the theatre
he claims that richard
mansfield once
kicked him out of the way
and then cried because
he had done it and
petted him
and at another time
he says in a case
of emergency
he played a bloodhound
in a production of

uncle tom s cabin
the stage is not what it
used to be tom says
he puts his front paw
on his breast and says
they don t have it any more
they don t have it here
the old troupers are gone
there s nobody can troupe
any more
they are all amateurs nowadays
they haven t got it
here
there are only
five or six of us oldtime
troupers left
this generation does not know
what stage presence is
personality is what they lack
personality
where would they get
the training my old friends
got in the stock companies
i knew mr booth very well
says tom
and a law should be passed
preventing anybody else
from ever playing
in any play he ever
played in
there was a trouper for you
i used to sit on his knee
and purr when i was
a kitten he used to tell me
how much he valued my opinion
finish is what they lack
finish
and they haven t got it
here

and again he laid his paw
on his breast
i remember mr daly very
well too
i was with mr daly s company
for several years
there was art for you
there was team work
there was direction
they knew the theatre
and they all had it
here
for two years mr daly
would not ring up the curtain
unless i was in the
prompter s box
they are amateurs nowadays
rank amateurs all of them
for two seasons i played
the dog in joseph
jefferson s rip van winkle
it is true i never came
on the stage
but he knew i was just off
and it helped him
i would like to see
one of your modern
theatre cats
act a dog so well
that it would convince
a trouper like jo jefferson
but they haven t got it
nowadays
they haven t got it
here
jo jefferson had it he had it
here
i come of a long line
of theatre cats

my grandfather
was with forrest
he had it he was a real trouper
my grandfather said
he had a voice
that used to shake
the ferryboats
on the north river
once he lost his beard
and my grandfather
dropped from the
fly gallery and landed
under his chin
and played his beard
for the rest of the act
you don t see any theatre
cats that could do that
nowadays
they haven t got it they
haven t got it
here
once i played the owl
in modjeska s production
of macbeth
i sat above the castle gate
in the murder scene
and made my yellow
eyes shine through the dusk
like an owl s eyes
modjeska was a real
trouper she knew how to pick
her support i would like
to see any of these modern
theatre cats play the owl s eyes
to modjeska s lady macbeth
but they haven t got it nowadays
they haven t got it
here

mehitabel he says
both our professions
are being ruined
by amateurs
                              archy

THE CRITICS AT WORK

America today is a paradise for critics, there is so much work to be done. Everything which is created in this country immediately becomes the subject of a critical report. Music, books, plays, movies, art—these must all be analyzed, praised, and damned, in the press; also women's underclothes, wines, architecture, sports, wall papers, motor cars—dozens of things. The accepted American journalistic practice is to present a critical estimate of a work of art five or ten minutes after it has been completed, before the paint is dry on the canvas, before the last act curtain has descended. In the Nineteenth Century the critics believed that a work of art should age for a few days, or years, before being passed upon. For this section of our book we have hunted up reviews for which it seemed likely the critic had had at least twenty-four hours to prepare himself before pronouncing a verdict.

Humor is a handy tool on a critic's workbench. The truth is, almost every good humorist is a critic of sorts. A knave like Ogden Nash, who is classified as poet and wit, is certainly at heart a critic, who attends life's every opening night; and Mark Twain apparently never had more fun than when he was taking something or somebody apart.

As well as giving you reviews in this section we have

thrown in Alexander Woollcott's own subtreasury of criti-
cism—an essay in which he has collected some of his favorite
critical bon mots and left jabs to the heart. Benchley's critical
article on the French newspapers, "La Presse Perverse,"
tickled us when we read it over, even though to read it in
these times is a melancholy pleasure. We are putting it in
the book confident that the newspapers of France will some
day again be free and, to a visiting American, full of wonder.

Mark Twain

FENIMORE COOPER'S LITERARY OFFENSES

The Pathfinder and *The Deerslayer* stand at the head of Cooper's novels as artistic creations. There are others of his works which contain parts as perfect as are to be found in these, and scenes even more thrilling. Not one can be compared with either of them as a finished whole.

The defects in both of these tales are comparatively slight. They were pure works of art.—*Prof. Lounsbury.*

The five tales reveal an extraordinary fullness of invention.

... One of the very greatest characters in fiction, Natty Bumppo....

The craft of the woodsman, the tricks of the trapper, all the delicate art of the forest, were familiar to Cooper from his youth up.—*Prof. Brander Matthews.*

Cooper is the greatest artist in the domain of romantic fiction yet produced by America.—*Wilkie Collins.*

It seems to me that it was far from right for the Professor of English Literature in Yale, the Professor of English Literature in Columbia, and Wilkie Collins to deliver opinions on Cooper's literature without having read some of it. It would have been much more decorous to keep silent and let persons talk who have read Cooper.

Cooper's art has some defects. In one place in *Deerslayer,* and in the restricted space of two-thirds of a page, Cooper has scored 114 offenses against literary art out of a possible 115. It breaks the record.

There are nineteen rules governing literary art in the domain of romantic fiction—some say twenty-two. In *Deerslayer* Cooper violated eighteen of them. These eighteen require:

1. That a tale shall accomplish something and arrive somewhere. But the *Deerslayer* tale accomplishes nothing and arrives in the air.

2. They require that the episodes of a tale shall be necessary parts of the tale, and shall help to develop it. But as the *Deerslayer* tale is not a tale, and accomplishes nothing and arrives nowhere, the episodes have no rightful place in the work, since there was nothing for them to develop.

3. They require that the personages in a tale shall be alive, except in the case of corpses, and that always the reader shall be able to tell the corpses from the others. But this detail has often been overlooked in the *Deerslayer* tale.

4. They require that the personages in a tale, both dead and alive, shall exhibit a sufficient excuse for being there. But this detail also has been overlooked in the *Deerslayer* tale.

5. They require that when the personages of a tale deal in conversation, the talk shall sound like human talk, and be talk such as human beings would be likely to talk in the given circumstances, and have a discoverable meaning, also a discoverable purpose, and a show of relevancy, and remain in the neighborhood of the subject in hand, and be interesting to the reader, and help out the tale, and stop when the people cannot think of anything more to say. But this requirement has been ignored from the beginning of the *Deerslayer* tale to the end of it.

6. They require that when the author describes the character of a personage in his tale, the conduct and conversation of that personage shall justify said description. But this law gets little or no attention in the *Deerslayer* tale, as Natty Bumppo's case will amply prove.

7. They require that when a personage talks like an illustrated, gilt-edged, tree-calf, hand-tooled, seven-dollar Friendship's Offering in the beginning of a paragraph, he shall not talk like a negro minstrel in the end of it. But this rule is flung down and danced upon in the *Deerslayer* tale.

8. They require that crass stupidities shall not be played upon the reader as "the craft of the woodsman, the delicate art of the forest," by either the author or the people in the tale. But this rule is persistently violated in the *Deerslayer* tale.

9. They require that the personages of a tale shall confine themselves to possibilities and let miracles alone; or, if they venture a miracle, the author must so plausibly set it forth as to make it look possible and reasonable. But these rules are not respected in the *Deerslayer* tale.

10. They require that the author shall make the reader feel a deep interest in the personages of his tale and in their fate; and that he shall make the reader love the good people in the tale and hate the bad ones. But the reader of the *Deerslayer* tale dislikes the good people in it, is indifferent to the others, and wishes they would all get drowned together.

11. They require that the characters in a tale shall be so clearly de-

fined that the reader can tell beforehand what each will do in a given emergency. But in the *Deerslayer* tale this rule is vacated.

In addition to these large rules there are some little ones. These require that the author shall

12. *Say* what he is proposing to say, not merely come near it.

13. Use the right word, not its second cousin.

14. Eschew surplusage.

15. Not omit necessary details.

16. Avoid slovenliness of form.

17. Use good grammar.

18. Employ a simple and straightforward style.

Even these seven are coldly and persistently violated in the *Deerslayer* tale.

Cooper's gift in the way of invention was not a rich endowment; but such as it was he liked to work it, he was pleased with the effects, and indeed he did some quite sweet things with it. In his little box of stage-properties he kept six or eight cunning devices, tricks, artifices for his savages and woodsmen to deceive and circumvent each other with, and he was never so happy as when he was working these innocent things and seeing them go. A favorite one was to make a moccasined person tread in the tracks of the moccasined enemy, and thus hide his own trail. Cooper wore out barrels and barrels of moccasins in working that trick. Another stage-property that he pulled out of his box pretty frequently was his broken twig. He prized his broken twig above all the rest of his effects, and worked it the hardest. It is a restful chapter in any book of his when somebody doesn't step on a dry twig and alarm all the reds and whites for two hundred yards around. Every time a Cooper person is in peril, and absolute silence is worth four dollars a minute, he is sure to step on a dry twig. There may be a hundred handier things to step on, but that wouldn't satisfy Cooper. Cooper requires him to turn out and find a dry twig; and if he can't do it, go and borrow one. In fact, the Leatherstocking Series ought to have been called the Broken Twig Series.

I am sorry there is not room to put in a few dozen instances of the delicate art of the forest, as practised by Natty Bumppo and some of the other Cooperian experts. Perhaps we may venture two or three samples. Cooper was a sailor—a naval officer; yet he gravely tells us how a vessel, driving toward a lee shore in a gale, is steered for a particular spot by her skipper because he knows of an *undertow* there which will hold her back against the gale and save her. For just pure woodcraft, or sailorcraft, or whatever it is, isn't that neat? For several years Cooper was daily in the society of artillery, and he ought to have noticed that when a cannon-ball strikes the ground it either buries itself or skips a hundred feet or so; skips again a hundred feet or so—and so on, till finally it gets tired and rolls. Now in one place he loses some "females"—as he always calls women—in the edge of a wood near a plain at night in a fog, on purpose to give Bumppo a chance to show off the delicate art of the forest before the reader. These mislaid people are hunting for a fort. They hear a cannon-blast, and a cannon-ball presently comes rolling into the wood and stops at their feet. To the females this suggests nothing. The case is very different with the admirable Bumppo. I wish I may never know peace again if he doesn't strike out promptly and *follow the track* of that cannon-ball across the plain through the dense fog and find the fort. Isn't it a daisy? If Cooper had any real knowledge of Nature's way of doing things, he had a most delicate art in concealing the fact. For instance: one of his acute Indian experts, Chingachgook (pronounced Chicago, I think), has lost the trail of a person he is tracking through the forest. Apparently that trail is hopelessly lost. Neither you nor I could ever have guessed out the way to find it. It was very different with Chicago. Chicago was not stumped for long. He turned a running stream out of its course, and there, in the slush in its old bed, were that person's moccasin tracks. The current did not wash them away, as it would have done in all other like cases—no, even the eternal laws of Nature have to vacate when Cooper wants to put up a delicate job of woodcraft on the reader.

We must be a little wary when Brander Matthews tells us that Cooper's books "reveal an extraordinary fullness of invention." As a rule, I am quite willing to accept Brander Matthews's literary judgments and applaud his lucid and graceful phrasing of them; but that particular statement needs to be taken with a few tons of salt. Bless your heart, Cooper hadn't any more invention than a horse; and I don't mean a high-class horse, either; I mean a clothes-horse. It would be very difficult to find a really clever "situation" in Cooper's books, and still more difficult to find one of any kind which he has failed to render absurd by his handling of it. Look at the episodes of "the caves"; and at the celebrated scuffle between Maqua and those others on the table-land a few days later; and at Hurry Harry's queer water-transit from the castle to the ark; and at Deerslayer's half-hour with his first corpse; and at the quarrel between Hurry Harry and Deerslayer later; and at—but choose for yourself; you can't go amiss.

If Cooper had been an observer his inventive faculty would have worked better; not more interestingly, but more rationally, more plausibly. Cooper's proudest creations in the way of "situations" suffer noticeably from the absence of the observer's protecting gift. Cooper's eye was splendidly inaccurate. Cooper seldom saw anything correctly. He saw nearly all things as through a glass eye, darkly. Of course a man who cannot see the commonest little every-day matters accurately is working at a disadvantage when he is constructing a "situation." In the *Deerslayer* tale Cooper has a stream which is fifty feet wide where it flows out of a lake; it presently narrows to twenty as it meanders along for no given reason, and yet when a stream acts like that it ought to be required to explain itself. Fourteen pages later the width of the brook's outlet from the lake has suddenly shrunk thirty feet, and become "the narrowest part of the stream." This shrinkage is not accounted for. The stream has bends in it, a sure indication that it has alluvial banks and cuts them; yet these bends are only thirty and fifty feet long. If Cooper had been a nice and punctilious observer he would have noticed that the bends were oftener nine hundred feet long than short of it.

Cooper made the exit of that stream fifty feet wide, in the first place, for no particular reason; in the second place, he narrowed it to less than twenty to accommodate some Indians. He bends a "sapling" to the form of an arch over this narrow passage, and conceals six Indians in its foliage. They are "laying" for a settler's scow or ark which is coming up the stream on its way to the lake; it is being hauled against the stiff current by a rope whose stationary end is anchored in the lake; its rate of progress cannot be more than a mile an hour. Cooper describes the ark, but pretty obscurely. In the matter of dimensions "it was little more than a modern canal-boat." Let us guess, then, that it was about one hundred and forty feet long. It was of "greater breadth than common." Let us guess, then, that it was about sixteen feet wide. This leviathan had been prowling down bends which were but a third as long as itself, and scraping between banks where it had only two feet of space to spare on each side. We cannot too much admire this miracle. A low-roofed log dwelling occupies "two-thirds of the ark's length"—a dwelling ninety feet long and sixteen feet wide, let us say—a kind of vestibule train. The dwelling has two rooms—each forty-five feet long and sixteen feet wide, let us guess. One of them is the bedroom of the Hutter girls, Judith and Hetty; the other is the parlor in the daytime, at night it is papa's bedchamber. The ark is arriving at the stream's exit now, whose width has been reduced to less than twenty feet to accommodate the Indians—say to eighteen. There is a foot to spare on each side of the boat. Did the Indians notice that there was going to be a tight squeeze there? Did they notice that they could make money by climbing out of that arched sapling and just stepping aboard when the ark scraped by? No, other Indians would have noticed these things, but Cooper's Indians never notice anything. Cooper thinks they are marvelous creatures for noticing, but he was almost always in error about his Indians. There was seldom a sane one among them.

The ark is one hundred and forty-feet long; the dwelling is ninety feet long. The idea of the Indians is to drop softly and secretly from the arched sapling to the dwelling as the ark creeps along under it at the rate of a mile an hour, and butcher the family. It will take the ark a minute and a half to pass under. It will take the ninety-foot dwelling a minute to pass under. Now, then, what did the six Indians do? It would take you thirty years to guess, and even then you would have to give it up, I believe. Therefore, I will tell you what the Indians did. Their chief, a person of quite extraordinary intellect for a Cooper Indian, warily watched the canal-boat as it squeezed along under him, and when he had got his calculations fined down to exactly the right shade, as he judged, he let go and dropped. And *missed the house!* That is actually what he did. He missed the house, and landed in the stern of the scow. It was not much of a fall, yet it knocked him silly. He lay there unconscious. If the house had been ninety-seven feet long he would have made the trip. The fault was Cooper's, not his. The error lay in the construction of the house. Cooper was no architect.

There still remained in the roost five Indians. The boat has passed under and is now out of their reach. Let me explain what the five did —you would not be able to reason it out for yourself. No. 1 jumped for the boat, but fell in the water astern of it. Then No. 2 jumped for the boat, but fell in the water still farther astern of it. Then No. 3 jumped for the boat, and fell a good way astern of it. Then No. 4 jumped for the boat, and fell in the water *away* astern. Then even No. 5 made a jump for the boat—for he was a Cooper Indian. In the matter of intellect, the difference between a Cooper Indian and the Indian that stands in front of the cigar-shop is not spacious. The scow episode is really a sublime burst of invention; but it does not thrill, because the inaccuracy of the details throws a sort of air of fictitiousness and general improbability over it. This comes of Cooper's inadequacy as an observer.

The reader will find some examples of Cooper's high talent for inaccurate observation in the account of the shooting-match in *The Pathfinder*.

A common wrought nail was driven lightly into the target, its head having been first touched with paint.

The color of the paint is not stated—an important omission, but Cooper deals freely in important omissions. No, after all, it was not an important omission; for this nail-head is *a hundred yards from* the marksmen, and could not be seen by them at that distance, no matter what its color might be. How far can the best eyes see a common house-fly? A hundred yards? It is quite impossible. Very well; eyes that cannot see a house-fly that is a hundred yards away cannot see an ordinary nail-head at that distance, for the size of the two objects is the same. It takes a keen eye to see a fly or a nail-head at fifty yards—one hundred and fifty feet. Can the reader do it?

The nail was lightly driven, its head painted, and game called. Then the Cooper miracles began. The bullet of the first marksman chipped an edge of the nail-head; the next man's bullet drove the nail a little way into the target—and removed all the paint. Haven't the miracles gone far enough now? Not to suit Cooper; for the purpose of this whole scheme is to show off his prodigy, Deerslayer-Hawkeye-Long-Rifle-Leatherstocking-Pathfinder-Bumppo before the ladies.

"Be all ready to clench it, boys!" cried out Pathfinder, stepping into his friend's tracks the instant they were vacant. "Never mind a new nail; I can see that, though the paint is gone, and what I can see I can hit at a hundred yards, though it were only a mosquito's eye. Be ready to clench!"

The rifle cracked, the bullet sped its way, and the head of the nail was buried in the wood, covered by the piece of flattened lead.

There, you see, is a man who could hunt flies with a rifle, and command a ducal salary in a Wild West show to-day if we had him back with us.

The recorded feat is certainly surprising just as it stands; but it is not surprising enough for Cooper. Cooper adds a touch. He has made Pathfinder do this miracle with another man's rifle; and not only that, but Pathfinder did not have even the advantage of loading it himself. He had everything against him, and yet he made that impossible shot; and not only made it, but did it with absolute confidence, saying, "Be ready to clench." Now a person like that would have undertaken that same feat with a brickbat, and with Cooper to help he would have achieved it, too.

Pathfinder showed off handsomely that day before the ladies. His very first feat was a thing which no Wild West show can touch. He was standing with the group of marksmen, observing—a hundred yards from the target, mind; one Jasper raised his rifle and drove the center of the bull's-eye. Then the Quartermaster fired. The target exhibited no result this time. There was a laugh. "It's a dead miss," said Major Lundie. Pathfinder waited an impressive moment or two; then said, in that calm, indifferent, know-it-all way of his, "No, Major, he has covered Jasper's bullet, as will be seen if any one will take the trouble to examine the target."

Wasn't it remarkable! How *could* he see that little pellet fly through the air and enter that distant bullet-hole? Yet that is what he did; for nothing is impossible to a Cooper person. Did any of those people have any deep-seated doubts about this thing? No; for that would imply sanity, and these were all Cooper people.

The respect for Pathfinder's skill and for his *quickness and accuracy of sight* [the italics are mine] was so profound and general, that the instant he made this declaration the spectators began to distrust their own opinions, and a dozen rushed to the target in order to ascertain the fact. There, sure enough, it was found that the Quartermaster's bullet had gone through the hole made by Jasper's, and that, too, so accurately as to require a minute examination to be certain of the circumstance, which, however, was soon clearly established by discovering one bullet over the other in the stump against which the target was placed.

They made a "minute" examination; but never mind, how could they know that there were two bullets in that hole without digging the latest one out? for neither probe nor eyesight could prove the presence of any more than one bullet. Did they dig? No; as we shall see. It is the Pathfinder's turn now; he steps out before the ladies, takes aim, and fires.

But, alas! here is a disappointment; an incredible, an unimaginable disappointment—for the target's aspect is unchanged; there is nothing there but that same old bullet-hole!

"If one dared to hint at such a thing," cried Major Duncan, "I should say that the Pathfinder has also missed the target!"

As nobody had missed it yet, the "also" was not necessary; but never mind about that, for the Pathfinder is going to speak.

"No, no, Major," said he, confidently, "that *would* be a risky declaration. I didn't load the piece, and can't say what was in it; but if it was lead, you will find the bullet driving down those of the Quartermaster and Jasper, else is not my name Pathfinder."
A shout from the target announced the truth of this assertion.

Is the miracle sufficient as it stands? Not for Cooper. The Pathfinder speaks again, as he "now slowly advances toward the stage occupied by the females":

"That's not all, boys, that's not all; if you find the target touched at all, I'll own to a miss. The Quartermaster cut the wood, but you'll find no wood cut by that last messenger."

The miracle is at last complete. He knew—doubtless *saw*—at the distance of a hundred yards—that his bullet had passed into the hole *without fraying the edges*. There were now three bullets in that one hole—three bullets embedded processionally in the body of the stump back of the target. Everybody knew this—somehow or other—and yet nobody had dug any of them out to make sure. Cooper is not a close observer, but he is interesting. He is certainly always that, no matter what happens. And he is more interesting when he is not noticing what he is about than when he is. This is a considerable merit.

The conversations in the Cooper books have a curious sound in our modern ears. To believe that such talk really ever came out of people's mouths would be to believe that there was a time when time was of no value to a person who thought he had something to say; when it was the custom to spread a two-minute remark out to ten; when a man's mouth was a rolling-mill, and busied itself all day long in turning four-foot pigs of thought into thirty-foot bars of conversational railroad iron by attenuation; when subjects were seldom faithfully stuck to, but the talk wandered all around and arrived nowhere; when conversations consisted mainly of irrelevancies, with here and there a relevancy, a relevancy with an embarrassed look, as not being able to explain how it got there.

Cooper was certainly not a master in the construction of dialogue. Inaccurate observation defeated him here as it defeated him in so many other enterprises of his. He even failed to notice that the man who talks corrupt English six days in the week must and will talk it on the seventh, and can't help himself. In the *Deerslayer* story he lets Deerslayer talk the showiest kind of book-talk sometimes, and at other times the basest of base dialects. For instance, when some one asks him if he has a sweetheart, and if so, where she abides, this is his majestic answer:

"She's in the forest—hanging from the boughs of the trees, in a soft rain—in the dew on the open grass—the clouds that float about in the blue heavens—the birds that sing in the woods—the sweet springs where I slake my thirst—and in all the other glorious gifts that come from God's Providence!"

And he preceded that, a little before, with this:

"It consarns me as all things that touches a fri'nd consarns a fri'nd."

And this is another of his remarks:

"If I was Injin born, now, I might tell of this, or carry in the scalp and boast of the expl'ite afore the whole tribe; or if my inimy had only been a bear"—[and so on].

We cannot imagine such a thing as a veteran Scotch Commander-in-Chief comporting himself in the field like a windy melodramatic actor, but Cooper could. On one occasion Alice and Cora were being chased by the French through a fog in the neighborhood of their father's fort:

"*Point de quartier aux coquins!*" cried an eager pursuer, who seemed to direct the operations of the enemy.
"Stand firm and be ready, my gallant 60ths!" suddenly exclaimed a voice above them; "wait to see the enemy; fire low, and sweep the glacis."
"Father, father!" exclaimed a piercing cry from out the mist; "it is I! Alice! thy own Elsie! spare, O! save your daughters!"
"Hold!" shouted the former speaker, in the awful tones of parental agony, the sound reaching even to the woods, and rolling back in solemn echo. "'Tis she! God has restored me my children! Throw open the sally-port; to the field, 60ths, to the field! pull not a trigger, lest ye kill my lambs! Drive off these dogs of France with your steel!"

Cooper's word-sense was singularly dull. When a person has a poor ear for music he will flat and sharp right along without knowing it. He keeps near the tune, but it is *not* the tune. When a person has a poor ear for words, the result is a literary flatting and sharping; you perceive what he is intending to say, but you also perceive that he doesn't *say* it. This is Cooper. He was not a word-musician. His ear was satisfied with the *approximate* word. I will furnish some circumstantial evidence in support of this charge. My instances are gathered from half a dozen pages of the tale called *Deerslayer*. He uses "verbal" for "oral"; "precision" for "facility"; "phenomena" for "marvels"; "necessary" for "predetermined"; "unsophisticated" for "primitive"; "preparation" for "expectancy"; "rebuked" for "subdued"; "dependent on" for "resulting from"; "fact" for "condition"; "fact" for "conjecture"; "precaution" for "caution"; "explain" for "determine"; "mortified" for "disappointed"; "meretricious" for "factitious"; "materially" for "considerably"; "decreasing" for "deepening"; "increasing" for "disappearing"; "embedded" for "inclosed"; "treacherous" for "hostile"; "stood" for "stooped"; "softened" for "replaced"; "rejoined" for "remarked"; "situation" for "condition"; "different" for "differing"; "insensible" for "unsentient"; "brevity" for "celerity"; "distrusted" for "suspicious"; "mental imbecility" for "imbecility"; "eyes" for "sight"; "counteracting" for "opposing"; "funeral obsequies" for "obsequies."

There have been daring people in the world who claimed that Cooper could write English, but they are all dead now—all dead but Lounsbury. I don't remember that Lounsbury makes the claim in so many words, still he makes it, for he says that *Deerslayer* is a "pure work of art." Pure, in that connection, means faultless—faultless in all details—and language is a detail. If Mr. Lounsbury had only compared Cooper's English with the English which he writes himself—but it is plain that he didn't; and so it is likely that he imagines until this day that Cooper's is as clean and compact as his own. Now I feel sure, deep down in my heart, that Cooper wrote about the poorest English that exists in our language, and that the English of *Deerslayer* is the very worst that even Cooper ever wrote.

I may be mistaken, but it does seem to me that *Deerslayer* is not a work of art in any sense; it does seem to me that it is destitute of every detail that goes to the making of a work of art; in truth, it seems to me that *Deerslayer* is just simply a literary *delirium tremens*.

A work of art? It has no invention; it has no order, system, sequence, or result; it has no life-likeness, no thrill, no stir, no seeming of reality; its characters are confusedly drawn, and by their acts and words they prove that they are not the sort of people the author claims that they

are; its humor is pathetic; its pathos is funny; its conversations are—
oh! indescribable; its love-scenes odious; its English a crime against the
language.

Counting these out, what is left is Art. I think we must all admit
that.

Ogden Nash

LET'S STAY HOME AND MAKE FRIENDS

May I give you a one-word comment on the average revue?
Pew!
Goodness sakes, couldn't they be a little less anatomical
And a little more comical?
Couldn't they have a few more jests
And a few less breasts?
Must they consist of nothing but scenes such as may be observed at
the Zoo in the monkey- or yak-house,
And revelry suggestive less of Bacchus than the backhouse?
Must all their skits on l'amour
Be fished from the sour?
Can the producers think of no subtler way of easing themselves into
Isottas and their girl-friends into sables
Than by luring a lot of people to pay a lot of money to look at a lot
of other peoples' nabels?
The undersigned obviously stands in strong need of a physic
If he is expected to find the above mentioned an aphrodysic.
Not that he proposes that all of our spectacular extravaganzas
Should be of the type that could be legally presented in Wichita,
Kansas;
Not that he insists that the female form should be fenced off as some-
thing of unmentionable sacredness;
Only that he believes that a bare finger in private is fraught with more
significance than any amount of public nacredness.

Alexander Woollcott

"MANHATTAN"

From time to time it is acrimoniously argued that the reviewers ought not measure the passing plays by their own perverse and epicurean taste nor commit themselves by applying any adjectives whatever—such as hilarious, febrile, dainty, narcotic, repulsive or the like—to the new piece of the night before. As a matter of fact, while much would be lost, something might be gained by barring adjectival indulgence from journalistic criticism, like firmly telling the cook that there must be no more thickening in the soup. One of the scribes, for instance, rather induced the impression that every new play was worth seeing the first six months after his first encounter with the word "intriguing" and the remote Louis Sherwin (before he shut his eyes, held his nose and jumped into the movies) was so abjectly devoted to the word "jejune" that he would lick it and paste it on every new play whether it was in the least jejune or not.

However, as we understand the contention, the desideratum is a severe, impersonal description of the play. Now it is quite impossible to accomplish that in terms of the first-night reception. If a first-nighter is pleased and entertained, he beats his palms together and laughs till he almost falls into the aisle. But watch him when he is bored. Then he beats his palms together and laughs till he almost falls into the aisle. So one is driven relentlessly back to bare description of the play's contents, its fabric, its design—in short, its plot.

Let us then consider the plot of the piece called "Manhattan," which launched one season at the Playhouse. The curtain rises on the library of the Van Norman home in Park Avenue. (It has been several years now since any dramatist has sheltered his more elegant characters on Riverside Drive or on Fifth or Madison Avenue. Only Clare Kummer —ever a bit wild and puckish in her fancy—has had the pioneer spirit to break from this tradition. Once, only once—it was in "The Robbery"—she went so far as to set the scene *in a cross street.* However, in most plays all the best people live on Park Avenue.)

Well, the aforesaid rising curtain reveals *Duncan Van Norman* busy writing an essay for *The Atlantic Monthly.* He is doing this in a snuggery so conveniently close to the front door that the butler has scarce disappeared in response to the door-bell when the room is a-swarm with laughing society folk, all eager to drag him off to some gayety. The *Van Normans,* as far as the play reveals, are a family of three—widowed mother, son and daughter. They have two bookcases and a butler. When *Miss Van Norman* has a burst of confidence, she does not skip up the plebeian stairs to her mother's boudoir and begin: "Mom, *what* do you think has happened?" Not she. Instead she rings for the butler and says: *"Paget,* tell my mother I wish to see her in the library and talk to her about something I want the audience to overhear." No, come to think of it, the last part of that sentence isn't actually spoken.

Well, *Duncan* isn't in the best of health. This is evidenced by his announcing that he does not care for any dinner beyond a biscuit and a glass of port—a dietetic arrangement which the authors in some way subtly associate with his writings for *The Atlantic.* However, both manifestations worry his gaudy old mother, who tries to persuade him that it is high time for him to go forth and cut up a bit. The same advice is then echoed by the family lawyer, who sends him a pretty little typist with the suggestion that he might seduce her, and, presumably, thereby become a contributor to *The Saturday Evening Post.* The typist arrives. She proves to be young, personable, poor. She is *Peg-o-My-Heart* all over again and again and again. She lacks the brogue and the red hair and Michael, to be sure, but she says "Gee" quite often; she is fond of poetry and she is so hard up that she agrees to copy "The Fourth Dimension in Ethics" for *The Atlantic.*

She copies it in a wretched little garret room south of Greenwich Village, which she shares with an Irish miss. This colleen is the good-natured kind who gives all her dinner to the poor starving girl next door. One gathers from the chit-chat of these three that a poor working-girl in New York has only to say the word—the word is "Yes" —to have sables and limousines galore. Indeed, one of their little circle appears to have said "Yes" recently, and they are all speculating on her happiness and wondering whether it was worth the price. There is some differen⸺ of opinion. Enter *Duncan Van Norman.* His arrival at this lowly spot might take the unsophisticated unawares, but the canny first-nighter knows full well that no manager, who has worked himself up to the point of paying Norman Trevor's salary, would ever allow an act to slip by without using him. Metaphorically speaking, *Duncan* has come in with a sable coat in one hand and a limousine in the other. He also mentions art, music, travel. He is spurned by the typist, who, however, does get five hundred dollars out of him for the poor starving girl next door and does consent to become his secretary.

The next act sees her thus installed in Park Avenue, where she takes hints from *Paget* and reads assiduously in *The Book of Etiquette,* all in an effort to "become a lady." Indeed, how she ever escaped from a novel by Frances Hodgson Burnett is one of the mysteries of modern letters. Well, naturally, you can imagine the talk caused in what the *Van Normans* call either "our world" or "the circle in which we move," when it is bruited up and down Park Avenue that *Duncan Van Norman* has a female secretary who comes right to his library every day and does his typing. There is so much scandal that *Duncan* offers marriage on the spot, which, despite his mother's efforts to buy the girl off, might settle matters and obviate the necessity of a last act, when in rushes that old family lawyer again, this time not to suggest that *Duncan* seduce some one else, but with the news that the little typist has just that moment inherited $450,000 of South African real estate. Of course, *Duncan* is horribly embarrassed by that, but she lands him at last by the expedient of locking herself in a room with him and throwing the key out the window.

And there you are. Though why "Manhattan"? To be sure, the scenes are *not* in Tallahassee, but then on that principle "Hamlet" might as well be called "Denmark" and "The First Year" might as well have been renamed "Redding, Illinois, and Joplin, Missouri." Why "Manhattan," do you suppose? Let's see. It's the name of an island and of a borough and of a transfer and of a cocktail and—oh, yes— of a storehouse.

CAPSULE CRITICISM

There is a popular notion that a dramatic criticism, to be worthy of the name, must be an article of at least one thousand words, mostly polysyllables and all devoted—perfectly devoted—to the grave discussion of some play as written and performed. To this notion, it must be sadly admitted, each generation of writers on the theater has lent some color.

In such an article it is presumed that there will be one judicious use of the word "adequate" and one resort to the expression "treading the boards"; also at least one regretful shaking of the head over the hopeless inferiority of the performance in question to (a) the way it was done in some other country two years before or (b) the way it would have been done in the critic's own country thirty years ago. Such ingredients are expected with reasonable confidence. But one thing is certain. The piece, to be real dramatic criticism, can scarcely be briefer than a thousand words.

The tradition of prolixity and the dullness in all such writing is as old as Aristotle and as lasting as William Archer. A man who will talk gaily of a play will yet feel a certain solemnity wetting down his spirits the moment he finds himself called upon to discuss it in print. Even Mr. Dickens, who could take his beloved theater lightly enough when he was weaving it into a novel and who always packed his letters full of the most engaging accounts of the farces and melodramas he was seeing, became rigid with self-importance and chill with scrupulosity the moment he knew he was reviewing a piece for publication. If he had undertaken to supply such comment to *The Examiner* or to our own *Atlantic,* a voice within him seemed to whisper, "Remember, now, you're a dramatic critic." And, lo! he was no more Dickensy than the merest penny-a-liner. This was true to some extent of Walt Whitman and certainly was true of Edgar Allan Poe. (The strangest people, it will be observed, have put in some time as dramatic critics; such people, for instance, as Eugene Field and Richard Harding Davis and Edward Bok and Elihu Root). Probably they were all verbose.

Yet I suspect it could be demonstrated that the most telling of all dramatic criticisms have found expression in less than fifty words. Also that the best of all were never written at all. To substantiate this, I have been raking my memory for the ones that have lodged there while longer and more majestical utterances have faded out of mind as completely as though they had never been written.

What we are looking for, of course, is the happy sentence that speaks volumes. As an example, consider the familiar problem presented by the players who can do everything on the stage except act. I have in mind a still celebrated beauty to whom that beauty opened wide the stage-door full thirty years ago. Since then she has devoted herself most painstakingly to justifying her admission. She has keen intelligence and great industry. She has learned every trick of voice and gesture that can be taught. She has acquired everything except some substitute for the inborn gift. Something to that effect, expressed, of course, as considerately as possible, ought, it seems to me, to be a part of any report on her spasmodic reappearances.

It usually takes about five hundred words. Yet Mr. Cohan managed it pretty well in a single sentence when he was passing on a similar case in one of his own companies. An attempt was made to argue with him that the veteran actor under review was a good fellow and all that. "He's a fine fellow, all right," Cohan assented amiably enough, and then added, with murderous good humor, "There's really only one thing I've got against him. He's stage-struck."

You see, often the perfection of these capsule criticisms are achieved by mere bluntness—are arrived at by the no more ingenious process than that of speaking out in meeting. I was struck with that on the melancholy occasion when John and Ethel Barrymore lent a momentary and delusive glamour to a piece called "Clair de Lune" by Michael Strange, the exquisitely beautiful poetess whom Mr. Barrymore had just married. By the time its third act had unfolded before the pained eyes of its first audience, there was probably not a single person in that audience who was not thinking that, with all the good plays lying voiceless on the shelf, Michael Strange's shambling and laboriously *macabre* piece would scarcely have been produced had it not been for the somewhat irrelevant circumstance of her having married Mr. Barrymore, the surest means, apparently, of engaging his priceless services for one's drama. Now, some such opinion, I say, was buzzing in every first-night head. All the critics thought just that. Yet they all described nervous circles around this central idea, dancing skittishly about it as though it had been a May-pole. Full of what Gladys Unger was once inspired to call "a dirty delicacy," reluctant, perhaps, to acknowledge the personal equation in criticism, and weighed down, probably, by an ancient respect for the marriage tie, they avoided all audible speculation as to why Mr. Barrymore had put the piece on at all. All, that is, except one. Mr. Whittaker of *The Chicago Tribune* —the same Mr. Whittaker, by the way, who married the fair Ina

Claire—cheerfully put the prevailing thought into three devastating words. He entitled his review: "For the Love of Mike."

That is not the only time I have seen the very essence and spirit of a review distilled in a single head-line. It happened on the occasion when the late Sir Herbert Tree, ever and always recognizable behind the most ornate make-ups, ever and always himself through all faint-hearted efforts at disguise, appeared for the first time in London in "The Merchant of Venice." It was on that occasion that his more illus-trious brother, Max Beerbohm, then merely the dramatic critic of *The Saturday Review,* went back-stage to felicitate the star but was overlooked in the crush of notables who were crowding around. When Tree chided him afterwards for unfraternal neglect, Max murmured: "Ah, I was there but you did not know me in your beard." Of course Max could not write the review of his own brother's performance—a task delegated, therefore, to John Palmer, whose comment on the play was awaited, naturally enough, with considerable interest. Palmer wrote a polite, though mildly derisive, review of the production and entitled it: "Shylock as Mr. Tree."

I find that the crispest reviews which come back in this effort at memory have taken many forms. For instance, when it was quite the leading American sin to attend the agitating performances of "Sapho" by Olga Nethersole, Franklin P. Adams made his comment in one quatrain:

> I love little Olga,
>   Her plays are so warm.
> And if I don't see them
>   They'll do me no harm.

The late Charles Frohman, on the other hand, was likely to sum up plays most felicitously in telegrams. Once, when he was producing an English comedy at his cherished Empire Theater in New York, he received just after the première a cable of eager, though decently nervous, inquiry from the author in London, who could not bear to wait until the reviews and the box-office statements reached him. "How's it going?" was the inquiry. Frohman cabled back: "It's gone."

Of course, many of the best capsule criticisms are classics. There was Warren's tart comment on Joe Jefferson's performance as *Bob Acres* in "The Rivals," a brilliant feat of comedic genius made out of whole cloth, so little origin did it have in the rôle as originally written. "Ha!"

quoth Warren, "Sheridan twenty miles away." And there was the feline stroke usually ascribed to Wilde—the one which said that Tree's *Hamlet* was funny without being vulgar. And there was the much-quoted knifing of still another *Hamlet* by an unidentified bandit who said, after the performance, that it would have been a fine time to settle the great controversy as to who wrote the play: one need merely have watched beside the graves of Shakespere and Bacon to see which one turned over.

Fairly familiar, also, are two ascribed by tradition to Eugene Field, in the days when he was dramatic critic of "The Denver Post" and used to go to the once-famous Tabor Grand to see "Modjesky ez Cameel," the days when the peak of the season for him was marked by the engagement of a vagrant, red-headed soubrette named Minnie Maddern. Of one performance of "Hamlet" there, Field's entire review consisted of two short melancholy sentences. He wrote: "So-and-so played Hamlet last night at the Tabor Grand. He played it till one o'clock." And it was Field who haunted the declining years of Creston Clarke with his review of that actor's *Lear*. Clarke, a journeying nephew of Edwin Booth, passed through Denver and gave there a singularly unimpressive and unregal performance in that towering tragedy. Field couldn't bear it and finally vented his emotions in one sentence. Said he: "Mr. Clarke played the King all evening as though under constant fear that some one else was about to play the Ace."

Of course some beautiful capsule criticisms are doomed to a lesser fame because it is so difficult to detach them from their circumstances and their context. This is true, for instance, of several deft summaries by Heywood Broun. When some years ago one Butler Davenport put on a juvenilely obscene little play at his own little theater in New York, Broun scowled and wrote, "Some one should spank young Mr. Davenport and take away his piece of chalk." Then there was the hilarious episode which grew out of the production for one afternoon in the spring of 1917 of Wedekind's "Frühlingserwachen," which Broun translated as "The Spring Offensive." In his little piece on the subject, he mentioned casually that to his mind an actor named Stein gave in the leading rôle the worst performance he had ever seen on any stage. Stein sued for damages, but the court decided, after some diverting testimony, that after all a critic was free to express his esthetic judgment, however incompetent, or however painful it might prove to the subject. Later it became Mr. Broun's embarrassing duty to review another performance by the same aggrieved Stein in another play. Broun evaded the duty until the last sentence, where he could have been found murmuring, "Mr. Stein was not up to his standard."

I am inclined to think, however, that the best of the tabloid reviews have been oral. Coleridge's famous comment on Kean's *Hamlet* —that seeing it was like reading Shakespere by flashes of lightning— was said by him but written by somebody else, wasn't it? Certainly the two best of my day were oral criticisms. One was whispered in my ear by a comely young actress named Tallulah Bankhead, who was sitting incredulous before a deliberate and intentional revival of Maeterlinck's "Aglavaine and Sélysette," a monstrous piece of perfumed posturing, meaning exactly nothing. Two gifted young actresses and a considerable bit of scenery were involved, and much pretentious rumbling of voice and wafting of gesture had gone into the enterprise. Miss Bankhead, fearful, apparently, lest she be struck dead for impiety, became desperate enough to whisper, "There is less in this than meets the eye."

The other was tossed off by that delightful companion and variegated actor, Beerbohm Tree. Hurrying from California to New York, he joined at the eleventh hour the already elaborated rehearsals of "Henry VIII," into which he was to step in the familiar scarlet of *Wolsey*. He was expected to survey whatever had been accomplished by his delegates and pass judgment. He approved cheerfully enough of everything until he came to the collection of damsels that had been dragged into the theater as ladies in waiting to the queen. He looked at them in pained and prolonged dissatisfaction and then said what we have all wanted to say of the extra-women in nearly every throne-room and ball-room and school-room scene since the theater began. "Ladies," said Tree, peering at them plaintively through his monocle, "just a little more virginity, if you don't mind."

S. J. Perelman

DOWN WITH THE RESTORATION!

Does anybody here mind if I make a prediction? I haven't made a prediction since the opening night of "The Women" year before last, when I rose at the end of the third act and announced to my escort, a Miss Chicken-Licken, "The public will never take this to its bosom." Since the public has practically worn its bosom to a nubbin niggling up to "The Women," I feel that my predictions may be a straw to show the direction the wind is blowing away from. I may very well open up a cave and do business as a sort of Cumaean Sibyl in reverse. You can't tell me people would rather climb up that Aventine Hill and have a man mess around with the entrails of a lot of sacred chickens when they can come down into my nice cool cave and get a good hygienic prediction for a few cents. So just to stimulate trade and start the ball rolling, here goes my first prediction: One of these days two young people are going to stumble across a ruined farmhouse and leave it alone.... Well, what are you sitting there gaping at? You heard what I said. That's my prediction.

Honest Injun, I hate to sound crotchety, and the last thing in the world I want to do is throw the editors of all those home-making magazines like *Nook and Garden* and *The American Home-Owner* into an uproar, but the plain fact is that I've got a bellyful. For over two years now, every time I start leafing through one of those excellent periodicals, I fall afoul of another article about a couple of young people who stumble across a ruined farmhouse and remodel it on what is inelegantly termed spit and coupons. Or maybe it's the same article. I couldn't be reading the same issue over and over, could I?

All these remodelling articles are written by the remodellers themselves and never by the ruined farmer or the man who didn't get paid for the plastering, which accounts for their rather smug tone. They invariably follow the same pattern. A young couple named Mibs and Evan (and if you checked up, I'll bet they were never married at *all!*)

have decided to return to the land. I see Mibs as one of those girls on the short side, with stocky legs, a low-slung posterior, and an untidy bun of straw-colored hair continually unwinding on the nape of her neck. Before anyone ever heard of Salzburg, she wore a high-bodiced dress with full skirts, a sort of horrid super-dirndl with home-cooked hems that have a tendency to hang down in back. She is usually engaged in reading a book written by two unfrocked chemists which tells women how to make their own cold cream by mixing a little potash with a dram of glycerine and a few cloves. Evan is a full-haunched young man in a fuzzy woollen suit (I don't suppose there's any such thing as a fuzzy cotton suit, but you know what I mean) who is forever rubbing a briar pipe along his nose to show you the beauty of the grain. He smokes his own mixture of perique, Latakia, and Imperial Cube Cut, for the very good reason that nobody else will smoke it, and he has probably read more of Arthur Machen than any man alive.

Well, as I say, your average remodelling yarn begins with Mibs and Evan stumbling across the most adorable ruin of an eighteenth-century farmhouse. It doesn't *have* to be a farmhouse; it can be a gristmill, or a tobacco barn, or a Mennonite schoolhouse, or—if Mibs and Evan are really lucky—an abandoned ropewalk. It can even be an early Colonial hen house, with delightful hand-hewn beams and perfectly sweet old tar paper scaling off the sides. Apparently nobody previous to Mibs and Evan has realized its possibilities, but Evan takes one look at it and says in a guarded tone, "Two hundred dollars would restore that beautifully if you didn't go crazy putting in a lot of bathrooms you didn't need." "Oh, Evan!" breathes Mibs, her eyes shining above her adenoids and her brain reeling with visions of Cape Cod spatter floors. "Dare we ... ?" That night, at dinner in the Jumble Shop, they put their heads together—Evan removes the pipe from alongside his nose, of course—and decide to jump at the chance. It involves giving up that trip to Europe, a choice the characters in these stories always have to make, but Mibs has always dreamed of a sunny garden filled with old-fashioned flowers of the type her mother used to read about in Max Schling's catalogue. So they bravely draw two hundred dollars out of their little hoard, leaving a hundred in case they ever want to take a really long trip to some place like Bali, and lay it on the line.

After considerable excitement, in which everybody searches the title like mad and Mibs discovers the quaintest old parchment deed describing their land in terms of rods, chains, and poods, they are ready to take the "Before" snapshots. Evan digs up one of the cameras used by Brady at the battle of Antietam, waits for a good cloudy-day, and focuses across a mound of guano at the most ramshackle corner of the "manse," as Mibs calls it with irreverent gaiety. The article generally carries several gray smudges captioned "Southwest corner of the house before work began," and you can't help wondering where those giant oaks came from in the "After" photographs. Maybe they sprang up from acorns dropped by the workmen while they were having lunch.

The first thing the high-hearted pair decide on is a new roof. This fortunately costs only eight dollars, as they use second-hand wattles and hire a twelve-year-old scab—all right, maybe he only mislaid his union card—to tack them on. The outside walls are a problem, but an amazing stroke of good fortune comes to their rescue. Opening a trapdoor they hadn't investigated, Mibs and Evan stumble across countless bundles of lovely old hand-split shingles which have been overlooked by previous tenants, like the hens. Two superb Adam fireplaces, hitherto concealed by some matchboarding, now make their appearance, in one of them a box of dusty but otherwise well-preserved pieces of Sandwich and Stiegel glass. "The attic!" shout Mibs and Evan simultaneously, suddenly remembering their resolution to look through it some rainy day, and sure enough, there they find a veritable treasure trove of pewter ware, cherry escritoires, Chippendale wing chairs, sawbuck tables, and Field beds, hidden away by survivors of the Deerfield massacre. "It just didn't seem *possible*," recalls Mibs candidly, up to her old trick of taking the words out of your mouth.

And now, suddenly, the place becomes a hive of activity. A salty old character named Lafe (who is really Paul Bunyan, no matter what *Nook and Garden* says) appears and does the work of ten men at the price of one. He pulls down trees with his bare hands, lays new floors, puts up partitions, installs electricity, diverts streams, forges the ironware, bakes porcelain sinks, and all but spins silk for the draperies. How this djinn ever escaped from his bottle, and where he is now, the article neglects to mention. The upshot is that in a little over two weeks, the last hooked rug—picked up by Mibs at an auction for ten cents after spirited bidding—is in place and the early Salem kettle is singing merrily on the hob. A fat orange tabby blinks before the fire and Evan, one arm around Mibs, is adding up a column of figures. "Think of it, lover," whispers Mibs with dancing eyes. "We did the whole thing for only *fifty-one dollars and eighteen cents!*" "Less than we'll get for that article in *The American Home-Owner,*" murmurs Evan exultantly, reaming the cake from his pipe. "Tell me, does oo love its 'ittle—" ... And now would you hate me if I stole out very quietly? I'm afraid there's going to be just a wee bit of baby talk.

Clifton Fadiman

GETTING GERTIE'S IDA

A rumor circulating a couple of months ago hinted that Gertrude Stein's new novel, "Ida," was really about the Duchess of Windsor. Now that I have tottered through "Ida," I find I cannot categorically deny the rumor. It is certainly as much about the Duchess of Windsor as it is about anything or anybody else. If it is not about the Duchess of Windsor, what *is* it about? Don't look at me; I'm not your man.

"Ida" is Miss Stein's first novel in eleven years. "It is presented faithfully to you," says the amiable Mr. Bennett Cerf, "by a publisher who rarely has the faintest idea of what Miss Stein is talking about, but who admires her from the bottom of his heart for her courage and for her abounding love of humanity and freedom." This statement would seem to mark an interesting departure in editorial policy. Doubtless we shall soon be reading the works of authors who cannot tell a lie, are kind to their younger brothers, or have contributed heavily to the Salvation Army.

Out of her abounding love of humanity, Miss Stein gives us an elusive creature named Ida. The story of Ida is divided, like a football game, into two halves, called, for purposes of ready reference, First Half and Second Half. The printer and binder have ingeniously arranged to make Second Half follow First Half, so quite an effect of sequence and coherence is produced. It's never made quite clear whether Ida (who dominates both halves) is on her own or whether she is twins. On page 43 we have this: "Ida decided that she was just going to talk to herself. Anybody could stand around and listen but as for her she was just going to talk to herself. She no longer even needed a twin." This seems a forthright statement, but at other points the twin situation is not as lucid as one would wish. On page 52, however, Ida is definitely not a twin. Fifty-two is my favorite page.

Ida (or her twin) has certain quirks: she is very careful about Tuesday, she always hesitates before eating, and she rests a good deal dur-

ing and between marriages. I should inform you that Ida is the marrying type. Among her various husbands is a man named Frank Arthur,
and why not? We do not learn much about her marital habits, but
we are told that "she was always good friends with all her husbands."

This goodness of Ida's also extends to other matters. "She was kind
to politics while she was in Washington very kind. She told politics
that it was very nice of them to have her be kind to them." No record
exists of politics' reply.

Furthermore, there is a man in the book named Philip. "Philip was
the kind that said everything out loud." This sentence about Philip appears on page 40, and he is never mentioned again. Philip is my favorite character.

I have a theory about Miss Stein's novel which—give me just a
second—I should like to outline for you. My notion is that Miss Stein
has set herself to solve, and has succeeded in solving, the most difficult
problem in prose composition—to write something that will not arrest
the attention in any way, manner, shape, or form. If you think this
easy, try it. I know of no one except Miss Stein who can roll out this
completely non-resistant prose, prose that puts you at once in a condition resembling the early stages of grippe—the eyes and legs heavy,
the top of the skull wandering around in an uncertain and independent
manner, the heart ponderously, tiredly beating. Take a sentence at
random: "Ida instead of going on the way she was going went back
the way she had come." Repeat it slowly once or twice and you will
find that your head has fallen to one side and your eyelids are a little
sandy. Try this: "Ida woke up. After a while she got up. Then she
stood up. Then she ate something. After that she sat down. That was
Ida."

See what I mean? Sleep tight.

FAULKNER, EXTRA-SPECIAL, DOUBLE-DISTILLED

At one point in "Absalom, Absalom!" William Faulkner makes Quentin Compson, who is telling the story, say to his auditor, "You can't
understand it. You would have to be born there." This seems to me
not merely one (or two) of the few comprehensible sentences in the
entire novel, but also beyond a doubt the truest. At any rate, it
is my particular Out. Not hailing from Mississippi (which Mr.

Faulkner, in his best Greek-tragedy mood, calls "a land primed for fatality"), I figure I'm not required to understand Mr. Faulkner's novels. I should like to state, therefore, in all humility, that I do not comprehend why "Absalom, Absalom!" was written, what the non-Mississippian is supposed to get out of it, or, indeed, what it is all about. Nor do I understand why Mr. Faulkner writes the way he does. And, having gone so far, I may as well break down and state my conviction that Mr. Faulkner's latest work is the most consistently boring novel by a reputable writer to come my way during the last decade. Duty also bids me report the opinion of the publishers, who see it as his major work, "his most important and ambitious contribution to American literature."

One may sum up both substance and style by saying that every person in "Absalom, Absalom!" comes to no good end, and they all take a hell of a time coming even that far. The story runs from 1807 to 1910, with the major action concentrated between 1833, when Thomas Sutpen appears in Jefferson, Mississippi, and 1869, when he is rather regretfully murdered by an old family retainer. Thomas Sutpen is a monomaniac, known familiarly to the other characters as The Demon. It is never quite clear what makes him so villainous, except that he has a habit of engaging in gouge-as-gouge-can fights with Negroes, and has the odd power of scaring ladies first into marrying him and then into conniption fits. However, he's the fellow you're supposed to shudder at, and if you understand Mr. Faulkner, you'll shudder. If you don't, I guess you just won't. The Demon's second wife, Ellen Coldfield, gives birth to two children, Henry and Judith, goes dotty, and dies after a while. Her younger sister, Rosa, is insulted by The Demon and also goes dotty, though it takes her much longer to die. The father of Rosa and Ellen goes nuts when the Civil War arrives, nails himself up in a garret, and perseveringly starves himself to death. Now, young Henry, upon finding out that his best friend, Charles Bon, engaged to be married to his sister Judith, is (a) his half-brother and (b) part Negro, also goes dotty in a complicated way, and finally shoots Charles dead. By the end of the story Henry has been reduced to straight, simple idiocy and is kept shut up in the attic. Judith, after some years passed in a vacant-eyed trance, passes out as a result of smallpox, a death so natural as to strike a rather jarring note. There is also Clytemnestra Sutpen, daughter of Thomas Sutpen (that's dat Ole Demon Sutpen) and a Negro slave. Clytie sets fire to herself and the idiot boy Henry, and so finishes her career in a fine blaze of pyromaniacal lunacy.

Then there are the Joneses. Wash Jones is a daft hanger-on of Ole Demon Sutpen. He has a granddaughter, Milly. Milly gives birth to a child (it's the Ole Demon's handiwork), Ole Demon insults her, Wash gets sore, shoots Milly, shoots the child, cuts Ole Demon in two with a scythe, and then commits suicide. The Joneses furnish the nearest thing to comic relief in the book. Now, if you'll think back a few lunatics or so, you will remember Charles Bon, preserved from incest and miscegenation by Henry Sutpen's fraternal bullet. Charles had an octoroon mistress, name and mental condition unrecorded, by whom he engendered the boy Charles Etienne. Charles Etienne, realizing that he is a few thirty-seconds Negro, promptly runs amuck. He dies rather dully, of smallpox, but not before he has begotten, with the assistance of a full-blooded Negress, a son Jim. Jim is the real McCoy, a legitimate idiot. (I mean one specifically so called by Mr. Faulkner.) At the end of the book, he is the only living descendant of the accursed Sutpens, which shows you what can happen to a family once they have committed themselves to Mr. Faulkner's tender care.

I think I've got them all in. There's a stray lunatic aunt here and there, but I'm no stickler for details. Come to think of it, there's the young man named Quentin Compson, whose grandfather had befriended Ole Demon Sutpen, and who tells the Sutpen saga to his college chum many years after all these murders, near-incests, fires, suicides, etc., occurred down on the Sutpen farm in Old Mississipp'. Neither Quentin nor his roommate carries on what you would call normal conversations, but as there is no evidence of either of them having married his grandmother, or roasted his grandfather over a slow fire (under the impression that the latter was merely a mulatto first cousin with a trace of chimpanzee blood), I think they should be accepted as Mr. Faulkner's concession to the gray, tawdry, non-Mississippian universe in which the rest of us poor folks live, if Mr. Faulkner can bring himself to call it living.

This cheerful little fable is filtered through the medium of a style peculiar to Mr. Faulkner. It seems peculiar to me, too. First, we have the Non-Stop or Life Sentence. The first two and a half pages of "Absalom, Absalom!" consist of seven sentences, composed of 123, 155, 9 (something wrong here), 146, 66, 93, and 135 words respectively.

Average: 104. To penetrate Mr. Faulkner's sentences is like hacking your way through a jungle. The path closes up at once behind you, and in no time at all you find yourself entangled in a luxuriant mass of modifiers, qualifications, relative clauses, parenthetical phrases, interjected matter, recapitulations, and other indications of a Great Style. All of Mr. Faulkner's shuddery inventions pale in horrendousness before the mere notion of parsing him.

After the Life Sentence comes the Far Fetch, or Hypertrope. Very few things in the book remain themselves. Each one reminds Mr. Faulkner of something else. "Her legs hung ... clear of the floor with that air of impotent and static rage like children's feet." See it? No? Join me at the foot of the class, where you belong.

Then we have what may be called Anti-Narrative, a set of complex devices used to keep the story from being told. Mr. Faulkner is very clever at this. He gets quite an interesting effect, for example, by tearing the Sutpen chronicle into pieces, as if a mad child were to go to work on it with a pair of shears, and then having each of the jagged divisions narrated by a different personage: the author, Rosa, Quentin, Quentin's father, Quentin's grandfather. All these people do a neat job of mixing up the time sequences, delaying climaxes, confusing the reader, and otherwise enabling Mr. Faulkner to demonstrate that as a technician he has Joyce and Proust punch-drunk. I should add that everybody talks the same language, a kind of Dixie Gongorism, very formal, allusive, cryptic. Apparently the entire population of Jefferson, Mississippi, consists of rhetoricians who would blench at the sight of a simple declarative sentence. On the other hand, it is only fair to say that there are a score of pages (Rosa Coldfield's section of the narrative) full of remarkable prose poetry, beautiful in itself, if magnificently irrelevant.

Seriously, I do not know what to say of this book except that it seems to point to the final blowup of what was once a remarkable, if minor, talent. I imagine that many of my respected colleagues will see in it a tragic masterpiece, a great lament for the old dead South, a Sophoclean study of a doomed family. Perhaps they are right. For me, this is a penny dreadful tricked up in fancy language and given a specious depth by the expert manipulation of a series of eccentric technical tricks. The characters have no magnitude and no meaning because they have no more reality than a mince-pie nightmare. If we are to have tales of violence and sadism, let the violence and sadism be drawn from the behavior of grownups, let them be more than the melodramatic gestures of childish maniacs. A study of defeat can have great tragic weight, but only if the defeated are akin to us, which these mumbling, muttering, frozen-faced Sutpens surely are not. I fail to see why we must go into a spasm of ecstatic shivering just because Mr. Faulkner is a clever hand at fitting up a literary asylum for the feeble-minded. It takes more than these fake sepulchral voices, these synthetic incests, these Monk Lewis allusions, to scare ordinary sober citizens. Ole Demon Sutpen is a mechanical bogeyman, and the rest of his gang are no better. The whole affair reminds one more of "The Tavern" than of Greek tragedy, and I have the horrid suspicion that if enough people were to say boo the entire structure of "Absalom, Absalom!" would disappear in smoke. Does anyone care to say boo?

Frank Moore Colby

WHEN NATURE LOVERS WRITE BOOKS

Nature lovers have found their way into print with rather unusual frequency of late. The success of this kind of writing is a healthy sign. A people cannot be far removed from innocence when books of this sort are widely read and when even the daily newspapers drop wars and politics, as they sometimes do, for a wholly irrelevant editorial rhapsody on cock-robin or autumn leaves. The London papers, especially, are given to these rustic interludes. There are more "rambles" and "bird-notes" than you would ever have supposed, and, if reviewers are to be believed, they are all written in the most charming style. But reviewers are not to be believed. No one ought to take time for many of these books if there are passages of Thoreau which he has not yet learned by heart. These writers are serviceable only when they give information. As interpreters they are of no use. For this business we must still rely on the masters, and how few of them there are!

A clergyman goes a-fishing and comes home well browned and ten pounds fatter. So he sits down and writes a book full of trite compliments to nature interspersed with a good deal of self-congratulation. He lays claim to the most refined and exquisite emotion you ever heard of—not one particle of which he succeeds in passing along. Yet because it is a good sort of thing for a clergyman to do and shows a fine appetite for wholesome fare the critics are absurdly easy on him. "Such a subtle sympathy with nature in her varying moods," they say. How do they know he has it? Just because he swears he has. There is no question of the man's sincerity or of the worth of what he writes about, but unfortunately these two are not the only elements of good writing. Here is a beautiful object, and there a genuine admirer. Yet the net result of bringing them together may be merely twaddle.

It is a rare man who can be agreeably articulate in these matters. They are hardly more communicable in speech than music is.

Some of these books are full of a sort of outdoor snobbishness, an air of having an especially fine make of soul and being proud of it. The writer will pity people who do not penetrate this or that of nature's secrets or participate in certain intimate joys. And he will tell you what these things do for him—how they strengthen him and uplift him and keep his heart pure and his mind clear. It may be true, but there should be some other evidence than his word for it. It is indelicate to be forever harping on nature's partiality for you. You cannot fancy his enjoying a thing quietly and for itself, but taking notes on each emotion in order to write it up afterward ostentatiously. How much of it is delight in objective nature and how much is satisfaction with the trim little intellectual outfit he surveys her with? Yet if there is one lesson she is supposed to din into everyone who comes close enough it is humility.

In England there are signs that in certain highly respectable magazines and newspapers they have a staff correspondent whom they never let indoors—a literary bird dog for whom the house is no place. If they catch him in the office they shoo him out with the broom to flush some small game for the next number. I gather from one of them that "the winter wind, unlike the entrancing night breezes of summer, is one of the few sounds that please even more when listened to indoors than out.... It sighs in the chimney, it moans round the walls; it whistles sometimes, at others it roars." From another I have learned that as a result of the bad weather of the week before the birds were "thoroughly worn out and uncomfortable," and "went to bed an hour before their time," though some of the partridges may have sat up somewhat longer. Some say it is the Englishman's love of nature, and would have you think it spontaneous. It is nothing of the sort. It is a clear case of compulsion. The wretches hate what they write of in nine cases out of ten. You can tell that from their style, and it is a pity they should be so tormented. Why try and squeeze a great, wild, forest joy out of a little cockney heart?

You could follow Thackeray's fancy in a cab. Dickens, though the sense of locality was as strong in him as in a cat, used nature only to emphasize pathos or punctuate joy. To Bulwer all outdoors was only stage carpentry and paint. Once if a writer did not wish to do it he did not have to try; but there is no getting out of it in these days, and the rarest gift of the generations is aped by everyone who writes.

NOVELS AND HATS

Considering how writers set about their tasks, it may be unreasonable to expect any sort of lifelike consequence. A novel is not a product of imagination. Novelists do not invent or observe; they rearrange their literary memories. Probably it is no more reasonable to look for human nature in a novel than to look for Nature in a woman's hat. For each being a work of customary or crowd-derived inspiration, their value in depicting life is much the same. One matches human nature as already published; the other matches Nature as already worn on hats. So with a host of virilities and vitalities, love-storms, moral whirl-winds, calls of the wild—you never meet the novelist who first employed them. You see the thousand hats that followed the example but never the great, brave, strong, protagonistic and outrageous hat that set it.

The call of the wild as seen on women's hats some seasons past proved no wild fancies in the heads beneath them. It was a call to precedent. When you found on a hat some singular bit from wildlife, say a weasel sleeping on its native beads or biting its light blue omelette, it was not a sign of any personal wildness. It had occurred on many hats before. And so with the novels then in season. The call of the wild in novels at that time was not a call to any special wildness; it was the peaceful call of one Jack London to another.

The hat, however, has somewhat the advantage, for women do sometimes more utterly let themselves go, feel more of that first, fine, careless rapture, in a hat than the novelist does in the novel. And as to the rule that the style is the man, I believe it could be easily proved that the hat is more exactly the woman. A novel always seems a form of self-concealment. Yet a woman otherwise quite subdued may suddenly appear in a hat that is all ablaze with feeling—no doubt imprisoned passion's single mad escape—and you sometimes meet a hot, infuriate hat, hardly venturing to look at the rabid face beneath, yet find there a countenance of great serenity. The riot of emotion had passed off in the hat, leaving the soul at peace. This is not true of novelists, who, on the contrary, seen in the flesh, show personal diversities not to be guessed from their books.

THE LOEB CLASSICS

I have been reading a review of the Loeb Classics by Professor Gilbert Norwood of the chair of Greek, University College, Cardiff. He says it is a magnificent task splendidly executed, and that the company of scholars engaged in it are in "a fair way to revolutionize the study of ancient literature as profoundly and in much the same way as the motor has revolutionized transport." His paper, like almost every other one I have read on this subject, is, for the most part, a mere rhapsody on the marvels of Greek and Latin authors coupled with praise of the Loeb Classics for reviving an interest in them. In regard to the translations he does not say one word of discriminating criticism, and the only improvement he suggests is that translations of poetry should always be in verse.

This sort of writing about the Loeb Classics is the worst thing that could happen to them. The editors of the Loeb Classics are not in a fair way to "revolutionize" anything; they are making a beginning, and a very crude beginning, in the revival of interest in the classics. Sensible men among them are well aware of their failures and they also know that the chief obstacle to success is an even flow of unmeaning, undiscriminating praise. They have no encouragement for doing their best if their worst is equally admired.

Take this latest eulogist for example. He says Dr. A. S. Way's translation of Euripides "is uninspiring but close to the Greek," while Professor Gilbert Murray's "is often loose, but marvelously beautiful." Patience with Way's Euripides is almost a proof of illiteracy. I suppose no man outside a government bureau at Washington ever wrote worse English than Professor A. S. Way, and he wrote it out of sheer love of bad English, for page after page of it has not the slightest excuse in the Greek. Even among Greek scholars who have forgotten the capacities of the English language without yet appreciating the Greek, the Way's version is known as an atrocity. Professor Gilbert Murray's Euripides has so little to do with Euripides that all compliments paid to it belong to Professor Murray himself. To call his Euripides "marvelously beautiful" is to pronounce a judgment on a contemporary verse writer. With Professor Way's close translation and Professor Gilbert Murray's loose and beautiful one, Professor Norwood thinks the people who cannot read the Greek of Euripides "stand in excellent case." I cannot imagine why. Professor Way's method resulted in murder and Professor Gilbert Murray's in oblivion.

Another instance of this writer's apathy is his mildness toward Professor H. E. Butler's version of Quintilian. To be sure he does says that where Quintilian uses thirty-five words Professor Butler uses sixty-eight, but he excuses Professor Butler on the ground that he probably wanted to let other scholars know that no suggestion implied in any one of Quintilian's words had escaped him. That is an absurd supposition to anyone who will read a few pages of Professor Butler. Loquacity is a native quality in Professor Butler. He had rather use sixty-eight words than thirty-five, and he will say the same thing twice over in order to do so. This is shown on page after page, when the thought is simple and the way to brevity perfectly open. Professor Butler takes the longest way because he likes it. When he sees seven words by Quintilian, he says to himself, "Why does the old chap waste his opportunity? I can put the same idea in forty." It is a difference in temperament. Quintilian likes to pack things into small space, skip an explanation, leave a little to inference. Professor Butler hates that kind of thing—thinks it selfish, and secretive. He dislikes Quintilian for it and thwarts him when he can. If there is any man in the world that I should hate to resemble, said Professor Butler, when he began this version, it's Quintilian, and his whole text is a demonstration of this incompatibility. Not once does he let Quintilian have his own way about anything. There is no doubt that Quintilian becomes modern by this method. You would swear he was a contributor to the London *Spectator*. I confess I never liked Quintilian at college. I thought him a man of mean outlook and low morality with a vile habit of saying things I knew already, but I did give him credit for putting a platitude into a nutshell, and I should never have dreamed of this long merciless revenge.

Wolcott Gibbs

CRYING IN THE WILDERNESS

Facile is the descent from the editorial chair of a fashionable women's magazine to the psychoanalyst's grim confessional. This is the gospel, according to Moss Hart, whose "Lady in the Dark" has just moved into the Alvin Theatre. To an old magazine man it would doubtless appear that Liza Elliott was fortunate beyond the wildest dreams of anybody in that unsavory racket. She had a fancy office in which nobody threw cigarette butts on the floor or scrawled telephone numbers on the walls; there was a rich backer with no exasperating theories about how things ought to be run; there were no disgruntled contributors or, as far as I could see, anything so vulgar as a typewriter in the joint. In fact, about the only professional problem confronting this lucky girl was the choice of what cover to put on the Easter issue. Mr. Hart's play has been generally described as a fantasy. It is, indeed.

In spite of all these advantages, however, Miss Elliott wasn't happy. Her case history, as outlined to the sawbones at twenty bucks a throw, was full of frustrations. As a very little girl she was plain, in embarrassing contrast to her beautiful mother, and her school days were just one damn thing after another. They wouldn't let her be the Princess in the Commencement play, for instance, and then when the class elections came around she was chosen Best Student, a disgusting thing, of course, to happen to anybody. As those of you who are familiar with the black magic of Vienna will realize, such experiences as these can set up bothersome complexes, and by the time Mr. Hart's heroine got to be an editor she was as mixed up emotionally as Mrs. Ethan Frome. In the end, I am happy to say, Dr. Brooks fixed everything, and Miss Elliott was able to find peace with an advertising man called Charley Johnson. It is obvious that the author classifies this as a happy ending, and who am I to argue?

All this, I'm afraid, is a preliminary to saying that I wasn't altogether carried away by "Lady in the Dark." The plot of a musical play, as a rule, is immune to rational criticism, but Mr. Hart clearly wishes his new piece to be taken seriously, as a dramatic work as well as a spectacle. On this basis, I can only report that Miss Elliott's wrestle with her subconscious, while spirited, would scarcely be likely to make any professional list of fascinating cases, and that, considered sheerly as a thing of beauty, the production at the Alvin may easily remind the captious of certain goings on at the Center Theatre, where giant turntables and similar miracles have also been used to astound the unwary.

Psychoanalysis, according to persistent rumor, has long been one of Mr. Hart's own best girls, beyond question or reproach, and this may account for something rather wide-eyed, reverent, and perhaps a little old-fashioned that crept into the scenes describing his heroine's conversations with her physician, as well as those dealing with her numerous suitors. It is harder to say why the musical sequences—the patient's fantasies and childhood memories—weren't altogether satisfactory either. Kurt Weill's tunes were pleasant, if not precisely memorable; Ira Gershwin's lyrics were always urbane, and often witty; the dances, supervised by Albertina Rasch, were brilliantly executed; and the costumes and settings, though stupendous, showed both imagination and taste. The total effect on me, however, was an almost perfect balance between rapture and fatigue. There were times when everything seemed wonderful, and there were others when I simply wished to see no more scenery split and dissolve, no more beautiful women rotate on turn-tables, no more ballets, each as pretty and expensive as a pure white yacht. I can't explain this peculiar reaction, except by saying that all this magnificence seemed exactly the sort of thing that could have been handled just as intelligently (and perhaps a little more magnificently) in Hollywood.

None of the above, of course, has anything to do with Gertrude Lawrence, who, in one carelessly chosen word, is superb, whether prone on her consultant's sofa, running over her symptoms, or merrily singing a fine, tough song called "The Saga of Jenny." Of the rest of the cast, I have only strength left to remark that Danny Kaye, Bert Lytell, Macdonald Carey, Margaret Dale, and Victor Mature (courtesy the Hal Roach Studio, Inc.) all deserve your respectful attention.

THE THEATRE IN FLUSHING

There is a sort of cock-eyed majesty in every project undertaken by Billy Rose, and the Aquacade is no exception. As far as I can see, it has everything—beauty, skill, size, humor, music, and, these chilly nights, a strong undertone of muted suffering. Of all the exhibits at the Fair, it is the one you are most likely to report to your grandson, though what he will be able to make out of your garbled and unlikely story I have no idea. There was a giant swimming pool anchored in a lake, you might tell him, and a grandstand to hold ten thousand people on the shore. These watched a hundred and seventy-seven young women (known as Aquafemmes, Aquagals, and Aquabelles, for our sense of humor in that dim yesterday may have been a little primitive) and seventy-seven young men (Aquadudes and Aquabeaux) swimming and diving and prancing in step. You could say that they were led by Johnny Weissmuller, a motion-picture star celebrated for impersonating apes, and Mr. Rose's fiancée, Miss Eleanor Holm, and that these two swam together in waltz time, an accomplishment both beautiful and unique.

None of these facts, however, would give him the faintest indication of what the Aquacade was really like. I'm afraid, in fact, that nobody who hasn't been to Flushing can hope to understand the strange balance of splendor and foolishness that Mr. Rose has achieved—the towers on the stage outlined pure and sharp against the sky, and the voice of God from somewhere telling everybody to buy Pabst Blue Ribbon beer and smoke Chesterfields (the man next to us borrowed a cigarette from Mr. Rose himself; it was a Lucky Strike), the perfect rhythm of the ballet and the gooseflesh on the childish limbs (it was 50° the night I went), the divers' bodies so lovely in the air and the distaste bordering on horror on every face confronted with the icy plunge.

In any case, I think you ought to go to Mr. Rose's unusual little party; a lot of water, I'm sure, will pass over Miss Holm before we shall see its like again. The only trend, incidentally, which I was able to note at the Aquacade is that the chorus girl of tomorrow will go in for a two-syllable Christian name, ending in "a." Lela, Lila, Glada, and Norma, they are called, Jona, Roma, Vela, and Willa.

Robert C. Benchley

LA PRESSE PERVERSE *

Paris, August 7, 1929.

In reading French newspapers there is always one consolation: no matter how little of the meaning you are able to get, you aren't missing a thing. News is the last thing a French editor worries about. Even when he finds himself saddled with a real news-story, he doesn't know what to do with it, and will just as likely as not run it on page 7 among the *Petites Annonces*. He can take the story of an Atlantic flight or a cabinet crisis and undress it until it looks like something in the Special Westchester Section of the Sunday *Times*. There is always plenty to read in a French newspaper, but it doesn't make any difference whether you read it or not.

The attitude of the French press towards news is shown by the fact that most French papers run the latest dispatches on the third page under a vague departmental heading like *"Dernière Heure"* or *"Dernières Nouvelles."* The front page they save for their essays.

The left-hand column of the front page is usually given over to a red-hot story called something like: "Molière During the Middle Period of his Productivity." The right-hand column is probably a signed outburst by the owner of the paper urging the restoration of the Bourbons or calling attention to the drought in what the French persist in calling *"Tchécoslovaquie."* In the middle of the front page the eager reader may devour biographical sketches of the bicyclists who are engaging in the *"Tour de France"* and who are now just passing through Toulon. And inside, on page 3, all nestled together in little two-line dispatches, will be the brief announcements that China is on fire and that a tunnel has been found already built under the English Channel.

All summer *Le Matin* has been giving over the two right-hand

* *This review of the French newspapers of 1929 was published in* The New Yorker's *"Wayward Press" department over the signature Guy Fawkes.*

558

columns of its front page to a series called "My Fishing Trip in New-foundland." This has been illustrated copiously each day with photo-graphs taken by the author, reproduced by means of cuts such as only French newspaper-engravers can make, presumably etched on pieces of bread. The date line on the most recent installment was April 30. (I read the first two or three laboring under a slight misapprehension owing to the word for "to fish" being the same as the word for "to sin" and hoping that someone had gone to Newfoundland on a "cam-paign of sinning." You couldn't have told from the pictures whether it was sinning or fishing the author was engaged in.)

But no matter what page you look at in a French paper, you will find America mentioned. Even the front-page essays on Rousseau manage to slip in a paragraph or two taking a crack at Oncle Sam. The ratification of the *dettes* has, of course, been the chief topic of com-ment, and from *L'Humanité* to *L'Écho de Paris* the general attitude toward the United States is one of boiling rage. Practically the only general news-notes from America that French papers will play up are those dealing with torch-murders, flag-pole-sittings and the extreme heat. It was, therefore, with considerable surprise that we saw a head-line on the front page of *L'Écho de Paris* reading *"Un Grand Améri-cain,"* but it turned out to be a tribute to Theodore Roosevelt and a lament that America had strayed so far from his teachings.

As near as we could detect, there was no mention made in the French press of the recently disclosed fact that American tourists paid over twice as much money into France last year as France paid to the United States. Well, they can't be expected to print every-thing.

In one department, however, the newspapers here excel, and that is in the reporting of crime. They love it. Crimes of violence which American papers would hardly think worth a stick of type are written up by the French with a zest and thoroughness which make of each one a special case in criminology. This is not because crimes are less frequent in France than in America, for such papers as *Le Petit Marseillais,* after a perfunctory story on how the debts and the bicycle-tour are coming on, settle down each day to five or six solid pages of murder, arson, sex and robbery which apparently have been occupy-ing the time of the entire citizenry the day before.

Even the most modest of crimes is treated in the Edgar Wallace manner, and it makes fascinating reading. Instead of, as in American accounts, beginning with the names and addresses of the policemen who discovered the crime, your French re-write man gets into a dressing-gown, lights his pipe and lets himself go like this (in rough translation):

"Toward 21 o'clock on the night of August 2, in the dark which resulted from there being no moon, Mme. Marie Plissy was walking toward her little shop in the rue Fourteenth-of-October when she suddenly found herself beaten down on the neck, falling dead at almost the same time. One is mystified."

Or even in more tantalizing fashion, under the mysterious headline "The Amorous Refusals," we are led on like this by *Le Petit Journal:* "André Gerome, 24 years, electrician, had known, for about four years, when he was a subaltern in the 2nd regiment of infantry, a young girl, Claudia Poncet, who had, at that epoch, 15 years and lived at the home of her parents, 15 rue Saint-Hippolyte."

Well, anything might be going to happen, you must admit. So we read on: "On his liberation, the young officer wished to become engaged and rendered a visit to the parents of the young Claudia who refused to give their consent. In order not to be disagreeable to her parents, Mlle. Poncet wished to romp (probably not the meaning of *rompre,* but good enough) and accepted a later rendezvous."

The rest of the story is really too sordid, but suffice it to say that when a M. Grafouillère came to knock on the door, he found that Mlle. Claudia had ceased to live owing to having received three balls in the chest and neck.

This will give you some idea of how things are going in sunny France and if one hasn't time to read *all* the stories of sudden death and crime one may take that excellent paper, *L'Éclaireur de Nice et du Sud-Est,* and turn to page 3 where, under the general heading of *Nouvelles Diverses,* one finds, in summary, that at Aix an infant of five years drowns itself in a basin, at Lisieux a grandmother is killed with a hatchet for her money, that at Les Baux two lovers are shot by a jealous, and that in Orange a little boy sets fire to the mayor (possibly a slipshod translation, but that's what it looks like).

Of all French papers *Le Temps* seems to be the dullest, having a makeup such as would be effected by spreading two pages of the *Congressional Record* out side by side and doubling the length of their columns. This unexciting layout is not enhanced in the least by a department which fills the right-hand column under the dreary heading: "*La Vie à Londres.*" There are no accounts of *crimes passionnels* in *Le Temps* and not even that concession to fresh air which most French newspapers make under the title "*La Vie Sportive.*" If we were to recommend a paper *not* to buy for general reading it would be *Le Temps,* followed closely by *Le Figaro.* Compared with them our own New York *Times* is a tabloid. (Incidentally, our own New York *Times,* even ten days late, comes with all the excitement of the monthly installments of "The Hound of the Baskervilles" when it was running serially in the *Strand Magazine.* We are sorry for anything we ever said disrespectfully of the New York *Times.*) Day in and day out *Le Matin* and *Le Quotidien* give the best imitation of real newspapers, although even they would deceive nobody. *Le Quotidien,* in the issue which has just come hot from the presses, bears a two-column scarehead on the front page biting out the following terse announcement, so that he who runs may read: "*La France Se Flattait Naguère de Posséder le Système Électoral le plus Large qui eût Jamais Existé. Va-t-elle Aujourd'hui Rester le Seul Pays où les Femmes ne Votent pas?*" Not only do French headlines not tell you anything. They must ask questions.

We can not bring this scholarly summary of French journalism to a close, however, without commending the theatrical newspaper *Comœdia* as being the best of its kind we have ever seen. It appears daily, and, although it, too, devotes its front page to gentlemen's essays on classical subjects and the reproduction of a painting of some old master, its inside pages are as handy a guide to what is going on in the theatre world of Paris as newspaper skill could devise. Every theatre is listed, with address, telephone number, name of current attraction and the names of the cast. If it were not for this department we should never have known that a cinema called "*Le Chanteur de Jazz*" with "*la grande vedette du film parlant Al Jolson*" is playing at the Aubert-Palace, or that at the Casino de Paris one is able to see "*Les 16 Smart Boys.*"

Edgar Allan Poe

WILLIAM ELLERY CHANNING*

In speaking of Mr. William Ellery Channing, who has just published a
very neat little volume of poems, we feel the necessity of employing
the indefinite rather than the definite article. He is *a,* and by no means
the, William Ellery Channing. He is only *the son* of the great essayist
deceased. He is just such a person, in despite of his *clarum et venerabile
nomen,* as Pindar would have designated by the significant term τις.
It may be said in his favor that nobody ever heard of him. Like an
honest woman, he has always succeeded in keeping himself from being
made the subject of gossip. His book contains about sixty-three things,
which he calls poems, and which he no doubt seriously supposes so to
be. They are full of all kinds of mistakes, of which the most important
is that of their having been printed at all. They are not precisely English—nor will we insult a great nation by calling them Kickapoo;
perhaps they are Channingese. We may convey some general idea of
them by two foreign terms not in common use—the Italian *pavoneg-
giarsi,* "to strut like a peacock," and the German word for "sky-rocket-
ing," *schwarmerei.* They are more preposterous, in a word, than any
poems except those of the author of "Sam Patch"; for we presume we
are right (are we not?) in taking it for granted that the author of
"Sam Patch" is the very worst of all the wretched poets that ever
existed upon earth.

In spite, however, of the customary phrase about a man's "making a
fool of himself," we doubt if any one was ever a fool of his own free
will and accord. A poet, therefore, should not always be taken too
strictly to task. He should be treated with leniency, and, even when
damned, should be damned with respect. Nobility of descent, too,
should be allowed its privileges not more in social life than in letters.
The son of a great author cannot be handled too tenderly by the critical

* *This book review has been cut. Mr. Poe took William Ellery Channing, Jr.,
apart with great thoroughness.*

Jack Ketch. Mr. Channing must be hung, that's true. He must be hung *in terrorem*—and for this there is no help under the sun; but then we shall do him all manner of justice, and observe every species of decorum, and be especially careful of his feelings, and hang him gingerly and gracefully, with a silken cord, as the Spaniards hang their grandees of the blue blood, their nobles of the *sangre azula*.

To be serious, then; as we always wish to be if possible. Mr. Channing (whom we suppose to be a *very* young man, since we are precluded from supposing him a *very* old one), appears to have been inoculated, at the same moment, with *virus* from Tennyson and from Carlyle. And here we do not wish to be misunderstood. For Tennyson, as for a man imbued with the richest and rarest poetic impulses, we have an admiration—a reverence unbounded. His "Morte D'Arthur," his "Locksley Hall," his "Sleeping Beauty," his "Lady of Shalott," his "Lotos Eaters," his "Ænone," and many other poems, are not surpassed, in all that gives to Poetry its distinctive value, by the compositions of any one living or dead. And his leading error—that error which renders him unpopular—a point, to be sure, of no particular importance—that very error, we say, is founded in truth—in a keen perception of the elements of poetic beauty. We allude to his quaintness—to what the world chooses to term his affectation. No true poet —no critic whose approbation is worth even a copy of the volume now hold in our hand—will deny that he feels impressed, sometimes even to tears, by many of those very affectations which he is impelled by the prejudice of his education, or by the cant of his reason, to condemn. He should thus be led to examine the extent of the one, and to be wary of the deductions of the other. In fact, the profound intuition of Lord Bacon has supplied, in one of his immortal apothegms, the whole philosophy of the point at issue. "There is no exquisite beauty," he truly says, "without some *strangeness* in its proportions." We maintain, then, that Tennyson errs, not in his occasional quaintness, but in its continual and obtrusive excess. And, in accusing Mr. Channing of having been inoculated with *virus* from Tennyson, we merely mean to say that he has adopted and exaggerated that noble poet's characteristic defect, having mistaken it for his principal merit.

Mr. Tennyson is quaint only; he is never, as some have supposed him, obscure—except, indeed, to the uneducated, whom he does not address. Mr. Carlyle, on the other hand, is obscure only; he is seldom, as some have imagined him, quaint. So far he is right; for although quaintness, employed by a man of judgment and genius, may be made auxiliary to a *poem,* whose true thesis is beauty, and beauty alone, it is grossly, and even ridiculously, out of place in a work of prose. But in his obscurity it is scarcely necessary to say that he is wrong. Either a man intends to be understood, or he does not. If he write a book which he intends *not* to be understood, we shall be very happy indeed not to understand it; but if he write a book which he means to be understood, and, in this book, be at all possible pains to prevent us from understanding it, we can only say that he is an ass—and this, to be brief, is our private opinion of Mr. Carlyle, which we now take the liberty of making public.

It seems that having deduced, from Tennyson and Carlyle, an opinion of the sublimity of everything odd, and of the profundity of everything meaningless, Mr. Channing has conceived the idea of setting up for himself as a poet of *unusual* depth, and *very* remarkable powers of mind. His airs and graces, in consequence, have a highly picturesque effect, and the Boston critics, who have a notion that poets are porpoises, (for they are always talking about their running in "schools,") cannot make up their minds as to what particular school he must belong. *We* say the Bobby Button school, by all means. He clearly belongs to that. And should nobody ever have heard of the Bobby Button school, that is a point of no material importance. We will answer for it, as it is one of our own. Bobby Button is a gentleman with whom, for a long time, we have had the honor of an intimate acquaintance. His personal appearance is striking. He has quite a big head. His eyes protrude and have all the air of saucers. His chin retreats. His mouth is depressed at the corners. He wears a perpetual frown of contemplation. His words are slow, emphatic, few, and oracular. His "thes," "ands," and "buts," have more meaning than other men's polysyllables. His nods would have put Burleigh's to the blush. His whole aspect, indeed, conveys the idea of a gentleman modest to a fault, and painfully overburthened with intellect. We insist, however, upon calling Mr. Channing's school of poetry the Bobby Button school, rather because Mr. Channing's poetry is strongly suggestive of Bobby Button, than because Mr. Button himself ever dallied, to any very great extent, with the Muses. With the exception, indeed, of a *very* fine "Sonnet to a Pig"—or rather the fragment of a sonnet, for he proceeded no farther than the words "*O* piggy wiggy," with the *O* italicized for emphasis—with the exception of this, we say, we are not aware of his having produced anything worthy of that stupendous genius which is certainly *in* him, and only wants, like the starling of Sterne, "to get out."

The best passage in the book before us, is to be found at page 121, and we quote it, as a matter of simple justice, in full:

> Dear friend, in this fair atmosphere again,
> Far from the noisy echoes of the main,
> Amid the world-old mountains, and the hills
> From whose strange grouping a fine power distills
> The soothing and the calm, I seek repose,
> The city's noise forgot and hard stern woes.
> As thou once said'st, the rarest sons of earth
> Have in the dust of cities shown their worth,
> Where long collision with the human curse
> Has of great glory been the frequent nurse,
> *And only those who in sad cities dwell*
> *Are of the green trees fully sensible.*
> *To them the silver bells of tinkling streams*
> *Seem brighter than an angel's laugh in dreams.*

The four lines italicized are highly meritorious, and the whole extract is so far decent and intelligible, that we experienced a feeling of surprise upon meeting it amid the doggerel which surrounds it. Not less was our astonishment upon finding, at page 18, a fine thought so well embodied as the following:

> *Or see the early stars, a mild sweet train*
> *Come out to bury the diurnal sun.*

But, in the way of commendation, we have now done. We have carefully explored the whole volume in vain, for a single additional line worth even the most qualified applause.

Were we to quote specimens under the general head of "utter and irredeemable nonsense," we should quote nine-tenths of the book. Such nonsense, we mean, as the following, from page 11:

> I hear thy solemn anthem fall,
>   Of richest song upon my ear,
> That clothes thee in thy golden pall
>   As this wide sun flows on the mere.

Now let us translate this: He hears (Mr. Channing,) a solemn anthem, of richest song, fall upon his ear, and this anthem clothes the individual who sings it in that individual's golden pall, in the same manner that, or at the time when, the wide sun flows on the mere—which is all very delightful, no doubt.

At page 37, he informs us that,

> ————It is not living,
> To a soul believing,
> To change each noble joy,
> Which our strength employs,
> For a state half rotten
> And a life of toys,

And that it is

> Better to be forgotten
> Than lose equipoise.

And we dare say it is, if one could only understand what kind of equipoise is intended. It is better to be forgotten, for instance, than to lose one's equipoise on the top of a shot tower.

Occupying the whole of page 88, he has the six lines which follow, and we will present any one (the author not excepted,) with a copy of the volume, if any one will tell us what they are all about:

> He came and waved a little silver wand,
>   He dropped the veil that hid a statue fair,
> He drew a circle with that pearly hand,
>   His grace confin'd that beauty in the air,
> Those limbs so gentle now at rest from flight,
> Those quiet eyes now musing on the night.

At page 102, he has the following:

> Dry leaves with yellow ferns, they are
> Fit wreath of Autumn, while a star
> Still, bright, and pure, our frosty air
>   Shivers in twinkling points
>   Of thin celestial hair
> And thus one side of Heaven anoints.

This we think we can explain. Let us see. Dry leaves, mixed with yellow ferns, are a wreath fit for autumn at the time when our frosty air shivers a still, bright, and pure star with twinkling points of thin celestial hair, and with this hair, or hair plaster, anoints one side of the sky. Yes—this is it—no doubt.

At page 123, we have these lines:

> My sweet girl is lying still
> In her lovely atmosphere;
> The gentle hopes her blue veins fill
> With pure silver warm and clear.
>
> O see her hair, O mark her breast!
> Would it not, *O!* comfort thee,
> If thou couldst nightly go to rest
> By that virgin chastity?

Yes; we think, upon the whole, it would. The eight lines are entitled a "Song," and we should like very much to hear Mr. Channing sing it.

Pages 36, 37, 38, 39, 40, and 41, are filled with short "Thoughts" in what Mr. C. supposes to be the manner of Jean Paul. One of them runs thus:

> How shall I live? In earnestness.
> What shall I do? Work earnestly.
> What shall I give? A willingness.
> What shall I gain? Tranquility.
> But do you mean a quietness
> In which I act and no man bless?
> Flash out in action infinite and free,
> Action conjoined with deep tranquility,
> Resting upon the soul's true utterance,
> And life shall flow as merry as a dance.

All our readers will be happy to hear, we are sure, that Mr. C is going "to flash out." Elsewhere at page 97, he expresses very similar sentiments:

> My empire is myself and I defy
> The external; yes, I rule the whole or die.

It will be observed here, that Mr. Channing's empire is himself, (a small kingdom, however,) that he intends to defy "the external," whatever that is—perhaps he means the infernals—and that, in short, he is going to rule the whole or die; all which is very proper, indeed, and nothing more than we have to expect from Mr. C.

Again, at page 146, he is rather fierce than otherwise. He says:

> We surely were not meant to ride the sea,
>   Skimming the wave in that so prisoned small,
> Reposing our infinite faculties utterly.
>   Boom like a roaring sunlit waterfall.
> Humming to infinite abysms: speak loud, speak free!

Here Mr. Channing not only intends to "speak loud and free" himself, but advises every body else to do likewise. For his own part, he says, he is going to *"boom"*—"to hum and to boom"—to "hum like a roaring waterfall," and "boom to an infinite abysm." What, in the name of Belzebub, *is* to become of us all? . . .

And this remarkable little volume is, after all, by William Ellery Channing. . . . There are many people in the world silly enough to be deceived by appearances. There are individuals so crude in intellect—so *green,* (if we may be permitted to employ a word which answers our purpose much better than any other in the language,) so green, we say, as to imagine, in the absence of any indication to the contrary, that a volume bearing upon its title-page the name of William Ellery Channing, must necessarily be the posthumous work of that truly illustrious author, the *sole* William Ellery Channing of whom any body in the world ever heard. There are a vast number of uninformed young persons prowling about our book-shops, who will be raw enough to buy, and even to read half through this pretty little book, (God preserve and forgive them!) mistaking it for the composition of another. But what then? Are not books made, as well as razors, to sell? The poet's name *is* William Ellery Channing —is it *not?* And if a man has not a right to the use of his own name, to the use of what has he a right? And could the poet have reconciled it to his conscience to have injured the sale of his own volume by any uncalled-for announcement upon the title-page, or in a preface, to the effect that he is not his father, but only his father's very intelligent son? . . .

Persis Greely Anderson

LENGTHY SYMPHONY

The opus rises to fortissimo
   While I, once more, resign myself to fate,
Hemmed in quite hopelessly by row on row
   Of music lovers, hushed, insatiate.
I know it is a sacrilege to sigh—
   The end is nearing, in all likelihood—
But one affrighted piccolo and I
   See no way out of this enchanted wood.

Phyllis McGinley

· PUBLIC JOURNAL

VERSES INSPIRED BY A DAY SPENT IN COMMUNION WITH THE BRIGHT
YOUNG MEN OF ENGLISH VERSE

Christopher Isherwood, Stephen Spender,
Auden and L. MacNeice—
I can't come along on an all-night bender,
But I'll have a quick one with you.

It is four in the afternoon. Time still for a poem,
A poem not topical, wholly, or romantic, or metaphysic,
But fetched from the grab-bag of my mind and gaudy with
Symbol, slogan, quotation, and even music.
And many a Marxian maxim and many allusions
To a daft system and a world-disorder.
I will mention machines and the eight hour day and
Czecho-Slovakia and the invaded border.

I will speak of love and I will do it slyly,
Unloosing the sacred girdle with a tired air,
Taking particular pains to notice the elastic garters
And the literal underwear.

I will put learning into my poem, for I acquired learning
At Cambridge or Oxford, it does not matter which.
But I'll freshen it up with slang which I got by ear,
Though it may sound a little off pitch.
And I'll be casual with rhymes for that is the trend,
Fashionable as the black hat of Anthony Eden.
I may put them at the middle of the stanza instead of the end,
For really amazing effect.
Or perhaps I'll find that assonance heightens the meaning better.
Yes, definitely, I prefer the latter.

Well, it will be sport, writing my private hates
And my personal credo.
I must bring in how I went to Spain on a holiday,
And how cold it was in Toledo.
There was a bootblack, too, in Madrid,
Who gave my shoes a burnish.
He told me something important which I cannot repeat,
For though I understand Spain, I do not understand Spanish.

I'll recall autumn weather in Birmingham,
Drearier than Boston.
And the pump-attendant there who sold me stormy petrol
For my thirsting Austin.

I will put tarts into my poem, and tenement people,
The poor but not the meek;
And pieces of popular songs for a hint of nostalgia,
And bits of Greek.

I shall be tough and ardent and angry-eyed,
Aware that the world is dying, gasping, its face grown pallid;
But quick to embalm it in language as an aspic
Enfolds the chicken salad.

Now it is five o'clock. The poem is finished
Like Poland, like the upper classes, like Sunday's roast.
I must straighten my waistcoat and see that it goes straight out
By the evening post.

For what is left for us? Only
The stanza a day,
And the American royalties, and an inherited income,
To keep the wolf at bay.

George Jean Nathan

BACK TO METHUSELAH

I surely advance no stunning morsel of news when I intimate to you that it has for some time now been the generous conviction of his many admirers that something ought to be done—by way of preserving the reputation he has antecedently established for himself—to make Mr. George Bernard Shaw shut up. To those of us who have been so greatly and so often soundly entertained by him for many years, the immediate institution and subsidy of an aesthetic Ku Klux with his muffling as its sole purpose would be a fond and gratifying thing. For, crossing the line of seventy some five or six years ago, the erstwhile Grand Old Boy of English drama and letters has, to the grief of the loving and yet judicious, made pretty much of a damned fool of himself. As damned fool is the exact phrase, I see no need for a more literary and genteel circumlocution. And not only has he made this damned fool of himself, but, in addition, he has turned out to be a very lamentable bore.

Any man, whether in his later or earlier years, is privileged to make something of a fool of himself if only he accompanies the act with a palliative dose of consoling humor or wit or with a persuasive and even slightly substantiating mocking philosophy. Any man is not only privileged to make a fool of himself, indeed, but, as human nature goes, is apparently pretty well by the Fates bound. Yet when a man of Shaw's previous humor, wit, intelligence and very considerable dialectical skill makes a monkey of himself and no longer displays the humor, wit, intelligence and dialectical skill to make his public not only swallow the fact but like it, it is high time that some kind friend took him gently by the ear, led him back home to mama and begged her, in his best interests, to keep a close eye on him and not let him out at night anymore. The trouble with Shaw is that, metaphorically, he has been going out at night when his venerable years and enfeebled powers have made it more or less obvious that he should have had his glass of hot milk by nine o'clock and been put safely to bed in his long woolen underwear. Yet what has he done? What he has done, careless of his literary, dramatic, critical and disputatious health, has been to persist in frisking anciently about under the young stars and the inhospitable winds of the new Springtime, with forced antic gayety croaking a song of the early Nineteen-Hundreds and with strained jocularity mimicking the noises of yon tree-top cuckoo. Where certain other quondam distinguished valetudinarians have, like the M. Maeterlinck, run off with a young girl, Shaw, being a vegetarian, has run off with an old joke.

Consider some of our erstwhile hero's septuagenarian monkey-shines. He has had his photograph taken in a state approximating the altogether. He has descended to a talking picture of himself wherein he has clownishly turned himself this way and that, instructing the onlookers to observe the rich beauty of his profile. He has made radio speeches in the language of Mr. Rube Goldberg's comic-strip "balloons." He has entered into Shakespearean discussions with prize-fighters, has played tag for the cameras on the Riviera with movie pantaloons, and has clambered laboriously atop a cannon in Moscow and cracked cheap vaudeville wheezes. He has engaged in sober philosophical discourse with one of the Four Marx Brothers and has given out interviews so silly that American newspaper editors, disbelieving that anything so juvenile could emanate from a mouth once so intelligent, have cabled to England for verification. He has taken up with the British *haute monde* and proudly posed for photographs with his bedizened hostesses. He has anticked for reporters at Malvern, performing circus-ring stunts with an umbrella. He has vainly insisted upon his youthfulness by going out in the rain bare-head and by being ostentatiously disgusted with persons who have sense enough to go in when it rains. He has made speeches on German railway platforms, on his return from a trip to Russia, so obviously manufactured for their publicity value that everyone has snickered at his performances. He has, in short, done just about everything that a dignified and still partly intelligent man could not think of doing. And, what is worse and what is our more immediate and relevant business, he has grown quite as dull and quite as stupid and quite as tiresome in his literary and dramatic enterprises as in his extra-literary and extra-dramatic.

In "The Apple Cart," we had a premonitory indication that a multiple, or brain, sclerosis had begun to attack Shaw. And now, in "Too True To Be Good," his latest substitute for playwriting, the doctor has told us the worst. I believe that I do not exaggerate when I say that, were any other name in the whole world of drama or literature attached to the play as author, no theatrical producer, white or black, would hesitate for a moment in throwing it forthwith into the trash-basket. Aside from one or two moderately fresh and faintly amusing flashes of paradox, it amounts in sum not only to a weary reiteration of all the antique Shavian opinions but to a restatement of various other opinions on the post-war dégringolade, the post-war spiritual uncertainty, the futility of carnage, etc., as stale and obvious as an old gin breath. It is dull, dull, dull, perhaps the dullest play, indeed, that a playwright of sometime high position has ever contributed to the theatre. And, being that dull, it carries with it a shade of sadness that its author, long so close to the admiring humor of most of us, has not at length the sagacity and wisdom to call it a day and, in some quiet corner of England, does not for the rest of his years sun himself peacefully and satisfiedly in the warm after-glow of his earlier career.

Dorothy Parker

THE HIGHLY RECURRENT MR. HAMILTON *

In advertising "Caste," the latest fantasy of that dreamer of dreams,
Mr. Cosmo Hamilton, the publishers state not only that it is "a superb
love story," but that it is "a biting social satire." In either of which
cases, I am the entire Hanneford family, including the nice white
horsie.

It is but fair to remark that this is my virgin try at any of the
works of Mr. Hamilton; and perhaps it is necessary to eat seven
before acquiring the taste. Until today, I walked square-shouldered
among my fellows, looked them in the composite eye, and said in
unshaken tones: "Anyway, there are two things I have never done.
I never resisted an officer, and I never read anything by Cosmo Hamilton." Today only the first half of that ringing boast is true. I made,
as usual, the wrong selection.

"Caste" is concerned with a Big Theme. Until this book, Mr.
Hamilton, they tell me, has been frittering away his time in writing
of that trifle, sex. Now he has lifted himself by his own spat-straps,
so to say, and cracked the race question wide open. He has dared
to tell, as only he can tell it, of the love of a fair young flower of
the most exclusive New York society for a—put your head down a
moment, while I whisper—for a Jew. Deliberately, the author has
made things as difficult as possible for himself, for his J-w is none
of your stereotyped Shylocks or Fagins. Mr. Hamilton's J-w is what
those who announce benevolently that they number some of them
among their best friends would call "a good J-w." Though of the
Chosen People, he is a gentleman; also, he is young, beautiful, romantic, cultured, a genius of the pianoforte, the toast of London and
the Continent, and you never see him lying drunk in a gutter. Indeed,
cries the author, crazed with liberalism, "He might have been a

* These two book reviews by Dorothy Parker were published in The New
Yorker over the signature Constant Reader.

Frenchman who had been educated at Harrow or Winchester." But neither you nor Mr. Hamilton can get around the fact that he is a J-w.

The full horror of the thing sweeps over you in that gripping scene where *Erskine Dalbeattie Farquhar,* the elegant father of the fair flower, demands of *Lord Warminster,* the fair flower's elegant uncle, the name of this Semite.

" 'It's Lorbenstein,' said Warminster, whose memory was good.

" 'Lorbenstein!'

"Farquhar shuddered, and a chill ran down his spine."

Well, from then on, hell rips loose. The United States rises and protests, practically in a body, against the proposed marriage of the fair flower and her J-w. The Old World stands up for young *Lorbenstein* something pretty, but America won't hear of the thing. The fair flower has "a mass of letters from her numerous friends, and in every one of them ... she has been begged to scratch her engagement and play the game by her set." Secretaries of Societies protest, members of the Ku Klux Klan protest, rival social leaders protest, bishops and strangers (the redundancy is Mr. Hamilton's) from all over America protest, I protest, thou protestest, he, she, or it protests, we protest, you protest, they protest. It is easy to see that things cannot go on at that rate; some one, and it looks like the author, must give way under the strain.

So the book ends with *Max Lorbenstein,* gentleman if J-w, Going Away, leaving "the young and lovely girl holding a few brave and beautiful words of renunciation and sacrifice in a shaking hand."

But before that, there are all sorts of elegances to be read through. One sees the reason for the popularity of Mr. Hamilton's opera; their writer is, beyond question, the wish-fulfillment king. His characters live high and wide and handsome. Nothing is too good for them; theirs is an atmosphere of see-what-the-boys-in-the-back-room-will-have lavishness. Consider, for example, *Erskine Dalbeattie Farquhar's* instructions to his butler, on the night of a quiet little dinner for fifty:

"I want you to tell the orchestra to pause after their fourth selection. I telephoned to the leader this afternoon to give him a list of tunes. At the moment when you serve the champagne, and for God's sake don't ice it as you did one night in the winter, the pipers will march in. I want you to tell them to go four times round the table, disappear, have dinner, and then form up on both sides of the staircase when the ladies leave the room."

Consider, further, that butler's highly trained reply: "Thank you, Sir. I have remembered the formula."

It is all that grand. Old brandy and sumptuous fabrics, loveless marriages and extra-mural affections, dinner-tables with "the civilized number of wineglasses to each place"—these and kindred luxuries troop through the pages of "Caste."

And all are described in Mr. Hamilton's inimitable, please God, style. My second favorite passage in the book is the glimpse of *Erskine Dalbeattie Farquhar's* nobly renounced lady-friend, "the woman who had acquired the art of gorgeous silences," although given to playing "several of the Chopin Preludes with an artist's touch." But my favorite, oh, my true favorite, is the chummily recurrent phrase, "the *hoi palloi*." Oh, Mr. Hamilton, Mr. Hamilton! Is that what you learned on the cricket field of Eton?

RE-ENTER MARGOT ASQUITH

"Daddy, what's an optimist?" said Pat to Mike while they were walking down the street together one day.

"One who thought that Margot Asquith wasn't going to write any more," replied the absent-minded professor, as he wound up the cat and put the clock out.

That gifted entertainer, the Countess of Oxford and Asquith, author of "The Autobiography of Margot Asquith" (four volumes, neatly boxed, suitable for throwing purposes), reverts to tripe in a new book deftly entitled "Lay Sermons." It is a little dandy if I have ever seen one, and I certainly have.

I think it must be pleasanter to be Margot Asquith than to be any other living human being; and this is no matter of snap judgment on my part, for I have given long and envious thought to the desirability of being Charles A. Levine. But the lady seems to have even more self-assurance than has the argumentative birdman. Her perfect confidence in herself is a thing to which monuments should be erected; hers is a poise that ought to be on display in the British Museum. The affair between Margot Asquith and Margot Asquith will live as one of the prettiest love stories in all literature.

In this book of essays, which has all the depth and glitter of a worn dime, the Countess walks right up to such subjects as Health, Human Nature, Fame, Character, Marriage, Politics, and Opportunities. A rather large order, you might say, but it leaves the lady with unturned hair. Successively, she knocks down and drags out each topic. And there is something vastly stirring in the way in which, no matter where she takes off from, she brings the discourse back to Margot Asquith. Such singleness of purpose is met but infrequently.

When she does get around to less personal matters, it turns out that her conclusions are soothingly far from startling. A compilation of her sentiments, suitably engraved upon a nice, big calendar, would make an ideal Christmas gift for your pastor, your dentist, or Junior's music teacher. Here, for instance, are a few ingots lifted from her golden treasury: "The artistic temperament has been known to land people in every kind of dilemma."..."Pleasure will always make a stronger appeal than Wisdom."..."It is only the fine natures that profit by Experience."..."It is better to be a pioneer than a passenger, and best of all to try and create." ... "It is not only what you See but what you Feel that kindles appreciation and gives life to Beauty." ... "Quite apart from the question of sex, some of the greatest rascals have been loved."..."I think it is a duty women owe not only to themselves, but to every one else, to dress well."

The Thames, I hear, remains as damp as ever in the face of these observations.

Through the pages of "Lay Sermons" walk the great. I don't say that Margot Asquith actually permits us to rub elbows with them ourselves, but she willingly shows us her own elbow, which has been, so to say, honed on the mighty. "I remember President Wilson saying to me"; "John Addington Symonds once said to me"; "The Master of Balliol told me"—thus does she introduce her anecdotes. And you know those anecdotes that begin that way; me, I find them more efficacious than sheep-counting, rain on a tin roof, or alanol tablets. Just begin a story with such a phrase as "I remember Disraeli —poor old Dizzy!—once saying to me, in answer to my poke in the eye," and you will find me and Morpheus off in a corner, necking.

Margot Asquith's is, I am sure, a naïve and an annoying (those two adjectives must ever be synonyms to me) and an unimportant book, yet somehow, grudge it though I do, there is a disarming quality to it and to its author. (There I go, getting tender about things, again;

it's no wonder men forget me.) Perhaps it is because the lady's cock-sureness implies a certain sort of desperate gallantry; perhaps it is because there is a little—oh, entirely unconscious, please, Your Grace—wistfulness in the recurrent references to the dear dead days of "The Souls," in the tales of the hunting-field when the high gentry were wont to exclaim, "You ride with such audacity, Miss Tennant!" I suppose that wistfulness is a fighting word to the Countess, but there it stands. She is, from her book, no master mind, God wot; but she is, also from her book, a game woman, gamer, I think, than she knows. I always have to cry a little bit about courage.

However (and how good it feels to get back to the nice, firm ground again), "Lay Sermons" is a naïve and an annoying and an unimportant book. The author says, "I am not sure that my ultimate choice for the name of this modest work is altogether happy." Happier I think it would have been if, instead of the word "Sermons," she had selected the word "Off."

THE REPORTERS AT WORK

In the preface to this book we gave reasons for abandoning funny newspaper stories. We probably would have given up the search for them earlier in the game if it hadn't been for a Frank Sullivan story from the World *which we had on hand. It was headed DECKHANDS IN RESCUE PARTY, and began this way:*

Philip Lamb, twenty-five, a deckhand on the tug *Thomas Howard,* moored at North First Street, Brooklyn, was boarding the tug yesterday when he slipped and fell into the river.

"Ahoy!" he cried.

Then he decided he had better start swimming, both to keep warm and afloat.

"Ahoy!" he cried.

"Ahoy!" cried a deckhand on the *Thomas Howard.*

"Ahoy!" cried Mr. Lamb.

"Awhere?" cried the deckhand.

"Ahere," informed Philip. "Ahoy ahere."

"Oh," said the deckhand, "down THERE. . . ."

It took us a long time to find out that we just couldn't locate an unlimited quantity of such news stories.

The profile of Timenterprise, by Wolcott Gibbs, is placed in this section rather than under Parody for arbitrary reasons;

it is *definitely a parody, and a superb one, but it is also humor in reporting.*

For the sake of the record it should be stated that "The Talk of the Town" pieces are often the work of two men—a reporter and a rewrite man, each as guilty as the other. In all news reports that are funny, imagination in fact-gathering is as important as the actual writing of the story.

There are two pieces in this section on the subject of birds and bird people. For some wholly mysterious reason birds began crowding into our book early. They came in like flies into a kitchen, and they kept on coming. It was an unexpected plague. We soon found ourselves with an embarrassing number of bird pieces, and had to start discarding good things for no other reason than that they pertained to birds and we didn't want the book to be preponderantly ornithological. Is there something about birds that attracts humorists, or vice versa?

Wolcott Gibbs

TIME...FORTUNE...LIFE...LUCE

Sad-eyed last month was nimble, middle-sized *Life*-President Clair Maxwell as he told newshawks of the sale of the fifty-three-year-old gagmag to *Time*. For celebrated name alone, price: $85,000.

Said he: *"Life* ... introduced to the world the drawings ... of such men as Charles Dana Gibson, the verses of ... James Whitcomb Riley and Oliver Herford, such writers as John Kendrick Bangs.... Be-

HENRY ROBINSON LUCE
For Cigarettes, $45,000?
(See FACTS, FIGURES)

ginning next month the magazine *Life* will embark on a new venture entirely unrelated to the old."

How unrelated to the world of the Gibson Girl is this new venture might have been gathered at the time from a prospectus issued by enormous, Apollo-faced C. D. Jackson, of Time, Inc.

"*Life*," wrote he, "will show us the Man-of-the-Week ... his body clothed, and, if possible, nude." It will expose "the loves, scandals, and personal affairs of the plain and fancy citizen ... and write around them a light, good-tempered 'colyumnist' review of these once-private lives."

29,000 die-hard subscribers to *Life*,* long accustomed to he-she jokes, many ignorant of King of England's once-private life (*Time,* July 25 *et seq.*), will be comforted for the balance of their subscription periods by familiar, innocent jocosities of *Judge*. First issue of new publication went out last week to 250,000 readers, carried advertisements suggesting an annual revenue of $1,500,000, pictured Russian peasants in the nude, the love life of the Black Widow spider, referred inevitably to Mrs. Ernest Simpson.

Behind this latest, most incomprehensible Timenterprise looms, as usual, ambitious, gimlet-eyed, Baby Tycoon Henry Robinson Luce, cofounder of *Time,* promulgator of *Fortune,* potent in associated radio & cinema ventures.

"High-Buttoned ... Brilliant"

Headman Luce was born in Tengchowfu, China, on April 3, 1898, the son of Henry Winters & Elizabeth Middleton Luce, Presbyterian missionaries. Very unlike the novels of Pearl Buck were his early days. Under brows too beetling for a baby, young Luce grew up inside the compound, played with his two sisters, lisped first Chinese, dreamed much of the Occident. At 14, weary of poverty, already respecting wealth & power, he sailed alone for England, entered school at St. Albans. Restless again, he came to the United States, enrolled at Hotchkiss, met up & coming young Brooklynite Briton Hadden. Both even then were troubled with an itch to harass the public. Intoned Luce years later: "We reached the conclusion that most people were not well informed & that something should be done. . . ."

First publication to inform fellowman was *Hotchkiss Weekly Record;* next *Yale Daily News,* which they turned into a tabloid; fought

* Peak of *Life* circulation (1921): 250,000.

to double hours of military training, fought alumni who wished to change tune of Yale song from *Die Wacht am Rhein*. Traditionally unshaven, wearing high-buttoned Brooks jackets, soft white collars, cordovan shoes, no garters, Luce & Hadden were Big Men on a campus then depleted of other, older Big Men by the war. Luce, pale, intense, nervous, was Skull & Bones, Alpha Delta Phi, Phi Beta Kappa, member of the Student Council, editor of the *News;* wrote sad poems, read the *New Republic,* studied political philosophy. As successful, less earnest, more convivial, Hadden collected china dogs, made jokes.* In 1920 the senior class voted Hadden Most Likely to Succeed, Luce Most Brilliant. Most Brilliant he, Luce sloped off to Christ Church, Oxford, there to study European conditions, take field trips into the churning Balkans.

Best Advice: Don't

Twenty months after commencement, in the city room of Paperkiller Frank Munsey's *Baltimore News,* met again Luce, Hadden. Newshawks by day, at night they wrangled over policies of the magazine they had been planning since Hotchkiss. Boasted the final prospectus: "*Time* will be free from cheap sensationalism ... windy bias."

In May, 1922, began the long struggle to raise money to start *Time.* Skeptical at the outset proved Newton D. Baker, Nicholas Murray Butler, Herbert Bayard Swope, William Lyon Phelps. Pooh-poohed *Review of Reviews* Owner Charles Lanier: "My best advice ... don't do it." From studious, pint-sized Henry Seidel Canby, later editor of Lamont-backed *Saturday Review of Literature,* came only encouraging voice in this threnody.

Undismayed Luce & Hadden took the first of many offices in an old brownstone house at 9 East 17th Street, furnished it with a filing cabinet, four second-hand desks, a big brass bowl for cigarette stubs, sought backers.†

---

* Once, watching Luce going past, laden with cares & responsibilities, Hadden chuckled, upspoke: "Look out, Harry. You'll drop the college."

† In return for $50 cash, original investors were given two shares 6% Preferred Stock with a par value of $25, one share Class A Common Stock without par value. 3,440 Preferred, 1,720 Class A Common were so sold.

170 shares of Class A Common, 8,000 shares of Class B Common, also without par value, not entitled to dividends until Preferred Shares had been retired, were issued to Briton Hadden, Henry R. Luce, who gave one-third to asso-

JPMorganapoleon H. P. Davison, Yale classmate of Luce, Hadden, great & good friend of both, in June contributed $4,000. Next to succumb: Mrs. David S. Ingalls, sister of Classmate William Hale Harkness; amount, $10,000. From Brother Bill, $5,000. Biggest early angel, Mrs. William Hale Harkness, mother of Brother Bill & Mrs. Ingalls, invested $20,000. Other original stockholders: Robert A. Chambers, Ward Cheney, F. Trubee Davison, E. Roland Harriman, Dwight W. Morrow, Harvey S. Firestone, Jr., Seymour H. Knox, William V. Griffin. By November Luce & Hadden had raised $86,000, decided to go to work on fellowman.

"Snaggle-Toothed ... Pig-Faced"

Puny in spite of these preparations, prosy in spite of the contributions of Yale poets Archibald MacLeish & John Farrar, was the first issue of *Time* on March 3, 1923. Magazine went to 9,000 subscribers; readers learned that Uncle Joe Cannon had retired at 86, that there was a famine in Russia, that Thornton Wilder friend Tunney had defeated Greb.

Yet to suggest itself as a rational method of communication, of infuriating readers into buying the magazine, was strange inverted Timestyle. It was months before Hadden's impish contempt for his

ciates, divided remainder equally.

In 1925, authorized capital of Time, Inc., was increased to 19,000 shares; of which 8,000 were Preferred, 3,000 Class A; as before, 8,000 Class B.

In June, 1930 (if you are still following this), the Preferred Stock was retired in full & dividends were initiated for both Common Stocks. Corporation at this time had 2,400 shares Class A, 7,900 Class B outstanding.

By the spring of 1931 *Time* had begun to march, shares were nominally quoted at $1,000. Best financial minds advised splitting stock on basis of twenty shares for one. Outstanding after clever maneuver: 206,400 shares Common.

In 1933, outlook still gorgeous, each share of stock was reclassified into 1/10th share of $6.50 Dividend Cumulative Convertible Preferred Stock ($6.50 div. cum. con. pfd. stk.) and one share of New Common Stock. New div. cum. con. pfd. stk. was convertible into a share and a half of New Common Stock, then selling around $40 a share, now quoted at over $200.

Present number of shares outstanding, 238,000; paper value of shares, $47,000,000; conservative estimate of Luce holding, 102,300 shares; paper value, $20,460,000; conservative estimate of Luce income from *Time* stock (shares earned $9.74 in 1935, paid so far in 1936, $6.50; anticipated dividend for full year, $8), $818,400; reported Luce income from other investments, $100,000; reported Luce bagatelle as editor of Time, Inc., $45,000; reported total Lucemolument, $963,400.

Boy!

readers,* his impatience with the English language, crystallized into gibberish. By the end of the first year, however, Timeditors were calling people able, potent, nimble; "Tycoon," most successful Tim-epithet, had been coined by Editor Laird Shields Goldsborough; so fascinated Hadden with "beady-eyed" that for months nobody was anything else. Timeworthy were deemed such designations as "Tom-tom" Heflin, "Body-lover" Macfadden.

"Great word! Great word!" would crow Hadden, coming upon "snaggle-toothed," "pig-faced." Appearing already were such mad-dening coagulations as "cinemaddict," "radiorator." Appearing also were first gratuitous invasions of privacy. Always mentioned as Wil-liam Randolph Hearst's "great & good friend" was Cinemactress Marion Davies, stressed was the bastardy of Ramsay MacDonald, the "cozy hospitality" of Mae West. Backward ran sentences until reeled the mind.

By March, 1924, the circulation had doubled, has risen since then 40,000 a year, reaches now the gratifying peak of 640,000, is still growing. From four meagre pages in first issue, *Time* advertising has now come to eclipse that in *Satevepost*. Published *Time* in first six months of 1936, 1,590 pages; *Satevepost*, 1,480.

No Slugabed, He ...

Strongly contrasted from the outset of their venture were Hadden, Luce. Hadden, handsome, black-haired, eccentric, irritated his partner by playing baseball with the office boys, by making jokes, by lack of respect for autocratic business. Conformist Luce disapproved of heavy drinking, played hard, sensible game of tennis, said once: "I have no use for a man who lies in bed after nine o'clock in the morning," walked to work every morning, reproved a writer who asked for a desk for lack of "log-cabin spirit."

In 1925, when *Time* moved its offices to Cleveland, bored, rebellious was Editor Hadden; Luce, busy & social, lunched with local bigwigs, addressed Chamber of Commerce, subscribed to Symphony Orchestra, had neat house in the suburbs. Dismayed was Luce when Hadden met him on return from Europe with premature plans to move the magazine back to New York. In 1929, dying of a streptococcus infec-

---

* Still framed at *Time* is Hadden's scrawled dictum: "Let Subscriber Good-kind mend his ways!"

tion, Hadden still opposed certain details of success-formula of *Fortune,* new, beloved Lucenterprise.

Oats, Hogs, Cheese ...

In January, 1930, first issue of *Fortune* was mailed to 30,000 subscribers, cost as now $1 a copy, contained articles on branch banking, hogs, glassblowing, how to live in Chicago on $25,000 a year. Latest issue (Nov., 1936) went to 130,000 subscribers, contained articles on bacon, tires, the New Deal, weighed as much as a good-sized flounder.*

Although in 1935 *Fortune* made a net profit of $500,000, vaguely dissatisfied was Editor Luce. Anxious to find & express "the technological significance of industry," he has been handicapped by the fact that his writers are often hostile to Big Business, prone to insert sneers, slithering insults. In an article on Bernard Baruch, the banker was described as calling President Hoover "old cheese-face." Protested Tycoon Baruch that he had said no such thing. Shotup of this was that Luce, embarrassed, printed a retraction; now often removes too-vivid phrasing from writers' copy.

¶ Typical perhaps of Luce methods is *Fortune* system of getting material. Writers in first draft put down wild gossip, any figures that occur to them. This is sent to victim, who indignantly corrects the errors, inadvertently supplies facts he might otherwise have withheld.

¶ *March of Time* in approximately its present form was first broadcast on March 6, 1931, paid the Columbia System for privilege, dropped from the air in February, 1932, with Luce attacking radio's "blatant claim to be a medium of education." Said he: "Should *Time* or any other business feel obliged to be the philanthropist of the air; to continue to pay for radio advertising it doesn't want in order to provide radio with something worthwhile?" So popular, so valuable to the studio was *March of Time* that it was restored in September of the same year, with Columbia donating its time & facilities. Since then *March of Time* has been sponsored by Remington-Rand typewriter company, by Wrigley's gum, by its own cinema *March of Time,* has made 400 broadcasts.† Apparently reconciled to philanthropy is Luce,

---

* Two pounds, nine ounces.

† By some devious necromancy, statisticians have calculated that *March of Time* ranks just behind *Amos & Andy* as most popular of all radio programs; reaches between 8,000,000 and 9,000,000 newshungry addicts.

because time for latest version will be bought & paid for by his organization.

¶ No active connection now has Luce with the moving-picture edition of *March of Time,* which was first shown on February 1, 1935, appears thirteen times a year in over 6,000 theatres, has so far failed to make money, to repay $900,000 investment. Even less connection has he with *Time's* only other unprofitable venture. Fifty-year-old *Architectural Forum,* acquired in 1932, loses still between $30,000 and $50,000 a year, circulates to 31,000.

¶ *Letters,* five-cent fortnightly collection of *Time's* correspondence with its indefatigable readers, was started in 1931, goes to 30,000, makes a little money.

¶ For a time, Luce was on Board of Directors of Paramount Pictures. Hoped to learn something of cinema, heard nothing discussed but banking, resigned sadly.

Fascinating Facts . . . Dreamy Figures . . .

Net profits of Time, Inc., for the past nine years:

1927	3,860
1928	125,787
1929	325,412
1930	818,936
1931	847,447
1932	613,727*
1933	1,009,628
1934	1,773,094
1935	$2,249,823†

In 1935 gross revenue of *Time-Fortune* was $8,621,170, of which the newsmagazine brought in approximately $6,000,000. Outside investments netted $562,295. For rent, salaries, production & distribution, other expenses went $6,594,076. Other deductions: $41,397. Allowance for federal income tax: $298,169.

Time's books, according to Chicago Statisticians Gerwig & Gerwig, show total assets of $6,755,451. Liabilities, $3,101,584. These figures,

---

* Hmm.

† Exceeded only by Curtis Publishing Co. (*Satevepost*): $5,329,000; Crowell Publishing Co. (*Collier's*): $2,399,600.

conventionally allowing $1 for name, prestige of *Time,* come far from reflecting actual prosperity of Luce, his enterprises. Sitting pretty are the boys.

Luce ... Marches On!

Transmogrified by this success are the offices, personnel of *Time-Fortune.* Last reliable report: *Time,* 308 employees; *Fortune,* 103; Cinemarch, 58; Radiomarch, 10; *Architectural Forum,* 40; *Life,* 47. In New York; total, 566. In Chicago, mailing, editorial, mechanical employees, 216. Grand total Timemployees on God's earth, 782. Average weekly recompense for informing fellowman, $45.67802.

From first single office, Timen have come to bulge to bursting six floors of spiked, shiny Chrysler Building, occupy 150 rooms, eat daily, many at famed Cloud Club, over 1,000 eggs, 500 cups of coffee, much bicarbonate of soda. Other offices: Cinemarch, 10th Avenue at 54th Street; Radiomarch, Columbia Broadcasting Building.

Ornamented with Yale, Harvard, Princeton diplomas, stuffed fish, terrestrial globes are offices of Luce & other headmen; bleak, uncarpeted the writer's dingy lair.

¶ Heir apparent to mantle of Luce is dapper, tennis-playing, $35,000-a-year Roy Larsen, nimble in Radio- & Cinemarch, vice-president & second largest stockholder in Time, Inc. Stock income: $120,000.

¶ Looming behind him is burly, able, tumbledown Yaleman Ralph McAllister Ingersoll, former Fortuneditor, now general manager of all Timenterprises, descendant of 400-famed Ward McAllister. Littered his desk with pills, unguents, Kleenex, Socialite Ingersoll is *Time's* No. 1 hypochondriac, introduced ant palaces for study & emulation of employees, writes copious memoranda about filing systems, other trivia, seldom misses a Yale football game. His salary: $30,000; income from stock: $40,000.

¶ Early in life Timeditor John Stuart Martin lost his left arm in an accident. Unhandicapped he, resentful of sympathy, Martin played par golf at Princeton, is a crack shot with a rifle or shotgun, holds a telephone with no hands, using shoulder & chin, chews paperclips. First cousin of Cofounder Hadden, joined in second marriage to daughter of Cunard Tycoon Sir Ashley Sparks, Timartin is managing editor of newsmagazine, has been nimble in Cinemarch, other Timenterprises, makes $25,000 a year salary, gets from stock $60,000.

¶ $20,000 salary, $20,000 from stock gets shyest, least-known of all Tim-editors, Harvardman John S. Billings, Jr., now under Luce in charge of revamped *Life,* once Washington correspondent for the Brooklyn *Eagle,* once National Affairs Editor for *Time.* Yclept "most important man in shop" by Colleague Martin, Billings, brother of famed muralist Henry Billings, is naïve, solemn, absent-minded, once printed same story twice, wanted to print, as news, story of van Gogh's self-mutilation, drives to office in car with liveried chauffeur, likes Jones Beach. ¶ Fortuneditor Eric Hodgins is thin-haired, orbicular, no Big Three graduate. Formerly on *Redbook,* boy & girl informing *Youth's Companion,* Hodgins inherited Pill-Swallower Ingersoll's editorial job two years ago when latter was called to greater glory, higher usefulness, still writes much of content of magazine, is paid $15,000; from stock only $8,000.

¶ Doomed to strict anonymity are *Time-Fortune* staff writers, but generally known in spite of this are former *Times* Bookritic John Chamberlain, Meistersinger Archibald MacLeish. Both out of sympathy with domineering business, both irked by stylistic restrictions, thorns to Luce as well as jewels they. Reward for lack of fame: Chamberlain, $10,000; MacLeish, $15,000; each, two months' vacation.

Brisk beyond belief are carryings-on these days in Luce's chromium tower. *Time,* marching on more militantly than ever, is a shambles on Sundays & Mondays, when week's news is teletyped to Chicago printing plant; *Fortune,* energetic, dignified, its offices smelling comfortably of cookies, is ever astir with such stupefying projects as sending the entire staff to Japan; new whoopsheet *Life* so deep in organization that staff breakfasts are held to choose from 6,000 submitted photographs the Nude of the Week; so harried perpetually all editors that even interoffice memoranda are couched in familiar Timestyle,* that an appointment to lunch with Editor Luce must be made three weeks in advance.

Caught up also in the whirlwind of progress are *Time, Fortune's* 19 maiden checkers. Bryn Mawr, Wellesley, Vassar graduates they, each is assigned to a staff writer, checks every word he writes, works hard & late, is barred by magazine's anti-feminine policy from editorial advancement.

---

* Sample Luce memorandum: "Let *Time's* editors next week put thought on the Japanese beetle. H. R. L."

Cold, Baggy, Temperate ...

At work today, Luce is efficient, humorless, revered by colleagues; arrives always at 9:15, leaves at 6, carrying armfuls of work, talks jerkily, carefully, avoiding visitor's eye; stutters in conversation, never in speechmaking. In early days kept standing at Luce desk like butlers were writers while he praised or blamed; now most business is done by time-saving memoranda called "Luce's bulls." Prone he to wave aside pleasantries, social preliminaries, to get at once to the matter in hand. Once to interviewer who said, "I hope I'm not disturbing you," snapped Luce, "Well, you are." To ladies full of gentle misinformation he is brusque, contradictory, hostile; says that his only hobby is "conversing with somebody who knows something," argues still that "names make news," that he would not hesitate to print a scandal involving his best friend.

Because of his Chinese birth, constantly besieged is Luce by visiting Orientals; he is polite, forbearing, seethes secretly. Lunch, usually in a private room at the Cloud Club, is eaten quickly, little attention paid to the food, much to business. He drinks not at all at midday, sparingly at all times, takes sometimes champagne at dinner, an occasional cocktail at parties. Embarrassed perhaps by reputation for unusual abstemiousness, he confesses proudly that he smokes too much.

Serious, ambitious Yale standards are still reflected in much of his conduct; in indiscriminate admiration for bustling success, in strong regard for conventional morality; in honest passion for accuracy; physically, in conservative, baggy clothes, white shirts with buttoned-down collars, solid-color ties. A budding joiner, in New York, Luce belongs to the Yale, Coffee House, Racquet & Tennis, Union, & Cloud Clubs; owns a box at the Metropolitan; is listed in *Who's Who* & *Social Register*.

Colder, more certain, more dignified than in the early days of the magazine, his prose style has grown less ebullient, resembles pontifical *Fortune* rather than chattering *Time*. Before some important body he makes now at least one speech a year, partly as a form of self-discipline, partly because he feels that his position as head of a national institution demands it. His interests wider, he likes to travel, meet & observe the Great. Five or six times in Europe, he has observed many Great & Near Great. Of a twenty-minute conversation with King Edward, then Prince of Wales, says only "Very interesting." Returning from such trips, he always provides staff members with 10 & 12-page memoranda carefully explaining conditions.

Orated recently of conditions in this country: "Without the aristocratic principle no society can endure.... What slowly deadened our aristocratic sense was the expanding frontier, but more the expanding machine.... But the aristocratic principle persisted in the United States in our fetish of comparative success.... We got a plutocracy without any common sense of dignity and obligation. Money became more and more the only mark of success, but still we insisted that the rich man was no better than the poor man—and the rich man accepted the verdict. And so let me make it plain, the triumph of the mass mind is nowhere more apparent than in the frustration of the upper classes." Also remarked in conversation: "Trouble is—great anti-social development—is the automobile trailer. Greatest failure of this country is that it hasn't provided good homes for its people. Trailer shows that."

Milestones

Good-naturedly amused by Luce tycoon ambitions was Lila Hotz, of Chicago, whom he married there on Dec. 22, 1923. In 1935, the father of two boys, Luce was divorced by her in Reno on Oct. 5. Married in Old Greenwich, Conn., without attendants, on Nov. 23, 1935, were Luce, Novelist-Playwright Clare Boothe Brokaw, described once by Anglo-aesthete Cecil Beaton as "most drenchingly beautiful," former wife of elderly Pantycoon George Tuttle Brokaw.

Two days before ceremony, "Abide with Me," by new, beautiful Mrs. Luce, was produced at the Ritz Theatre. Play dealt with young woman married to sadistic drunkard, was unfavorably reviewed by all newspaper critics.*

In a quandary was Bridegroom Luce when *Time's* own critic submitted a review suggesting play had some merit. Said he: "Show isn't that good.... Go back.... Write what you thought." Seven times, however, struggled the writer before achieving an acceptable compromise between criticism, tact.

---

* Of it said Richard Watts, blue-shirted, moon-faced *Tribune* dramappraiser:
"One almost forgave 'Abide with Me' its faults when its lovely playwright, who must have been crouched in the wings for a sprinter's start as the final curtain mercifully descended, heard a cry of 'author,' which was not audible in my vicinity, and arrived onstage to accept the audience's applause just as the actors, who had a head-start on her, were properly lined up and smoothed out to receive their customary adulation."

A Million Rooms, a Thousand Baths ...

Long accustomed to being entertained, entertaining, is Mrs. Luce, intimate of Mr. & Mrs. A. Coster Schermerhorn, Bernard M. Baruch, Jock Whitney, glistening stage & literary stars. Many were invited last summer to 30-acre estate in Stamford to play tennis, croquet, swim; many more will be when Mrs. Luce has finished her new play, "The Women," * when *Life's* problems, budding policies have been settled by Luce.

Many, too, will come to 7,000-acre, $100,000 Luce plantation, near Charleston, S. C.; will sleep there in four streamlined, prefabricated guest cottages. Given to first Mrs. Luce in divorce settlement, along with $500,000 in cash & securities, was French Manoir at Gladstone, N. J., where Luce once planned to raise Black Angus cows, to become gentleman farmer.

Described too modestly by him to Newyorkereporter as "smallest apartment in River House," † Luce duplex at 435 East 52nd Street contains 15 rooms, 5 baths, a lavatory; was leased furnished from Mrs. Bodrero Macy for $7,300 annually, contains many valuable French, English, Italian antiques, looks north and east on the river. In décor, Mrs. Luce prefers the modern; evasive is Luce. Says he: "Just like things convenient & sensible." Says also: "Whatever furniture or houses we buy in the future will be my wife's buying, not mine."

Whither, Whither?

Accused by many of Fascist leanings, of soaring journalistic ambition, much & conflicting is the evidence on Luce political faith, future plans. By tradition a Tory, in 1928 he voted for Alfred E. Smith, in 1932 for Herbert Hoover, this year for Alfred M. Landon. Long at outs with William Randolph Hearst, it was rumored that a visit last spring to California included a truce with ruthless, shifting publisher. Close friend for years of Thomas Lamont, Henry P. Davison, the late Dwight Morrow, it has been hinted that an official connection with the House of Morgan in the future is not impossible. Vehemently denies this Luce, denies any personal political ambition, admits only that he would like eventually to own a daily newspaper in New York.

---

* Among backers are sad, ramshackle George S. Kaufman, high-domed fur-bearing Moss Hart.

† Smallest apartment in River House has six rooms, one bath.

Most persistent, most fantastic rumor, however, declares that Yale-man Luce already has a wistful eye on the White House. Reported this recently Chicago's *Ringmaster,* added: "A legally-minded friend ...told him that his Chinese birth made him ineligible. Luce dashed to another lawyer to check. Relief! He was born of American parents and properly registered at the Consulate."

Whatever the facts in that matter, indicative of Luce consciousness of budding greatness, of responsibility to whole nation, was his report to *Time's* Board of Directors on March 19, 1936. Declaimed he: "The expansion of your company has brought it to a point beyond which it will cease to be even a big Small Business and become a small Big Business.... The problem of public relations also arises. *Time,* the Weekly Newsmagazine, has been, and still is, its own adequate apolo· gist. Ditto, *Fortune.* But with a motion-picture journal, a nightly radio broadcast, and with four magazines, the public interpretation of your company's alleged viewpoint or viewpoints must be taken with great seriousness." Certainly to be taken with seriousness is Luce at thirty-eight, his fellowman already informed up to his ears, the shadow of his enterprises long across the land, his future plans impossible to imagine, staggering to contemplate. Where it all will end, knows God!

Joseph Mitchell

TANYA

At one time or another I have talked with several of the lovely young women who hope to become the Sally Rand of the New York World's Fair of 1939. Of them all, Florence Cubitt is my favorite. She was the Queen of the Nudists at the California Pacific International Exposition at San Diego in 1936. The nudists—twenty girls and five bearded men—were segregated behind a fence in a big field, and the customers paid forty cents to go in and watch from a distance while they played games. Her Exposition name was Tanya Cubitt, she told me, because "Tanya sounds more sexy than Florence." I met her on St. Patrick's Day in 1936, and I spent several hours of a rainy afternoon listening to her talk in her room at the Hotel New Yorker.

Miss Cubitt was sent here to get some publicity for the San Diego Exposition. The officials of the San Diego fair, which was supposed to "tell the story of mankind's restless urge toward achievement," also said they would ban "all but the highest type of concession," but when customers stayed away by the million, they decided that Miss Cubitt's nudist concession was of an extraordinarily high type. More than one American exposition has been saved from bankruptcy by uninhibited young women.

The newspaper for which I work sent me up to interview Miss Cubitt the day after she arrived in New York. A photographer went along with me. I saved all my notes, and I want to tell you about Miss Cubitt because I think she will be one of the sensations of the Midway at Mr. Whalen's Fair.

We were met at the door of Miss Cubitt's room by one of the Exposition's press agents, a brisk young man named Jack Adams. We went in and sat down, and he said the Queen—he called her the Queen every time he referred to her—would be out in a minute. I had a bad cold that day and did not particularly like the assignment. I liked it even less when Mr. Adams began telling me about the Queen. He said she did not approve of the girls in the New York night-club shows because she felt they besmirched the cause of nudism. He said she ate uncooked carrots, took an orange-juice bath about once a week, and lived almost entirely off raw herbs.

He was telling about the Queen's dietary habits when she came in. She was naked. It was the first time a woman I had been sent to interview ever came into the room naked, and I was shocked. I say she was naked. Actually, she had a blue G-string on, but I have never seen anything look so naked in my life as she did when she walked into that room. She didn't even have any shoes on. She was a tall girl with a cheerful, baby face. She had long, golden hair and hazel eyes. The photographer was bending over his camera case, screwing a bulb into his flashpan, when she came in. As soon as he saw her, he abruptly stood erect.

"My God!" he said.

Mr. Adams introduced the Queen, and she shook hands with me and smiled. Then she shook hands with the photographer.

"Pleased to meet you," said the photographer.

"Likewise," said Miss Cubitt, smiling.

She went over and sat down in one of the hotel's overstuffed chairs and said she hoped we wouldn't mind if she didn't put anything on, and we shook our heads in unison. The telephone rang and Mr. Adams answered it. When he got through with the telephone, he said he would have to beat it, that he had an appointment with an advertising agency, and he said goodbye. The rain was beating against the windows, and when Mr. Adams got to the door, Miss Cubitt yelled, "You better wear your rubbers." The photographer was still standing in the middle of the floor with his flashpan in his hand, staring open-mouthed at the young woman. I didn't know how to begin the interview.

"Well, Miss Cubitt," I said, tentatively, "Mr. Adams just told me you eat a lot of raw carrots."

"Why," she said, sitting upright in the overstuffed chair, "I never ate a raw carrot in my life. I eat like anybody else. My mother cooks me great, big, old steaks and French-fried potatoes. That's what I eat. In the nudist colony, the men nudists eat a lot of that stuff. The men nudists are a bunch of nuts. Why, they eat peas right out of the pod. They squeeze the juice out of vegetables and drink it, and they don't eat salt. Also, they have long beards. They don't have any ambition. They just want to be nudists all their lives. I want to be a dancer, myself. I'm going to come to the New York World's Fair with my dance, and I bet it will make me a reputation."

I saw that the young woman was articulate, and that I wouldn't have to ask a lot of questions. When I said I had a bad cold, she said, "You poor man," and telephoned room service to send up whiskey. At the same time she ordered some sandwiches, some corned-beef sandwiches, saying, "I'm so hungry I could eat the flowers off the plate." While she was holding the telephone in her hand, waiting for room service to answer, she said she was only nineteen years old and that she had eight sisters, four of whom had been working with her in the nudist colony. Their names, she told me, were Ruthie, Bobbie, Lucille, and Diane. She said her mother was glad they were working in the colony.

"It keeps us out in the open," said Miss Cubitt. "It doesn't keep us out late at night, and we have a healthy atmosphere to work in. My girl friends think we have orgies and all, but I never had an orgy yet. Sometimes when the sun is hot, nudism is hard work."

She was a pretty girl. Her skin was ivory-colored and she had freckles on her cheeks, like Myrna Loy. In fact, she looked a little like Myrna Loy. She was obviously healthy, and she said she played a lot of tennis and handball. She said she sometimes posed for artists. "Once one of them told me I looked like a Madonna," she said, "and I said, 'O.K.'" I think she was the least inhibited person I ever saw. She reminded me of Reri, the Polynesian girl Florenz Ziegfeld brought to New York in 1931. Reri's feet were always dirty, because she insisted on walking about the theatre barefooted, and she used to sit in her dressing room at the "Follies" reading a movie magazine and wearing nothing but a pair of men's trunks.

"Mr. Adams told me you don't approve of the dancers in night clubs here," I said when she sat down again, "because you feel they besmirch the cause of nudism."

Miss Cubitt giggled.

"Well," she said, "you can put that in the paper if you want to, but I went to a night club last night and I thought the girls were real sweet. I would like to get a job in one. I sure do like New York. I've had lobsters every meal since I got here, and last night I had some real French champagne."

After the photographer had been introduced to the Queen, he had slumped into a chair and had remained there, staring. Now he roused himself and said he wanted to make some shots in a hurry, because he had to leave and cover the St. Patrick's Day parade. The young woman enjoyed posing and seemed to be sorry when the photographer finished, although he made about five times as many pictures as we needed. A few minutes after he left, a waiter, bringing the whiskey and the corned-beef sandwiches, knocked on the door. The waiter was either extremely sophisticated or had waited on the Queen before, because he did not seem to notice that she was not wearing anything. His eyes were respectfully averted, but he acted as if all the young women he waited on were nudists. When he had arranged his plates and glasses on a table, he handed Miss Cubitt the check. She signed it, and he bowed and left.

While we were eating the sandwiches, she told me of the dance she was working on, saying she called it the Tiger Lily dance. Why she called it that was a secret, she said.

"A World's Fair," the Queen remarked, "is a good place for a girl to make a reputation. When you get a reputation, you are fixed. Look at Sally Rand. What's she got I haven't got? I've seen her, and she's no world-beater. Look at Rosita Royce and her butterfly dance. Look at Toto La Verne and her swan dance. They're all World's Fair girls. If I can put my Tiger Lily over at the World's Fair, I'll be fixed."

I warned her that she might live to regret a World's Fair reputation, and mentioned the career of Mrs. Frieda Spyropolous, the Syrian girl whose dance as Little Egypt at the World's Columbian Exposition in 1893 attracted more attention than the seventy-ton telescope or any of the other educational exhibits. I told her how this Little Egypt had married the respectable Mr. Andrew Spyropolous, a Greek restaurant proprietor, not long after the Columbian Exposition closed, expecting to settle down to a peaceful way of life, and how the scandalous behavior of the hundreds of other Little Egypts who began doing her dance in low places all over the country had caused her acute anguish the rest of her life.

"Oh, I won't regret it," said the Queen, chewing on her sandwich. "I won't do anything unless it's artistic. Why, out at San Diego they even wanted me to do a Lady Godiva on a big white horse. I didn't do it because my boy friend made me mad. He said to go ahead and be Lady Godiva. He said he would sure pay forty cents to see me do it, because it had been years and years since he'd seen a horse."

Miss Cubitt giggled.

After we finished the sandwiches, we sat at a window and looked at the drizzle. I pointed out a few skyscrapers, but they didn't interest her. She wanted to talk about her career.

"It's swell being a nudist," she said, "but I wouldn't want to make it my life's work. I think the whole world should go nudist in the summer. You save so much on clothes. But then I don't know. I was in a real nudist colony once, and there were a lot of big, fat men there, and some women that must have weighed a ton. No kidding, you sure do see some terrible shapes in a nudist colony. Out at San Diego, we go on duty in the colony at noon and work until nine. It's like going back to your childhood—all you do is lie in the sun and play games. It's kind of silly, too. Sometimes me and my sisters get to laughing when we figure that already more than two million people have paid forty cents to see us girls running around naked. At the colony, we are a good distance from the customers, and they stand up there at the fence and strain their eyes. Sometimes I say to Ruthie, 'Ruthie, one of those psychologists would have a picnic down here.'"

By the time I got ready to go, my cold had vanished. Miss Cubitt went to the door with me. We were standing in the hall, shaking hands, when an elderly couple, a man and a woman, came out of a nearby room and started down the hall to the elevator. When they saw Miss Cubitt, their chins dropped. When they walked past us, they turned and stared. They did not appear to disapprove. They just seemed to be startled. Miss Cubitt giggled. She backed into her room.

"I guess I better say goodbye now," she said. "See you at the World's Fair."

Alva Johnston

HOW TO BECOME A GREAT WRITER*

Everybody sooner or later turns out to be a writer. Get deep enough into anybody's confidence, and you find that he has manuscripts. Psychoanalysts build a false science on the theory that millions of people are maladjusted lovers; a better knowledge of the world would teach that they are maladjusted writers.

David Binney Putnam launched himself on a serious literary career by wearing overalls, growing a beard and setting out to get the life stories of derelicts; the first derelict he met was a writer who took out a notebook and insisted on having young Putnam's life story.

Harold Ross, editor of The New Yorker, finding himself sick of New York City's 7,300,000 writers, tried to hunt a spot where there were no writers. He and Harpo Marx drove a car far into the Rockies. En route Harpo turned out to be a secret writer. The car broke down. The editor followed a trail leading to a cabin in a lonely mountain valley. In the cabin he found a writer writing a novel.

All this shows that, as Ed Howe put it, the people are smart. They are on the right trail. Writing is the shortest cut to affluence except inheriting big money. Today is the harvesttime for writers, and tomorrow's prospect is still better. A sure-hit writer can get $5000 a week and upwards in Hollywood. A good radio-script man or woman is worth four figures a week. Magazine editors and book publishers go out in posses after any promising writer. Writing is the royal road to statemanship; there is an enormous demand on the part of public men in Washington and elsewhere for artists in the oration-writing department of belles-lettres. Television holds a promise of becoming a writers' paradise; if it is a success it will require legions of writers to feed the television studios with scripts.

The paradox of the literary situation is that, while everybody is a writer, there is a shortage of writers for the thousand-a-week spots

This Saturday Evening Post *article has been cut.*

and the five-thousand-a-week spots. According to Pandro Berman. head of the RKO picture studio. Hollywood can't get one tenth of the good writers it needs. His solution of the problem is for the universities to stop concentrating on the second-rate professions, which are already overcrowded, and to devote themselves to turning out big-money master writers, who are needed by the thousands. Law, medicine, engineering and the sciences have proved themselves to be excellent stopgaps and steppingstones for writers, but the demand of the time is for direct literary training which will enable young men and women to assume the thousand-a-week burdens immediately on graduation.

The main difficulty with Berman's suggestion is that of organizing the courses. Nobody seems to have worked out a satisfactory method of training writers to write. Colleges are good on punctuation marks, but not on what to put between them. Famous writers seem to have left few hints that are useful to beginners. Ring Lardner said it was a matter of selecting pencils of the right colors. Anthony Trollope said it was a matter of attaching the writer's pants to the chair with bees-wax. Goethe attributed his output to a chair in which it was impossible to get into a restful position. In the vast literature about Dr. Samuel Johnson, only one practical rule of writing is to be found, and Doctor Johnson had that from an old schoolmaster; the rule being that, if you think any sentence you write is particularly good, strike it out. Dickens picked up his technique by accident. As a Parliamentary shorthand reporter during the decadence of parliamentary oratory, he learned the comic effect of presenting trivialities in ornate and sounding prose.

The subject has to be simplified before the universities can turn out prose masters on belt conveyors. A new approach to the problem would be to take the greatest living writer and make a thorough analysis of the factors which caused his greatness. Because of differences of opinion as to who is the greatest living writer, it is necessary to adopt arbitrary tests to identify him.

These tests are: 1. The size of the writer's public. 2. His success in establishing a character in the consciousness of the world. 3. The probability of his being read by posterity.

Judged by these tests, Edgar Rice Burroughs is first and the rest nowhere.

No other literary creation of this century has a following like Tarzan. Another character with a world-wide public is Mickey Mouse, but he belongs to a different art. The only other recent works of imagination in this class are Charlie McCarthy and The Lone Ranger, but their vogue is confined to the English-speaking peoples and they are still novelties rather than assured immortals.

Twenty-five million copies of the Tarzan books have been sold. Tarzan has established his durability; the first book on the ape boy came out a quarter of a century ago, and he is today more popular than ever. A writer's foreign following has been described as a contemporary posterity; Tarzan books have been translated into fifty-six languages and dialects. Hundreds of baseball players, football players, wrestlers, fighters and other athletes are nicknamed Tarzan. Extra-large schoolboys are called Tarzan in admiration, and undersized ones are called Tarzan in derision. Sherlock Holmes, Peter Pan, Pollyanna and Babbitt are perhaps the only literary creations of the last fifty years whose names are rooted in the English language as strongly as Tarzan; and Tarzan is a household word on every continent and on the larger islands from Iceland to Java.

Tarzan is a pillar of the American fiscal system. Through his author, his motion-picture company, his cartoon-strip syndicate, his radio sponsors and his various other concessionaires, the African ape boy contributes enough in taxes to pay the salaries of most of the United States senators.

Burroughs is clearly the man to tell the 130,000,000 American writers how to write. His life story ought to be the supreme textbook. The main rules for literary training that can be gathered from the experiences of Burroughs are:

1. Be a disappointed man.
2. Achieve no success at anything you touch.
3. Lead an unbearably drab and uninteresting life.
4. Hate civilization.
5. Learn no grammar.
6. Read little.
7. Write nothing.
8. Have an ordinary mind and commonplace tastes, approximating those of the great reading public.
9. Avoid subjects that you know about.

Burroughs had been an ill-paid employee and an unsuccessful small businessman for fifteen years before he wrote a word of fiction. The great difficulty in basing a college training on his rules is that of compressing into four years all the dullness, wretchedness and futility which it took Burroughs fifteen years to assimilate.

Burroughs started at twenty as a cattle drover and then became an employee on a gold dredge in Oregon. For a time he was a railroad policeman in Salt Lake City. He put in stretches as an accountant, as a clerk and as a peddler. His most important position was that of head of the stenographic department of Sears-Roebuck, in Chicago. A docile employee, he was never fired. An inveterate reader of help-wanted ads, he was constantly obtaining new positions not quite equal to his old ones. Added to that, he was always ready to join his own pennilessness to the pennilessness of some other man, and to found a partnership on any naïve dream of avarice.

Combining their resources of no capital, no experience and no contacts, Burroughs and a partner founded an advertising agency, which failed.

Having no experience with salesmanship beyond that of being repulsed by housewives when he tried to sell sets of Stoddard's Lectures, Burroughs wrote a correspondence course in salesmanship. After studying by correspondence for a few weeks, his students were to be graduated into field work. Small stocks of aluminum pots and pans were sent to them with instructions to sell them from door to door and remit the money to the home office.

Burroughs and his partner thought there were millions in it. They regarded themselves as aluminum kings about to corner the pot-an-pan trade with the help of peddlers who would pay tuition fees for the privilege of peddling. But the students all quit when they got to the field-work stage. Some failed to send back either the money or the pots and pans.

The Burroughs family had been rich when Edgar was a boy, but had lost its money. His allowance at prep school had been $150 a month. During his entire business career he never earned as much as his prep-school allowance. Twice he was compelled to pawn his family heirlooms in order to buy food for his wife and children. His failure as a businessman was so complete that he was reduced to earning a living by writing hints on how to become a successful businessman.

The businessman's bible three decades ago was *System, the Magazine of Efficiency*. It was a pioneer in introducing charts and graphs. Many businessmen worshiped charts and graphs as religious symbols. It was their belief that, if they stared long enough at these mystic curves and angles, red ink would turn into black.

A new department was introduced by the magazine. On payment of fifty dollars a year, a businessman could write to the magazine as often as he liked, and receive detailed advice on his business problems. Burroughs was hired to give the detailed advice. There was also a detailed-advice department for bankers, which was handled by a youth of twenty-one years. Burroughs sat at his desk from morning until night, writing counsel to merchant princes and captains. He used words that rumbled with portentous business wisdom, but were too vague to enable any industrial baron to act on them. Burroughs had a conscience, and it was always his fear that, if his advice ever became understandable, it would land his clients in the bankruptcy courts. With his letters he would enclose some of the awe-inspiring hieroglyphics now known as "barometrics."

Burroughs' advice never brought a complaint, and he may have been as good as anybody else in this field. Nothing is definitely known on the subject today except that the more the charts and graphs flourish, the faster business decays.

Burroughs' first contact with literature came in 1911 through his connection with Alcola, a cure for alcoholism. Alcola cured alcoholism all right, but the Federal Pure Food and Drug people took the position that there were worse things than alcoholism, and forbade the sale of Alcola.

One of Burroughs' duties in the Alcola firm was that of putting advertisements in the pulp fiction magazines. He bought the magazines in order to make sure that his ads were printed. He detested fiction, but when he looked at the ads some of the reading matter entered his field of vision. His reaction was approximately that of Dean Swift, who, under similar circumstances, exclaimed, "No man alive ever writ such damned stuff."

His next thought was that, if this was literature, any man could be a man of letters if he would abandon his mind to it. He wrote a novel. Thomas Newell Metcalf, editor of the *All-Story Magazine*, accepted it and sent Burroughs a check for $400. It was published as a serial in *All-Story* in 1912, under the title of "Under the Moon of Mars."

Metcalf wanted to make a Sir Walter Scott out of Burroughs. He induced him to spend months of research on the Wars of the Roses. The result was a novel entitled "The Outlaw of Torn." Metcalf rejected it.

Burroughs saw the folly of research. He had located his first novel on Mars because nobody knew the local color of that planet or the psychology of the Martians, and nobody could check up on him. A similar motive influenced him partly in writing his first Tarzan book, "Tarzan of the Apes." He created a new race of apes, bigger than gorillas, and placed them in an unknown part of Africa. He knew that nobody could trip him up on the psychology, customs and language of his own private anthropoids.

For African local color he read Stanley's "In Darkest Africa." He got his flora all right, but he made a blunder in his fauna. One of his important characters was Sabor, the tiger. There are no tigers in Africa. Letters from readers were printed in *All-Story* on this point. A man in Johannesburg confounded the critics, however, by writing that everybody in Africa referred to leopards as tigers. Nevertheless, Burroughs later changed Sabor to a lioness. He got a check for $700 from *All-Story* for "Tarzan of the Apes."

Burroughs had by this time retired from his last business, that of selling a pencil sharpener, and was devoting all his time to writing. His business career had, by its dreary futility, been a genuine literary apprenticeship. During his last few years in commercial pursuits, life had become almost intolerable to him.

He was too poverty-stricken to pay for any of the tired businessman's relaxations, but he hit upon a free method of making himself feel better. When he went to bed he would lie awake, telling himself stories. His dislike of civilization caused him frequently to pick localities in distant parts of the solar system. Every night he had his one crowded hour of glorious life. Creating noble characters and diabolical monsters, he made them fight in cockpits in the center of the earth or in distant astronomical regions. The duller the day at the office the weirder his nightly adventures. His waking nightmares became long-drawn-out action serials.

Psychiatrists consider these reverie addicts borderline cases. If Burroughs' family had known of his mental state, they would have called in a medical man, who would have probably insisted on having his teeth out, according to the fashionable method of treating such patients in 1911. Twenty years later, Burroughs would have been advised to save up his money for a few years and go to a psychoanalyst, who would have cured him of an incipient $10,000,000 affliction. A raise of twenty-five dollars a month in 1911, according to Burroughs' estimate, would have made him happy and caused him to put in nights of sound, refreshing slumber, instead of constructing penny-dreadful deliriums for himself.

Burroughs had given away serials to himself for five years or more before he learned that he could sell them. He had become a master of the slaughterhouse branches of fiction. It is clear from reading the Tarzan and other Burroughs books that he devoted little of his twilight sleep to tea-table and boy-meets-girl imbroglios.

Five years of dark and bloody mysteries gave his pen a high professionalism in pyramiding climaxes and piling up horror; but he was an awkward novice when the structure of his novel required him to introduce scenes of society life or hearts-and-flowers passages. Burroughs is great when Tarzan has a half nelson on a lion or a gorilla, but he has no talent for drawing-room hubble-bubble or boudoir hanky-panky. There is a trace of Homer in him, but not any Noel Coward.

In "Tarzan of the Apes" the reader can put his finger on the passages where Burroughs is the dream-disciplined artist and on the passages where he is the self-conscious amateur. He wanted to endow his ape-reared infant with a magnificent heredity. He was under the impression that the way to have a glorious moral, mental and physical inheritance was to be a scion of the British aristocracy. So Tarzan's parents were Lord and Lady Greystoke, the flower of the old nobility. Burroughs created them out of condescending sawdust.

It is obvious that Burroughs in his nightly trances had wasted no time messing around with lords and ladies. The Burroughs noblemen cause the reader to turn instinctively to P. G. Wodehouse for a sympathetic picture of the British aristocracy. But when the real Burroughs gets to work on his wild boy, his colossal anthropoids, his giant carnivora and his cannibals, it is not difficult to see why 3,000,000 copies of "Tarzan of the Apes" have been sold and why Tarzan is the best-known literary character of the twentieth century.

Burroughs says that his ordinariness explains his success. When he wrote his first novel for *All-Story,* he used the nom de plume of Normal Bean, meaning common head. By accident the editor changed it to Norman Bean. Burroughs was unwilling to use his own name at the time because he thought it would hurt his standing in the unsuccessful business world. He believes today that his novels are in demand because the things that interest him are bound to interest the ordinary people, who are abundant. Undoubtedly a certain galloping commonplaceness is one of his assets, but he has others. He did not win his world public solely through mediocrity. There are pages of his books which have the authentic flash and sting of storytelling genius.

One brilliant passage is that in which the half-grown Tarzan identifies himself as the being who is reflected in a pool of water. Tarzan had already had reason to suspect that he was not a trueborn ape. Gazing at himself in the waters, he discovers what a poor relation of the higher anthropoids he really is. Burroughs is in a high literary vein when he describes the boy's chagrin in comparing his parody of a countenance with the pretentious physiognomies of his playmates. Instead of nostrils that spread half across his face, he had a despicable imitation of an organ of smell. He had trifling bits of ivory where competent tusks should have been. Self-pity overwhelmed him when he discovered that his eyes were an insipid gray instead of being big, black and bloodshot. On realizing that he was hairless like a snake, he plastered himself from head to foot with mud.

Tarzan had already suspected that he was not a true ape, because he had discovered in a deserted cabin a number of kindergarten books with pictures of animals. He had begun to fear that he resembled the apes less than he resembled another animal, whose picture was always printed with what appeared to be three little bugs—*B, O* and *Y.* The painful conviction was forced upon him that he was a *B-O-Y.*

Using these three bugs as a clue, Tarzan works out the secret of all the twenty-six bugs in the alphabet. He learns written English without knowing how to pronounce it. Burroughs' handling of Tarzan's self-education is better than the cipher sequences in "The Gold Bug" or "The Dancing Men."

Tarzan's discovery that he is a member of the human species later lands him in a beautiful ethical dilemma. Having killed an African tribesman, Tarzan is about to help himself. Certain doubts assail him. His bringing up had taught him that eating a member of one's own species was not done. He has eaten raw gorilla, but the gorilla does not belong to his set. Tarzan now knows himself to be a man, and he recognizes the dead African as a man. On the other hand, Tarzan is hungry, and his political sympathies are all with the apes. It is a pretty case of conscience, and Burroughs does justice to it. In the end Tarzan takes the high ethical stand and never refreshes himself with an African.

One sequence in "Tarzan of the Apes" will bear comparison with the much-admired passage in "Gulliver's Travels" in which the Lilliputians, in an official report on the effects removed from Gulliver's pockets, suggest that his watch is his god because of the frequency with which he consults it. Tarzan sees Kulonga, son of a savage chief, cook a wild boar and eat it. Tarzan knows fire only as Ara, the lightning. He cannot understand why anybody would spoil raw meat by plunging it into fire. He concludes that Kulonga is a friend of the god of lightning and is sharing the wild boar with him. There is occasionally a touch of poetry in Burroughs, as in describing Tarzan's grass-woven lasso as "his long arm of many grasses."

Another source of the author's strength is his strong grip of character. Not only Tarzan but the apes and animals are highly individualized beings who seldom step out of character. Burroughs edits the Tarzan movies and newspaper strips to see that no liberties are taken with the Tarzan psychology. In one movie scene, for example, Tarzan threw his head back and laughed long and boisterously. "Strike it out," ordered Burroughs. Tarzan, in spite of his violent activity, is as reserved and contemplative as Hamlet. Nothing could be farther from his personality than brainless uproariousness.

One of the handsome passages in "Tarzan of the Apes" is the ape-bred boy's first encounter with white womanhood. Tarzan rescued the heroine, a glamorous but educated American girl, from the clutches of a mate-hunting giant ape. The bronzed and sun-baked Tarzan, accustomed to seeing none but ape women and blacks, was conscious of a sudden prejudice in her favor, in spite of her white body. He wanted her to know that he was favorably disposed toward her. His good will took the form of pawing and nuzzling. She slapped him. Tarzan was astonished. He had assumed that, when a member of a species showed a nice spirit toward another member of the same species, that spirit would be reciprocated. He could not understand why she was returning evil for good.

Burroughs was told that Kipling liked Tarzan and supposed that Tarzan was patterned after Mowgli of "The Jungle Book." According to Burroughs, Tarzan is a literary descendant, not of Mowgli but of Romulus and Remus, who got such a raising from a she-wolf that they founded Rome. Burroughs credits himself with only one stroke of genius—the naming of Tarzan. The impact of those two syllables on the eardrum is, in his opinion, largely responsible for the world success of the Tarzan books. This is one of the few literary secrets of Burroughs that is communicable. In christening his characters he works with syllables as some composers work with musical notes. He tests one sound against another until, after trying perhaps hundreds of combinations, he has a name that rings like a fire bell.

The early life of Burroughs was more interesting than his business career, but it furnishes few hints toward becoming a great writer. His father, who had been a major in the Civil War, grew rich in the distilling business. Later he became a manufacturer of electrical batteries. He had a habit of reading aloud, which partly caused young Edgar's aversion to literature. When, for example, his father read "Dombey and Son," Edgar hated Dombey and had the impression that Dombey and Dickens were one and the same person. When he learned the difference, it was too late for him to overcome his ingrained prejudice against Dickens. He has also cherished a lifelong dislike for Shakespeare, but is big enough to state that he assumes it to be his fault rather than the poet's.

Burroughs' escape from grammar was a lucky accident. He was sent first to a private school in Chicago which held that the teaching of English grammar was nonsense and that students should absorb grammar through Latin and Greek. Edgar absorbed no Latin and Greek. He was then sent to Phillips Andover, which, assuming that all freshmen were thoroughly drilled in grammar, ignored that subject. Phillips Andover quickly waived on young Burroughs, and he was sent to military academy, which paid no attention to grammar. Edgar thus became an uninhibited writer, free from the anxieties about moods and tenses which kill spontaneity. Burroughs doesn't know whether he is grammatical or not, and cares less. He always writes or dictates at top speed in order to get his thoughts on paper while they are fresh and hot. No grammar-scared writer can do that. Burroughs never makes corrections unless he finds an inconsistency in his development of plot.

The battery business led the elder Burroughs to become interested in an electrical horseless carriage. Edgar demonstrated it at the World's Fair, in 1893. The only time he ever felt that he amounted to something was when he drove a nine-seater horseless surrey about the fairgrounds, starting runaways every hundred feet or so.

In his youth Burroughs had a craving for glory. He preferred the military variety because his father had been a soldier. After graduating from the Michigan Military Academy he joined its faculty as a cavalry instructor. After the Sino-Japanese War of 1894-5, China, which had been defeated because her armament consisted largely of drums and dragon banners, started to reorganize her army. Burroughs sought a commission in the Chinese army, but failed. Later he obtained a commission in the Nicaraguan army, but his family interfered. At the age of twenty he enlisted in the Seventh Cavalry and was sent to Arizona against Geronimo. Instead of cavalry charges, however, the campaign consisted mainly of ditch-digging. Wires were pulled, and, because Burroughs had enlisted while under age, he was discharged. In 1898 he volunteered for the Rough Riders, but received a polite letter of regret from Theodore Roosevelt.

During his brief Regular Army service, Burroughs had committed two grave infractions of the military code. On sentry duty, he was required to shoot to kill if anyone disregarded his warning of "Halt, or I fire." His warning was twice disregarded, but Burroughs did not shoot. In each case he wrongfully saved the life of a drunken member of his own outfit. He escaped disgrace, his unsoldierly conduct never becoming known.

From the Army Burroughs went directly into cow handling, and then into gold dredging. Years later, after establishing himself as a writer about imaginary worlds and countries, he wrote "The Bandit of Hell's Bend," based on his Western experience. This was a violation of his custom of not writing things personally known to him; but Alexander Grosset, of the publishing house of Grosset & Dunlap, pronounced "The Bandit of Hell's Bend" the greatest Western ever written.

The old craving for glory was roused in Burroughs only once after the Spanish-American War. He happened to see the regal state in which the president of the Oregon Short Line traveled. He took the only railroad job he could get. In hot pursuit of glory, Burroughs chased bums out of boxcars in the Salt Lake City railroad yards for six months. But the idea of becoming a railroad president—last of his high ambitions—faded, and he drifted into the business career which punished him until he took refuge in literature.

The first Tarzan story did not immediately make Burroughs rich. The idea of bringing it out in book form was rejected by publishing houses, one reason being that they felt that the title, "Tarzan of the Apes," would shock refined people. Burroughs wrote a sequel, "The Return of Tarzan." It was declined by the Munsey publications, without the knowledge of Bob Davis, editor-in-chief of that organization.

Davis was furious when the Tarzan sequel was printed in a rival magazine. The famous editor took Burroughs under his wing and insisted on publishing everything he wrote. Even Davis, however, did not see the future of Tarzan. He induced Burroughs to cause the original Tarzan to assume his title of Lord Greystoke and take his seat in the House of Lords, while the series was carried on with the son of Tarzan. This caused confusion, and Burroughs finally went back to Tarzan the First. According to rigid rules of biology, the African wild boy is now a grandfather.

In less than a year after his first work was published, Burroughs was a big pulp name and a ten-cents-a-word writer. As his literary labor consisted largely of transcribing from memory the old phantasmagorias with which he soothed himself during his business life, his production was large. He was making more than $20,000 a year before his first book was published. On his banner day he wrote 9100 words—$910 worth.

Big money did not immediately soften Burroughs' hatred of modern life. His great aim was to escape from civilization, and, as soon as he had money, he went to Southern California. In 1919, after he had become wealthy, Burroughs bought the 600-acre Harrison Gray Otis ranch in the San Fernando Valley and founded the town of Tarzana, about half an hour's auto ride from Hollywood. He delighted to ride, stetson on head, gun across saddle, over his hills and through his valleys and his canyons.

He started to ranch on a large scale with pedigreed animals. It was necessary to write furiously to support the ranch. Scarcity of wells and springs was the trouble. Water had to be brought in from the outside. After some experience with water rates, he found it would be cheaper to take his cattle to a soda fountain. The ranch was turned over to the El Caballero Golf Club, which failed. After running it as a public golf course for a while, Burroughs sold out.

Burroughs had been writing four years before a publishing house would take a chance on printing his novels in book form. The late J. H. Tennant, editor of the *New York Evening World,* had read "Tarzan of the Apes" in *All-Story* and bought the right to print it in his newspaper. Other papers followed suit, and Tarzan fans became an important bloc in the community. A. C. McClurg & Co., one of the many publishers which had previously rejected "Tarzan of the Apes," began publishing the Tarzan books and then other Burroughs novels. Millions of boys took to leaping from limb to limb and from tree to tree. The nation resounded with the Tarzan yell and the snapping of collarbones.

Today Burroughs has forty-nine books in print. The sales have exceeded 30,000,000 copies. The Tarzan books are still in great demand in nearly every part of the world except Germany. In 1925 Burroughs was taking more royalties out of Germany than any foreign author, but in that year a German writer printed a book entitled "Tarzan the German Devourer." During the World War, Burroughs had, in "Tarzan the Untamed," caused Tarzan to do his bit by capturing German officers and feeding them to lions. The sensitive Teutons boycotted Burroughs after 1925.

Tarzan is a radio star today. The Tarzan comic strip is printed in about 150 American newspapers and forty foreign ones, including journals in Java and Ceylon. Tarzan has been a great money-maker in the movies for more than twenty years. Johnny Weissmuller is the ninth actor to play the part in the films.

Tarzan's importance in the films increased greatly in 1932, when the late Irving Thalberg took charge of his career. Thalberg and Burroughs agreed that Tarzan pictures should be great spectacles and should come out once a year, like a circus. Thalberg's first two pictures cost more than a million each, and the third, "Tarzan Escapes," cost more than a million and a half. After Thalberg's death, the Metro-Goldwyn-Mayer Company dropped Tarzan as too expensive. But the final audit showed that "Tarzan Escapes" had grossed more than $2,000,000, and the series was resumed.

The expensiveness of the Tarzan films lies partly in the nature of things and partly in the maniacal perfectionism of Hollywood. In the last picture, "Tarzan Finds a Son," the producers wanted an effect of steam rising from a lake. They ransacked the country for steamy lakes and at last found the one they wanted in Florida. The lake refused to steam for them. They found that it would steam only on certain days and then only for about fifteen minutes in the morning. It took the location company seven days to get the pictures they wanted.

Most of the Tarzan scenes are taken out of doors. Bad weather causes losses running into hundreds of thousands of dollars in salaries of actors, technical men and mobs of extras. But the greatest expense is that of getting animals to perform. In making the last picture a lion cost the company tens of thousands of dollars by refusing to chase a small boy. The lion would either walk or lie down or lope off in the wrong direction. When he finally took after the boy, the boy forgot to run. The pay roll ran wild for ten days before the scene could be shot. Flamingos, zebras and other live items of African background, after hours had been consumed in maneuvering them into their places, walked off the set just before the cameras started.

It took weeks to teach the big elephant, Queenie, to limp when she was supposed to have been shot in the foot. In the meantime the baby elephant, Bea, was limping sympathetically, and it took weeks to break her of the habit. A herd of hippopotamuses broke out of their stockade in Sherwood Lake and ate up $25,000 worth of horticulture in the neighborhood. Fresh ostrich eggs, which were used by Tarzan's mate in making omelets, cost twenty-five dollars each.

M-G-M spared no expense on the Tarzan yell. Miles of sound track of human, animal and instruments sounds were tested in collecting the ingredients of an unearthly howl. The cry of a mother camel robbed of her young was used until still more mournful sounds were found. A combination of five different sound tracks is used today for the Tarzan yell. These are: 1. Sound track of Weissmuller yelling, amplified. 2. Track of hyena howl, run backward and volume diminished. 3. Soprano note sung by Lorraine Bridges, recorded on sound track at reduced speed; then re-recorded at varying speeds to give a "flutter" in sound. 4. Growl of dog, recorded very faintly. 5. Raspy note of violin G-string, recorded very faintly. In the experimental stage the five sound tracks were played over five different loud-speakers. From time to time the speed of each sound track was varied and the volume amplified or diminished.

When the orchestration of the yell was perfected, the five loud-speakers were played simultaneously and the blended sounds recorded on the master sound track. By constant practice Weissmuller is now able to let loose an almost perfect imitation of the sound track.

Sanderson Vanderbilt

OWL MAN

Somehow or other, Miss Emily Nathan, publicity manager for the Audubon Society, got the idea that a barn owl sleeps every night with Mr. Irving Kassoy at his apartment in the Bronx at 817 Faile Street. Maybe it was because a *stuffed* barn owl is perched on the bureau in Mr. Kassoy's bedroom and he knows where there *is* a live barn owl. Miss Nathan, with other things on her mind, didn't catch the distinction. At all events she got word to me that Mr. Kassoy had an owl sleeping with him and that I could have an interview with Mr. Kassoy. "Besides," said Miss Nathan, "the National Association of Audubon Societies gets all its owl reports from Mr. Kassoy."

I met Mr. Kassoy at six that evening at the Audubon Society's headquarters, at Fifty-seventh Street and Broadway, after he had completed his day's work. He is a slim little fellow of thirty-two, very pale and somewhat bald. His chin is pointed and his skin is drawn taut from his cheeks up to his wide forehead. You couldn't help noticing his grave eyes because of the thick glasses he wears. Even to one not knowing the nature of his hobby, Mr. Kassoy's general appearance would be hauntingly suggestive of owls.

Mr. Kassoy was sitting there in the anteroom of the Audubon offices telling Miss Nathan about the difference in behavior between male and female owls. As soon as I came in, Miss Nathan broke the bad news to me that Mr. Kassoy's barn owl did not roost in Mr. Kassoy's bedroom, after all. Even if it did, it had occurred to Miss Nathan, it would be unlikely that an owl would stay home after dark to be visited. It occurred to me that I ought to have thought of that myself. Mr. Kassoy immediately moderated my dismay by saying that he could take me to the home of a barn owl resident in New York City if I cared to make a rather strenuous trip, and I impulsively accepted his invitation. With very little more conversation we started off, after saying good night to Miss Nathan.

Crossing town on Fifty-ninth Street, Mr. Kassoy told me that when he is not checking up on owls, he works as a jewelry salesman in mid-town Manhattan. Then he went on eagerly to give me a brief intro-duction to the owl situation in the city. He said there might very likely be a pair of screech owls living right over there in Central Park and that the short-eared owl, the saw-whet owl, the great horned owl, and two or three other owls are seen around there occasionally on their way through town during migration seasons. But his interest was primarily in the barn owl, he said, because that's the kind that lives here all year round. As he talked, it developed that he was interested, actually, in only one barn owl, because, as far as he can find out, only one barn owl now lives in New York.

"Pelham Bay Park is the only place in the city where you can definitely go to see a barn owl when you want to see one," said Mr. Kassoy, picking his phrases with scientific care. "And, as a matter of fact, there's only one of the birds up there now. I've looked every-where for more of them—last May there was a pair in a church over in Flushing, and a few years ago (you'd hardly believe it, would you?) there were some in a factory up on East 138th Street—but the only barn owl I know of now is in Pelham Bay Park. I suppose you can't print this, but a man who is familiar with barn owls can always tell where they are by the droppings outside the place they're nesting in. I mean, he knows it's a barn owl and not a pigeon or some other kind of bird. Barn owls generally live in church belfries. I've been looking at a lot of belfries but I haven't covered them all as yet. There are so many churches in New York."

We went into the subway at Bloomingdale's and got on an uptown local. It was crowded, and Mr. Kassoy shouted above the roar that he had first heard of barn owls living in Pelham Bay Park in 1932. A pair of them had built a nest in a ventilator over the library of the old Huntington mansion, erected by the railroad magnate and now used by the Parks Department as a sort of warehouse. The next spring the female laid six eggs, and five of them hatched. It was then that Mr. Kassoy began to develop what he described as his monomania. Owl study isn't very exciting when there are no young birds, because the adults won't stay on their nests to be observed. All you get is a glimpse of them at dusk darting forth in search of food. But when there are babies, the female stands guard over them all night long while the father bird brings in the food. You can observe them then to beat the band, it seems.

Mr. Kassoy first of all got permission and some keys from the Parks Department to visit the Huntington mansion at all hours. Then he set a birdhouse against the interior opening of the ventilator. The owls seemed to like the birdhouse, and even stayed right on when Mr. Kassoy installed in it a little electric light operated by a dry-cell battery. Finally, he rigged up a piece of glass so that when it was dark outside and the light was turned on inside the cage, Mr. Kassoy could see the owls but the owls couldn't see Mr. Kassoy.

Three of that first batch of baby owls waddled through the ventilator, fell two stories to the ground, and died. The two others grew up and flew away. Mr. Kassoy never saw them again. The parents stayed on and Mr. Kassoy observed them every night. Then, in March, 1934, Mr. Kassoy found the female dead on the nest. *That's* the one, stuffed and mounted, in his bedroom. The male had a new mate in ten days. "A commentary on the possible abundance of the barn owl in New York," Mr. Kassoy said as the train pulled into Ninety-sixth Street.

Well, the new female deposited four eggs and three of them hatched out, and Mr. Kassoy put up a little platform outside the ventilator to protect the young from the fate of their predecessors. "When they were only eighteen days old," said Mr. Kassoy, pushing a straphanger's *Evening Journal* out of his face, "the barn owl's ancient enemy, the crow, chased the mother out over Eastchester Bay, where some herring gulls took up after her, pounced on her, and apparently finished her off."

Within a fortnight, he went on, the widower had a new companion, and *that's* the owl over which Mr. Kassoy now keeps lonely vigil in Pelham Bay Park and the one he was now taking me to see. She would have nothing to do with rearing her predecessor's offspring, he said, and kept disappearing from time to time. While the father owl labored to bring up his half-orphans, she'd go away for as long as a fortnight at a stretch. Finally, when the youngsters grew up, she settled down and hatched out five of her own. They came along pretty late in the season.

It snowed heavily in January and February of 1935, but Mr. Kassoy floundered from the end of the subway line through the drifts in the park to the Huntington mansion two or three nights a week. Some of the young owls died of starvation and the others went away. Finally the male vanished, and since that time Mr. Kassoy has had only the movements of the lone female to observe.

"There was every indication during March of 1935 that she was seeking a new mate," Mr. Kassoy shouted down the neck of a bouncing matron in front of him. "But she was not successful, and in April she disappeared. I thought it was all over then, but she came back in June. Last spring it was the same thing—she went away for a long while but came back. No mates, so far as I could learn."

At the Hunts Point station we got out of the subway to pick up a flashlight at Mr. Kassoy's home. By this time we were both referring to the long series of bird tenants at the Huntington mansion as "female number one," "female number two," and "female number three." As we climbed the stairs to the street, I asked Mr. Kassoy if he had some pet name, like Lizzie or Iphigenia, for the last female barn owl whose life he had studied during the last two and a half years.

"Why should I?" he asked gravely. "The bird doesn't know me."

We walked up four flights to the apartment where Mr. Kassoy lives with his parents. Down the long hallway I could see them at dinner, but we just went into Mr. Kassoy's little bedroom, where the only ornaments were that stuffed owl on the bureau and a mounted duck on the bookcase. Mr. Kassoy told me he had been born in Russia and was brought to the Bronx when he was a few weeks old. He is unmarried. He asked me if I had had dinner, and when I told him I had, he said he'd had a late lunch and didn't want any. Then he called to his parents, "I'm going out," and we started downstairs.

We went back to the subway and continued on our way to Pelham Bay Park. The train was almost empty that far uptown, and the only person in the car with us was an extremely pretty girl who sat directly opposite. Mr. Kassoy was telling me about "the guttural, vibrant quality of the barn owl's call just before copulation" when the train ground to a halt and his voice suddenly became painfully audible. The young woman looked up and studied Mr. Kassoy intently. After appraising his shiny blue suit, his pink shirt, and his sweat-stained felt hat, she unexpectedly smiled directly at his earnest, wan face. Mr. Kassoy was looking in her direction, but I don't think he even saw her. He began to tell me about the winter night he tried to keep his owls from starving.

"It was in 1935, when the male disappeared, and we were having a heavy snow that night," he explained. "The next morning I said, 'Well, the barn owls are having a tough time up there, but I guess they'll weather it.' The next night it snowed again and there was a gale, so that evening I took two pounds of raw beefsteak up there. It was a Saturday night, and there was about a foot of snow on the ground. I had quite a time breaking a track through, and when I got there the keeper had locked up his home. (I have to go there to get the keys to the mansion.) It was midnight by that time. I couldn't get in, so I scattered the meat around outside."

Generally speaking, however, Mr. Kassoy does not like to feed his owl, because of a strange gastronomic process peculiar to the birds. Barn owls live mostly on mice and rats, which they swallow whole. Their digestive juices get to working on the mess and peel the meat from the skeleton sort of like boiling a soup bone. On the way home, the owl's insides roll up the bones, along with the fur, into a black pellet about the size of a horse chestnut. It would seem more conducive to pleasant living if the owl got rid of this somewhere outdoors, but it doesn't. It waits until it reaches its nest and then disgorges the pellet. Nasty as it sounds, the habit is a godsend to Mr. Kassoy, for it has afforded him his principal contact with his owl since the last batch of young went away, nearly two years ago. By opening up the pellets and examining the little rodents' skulls inside them, Mr. Kassoy can tell just how well his owl has been eating. He also can determine, from the consistency of the pellet, whether the owl has been home recently or whether she is out on one of her periodic wandering sprees. He seldom sees his owl any more, but feels that the pellets keep him on quite intimate terms with her.

The train reached the end of the line and we got off. Mr. Kassoy wanted to get some cigarettes, so we went into a neighborhood bar and grill. The bartender came forward with a smile. Mr. Kassoy asked him if he sold cigarettes and the man pointed to a vending machine. "You know," Mr. Kassoy told me, as he poked his coins into the device, "no one ever made a study of barn owls' behavior on the nest before."

We headed off cross-country through Pelham Bay Park. Mr. Kassoy flicked his flashlight on and off, but not to find our path. He kept flashing it up into the trees, hoping, he told me, to spot the sparkle of an owl's eye. There didn't seem to be any around. Then we stood still while Mr. Kassoy whistled low and mournfully. He said if there were any screech owls in the vicinity, they'd answer that. The only thing we heard was the rumble of our subway train, far behind us, starting back toward Manhattan.

"I wish you could hear a barn owl," Mr. Kassoy said, leading the way confidently through the darkness. "It's sort of a long, drawn-out, rasping scream. In fact, I wouldn't be surprised if it gave rise to the banshee legends in Ireland."

"You wouldn't?" I inquired, absently, as I stumbled through the underbrush.

"No," he replied, "but it's just an unsubstantiated theory of mine, so maybe you'd better not mention it."

After half a dozen more unanswered calls for screech owls, we saw a light through the trees. It came from the park caretaker's cottage, where Mr. Kassoy always has to stop to pick up the keys to the Hunt-ington mansion. Mr. Kassoy told me that the caretaker, Mr. Devine, thinks the mansion is haunted and that anyone who'd sit up alone in it all night long looking for owls is mad.

The keys were in a little box on Mr. Devine's back porch. Mr. Kassoy called a cheery greeting to the caretaker, who was sitting in the living room in his shirtsleeves. Mr. Devine replied with a curt "Hello." Then we continued toward the mansion.

It was a gloomy place, all right. At one end of the library, Mr. Kassoy's light picked out a huge tree—an elm, I think he said it was—which, he said, in season, has such thick foliage that it's almost as dark as night underneath it on a summer afternoon. The building itself was covered with ivy, which rustled in the chilly evening air. Up near the eaves, Mr. Kassoy's flash spotted the little ventilation opening through which passes the only known barn owl in New York City.

We stood around in the courtyard for a while, looking for owls but not seeing any, and then Mr. Kassoy led the way around to the car-riage entrance. "Gosh, I love this place!" he said as he fumbled with the lock. "After four years of coming up here nights alone and all the things I've seen here and all—I love it, you know."

The Parks Department keeps seeds in the old library, and the place smelled moist and warm. I found myself tiptoeing. Suddenly, Mr

Kassoy opened the door to a stairway and flashed his light quickly upward. "Hmm, that's funny," he said. "Generally, there's a rat on these stairs. Runs up ahead of me every night." Two flights up we came to a trapdoor. Mr. Kassoy had a key for that, too. That brought us to the eaves and the ventilator. Mr. Kassoy fiddled around with some batteries in one corner and pretty soon a pale light appeared near the floor. It was in the barn owl's nest—a plain box with an open top, pushed up against the entrance afforded by the ventilator.

Removing one of the boards, Mr. Kassoy bent tenderly over the cubby-hole, which was foul. He picked up a buff-colored feather and told me it had been part of his barn owl's plumage.

Then Mr. Kassoy began inspecting the pellets left in the nest since his last visit. Nearly every one of them contained two rat skulls. A few of the pellets were old and dry, but presently Mr. Kassoy came upon a fresh one and he became visibly excited. "That was left just today," he said. "The owl was here last night!"

Sitting there in the faint light from the cage, I suggested to Mr. Kassoy that time must pass slowly during an all-night, solitary watch over the nest. But he said no, it didn't, and that Saturday nights were particular treats, because then he could sleep the next day.

"I remember one time, though," he went on. "It was about two o'clock on a Sunday morning. It was so quiet up here I could hear my watch ticking in my pocket. Suddenly, someone slammed the door downstairs. I knew I was the only one with a key to the place and that I had locked the door. And I knew whoever it was down there had no business in the house.

"Well, I never knew before that it really could happen, but my hair actually stood out on the sides of my head. Then I heard footsteps in the hall downstairs, and then they started coming upstairs. I heard them coming right up that stairway to the trapdoor. Just then, though, one of the owls flew in to feed the young and I had to make a note of that in my records. So I forgot all about the footsteps."

Mr. Kassoy paused—for dramatic effect, I suspected. He said no more. "What about the intruder?" I finally asked.

"I don't know," said Mr. Kassoy. "After I'd made my notes, I didn't hear the footsteps any more."

On the way back to the subway, I asked Mr. Kassoy where his owl went at night. He admitted, sadly, that he wasn't sure. "She generally starts out over Eastchester Bay," he said. One time Mr. Kassoy went over to the other side of the bay every evening for a week, hoping to catch a glimpse of the bird arriving there. After seven fruitless evenings, he returned to the nest and checked up on the pellets. His owl hadn't been home once during the whole week. She stayed away a month that time.

E. J. Kahn, Jr.

AT HOME WITH THE PALEYS

I am pretty sore at the William S. Paleys. They will be surprised to hear this, if they do, because they don't know me and I don't know them. I do know, of course, that Mr. Paley is the president of the Columbia Broadcasting System and that Mrs. Paley is a member of café society in good repute. Unless *Vogue* and *Harper's Bazaar* have been misinforming me, she is even a friend of Elsa Maxwell's. I am not a friend of Elsa Maxwell's, and the reason I am sore at the Paleys is that a while ago I went to call on them, in their own home, and they were out. I had seen in the papers that on a certain afternoon it would be possible for anyone—anyone with six dollars, that is—to visit half a dozen charming hostesses in their own salons. The money, I read, would go to the Neighborhood Playhouse Scholarship Fund, and it seemed like a worthy cause. I sent in my six dollars and received a nice printed card of admission—to six houses, I thought expectantly, full of gay people, sparkling repartee, and tall, tinkling glasses. Lily Pons and Elizabeth Arden were on the list, but I preferred to call upon the Paleys. I wanted to see Mr. Paley standing hostlike in the background, muttering about Martians while his wife passed the *pâté de foie gras*, looking just like a picture out of El Morocco. When I got there, the only thing I found that reminded me at all of El Morocco was a large carpet made of zebra skins, running up a staircase. There was not a sign of Mr. Paley, Mrs. Paley, Elsa Maxwell, or the Countess di Zoppola.

As a matter of fact, when my cab pulled up at the house I thought for a moment I was at the wrong address. Beekman Place is a section I rarely get to, and there wasn't a limousine parked within twenty yards of the door my driver pointed to, but the number 29 was unmistakably on it, so I went in, across a tarpaulin that had been thrown over the front steps to protect the Paley threshold from such humble feet as mine. The door was open, and when I went in there was no sound of carefree banter, no gentle hum of conversation. Not even an exploding flash bulb. There were simply two bored ladies sitting at a table in the entrance, in neither of whose faces I recognized those lovely characteristics that have endeared Mrs. Paley to many a roto-gravure reader like myself. "This *is* Mrs. Paley's, isn't it?" I asked for reassurance.

"Yes," said one of the ladies, looking at me peculiarly. "Have you a card?"

I produced it and they examined it critically, checked it with a list in front of them, and then handed it back to me. They had more or less the attitude of women selling doughnuts at a charity bazaar—women who had had no particular desire to make the doughnuts in the first place and knew they tasted like old cloth.

One of the ladies said, with no great enthusiasm, "I guess you'll want to see the rooms down here," and let me peer briefly into what appeared to be a reception room and a dining room. Then she led me to the foot of the zebra-striped stairs. I stood there for a moment, waiting for something to happen, and she said, "Well, don't you want to go up?" I nodded, and she called "June, coming up!" and went back to her table.

June was a girl in a reddish-brown dress, with a tassel on her hat. Neither of us could think of anything to say when we met on the second-floor landing, beside a large potted plant, so I took out a cigarette. "Oh, you can't do that," she said apologetically. "We aren't allowed to smoke here." Then she led me into the living room, a chamber containing a number of fragile knickknacks and, in one corner, a pair of orchids growing in a pot. There were a lot of modern paintings, too. In this and the other rooms, I saw and admired works by Cézanne, Matisse, Derain, Picasso, Degas, Gauguin, and Cecil Beaton. Beaton's were photographs, mostly of Mrs. Paley, and all signed with his name in prominent red letters. One stood near a sketch of Mrs. Paley—by Picasso, I think, or maybe by Matisse. In both portraits she was shown with her chin resting in her hand, and June drew my attention to the coincidence. "Notice that same lethargic, contented look," she said. It was the only information anyone there offered me about my absent hostess's character.

"Where is Mrs. Paley?" I asked.

"She's away somewhere," said June matter-of-factly. "She spends most of her time in the country."

Then June led me into the library, where my hopes rose at the sight of a table laden with bottles of whiskey and soda water. June didn't say anything about them, though, and I noticed that they were all unopened. I guess they were meant to stay that way.

"Well," said June, "that's that. . . . Polly, coming up!"

I recognized my cue and climbed another flight. Polly was an amiable, harassed-looking brunette with a corsage of wilting gardenias. She greeted me with "My God, what I'd give for a cigarette!"

I suggested that we go outside and have one, but she wouldn't do it. "I have to stay here till someone comes to relieve me," she said. "It's not that we don't trust people, but you know, they might burn holes in the furniture. My mother always used to worry about me burning holes in her furniture."

I nodded sympathetically. "You're a friend of the Paleys, I suppose?"

"Lord, no. Never saw the place before. I just came down from Elizabeth Arden's and they stuck me up here," she said.

Polly then showed me the ingenious devices by which the Paley art is lighted. For instance, should Mr. Paley be in his bedroom and want to meditate upon a Matisse, all he has to do is throw a switch and flash! there's a Matisse, all nicely and directly illuminated. The wiring system in the house is so contrived that almost every painting has its own tiny spotlight concealed in a molding or an end table. God knows what would happen if the Paleys decided to redecorate. Mr. Paley also has three telephones to play with at his bedside, which I daresay is more than Mr. Lohr of N.B.C. has. The most distinguishing feature of Mrs. Paley's bedroom is her bed. It's a tremendous four-poster affair with a silvery canopy and mirrored posts. It looks as if a queen might have died in it.

In Mrs. Paley's bedroom there is also a growing camellia plant and other flora that at first sight appear to be growing right out of the top of a table. The pots are built in. But her dressing room and bath are the killer-dillers. They are all done in mirrors, and when you sit at the dressing table, as I did at Polly's invitation, you see yourself not only from all sides but from above as well. I don't know how Mrs. Paley feels in the morning, but I'd hate to wake up and have to look down at the top of my own head. Mr. Paley's bathroom has no more than an ordinary quota of mirrors, but it has a radio in it—the only one I saw in the house.

There was still another flight of stairs leading up from the third floor, but Polly barred the way. "I'd like to let you go up," she said, "but the children are there. I keep hearing them shuffling around; makes me nervous."

It was nice to know there was a Paley in the house, but since it was evident that I wasn't going to get to see even a little one, I started downward. When I reached June again, she had two strangers in tow: a young man whom I took to be an interior decorator, and a young lady who looked as if she had just stepped out of the nearest branch of the Y.W.C.A. She was probably an applicant for one of those Neighborhood Playhouse scholarships, and I could see my six dollars making it possible for her to play Desdemona, with a slight lisp. It was a discouraging thought, but still these were fellow-visitors, and I joined them for a moment in the library. The girl had just made a remark about some white upholstered chairs and a matching couch, I gathered.

"They come from Russia, I think," she was saying.

"Not Russia!" exclaimed the young man in a voice of horror. "Nothing good comes from Russia."

"Well, I was told they come from Russia," said the girl stubbornly.

"Maybe they come from Georgia," said the young man hopefully.

I went outside then to have a cigarette, and I didn't go back. If I ever call on the Paleys again, they had better be home.

John McNulty

ATHEIST HIT BY TRUCK

This drunk came down the "L" stairs, and at the bottom he made a wrong turn. This led him into the gutter instead of onto the sidewalk, and a truck hit him and knocked him down.

It is a busy corner there at Forty-second Street and Second Avenue, in front of the Shanty, and there's a hack line there. Naturally, a little crowd and a cop gathered around the drunk and some hackies were in the crowd.

The cop was fairly young. After he hauled the guy up and sat him on the bottom step of the "L" stairs, he saw there wasn't much wrong with him. His pants were torn and maybe his knee was twisted slightly —maybe cut.

The cop got out his notebook and began asking questions and writing the answers down. Between questions he had to prop the man up. Fellow gave his name—Wilson, Martin, some noncommittal name —and his address. Everybody around was interested in these facts.

The blind man in the newspaper hut under the stairs felt a little put out because nobody was telling him what was going on, and he could hear beguiling fragments of it. "What happen? What happen?" the blind man kept asking, but the event wasn't deemed sensational enough for anybody to run and tell him, at least until afterward.

"What religion are yuh?" the policeman asked the man, who propped himself up this time and blurted out, "Atheist! I'm an atheist!"

For some reason, a lot of people laughed.

"Jeez, he's an atheist!" one of the hackies said. He shouted to a comrade who was still sitting behind the wheel of a parked cab at the corner, "Feller says he's an atheist!"

"Wuddaya laughing at?" the cop asked, addressing himself to the crowd generally. "Says he's an atheist, so he's an atheist. Wuddaya laughing at?" He wrote something in the book.

Another policeman, from over by Whelan's drugstore, where there was a picket line, strolled up. He was an older cop, more lines in his face, bigger belly, less humps around his hips, because the equipment —twisters, mace, and all that stuff—fitted on him better after all these years. "Wuzzamadder with 'im?" he asked his colleague.

"This here truck hit him. He isn't hurt bad. Says he's an atheist."

"I *am* an atheist!" the man yelled.

The crowd laughed again.

"Did you put that down—atheist?" the older cop asked.

"Yuh, I put it in where it says 'religion.'"

"Rubbid out. Rubbid out. Put in Cat'lic. He looks like a Cat'lic to me. He's got an Irish name? Anyway, rubbid out. When he sobers up, he'll be sorry he said that atheist business. Put in Cat'lic. We gotta send him to Bellevue just for safety's sake." The young cop started for the drugstore to put in a call.

"Never mind safety's sake. I'm an atheist, I'm telling you," the drunk said, loud as he could.

"Cuddid out, cuddid out," the older cop said. Then he leaned over like a lecturer or somebody. "An' another thing—if you wouldn't go round sayin' you're an atheist, maybe you wouldn't be gettin' hit by trucks."

The crowd sensed a great moral lesson and didn't laugh.

"Jeez! The guy says he's an atheist," the hackie said again.

A little later the Bellevue ambulance came.

"I yam a natheist," the man kept muttering as they put him into the ambulance.

A. J. Liebling

IN MULBERRY STREET*

In the middle of any New York block there is likely to be one store that remains open and discreetly lighted all night. This is the undertaker's. The undertaker or an assistant is always in attendance, waiting for something to turn up. Undertakers are sociable men; they welcome company during their unavoidable periods of idleness. High school boys study for their State Regents' examinations in undertakers' offices on hot June nights. The door is always open, the electric fan soothing, the whole environment more conducive to reflective scholarship than the crowded apartment where the boy lives. Policemen going off duty sometimes drop in for a visit with the undertaker before climbing into the subway for the long trip home to another part of the city.

There is no merchandise in the front part of an undertaker's store. Usually there are a few comfortable chairs for bereaved relatives, and policemen sit in these chairs. During the day, the undertaker acts as a referee in the disputes of children. Housewives tell him their troubles; priests appeal to him to head church committees. Ten to one he becomes the biggest man in the neighborhood, like my friend Mayor Angelo Rizzo of Mulberry Street. Some New York streets have Mayors, but they are not elected. A man lives on a street until the mayoralty grows over him, like a patina. To Mayor Rizzo Elizabeth Street, although but two blocks east of Mulberry, is an alien place. For the feast of San Gennaro, who is the Mulberry Street Saint, Mayor Rizzo usually heads at least three committees and festoons his shop-front with electric lights. A celebration on Elizabeth Street leaves him unmoved. "Just one of them Sicilian saints," he says.

Once Mayor Rizzo told me he was hard put to keep track of his constituents' baths. "I think I will have to get a secretary," he said, as he

---

* Chapter I of A. J. Liebling's "Back Where I Came From." In the book it was titled "Beginning with the Undertaker."

improved the taste of a casket salesman's gift cigar with a swig of iced barbera wine. He sat in front of 178 Mulberry Street, enthroned upon one of the elegant portable chairs which he is prepared to furnish in any number for correct funerals. "They should call this cigar a La Palooka," he remarked on the side.

"Mrs. Aranciata is getting crazy because she don't remember whether Jimmy has been to Cooney Island twenty-two times or twenty-three times. So she come to me and said I should tell the kid not to go no more, because maybe that will make it an even number of times and he will get rheumatism. So I said to her, 'But suppose he has been only twenty-two times? Then by keeping him home you will be preventing him getting on the odd number again, and the rheumatism will be your fault.'

" 'Oh, Madonna mia,' she says, 'and what will I do?'

"So I says, 'Why don't you forget all about it and purtend this is a new year. Start all over again and when he goes to Cooney tell me, and I will keep track of it on a piece of paper.' So she is delighted and the next thing I know she tells all her friends and now I got about fourteen women coming in wanting me to keep score how many times the family goes swimming.

"It is like when I feed one cat spaghetti a couple of winters ago and in a week I got a waiting line of 598 cats, including a lot of Sicilian cats from Elizabeth Street."

"But what difference does it make how many times you go swimming—at Coney or any place else?" I asked.

"What difference does it make?" shouted Mr. Rizzo. "Do you mean to tell me that you, an educated man, do not know that salt water baths are only good for you if you go an odd number of times? Any old woman on Mulberry Street knows that much."

To prove his point Mayor Rizzo called the cop on the beat.

"You are an Italian," said His Honor. "Which is it lucky to take baths, an odd number or an even number?"

"Odd number," answered the officer promptly. "My mother-in-law, she keeps count on her fingers. She would never go in the water two times, or four times, in an afternoon, but always three times or five times."

The argument became a little involved here. Some of the folklore hydrotherapists held that each immersion counts as a bath, and if you go in the drink an odd number of times at each visit to the beach, your health will not suffer.

Others maintain that you must keep track of the total number of days' bathing, and be sure to wind up the season on an odd.

"I remember when I was a kid an old lady from Calabria made me go in fifty-one times one summer," said Al Gallichio, the restaurant man.

An antique and gracious lady waddling past with a bag of zucchini, was invoked as a superior authority.

"Pardon me, madame," said Mayor Rizzo, "but I would wish to request a word with you."

"Voluntarily," she replied.

"When you are accustomed to go bathing, which is the more auspicious, to go an even or an uneven number of times?"

"Childish," said the dame. "It makes no difference. But once you have begun to go you must go at least fifteen times, else your bones rot. It is for that reason I have not gone to the sea, this year, because I might not be able to afford fifteen visits."

She was an exception, because the odd-and-even belief, in one or other of its two forms, is prevalent all the way from Bleecker Street down to Park Row.

"It is very important this year," said the Mayor, "because we got no public bath in the neighborhood. There used to be a bathhouse on Center Market Place where the fellow would let you take a shower for a nickel. Of course, even the old-timers do not count whether a shower is odd or even. But now the Broome St. Tamanacle Church has bought the building. A lot of these old houses have no bathtubs even, so the nearest place the people can get a bath is Allen Street and they figure they might just as well go out to Cooney.

"Do I believe in this odd-and-even business?" he said. "Well, I tell you. I went swimming off the Battery just once, which is an odd number, and a kid pushed my head under and nearly drowned me, so I figured if I went back that would be an even number and even worse luck and I probably would remain drowned, so now I do all my swimming in a bathtub."

The Talk of the Town *

SUITS FOR JIMMY

October 20, 1928

Seven new suits are now under construction for Mayor Walker. For this important work, Jeann Friedman, tailor to His Honor, has moved his shop from Thirty-fourth Street up to Forty-sixth Street, opposite the Ritz. Here, behind heavily panelled walls, we found a squad of men on their haunches, stitching away at the royal garments.

Mr. Friedman, who knows our unflagging interest in the Mayor's appearance, telephoned last week, inviting us to inspect the new raiment, and when we called received us personally in his reception room and let us finger the executive swatches. One series is called the Hyde Park Ensemble. Another the Biarritz Casino. Both are new departures, featuring jackets of plain cloth, with pants of a slightly different hue, vigorously striped—like the Bush Terminal Building. Five of the new suits now under the needle are of the Hyde Park (different-color-pants) type. Two are of the standard (pants-match-coat) variety. At the moment the Mayor is in an autumnal mood and leans toward brown. Among the ensembles there will be one reddish brown, two oak leaf (or Broadway) browns, one blue, one gray.

The Biarritz group is a sports group. (There is always a suspicion in Mr. Friedman's mind that the Mayor may be going south.) As a group it has not been recommended to His Honor's attention yet. "Just now am I just studying them," said Mr. Friedman. "These combination effects, only for an outstanding man they are, different from other people." And he showed us exactly how the Biarritz Casino garment works—coat of dark gray, knickers of thatched-roof motif, flannels of light gray stripes—"for lolling."

To fend off cold winds, three topcoats of pure cashmere are also being built for Mr. Walker. He already owns two fur coats, one black,

* The following nine short news stories are from The Talk of the Town department in The New Yorker.

one brown, and will be able to get through the winter inside of these, Mr. Friedman thinks. The brown is worth ten thousand dollars, on account of a very fine collar that a fellow brought the Mayor from Russia.

About seventy suits comprise the Walker wardrobe. Many have been around the house for years. Ten of them hang in the tailor shop all the time. No room at home. "He leaves things laying around," Mr. Friedman confided, pulling out a dandy cocoa-colored specimen, said to be a favorite. The Mayor spends three thousand dollars a year on this kind of equipment, and enjoys every cent of it.

Life has opened up like a flower for Jeann Friedman since becoming tailor to Mr. Walker. Fifteen years ago he made a suit for a friend of Jimmie's, and the snappy effect so took the Walker fancy that Jeann has done the tailoring ever since. Other tailors try with siren notes and custom effects to lure the Mayor away, but Jeann makes the Walker pants twenty inches at the knee, eighteen and a half inches at the bottom, no break at the instep; makes the Walker lapels sit up where they belong; and Jeann now has a nice shop with ashtrays in the reception room and a view of the Ritz. Also he has attracted attention in the trade. A writer for a fashion magazine interviewed him and quoted him as saying: "It is not so much a matter of a designing system, but accomplishment which comes through the trained, artistic eye visualizing the finished product according to the individuality of the customer." Jeann sits among his ashtrays and reads that statement over and over.

———

ISADORA'S BROTHER

December 7, 1929

Raymond Duncan is in town with the idea of starting a branch of his academy here. He serves tea every afternoon in his studio in West Seventy-fifth Street, surrounded by his fabrics, his poems, his shepherdess, and his disciples. Reclining on a couch, he talks with you about the future, which he believes must be prepared for by throwing off the past and learning to perform the simple motions of life, such as digging and making sandals. His poems are five dollars, his "Eternal Beauty" is two dollars, and his fabrics run from four dollars on up. The couch is very hard.

The little brother of Isadora is getting on in years, and looks more like a witch than a shepherd. His long gray locks are held back by a ribbon, his tunic flows classically from his shoulders, and his chubby little arms that have woven so many yards of piece goods look rather flabby and old. After years of tending donkeys and goats on the Acropolis with Penelope, organizing refugees, rebuilding a city in Albania, weaving rugs, digging holes, dyeing linen, writing poems, and administering academies and temples of arts, always clinging tight to the immortal and somewhat elusive spirit of his inspired sister, he is still hopeful. He hasn't had on a pair of pants in nineteen years, man and boy.

While we were reclining with him, doing our best to look like a goatherd despite our sack suit, a lady entered the room and asked him "if it would brutalize him if she suggested a cup of tea." "My dear Julia," he replied, "the whole world is trying to brutalize me."

Brute that we were, we drank the tea, bought a small doily, and departed, our sandals clinking merrily along the pave.

TEA PARTY

October 24, 1931

Simon & Schuster gave a tea last week called the "Believe-It-or-Not" party, the occasion being the publication of a new book by that name. The idea was to get up a party which would be like the book—that is: incredible but true—and it was a success. About a hundred and fifty people, mostly literary figures, moved about with teacups and fountain pens, drinking tea and autographing books. Gene Tunney was there and he autographed a book for Sir Hubert Wilkins, who was autographing a book for Count Felix von Luckner. Tunney wore a brown suit, with soft tan shirt and dark red tie, secured by a small gold pin. Count von Luckner wore a blue suit and a hard shiny collar. Both looked debonair but unreal.

Everybody had to sign a huge book at the door. It contains the oddest collection of names in the world and is probably worth a great deal of money. Count von Luckner was the third person to arrive. His signature, "Felix Count Luckner," was fourteen inches long and two inches high. A Mr. Joe Rosenblatt signed right under him, taking up only the same amount of space as the word "Count." Ely Culbertson signed right after we did. Sidney Lenz arrived eight signatures later. The two, as you know, have for months been challenging each other to a contract-bridge game. To everybody's surprise, the game was not played at the party. Some people thought they wouldn't even speak, but they signed each other's book and the news spread quickly through the crowd. Then Eddie Cantor signed Culbertson's book and Tunney signed Lenz' and Lenz signed Major James Doolittle's. A Mr. Sam Weisenhouse signed ours and asked us if Hendrik Van Loon had arrived yet. It was all very crowded and now and again you signed somebody's book or somebody signed yours by accident, due to jostling. Somebody said one book was signed "Count von Wilkins," due to jostling, but we didn't see it. The Count and the Sir talked together for a long time, and we edged up to hear what was being said. Count von Luckner was saying: "Our two countries should never have fought." We were introduced *to* Tunney and *as* Tunney. A strange woman in a green hat, mistaking us for somebody else, said: "Where was you?" We said: "To the taxidermist's" and she went around telling people we were Ring Lardner. Sir Hubert thereupon came over and praised us for "The Outline of Science."

Simon & Schuster's is a lot of bright, ivory-colored rooms joined together, containing pictures of Thomas Mott Powys and Will Durante, Simon & Schuster authors. People moved from room to room, passing sandwich tables, passing Tunney, passing a radio to which one couple was dancing, passing a ping-pong table at which two women, wearing fur coats, were playing. At the end of three hours, we hadn't met Ripley, the so-called guest of honor. We hadn't met One Long Hop, the Chinaman who was named after Lindbergh's flight, either. He was there. We asked a young lady how to find Ripley. "He's got spats," she said. A man who looked like Coolidge arrived. Believe it or not, it wasn't Coolidge.

GTDE STEIN

November 24, 1934

Miss Stein was seven or eight minutes late for her autographing at Brentano's last week and about fifty people were waiting restlessly for her when she solidly arrived with Alice B. Toklas pertly in tow. On a table were arranged solid stacks of Miss Stein's books and next to the table was a big desk at which she sat solidly down. She was calm, quick, and smiling throughout the ordeal. Of course, it wasn't as exciting as the immortal Hugh Walpole-Gene

Tunney autographing, but it had its moments. As soon as she sat down, Miss Stein looked up expectantly and people began pushing toward the desk, carrying books. Clerks fluttered about selling the pushers whatever book of Miss Stein's they might want: the books ran in price from ninety-five cents (the Modern Library edition of "Three Lives") to $3.50. At an autographing, you are supposed to write down on a card your name, or Aunt Lisbeth's name, or the name of whomever you are buying the book for, and hand the book and the card to the autographer. This speeds things up, because people standing in front of an author and meeting the author's eyes are likely to get timid and dry-throated and say "Zassfrank Dooselinch" or what sounds like "Zassfrank Dooselinch" to the author. Miss Stein doesn't like people to be incoherent about names.

She signed two hundred and seventy-five books in all, and her signing time was a little under an hour and a half. She wrote with a big pen, vigorously. We bought one of her books and got in line behind a man named Twifflefinks, Moited Twifflefinks (he hadn't written his name on a card). That was straightened out after a while—Miss Stein is always gracious and patient. We just handed our book to her, and she glanced at us with her keen, humorous eyes and, seeing that we didn't have a name, simply put her own name on the flyleaf, and the date. She signs herself always Gtde Stein. Now and again somebody (once it was a girl of twelve) would slip her an autograph book or a blank sheet of paper, but she would push these away and say "No," and these autograph-hunters would retreat in humiliation. There are ethics in autographing: you can't just walk into a bookstore out of the street and get an author to sign his name for you. You have to buy or bring one of the author's books.

One confused man somehow found himself standing in front of Miss Stein without a book, so he shouted at a clerk, " 'Three Saints'! 'Three Saints'!" he said. "Give me a 'Three Saints'!" The right title is "Four Saints." A clerk corrected the gentleman coldly. Miss Stein just laughed. She doesn't get peeved about things like that. Behind us was a lady named Mielziner. Miss Stein, hearing the name, looked up and asked about Leo Mielziner, Jr. "Leo Mielziner is Kenneth MacKenna," said the lady. Miss Stein took that in her stride. Now and again someone would ask the hovering Toklas to sign a book, and she always did. Somebody asked Miss Stein what had been her greatest thrill in America. She said her airplane trip to Chicago.

A friend of ours who heard the great lady lecture a few days after the autographing said it was very interesting and seemed to make sense. Our friend, however, copied down a few sentences that Miss Stein said and showed them to us. Our favorite was "When the inside had become so solidly inside that all the outside could be outside and the inside inside." The lady who listened said that when you hear Gtde talk that way, you can see what she means, or think you can. People who hear her always like her as a person. After her lectures she will answer any questions—if they are sensible. Once she waved her hand and said pooh at a woman who asked her what she thought of the effect of psychology on literature. She then said that psychology hasn't any effect on literature. She told some other questioner that she doesn't believe much in the subconscious. "It's subconscious because it's inarticulate," she said.

This is probably all we're going to tell you about Miss Stein.

UNDER THE LINDENS

June 27, 1936

The open-air Promenade Café, in the sunken plaza of Rockefeller Center, opened Wednesday evening, June 17th. A tropical disturbance, which had been moving northeastward, was centered about four hundred miles south of Cape Race when the first diners arrived. All afternoon the southeasterly breeze had been freshening, and at sundown it hauled into the south and increased to a velocity of 25. At nine o'clock, with the glass hovering around 29.9 and with our lady on our arm, we entered the café, where one of the captains took us in tow, skirted some cedar hedges, and led us to a fountain-side table right abeam of Prometheus's groin. By this time the restaurant was beginning to roll a bit, and some of the smaller tables were trying to shorten sail. Tablecloths whipped in the wind, umbrellas tugged at their moorings, and the eight linden trees bent to the gale while their wire rigging sang. In the west, right above our heads, the enormous waterspouts shot noisily into the air, were caught by the downdraft from the R.C.A. Building, and sprayed out in a fine mist over the decks. It was difficult to hear anything above the roar. A waiter came up, his hair in his mouth.

"What'll you have?" he yelled.

"Two Martinis and some oilskins!" we called back, and he was off, bending low. As he departed, the fog shut down, and we couldn't see our own partner but could feel her knee against ours under the table. Steep seas were making up in the basin of the fountain, and a cross-current from the jets of Prometheus churned up a nasty chop. Over to the eastward near Al Donahue and his orchestra, a silver platter came adrift and went down with a deafening crash. The fog lifted. Some mint from the fruit cup of the people at the next table blew across our nostrils in a fine green dust. Ladies in thin evening clothes clutched at their back hair, while their men shifted the dinner service around crazily, in an attempt to batten down the meal. A singer from the Music Hall fought her way to the microphone and sang "Let Your-self Go." Even then we didn't realize how hard the wind was blowing till we looked down at our butter plate and noticed that the hard roll was rocking slowly back and forth, back and forth.

In the north we could see tier on tier of the common people lined up behind the hedges on Fiftieth Street, gazing down into the cave of the winds at us. Spotlights burned down from the roof of the Brit-ish Building, so that one's shoulders threw one's food into deep shadow. At about half past nine, an unseen right-minded mechanical wizard turned Prometheus off, and the noise abated but not the wind. A cigarette girl, dressed in a cutaway and wearing a monocle, tacked back and forth across our bow, and once, when we looked up from our hearts of lettuce with fines herbes et fines Lucky Strike ashes, we saw the wind tear the glass right out of her eye. At eight minutes after eleven, a man's straw hat went by, bottom up, in the green, angry waters of the fountain. Toward midnight, it became apparent that the worst of the blow was over, and guests made things as snug as pos-sible and settled down to enjoy the dancing and the food. Spots went out, the dark came, the lindens rustled, and violin music drifted out over the garden. The precision dance of the Rockettes, on the plat-form with the waving trees throwing leaf shadows on them, was a surprisingly beautiful and almost unearthly sight—the Rockettes, who had heretofore been merely puppets seen indoors at a distance of a quarter of a mile, now suddenly translated into living girls dancing in the clean bright night in a big wind. We saw them again, later, in the British bar, at even closer range, and were surprised at their faces, which were earnest rather than gay.

The Promenade Café, we learn on inquiry, serves table d'hôte lunches from $1 up, table d'hôte dinners from $1.50 up. Also à la carte for lunch and dinner. It is open for cocktails in the afternoon, and for supper at night. The dance platform remains throughout the summer for dancing. There is no cover charge at any time. There is an indoor section on the north side called the English Grill, which has a bar, and an indoor section on the south side called the Restaurant Français, which hasn't. On calm nights, with Prometheus idling, or shut off entirely, we should think it would be a rather pleasant spot.

THE JAPANESE ARMY

March 5, 1938

The Japanese army is listed in the Manhattan telephone directory, on page 494—"Japanese Army, 1775 Broadway, CIrcle 7-4466." We didn't find this out until last week, but the minute we did we dropped everything and hurried around to investigate. We found the Japanese army firmly entrenched just off Columbus Circle, on the sixth floor of the General Motors Building. It occupies a modest office suite and has no sentry or receptionist. When we entered (without knocking), we found ourself looking across a waist-high partition and gate into a biggish room in which a half-dozen Japanese, all in mufti, were engaged in some sort of clerical work. One of them, a short, dark gent with horn-rimmed glasses and hair parted in the middle, got up and came toward us, stopping on the other side of the gate. We introduced ourself and right off, without subterfuge, asked him why the Japanese army had a New York office. "You go do this up?" he said. We said yes, we'd like to write a piece about it. "No true," he said in rather a heated tone. "You think we only army with office? Hah, you not know all armies have office in New York? Go, go learn others, then have purpose do this up." He thereupon turned from us and went into the inner office, followed by all his colleagues.

This sudden retreat left us in complete command of the field but uncertain as to whether or not the interview was at an end. We held our gains, observing what we could of the Japanese army's New York equipment. It wasn't much—just books, filing cabinets, a safe, and a couple of things which we took to be Japanese multigraphing machines. For a moment we caught excited mumbling from the inner office, then this stopped and there was complete Oriental quiet. We were almost on the point of going away when we noticed that the inner office door was ajar and that a man was peeking at us. We motioned to him to come out, and he did, somewhat hesitantly. This was another army man, tall and slender, with thin hair and no eyebrows. Deciding to try a different gambit with him, we asked if we might see the general. "No general," he said, smiling and showing pale gums. "One lieuten' colonel, two major." We asked if we could see the lieutenant colonel, whereupon he withdrew again to the inner office. He returned in a moment with the news that the lieutenant colonel was "bissy with friend." So were both the majors. "All time bissy with friend," he said, with another pale smile that hardly seemed to include us as a friend. Why, we asked, getting back to the original point, did the Japanese army have an office in New York? "You know," he said slowly, "the purchases. We inspect." All of them? we asked. "All." Where? "Here." To whom was the New York office of the Japanese army responsible, the Japanese consulate? He shook his head, arching what could have been his eyebrows. The embassy? "No." The Emperor? "No.... Yes." With that, the second Japanese army man who ever came into our life grinned, backed away, and disappeared into the inner office. Again all was quiet as a Japanese flower garden, so we left.

We snooped around the General Motors Building a bit and learned that the Japanese army has been a tenant for about seven years. It's the irritated opinion of several of the building employees that the army can speak perfectly good English if it wants to. Nobody, not even the postman or the superintendent, has been in the inner office.

WIND AND WATER

February 10, 1940

Too many buildings in this city were erected without the slightest regard for devils. The Chinese manage things better. In China, when a building is to go up, a geomancer is called in to pass on the site. A geomancer is a practitioner of *fung sui*—a doctor of the wind and the water. He corresponds roughly to our architect, except that he has a better grasp of the situation.

This much you know if you read Carl Crow's book, "Four Hundred Million Customers." Mr. Crow made the statement that geomantically the Empire State Building is in a very dangerous condition, while the Hotel New Yorker is fine, and this eventually got us started to Chinatown, where we found an old retired geomancer named Loo Chan, whose father practiced extensively in China and who himself once had hopes of practicing here. A good building, he says, must be designed to repel and confound evil spirits. Demons avoid pagodas, national banks and trust companies, and running water. They are stupid and fly always in a straight line. Therefore it is possible to plan your building accordingly. Take, for example, the New Yorker Hotel. An evil spirit, flying at the New Yorker Hotel at a low altitude, would crash into surrounding buildings and become baffled. If it flew at a high altitude, it would be met by the house spirit of the New Yorker, which, from its perch on a setback, would grapple with the demon. You never hear of anybody in the New Yorker Hotel getting boils, or scurvy, do you? Well?

The Empire State Building, on the contrary, violates every principle of *fung sui*. It is the butt of all the wandering devils in midtown Manhattan. From about the thirtieth story up, it rises perpendicularly, a vast unprotected expanse, no surrounding obstructions, no pagodas, no running water—except the occasional flow in the lonely lavatories. No place for the house spirit to perch until you get clear to the top. You notice that all that middle section of the building is vacant, don't you? Well?

Since learning about geomancy, we study every building we pass with an eye to its vulnerability. We have noticed that the Chinese Consulate (in fact, our geomancer pointed this out) is in a cozy spot in Radio City, strategically located behind a setback and enjoying the beneficent influence of St. Patrick's, a nearby pagoda. There is also a good deal of running water in the fountain. The Japanese Consulate is wide open. It is in the Salmon Tower and is in the path of devils working north from Lord & Taylor's. The Waldorf is well-nigh impregnable. It has St. Bartholomew's, the Chemical Bank & Trust Co., and a fire station, which makes a lot of noise and scares spirits off.

Loo Chan says there is no chance of a *fung-sui* practitioner making a living in New York (some years ago he went into the rice-cake business) because Chinese don't build buildings or bury their dead here. (Locating graves is really the principal task of the geomancer; a proper grave should be on a hill, near a stream and a pagoda—like Grant's tomb.) Residents of Chinatown are content with the narrow, winding streets of their district. Makes it tough for devils, and if the neighborhood engine company isn't kicking up a rumpus, you can always shoot off firecrackers. The Chinese revere the art of *fung sui* because of their desire to have everything on their side. They think this life is a peculiar one.

We are sorry to say that our own office building is badly planned. Spirits skirt around the Guaranty Trust Company and come in across a parking lot. There are continual distempers and fevers. We asked the receptionist the other day if she was ever troubled by devils getting off the elevator.

"You mean the ones that have been to art school?" she replied, sullenly.

We noticed she had a racking little cough.

———

PASTORAL SCENE
February 22, 1941

Next time a broker, toying wanly with his frayed cuffs, tells you a seat on the Stock Exchange recently sold for $27,000 and that the daily average of shares traded this January was 512,000, as compared to 4,300,000 in January, 1928, you might enter into the spirit of things by telling *him* how the amount of waste-paper swept up from the Exchange floor at the close of a day's trading stacks up against the amount swept up ten years ago. Current sweepings, consisting of brokers' orders, memorandums, and quotation slips, are only about two-thirds what they used to be: in 1931 they averaged twenty-one bags, or 1,500 pounds, a day; today they hover around thirteen bags, or 950 pounds. Moreover, the figures jotted on these scraps of paper are substantially lower than they were in the days when stockbrokers warned their sons against becoming college professors, poets, or harmonica players, and their daughters against marrying same.

We obtained this interesting wastepaper statistic, and a few sidelights that may be of value to some morbid historian, when we visited the Exchange last week. An official guide took us to the visitors' gallery, from which, around noon, we watched the following sluggish scene unfold itself. At Trading Post 6, a bald-headed broker was sitting down, reading a copy of *Time,* no doubt the "Business & Finance" section. At Post 2, another broker was working on the *Herald Tribune* crossword puzzle. At Post 4, where General Motors is traded, three members were talking; one was sitting, two standing. Our guide pointed to the left of Post 2, where U.S. Steel is traded, and said, "There's the steel crowd." The steel crowd consisted of four brokers and one Stock Exchange employee, all conversing without animation. Another crowd of four brokers stood about Post 10, where Bethlehem Steel is traded; under our very eyes one of them walked away from the others and wrote something on a pad. Our guide advised us to keep on watching him, because it looked as though the man was about to trade. "Yes," the guide said breathlessly a moment later, "he did trade, he did trade."

Around this time the annunciator board, which is used to call members from the floor to their phones and is equipped with a thousand numbers, had sixteen numbers up. In the old days, three or four hundred numbers showing was nothing unusual. Brokers' carnations have declined even more sensationally. Formerly about half the members sported them; the day we were there all buttonholes were bare. According to E. Burd Grubb, a governor of the Exchange, most brokers have given up lunch, along with the carnations. Mr. Grubb told us he stopped eating lunch a year and a half ago. "It's an easy way to save a dollar and a half," he said. He just has a bigger dinner when he gets home. A few of the more improvident, or hungrier, brokers have sandwiches sent in, or go to Walgreen's, or patronize a recently installed sandwich bar in the Luncheon Club. The smoking room is more popular than it used to be, since members go there increasingly to read, complain, do crossword puzzles, and talk deferentially about such profitable ventures as photography and stamp-collecting. Backgammon stakes in this room, once a quarter a point, are now generally a nickel.

We asked a broker about the horseplay and practical jokes which have long been an Exchange tradition and were told that the last prank occurred before the election, when a trader, having bought a carton of eggs from John Conklin, a broker who has a farm in New Jersey and peddles seventy dozen eggs a week to his colleagues, checked his carton in the cloakroom. Another member, apparently feeling Willkie was going to be elected, giddily removed the eggs, had them hardboiled at a restaurant across the street, and returned them to the cloakroom. The owner's wife later tried to make some scrambled eggs, and the joke was judged a success. By the end of the year, however, no one felt humorous, and December 31st, formerly an occasion marked by revelry, song, two bands, paper hats and noise-makers, was celebrated gloomily with prolonged booing at the three-o'clock close. The man who told us this went on to say that no one has had the initiative to haze the two newest members; that the Stock Exchange theme song, "Wait Till the Sun Shines, Nellie," formerly rendered by all hands when something good happened in the market, hadn't been sung for months; that no one whistles at girls in the visitors' gallery any more; and that James Seligman, once one of the wittiest men on the floor, had given up conversation altogether. "You don't crack jokes at a funeral," our informant said.

YOUNG MAN IN THE BED

March 1, 1941

Having a healthy interest in both the drama and the human head, we called at four o'clock last Thursday afternoon on Victor Mature, who plays opposite, or almost opposite, Gertrude Lawrence in Moss Hart's psychoanalytical play, "Lady in the Dark." Although only twenty-six years old, Mr. Mature has been singled out by the Harvard *Lampoon* as "the actor least likely to succeed," has already made a fool of the Harvard *Lampoon,* has met socially in recent weeks various Paleys, Swopes, Hearsts, Vanderbilts, Harrimans, and other resourceful hosts and hostesses, and has been mentioned in the gossip columns as being alarmingly handsome. We found him in bed in a room at Essex House, discussing some sample suitings with a tailor and drinking Coca-Cola out of a bottle. He motioned the tailor to a chair in a corner and apologized to us for not being up, explaining that he had stayed out late the night before. "I used to have low moments and they were just low moments," he remarked abruptly, "but since this play, when I have low moments I worry about them. The other night I got to worrying about the face of the stage manager looking through the square hole in the wings and I couldn't concentrate and I knew my performance was stinking and later I couldn't get my mind off it and I thought 'Lord! Maybe there *is* something wrong with my complexes and stuff.' "

"Just lie back and say whatever comes into your mind," we suggested.

"I can't figure it out," he went on, putting his hands under his head. "I've got to find something to do with these afternoons. In Hollywood, since I got a break a year and a half ago, I've had a little house and a tennis court and a car and I had confidence and was happy just getting ahead and pushing. Now here in New York, for instance, I have

to get all these new suits because all the ones I had were the sports outfits which you wear out there exclusively, and these New York clothes
make me feel sharp. Too sharp, see? Mr. Hart and everybody have
been wonderful, and this is what I want, this is *it,* this is strictly the
good thing, and my God, meeting the Paleys and all those and so
forth—why, think of it, when I went to Hollywood in 1935, when I
was nineteen, I lived in a garage that was all charcoal inside and only
last week I'm at the Paleys', stumbling over Swopes and stuff."

"You lived in a garage that was all charcoal inside?" we asked
softly.

"It was only eight dollars a month," he said. "That's why—because
it had had a fire in it and was burned out, only not burned *down.* It
was fixed up like an apartment but it was really a garage and all the
wood inside was charred and came off black on your fingers. I got
to Hollywood from my home in Louisville, Kentucky, with eleven
cents left after I paid this eight dollars' rent and I wired Dad saying
I had eleven cents and he wired back saying that was six cents more
than he'd had when he came over from Austria and he couldn't speak
English, but *I* could. Dad used to grind scissors in Louisville and he
got into the refrigeration business later and made a good deal of
money, so he thought acting was unsound and wanted me to go into
his business. I was an only child. We never had any real quarrel or
anything and you ought to see them now—Dad and Mother. Boy, are
they proud! Mature's my real name, you see—same as theirs. I had a
tough time in Hollywood but it was constructive and did me good and
I'm glad Dad didn't send me any dough. The tough going gave me
an insight, which is strictly a good thing."

"It's what parents ought to do instead of mollycoddling," said the
tailor emphatically.

"There you are wrong, old man," said Mature. "You can't generalize.
Now, for me it was right, it was *it,* but for some other kid it would
not have been constructive. I was pushing, and the works were *proper*
and they still are, only—well, like I've just been reading six movie
magazines with features about me: 'Mature's opinion on love,' 'Mature's taste in dames.' I never gave any of them out, but it's O.K., it is
strictly the stuff, it is *it,* only I worry more now and I'm not as happy
with myself—O.K. but not *as* O.K. I watch my step. This way? That
way? Lord, sometimes I think maybe I'll talk to one of these psycho

guys, like Mr. Hart did. But nuts! I got to figure out something to do with these afternoons. I may walk in the Park a little. I may join the New York Athletic Club. I may take some courses at Columbia. But nuts!"

Geoffrey Hellman

BOY MEETS BULLFINCH*

Dr. Frank M. Chapman, who has been Curator of Ornithology at the American Museum of Natural History since 1908, has probably spent more time in the society of birds than any other man alive. For over sixty years he has patiently concealed himself in bushes and blinds all over North and South America in order to study at close range the habits of everything from the blue jay and the pelican to the vulture and the dusky-tailed ant tanager. He has reported his findings in some two hundred scientific papers, in *Bird-Lore,* an ornithological magazine which he founded in 1899 and edited for thirty-six years, and in fifteen books, which have sold, all told, over a quarter of a million copies. His "Handbook of Birds of Eastern North America," first published in 1895, still sells around 800 copies a year. Since going to work at the Museum in 1888, Dr. Chapman has helped build up its collection of bird specimens from about 10,000 to over 750,000 and to make its bird department the best in the world.

With the exception of a few species which he dislikes, like starlings and English sparrows, Chapman has a whole-souled admiration for birds. His approach to his subject is aesthetic and social rather than physiological, and he is more concerned with a bird's appearance, song, and way of life than with its underlying bone structure. His book "The Warblers of North America" for example, carefully classifies warblers into such groups as Warblers Which Have Loud, Whistled Songs; Warblers Which Have Not Loud, Whistled Songs; Warblers Which Have Songs of the Wee-Chee or Cher-Wee Type, with a Whistled Quality; Warblers Whose Songs Possess Pebbly, Twittering Notes or Which Suggest a Song of the Chipping Sparrow or Junco Type; and Warblers in Whose Songs There Is a Pronounced Zee Quality. This book contains plenty of the sort of prose which has made Dr. Chapman the most influential man since Audubon in interesting people in

* This is the first half of a Profile from The New Yorker, *March, 1939.*

birds, prose which in its way tells a good deal about Dr. Chapman himself:

> All the sweetness and promise of spring seems stored in Parula's little sizzling gurgle; there is good cheer and sunshine in Yellow Warbler's lay; peace and rest in the quaint *zeeing* of the Black-throated Green.... If, however, you would see the [Yellow-Breasted] Chat satisfactorily, fight him with his own fire. Seat yourself in the thicket where as pursuer you are at the bird's mercy, and with pursed lips *squeak* gently but persistently. Soon there will be an answering *chut,* and with due patience and discretion you may induce this elusive creature to appear before you. I do not recall a more suspicious bird than the Chat.... The song of the Redstart can be readily recognized by those who know it but like so many Warblers' songs of what may be called the *weechy* type, loses all character when it is reduced to syllables.

Dr. Chapman's idea of a tremendous compliment is to compare a person to a bird, and he recently said of the late Lord Grey, bird-loving statesman, "Grey was the most charming host and companion, just like a bird." Dr. Chapman likes to think that birds are fond of him, too, and enjoys telling friends of the time an English wild eider duck permitted him to stroke her as she sat on her eggs. "She turned and pecked my finger gently, almost caressingly, I thought," he says. A good many birds have come to tolerate Dr. Chapman during his long career, and this pleases him immensely. One winter in Florida he spent the better part of three days forty-five feet up in a cypress tree, in a blind consisting of a green umbrella and a lot of Spanish moss, in order to observe herons and egrets. The birds in the vicinity kept their distance for a while, but toward the end of the third afternoon a spoonbill and two snowy egrets came and roosted in the same tree with him. Dr. Chapman, then a young man, felt he had arrived. "Surely," he later wrote in the first of several autobiographical books, "Camps and Cruises of an Ornithologist," "this was an honor these rarest of American birds have accorded few ornithologists." He did not allow the experience to turn his head, however, and went on to report in a matter-of-fact way that the adult egret says "Cuk-cuk-cuk," while young egrets say "Kek-kek-kek."

For the last thirty-five years, Dr. Chapman, along with most North American birds, has migrated South in the winter, usually going to Florida, South America, or Panama. In the spring he comes North again with the first robin. He is able to reproduce the songs of any number of birds by whistling and likes nothing better than to fool a bird into thinking he is another bird. By answering their songs in the woods, he has astonished many varieties of birds, who have come up within a few feet of him and looked at him closely. Since some of them sing only to attract mates, Dr. Chapman's replies have led to a certain amount of disappointment, misunderstanding, and bad feeling among birds. He often used to imitate an owl's cry while walking in the country, in order to get a flock of crows, who despise owls, to fly up and caw at him. He once played this trick when a real owl was around. Crows flew up and attacked the owl, which was quietly taking a nap. The owl was amazed. Dr. Chapman, who likes an owl as well as the next bird, has not done this since. He did, however, in the interests of science, play a rather elaborate trick not long ago on some blue jays. He wanted to see, at close range, the jays feed their young, and after spending several fruitless hours near a blue-jay nest, while concealed in a canvas affair painted to resemble tree bark and liberally draped with poison-ivy vines, he hit on the idea of wiring a mounted blue jay to a limb below the nest. He thought the parent jays, who were frightened away by his blind, would come back to evict the stranger loitering near their home. Instead, the mother at once returned and fed her young, apparently reassured by the mounted bird, whom she took for an old friend of the family's. Dr. Chapman next removed the dummy jay and replaced it with a mounted screech owl, which is a great enemy of the jay. The parent jays screamed in horror and attacked the owl, which they knocked over so that it hung upside down, still wired to the tree. Even in this position it continued to terrify the jays, and Dr. Chapman, who thought the thing had gone far enough, finally removed it.

Dr. Chapman has on several occasions occupied the nests of some of the larger birds himself. Some years ago, marooned by a storm on a small island in a Canadian lake, he moved three pelican eggs from one nest to another and climbed into the vacant nest, which was made of heaped-up sand and pebbles and was well above water level. He sat there in comparative snugness until the downpour was over, feeling exactly like a pelican. Another time, on a beach in the Bahamas, he passed several days in an unoccupied nest in the middle of a settlement of two thousand flamingos, making notes and taking photographs. The flamingos accepted Dr. Chapman as one of themselves and poked about right under his nose. "Seated on the deserted nest," he reported, "I myself seemed to have become a flamingo." For all this, Dr. Chapman realizes that he is actually neither a flamingo nor a pelican. He deplores the fact that there is no real communication between men and birds and that consequently he is unable to let certain birds know how much he enjoys their singing. "I often wish there were some way of assuring vireolanius that he is doing more than his duty," he once said.

Most of the time when he has not been directly fraternizing with birds, Dr. Chapman has spent classifying them, skinning them, writing about them, agitating to get them off women's hats, helping establish sanctuaries for them, and lecturing on them. He began to lecture in the eighteen-nineties in order to supplement the modest salary he was then getting as associate curator of the Museum's Department of Ornithology and Mammalogy. He made his first talk at the Ogontz School, a girls' institution near Philadelphia. Dr. Chapman, who in those days felt more at home in a cypress tree than on a lecture platform, pretended to himself that he was talking to a group of birds, and everything went smoothly. He soon became known as the most articulate ornithologist in the country and was invited to give lecture courses at places ranging all the way from the University of Indiana to the Lowell Institute in Boston. In 1901 he got a letter from the New York Farmers, an organization he had never heard of, asking him to speak on farm birds at their annual dinner. Dr. Chapman, then a rising young ornithologist of thirty-seven, was reluctant to waste an evening before a group of agriculturalists and rather offhandedly recommended another speaker, pleading a prior engagement. The next year the Farmers invited him again. Not wishing to be rude, he accepted and found himself at a dinner at the Metropolitan Club, surrounded by such farmers as J. P. Morgan, George F. Baker, Cleveland H. Dodge and Adrian Iselin. The New York Farmers turned out to be a group of part-time country gentlemen who met once a year to eat an enormous meal and discuss the problems of Long Island and Westchester estates. The private dining room where Dr. Chapman addressed them was embellished with moss, plants, a small log cabin, and dozens of mounted birds. Dr. Chapman was torn between pleasure at the company and dismay at the arrangement of the stuffed birds. "Without regard to haunt or habit, 100 or more of these specimens were distributed where they could be most easily attached or seemed to produce the best effect," he wrote in his autobiography. "It was a Habitat group such as never was seen before or since. There were Terns in the evergreens and Swallows on the forest floor, while birds of the Temperate and Tropic Zones met in a hitherto unheard-of association."

Dr. Chapman will be seventy-five in June. In recent years he has had to give up lecturing, but he still likes to talk about birds by the hour to friends and visitors at the Museum, and he is writing his sixteenth book about the subject with which he has been in love all his life. He was born in 1864 on his family's forty-acre farm in Englewood, N. J. The place was full of birds and he was conscious of the songs of wrens, bluebirds, and red-winged blackbirds from the start. He was the first birdman in the Chapman line. His father, a lawyer associated with Joseph H. Choate's firm, paid no particular attention to birds. Frank thinks he may have inherited from his grandfather the patience which has enabled him to set down long, detailed classifications of birds. His grandfather was Lebbeus Chapman, a banker who between July 1, 1846, and May 25, 1847, copied the entire Bible in longhand, averaging four hours a day at this work.

Dr. Chapman recalls seeing his first cardinal at the age of eight while visiting his grandparents in Georgia. This visit also brought him into contact with a European bullfinch, owned by a neighbor of his grandparents, which made a deep impression on him. He memorized the song of this bird and still whistles it occasionally. It takes twenty-three seconds, which is long for a birdcall. An uncle to whom he whistled the bullfinch song was so favorably affected that he gave Frank his first book about birds, Johnson's "Natural History," and later sent him some pelican feathers. These became the nucleus of a rather large accumulation of feathers. Frank got his mother's cook to give him wings of prairie hens, then common in butcher shops, and enlarged his collection of feathers by shooting robins, blue jays, Carolina parakeets, and cedar waxwings, and by trapping bobolinks. Today he wouldn't think of trapping a bobolink. He has followed the bobolink to its winter quarters in the Argentine and has pronounced it his favorite American bird. "I like it for its sweet song," he wrote in one of his books, "for its high character, for its habits, and for its extraordinary migrations." He feels different about ducks, and has been an active duck-shooter most of his life, pursuing this sport somewhat surreptitiously in later years out of deference to an anti-duck-shooting bloc in the Audubon Society.

Dr. Chapman graduated from Englewood Academy in 1880 and

then went to work for the American Exchange National Bank in New York. He had an independent income of around $2,000 a year, left to him by his father, and although he had no particular desire for more money, he thought he should find some sort of conventional career. He commuted every day and on the train fell in with a couple of Hackensack bird-lovers, who lent him ornithological books, showed him their collections of mounted birds, and introduced him to other birdmen. Dr. Chapman toiled faithfully at the bank, but his heart was in the woods and he frequently stimulated his colleagues by whistling bird songs as he worked. He became a faithful reader of *Forest & Stream* and in 1884 answered an appeal in this publication, issued by Dr. C. Hart Merriam, chairman of the committee on bird migration of the recently organized American Ornithologists' Union, calling for volunteers to observe and report on the seasonal movements of birds. In the line of duty, Dr. Chapman rose at dawn every morning from March 10th through May 23rd and went into the woods to shoot birds. He followed a route which got him to the West Englewood station at 7:30, where he checked the birds, changed from rough clothes to a double-breasted blue suit, and boarded the 7:39 train to business. In the evening he would pick up the birds at the station and usually shoot more specimens before dinner. After dinner he skinned the day's haul and took notes. During this period he turned up at the bank every day except May 15th, when he got so excited after getting a Brewster's warbler that he took the day off. His report was pronounced the best in the Atlantic Division and he was invited to join the Linnæan Society of New York, a natural-history group which specializes in birds. Through this organization he got to meet still more birdmen. In 1885 he was elected an associate member of the Ornithologists' Union. His passion for birds made him dissatisfied with his work at the bank but didn't interfere with his business progress, and in the fall of 1886 he was placed in charge of the city collecting department. He saw ahead long years of steady advancement and this discouraged him. He resigned at once. He had decided to become a full-time bird-man.

St. Clair McKelway and A. J. Liebling

WHO IS THIS KING OF GLORY?*

Father Divine has said on more than one occasion that he is God. On the walls of his various Heavens here and in other cities hang banners which state that

FATHER DIVINE IS GOD ALMIGHTY

and on the buses which take his followers on joyous excursions from the Harlem Heavens to the Heavens of Newark and Jersey City is the invariable, red-lettered inscription:

FATHER DIVINE
(God)

The effect of this bold claim, on the press and government of the city in which he makes his headquarters, has been remarkable. The papers, on the whole, have appeared to regard his works as miraculous. The city government has been singularly deferential in its attitude toward him. The two principal candidates for Mayor of New York called on him at one of the nightly meetings in his Harlem Heaven in 1933. "I came here tonight," said Mr. LaGuardia, "to ask Father Divine's help and counsel. Whatever he wants, I'll do it for him." Mr. O'Brien, appearing before the meeting a little earlier, had said, "Peace! Come what may, adversity, joy, or sorrow, you can meet it by reason of your leadership under Father Divine. Peace!" It looks sometimes as if a good many people besides Father Divine's followers think maybe he *is* God.

Father Divine would like everybody to believe that he was born mature, and only a few years ago, in Providence, which is neither in Rhode Island nor the sky, but right here (or over there), like the

---

* *This is part of a long portrait of Father Divine which was published in* The New Yorker *in June, 1936.*

654

pantheistic Deity or the Buddhists' eternal life. "Except a man be born again," Jesus told Nicodemus, "he cannot see the Kingdom of God." Father Divine not only sees the Kingdom of God every day, but leases it and lives in one of the main apartments himself. Naturally, he says, he had to be born again before that could be. He insists that he can't remember who he was or what he was like before that happened. "Can you remember back to before you were born?" he has asked skeptics who have questioned him on this point.

If you bear firmly in mind the fact that the Father is a short, dignified colored man with a bald head, the true story of his life is more impressive than his story of divine rebirth. It is a story of arduous struggle, onward and upward, from obscurity to national prominence, from rags to riches. In a mere forty years, he rose from hedge-clipper and grass-cutter to evangelist, from evangelist to The Messenger, from The Messenger to Major J. Devine, from Major J. Devine to the Rev. J. Divine, and from the Rev. J. Divine to Father Divine (God).

He is around sixty now, and the earliest records of his life are obscure. People who knew him when he was in his twenties think he came from Georgia, or Florida, or Virginia. They are not sure which. But in 1899, beyond all question, he was a man named George Baker and was earning an honest living in Baltimore, mostly by clipping hedges and mowing lawns. He had a scythe and a pair of pruning shears, and he would canvass the white residential districts in spring and summer, offering his services for fifty cents a day. He was frugal, and when winter came he had usually saved up enough money to loaf for a while. If his store of coins began to get too low, he would find odd jobs on the docks. He did not seem to be very ambitious.

On Sundays he taught in the Sunday school of the Rev. Mr. Henderson's Baptist Church on Eden Street. He was a serious-minded young fellow and worried a lot about God. He didn't feel, or claim to be, closer to God than any of the other members of the Rev. Mr. Henderson's colored congregation. He just taught his Sunday-school class, read his Bible, and went about his work during the week with his head full of large words and sounding phrases. At Wednesday-night prayer meetings in the church he sometimes made little speeches, as any member of the congregation had a right to do, and in these he almost always would get tangled up with some tremendous thought, such as "God is personified and materialized." He would grasp the thought firmly and wrestle with it. "God," he would say, "is not only personified and materialized. He is repersonified and rematerialized. He rematerializes and He rematerial*ates*. He rematerial*ates* and He is rematerial*izatable*. He repersonificates and He repersoni*fitizes*." He would go on like that for a while, sweating, his eyes bulging a little, and then he would stop abruptly and resume his seat. People liked to hear him talk even then. There would be cries of "Amen, brother!" and "Brother, ain't it so!" between his words and sometimes between the syllables of his words. But he wasn't the superb orator then that he is now, and he never seemed to be quite sure what it was he was driving at.

*   *   *

Twenty years later, George Baker, who by a process of multiple birth had become The Messenger and then Major J. Devine, was born a fourth time, and then a fifth time, almost as soon as he established himself in Sayville, Long Island, in 1919. He became Rev. J. Divine, dropping the military title and adopting a vowel which gave the name a supernatural significance. Then almost immediately afterward he became Father Divine (God). He has been God ever since. A few weeks ago his disciples in Harlem stretched a streamer of black-and-gold silk across the throne of Heaven, the headquarters of the cult, on West 115th Street, with the blaring legend:

FATHER DIVINE IS DEAN OF THE UNIVERSE

But that is rank hyperbole. The promotion to Dean of the Universe is simply a gratuitous expression of the enthusiasm of his followers and does not represent a formal rebirth. Neither in the early years in Sayville nor in the later years in Harlem has Father Divine ever hinted that he considers himself to be anything more than God.

As God, after he had settled down in Sayville, he was modest and almost entirely without affectation. His white neighbors on Macon Street were never exactly friendly with him, but they didn't object to him particularly. It was not a pretentious street. The houses, set back from the curbs in comfortable, shady yards, were occupied mostly by people who worked in the village the year round. The summer colony was on the other side of the Merrick Road and the hotels and great estates were still further away. To his neighbors, Father Divine was

known not as Major J. Devine, the name he had signed to the deed
when he bought his house, but as the Rev. J. Divine, and he told them
he was operating an employment agency. He seemed to be an excep-
tionally clean, upright, and dignified colored man, with soft doe eyes
and gentle manners. The neighbors did not know until some years
later that he was supposed to be God. They used to see him doing odd
jobs around his yard in his spare time, pruning the shrubbery, cutting
the grass, and tidying up the places where the former owner had
allowed rubbish to accumulate. He was alone all day except for a
cook. The twenty-odd men and women who lived with him were
workers. Some of them were in New York except on Sundays; others
left the house in the morning and returned in the evening. They were
decent, orderly colored folk, and bothered nobody. They sang a good
deal at night, especially on Sunday, but the singing was soft and they
never kept it up much later than nine o'clock. Inside the house George
Baker was called Father Divine, and all his followers were sure that he
was God.

Once each week Father Divine walked to the office of the *Suffolk
County News,* down the block from the Oystermen's Bank & Trust
Company, and placed a classified advertisement offering reliable colored help for all work. Whenever a householder answered the advertisement, Father Divine would call in person, bearing a business card
marked "Rev. J. Divine." He would remove his hat and, standing on
the doorstep, would say, "I can guarantee and *re*guarantee the character and probity and uprighteousness of all my clients." People liked
him, and within a year or so, working at a leisurely pace, he got jobs
in and near Sayville for all of the early disciples. This relieved the communal purse of the cost of commuting, which had been a considerable
strain.

These early followers of Father Divine had never had much to give
him but their wages, and their wages were never high. They were poor
people who labored on the outer fringe of domestic service. None
of them was expert as cook or laundress. They worked mostly for
families of three or four who could afford one servant and who paid
not more than $10 or $12 a week. But now Father Divine began to
attract from the kitchens and butlers' pantries of the summer hotels
and big houses of Nassau and Suffolk Counties a new kind of disciple
—colored people of some means, who earned sometimes as much as
$100 a month, slept and ate in their employers' houses, and had bank

accounts and insurance policies. To these people Father Divine seemed to be God in an even more wonderful degree than he had been to the early followers. As he became acquainted with the better class of colored folk in Sayville and neighboring towns, he began to invite them to Sunday dinners at his house; he preached to them after dinner, and never took up a collection. When the guests asked him candidly how he managed to give them free dinners, he would say cheerfully, "Father will provide," and his disciples would say, "It's wonderful! Ain't it wonderful? Sweet Father is God Almighty!" He enjoyed no sudden popularity. He attracted people to his house only by twos and threes. Some Sundays there were no outside guests at all; on others there might be three or four. For six or seven years Father Divine's progress was slow. It was not until the late nineteen-twenties that things began to boom.

The experiences of a butler-and-cook couple named Thomas and Verinda Brown, who worked for a substantial white family in Forest Hills and earned a joint salary of $150 a month, plus board and room, are typical of the experiences of scores of disciples who joined the cult of Father Divine about this time. Thomas and Verinda occupied prominent places in Father Divine's Heaven from 1930 until 1933. They were what Father Divine calls Angels, a title conferred upon any person who assigns all his property to Father Divine, hands over all the money he earns, and takes a new name. Verinda was called Rebecca Grace, and throughout one Sunday dinner in 1931 sat at the right hand of God. Thomas was called Onward Universe and for a while was one of God's favorite Angels. Now the two are Thomas and Verinda again and are back in Forest Hills, working for the same family they were with when they first met Father Divine. They no longer believe that he is God.

Verinda is a very tall, very healthy-looking middle-aged woman, the color of a fine mink coat. Her features are large and frank—a great nose, an enormous jaw, a mouth that opens and shuts decisively. Her natural expression is an expansive grin. Thomas is shorter, darker, less vivacious, a sort of understatement of Verinda. His eyes are drowsy and slow-moving. He is deliberate, methodical, and thoughtful by nature. Verinda comes from Barbados, Thomas from the Bahamas. Both have been in this country thirty years or more and they have been married ten. Both are excessively neat; Thomas is even something of a dude, and at one time owned sixteen suits of clothes, all of them in fair condition. Verinda is a fine cook and a capable children's nurse; as a butler and house man, Thomas is efficient and has a soothing manner. They are decent, honest people. They estimate that during the time they were Angels in Sayville they gave Father Divine, freely and of their own accord, something over $5,000, itemized as follows:

Savings withdrawn from the Railroad Coöperative Building & Loan Association	$ 700
Verinda's salary of $75 a month from April, 1930, to October, 1933	3,225
Gold coins	100
Seven Florida lots (estimated value)	350
Thomas's salary, averaging $75 a month, for six months in 1930	450
Thomas's earnings at odd jobs in Sayville during eighteen months of 1931-32	750
Fifteen suits of clothes relinquished by Thomas (estimated value)	85
Total	$5,660

The manner in which Verinda and Thomas became acquainted with Father Divine seemed to them for a long time afterward to be clearly miraculous. One day in the spring of 1929, after Father Divine's Sunday dinners had become quite an event for the colored population in and near Sayville without attracting attention in other quarters, a laundryman in Forest Hills made a mistake and left some strange clean clothes at the home in which Thomas and Verinda worked. Thomas knew that another family down the street patronized the same laundry, so he took the bundle to the servants' entrance of that house and introduced himself to the cook. He asked if by any chance the laundry bundles for the two houses had been transposed, and found that was just what had happened. The cook was a happy colored woman who said her name was Priscilla Paul. "After the Apostle," she explained. Thomas himself was a constant reader of the Bible and he and Priscilla exchanged, along with the laundry bundles, a few Biblical texts. They parted friends. "Peace! It's wonderful!" Priscilla said as Thomas started off, and Thomas still remembers how pleasant and reassuring it sounded. ("It's a catching phrase," he says now, in the depths of his agnosticism.)

That night Priscilla Paul came to see Verinda and Thomas in their kitchen. "Peace!" she said as she entered. "It's wonderful!" She invited them to come to the evening meal at her father's house in Sayville the next Sunday. She explained that she went to Sayville every Sunday herself and suggested they go with her on the bus. They accepted, and on Sunday were surprised but not displeased to find themselves at a sort of religious meeting. The dinner was very good. The fact that each plate, before it was passed to the eater, was blessed by the man Priscilla and all the other diners called "Father" rather appealed to Verinda and Thomas. Father Divine said nothing memorable in his sermon after dinner. He did not say he was God, or even intimate it, but his phrasemaking was glorious, and Thomas especially liked the Biblical sound of the things Father Divine said. Verinda thought Father Divine had the loveliest, softest eyes she had ever seen.

Verinda and Thomas had Sundays off after midday dinner, and they became regular visitors at Father Divine's house. They asked him if they shouldn't pay for the meals they had every Sunday— told him they'd be more than glad to, because they enjoyed themselves so much. But he would always wave them away with a cheerful smile and say, "Father will provide." It was wonderful. As they got to know the other disciples—a preoccupied and prim old fellow named Gabriel; an elderly woman named Susanna, who sang beautifully; and others named Ruth Rachel, Hozanna Love, Faith Sweetness, Frank Incense, Blessed Charity, and so on—they began to learn how much more wonderful it was than they had dreamed. Not only did the Father provide a dinner every week that must have cost $15 or $20; he worked other miracles besides. The loaves-and-fishes trick, to him, was just a routine. He was a healer, too. Everybody there, it seemed, had been cured of some physical or spiritual disorder. After dinner in the evenings, between songs like:

> Father Divine is the Perfect God,
> Perfect God,
> Perfect God . . .

and

> I love to sing the praise of thee,
> Sweet Father Divine.
> I love to sing the praise of thee,
> Be practical all the time,

testimonials would be given by the Angels. This phase of the meeting was a sort of burnt-cork Buchmanism. Verinda and Thomas were perfectly healthy physically, but both had stern consciences and they managed to join in by telling about things they had done wrong, and explaining that, since they had come to know the Father, they didn't do wrong any more.

In the Father's sermons at this time there ran a refrain which had to do with "conscious mentality." He would say, "Relaxation of the conscious mentality is the super-mental relaxativeness of mankind." The Angels, who sat nearest to him at the big dinner table, had achieved this sublime state, it seemed. They had relaxed their conscious mentalities until they had been born again as Angels, they had got fine new names, and they didn't remember anything that had ever happened to them in the past. Verinda and Thomas thought the Angels, and everything about them, were enviable, and they began to try to relax their conscious mentalities. The way to do this, they were told, was to love the Father and think about him all the time.

The employers of Verinda and Thomas were puzzled, and somewhat unnerved, when, during this period, their splendid servants seemed to be going to pieces. Upon being reprimanded for breaking dishes or being slow with the cocktail things, Verinda and Thomas would explain mournfully that they were trying to relax their conscious mentalities. They seemed preoccupied, sad, and solemn, and they probably would have lost their jobs had they not been faithful servants for nine years past. Besides the worry over their conscious mentalities, they had anxieties which their employers did not understand. Thomas and Verinda had grown to love Father Divine. He had been so kind to them during those first months, and he had seemed to know everything, to feel everything, to be so confident when he said, over and over at the dinners, "Your Father is rich in all your needs and all your wants shall be supplied." Those ecstatic shouts of "Yes, Father, you are *so* wonderful!" and "Thank you, Father!" which came from the Angels were impressive and contagious. There was something keenly satisfying and delightful about the idea of putting one's trust in somebody as the Angels put their trust in Father Divine. Verinda and Thomas had begun to think of him as God. And now, just when they were loving him so, and were trying so hard to please him, he seemed not to notice them at all. They found themselves seated further and further away from him every Sunday. When he looked at them at all, it was as if he despised them. He was always talking these days about sacrifice and self-denial and consecration, building the words up till they seemed four times as big as they really were. "He who would enter into the Kingdom of God must have nothing he can call his own," he would say sometimes, candidly. He preached against life insurance, against all forms of insurance, and said that anybody who stood to benefit by an insurance policy was a murderer or an incendiarist at heart. "Look," he would say, "at the Snyder-Gray case. If Albert Snyder hadn't been insured, he would never have been killed. He was putting temptation in the way of the iniquitous. Live right and keep my commandments and you shall never die. It is so written. He who insures his life or his property is a man of little faith." He did not tell his followers that he had insured his house against fire with the Firemen's Insurance Company, the Glens Falls Insurance Company, and the National Liberty Insurance Company, but he had.

When Verinda and Thomas heard the speech against insurance they were delighted. It seemed to be addressed directly to them. They had small insurance policies of the kind that may be cashed in, and they applied for the money that Monday. When they got the cash the next week, Verinda bought a trunk for Thomas and Thomas bought a diamond ring for Verinda. Then they made a special night trip to Sayville to tell the Father about it, feeling sure that he would be pleased.

"Why didn't you ask me what to do with the money?" he demanded bluntly, and added in a more Godlike tone, "He that loveth father or mother, son or daughter, husband or wife, more than me is not worthy to enter the Kingdom of God." They were abashed. Verinda, quicker of tongue than Thomas, said she was so sorry and asked the Father's forgiveness. They had, she said after a silence, a joint account in the Railroad Coöperative Building & Loan Association that contained about $700. They would do anything Father wished with that, she said. Father Divine said, "Draw it out. Lay not up treasures on earth where moth and thief and mouse break in and steal, but lay it up in Heaven with your Father."

This they did. Father Divine got the $700 that Friday.

Then, for a while, Thomas and Verinda dwelt in a state of beatitude. They were told that they had achieved the rank of Angels and were permitted to choose new names for themselves. Verinda chose Rebecca Grace, after some advice from the other Angels. Thomas had already thought up Onward Universe for himself, and he adopted it forthwith. They remained Thomas and Verinda to their employers, but they explained one day that their old names were really just nicknames, that their real names now were Rebecca Grace and Onward Universe. "But you just keep calling us Thomas and Verinda," Thomas said to his master. "That will be perfectly all right."

Thomas and Verinda were happy now. They were moved back nearer the head of the table, and Father Divine beamed on them with heart-warming affection. As a matter of course, without being invited to do so by the Father, they began at once to turn over their wages to him every week, as all the other Angels did. Thomas took the deeds to his Florida lots out of his trunk and signed them over to the Father. When Verinda's mistress, the following year, gave her a bonus of $100 in gold, Verinda turned that over to the Father. For one Sunday, Verinda sat on the right hand of God, and Thomas, only a few seats away, found himself talking intimately with God during dinner. They never talked with the other Angels about the money they were giving to Father Divine because part of the gospel taught at Heaven was that true believers "relaxed all recollection of material transactions." This was a phrase which, with prefixes and suffixes, Father Divine built into something of impressive proportions.

Father Divine was a keen-eyed God. He noticed that Thomas had on a different suit nearly every time he came to Heaven, and one day he asked Thomas about that and learned that Thomas had sixteen suits. "Bring me fifteen of those suits," he told Thomas. "Look how the lilies of the field are clothed, and they spin not."

He was a jealous God, too. In Brooklyn he had always preached the gospel of celibacy to the followers who lived in the flat with him, and now, in Sayville, with about twenty Angels living with him and forty living with their employers, he preached the same gospel with even more determination. When the conscious mentality is really relaxed, he argued, all love except for the Father has to relax, too. Verinda and Thomas were a devoted couple and they slept at night in a double bed. They took the Father's preaching literally and seriously, and Thomas faced the same hardships as those third-century monks who used to exorcise themselves by inviting attractive women to come to the monastery and tempt them. As Gibbon said of the monks, outraged nature sometimes vindicated herself. Whenever that happened, Verinda and Thomas would appear before the Father ill at ease and heavy of conscience, and he, looking at them, would say, "I see you have sinned. You cannot hide from God. I am everywhere. I see all. I know all." And they would moan and cry, "Oh, Father! Yes, Father! Forgive us, Father! You are *so* wonderful, Father!"

A man of Thomas's abilities was needed in Heaven, and six months after Thomas became Onward Universe, he left his job and his Verinda, and came to live in the house on Macon Street. He was one of the principal Angels, and for a while used to hold long Biblical discussions with the Father on weekday evenings. He is handy with tools, and by day he worked around Heaven, putting up partitions where the Father wanted them, repairing the roof, and doing other useful chores. Evidently it was worth the loss of Thomas's salary to Father Divine to have Thomas around. When there was nothing for Thomas to do, he found odd jobs in the village and earned a little cash from time to time, which he turned over to the Father. Verinda kept her job in Forest Hills and came to Heaven only on Sundays, as in the past. She used to meet Thomas there, but never clandestinely, and when they spoke to one another it was just to say, "Peace! It's wonderful!" For a long time it seemed to them that they were happier than they had ever been before. Verinda remained a faithful follower of Father Divine until the fall of 1933. By that time she had become just one of sixty-odd Angels, she was beginning to have her doubts about the divinity of the Father, and she was tired of not having any spending money. Her employers in Forest Hills, who were fond of her, advised her to quit going to Father Divine's meetings, and finally she took their advice. Thomas stayed with Father Divine until last year, by which time he had been demoted to furnace man in the Harlem Heaven. Then one day he walked out, got his old job back, and his Verinda, and never returned.

A good many other Angel couples became estranged in the same way during the Sayville period. Some of them lived separately in Heaven itself and some lived separately outside, and all of them were lonely, their hearts were full of affection, and they didn't love anybody but God. He looked after everything. As he had done in Brooklyn with his early disciples, he now provided second-hand clothes for his Angels, skillfully altered and made over by Angel seamstresses. The Angels had no outside expenses to speak of. They had no doctors' bills to pay. Father Divine preached against doctors and dentists. "Father is the Doctor" became the refrain of one of the Heavenly songs. If a disciple was in the habit of going to a clinic for treatment of some disease, even the most contagious ones, Father Divine frowned upon him and told him not to be of little faith. Death, he said, could not come to a true believer. If it did come, it was a proof that the dead Angel had not been a true believer. At least one Angel died at the Sayville Heaven. This was a woman named Bowman. It was recorded at the time that she was a pauper, with no relatives to pay for her funeral, and she was buried in the town's potter's field.

How much money Father Divine was taking in during the winter of 1929-30 is anybody's guess. Figuring that sixty skilled and unskilled disciples earned an average of $15 a week apiece (some of them in those boom years were making $40 and $50), the total, aside from insurance policies and savings accounts which he took over, would have been $900 a week.

The Sunday dinners had become large affairs by the spring of 1930. Word of the strange preacher who seemed to be God, who gave free Sunday dinners, and who never took up a collection, had got back to Harlem. People began to go out to Sayville from Harlem to see for themselves and to eat the miraculous dinners. But they, like the new disciples, were not riffraff. The round-trip ticket from New York to Sayville cost $2.40 and it was cheaper for people who had to count the pennies to eat at home. Only the well-to-do class of Negroes came to Father Divine's Sunday dinners. Some of them became Angels. A few newspaper stories appeared, all of them marvelling at the hospitality of Father Divine, and after the publicity white people began to go to the Sunday dinners in Sayville. There was a Mrs. Withers, of Long Island City, for instance, who went through the customary initiation and eventually became an Angel named Sister Everjoy. She had been a Christian Scientist, had lost a child, and was vulnerable to any kind of new faith that came along. There was J. Maynard Matthews, an automobile dealer of Brookline, Massachusetts, who had tried Divine Science, Unity, and a number of swamis and yogis without having found what he wanted. He presented Father Divine with a Cadillac, abandoned his business, and became the Father's secretary. His name is John Lamb and he is one of the most important Angels in the movement. Other white followers arrived from all over the country, not in great numbers, but singly, one at a time—a widow from Charlotte, North Carolina; a doctor from Chicago; a young accountant from Kansas City. They were solitaries, marked by that peculiar, agonized look which profound faith seems to bring to people's eyes, and they were all looking for some new kind of life on earth.

By midsummer that year, the Sayville police on Sundays had to put no-parking signs up and down the block in which Heaven stood, to prevent hopeless traffic jams. Trucks and buses were bringing scores of Negroes out from Harlem every week. Father Divine's neighbors rented parking space in their front yards, thus combatting the nascent depression. Not more than seventy-five persons could be seated in Father Divine's dining-room, and he served the Sunday dinners to hundreds, in shifts, all day long and into the evening. A new technique of serving these meals was introduced about this time. The hungry visitors would sit down around the table and Father Divine would bless, first of all, the coffee and tea, and those drinks would be served. There would be an interval of thirty minutes or so, during which everybody was urged to have four or five cups apiece. Then, when the diners had reached a bloated condition, great platters of spaghetti, potatoes, Lima beans, and other starches would be blessed and served. Another half-hour would go by before the impressive hams, roasts, chickens, and turkeys would appear. Usually these dishes, having been blessed and offered to everybody, would leave the table almost intact, to be blessed and served again at successive meals for the rest of the day, and to turn up again on quiet week nights when the Angels sat down to dinner. Father Divine himself found the Heavenly meals unsatisfactory. He used to call on Verinda a little before noon on Sundays in her kitchen in Forest Hills and she would invite him to have a bite to eat. "I can't do that," he would say, drawing himself up to the table. "My Angels are waiting on me in Sayville, to bless their food," he would protest. Verinda would cook up some scrambled eggs, pancakes, sausage, fried potatoes, and coffee, and the Father would fall to, remarking that he might have a snack, at that, to strengthen him on his drive back to Sayville. "When I scrambled eggs for him," Verinda says now, "I always scrambled six."

As Father Divine's fame increased, so did the suspicions of many people outside his cult. Letters were sent to him containing cash, money orders, and checks, by investigators in the pay of the Sayville police authorities, who thought he might be open to prosecution on a federal charge of using the mails to defraud. In every case the enclosure was returned with a note that said, "Father will provide." The Suffolk County District Attorney planted two colored women from Harlem in Father Divine's Heaven in an effort to find out where his money came from, but at the end of two weeks they told him they hadn't been able to find out anything. This procedure was doomed from the start, for the reason that the two colored women were Harlem followers of Father Divine and were well on the way toward becoming Angels themselves. In the end, the Suffolk County authorities ceased trying to work up a criminal case against Father Divine. Nobody could with authority challenge his claim that his money came to him out of the sky. "Everything comes to him automatically because he's God," the Angels used to say, and it seemed to be the only possible explanation.

By fall of that year, there were so many Angels in Heaven that Father Divine had to expand. Property in his block had declined in value somewhat since the big meetings had begun, and he bought the house next door, at No. 64 Macon Street. It is a smaller house than the other one, and was used as a dormitory for female Angels. This left room in Heaven for an extra dining-room to accommodate the guests who came each Sunday in increasing numbers. Father Divine had by this time about a hundred and fifty Angels living with him. In the summer of 1931, he leased a house across the street for white Angels exclusively. About the same time he established what he called an Extension Heaven in Harlem, a flat of five or six rooms on Fifth Avenue at 128th Street. Some twenty Angels who worked in New York lived in the Extension Heaven just as the suburban Angels lived in the one at Sayville. The sexes were segregated, and one of Father Divine's principal Angels looked after the marketing, directed the household work, and collected the wages of all the Angels every payday.

By the fall of 1931, the police authorities in Sayville and the Suffolk County District Attorney had decided that Father Divine was a public nuisance, and he was arrested on that charge on November 16th of that year. After a change of venue had been obtained, he was brought to trial in Nassau County, before Justice Lewis J. Smith, who turned out to be the man who contributed as much as anybody to the present greatness of Father Divine. The Justice, according to the opinion of the higher court which subsequently overruled him, permitted prejudice to enter into the trial and charged the jury in a manner that virtually demanded a verdict of guilty. Father Divine was convicted and Justice Smith fined him $500 and sentenced him to one year in jail. Four days after Justice Smith pronounced this sentence, he died. He had been a robust man and was only fifty-five years old. His physicians said his death was caused by heart failure. It was obvious to all of Father Divine's followers, and to thousands of people, both white and colored, all over the country who read about it in the newspapers, that Father Divine had struck down the Justice. The appeal was handled brilliantly by James C. Thomas, a Negro attorney who is a former Assistant United States District Attorney. He donated his services because he believed the issue to be one of racial prejudice. When the Appellate Division reversed the conviction in January, 1933, it was accepted as further evidence of the divinity of Father Divine. The Angels gave Mr. Thomas no credit at all for the victory.

During the five weeks Father Divine had been held in jail without bail, scores of new followers joined his cult. The Heavens in Sayville, and the branch in Harlem, had been efficiently maintained by a few trusted Angels, who came to him often at the Nassau County Jail for instruction and advice. He was ready now to expand still further, and he selected Harlem as his new headquarters. Leaving a few elderly Angels to look after his property in Sayville, he moved to New York. By this time not fewer than three hundred Angels were turning over to him everything they earned.

* * *

When Father Divine addresses his followers these days in Heaven, a roomy, five-story structure at 20 West 115th Street, his demeanor is marked by an alertness which suggests that he is an extremely nervous man. One of his favorite routines is that of leading a chant which starts like this:

One million blessings,
Blessings flowing free,
Blessings flowing free.
There are so many blessings,
Blessings flowing free for you.

Then it goes:

One *billion* blessings,
Blessings flowing free,
Blessings flowing free,
There are so many blessings,
Blessings flowing free for you,

and so on—trillion, quadrillion, quintillion, and on up to what he calls septdecillion. He shouts the catch line of each verse and then, as he hums the chorus and the followers sing, his soft eyes begin to wander. They shift rapidly over the audience, they glance for an instant at the entrance door, at the exits, and once or twice during the singing of a verse he turns half about and looks sharply behind him. He seems agitated and apprehensive, and it is clear that there is more on his mind than the task of conducting a religious meeting. He has the detached, preoccupied manner of a bartender in the early days of prohibition who, while mixing a highball, was always wondering when the police would come in.

VERSE

It is grim business being a minor poet, so little is expected of you. Perhaps for this very reason the writers of non-serious verse give the reader such good measure—they give him poems which sometimes contain music, emotion, and humor, all at once. Even loaded with these noble burdens, the stuff gets called "light."

The editors here offer a few of the heaviest poems they could collect. Others will be found scattered through the book.

Don Marquis

THREE SONNETS TO A RED-HAIRED LADY

Suzanne, I bid you fling aside your comb
And down the wind let stream your burning hair!
My soul, perchance, through midnights of despair,
May see it, Sultry Kid, and flutter home!
Or is there danger in that flaming dome? ...
Suppose I fluttered moth-like, frying there
Unto a crackling, Susan! ... would you care,
My pink-beaned Venus crowned with fiery foam?

My Fifth Wife had a wad of hair herself;
She used to wash and wash and wash the stuff;
I canned her, Sue; I put her on the shelf;
I like clean hair, but still, enough's enough....
She'd get it dry the radiator way....
How these old griefs return! Ah, welladay!

~~~~~~

I saw some bright flowers swaying in the park
And thought how like their life your red locks blow....
My Flame! My Sunrise and mine Afterglow!
My genial Hearthfire blazing through the dark!
My Gaudy Kid! Upon life's headlands, stark
And bleak, over the treacherous tides that flow,
A beacon light your Fiery Bean doth throw....
I steer by you and save my giddy bark.

How I should hate it, Lighthouse tall and slim,
If you should cut your hair and dim your fire!
My Seventh Wife did that; she doused her glim,
And dousing it, she damped my soul's desire—
I took a brick and shaved the rest away,
But still her memory stirs me.... Welladay!

When I grow older will you be my wife?
Not now, Suzanne...in twenty years or more.
Unless I change my mind, I'd like you for
A Bonfire in the Autumn of my Life.
But, no! You may be faded then with strife
Of living...marry another, I implore!
And raise me up your daughter to adore,
Red-Haired, with your own candent beauty rife.

My Fourteenth Wife had *unresponsive* hair,
As drab in tone, inert to touch, as clay;
She wore it in an ugly little knot;
She had a morbid interest in prayer,
Which vexed me so I had to have her shot....
She's with the angels now! Ah, welladay!

Angela Cypher

WOMAN OUT OF TAXI

Any woman
　　When she's grown
And goes to parties
　　All alone

Finds taxicabs
　　Exert a spell
That segregate her
　　Like a shell

Wherein detached
　　From life she's whirled
Through this exciting
　　Clamorous world.

Within a cab
　　She grows compact,
A separate, keen,
　　Dynamic fact,

Unentertained,
　　Untouched, unspent,
Safe in her own
　　Integument.

Out of the taxi
　　She will come
From an emotional
　　Vacuum,

Out of the darkness
  Into the light,
As highly charged
  As dynamite.

She draws her cloak
  About her hips,
Twists her bracelet,
  Bites her lips,

From head to toe
  Grows tense and narrow,
Simple and dangerous
  As an arrow

Aimed at a door
  That may, by chance
Swing inward, brightly,
  On romance.

Ogden Nash

CAT NAPS ARE TOO GOOD FOR CATS

Oh, early every afternoon
I like a temporary swoon.
I do not overeat at luncheon,
I do not broach the bowl or puncheon;
Yet the hour from two to three
Is always sleepy-time to me.

Bolt upright at my desk I sit,
My elbows digging into it,
My chin into my hands doth fit,
My careful fingers screen my eyes,
And all my work before me lies,
Which leads inquisitive passer-bys
Who glance my way and see me nod,
To think me wide awake, if odd.

I would not sell my daily swoon
For all the rubies in Rangoon.
What! sell my swoon? My lovely swoon?
Oh, many and many's the afternoon
I've scoured the woods with Daniel Boone,
And sipped a julep with Lorna Doone,
And Former Governor Ruby Laffoon.
I'll sell my soul before my swoon,
It's not for sale, my swoon's immune.

From two to three each afternoon
Mine are the Mountains of the Moon,
Mine a congenital silver spoon.
And I can lead a lost platoon

Or dive for pearls in a haunted lagoon,
Or guide a stratosphere balloon.
Oh, where the schooner schoons, I schoon,
I can talk lion, or baboon,
Or make a crooner cease to croon.
I like to swoon, for when I swoon
The universe is my macaroon.
Then blessings on thee, my afternoon torpor,
Thou makest a prince of a mental porpor.

"MY CHILD IS PHLEGMATIC..."

—ANXIOUS PARENT

Anxious Parent, I guess you have just never been around;
I guess you just don't know who are the happiest people anywhere to
be found;
I guess you just haven't ever been to the Beaux Arts or Kit Kat or
Cholly Knickerbocker or Old Guards Ball;
I guess you just haven't had any experience of life at all.
So you are worried, are you, because your child is turning out to be
phlegmatic?
Forgive me if I seem a trifle unsympathatic.
Why do you want your child to be a flashing, coruscating gem?
Don't you know the only peace the world can give lies not in flame
but in phlegm?
Don't you know that the people with souls of putty
Are the only people who are sitting prutty?
They never get all worked up at the drop of a pin or a feather or a hat,
They never go around saying bitterly to themselves: "Oh God, did I
really do, did I really say *that?*"
They never boil over when they read about stool pigeons getting girls
into reformatories by making treacherous advances;
They never get perfectly futilely harrowed about Sacco and Vanzetti
or Alice Adamses who don't have good times at dances;
They never blink an eyelash about colleges that are going to the dogs
because of football overemphasis;
They never almost die with indignation when some colored person is
lynched in Natchez or Memphis.

No, when they eat they digest their food, and when they go to bed
they get right to sleep
And four phlegmatic angels a stolid watch over them keep.
Oh to be phlegmatic, oh to be stolid, oh to be torpid, oh to be calm!
For it is only thus, Anxious Parent, that we can get through life with-
out a qualm.

THE SONG OF SONGS

Is anybody here in favor of a redistribution of wealth?
Because I think it ought to be redistributed, only not by force or by
stealth,
Because it is only when other people have it and you haven't that it
is evil,
So we had better try to correct the situation before it is made worse
by a revolution or an upheaval.
Let us not be like the Soviets and fall prey to any communistic
demagog.
No, surely we have more sense than a mujik and would yawn at
arguments that keep them agog;
And let us not be sheep like a Fascist audience
Who get played on by their leaders like concertinas or accaudience;
Let us rather correct in our own 100% American way the wrongs that
annoy and disgust us,
And correct them so the corrections will not offend the Constitution
and Mr. Hughes, our imposing Chief Justice;
Let us handle it in the manner of Washington and Jefferson and
Jackson
And keep very level-headed and Anglo-Saxon.
There are several things standing in the way of a natural distribution
of wealth, but if you want to know which is the chief thing, well,
I will tell you which:
The rich marry only the rich.
It is one of our national disasters
That, broadly speaking, Astors and Vanderbilts and Rockefellers and
Morgans never marry anybody but Morgans and Rockefellers and
Vanderbilts and Astors,

Whereas if they only bestowed their affections on somebody in a
    lower crust,

Why money would be distributed over this broad land of ours like
    dust,

So I think they may all be rich but honest,

But I think their matchmaking proclivities ought to be harnessed.

Yes, if money marrying money were prohibited,

How speedily and how painlessly it would be redistributed.

Yes, yes, the rich and the poor can settle and forget their differences
    just as the Blue and the Gray have

As soon as we have a law saying that people can only marry people
    who have a lot less money than they have,

And that will be the end of all your present and future Townsends
    and Coughlins and Longs,

And that is why I call this piece the Song of Songs.

H. C. Bunner

BEHOLD THE DEEDS!

(Being the Plaint of Adolphe Culpepper Ferguson, Salesman of Fancy Notions, held in durance of his Landlady for a failure to connect on Saturday night.)

I.

I would that all men my hard case might know;
    How grievously I suffer for no sin:
I, Adolphe Culpepper Ferguson, for lo!
    I, of my landlady am lockéd in,
For being short on this sad Saturday,
Nor having shekels of silver wherewith to pay;
    She has turned and is departed with my key;
    Wherefore, not even as other boarders free,
        I sing (as prisoners to their dungeon stones
When for ten days they expiate a spree):
        Behold the deeds that are done of Mrs. Jones!

II.

One night and one day have I wept my woe;
    Nor wot I when the morrow doth begin,
If I shall have to write to Briggs & Co.,
    To pray them to advance the requisite tin
For ransom of their salesman, that he may
Go forth as other boarders go alway—
    As those I hear now flocking from their tea,
Led by the daughter of my landlady
        Piano-ward. This day for all my moans,
Dry bread and water have been servéd me.
        Behold the deeds that are done of Mrs. Jones!

III.

Miss Amabel Jones is musical, and so
  The heart of the young he-boardér doth win,
Playing "The Maiden's Prayer," *adagio*—
  That fetcheth him, as fetcheth the banco skin
The innocent rustic. For my part, I pray:
That Badarjewska maid may wait for aye
  Ere sits she with a lover, as did we
  Once sit together, Amabel! Can it be
   That all that arduous wooing not atones
For Saturday shortness of trade dollars three?
  Behold the deeds that are done of Mrs. Jones!

IV.

Yea! she forgets the arm was wont to go
  Around her waist. She wears a buckle whose pin
Galleth the crook of the young man's elbów;
  I forget not, for I that youth have been.
Smith was aforetime the Lothario gay.
Yet once, I mind me, Smith was forced to stay
  Close in his room. Not calm, as I, was he;
  But his noise brought no pleasaunce, verily.
   Small ease he gat of playing on the bones,
Or hammering on his stove-pipe, that I see.
  Behold the deeds that are done of Mrs. Jones!

V.

Thou, for whose fear the figurative crow
  I eat, accursed be thou and all thy kin!
Thee will I show up—yea, up will I shew
  Thy too thick buckwheats, and thy tea too thin.
Ay! here I dare thee, ready for the fray!
Thou dost *not* "keep a first-class house," I say!
  It does not with the advertisements agree.
  Thou lodgest a Briton with a puggaree,

And thou hast harboured Jacobses and Cohns,
Also a Mulligan. Thus denounce I thee!
   Behold the deeds that are done of Mrs. Jones!

ENVOY

Boarders! the worst I have not told to ye:
She hath stolen my trousers, that I may not flee
   Privily by the window. Hence these groans,
There is no fleeing in a *robe de nuit*.
   Behold the deeds that are done of Mrs. Jones!

Franklin P. Adams

TO A THESAURUS

O precious codex, volume, tome,
  Book, writing, compilation, work
Attend the while I pen a pome,
  A jest, a jape, a quip, a quirk.

For I would pen, engross, indite,
  Transcribe, set forth, compose, address,
Record, submit—yea, even write
  An ode, an elegy to bless—

To bless, set store by, celebrate,
  Approve, esteem, endow with soul,
Commend, acclaim, appreciate,
  Immortalize, laud, praise, extol.

Thy merit, goodness, value, worth,
  Expedience, utility—
O manna, honey, salt of earth,
  I sing, I chant, I worship thee!

How could I manage, live, exist,
  Obtain, produce, be real, prevail,
Be present in the flesh, subsist,
  Have place, become, breathe or inhale,

Without thy help, recruit, support,
  Opitulation, furtherance,
Assistance, rescue, aid, resort,
  Favor, sustention, and advance?

Alas! alack! and well-a-day!
  My case would then be dour and sad,
Likewise distressing, dismal, gray,
  Pathetic, mournful, dreary, bad.

                    * * *

Though I could keep this up all day,
  This lyric, elegiac song,
Meseems hath come the time to say
  Farewell! adieu! good-by! so long!

LINES TO THREE BOYS, 8, 6½, AND 2 YEARS OF AGE

Gentlemen, I love and like you,
Caring little for your IQ.

ADVICE TO YOUNG MEN

Never smash thy promise, lad;
  Never break thy word;
Never kiss a lady's lips,
  Lest thou seem absurd.

Be a rock the girls can trust;
  Never tell a lie;
Never come thou back again
  When they say good-by.

Never let them wonder, lad,
  If thou'lt be on time;
Pay thy debts with diamonds,
  Never with a rhyme.

Never be a wastrel, lad;
  Never fool a maid;
Make of honor a business,
  Make of truth a trade.

Do thou as I tell thee, lad;
  Be the best of men:
And girls won't write of thee in verse,
  Nor think of thee again.

Louis Untermeyer

A. E. HOUSMAN TURNS "GEORGEY PORGEY"
INTO A SHROPSHIRE LAD

Where lanes are bright with basil
   And the blue Severn twirls,
Young Georgey ran to dazzle
   And kiss the rose-lipt girls.

No love as light as Georgey's
   Who gave his heart at will,
And there were rustic orgies
   On many a moonlit hill.

But Spring's first tender buddings
   Oft bear a bitter fruit;
And age prefers its puddings
   To the unchaste salute.

Now when the dusk is humming
   And girls come out to play,
Old Georgey sees them coming
   And, oh—he runs away!

Clarence Day

SCENES FROM THE MESOZOIC

I

The parting injunctions
Of mothers and wives
Are one of those functions
That poison their lives.

II

The real objection to the nude,
   Apart of course from chill,
Is that it looks a trifle crude;
   It doesn't fill the bill.

The fact is we need some disguise,
At least in other people's eyes;
Though not so very long ago,
Tradition says, this wasn't so.

The well-dressed beast in ages gone
Had absolutely nothing on,
And yet—if one of the elect—
Achieved with ease the right effect.

III

In mesozoic days a war,
However short, went quite as far
As those du Pont equips, or Krupp.
Like us, they ate each other up.

IV

Soundless is her laughter grim
As he stumbles through the storm.
Fate, he knows, is trailing him,
And the back of his neck feels warm.

V

Farewell, my friends—farewell and hail!
I'm off to seek the Holy Grail.
   I cannot tell you why.
Remember, please, when I am gone,
'Twas Aspiration led me on.
Tiddlely-widdlely tootle-oo,
All I want is to stay with you,
   But here I go. Goodbye.

Irwin Edman

INTERMISSION, PLEASE!

What poet wrote these lovely lines?
What theme is this, from what sonata?
What king invented minus signs?
What's English for *persona grata*?

    The aria we now shall hear
    Is sung by basso, alto, tenor—?
    What actress first played "Chanticler"?
    What's *Lebensraum?* What's *Sprachenkenner?*

Whichever way I turn the dial,
Somebody's asking someone something,
Somebody's learning is on trial,
Someone is being proved a dumb thing.

    Where is the Yard? The Hook of Holland?
    The Taj Mahal? The Iron Lung?
    What college sings the Song of Roland?
    How do you tie a person's tongue?

The famous crowd the microphones
Primed with *bon mots* and information—
A movie star on postal zones,
A prince on pin-point carbonation.

    Name four, name six, name three, name two.
    Send the tinfoil, send in the bottle.
    Send in your question; we'll send you
    A full Greek text of Aristotle.

I listen as they quip and quiz
And get a joke or get an answer:
    What's the pluperfect tense of *Is?*
    Whose head was carried by what dancer?

And as the quizzes end I go
(Sometimes I last but half-way through them)
To study hard until I know
So much I needn't listen to them.

Stephen Vincent Benét

FOR CITY SPRING

Now grimy April comes again,
Maketh bloom the fire-escapes,
Maketh silvers in the rain,
Maketh winter coats and capes
Suddenly all worn and shabby
Like the fur of winter bears,
Maketh kittens, maketh baby,
Maketh kissing on the stairs.
Maketh bug crawl out of crack,
Maketh ticklings down the back
As if sunlight stroked the spine
To a hurdy-gurdy's whine
And the shower ran white wine.

April, April, sing cuckoo,
April, April, maketh new
Mouse and cockroach, man and wife,
Everything with blood and life;
Bloweth, groweth, flourisheth,
Danceth in a ragged skirt
On the very stoop of Death
And will take no mortal hurt.
Maketh dogs to whine and bound,
Maketh cats to caterwaul,
Maketh lovers, all around,
Whisper in the hall.

Oh, and when the night comes down
And the shrieking of the town
Settles to the steady roar
Of a long sea-beaten shore,

April hieth, April spieth
Everywhere a lover lieth,
Bringeth sweetness, bringeth fever,
Will not stop at "I would liever,"
Will not heed, "Now God a mercy!"
Turneth Moral topsy-versy,
Bringeth he and she to bed,
Bringeth ill to maidenhead,
Bringeth joyance in its stead.
By May, by May, she lieth sped,
Yet still we praise that crocus heaα,
April!

Carolyn Wells

FAMOUS BATHS AND BATHERS

The baths of Caracalla
Beat those in Walla Walla;
Their emblems and omens
Appealed to the Romans.

The baths of Diocletian
Were filled to repletion
With aediles and eunuchs
In togas and tunics.

Susanna, young fool,
Bathed in the pool;
The elders in the shrubbery
Kicked up a bobbery.

Diogenes, old chap,
Just turned on a tap;
(No, that couldn't be,
For he lived in B.C.)

Brave Sir Launcelot
Liked the water hot;
While the old Ettrick shephe'd
Preferred his quite tepid.

Marat, we know,
Used a bathtub, and so
Was put out of the way
By Charlotte Corday.

All of the Pitts
Always used Sitz;
The family tradition
Decreed this position.

But E. Humperdinck
Washed at the sink;
He said, "It saves time
And it takes off the grime."

Samuel Hoffenstein

POEMS IN PRAISE OF PRACTICALLY NOTHING

I

You buy some flowers for your table;
You tend them tenderly as you're able;
You fetch them water from hither and thither—
What thanks do you get for it all? They wither.

II

Only the wholesomest foods you eat;
You lave and you lave from your head to your feet;
The earth is not steadier on its axis
Than you in the matter of prophylaxis;
You go to bed early, and early you rise;
You scrub your teeth and you scour your eyes—
What thanks do you get for it all? Nephritis,
Pneumonia, appendicitis,
Renal calculus and gastritis.

III

You get a girl; and you say you love her;
You pan the comparative stars above her;
You roast the comparative roses below her;
You throw the bull that you'll never throw her—
What thanks do you get? The very first whozis
Who tips his mitt, with him she vamooses.

IV

You buy yourself a new suit of clothes;
The care you give it, God only knows;

The material, of course, is the very best yet;
You get it pressed and pressed and pressed yet;
You keep it free from specks so tiny—
What thanks do you get? The pants get shiny.

V

You practise every possible virtue;
You hurt not a soul, while others hurt you;
You fetch and carry like a márket basket;
What thanks do you get for it? Me don't ask it!

VI

You leap out of bed; you start to get ready;
You dress and you dress till you feel unsteady;
Hours go by, and you're still busy
Putting on clothes, till your brain is dizzy.
Do you flinch, do you quit, do you go out naked?—
The least little button, you don't forsake it.
What thanks do you get? Well, for all this mess, yet
When night comes around you've got to undress yet.

LOVE SONG

The honey of the Hybla bees
Is not so sweet as kissing you;
Nor autumn wind in dying trees
So wistful is as missing you.

And when you are not mine to kiss,
My every thought is haunting you;
And when your mouth is mine, I miss
The wistfulness of wanting you.

David McCord

SONNETS TO BAEDEKER

I

My old companion on the beaten track,
Who brought me villages and bed and board,
Settled the day and laid me on my back
At inns whose tariff I could not afford;
Sweet *vade mecum* of the *Tuileries,
And audible in naves and barrel vaults,
Still smelling of an earlier Cheddar cheese,
Or blemished with red wines and English malts;
So I remember with what crafty charm
Of small italics and appropriate miles
Distinguished pages loosened a new swarm
Of ancient *Ninevehs* and distant *Niles,*
And played upon my mind as men at chess,
And sold me to AMERICAN EXPRESS.

II

Once it was Paris of *la Reine Pédauque,*
With *SACRÉ-CŒUR like loaves of a young yeast,
And people trading in a foreign talk
For seriatims of the *bouquiniste.*
O glory then upon the face of France:
Who painted what, and where the most is hung,
Such royal chambers of strange occupance
As burned to envy the guide's eager tongue.
Figures and dates assigned at *ST.-SULPICE,

And when the garlic boats ran down the *Seine;*
Recumbent *Abélard and Héloïse,*
The streets that saw a thousand Shelleys plain.
Fine view **(adm. gratis).** Was it Psyche?
Or Cook's own clients round the nerveless ****Nike?**

III

The Coast of Normandy, whose sands are quick,
But troubled by the rock **Mont St. Michel**
Where omelette, *langouste,* and heretic
Mix with the fragrant French monastic smell;
Cathedral towns, the rose-stained glass of **Chartres,**
Septentrional winds upon the mouth,
Vie in the blood with memories **Montmartre,*
The Château country lying to the S.
Travelers' cheques (*sigaro, pourboire, tip*)
Cashed to the least advantage of exchange,
Silver the RIVIERA as we trip
The marquised beaches or what you arrange;
Dining on balconies and running bills,
With sidelong glances toward the Spanish hills.

IV

They called him Ishmael. I call you Karl,
Who printed London on a Leipzig press,
And left delirious in simple snarl
What most obliges of her great noblesse.
Out of red covers wells the million sound
Of tram and lorry over Oxford Circ.,
And from the purlieus of the underground
The actual Londoners emerge to work.
Sweet catalogue, beyond the last inhab.
Who dwell in *Claridges and BERKELEY SQS.,
Or blithe Americans by taxicab
Ascending thus her golden British stairs—
Open to **Simpson's* and a London play,
And let me read and eat my heart away.

V

Then up to **Bicester** and the English towns:
Hail *Royal George (Pl. a; B, 4) and how!
Green separate spots of separate renowns,
As where some stout Archbp. made his vow.
Perp. churches, sir, cathedrals, E. E. style,
Castles to open **Wed. 10-3**;
Or Roman ruins of a domicile,
And *Keeps,* 12th cent. (restored), for a small fee.
Number of miles to **Tottenham** and back
(*Cycle or motorbus, afoot or train*),
The kind of villages one used to sack,
And what the Duke said to the King of Spain;
Who died wherever, and God rest their bones,
And why the *Druids* left such funny stones.

VI

But chief, in the moist latitudes of Skye,
You burred the difficult names of Scottish breed:
Blairgowrie, Tomnahurich, Morven—aye,
Of glens and invers to the trouty *Tweed*.
The grandest moors upon the purpled airth,
A Celtic twilight, and Midlothian heart
Commingle sadly in the sound of 'Perth'
As strong rfmt. offered by a bart.
Good patient soul, you spelled the Gaelic word,
Say *usquebaugh* for whiskey, in the notes;
Selected curlew, gannets, the wild bird
That screams the cowried shore by **John o' Groats**;
And where *Auld Reekie* stands eternal guard
You led me to the city ***triple-starred.

Arthur Guiterman

ANTHOLOGISTICS

Since one anthologist put in his book
Sweet things by Morse, Bone, Potter, Bliss and Brook,
All subsequent anthologists, of course
Have quoted Bliss, Brook, Potter, Bone and Morse.
For, should some rash anthologist make free
To print selections, say, from you and me,
Omitting with a judgment all his own
The classic Brook, Morse, Potter, Bliss and Bone,
Contemptuous reviewers, passing by
Our verses, would unanimously cry,
"What manner of anthology is this
That leaves out Bone, Brook, Potter, Morse and Bliss!"

SEA-CHILL

When Mrs. John Masefield and her husband, the author of "I Must Go
Down to the Seas Again," arrived here on a liner, she said to a reporter,
"It was too uppy-downy, and Mr. Masefield was ill."—*News item.*

I must go down to the seas again, where the billows romp and reel,
So all I ask is a large ship that rides on an even keel,
And a mild breeze and a broad deck with a slight list to leeward,
And a clean chair in a snug nook and a nice, kind steward.

I must go down to the seas again, the sport of wind and tide,
As the gray wave and the green wave play leapfrog over the side.
And all I want is a glassy calm with a bone-dry scupper,
A good book and a warm rug and a light, plain supper.

I must go down to the seas again, though there I'm a total loss,
And can't say which is worst, the pitch, the plunge, the roll, the toss.
But all I ask is a safe retreat in a bar well tended,
And a soft berth and a smooth course till the long trip's ended.

Phyllis McGinley

ODE TO THE END OF SUMMER

Summer, adieu.
        Adieu, gregarious season.
Goodbye, 'revoir, farewell.
Now day comes late; now chillier blows the breeze on
Forsaken beach and boarded-up hotel.
Now wild geese fly together in thin lines
And Tourist Homes take down their lettered signs.

It fades—this green, this lavish interval,
This time of flowers and fruits,
Of melon ripe along the orchard wall,
Of sun and sails and wrinkled linen suits;
Time when the world seems rather plus than minus
And pollen tickles the allergic sinus.

Now fugitives to farm and shore and highland
Cancel their brief escape.
The Ferris wheel is quiet at Coney Island
And quaintness trades no longer on the Cape;
While meek-eyed parents hasten down the ramps
To greet their offspring, terrible from camps.

Turn up the steam. The year is growing older.
The maple boughs are red.
Summer, farewell. Farewell the sunburnt shoulder,
Farewell the peasant kerchief on the head.
Farewell the thunderstorm, complete with lightning,
And the white shoe that ever needeth whitening.

Farewell, vacation friendships, sweet but tenuous.
Ditto to slacks and shorts.
Farewell, O strange compulsion to be strenuous

Which sends us forth to death on tennis courts.
Farewell, Mosquito, horror of our nights;
Clambakes, iced tea, and transatlantic flights.

The zinnia withers, mortal as the tulip.
Now from the dripping glass
I'll sip no more the amateur mint julep
Nor dine al fresco on the alien grass;
Nor scale the height nor breast the truculent billow
Nor lay my head on any weekend pillow.

Unstintingly I yield myself to Autumn
And Equinoctial sloth.
I hide my swim suit in the bureau's bottom
Nor fear the fury of the after-moth.
Forswearing porch and pool and beetled garden,
My heart shall rest, my arteries shall harden.

Welcome, kind Fall, and every month with "r" in
Whereto my mind is bent.
Come, sedentary season that I star in,
O fire-lit Winter of my deep content!
Amid the snow, the sleet, the blizzard's raw gust,
I shall be cozier than I was in August.

Safe from the picnic sleeps the unlittered dell.
The last Good Humor sounds its final bell,
And all is silence.
                    Summer, farewell, farewell.

SONG FROM NEW ROCHELLE

WITH A REFRAIN TO BE CHANTED SOLEMNLY BY A CHORUS CONSISTING
OF N. Y., N. H. & HARTFORD R. R. CONDUCTORS, PASSENGER
AGENTS, AND JOHN COOLIDGE

Monday's child is fair of face,
    And her chauffeur's a handsome fellow.
Tuesday's child is full of grace,
    So she gracefully hails a Yellow.

Wednesday's child has a red coupé
   With a little black horn she toots,
But I was born on a Saturday,
   And Saturday's child commutes!

CHORUS:

No responsibility is assumed for errors in time tables, nor for inconvenience or damage resulting from delayed trains or failure to make connections.

They that live on Washington Square
   May sleep as long as they please.
And they slumber deep and they slumber fair
   In the affluent seventies.
In Tudor City, the good and mild
   Lie late with a brow serene,
But I am only Saturday's child
   So I get the eight-sixteen.

CHORUS:

Buy tickets before boarding trains and avoid payment of extra charge.

The other girls go out to play
   In the fields of corn and clover.
And the other girls can always stay
   Until the party's over.
But just when the height is at its fun
   And the yodelers growing vocal,
I am the one who needs must run
   To catch the Stamford Local.
It's I that hostesses yearn to shelve;
   The bridge-table Blight am I.
(If Cinderella went home at twelve,
   She probably lived in Rye.)
Before the chorus has ceased to smile
   Or the maestro dropped his baton,
I am the lass in the middle aisle
   Who's trying to get her hat on.

O, gayety dwells
In the best hotels,
   But little to me it boots,
For I was born
On Saturday morn,
   And Saturday's child commutes.

CHORUS:

The schedules shown herein are subject to change without notice.

A HOBBY A DAY KEEPS THE DOLDRUMS AWAY

OR THE PROJECTS OF OLIVER AMES

This is Oliver's garden...
Here is the earth we watched him splinter
When spring was baying the tracks of winter,
Here are the bountiful beds he laid out
The earliest day he could get his spade out.
These are his borders—you couldn't miss 'em—
Of ageratum and sweet alyssum.
These are the plots where he put his signs up,
Yonder his trellis to lure the vines up,
And here are the flowers he let go *their* ways
When "Fore" resounded along the fairways;
The blooms I reared in the sweat of my brow.
For it's *my* garden now.

This is Oliver's workshop...
Behold the nook where my hero planned to
Build whatever he set his hand to.
Observe his hammers and saws and wrenches,
His braces and bits, his drawers and benches.
These are his cupboards—a costly come-on.
This is the tool that he cut his thumb on,
And here is the table he almost finished
Before his masculine zeal diminished,

When he decided perhaps he might
Leave some of the laurels for Hepplewhite;
While here are the cobwebs that coil and cluster
For *my* broom and duster.

> *Sing hey for Oliver's playthings...*
For the wireless set that he cannot send with,
For the tropical fish that I contend with,
For the herbs I hang when he tires of cookery,
For the books I shelve in his unread bookery,
For the faithful hound of a doting master
That I take out to avoid disaster;
The trays and acids in which I traffic
When palls the interlude photographic;
The grain he buys for the snowbound starlings
That I distribute—they're all my darling's.
Each for the moment his one, his true love,
And mine to store when he takes a new love.

For Man proposes the Fuller Life,
But the debris's disposed of by his wife.

Bert Leston Taylor

THE PASSIONATE PROFESSOR

But bending low, I whisper only this:
"Love, it is night."
> —Harry Thurston Peck.

Love, it is night. The orb of day
Has gone to hit the cosmic hay.
  Nocturnal voices now we hear.
  Come, heart's delight, the hour is near
When Passion's mandate we obey.

I would not, sweet, the fact convey
In any crude and obvious way:
  I merely whisper in your ear—
        "Love, it is night!"

Candor compels me, pet, to say
That years my fading charms betray.
  Tho' Love be blind, I grant it's clear
  I'm no Apollo Belvedere.
But after dark all cats are gray.
        Love, it is night!

Morris Bishop

A WORM-CHORUS

Rain, wind, and rain!
The heavens are of ashen hue,
They kiss with their celestial dew
Walks of cement, and flagstone too—
Rain, wind, and rain!

Spring, joy of Spring!
Let's break the prison where we're pent
And heed the Spring's admonishment
To bask upon the wet cement!
Spring, joy of Spring!

—Stay yet a while!
Ye know the song the old worms sing
Of them that went adventuring,
Their long abdomens mad with Spring;
Stay yet a while!

Oh, wise old worms!
For home they brought the rovers, dead,
Smit by a Herculean tread,
Their long abdomens all outspread!
Oh, wise old worms!

—Pooh, old worms' tales!
E'en were their drowsy mumbling sooth
(And old worms rarely speak the truth)
Death cannot daunt the heart of youth!
Faugh, old worms' tales!

Rain, wind, and rain!
The asphalt calls us, let us fly;
Forward! We urge with purpose high
Our long abdomens forth to die!
Rain, wind, and rain!

OZYMANDIAS REVISITED

I met a traveller from an antique land
Who said: Two vast and trunkless legs of stone
Stand in the desert. Near them on the sand,
Half sunk, a shatter'd visage lies, whose frown
And wrinkled lip and sneer of cold command
Tell that its sculptor well those passions read
Which yet survive, stamp'd on these lifeless things,
The hand that mock'd them and the heart that fed;
And on the pedestal these words appear:
"My name is Ozymandias, king of kings:
Look on my works, ye Mighty, and despair!"
Also the names of Emory P. Gray,
Mr. and Mrs. Dukes, and Oscar Baer
Of 17 West 4th St., Oyster Bay.

Dorothy Parker

LITTLE WORDS

When you are strayed, there is nor bloom nor leaf
  Nor singing sea at night, nor silver birds.
And I may only stare, and shape my grief
  In little words.

I cannot conjure loveliness, to drown
  The bitter woe that racks my chords apart.
The staggering pen that sets my sorrow down
  Feeds at my heart.

There is no mercy in the shifting year;
  No beauty wraps me tenderly about.
I turn to little words—so you, my dear,
  Can spell them out.

THE SEARCHED SOUL

When I consider, pro and con,
What things my love is built upon—
A curly mouth; a sinewed wrist;
A questioning brow; a pretty twist
Of words as old and tried as sin;
A pointed ear; a cloven chin;
Long, tapered limbs; and slanted eyes
Not cold nor kind nor darkly wise—
When I so ponder, here apart,
What shallow boons suffice my heart,
What dust-bound trivia capture me,
I marvel at my normalcy.

TOMBSTONE FOR AN ACTRESS

Her name, cut clear upon this marble cross,
   Shines, as it shone when she was still on earth;
While tenderly the mild, agreeable moss
   Obscures the figures of her date of birth.

Clarence H. Knapp

AIN'T THERE AT LEAST ONE GEN'LEMAN HERE?

A MODERN SOB BALLAD

I

A travelling man once entered
  Into a cabaret.
'Twas midnight and quite naturally
  The throng there all was gay.
He sat down to a table
  And ordered a Port wine.
Right near him was a party,
  Most of whom felt fine.
Now one of this fast comp'ny
  Was a youth too full of beer,
Who rose unsteady from his seat
  And said so all could hear:
"That dancing girl looks good to me,
  A kiss I'm going to steal."
The girl cried out as he drew near,
  Then made this sweet appeal:

REFRAIN

"Ain't there at least one gen'leman here,
  One who ain't full of whiskey or beer,
One who remembers his wife or his mother,
  One who will act just like a big brother?
Don't think 'cause I dance midst these lights and these lures,
  That my feelings ain't hurt as easy as yours.
And though dancing girls are sporty 'tis claimed,
  I've never done nothing of what I'm ashamed."

716

II

The travelling man rose from his seat,
  And picking up a chair,
He threat'ningly strode toward the youth
  So near that dancer fair.
Said he, "Miss, I heard your plea
  And I'll protect your name."
The drunken youth then did shrink back
  In terror and in shame.
The man glanced at the girl once more,
  The frown from his face fell.
He recognized to his surprise
  His boyhood's sweetheart, Nell.
He cried, "At last I've found you, Nell.
  We'll leave this place and wed."
She whispered, "Bert, I knew you'd come
  When those words I had said:

REFRAIN

" 'Ain't there at least one gen'leman here,
  One who ain't full of whiskey or beer,
One who remembers his wife or his mother,
  One who will act just like a big brother?
Don't think 'cause I dance midst these lights and these lures
  That my feelings ain't hurt as easy as yours.
And though dancing girls are sporty 'tis claimed,
  I've never done nothing of what I'm ashamed.' "

E. B. White

HARPER TO MIFFLIN TO CHANCE

Among the authors who have recently gone to other publishers are H. G. Wells, who left Doubleday Doran for Macmillan; Charles Morgan, author of "The Fountain," who went to Macmillan from Knopf; Harold Bell Wright, who left Appleton's for Harper's; Aldous Huxley, who left Doubleday Doran for Harper's; Louis Bromfield, who left Stokes for Harper's; Tiffany Thayer, who left Claude Kendall for Liveright; and J. P. McEvoy, who went from Simon & Schuster to Houghton Mifflin.—*The Times.*

Come Harper, come Schuster, come Appleton all,
The winter is coming, and gone is the fall,
The authors are restless and pining to go
And Santa is poorly and we shall have snow!
   Come *on,* Harper!

Come Huxley, come Morgan, come Harold Bell Wright,
The dew's on the turnip—the publisher's blight;
Come Bromfield and Thayer, come all God's chillun,
Goodbye to Knopf, sir, and ho for Macmillan!
   Come *on,* Macmillan.

Ho ho! for the writers who pass in the night,
Hey hey! for Al Huxley and Harold Bell Wright,
For the moon on the crest of the new fallen snow
And the luster of Doubleday all in a row.
   Come *on,* Doubleday!

Come author, come poet, come scriveners bold,
The royalty's gone and the days grow cold,
So put on the imprint of Simon & Schuster
And sell a lot more than you formerly uster!
   Come *on,* Simon!

Come Appleton, Harper, come Mifflin and all!
To the top of the list, to the top of the wall!
Your authors are dressed in their last year's loyalty,
They'll kiss you goodbye for the first pretty royalty.
  Come *on,* Pater.

Kenneth Allan Robinson

THE MESECKS

(Respectfully Dedicated to the Meseck Towing Line)

Swaggering up the harbor,
  With Quarantine left behind you,
Your liner stops and tootles for help,
  And who comes out to find you?
Who comes out to help you
  But Mesecks all in a flock—
A fleet of little Mesecks,
Of hovering, anxious Mesecks,
Of scurrying tugboat Mesecks,
  To waggle you into dock.

Walter Meseck, and Bessie Meseck, and Meseck, Carrie T.,
Margaret, Madeline, William Meseck, and Meseck, Mary E.

I've never come up the harbor
  At the end of a six days' journey
But the Meseck names have taken my gaze
  Like unknown knights at a tourney.
Mary and Bessie and Carrie,
  Madeline, Walter, and Bill—
What are they like, those Mesecks,
Those veiled, mysterious Mesecks,
Those secret, glamorous Mesecks
  Whose navies are never still?

Walter Meseck, and Bessie Meseck, and Meseck, Carrie T.,
Margaret, Madeline, William Meseck, and Meseck, Mary E.

I never have met the Mesecks
  —Though I pray that they're hale and hearty—
And I'm never a guest at a dinner
  Or a large, superior party
But I hope that my host or hostess
  Will hail me before I go
With "Haven't you met the Mesecks?
Come here and meet the Mesecks,
Come here and meet *all* the Mesecks,
  They're *such* nice people to know:

Walter Meseck, and Bessie Meseck, and Meseck, Carrie T.,
Margaret, Madeline, William Meseck, and Meseck, Mary E."

Oliver Wendell Holmes

CACOËTHES SCRIBENDI

If all the trees in all the woods were men,
And each and every blade of grass a pen;
If every leaf on every shrub and tree
Turned to a sheet of foolscap; every sea
Were changed to ink, and all earth's living tribes
Had nothing else to do but act as scribes,
And for ten thousand ages, day and night,
The human race should write, and write, and write,
Till all the pens and paper were used up,
And the huge inkstand was an empty cup,
Still would the scribblers clustered round its brink
Call for more pens, more paper, and more ink.

REMINISCENCE

Humorists have wonderful memories, or think they have. They are constantly recording emotional fragments of their lives, as recalled in tranquillity—or in drink. As for the truth of what they put down on paper, it is questionable: we can assure the reader that the reminiscences on the following pages range from straight fact to the most barefaced lies.

When grilled about the faithfulness of their memoirs, different humorists tell different stories. Clarence Day always insisted that his pieces about the Day family were true in every detail, and he believed this himself. James Thurber never used to claim that his memories were wholly factual, but he has by now almost persuaded himself that the Columbus, Ohio, of his childhood was as fantastic as he describes it. (It is easy to believe the Thurber household was an unusually active one, but surely the most tempestuous and busy spot in the whole place was the mind of little Jamie.) Bemelmans, we believe, states that his stories of the Hotel Splendide are fiction written in autobiographical form. The reader can reasonably accept this as true, at the same time realizing that in setting up a background for his plots, memory has served Mr. Bemelmans well.

Clarence Day

THE NOBLEST INSTRUMENT

Father had been away, reorganizing some old upstate railroad. He
returned in an executive mood and proceeded to shake up our home.
In spite of my failure as a singer, he was still bound to have us taught
music. We boys were summoned before him and informed that we
must at once learn to play on something. We might not appreciate
it now, he said, but we should later on. "You, Clarence, will learn the
violin. George, you the piano. Julian—well, Julian is too young yet.
But you older boys must have lessons."

I was appalled at this order. At the age of ten it seemed a disaster
to lose any more of my freedom. The days were already too short
for our games after school; and now here was a chunk to come out
of playtime three days every week. A chunk every day, we found
afterward, because we had to practice.

George sat at the piano in the parlor, and faithfully learned to
pound out his exercises. He had all the luck. He was not an inspired
player, but at least he had some ear for music. He also had the advantage of playing on a good robust instrument, which he didn't have
to be careful not to drop, and was in no danger of breaking. Furthermore, he did not have to tune it. A piano had some good points.

But I had to go through a blacker and more gruesome experience.
It was bad enough to have to come in from the street and the sunlight and go down into our dark little basement where I took my
lessons. But that was only the opening chill of the struggle that followed.

The whole thing was uncanny. The violin itself was a queer, fragile,
cigar-boxy thing, that had to be handled most gingerly. Nothing sturdy
about it. Why, a fellow was liable to crack it putting it into its case.
And then my teacher, he was queer too. He had a queer pickled smell.

I dare say he wasn't queer at all really, but he seemed so to me,
because he was different from the people I generally met. He was

725

probably worth a dozen of some of them, but I didn't know it. He was one of the violins in the Philharmonic, and an excellent player; a grave, middle-aged little man—who was obliged to give lessons.

He wore a black, wrinkled frock coat, and a discolored gold watch-chain. He had small, black-rimmed glasses; not tortoise-shell, but thin rims of metal. His violin was dark, rich, and polished, and would do anything for him.

Mine was balky and awkward, brand new, and of a light, common color.

The violin is intended for persons with a passion for music. I wasn't that kind of person. I liked to hear a band play a tune that we could march up and down to, but try as I would, I could seldom whistle such a tune afterward. My teacher didn't know this. He greeted me as a possible genius.

He taught me how to hold the contraption, tucked under my chin. I learned how to move my fingers here and there on its handle or stem. I learned how to draw the bow across the strings, and thus produce sounds....

Does a mother recall the first cry of her baby, I wonder? I still remember the strange cry at birth of that new violin.

My teacher, Herr M., looked as though he had suddenly taken a large glass of vinegar. He sucked in his breath. His lips were drawn back from his teeth, and his eyes tightly shut. Of course, he hadn't expected my notes to be sweet at the start; but still, there was something unearthly about that first cry. He snatched the violin from me, examined it, readjusted its pegs, and comforted it gently, by drawing his own bow across it. It was only a new and not especially fine violin, but the sounds it made for him were more natural—they were classifiable sounds. They were not richly musical, but at least they had been heard before on this earth.

He handed the instrument back to me with careful directions. I tucked it up under my chin again and grasped the end tight. I held my bow exactly as ordered. I looked up at him, waiting.

"Now," he said, nervously.

I slowly raised the bow, drew it downward....

This time there were *two* dreadful cries in our little front basement. One came from my new violin and one from the heart of Herr M.

Herr M. presently came to, and smiled bravely at me, and said if I wanted to rest a moment he would permit it. He seemed to think

I might wish to lie down awhile and recover. I didn't feel any need of lying down. All I wanted was to get through the lesson. But Herr M. was shaken. He was by no means ready to let me proceed. He looked around desperately, saw the music book, and said he would now show me that. We sat down side by side on the window-seat, with the book in his lap, while he pointed out the notes to me with his finger, and told me their names.

After a bit, when he felt better, he took up his own violin, and instructed me to watch him and note how he handled the strings. And then at last, he nerved himself to let me take my violin up again. "Softly, my child, softly," he begged me, and stood facing the wall....

We got through the afternoon somehow, but it was a ghastly experience. Part of the time he was maddened by the mistakes I kept making, and part of the time he was plain wretched. He covered his eyes. He seemed ill. He looked often at his watch, even shook it as though it had stopped; but he stayed the full hour.

That was Wednesday. What struggles he had with himself before Friday, when my second lesson was due, I can only dimly imagine, and of course I never even gave them a thought at the time. He came back to recommence teaching me, but he had changed—he had hardened. Instead of being cross, he was stern; and instead of sad, bitter. He wasn't unkind to me, but we were no longer companions. He talked to himself, under his breath; and sometimes he took bits of paper, and did little sums on them, gloomily, and then tore them up.

During my third lesson I saw the tears come to his eyes. He went up to Father and said he was sorry but he honestly felt sure I'd never be able to play.

Father didn't like this at all. He said he felt sure I would. He dismissed Herr M. briefly—the poor man came stumbling back down in two minutes. In that short space of time he had gallantly gone upstairs in a glow, resolved upon sacrificing his earnings for the sake of telling the truth. He returned with his earnings still running, but with the look of a lost soul about him, as though he felt that his nerves and his sanity were doomed to destruction. He was low in his mind, and he talked to himself more than ever. Sometimes he spoke harshly of America, sometimes of fate.

But he no longer struggled. He accepted this thing as his destiny. He regarded me as an unfortunate something, outside the human species, whom he must simply try to labor with as well as he could. It was a grotesque, indeed a hellish experience, but he felt he must bear it.

He wasn't the only one—he was at least not alone in his sufferings. Mother, though expecting the worst, had tried to be hopeful about it, but at the end of a week or two I heard her and Margaret talking it over. I was slaughtering a scale in the front basement, when Mother came down and stood outside the door in the kitchen hall and whispered, "Oh, Margaret!"

I watched them. Margaret was baking a cake. She screwed up her face, raised her arms, and brought them down with hands clenched.

"I don't know what we shall do, Margaret."

"The poor little feller," Margaret whispered. "He can't make the thing go."

This made me indignant. They were making me look like a lubber. I wished to feel always that I could make anything go. . . .

I now began to feel a determination to master this thing. History shows us many examples of the misplaced determinations of men— they are one of the darkest aspects of human life, they spread so much needless pain: but I knew little history. And I viewed what little I did know romantically—I should have seen in such episodes their heroism, not their futility. Any role that seemed heroic attracted me, no matter how senseless.

Not that I saw any chance for heroism in our front basement, of course. You had to have a battlefield or something. I saw only that I was appearing ridiculous. But that stung my pride. I hadn't wanted to learn anything whatever about fiddles or music, but since I was in for it, I'd do it, and show them I could. A boy will often put in enormous amounts of his time trying to prove he isn't as ridiculous as he thinks people think him.

Meanwhile Herr M. and I had discovered that I was nearsighted. On account of the violin's being an instrument that sticks out in front of one, I couldn't stand close enough to the music book to see the notes clearly. He didn't at first realize that I often made mistakes from that cause. When he and I finally comprehended that I had this defect, he had a sudden new hope that this might have been the whole trouble, and that when it was corrected I might play like a human being at last.

Neither of us ventured to take up this matter with Father. We knew that it would have been hard to convince him that my eyes were not perfect, I being a son of his and presumably made in his image; and we knew that he immediately would have felt we were trying to make trouble for him, and would have shown an amount of resentment which it was best to avoid. So Herr M. instead lent me his glasses. These did fairly well. They turned the dim grayness of the notes into a queer bright distortion, but the main thing was they did make them brighter, so that I now saw more of them. How well I remember those little glasses. Poor, dingy old things. Herr M. was nervous about lending them to me; he feared that I'd drop them. It would have been safer if they had been spectacles: but no, they were pince-nez; and I had to learn to balance them across my nose as well as I could. I couldn't wear them up near my eyes because my nose was too thin there; I had to put them about half-way down where there was enough flesh to hold them. I also had to tilt my head back, for the music-stand was a little too tall for me. Herr M. sometimes mounted me on a stool, warning me not to step off. Then when I was all set, and when he without his glasses was blind, I would smash my way into the scales again.

All during the long winter months I worked away at this job. I gave no thought, of course, to the family. But they did to me. Our house was heated by a furnace, which had big warm air pipes; these ran up through the walls with wide outlets into each room, and sound traveled easily and ringingly through their roomy, tin passages. My violin could be heard in every part of the house. No one could settle down to anything while I was practicing. If visitors came they soon left. Mother couldn't even sing to the baby. She would wait, watching the clock, until my long hour of scale-work was over, and then come downstairs and shriek at me that my time was up. She would find me sawing away with my forehead wet, and my hair wet and stringy, and even my clothes slowly getting damp from my exertions. She would feel my collar, which was done for, and say I must change it. "Oh, Mother! Please!"—for I was in a hurry now to run out and play. But she wasn't being fussy about my collar, I can see, looking back; she was using it merely as a barometer or gauge of my pores. She thought I had better dry myself before going out in the snow.

It was a hard winter for Mother. I believe she also had fears for the baby. She sometimes pleaded with Father; but no one could ever tell Father anything. He continued to stand like a rock against stopping my lessons.

Schopenhauer, in his rules for debating, shows how to win a weak case by insidiously transferring an argument from its right field, and discussing it instead from some irrelevant but impregnable angle. Father knew nothing of Schopenhauer, and was never insidious, but, nevertheless, he had certain natural gifts for debate. In the first place his voice was powerful and stormy, and he let it out at full strength, and kept on letting it out with a vigor that stunned his opponents. As a second gift, he was convinced at all times that his opponents were wrong. Hence, even if they did win a point or two, it did them no good, for he dragged the issue to some other ground then, where he and Truth could prevail. When Mother said it surely was plain enough that I had no ear, what was his reply? Why, he said that the violin was the noblest instrument invented by man. Having silenced her with this solid premise he declared that it followed that any boy was lucky to be given the privilege of learning to play it. No boy should expect to learn it immediately. It required persistence. Everything, he had found, required persistence. The motto was, Never give up.

All his life, he declared, he had persevered in spite of discouragement, and he meant to keep on persevering, and he meant me to, too. He said that none of us realized what he had had to go through. If he had been the kind that gave up at the very first obstacle, where would he have been now—where would any of the family have been? The answer was, apparently, that we'd either have been in a very bad way, poking round for crusts in the gutter, or else nonexistent. We might have never even been born if Father had not persevered.

Placed beside this record of Father's vast trials overcome, the little difficulty of my learning to play the violin seemed a trifle. I faithfully spurred myself on again, to work at the puzzle. Even my teacher seemed impressed with these views on persistence. Though older than Father, he had certainly not made as much money, and he bowed to the experience of a practical man who was a success. If he, Herr M., had been a success he would not have had to teach boys; and sitting in this black pit in which his need of money had placed him, he saw more than ever that he must learn the ways of this world. He listened with all his heart, as to a god, when Father shook his forefinger, and told him how to climb to the heights where financial rewards were achieved. The idea he got was that perseverance was sure to lead to great wealth.

Consequently our front basement continued to be the home of lost causes.

Of course, I kept begging Herr M. to let me learn just one tune. Even though I seldom could whistle them, still I liked tunes; and I knew that, in my hours of practicing, a tune would be a comfort. That is, for myself. Here again I never gave a thought to the effect upon others.

Herr M., after many misgivings, to which I respectfully listened—though they were not spoken to me, they were muttered to himself, pessimistically—hunted through a worn old book of selections, and after much doubtful fumbling chose as simple a thing as he could find for me—for me and the neighbors.

It was spring now, and windows were open. That tune became famous.

What would the musician who had tenderly composed this air, years before, have felt if he had foreseen what an end it would have, on Madison Avenue; and how, before death, it would be execrated by that once peaceful neighborhood. I engraved it on their hearts; not in its true form but in my own eerie versions. It was the only tune I knew. Consequently I played and replayed it.

Even horrors when repeated grow old and lose part of their sting. But those I produced were, unluckily, never the same. To be sure, this tune kept its general structure the same, even in my sweating hands. There was always the place where I climbed unsteadily up to its peak, and that difficult spot where it wavered, or staggered, and stuck; and then a sudden jerk of resumption—I came out strong on that. Every afternoon when I got to that difficult spot, the neighbors dropped whatever they were doing to wait for that jerk, shrinking from the moment, and yet feverishly impatient for it to come.

But what made the tune and their anguish so different each day? I'll explain. The strings of a violin are wound at the end around pegs, and each peg must be screwed in and tightened till the string sounds just right. Herr M. left my violin properly tuned when he went. But suppose a string broke, or that somehow I jarred a peg loose. Its string then became slack and soundless. I had to re-tighten it. Not having an ear, I was highly uncertain about this.

Our neighbors never knew at what degree of tautness I'd put such a string. I didn't myself. I just screwed her up tight enough to make a strong reliable sound. Neither they nor I could tell which string would thus appear in a new role each day, nor foresee the profound transformations this would produce in that tune.

All that spring this unhappy and ill-destined melody floated out through my window, and writhed in the air for one hour daily, in sunshine or storm. All that spring our neighbors and I daily toiled to its peak, and staggered over its hump, so to speak, and fell wailing through space.

Things now began to be said to Mother which drove her to act. She explained to Father that the end had come at last. Absolutely. "This awful nightmare cannot go on," she said.

Father pooh-poohed her.

She cried. She told him what it was doing to her. He said that she was excited, and that her descriptions of the sounds I made were exaggerated and hysterical—must be. She was always too vehement, he shouted. She must learn to be calm.

"But you're downtown, *you* don't have to hear it!"

Father remained wholly skeptical.

She endeavored to shame him. She told him what awful things the neighbors were saying about him, because of the noise I was making, for which he was responsible.

He couldn't be made to look at it that way. If there really were any unpleasantness then I was responsible. He had provided me with a good teacher and a good violin—so he reasoned. In short, he had done his best, and no father could have done more. If I made hideous sounds after all that, the fault must be mine. He said that Mother should be stricter with me, if necessary, and make me try harder.

This was the last straw. I couldn't try harder. When Mother told me his verdict I said nothing, but my body rebelled. Self-discipline had its limits—and I wanted to be out: it was spring. I skimped my hours of practice when I heard the fellows playing outside. I came home late for lessons—even forgot them. Little by little they stopped.

Father was outraged. His final argument, I remember, was that my violin had cost twenty-five dollars; if I didn't learn it the money would be wasted, and he couldn't afford it. But it was put to him that my younger brother, Julian, could learn it instead, later on. Then summer came, anyhow, and we went for three months to the seashore; and in the confusion of this Father was defeated and I was set free.

In the autumn little Julian was led away one afternoon, and imprisoned in the front basement in my place. I don't remember how long they kept him down there, but it was several years. He had an ear, however, and I believe he learned to play fairly well. This would have made a happy ending for Herr M. after all; but it was some other teacher, a younger man, who was engaged to teach Julian. Father said Herr M. was a failure.

Joseph Mitchell

THE DOWNFALL OF FASCISM IN
BLACK ANKLE COUNTY

Every time I see Mussolini shooting off his mouth in a newsreel or
Göring goose-stepping in a rotogravure, I am reminded of Mr. Catfish
Giddy and my first encounter with Fascism. In 1923, when I was in
the ninth grade in Stonewall, North Carolina, Mr. Giddy and Mr.
Spuddy Ransom organized a branch of the Knights of the Ku Klux
Klan, or the Invisible Empire, which spread terror through Black
Ankle County for several months. All the kids in town had seen "The
Birth of a Nation," and they were fascinated by the white robes and
hoods worn by the local Klansmen, and by the fiery crosses they
burned at midnight on Saturdays in the vacant lot beside the Atlantic
Coast Line depot. On Tuesday and Friday, the Klan's meeting nights,
the kids would hide in the patch of Jerusalem-oak weeds in the rear
of the Planters Bank & Trust Company and watch the Klansmen go
up the back stairs to their meeting hall above the bank. Sometimes
they reappeared in a few minutes, dressed in flowing white robes, and
drove off mysteriously. I spent so many nights hiding in the weed
patch that I failed my final examinations in geometry, history, French,
and Bible, and was not promoted, which I did not mind, as I had
already spent two years in the ninth grade and felt at home there.

Now, when I look back on that period and reflect on the qualities
of Mr. Giddy, Mr. Ransom, and their followers, I wonder why the
people of Black Ankle County, particularly the people of Stonewall,
stood for the Ku Klux Klan as long as they did. Traditionally, the
people of Stonewall are sturdy and self-reliant. In fact, the town was
named General Stonewall Jackson, North Carolina, when it was
founded right after the Civil War; later the name was shortened to
Stonewall. There was certainly nothing frightening about Mr. Giddy,
the Führer of the local Klan. His full name was J. Raymond Giddy,
but he had a mustache on his plump face which he treated with bees-

wax and which stuck out sharply on both sides, and consequently he
was almost always referred to as Mr. Catfish Giddy, even in the columns of the weekly *Stonewall News*. He was rather proud of the nickname. He used to say, "I may not be the richest man in Black Ankle
County, but I sure am the ugliest; you can't take that away from me."
Mr. Giddy was a frustrated big businessman. Before he got interested
in the Klan, he had organized the Stonewall Boosters and a Stonewall Chamber of Commerce, both of which died after a few meetings.
He was always making speeches about big business, but he was never
much of a big businessman himself. At the time he and Mr. Ransom
organized the Klan he was a travelling salesman for a chewing-tobacco
concern. When he returned from a trip he would never brag about
how many boxes of cut plug he had sold. Instead, he would brag that
the cut plug manufactured in North Carolina in one year, if laid end
to end, would damn near reach to Egypt, or Australia, or the moon,
or some other distant place.

"In the manufacture of chewing tobacco, my friends," he would
boast, "the Tarheel State leads the whole civilized world."

He was the town orator and the town drunk. In his cups, he would
walk up and down Main Street, singing. He had a bass voice and
his favorite songs were "Old Uncle Bud," new verses for which he
would make up as he went along, and a song about Lydia Pinkham's
vegetable compound and its effect on the human race, a song he had
learned when he was a young man attending a business college in
Atlanta. The high-school boys and girls, drinking Coca-Colas in the
Stonewall Drug Company, would run to the door and stare and giggle
when Mr. Giddy got drunk and marched up Main Street. "Old Uncle
Bud," he would sing, "is the jelly-roll king. Got a hump on his back
from shaking that thing." At that time, the shimmy, introduced by
some tent-show girls at the Black Ankle County Fair, was popular
in Stonewall, and the young people called it the "jelly roll."

Mr. Ransom was far more frightening than Mr. Giddy. He was a
gaunt, wild-eyed farmer. He was a religious fanatic, always screaming
about wickedness. Even when he was dressed in his Ku Klux Klan
outfit, he could easily be identified because he walked with a peculiar,
hobbledehoy gait. He was a deacon in the Stonewall Jackson Baptist
Church, the church I went to, and he used to ring the bell before
services until he got a little too impassioned one Sunday morning and
pulled the rope so hard the bell came unscrewed and fell out of the

loft, landing on his left shoulder. After that accident he always walked as if his next step would be his last. Like Mr. Giddy, he had a nickname. He was christened John Knox Ransom, but he was called Mr. Spuddy because he habitually argued that the Southern farmer should quit planting cotton and tobacco and plant Irish potatoes. "Something you can eat," he would argue, smacking his palms together for emphasis. "Goodness gracious, my friends, if you can't sell your crop, you can put it on the table and eat it." One winter he tried to live on Irish potatoes and got so thin his belt wouldn't hold his pants up. His worried wife would urge him to eat some meat to get his strength back, and he would shout, "Is a mule strong? Does a mule eat meat?" His wife, who was a sensible woman, would ask meekly, "Does a mule eat Irish potatoes?"

I don't think Mr. Giddy, the drunken drummer, and Mr. Ransom, the fanatical deacon, thought very highly of each other until Mr. Giddy returned from a selling trip in the winter of 1923 with some booklets about the Klan he had picked up in Atlanta. Mr. Giddy discreetly distributed the booklets among some of the loafers in Stonewall, and Mr. Ransom got one. After reading it, he decided that the best way to fight wickedness, the best way to drive corn-whiskey distillers, gipsy mule traders, loose women, profane men, and Holy Roller preachers out of Black Ankle County was to organize the Klan there.

He and Mr. Giddy got together, hired the hall over the bank, painted the windows black for the sake of secrecy, and enrolled seventeen men in the Klan. They included a tobacco auctioneer, an undertaker, a grocery clerk, an indolent house painter, and a number of farmers. The farmers were all like Mr. Ransom in that they spent less time in their fields than they did around the pot-bellied stove of the Stonewall Hardware & General Merchandise Company, arguing about religion and politics. Most of the men joined the Klan because it gave them an excuse to get away from their wives at night and because it seemed to them to have even more mystery and ceremony than the Masons or the Woodmen of the World. The undertaker and Mr. Ransom were the only "respectable" men in it; most of the others, according to the rather rigid standards of Stonewall, were either "common" or "sorry." Some were both—the house painter, for example. I once heard him summed up by an old woman in Stonewall, who said, "He's common. Fishes in the summer and hunts in the winter, and when it rains he sits by the stove and plays checkers. He sure is one sorry man."

The fathers of some of my friends joined the Klan and gradually I learned many of the Klan secrets. I learned that the initiation fee was ten dollars and that the robe and hood cost six-fifty. A friend of mine swiped his father's Klan books. One was called "The Platform of the Invisible Empire." I persuaded him to let me have it in exchange for Zane Grey's "Riders of the Purple Sage." I still have it. On the cover is this declaration: "The Ku Klux Klan stands on a platform of 100-per-cent Americanism, white supremacy in the South, deportation of aliens, purity of womanhood, and eradication of the chain store." In the book are a number of denunciations of Catholics, Jews, Negroes, and labor unions. The kids in Stonewall spied on the Klan much as kids now play G-men and gangsters; it was a game. We were frightened by the Klansmen, but not too frightened to hide in the weed patch and watch them come and go. I remember one kid, lying beside me in the weeds, pointing to a robed figure and hoarsely whispering, "There goes Pa."

Mules are used almost exclusively instead of horses in the tobacco and cotton fields of Black Ankle County, and during the first weeks of the Klan's existence in Stonewall the members rode plough mules on their night rides about the countryside. They preferred to ride cross-country, and they could not use automobiles because they would quickly bog down in the sticky mud of the fields, the black mud which gives the county its name. The mules were supplied by Mr. Ransom and by other members who were farmers. That lasted until Mr. Giddy and Mr. Ransom, as the leaders, sent to Atlanta for some white horse robes. They draped the robes over their mules one dark night and rode out to a sawmill in a swamp to keep a rendezvous with their followers. When they galloped up on their shrouded steeds the mules of the other Klansmen got frightened; they let out angry neighs, reared back on their heels, and stampeded into the swamp with their riders. One Klansman was thrown from his mule and suffered a broken leg and three fractured ribs. After that the Klansmen gave up cross-country riding. They stuck to the highways and used automobiles. Fat Mr. Giddy undoubtedly felt out of place on the sharp back of a plough mule, anyway.

The Klansmen began their terrorism by burning fiery crosses, huge crosses made of fence rails sprinkled with kerosene, in the yards of all the Negro churches in the lower part of the county. Then they kidnapped an aged, irritable blacksmith who was celebrated for his profanity. They covered him with tar. They sprinkled chicken feathers over the tar. Then they tossed him into Bearcat Millpond. I have heard that the old blacksmith crawled out of the millpond with ten brand-new oaths. A few nights later the Klansmen went after a mentally defective woman who used to wander about the county with her fatherless children, sleeping in tobacco barns and haylofts. They flogged her, clipped her hair close to her scalp, and branded a "K" on her head. Next day a rural policeman found the bleeding, frantic woman on a ditch bank beside a country road and took her to a hospital. Later she was sent to an asylum. One night, a few weeks later, they broke into a chain grocery in Stonewall, the A. & P., and wrecked it. The same night they went to a Negro café in the Back Alley, the Negro section of Stonewall, and smashed a big, loud Edison phonograph, which the proprietor of the café had mortgaged her home to buy. Then they began threatening a quiet, lonesome Jew who lived above his dry-goods store on Main Street. Some of the members of the Klan had charge accounts, long unpaid, at his store. At the post office one night, waiting around for the evening mail to be sorted, I heard Mr. Giddy talking about him. He said, "He sits up there all night long, reading books. No telling what he's plotting." The dry-goods merchant went to the hardware store one morning at a time when some of the Klan members were sitting around the stove and bought a double-barrelled shotgun and three boxes of twelve-gauge shells. He was not threatened any more.

Late that spring it was rumored in Stonewall that the Klan had decided to do something about the corn-whiskey-distilling situation. The biggest distiller was Mr. Sledge MacKellar; he employed four men at his copper still in Pocahontas Swamp. We knew he was immune from the Klan because he was Mr. Giddy's personal bootlegger, because he was fabulously expert with a shotgun, and because he had publicly served notice on the Klan. Mr. MacKellar came out of the swamp one afternoon and said he was prepared for "the Bed-Sheets." By that time Klansmen were called "the Bed-Sheets." He said, "I'm a Democrat and I got my rights. The first time one of them Bed-Sheets sticks his head in my front gate, I'm going to take his head right off. I got a shotgun and I got it loaded and I'm just aching to pull the trigger."

We knew the distillers the Klan had in mind were the Kidney boys, and we were not surprised when we heard that a date had been set on which they were to be tarred and feathered. The Kidney boys were three drunken Irish brothers who lived in a house about two and a half miles out from Stonewall and operated a still in Big Cherokee Swamp, behind their house. Their names were Patrick, Pinky, and Francis. They drank about half the whiskey they manufactured. When they came to town that week for supplies, the clerks in the stores kidded them. "I hear the Bed-Sheets are going to call on you boys for a pot of tea Friday night," one clerk said.

The Kidney boys had a hired man, an aged Negro named Uncle Bowleg, who later worked for a relative of mine. One time Uncle Bowleg told me how the Kidney boys brought about the downfall of the Invisible Empire in Black Ankle County. There were three entrances to the Kidney house—a front door, a back door, and a side door. When they heard the Klan was planning a call on Friday night, the brothers rented three dynamite outfits from a man who made his living blasting out tree stumps. They swapped him a gallon of charcoal-cured corn whiskey for the use of the outfits. They buried three great charges of dynamite in the yard, under the three paths leading to the entrances of the house. Wires led from the buried dynamite to batteries, to which switches were attached. The Kidney boys placed the batteries in the house, beneath three windows where they could sit and watch for approaching Klansmen. They planned to throw a switch the moment the Klansmen walked up one of the paths.

That night the Kidney boys turned off all the lights and took places at the windows with the dynamite batteries and switches in their laps. Uncle Bowleg was in the house with them. The Kidneys soon got tired of staring out into the yard, waiting for Klansmen, and ordered Uncle Bowleg to fetch them a jug of whiskey and a pitcher of water. Uncle Bowleg said he was kept busy running from one Kidney to another with the whiskey. The whiskey made them happy and they began to talk, speculating on how much noise their blasts would make. "We'll blow those Bed-Sheets to Kingdom Come," said Pinky.

About ten o'clock, when the moon was high, Francis Kidney, who was guarding the side door, decided he could wait no longer. The whiskey had given him an irresistible desire to throw the switch on his battery.

"Get ready!" he shouted suddenly. "I just can't wait no longer. I'm going to test this dynamite. The Bed-Sheets won't come in by the side door, anyway."

He threw the switch and there was a blast that shook the entire lower half of Black Ankle County. It caused people to leap out of their beds. We heard the blast in my home, and I remember that my grandmother said she thought that Judgment Day or the Second Coming was at hand.

Uncle Bowleg said the blast tore up a massive longleaf pine tree in the yard of the Kidney house and threw it into the highway. Uncle Bowleg was so frightened he jumped under a bed and hid. The Kidneys ran to the front porch and looked at the great tree lying in the highway. It pleased them. They laughed and slapped each other's shoulders. They came in and poured themselves some drinks. Then Patrick and Pinky took their places again, but Francis had thrown his switch, so he lost interest and went to sleep in his chair. In about half an hour, Patrick Kidney, who was guarding the rear door, heard a rustle out in back of the house. He knew it was the wind rustling the leaves on the chinquapin bushes, but all he wanted was an excuse to throw his switch.

"I think I hear them coming!" he shouted to Pinky, who was sitting at the front door with his hand on his switch. "Get ready. I'm going to let go."

Pinky needed some excitement, too. "Throw the switch!" he yelled.

Patrick threw his switch. The blast rattled Pinky and he threw his switch, too. The blasts were almost simultaneous. The slats fell out of the bed under which Uncle Bowleg was hiding and bruised him all over. A big framed picture of the mother of the Kidney brothers fell off the wall and hit Francis on the head. The legs dropped off the kitchen range and it fell apart. The entire back porch was torn loose from the house. The blast blew up the chicken house and a barrel in which the two hounds slept. All the chickens were killed, except an old rooster, and he never crowed again. Next morning there were six dead hens on the roof of the house and dead hens and ducks were scattered all over the yard. The South Carolina line runs near the rear of the Kidney house, and Uncle Bowleg swears that the hounds landed in South Carolina and were so shocked and outraged they never crossed back into North Carolina again. The mule's stall fell in.

"The roof fell down on that old mule," Uncle Bowleg told me later, "and he pounced out into the yard with the roof on his back like a saddle and galloped two miles before he felt safe enough to slow down and look around. And there was a rocking chair on the back porch and the dynamite set it to rocking. Next morning it was still rocking."

When the noise died down that night, and when things stopped falling apart, the Kidney brothers looked at each other. They were shamefaced. Suddenly they felt frightened. Without their dynamite, they felt naked and defenceless. "If the Bed-Sheets come now, we're sure done for," Francis said. His mother's picture was raising a bump on his head. All of a sudden the Kidney boys ran out of the house and made a dash for Big Cherokee Swamp, with Uncle Bowleg following. Early next morning Uncle Bowleg got hungry and went back to the house for something to eat but the Kidney boys stayed in the swamp until noon.

As a matter of fact, they would have been just as safe in their wrecked house as they were in the swamp, because the Ku Klux Klan never did show up. The Klan had postponed its scheduled call because Mr. Giddy had arrived at the hall over the bank too drunk to take any interest in Klan matters. However, while the Kidneys were still snoring in the swamp, Mr. Ransom, who hadn't been able to get any sleep because of the three strange blasts, drove into Stonewall in his Ford and picked up Mr. Giddy. Mr. Ransom was sleepy and irritable and Mr. Giddy had a bad hangover, and they were not a happy pair. They drove out to the Kidney house to see what had happened during the night. When they arrived, Uncle Bowleg was sitting in the rocking chair on the front porch, eating a plate of corn bread and molasses. Mr. Giddy and Mr. Ransom walked into the yard and looked into the three gaping holes. Uncle Bowleg watched them like a hawk.

"Spuddy," said Mr. Giddy as he peered into the hole out of which the longleaf pine had come, "that sure is a damned big hole. I sure am glad I wasn't around when those holes were dug."

"Catfish," said Mr. Ransom in a frightened voice, "somebody might of got murdered last night. It's a good thing the Klan didn't ride last night."

Uncle Bowleg said they both stared into the holes and shuddered. Then they got into the Ford and drove away rapidly. During the day all the members of the Invisible Empire took occasion to drive by the Kidney house. They also shuddered when they saw the dynamite pits.

Late that afternoon Mr. Giddy showed up on Main Street. He was drunk again. He walked down Main Street, but he didn't sing. He stopped each person he met and said, "Friend, I have resigned." "Resigned from what, Mr. Catfish?" people asked. "Don't make no difference what I resigned from," he answered. "I just want you to know I resigned." The Ku Klux Klan never held another meeting in Stonewall. In a week or two the black paint was scraped off the windows in the hall above the bank and a "For Rent" sign was hung out. One woman ripped up her husband's Klan robe and made a pillowcase out of the cloth. Others heard about it and did the same. Mrs. Catfish Giddy ripped up her husband's robe and told her friends he was so fat she found enough material in it for two pillowcases, an apron, and a tablecloth.

Last summer I went back to Stonewall for a visit. North Carolina is a local-option state and Black Ankle is a dry county, and I wondered if the Kidneys were still making whiskey. One afternoon I drove by the Kidney house. The gaping dynamite pits were still in the yard. Pinky Kidney was sitting on the front porch in a rocking chair, smoking his pipe, and I stopped and had a talk with him.

"The mosquitoes breed in those holes," he said, motioning toward the dynamite pits with the stem of his pipe. "We been aiming to fill them up, but we keep so busy 'stilling whiskey down in the swamp that we just never get around to it."

Richard Lockridge

WHAT DID YOU DO, GRANDFATHER?

Recent editorial speculations about the next war and all the trouble it is going to make for everybody got me to thinking about the last war and all the trouble I made for the United States Navy. The next war I expect to spend with the rest of the civilian population, being blown into small pieces, but during the other war I was, in a manner of speaking, a combatant. Or, if that is too strong a word, I was at least a member of the U.S.N.R.F., which meant United States Naval Reserve Force and was usually interpreted by its members, and others, as meaning "You shall never reach France."

I was nineteen when I got into it, and barely twenty when the Navy, with a sigh of relief which could be heard all over the Brooklyn Navy Yard, got me out. I went in for a variety of reasons, none of any particular interest. I got out, I have always felt, because the Navy decided it couldn't take the responsibility any longer. The final straw, so far as the Navy was concerned, was when I very nearly did die for my country, or at any rate for the coal bunkers of the U. S. S. North Dakota.

My naval career up to the time I actually got aboard ship was not particularly remarkable. All through the training period, which took me from Kansas City to Chicago, and from Chicago to Newport, and from Newport to Hampton Roads, things were moderately quiet. I learned the manual of arms at Newport well enough; I even got to be a color guard. I learned how to get the smallest-size issue leggings, bleach them as near white as possible, and wear my trousers bagging out over them, and I learned, too, that you had to stitch your white hats round and round until the brim stood up stiffly. These things were "seagoing." I also, during long hours in the sail loft, learned to tie a number of knots and to make a serviceable if not particularly neat eye splice. I also, being adaptable in certain ways, learned a great deal about keeping out of work.

The Navy puzzled me somewhat, of course, as it puzzled everybody. It patently regarded me as a contributor of brawn—my weight went up to a hundred and thirty, thanks to the regular hours and beans for breakfast—and it firmly declined to take any chances on the quality of my brainwork. I had wanted to be a radio operator, heaven knows why, and the Navy merely ignored that. It let me take, and pass, an examination for submarine listener, which was probably one of the worst jobs it offered but at least sounded more interesting than chipping paint, and then moved my whole company hurriedly away so it wouldn't have to send me to Pelham for training. I have never understood why, later, it asked all who wanted to become signalmen to step forward and then picked for training all those who *hadn't* stepped forward. And I doubt whether there was any malicious connection between the fact that the smell of paint always made me ill and the fact that never once, during the nine months of my enlistment, did I miss a painting detail. I gained considerable art in dodging through those months and toward the end I even got out of swabbing decks. But when there was painting, particularly in one of the lower and more airless compartments, they always caught me.

But these were items in the common fate, and I didn't stand out until I got aboard the North Dakota. She was one of the older ships —she was junked not long after the war—and when I went aboard with a draft she was in the yard in Brooklyn having new engines put in. She remained there, as it happened, until after the armistice; the finishing touches were put on and she was ready for service, as I recall it, November 12, 1918. This kept her crew safe from the ordinary dangers of war, although it subjected them pretty steadily to the dangers of New York City, all of which they enjoyed very much indeed.

Even aboard ship my misadventures were minor until almost the end, and merely aroused a general suspicion of my ability to take care of myself without definitely confirming it. There was, for example, the time I almost got both legs taken off by a dummy powder bag which was being hurled through a dummy gun breech by what the petty officer in charge obviously regarded as a dummy gun crew. I had just wandered behind the breech, which was set up on a bracket screwed into the deck, for some reason. Everybody yelled a warning when the bag, which weighed a couple of hundred pounds, came hurtling through from the other side, and I had time to jump straight up in the air. Things like that might, I think, have happened to anybody.

So, certainly, might the rather unfortunate contretemps in No. 3 turret in the middle of one night. I was on watch there, with nothing to watch, of course, except a telephone. At fifteen-minute intervals somebody would call through the telephone and you were supposed to answer. He'd say "No. 3 turret?" and you'd answer "Aye, aye, sir" or something of the kind. The telephone was a small hand-set device and I yelled into it every time I was asked to. The conversations puzzled me a little. "No. 3 turret?" "Aye, aye, sir." "No. 3 turret?" "Aye, aye, sir." "No. 3 *turret!*" "Aye, aye, sir." It was after this had happened three times that a chief petty officer, an ensign of my section, the officer of the deck, and a couple of seamen poked their heads up into my cranny, where I was reading a book. They were indignant and worried. It turned out there was a button to press on the telephone before your voice became audible through it, and the whole ship had thought that somebody had stolen No. 3 turret and me.

There was also the time I went to sleep while standing up, again on watch, at the head of the crew gangplank and almost fell off onto the dock, being saved only at the last minute by a Marine who was also guarding. There was the time when somebody grabbed me just as I was about to be blown off the deck by a little wind we had off the coast of Maine on the shakedown cruise. None of these things was anything much in itself, but all of them together sort of made the Navy begin to wonder. The Navy quit wondering the day we coaled ship.

That was after the shakedown cruise, and about three weeks after the armistice. All of us who were in for the duration had immediately put in applications for discharge from active service as soon as we were given the forms, and we hoped to get out right away. We went on the cruise first, however, and it wasn't until we came back that they posted a list of names of those who were, two days later, to be allowed to go home. All of us crowded around, and whenever one of us read his name he jumped up in the air and yelled. I read the list over twice before I was finally convinced that my name wasn't there and that I was going to stay on the North Dakota.

The elation of the lucky ones was calmed a bit when they found out that before they went home they were going to help the rest of us coal ship. They felt the Navy had pulled rather a mean trick on them, as in fact it had. Nobody who has never coaled ship can imagine how mean a trick, as we all found out when the barges were brought alongside and we were sent into them to fill great canvas bags with coal dust. We started right after breakfast and didn't stop until evening. They sent down sandwiches at noon so we wouldn't lose any time. The sandwiches gritted between our teeth and stuck on the coal dust in our throats.

We finished the job, finally, and the barges were empty and riding light when I provided the drama in a dull day. We formed lines, roughly, and began to jump from the barges to the five-inch-gun ports, from which we could clamber to the North Dakota's deck. It wasn't much of a jump and the barge I happened to be on was bobbing only slightly. Subsequent events cleared my mind of the precise details, but perhaps my foot slipped. Perhaps I merely stopped to think matters over in mid-jump. Anyhow, I missed the port.

I missed the port and fell, like the blackened stick of a skyrocket, straight down between the ship and the barge. There was about a yard separating them at the waterline, and I didn't graze either one. I hit the water and kept on going down and not expecting ever to come up again. For what it is worth, my evidence is that you don't remember your past life and aren't particularly scared. You just think the whole thing is preposterous and decide it is happening to somebody else. "This can't be happening to me," you tell yourself, particularly if you know that what is happening is pretty serious. What was happening to me was serious, all right. I couldn't swim, but that wasn't the point—the point was that the chances were at least even that the barge would bob in and rub affectionately against the ship again, as it had been doing off and on. And that I would be in between. Or I might come up under the barge and just stay there.

I began clawing instinctively as soon as I hit water, and after a while I quit going down. Then I even began going up again, and a couple of hours later, while I was still wondering who this was happening to, somebody grabbed my hand. A boatswain's mate dragged me out then, excitedly, and the next moment the barge nuzzled gently up against the side of the ship. Everybody looked at me with astonishment and, after the first surprise wore off, disapproval. The whole deck force lined up and looked.

The next day there was a special supplementary list posted of those who were to go home. It read: "Lockridge, Richard, S2c." I thought this was a trifle pointed, but I was glad enough to go.

Lee Strout White

FAREWELL, MY LOVELY!

I see by the new Sears Roebuck catalogue that it is still possible to buy an axle for a 1909 Model T Ford, but I am not deceived. The great days have faded, the end is in sight. Only one page in the current catalogue is devoted to parts and accessories for the Model T; yet everyone remembers springtimes when the Ford gadget section was larger than men's clothing, almost as large as household furnishings. The last Model T was built in 1927, and the car is fading from what scholars call the American scene—which is an understatement. because to a few million people who grew up with it, the old Ford practically *was* the American scene.

It was the miracle God had wrought. And it was patently the sort of thing that could only happen once. Mechanically uncanny, it was like nothing that had ever come to the world before. Flourishing industries rose and fell with it. As a vehicle, it was hard-working, commonplace, heroic; and it often seemed to transmit those qualities to the persons who rode in it. My own generation identifies it with Youth, with its gaudy, irretrievable excitements; before it fades into the mist, I would like to pay it the tribute of the sigh that is not a sob, and set down random entries in a shape somewhat less cumbersome than a Sears Roebuck catalogue.

The Model T was distinguished from all other makes of cars by the fact that its transmission was of a type known as planetary—which was half metaphysics, half sheer friction. Engineers accepted the word "planetary" in its epicyclic sense, but I was always conscious that it also meant "wandering," "erratic." Because of the peculiar nature of this planetary element, there was always, in Model T, a certain dull rapport between engine and wheels, and even when the car was in a state known as neutral, it trembled with a deep imperative and tended to inch forward. There was never a moment when the bands were not faintly egging the machine on. In this respect it was like a horse, rolling the bit on its tongue, and country people brought to it the same technique they used with draft animals.

Its most remarkable quality was its rate of acceleration. In its palmy days the Model T could take off faster than anything on the road. The reason was simple. To get under way, you simply hooked the third finger of the right hand around a lever on the steering column, pulled down hard, and shoved your left foot forcibly against the low-speed pedal. These were simple, positive motions; the car responded by lunging forward with a roar. After a few seconds of this turmoil, you took your toe off the pedal, eased up a mite on the throttle, and the car, possessed of only two forward speeds, catapulted directly into high with a series of ugly jerks and was off on its glorious errand. The abruptness of this departure was never equalled in other cars of the period. The human leg was (and still is) incapable of letting in a clutch with anything like the forthright abandon that used to send Model T on its way. Letting in a clutch is a negative, hesitant motion, depending on delicate nervous control; pushing down the Ford pedal was a simple, country motion—an expansive act, which came as natural as kicking an old door to make it budge.

The driver of the old Model T was a man enthroned. The car, with top up, stood seven feet high. The driver sat on top of the gas tank, brooding it with his own body. When he wanted gasoline, he alighted, along with everything else in the front seat; the seat was pulled off, the metal cap unscrewed, and a wooden stick thrust down to sound the liquid in the well. There were always a couple of these sounding sticks kicking around in the ratty sub-cushion regions of a flivver. Refueling was more of a social function then, because the driver had to unbend, whether he wanted to or not. Directly in front of the driver was the windshield—high, uncompromisingly erect. Nobody talked about air resistance, and the four cylinders pushed the car through the atmosphere with a simple disregard of physical law.

There was this about a Model T: the purchaser never regarded his purchase as a complete, finished product. When you bought a Ford, you figured you had a start—a vibrant, spirited framework to which could be screwed an almost limitless assortment of decorative and functional hardware. Driving away from the agency, hugging the new wheel between your knees, you were already full of creative worry. A Ford was born naked as a baby, and a flourishing industry grew up out of correcting its rare deficiencies and combatting its fascinating diseases. Those were the great days of lily-painting. I have been looking at some old Sears Roebuck catalogues, and they bring everything back so clear.

First you bought a Ruby Safety Reflector for the rear, so that your posterior would glow in another car's brilliance. Then you invested thirty-nine cents in some radiator Moto Wings, a popular ornament which gave the Pegasus touch to the machine and did something godlike to the owner. For nine cents you bought a fan-belt guide to keep the belt from slipping off the pulley.

You bought a radiator compound to stop leaks. This was as much a part of everybody's equipment as aspirin tablets are of a medicine cabinet. You bought special oil to prevent chattering, a clamp-on dash light, a patching outfit, a tool box which you bolted to the running board, a sun visor, a steering-column brace to keep the column rigid, and a set of emergency containers for gas, oil, and water—three thin, disc-like cans which reposed in a case on the running board during long, important journeys—red for gas, gray for water, green for oil. It was only a beginning. After the car was about a year old, steps were taken to check the alarming disintegration. (Model T was full of tumors, but they were benign.) A set of anti-rattlers (98c) was a popular panacea. You hooked them on to the gas and spark rods, to the brake pull rod, and to the steering-rod connections. Hood silencers, of black rubber, were applied to the fluttering hood. Shock-absorbers and snubbers gave "complete relaxation." Some people bought rubber pedal pads, to fit over the standard metal pedals. (I didn't like these, I remember.) Persons of a suspicious or pugnacious turn of mind bought a rear-view mirror; but most Model T owners weren't worried by what was coming from behind because they would soon enough see it out in front. They rode in a state of cheerful catalepsy. Quite a large mutinous clique among Ford owners went over to a foot accelerator (you could buy one and screw it to the floor board), but there was a certain madness in these people, because the Model T, just as she stood, had a choice of three foot pedals to push, and there were plenty of moments when both feet were occupied in the routine performance of duty and when the only way to speed up the engine was with the hand throttle.

Gadget bred gadget. Owners not only bought ready-made gadgets, they invented gadgets to meet special needs. I myself drove my car directly from the agency to the blacksmith's, and had the smith affix two enormous iron brackets to the port running board to support an army trunk.

People who owned closed models builded along different lines: they bought ball grip handles for opening doors, window anti-rattlers, and deluxe flower vases of the cut-glass anti-splash type. People with delicate sensibilities garnished their car with a device called the Donna Lee Automobile Disseminator—a porous vase guaranteed, according to Sears, to fill the car with a "faint clean odor of lavender." The gap between open cars and closed cars was not as great then as it is now: for $11.95, Sears Roebuck converted your touring car into a sedan and you went forth renewed. One agreeable quality of the old Fords was that they had no bumpers, and their fenders softened and wilted with the years and permitted the driver to squeeze in and out of tight places.

Tires were 30 x 3½, cost about twelve dollars, and punctured readily. Everybody carried a Jiffy patching set, with a nutmeg grater to roughen the tube before the goo was spread on. Everybody was capable of putting on a patch, expected to have to, and did have to.

During my association with Model T's, self-starters were not a prevalent accessory. They were expensive and under suspicion. Your car came equipped with a serviceable crank, and the first thing you learned was how to Get Results. It was a special trick, and until you learned it (usually from another Ford owner, but sometimes by a period of appalling experimentation) you might as well have been winding up an awning. The trick was to leave the ignition switch off, proceed to the animal's head, pull the choke (which was a little wire protruding through the radiator), and give the crank two or three nonchalant upward lifts. Then, whistling as though thinking about something else, you would saunter back to the driver's cabin, turn the ignition on, return to the crank, and this time, catching it on the down stroke, give it a quick spin with plenty of That. If this procedure was followed, the engine almost always responded—first with a few scattered explosions, then with a tumultuous gunfire, which you checked by racing around to the driver's seat and retarding the throttle. Often, if the emergency brake hadn't been pulled all the way back, the car advanced on you the instant the first explosion occurred and you would hold it back by leaning your weight against it. I can still feel my old

Ford nuzzling me at the curb, as though looking for an apple in my pocket.

In zero weather, ordinary cranking became an impossibility, except for giants. The oil thickened, and it became necessary to jack up the rear wheels, which, for some planetary reason, eased the throw.

The lore and legend that governed the Ford were boundless. Owners had their own theories about everything; they discussed mutual problems in that wise, infinitely resourceful way old women discuss rheumatism. Exact knowledge was pretty scarce, and often proved less effective than superstition. Dropping a camphor ball into the gas tank was a popular expedient; it seemed to have a tonic effect on both man and machine. There wasn't much to base exact knowledge on. The Ford driver flew blind. He didn't know the temperature of his engine, the speed of his car, the amount of his fuel, or the pressure of his oil (the old Ford lubricated itself by what was amiably described as the "splash system"). A speedometer cost money and was an extra, like a windshield-wiper. The dashboard of the early models was bare save for an ignition key; later models, grown effete, boasted an ammeter which pulsated alarmingly with the throbbing of the car. Under the dash was a box of coils, with vibrators which you adjusted, or thought you adjusted. Whatever the driver learned of his motor, he learned not through instruments but through sudden developments. I remember that the timer was one of the vital organs about which there was ample doctrine. When everything else had been checked, you "had a look" at the timer. It was an extravagantly odd little device, simple in construction, mysterious in function. It contained a roller, held by a spring, and there were four contact points on the inside of the case against which, many people believed, the roller rolled. I have had a timer apart on a sick Ford many times, but I never really knew what I was up to—I was just showing off before God. There were almost as many schools of thought as there were timers. Some people, when things went wrong, just clenched their teeth and gave the timer a smart crack with a wrench. Other people opened it up and blew on it. There was a school that held that the timer needed large amounts of oil; they fixed it by frequent baptism. And there was a school that was positive it was meant to run dry as a bone; these people were continually taking it off and wiping it. I remember once spitting into a timer; not in anger, but in a spirit of research. You see, the Model T driver moved in the realm of meta-physics. He believed his car could be hexed.

One reason the Ford anatomy was never reduced to an exact science was that, having "fixed" it, the owner couldn't honestly claim that the treatment had brought about the cure. There were too many authenticated cases of Fords fixing themselves—restored naturally to health after a short rest. Farmers soon discovered this, and it fitted nicely with their draft-horse philosophy: "Let 'er cool off and she'll snap into it again."

A Ford owner had Number One Bearing constantly in mind. This bearing, being at the front end of the motor, was the one that always burned out, because the oil didn't reach it when the car was climbing hills. (That's what I was always told, anyway.) The oil used to recede and leave Number One dry as a clam flat; you had to watch that bearing like a hawk. It was like a weak heart—you could hear it start knocking, and that was when you stopped and let her cool off. Try as you would to keep the oil supply right, in the end Number One always went out. "Number One Bearing burned out on me and I had to have her replaced," you would say, wisely; and your companions always had a lot to tell about how to protect and pamper Number One to keep her alive.

Sprinkled not too liberally among the millions of amateur witch doctors who drove Fords and applied their own abominable cures were the heaven-sent mechanics who could really make the car talk. These professionals turned up in undreamed-of spots. One time, on the banks of the Columbia River in Washington, I heard the rear end go out of my Model T when I was trying to whip it up a steep incline onto the deck of a ferry. Something snapped; the car slid backward into the mud. It seemed to me like the end of the trail. But the captain of the ferry, observing the withered remnant, spoke up.

"What's got her?" he asked.

"I guess it's the rear end," I replied, listlessly. The captain leaned over the rail and stared. Then I saw that there was a hunger in his eyes that set him off from other men.

"Tell you what," he said, carelessly, trying to cover up his eager-ness, "let's pull the son of a bitch up onto the boat, and I'll help you fix her while we're going back and forth on the river."

We did just this. All that day I plied between the towns of Pasco and Kennewick, while the skipper (who had once worked in a Ford garage) directed the amazing work of resetting the bones of my car.

Springtime in the heyday of the Model T was a delirious season. Owning a car was still a major excitement, roads were still wonderful and bad. The Fords were obviously conceived in madness: any car which was capable of going from forward into reverse without any perceptible mechanical hiatus was bound to be a mighty challenging thing to the human imagination. Boys used to veer them off the highway into a level pasture and run wild with them, as though they were cutting up with a girl.

Most everybody used the reverse pedal quite as much as the regular foot brake—it distributed the wear over the bands and wore them all down evenly. That was the big trick, to wear all the bands down evenly, so that the final chattering would be total and the whole unit scream for renewal.

The days were golden, the nights were dim and strange. I still recall with trembling those loud, nocturnal crises when you drew up to a signpost and raced the engine so the lights would be bright enough to read destinations by. I have never been really planetary since. I suppose it's time to say goodbye. Farewell, my lovely!

Ruth McKenney

THE SOCK HUNT

I suppose, what with the passing years and the girls he's met since, that young Mr. Randolph Churchill, the scion of the London Churchills, does not remember me. Still, looking back on it all, I should think he would. I certainly do. Precisely as I can never, for so long as I walk this earth, forget the time I fell down at my high-school senior prom, right smack in front of the orchestra with my best beau sprawled beside me, so can I never put aside the memory of young Mr. Churchill. My flesh still crawls. Not that Mr. Churchill is anything to make a girl's flesh crawl. Not at all. In a certain way, like the men in the breakfast-food ads, he is quite handsome.

Mr. Churchill and I met in a purely professional capacity. It was the late fall of 1930. He was touring America, speaking before literary clubs, Rotary Clubs, university clubs, and the like on a variety of light topics, including "Fate of an Empire" and "Why I Am a Conservative." He was then nineteen, and I was the daisy-eyed star reporter on the *Ohio State Lantern,* a newspaper published daily, except Saturday and Sunday, by the students of journalism at Ohio State University.

Young Mr. Churchill arrived in Columbus, Ohio, on the flood tide of a lot of awe-struck advance notices. He was to address a local men's dinner club which for pure hauteur would make the Union Club look sick any day. All the speeches before this tony oufit were dead secret; no reporters allowed. Furthermore, celebrities who appeared before these hallowed few were never interviewed by the Columbus press. The editors of the papers were all members of the club, and that was that.

Well, my mouth watered to interview Mr. Churchill. I had never seen a real Englishman in the flesh, for one thing. For another thing, my deadly rival on the *Lantern* staff, a chap of considerable energy and no ethics, had publicly stated that he considered the feat of obtaining an interview with Mr. Churchill too great even for his remarkable talents. After this, nothing could hold me. I marched forward with determination to my doom.

I arrived at the hotel lobby at 4:35 P.M. and briskly set about finding out Mr. Churchill's room number. Then, with success almost in the hollow of my hand, I collapsed on a lobby lounge with an attack of acute panic. This lasted until 5:22 P.M., when a man insulted me. At least he came directly over to my lounge and said, in a chummy tone, "Waiting for somebody?"

This drove me to Mr. Churchill. I fled from my insulter and arrived at the forbidding door of Mr. Churchill's hotel room, still unnerved. I knocked valiantly. I had mapped out my strategy well in advance. When Mr. Churchill asked, "Who's there?" I intended to reply, "Maid, with towels." Then, when he opened the door, I planned to stick my foot in the crack and ask him a lot of questions very fast. I think a scene such as this had been in a newspaper film about that time.

Anyway, Mr. Churchill ruined my pretty plans by replying, to the knock, "Come in." I hesitated, getting a burning sensation in my throat. I was nineteen and lived with my grandmother, who would have been absolutely horrified at the thought of any young woman traipsing into a man's hotel room alone.

"Come IN!" roared Mr. Churchill from behind the door. He sounded rather angry. I kept telling myself that after I got out of school and got a real job on a newspaper, I would look back on this moment and laugh. As it turned out, however, in spite of a lot of jobs on newspapers, genuine daily ones, the mere thought of that frightful moment, with Mr. Churchill bellowing "Come IN" on one side of the door and me trembling on the other, has never brought even the sickliest of smiles to my face. It still makes my hair prickle.

Finally I opened the door very timidly indeed, and beheld Mr. Churchill, surely the blondest young man in the world, seated at a desk, writing. He wore a smoking jacket over his dinner trousers, black vest, and starched shirt front. His bare feet were stuck in floppy leather slippers. Mr. Churchill looked so very public-school English he was faintly incredible. Maybe he's grown out of that now, but in 1930 he was certainly breath of Empire. You could—or at least I could—just see him wolfing down supper off in the tropics, dressed to the teeth in tails and white tie. Mr. Churchill's eyes were a china blue and his smoking jacket was the same, overlaid, however, with old rose and gold.

I stood by the door for several seconds while Mr. Churchill continued to scratch away at his desk. Now, a cynical old interviewer of ripened years, I fear that Mr. Churchill was attempting to impress me. But on that trying evening I felt that I had intruded on the literary labors of a young genius. Finally Mr. Churchill lifted his blue eyes to mine.

"Ah," he said, leaping gallantly to his feet, "a lady! I beg your pardon. Pray do forgive me."

My mouth sagged. Mr. Churchill drew up a chair beside his desk and, with a cozy gesture, beckoned me over. I went.

"Pray excuse me," said Mr. Churchill. "I must finish this wireless message." On his desk lay eleven or twelve Western Union blanks covered with writing.

"What?" I said. The reason I said this was that I could not understand very much of what he said. His accent, which I had so longed to hear, a real, bona-fide Oxford accent, was so broad that unfortunately he might as well have spoken French. I can get every other word a Frenchman says, too, which is fairly good, considering I studied French in the Ohio public schools for only eight years.

Young Mr. Churchill now turned to me and said in a fierce tone, "What would you say if you wanted to tell your manager you did not want ladies to give you flowers at lectures?" At least that is what I thought he said. It was so difficult for me to decipher Mr. Churchill's accent, and the question seemed so entirely improbable, that, after agonized reflection, I simply shook my head.

Mr. Churchill didn't note my silence. He apparently hit on just the right words, for he signed his name with a flourish I am sure no American operator ever spelled out, and turned briskly to me, saying, "Now, what may I do for you?"

I explained haltingly that I was a newspaper reporter. Mr. Churchill didn't ask, so I didn't find it necessary to tell him that the paper I was interviewing him for was only, alas, the university daily. I simply trotted out all my carefully prepared questions. I asked him about Ramsay MacDonald and Hoover and Briand and a few other such people. Mr. Churchill roundly denounced them all, for different reasons. MacDonald was too far left, and even Mr. Hoover was pretty much of a Socialist. I asked him about the future of English youth, and Mr. Churchill said that if only a few more young people of his class would awaken to their responsibility, the future of England was safe. I was slightly shaken at Mr. Churchill's firm Tory opinions. He seemed quite young to be so fierce.

However, I drew a breath and started off on the English public-school system. Just at this point Mr. Churchill created a diversion.

In an ordinary speaking voice, as distinguished from the voice in which he denounced Mr. Hoover or Mr. MacDonald, he said, "Would you care for a drink?"

This unnerved me again. I could explain the interview to Grandma and my conscience, but drinking with a total stranger in his hotel room certainly seemed excessive. In those days, most college students —at least at my school—still thought drinking, no matter where, was pretty darned daring. Mr. Churchill, however, had already unearthed from his suitcase a bottle of what he assured me was fine Scotch, straight from England.

I was no judge. Up to that very moment I had never tasted anything in alcoholic beverages except a variety of bootleg liquor called "New Straitsville corn," because it was distilled in some abandoned mines near New Straitsville, Ohio. New Straitsville corn burned your throat and made you sick. Also, it hurt so to choke down New Straitsville corn that you were acutely conscious of every drink. It was the suave, sneaking quality of Mr. Churchill's fine liquor which undid me. You hardly knew you were drinking it, until afterward.

Mr. Churchill and I soon forgot serious topics. I asked him whether he really enjoyed lecturing about "Fate of an Empire." He said he did not, and also that he hated America and couldn't wait to get home. After a while Mr. Churchill thought we ought to eat something.

"I say," he said, "how about a spot of food, what?" He really talked just like that.

"O.K.," I said. "Let me order, though. They can't understand you over the phone. You talk so funny."

Mr. Churchill glowered. He said I was the one who had a peculiar accent.

"You talk through your nose," he said, with truth, "and you pro-nounce all your 'r's. They aren't supposed to be pronounced."

"That's what you think," I said, feeling hilarious, "Old Mush-mouth."

For some reason, Mr. Churchill thought that was very funny. "'Mushmouth!'" he shouted joyously, amid peals of real upper-class

English laughter, very high-pitched, like a whinny. "'Mushmouth'! Deah me, I must remembaw that."

We ate lamp chops, a lot of them. "Tell them to send up a bally lot of them!" Mr. Churchill roared while I telephoned. "I want six lamb chops all for myself. After all, I must lecture on the 'Fate of an Empire.'"

While we were gnawing on lamb-chop bones we traded opinions on moving pictures. Mr. Churchill was a fan, and so was I. It turned out we both adored Vilma Banky. Suddenly Mr. Churchill said, "What about my lecture?"

"Well," I said, "what about it?"

"I won't do it," Mr. Churchill said. "Let the Empire go rot for tonight. Let's go to the cinema. You and I."

For a moment I was sorely tempted. Then I pictured the fearful scandal. The lecturer disappears. The town's leading citizens are left waiting. Among the leading citizens was the publisher of the Columbus *Dispatch*. I was the campus correspondent for the Columbus *Dispatch,* and I lived—in a very meagre way, to be sure, but still I lived—on the weekly wages the *Dispatch* paid me. In my fancy I saw the publisher of the *Dispatch* discovering that his most minor employee had practically kidnapped young Mr. Churchill.

"No," I said firmly. "You have to make that speech."

Mr. Churchill sighed. "Well, then," he said, "I have to put on my dinner jacket." He found that all right; also his white scarf and his black overcoat and his two patent-leather pumps. But alas, as the hour approached nine, he could find only one black sock. The club was to send a committee at nine, to escort Mr. Churchill to the lecture hall.

"What shall I do?" Mr. Churchill inquired frantically. "I can't lecture with only one sock." I rose from the dinner table, still gnawing a bone, and cast a quick look over the room.

"Be calm," I said. "They'll never notice."

"Oh, yes they will," Mr. Churchill said. "Besides, I won't go unless we find that sock. And I only have one black pair with me. The rest of them are in Pittsburgh."

"Wear another color," I said lightly. "What happened to the socks you had on this afternoon?"

"Tan socks," Mr. Churchill shouted, "with a dinner coat?"

I observed Mr. Churchill's frenzy with a motherly eye. "There, there," I said. "Relax. I'll find it."

Mr. Churchill sat down, putting a childish faith in me. I failed. I trotted around in circles, afraid to look in his luggage—for after all, that would hardly be proper—and unable to spot a stray black sock in the immediate surroundings.

Suddenly Mr. Churchill shouted, "I bet it's under the bed. I unpacked my things on the bed, and maybe it fell off on the floor." He threw himself down beside his bed and stuck his head under the springs.

"I can't see it," he said dismally, sounding muffled. "You have a look from the other side."

I obligingly sprawled out under the wall side of the bed, and peered around, coughing in the dust. At this moment precisely, there was a knock on the door.

"Come in!" bellowed Mr. Churchill, before he thought. I gave a faint scream, and too late Mr. Churchill considered the informality of his position. He tried to get up, too suddenly, and bumped his head severely on the bed slats. He relapsed, groaning, just as the committee of super-leading citizens walked in.

Fortunately, I do not now remember the names of those three well-starched, beautifully tailored citizens who marched in on that sock-hunting expedition. It would be frightful to be haunted all my life by their names as well as their faces.

"Mr. Churchill?" said the first leading citizen, in a tone of pained surprise.

Young Mr. Churchill showed the heritage of generations of gentlemen. Still reclining on the floor, he turned his head, nodded an acknowledgment, and said in a loud, belligerent voice, "I'm looking for my lost black sock." The second leading citizen went directly to the bureau and picked up the lost black sock.

"Your sock, sir," he said. Mr. Churchill rose, bowed slightly, and said, "I thank you very much." Then he shouted to me, "Get up! We've found it."

I hesitated. I wanted to stay under that bed and just die there peacefully, without ever having to rise and face those three leading citizens. I did get up, though, feeling the way you do in dreams when you have no clothes on at a gala performance of "Aïda" in the Metropolitan. I suppose, from the expression on the faces of the three leading citizens, that they had not realized until the moment my face slowly emerged from behind the bed that there was a young lady in the room. Each leading citizen did a combination gasp and snort.

"She's coming to hear my lecture," Mr. Churchill announced as he put on his sock. The purple staining my cheeks now rose to my hairline.

"I couldn't," I said weakly. "I couldn't indeed. It's private. They don't allow women in."

"Nevertheless," said Mr. Churchill briskly, "I don't speak unless you come."

The three leading citizens looked so grim I thought I should really faint, although I never had in my whole life. Mr. Churchill and I and the committee now left the room and boarded the elevator. All the way down, Mr. Churchill maintained his position. I was to come or he wouldn't speak. The three leading citizens took turns saying, "But that is impossible, Mr. Churchill. The rules of the club do not permit ladies."

As we got off the elevator, one of the leading citizens, a tall, white-haired man with a large stomach, managed to fall in step with me while the two other leading citizens took Mr. Churchill by the arms.

"Now," said my sudden escort, "you go away fast, and stop bothering Mr. Churchill."

"Me?" I said in honest astonishment. "I never bothered him."

The leading citizen did not stop to argue. "Go away," he hissed, giving me a slight push into the lobby. I went. I was never so glad to leave any place in my life. I wrote my interview that night, and it was a big success. My rival, Ernest, was a picture of jealous confusion when he read it next day. But even the sweet rewards of college fame and my colleagues' envy did not erase the memory of that hideous moment when I was caught, red-handed, looking for Mr. Churchill's sock. It is comparatively easy to recover from honest sorrows, but I wake up in the dead of night at least twice a year and my heart fills with agony, remembering that unspeakable moment when, like a rising moon, my face slowly appeared from behind Mr. Churchill's bed, to confound the three leading citizens of Columbus, Ohio.

Life can hold no further terrors for me.

M. R. A.

MEMOIRS OF A MASTER

There were always servants in my father's house, and now there are servants in mine. This morning, from a vantage point in the upstairs hall of my house in the city, I counted five. We have a cook, a chambermaid-and-waitress, a nurse, a laundress, and a furnace man. There are times when amity and peace brood over the home, when the servants remain with us and I begin to have a bowing acquaintance with some of them. There are other periods when the arrivals and departures are frequent and dramatic, and the house takes on the momentous character of the North Beach Airport.

Whenever a new servant is due to arrive, my wife and I always prepare the room for her with our own hands—with a sort of loving suspicion, as you might make a nest for a litter of lion cubs. I have just this minute come from the top floor, where we are fixing up a room for an incoming cook. Her name is said to be Gloria. It sounds implausible; but to me, an old master, nothing is impossible, not even a cook named Gloria. Nothing is even remotely unlikely. I await Gloria with head held high. The encounter with Gloria's bedroom suite, however, has exhausted me; and as I sit here on my study couch, I feel a great wave of fatigue engulf me—the peculiar weariness that afflicts a man who has always had everything done for him. I call it *Meisterschmerz*. I realize that I am not getting any younger and that the day may come when I shall no longer have the physical stamina to be waited on hand and foot by a corps of well-trained domestics.

When bachelors enjoy a reverie, I understand that all the girls of their past float before their eyes in rings of smoke from their pipe. My benedictine smoke dreams are full, not of past loves but of former servants. I dream of Alma, Estelle, Mrs. Farrell, Sylvia, Susan, Anna (who chose a brief interlude with us to have gallstones), Gaston and Eugénie, Elaine the beautiful, Zelda, Otto and Mildred, Mrs. Farnsworth, Joan, Claire. I like to sit here now and dream about them, count them over, like beads in a rosary, and think of all the bright, fierce times I have had with them, sharing their sorrows and their joys, their sickness and their health, taking their phone calls, filling in for them on their days out, driving them to distant churches in remote country districts. They have had some magnificent sicknesses, these old friends of mine, vivid bits of malaise, and truly distinguished indispositions. Every name calls up some bright recollection of bygone days.

Sylvia, for example. Sylvia to me means Christmas, and Christmas in turn means pneumonia. Someone in my family is always sick at Christmas, and when it isn't I, it is quite apt to be a servant. The year we had Sylvia, it was she. Sylvia had been looking a bit stringy for several days before the twenty-fifth, and we could feel something coming on. We nursed her along and refused to let her do any work, but her fever began on the twenty-fourth, with the early-afternoon carol singing, and rose steadily with the dusk. At last her conversation faded out and she just mumbled something and went to bed. I wasn't feeling any too fit myself, so at six o'clock my wife took first Sylvia's temperature and then mine. Sylvia had me by four and two-tenths degrees, and it was decided that *she* would be the one to go to the hospital. Our doctor verified this and mentioned pneumonia. I simply picked up the phone and said those magic words which I had read so many times on the cover of the directory: "I want an ambulance."

To my astonishment, an ambulance soon appeared in the street below. Police arrived with it, and the living room soon smelled pleasantly of balsam wreaths and Irishmen. The children, of course, adored having police on Christmas Eve—it gave a gala touch to the holiday—but the whole business presented special problems to us parents because all the gifts were hidden in Sylvia's room, and we had the devil's own time keeping the youngsters from running in and out with the cops.

None of us could think of Sylvia's last name, not even Sylvia; but I gave "Cassidy" to the ambulance doctor, and he bundled her downstairs to the waiting car, and away she went through the merry streets, myself following along afoot (with my lowgrade fever) like one of the Magi, to attend to the admittance problem—which is part of the servant problem. I shall never forget the hospital's reception of Sylvia.

To begin with, the place was jammed—the holiday rush—and the pneumonia ward was full to bursting. Sylvia was rolled into a downstairs corridor and parked there for about half an hour, while sisters of mercy flitted about conjuring up an extra bed. Finally it was arranged, and I accompanied Sylvia up to the ward to tuck her in and wish her a last Merry Christmas, although the poor girl was barely conscious by this time of what was going on. It was after nine o'clock, and the corridor was lit only by a small red night light. Just as our little procession groped its way into the ward, with its dim forms of sickness and the smell of calamity, we were welcomed by a woman's delirious scream.

"Sylvia!" the voice cried, in unwordly pain. "Seeelvyah!" And then a short, rapid "Sylvia, Sylvia, Sylvia," ending with a mournful wolf note, "Seeeeeeelvyah!"

It was the cry of a female who must have had a Sylvia in her family, or in her past, or both. But it was too much for my Sylvia. I think she imagined herself crossed over into purgatory. "Dear God!" I heard her mumble. "Dear God, get me out of here!" Feeling definitely pneumonic myself, and damn sorry for Sylvia and for the world in general, I trudged shakily home and spent the rest of the holy night putting together a child's fire truck, which had arrived from a department store that must have known of our domestic quandary, for they sent the thing in knockdown form—a mass of wheels, axles, bolts, screws, nuts, bars, and cotter pins.

Well, that was all a long while ago. Sylvia pulled through all right, but took a place in the country, where the air would be better for her. I thought, in those days, that I knew what sickness was; but I tell you now that nobody knows what sickness is till he's had an upstairs maid with gallstones. Anna had been with us only six days when her seizure came. In fact, I had never actually seen Anna— her paths and mine never crossed—and I knew her only by hearsay and by the sound of her typewriter tap-tapping on the floor above me. She was an elderly sort, my wife said, with eyes set too near together, like Franklin D. Roosevelt's. I inquired about the presence of the typewriter and my wife explained that Anna had taken up typing, hoping to improve herself. I couldn't very well object, because I had been up to the same trick myself for some years.

Anna, it turned out, was more than a typist—she was a Christian Scientist as well, and she waited grimly through three hours of torture before letting out the yell that began our acquaintanceship. The yell came at four o'clock in the morning, and my wife and I sprang out of bed and instinctively rushed up one flight to see what was the matter.

"Mister," groaned Anna, recognizing me instantly as a friend, "please get me some morphine—it's my gallbladder!"

"Call the doctor!" said my wife. "And," she added peremptorily, "you better get dressed, you may have to go somewhere and you might as well be ready."

As I pattered downstairs, I remember trying to decide between my blue unfinished worsted (whose pockets contained everything necessary for a gallstone operation, such as money, fountain pen, and keys) and my brown tweed, which seemed a more workaday proposition but needed servicing. I knew the day would come and go before I slept again, and I figured I might as well be dressed correctly.

When the doctor arrived, I was fully attired in the blue, and ready for anything. He seemed suspicious of Anna's familiarity with morphine, but admitted that her gallbladder might be on the blink and said we'd better get in touch with her relatives. Now, the relatives of domestics are an even more mysterious band of people than domestics themselves. I knew from experience that sometimes they didn't even have names. I also knew that they never had telephones, although they sometimes lived in the same building with a telephone. However, we grilled Anna on the subject of relatives, after the doctor had relieved her, and eventually, by an elaborate bit of telephoning through third parties, we dug up a beauty—a niece, Anna said she was. We asked her to come as soon as possible. She turned out to be one of the most beautiful women I have ever seen in my life. She arrived about nine that morning, with a fourteen-month-old child in rather bad repair. I let her in, and she immediately handed the baby to me. "Would you mind?" she said. "I have a terrible hangover and can hardly stand up. Isn't it a shame about Bumpo?"

"About who?" I asked.

"Bumpo," she said. "That's what we call my Aunt Anna."

"Oh, I didn't know," I replied. "Yes, it's a dreadful thing, with much pain. I'm sorry *you* don't feel good, either," I added courteously.

"I'll be all right as soon as I get a drink," she said. "I was on a bender last night after the show. I have a walk-on part in the 'Scandals,' you know. Have you seen it?"

"No, but I will," I replied.

Together we marched upstairs. The baby was heavy and soggy, a rather spiritless child. With him in my lap, I made a quick phone call to the office and told them that it didn't look as though I'd be in till afternoon.

I sometimes think that that morning, as I stood around pacifying the grand-nephew of a stricken domestic named Bumpo, my career as a master reached a minor pinnacle, achieved something like nobility. It didn't last, though. Anna had been gone hardly an hour when my wife and I found ourselves engaged in the cheap, vulgar trick of reading the diary which she left behind her. We discovered it on her bureau. Our intentions were honorable enough at first—we were simply thumbing through it hoping to come across her niece's address, which in the confusion she had neglected to leave us. Gradually, however, we became absorbed; Anna's story began to grip us and sweep us along. Written in ink, in a fine, close hand, the diary covered a period of about two years and chronicled her goings and comings in two previous places. For the most part it was a rather dreary recital of a cheerless life. "The madam out this afternoon." "Getting colder." "Robert Taylor was at the Strand yesterday but didn't get to go." We waded, fascinated, through page after page of this commonplace stuff, and suddenly, as though we had been hit across the eyes with a board, we came upon the following terse item: "Phoned Milwaukee police today."

That was all there was to it. Nothing led up to it. Nothing led away from it. It stood there all alone a tiny purple chapter in a gray little book. We still don't know what it was all about, and we still dream about it sometimes.

Anna had her stones out in good shape and soon grew fit again. We volunteered to pay for the operation, but she refused financial help. Although we held the situation open for her, she never came back to us—which rather disappointed me, as I wanted to get to know her well enough to call her Bumpo. She is probably even now tapping away at her portable machine somewhere—a one-act play, perhaps, or a friendly note to the Department of Justice.

The presence in my house of a group of persons with whom I have merely a contractual relationship is a constant source of wonder to me. Left to my own devices, I believe I would never employ a domestic but would do my own work, which would take me about twenty minutes a day. However, all matters pertaining to the operation of the home are settled agreeably and competently for me by my wife, who dearly loves complexity and whose instinctive solution of any dilemma like marriage is to get about four or five other people embroiled in it. Although the picturesque and lurid rôle of householder saps my strength and keeps me impoverished, I must admit it gives life a sort of carnival aspect, almost as though there were an elephant swaying in the dining room. And then, once in a lifetime, some thoroughly indispensable and noble person walks casually into one's home, like Antoinette Ferraro, who proceeds to become a member of the family, blood or no blood. Antoinette has been fooling around our house for thirteen or fourteen years, and we would as lief part with her as with our own children. There is no danger of any separation, however. I am perfectly sure that when I draw my last breath, Antoinette will still be somewhere about the premises, performing some grotesquely irrelevant act, like ironing a dog's blanket.

Her name is really Antonietta, and I suspect that I had better not go on with these memoirs without taking her up in some detail, as she is the core of our domestic apple. Without her we should perish; and *with* her (such is the pressure of her outside obligations) we very nearly do. The other night, as my wife and I were sitting by Antoinette's side in the crowded auditorium of a trade school, watching her legitimate son Pietro graduate with honors in my blue serge suit, I had a chance to study the beatific face of this remarkable woman and brood about my good fortune in having encountered her in this world. She was born, I believe, in northern Italy, and speaks an impartial blend of Italian, French, and English. The only form of an English verb which appeals to her, however, is the present participle. In fact, she speaks almost entirely in participles, joining them by French conjunctions, to which she is loyal. If you ask if she'd be good enough to boil you an egg, her reply is simply, *"Oui,* I'm boiling." Once, on New Year's, she got a little tight on some mulled wine of her own concoction, and when we inquired of her next day if she had reached the Sixth Avenue "L" safely the night before, she blinked her long lashes shyly and said, "Oh, *oui*. Hah! I'm so running! Oh, my!"

Although she ostensibly works full time for us, and gets paid for it, this is merely a mutual conceit on our parts, for she has a full, absorbing life of her own—an apartment full of birds and plants, a son on whom she pours the steady stream of her affection, two boarders for whom she prepares two meals a day, and a thoroughbred Cairn bitch, which (like Antoinette herself) is forever being taken advantage of by an inferior male. The last time this animal had puppies, Antoinette brought one over, tenderly, for us to see. It was something of a monster, with chow characteristics and a set of inflamed bowels. When we offered our condolences on the continuance of the bitch's bitter destiny, Antoinette sighed. *"Ah, oui,"* she said, dreamily. "Wazz that night on the roof."

I marvel that we go on paying Antoinette anything. It takes her two hours and a half to dust one side of a wooden candlestick, and even then she forgets to put it back on the mantelpiece and our Boston terrier carries it to the cellar and worries it in the coalbin. All we gain from the arrangement is Antoinette's rich account of the little adventure, including a perfect imitation of the dog. "He so hoppy," she will explain, "holding in mouth, like beeg cigar, *mais* never dropping. Oh, he barking, he jomping . . ."

It doesn't sound reasonable, I know, that we should pay anyone to sit around our house and imitate a dog, but we do, nevertheless. One morning she showed up, ready for work, accompanied by a sick bird in a gilded cage, her bitch (again pregnant), and her own family wash, which she always seems to do on our time. "Antoinette," said my wife, exasperated, "I honestly don't see how you expect to do anything for *us* today." Antoinette fluttered her wonderful lashes. "Is all right," she announced, "I'm doing." She never leaves any opening for you at the end of a sentence.

She is a magnificent cook, easily the best we ever encountered, but, because our hours interfere with the proper functioning of her own domestic establishment, she has given up cooking for us and prepares food now only for our dog, kneading raw meat and carrots with kindly red hands and adding a few drops of "colliver oily" as cautiously and precisely as a gourmet fussing over a salad dressing. There have been times when I have looked into the dog's dish with unfeigned envy, for the instant Antoinette's hand touches food, it becomes mysteriously delectable. When I think of her risotto, the tears come to my eyes.

I suppose our affection for Antoinette is temperamental: she likes the same things we do, has the same standards, reacts the same in any situation. She drinks moderately and likes to see other people drink and have a good time; consequently, when you ask her to bring you some ice, she does it with gusto and a twinkle in the eye. We usually manage to sneak her a glass of wine at night, when the other more straitlaced members of the staff aren't looking. She smokes our brand of cigarettes, and is a chain smoker. She is fond of dogs, and indeed is the only domestic of my acquaintance whose first concern, when a dog is sick on the rug, is for the dog. I can't help liking that in her, even though I often have to clean the rug myself while she is comforting the animal. If you give her an old flannel shirt to launder, she lavishes all her love and skill upon it, and it comes back to you the same size as when it went to the tub. And then, Antoinette has that great Latin quality: she is a realist. Life is life, and it's the way it is. We had a manservant one time—a middle-aged Belgian who went hog wild one morning about ten o'clock, kicked pots and pans all over the pantry, and wound up by taking off all his clothes and running naked up and down the laundry, hoping by this sudden noisy revel to engage Antoinette's fancy. Neither my wife nor I was home, and when we apologized later to Antoinette for this unexpected bit of goatishness, she chuckled reminiscently. "La, that old fellow," she snickered. "Is nothing."

This same old fellow who was nothing was my first experience with a manservant. His name was Gaston, and his career with us was brief but colorful. He was one half of a "couple," and nobody has had any experience of a domestic nature till he has employed a couple. I was against the idea, but my wife assured me that a couple would be more economical because then the man could tend the furnace. Unimpressed by this flimsy bit of logic, I went to a nursemaid then in our employ and asked her if she had ever worked in the same house with a couple. "Oh, sure, I like it," she replied. "It's fun to come down in the morning and see which one has the bruises."

I really held out for quite a while against a couple.

"But why?" asked my wife doggedly. "What earthly reason is against it?"

"Well," I said, "I'm not going to have any man pussyfooting around this house, bowing and scraping."

"What's wrong with a man?"

"Well, I don't know," I cried, "it's just sort of immoral, that's all."

"Immoral! What kind of crazy reason is that? It's no more immoral than having *you* around."

"You know what menservants do sometimes, don't you?" I asked.

"What do they do?"

"They steam open your letters. I saw one do it in the movies one time."

"Oh, my God," said my wife, and the talk ended. Gaston and Eugénie arrived the following Monday, in a cab.

They were, as I have said, Belgians. It seemed to me then, and still seems, an inspired bit of deviltry on my wife's part to engage a couple neither of whom could speak or understand English. I myself neither speak nor understand any other language. I can usually grasp Antoinette's meanings, because she puts in a liberal dash of English participles and nouns. Gaston and Eugénie spoke a mixture of French and Flemish, which gave even my bilingual wife a little trouble. In fact, until Gaston and I worked out a system of arm signals and small guttural cries, there was practically no communication between any of us in the home.

"He'll soon learn English," my wife assured me. And indeed the old fellow did make a stab at it. One evening, after a formal dinner party at which Gaston had officiated, we men stepped out into the garden for a smoke while the ladies withdrew, genteelly, to the living room upstairs. I was half through a cigarette when Gaston appeared in the garden, his bald streak shining in the moon, his gray curls festooned like tiny vines around his big, rascally ears. With his index finger pointing upward, he placed his heels neatly together, bowed, and said, *"Pardon, M'sieu. Café* oops."

"How's that, Gaston?" I said sheepishly, while my fascinated guests watched. *"Café* what?"

"Café oops, *M'sieu.* Oopstair."

"Ah, oui. Ah, oui, Gaston," I replied glibly, and led the gentlemen aloft to their coffee.

In the long roster of persons who have been attached at one period or another to our house, Gaston and Eugénie were far from being the most successful, but they were in many ways the most distinguished.

The head of the employment agency where my wife found them had been most enthusiastic—they were the "perfect servants" and had been trained in the household of a Washington diplomat, an ambassador, I believe. I think my wife was just a shade impressed by this. Anyway, she failed to foresee the unhealthy effect it would have on Gaston to go straight from serving an ambassador to serving a screwball like me. I was always rather sorry for the old boy, with his courtly manner and his bucktoothed little wife, who grinned and said yes even when she didn't understand what you said, which was always: The very first meeting between Gaston and myself was unpropitious and drab. I had a rotten cold on the Monday when he arrived, and spent the morning wrapped in an old button-up-the-front sweater in my third-floor study among some diseased house plants and empty picture frames. My wife left early in the morning, to be gone all day, and had given instructions to the breathless new couple to prepare for me, the unseen master, a lunch, explaining that I was unwell, in the chambers above, but would descend to the dining room for the noon meal.

"*M'sieu est* grippy," she said, in her best Flemish.

"*Oui, Madame,*" Gaston had replied respectfully.

At one o'clock, I heard stealthy footsteps outside the door, then a rap. "Yes?" I said. The door opened, and there he was—a faded, gray little man, beautifully if unsuitably attired in tails. There was something tragic about the appearance, in my dismal doorway on a Monday noon, of a Belgian husband in evening dress. Against the peeling plaster walls, he looked wrong, and I knew then and there that our adventure with a couple was ill-starred. His skin was a cigarette-ash gray, and his bow tie was not much less dingy. Having been instructed by my wife never to address me in French or Flemish, and being incapable of announcing lunch in any other tongue, he simply raised one arm in a long, eloquent sweep toward the stairs and the smell of meat balls, and departed.

Lunch turned out to be a considerably gayer occasion than I reckoned on. I was joined at table by my small son, Bertrand, and our Boston terrier, Palsy. The latter, far from being depressed by the sight of a tailcoat at noontide, was exhilarated. He took up a wing-back position near the woodbox and executed a brilliant series of line bucks through Gaston's skinny legs. Ordinarily, Bertrand would have welcomed a free-for-all of this sort with howls of encouragment, but to my amazement the little boy sat spellbound and quiet, his steady gaze never wavering from Gaston's contorted features, his grave demeanor in strange contrast to Palsy's clowning. There was something genuinely compelling in Gaston's hauteur, and throughout the meal Bertie spoke only in whispers. I kept blowing my nose and scolding Palsy, but there wasn't much use in it. Finally I said to Gaston, "I am sorry, Gaston, that the little dog attacks you foolishly. Soon he will get to know you."

"M'sieu?" queried Gaston, trembling with incomprehension.

"The little dog," I said, pointing. "I fear he is a great trouble to you."

Gaston considered this speech carefully, searching for meanings. Then his features composed into a hideous smile. Picking up a meat ball between thumb and forefinger, he bent stiffly from the waist and handed it to Palsy, dreaming, I do not doubt, of his life in Washington, among decent people.

When we fired Gaston and Eugénie for Gaston's vile interlude in the laundry, he put on quite a scene, at first refusing flatly to accept the dismissal. I stood by while my wife alternately discharged him in French and translated his protests to me in English. We were, he said (and his great, melodious voice dipped deep into the lower register and then swooped up again like some dark bird), making the supreme mistake of our lives, dispensing with the services of himself and his so talented wife. We countered. Liquor, we said, had unquestionably debased him. Eugénie, hearing the word "liquor," nodded violently in agreement: liquor had made Gaston gross, but we should not concern ourselves with such harmless derelictions. Gaston grew more and more surly. A discharge was out of the question, and he was willing to lay the whole unfortunate affair to our inexperience as master and mistress of a household. "He says we're inexperienced, darling," said my wife.

This, for some reason, made me mad, for I remembered Anna's gallstones and a thousand and one other nights. "By God, nobody's going to stand there and call me inexperienced!" I shouted. "You get out of here, you lecherous old scarecrow."

Half an hour later they were gone, but not before Gaston had got in the last word. He appeared on the second-floor landing with his trunk, set it down, and turned to salute us.

"S'il faut partir, il faut partir. Pfui!" And with a quick little push,

he launched the trunk into the air and watched it go roaring down to the floor below, chipping off pieces of stair as it went. Thus departed the perfect servant.

My wife is not easily discouraged, and Gaston and Eugénie were followed closely by another wedded pair, Otto and Mildred. They were young Germans, but they spoke English clearly enough—it just came natural to them. Otto was the *Turnverein* type, big, blue-eyed, vain, and strong; well-being oozed from every pore. I always felt that he should wear shorts and a small rucksack when waiting on table. He loved moving heavy objects, because it showed off his strength, and he frequently went down cellar and threw boxes and crates around for no particular reason. When my Aunt Helen, who is a fairly fleshy old lady, returned to our house to convalesce after she'd had her appendix out, the problem came of getting her upstairs. "Dot's nudding," said Otto, appraising her quickly. And before any of us could stop him, he gathered Aunt Helen in his arms, scar tissue and all, and bounded up two flights of stairs with her. "So!" he said, plopping her down on the bed.

Otto loved to be in the same room with me. When he discovered I was a writing man, he determined to be of the greatest possible assistance to me, and was always busting into my study, clad in a zipper campus jacket and bearing a greasy clipping from the *Daily Mirror*. "Here's a tchoke for you," he would announce, handing me some unattractive oddity in the news, such as a cat mothering a baby robin. I had to give up trying to work at home during the time he was with us. I used to go to the reading room of the Public Library and sit with other escapists at long oak desks.

There is something about our household which invariably makes it seem like a comedown to servants after other houses they have been in. Gaston and Eugénie were gravely disappointed that our home wasn't an embassy. Otto was crushed when he found out I didn't own two Duesenbergs. The man he worked for just before he came to us had two Duesenbergs, and Otto kept throwing them in my face. Even had I allowed Otto to drive my old Hudson sedan, which I never did, I'm sure it wouldn't have filled the void in his life. I think it was the humdrum of our home that drove him into aviation as a sideline. He managed to combine the two vocations charmingly—

waiting on table here and spending his Thursday and Sunday after-noons off at an airfield in Flushing, taking flying lessons.

I asked him if it wasn't pretty expensive. "Na," he replied. "Ten dollars an hour, dot's all." His goggles, which he showed me one day, cost $27.50.

He progressed rapidly in the air. When he got so he could solo, he used to fly across the river and circle above our house, banking sharply at the prescribed altitude and showing off as much as he could without violating the Bureau of Air Commerce regulations. It was a perfect outlet for his Aryan spirits, but it was just one more straw for my tired old back. I got damned sick of hearing the drone of my em-ployee's plane over my rooftop, and I never got quite used to having my Friday-morning coffee poured by a man lately down from the skies. I felt earthbound, insignificant, and stuffy; and I began to compensate for this, unconsciously, in my attitude toward Otto.

"Well," I would say sourly, "I see you didn't break your neck yesterday." Otto would laugh—a loud, bold laugh.

"Na, I'm too schmart."

He *was* too smart, too. He left our household not as the result of any aerial mishap but because he couldn't get on with Bertrand's nurse, Katie, a pretty little Irish girl who called him Tarzan behind his back and was no more impressed by his gorgeous torso than I was.

I guess Otto's most notable quality was his readiness to answer all questions, at table. We first noticed this in him the day Aunt Helen went to the hospital for her appendectomy, which was very soon after Otto's arrival.

"I wish I knew how much the operation is going to cost," I re-marked to my wife at dinner.

"Fifty dollars," replied Otto, coming up on my left with a dish of broccoli.

I was delighted at this sign of alertness in him and soon discovered that his store of information covered every subject. If a guest, for example, filled in a dull pause at dinner by remarking that she had found a terribly nice little flower shop but she couldn't remember whether it was on Fifty-first Street or Fifty-second Street, Otto would pipe up, "Fifty-first." If you speculated as to what theatre a certain show was playing in, Otto would announce, "Broadhurst."

I never knew him to be right about anything, but he was an

enormous comfort just the same. There are lots of times when you like to get a quick answer, even though it means nothing.

Another thing I rather enjoyed about Otto was his identification with the world of crime. Otto hadn't been with us three days when a jeweller's wife was murdered in a small suburban apartment building by a lover in a state of pique.

"It's funny how dot feller got in her hallway," said Otto, taking a quick glance over my shoulder at the newspaper.

"What's so funny about it?" I replied. "He got in by pushing some-body else's bell and walking in when they clicked."

"Dot's what *you* think," said Otto. "But dot building ain't dot way. You godda be let in."

"How do you know so much about it?"

"I worked there."

It soon became clear that Otto had worked not only at the scene of that crime but at the scene of all crimes. While police wallowed in the darkness of an unsolved mystery, Otto and I walked in the light of exact knowledge. I consulted him whenever I was in doubt about any point, and always got a direct, clear answer.

Smoke dreams! How charmingly these dear people drift before me as I sit here with my pipe and my memories! I think back to the soft spring evening, ten years ago, when I was in the dining room lingering over coffee. The door opened and a young peasant woman entered, carrying a dustpan full of horse manure. It was some which she had discovered in front of the house, following the fitful passage through our street of a Borden's delivery wagon. The young woman, surprised to find me still in the dining room, blushed prettily, then carried her treasure out into the back garden and spread it tenderly on the exhausted little plot of soil which supported our privet bush.

The smoke curls in wreaths around my head. I see the thin, com-petent form of Mrs. Farrell, whom Antoinette always called Farola and who in turn called me Dearie. I think of Minnie, the Bahai, whose piety allowed her to partake of food only before sunrise and after sundown, and whose abstinence so weakened her that she used to run the egg-beater in the kitchen to drown out the noise of her lamentation. And of Mrs. Farnsworth, the aged eccentric, whom, in the course of a five-hundred-mile motor journey, I regaled with a dollar-and-a-quarter chicken dinner only to see her sweep the entire contents of her plate off into her purse, to take to the little dog that was the delight of her life.

I count them over, one by one. Today, however, I feel a great lethargy creep over me. Sometimes I wish I could relive all those strange and golden times; but there are other moments, when the radio is particularly loud in Francine's room and the *Meisterschmerz* is strong upon me, when I know that all I want is peace.

Wolcott Gibbs

RING OUT, WILD BELLS

When I finally got around to seeing Max Reinhardt's cinema version of "A Midsummer-Night's Dream," and saw a child called Mickey Rooney playing Puck, I remembered suddenly that long ago I had taken the same part.

Our production was given on the open-air stage at the Riverdale Country School, shortly before the war. The scenery was only the natural scenery of that suburban dell, and the cast was exclusively male, ranging in age from eleven to perhaps seventeen. While we had thus preserved the pure, Elizabethan note of the original, it must be admitted that our version had its drawbacks. The costumes were probably the worst things we had to bear, and even Penrod, tragically arrayed as Launcelot in his sister's stockings and his father's drawers, might have been embarrassed for us. Like Penrod, we were costumed by our parents, and like the Schofields, they seemed on the whole a little weak historically. Half of the ladies were inclined to favor the Elizabethan, and they had constructed rather bunchy ruffs and farthingales for their offspring; others, who had read as far as the stage directions and learned that the action took place in an Athenian wood, had produced something vaguely Athenian, usually beginning with a sheet. Only the fairies had a certain uniformity. For some reason their parents had all decided on cheesecloth, with here and there a little ill-advised trimming with tinsel.

My own costume was mysterious, but spectacular. As nearly as I have ever been able to figure things out, my mother found her inspiration for it in a Maxfield Parrish picture of a court jester. Beginning at the top, there was a cap with three stuffed horns; then, for the main part, a pair of tights that covered me to my wrists and ankles; and finally slippers with stuffed toes that curled up at the ends. The whole thing was made out of silk in alternate green and red stripes, and (unquestionably my poor mother's most demented stroke) it was covered from head to foot with a thousand tiny bells. Because all our costumes were obviously perishable, we never wore them in rehearsal, and naturally nobody knew that I was invested with these peculiar sound effects until I made my entrance at the beginning of the second act.

Our director was a man who had strong opinions about how Shakespeare should be played, and Puck was one of his favorite characters. It was his theory that Puck, being "the incarnation of mischief," never ought to be still a minute, so I had been coached to bound onto the stage, and once there to dance up and down, cocking my head and waving my arms.

"I want you to be a little whirlwind," this man said.

Even as I prepared to bound onto the stage, I had my own misgivings about those dangerously abundant gestures, and their probable effect on my bells. It was too late, however, to invent another technique for playing Puck, even if there had been room for anything but horror in my mind. I bounded onto the stage.

The effect, in its way, must have been superb. With every leap I rang like a thousand children's sleighs, my melodies foretelling God knows what worlds of merriment to the enchanted spectators. It was even worse when I came to the middle of the stage and went into my gestures. The other ringing had been loud but sporadic. This was persistent, varying only slightly in volume and pitch with the vehemence of my gestures. To a blind man, it must have sounded as though I had recklessly decided to accompany myself on a xylophone. A maturer actor would probably have made up his mind that an emergency existed, and abandoned his gestures as impracticable under the circumstances. I was thirteen, and incapable of innovations. I had been told by responsible authorities that gestures went with this part, and I continued to make them. I also continued to ring—a silvery music, festive and horrible.

If the bells were hard on my nerves, they were even worse for the rest of the cast, who were totally unprepared for my new interpretation. Puck's first remark is addressed to one of the fairies, and it is mercifully brief.

I said, "How now, spirit! Whither wander you?"

This unhappy child, already embarrassed by a public appearance in cheesecloth and tinsel, was also burdened with an opening speech of sixteen lines in verse. He began bravely:

"Over hill, over dale,
   Thorough bush, thorough brier,
Over park, over pale,
   Through flood, through fire..."

At the word "fire," my instructions were to bring my hands up from the ground in a long, wavery sweep, intended to represent fire. The bells pealed. To my startled ears, it sounded more as if they exploded. The fairy stopped in his lines and looked at me sharply. The jingling, however, had diminished; it was no more than as if a faint wind stirred my bells, and he went on:

"I do wander every where,
   Swifter than the moone's sphere..."

Here again I had another cue, for a sort of swoop and dip indicating the swiftness of the moone's sphere. Again the bells rang out, and again the performance stopped in its tracks. The fairy was clearly troubled by these interruptions. He had, however, a child's strange acceptance of the inscrutable, and was even able to regard my bells as a last-minute adult addition to the program, nerve-racking but not to be questioned. I'm sure it was only this that got him through that first speech.

My turn, when it came, was even worse. By this time the audience had succumbed to a helpless gaiety. Every time my bells rang, laughter swept the spectators, and this mounted and mingled with the bells until everything else was practically inaudible. I began my speech, another long one, and full of incomprehensible references to Titania's changeling.

"Louder!" said somebody in the wings. "You'll have to talk louder." It was the director, and he seemed to be in a dangerous state.

"And for heaven's sake, stop that jingling!" he said.

I talked louder, and I tried to stop the jingling, but it was no use. By the time I got to the end of my speech, I was shouting and so was the audience. It appeared that I had very little control over the bells, which continued to jingle in spite of my passionate efforts to keep them quiet.

All this had a very bad effect on the fairy, who by this time had many symptoms of a complete nervous collapse. However, he began his next speech:

"Either I mistake your shape and making quite,
    Or else you are that shrewd and knavish sprite
    Call'd Robin Goodfellow: are you not he
    That..."

At this point I forgot that the rules had been changed and I was supposed to leave out the gestures. There was a furious jingling, and the fairy gulped.

"Are you not he that, that..."

He looked miserably at the wings, and the director supplied the next line, but the tumult was too much for him. The unhappy child simply shook his head.

"Say anything!" shouted the director desperately. "Anything at all!"

The fairy only shut his eyes and shuddered.

"All right!" shouted the director. "All right, Puck. *You* begin *your* next speech."

By some miracle, I actually did remember my next lines, and had opened my mouth to begin on them when suddenly the fairy spoke. His voice was a high, thin monotone, and there seemed to be madness in it, but it was perfectly clear.

"Fourscore and seven years ago," he began, "our fathers brought forth on this continent a new nation, conceived..."

He said it right through to the end, and it was certainly the most successful speech ever made on that stage, and probably one of the most successful speeches ever made on any stage. I don't remember, if I ever knew, how the rest of us ever picked up the dull, normal thread of the play after that extraordinary performance, but we must have, because I know it went on. I only remember that in the next intermission the director cut off my bells with his penknife, and after that things quieted down and got dull.

H. L. Mencken

BRIEF GUST OF GLORY

When I was a boy in the Aurignacian Epoch of Baltimore, the favorite bivouac and chapel-of-ease of all healthy males of tender years was the neighborhood livery stable. I have since learned, by a reading in the social sciences, that the American livery-stables of that era were seminaries of iniquity, with a curriculum embracing cursing and swearing, gambling, cigarette-smoking, tobacco-chewing, the classical or Abraham Lincoln répertoire of lewd anecdotes, the design and execution of dirty pictures, and even the elements of seduction, burglary, and delirium tremens. It may have been true, for all I know, in the pathological small towns that all social scientists appear to hail from, but certainly it was not true in West Baltimore, a sedate and sequestered section of a great American seaport. I was a regular student at Reveille's stable in Stricker Street from the beginning of my seventh year to the end of my nonage, and a special student at Coblens's stable in Paca Street, off and on, for most of the same period, but so far as I can recall I never heard a word uttered in either of them, or beheld any human act, transaction, or phenomenon, that might not have been repeated before a bench of archbishops.

On the contrary, they were both schools of decorum, operated by proud and even haughty men, and staffed by blackamoors of a generally high tone. No palpably dipsomaniacal or larcenous coon could survive more than a few days in any such establishment. There were too many valuable horses and rigs on hand to be trusted to the former, and too many valuable carriage robes, buggy whips, hassocks, etc., to be exposed to the latter. My father's No. 1 whip, hung up by the snapper in Mr. Reveille's office, had a gold band around the handle engraved with the insigne of the Ancient Arabic Order of Nobles of the Mystic Shrine, and in Mr. Coblens's office, where my father commonly kept his No. 2 whip, there was also a buffalo robe that he set great store by, although I should add that its hair had pretty well played out, and that after his death I gave it freely to the poor.

Mr. Coblens was a man of erect bearing, reserved manner, and great dignity. He wore none of the loud checks associated with his vocation, but was always clad in plain colors, and not infrequently appeared in a black cutaway. His only concession to the public expectation was a gray derby, very high in the crown. If you can imagine a Jewish colonel of a swagger cavalry regiment, then you have got him to the life. My father had a high regard for him, and often paused to discuss horses with him—a subject about which he knew everything and my father next to nothing. Mr. Coblens seldom descended from his heights to speak to my brother or me. He knew us very well and would indicate by a vague flicker of his eyes that he was aware of our presence, but it was not often that he said anything.

His cousin Felix was a far more cordial fellow. Felix was a bachelor in those days, and apparently a somewhat gay one, for more than once I saw him set out of an afternoon in a buggy shining like a hundred-dollar coffin, with sometimes a blonde lady beside him and sometimes a brunette. My brother and I, boylike, regarded his ease and success at gallantry with great respect. He was, indeed, one of our heroes, and also one of our friends. He was never too busy to explain to us, with the use of living models paraded by his blackamoors, the points of a harness horse, and he also had illuminating ideas about buggy architecture. When I was eight years old and my brother six, my father gave us a pony named Frank, and it was Mr. Felix who taught us how to handle it—no mean art, I assure you, for Shetland ponies not only kick like mules but also bite like dogs, and no doubt would scratch like cats if they had claws. To this day I have a scar on my bosom, often passing for a war wound, that proves how effectively Frank could use his teeth.

In 1890 or thereabout my father traded two cases of leaf tobacco and a Swiss repeater watch for a gelding bearing the strange name (for a horse) of John. John was a trotter, and supposedly of some speed in harness, but my father could never get it out of him. The two did so badly together, indeed, that my father concluded that John must have rheumatism, and thereafter, for a year or so, the poor beast was the patient of a veterinarian who sent in large bottles of a fiery, suffocating liniment and even larger bills, but never did John any good. Mr. Felix, it appeared, had suspected all the while that the trouble was predominantly in the driver rather than in the horse, and eventually he volunteered to go out with my father some afternoon and make a scientific review of his driving. He returned downcast. "Your pa," he said to me the next time I dropped in, "is hopeless. It would take him two or three hundred years to learn to drive a cart horse, let alone a trotter. He holds the lines like a man dealing cards. If he ever got John to really stepping, he would fall out of the buggy and break his neck."

A few days later, as if reminded by conscience that he might have been hasty in dismissing his duty to the family, he amazed and delighted me by offering to give *me* a few lessons. It was a colossal opportunity to a boy of eleven, for Mr. Felix was an eminent figure in the trotting world of Baltimore and seldom condescended to pedagogy. I had, as I recall it, only four or five lessons, but when they were over, Mr. Felix was so complimentary that I developed on the spot a complacency which still survives after nearly fifty years, protecting me like an undershirt of concrete from the contumely of mankind. Indeed, he said flatly, and I believe he meant it, that I had in me the makings of a really smart harness driver. "By the time you begin to shave," he concluded, "you'll be showing 'em."

By that time, alas, I had turned from equestrology to chemistry, and a little while later I abandoned chemistry (to my sneaking regret on many a rainy day) for the kind of beautiful letters on tap in newspaper offices. But for two or three years I drove John every day, and so gradually improved and mellowed my technique. On summer afternoons, when my father and I were driving home to the country, and the clomp-clomp of a trotter's scissoring hooves began to sound behind us on the Pimlico Road, he would silently hand me the reins and settle back to be torn between parental pride and personal humiliation. I seemed to hear him groan now and then, but he never said anything. When John, who was really very fast, had left the other nag behind, and the brush was over, my father would quietly revive his cigar with a few sad puffs and resume the reins. He never complimented me: it would have been ruinous to his dignity as a harness driver. Despite the unction to my vanity that flowed out of these episodes, there was also melancholy in them, and they implanted in me a lifelong conviction that children, taking one day with another, must be damned pests.

It was not the Coblens stable, however, but the Reveille stable that was my chief haunt in boyhood. The Coblens stable was downtown near my father's place of business; the Reveille stable was only two blocks from our home on Hollins Street. My brother and I spent many happy hours there, watching the blackamoors currying and feeding the horses, plaiting their tails, excavating and blacking their hooves, dosing them with Glauber's salts and condition powders, and treating their lampas (pronounced "lampers") with red-hot pokers. This last was a horrifying spectacle, for lampas is an overgrowth of tissue behind the upper incisor teeth, and burning it out involved thrusting the poker into the poor horse's gaping mouth. But I learned before long that horses have very little sense of pain, if indeed any at all; and years afterward I saw one, with a leg cut off by a trolley car, munching the grass between the cobblestones as it lay on a Baltimore street, waiting for a cop to shoot it.

Mr. Reveille was a Frenchman who seemed venerable and even ancient to my brother and me, for he wore a straggling beard and always had on a black coat. He had two grown sons, both stout and hearty fellows, but, like their father, very dignified. There was a period when both the trotter John and our pony Frank were quartered in the Reveille stable, along with two buggies, a pony cart, and several other rigs, so my brother and I had plenty of excuse for hanging about. The Reveilles always welcomed us gravely, and let us warm up, in winter, in their tiny office, which was so filled with robes that there was scarcely room for the stove, always verging on white-hot. We admired especially the rack of whips, which included some virtuoso pieces by the Baltimore master craftsmen of the time. A good whip might cost as much as $25. We figured that the whole lot must be worth at least $1,000, and toyed for a while with a plan to break in some dark night, smouch them all, sell them to the cattle-herders at the Calverton stockyards, and go West with the proceeds to fight the Indians. What the herders would do with puny buggy whips we never paused to figure out. In the end, we abandoned the scheme as probably unlawful.

The colored brethren who pontificated at Reveille's have all faded, with the flight of the years, into a brown smudge—all, that is, save Old Jim. Jim was the carriage-washer, and a fellow of vast size and unparalleled amiability. He was coal-black and built like a battleship, and when he got into his hip-high rubber boots and put on his long rubber apron he had the imposing presence of an emperor in Hell. Jim's atelier was a skylighted space at the rear of the carriage house, paved with cobblestones and always flowing with water. He got to work at six in the morning, and was sometimes still going hard at nine at night. He had the care of fifty or more buggies, and of perhaps as many other vehicles, and he kept them clean and shining. His hardest time came on Sunday morning, when he had to wash and polish all the buggies in preparation for the pleasure jaunts of the afternoon. For this business he brought out his newest sponges and cleanest chamois skins. Also, he put on a black derby, never worn on weekdays.

In the intervals of his washing and polishing, Jim took out rigs to the homes of clients of the stable, and thereby sometimes acquired quiet brannigans, for it was the custom to reward him not with money but with drinks. My father kept a special jug for the purpose. It was shared by the iceman, but Jim got most of it, for in view of his great bulk he was given a much larger drink than the iceman. He always downed it at a gulp, and after it was down he would blink his eyes, rub his belly, and say "Ah-h-h-h-h!" This ritual was a Baltimore custom of the time, practiced by most of the nobility and gentry and imitated by serving folk. Sometimes Jim also got a cigar. He would light it at once and stalk back to Reveille's smoking it at an angle of forty-five degrees. Smoking was forbidden to the faculty at the stable and when he reached there he would choke it carefully and deposit it on a high ledge in the brick wall. Some of its other members had sharp eyes for likely stumps and the cigar was out of their reach there, but not out of his.

My brother and I greatly admired Jim, and delighted in watching him at work. He had a way of spinning buggy wheels that was really magnificent, and he worked with larger sponges and broader chamois skins than any other carriage-washer in West Baltimore. The buggies of those days all had carpets, and when there was nothing else to do he would get out a dozen or so of them and beat them. Sometimes he would find a nickel or a dime under one of them. It always went into his pocket, for it was the theory among the colored proletariat of Baltimore in those days that whatever a white person lost or mislaid he really didn't want. If he wanted it, he would ask for it, and probably raise hell about it. Jim's income from this source was not large, for he found a great many more pins than nickels. He always laid them aside and then threw them into the manure pit, for a pin in the frog of a horse's hoof might bring on calamity.

One day my brother and I were astonished to find Jim missing; it seemed almost as strange as finding Mr. Reveille missing, or the stable itself. His *locum tenens,* a short, spotty colored man named Browny, ordinarily a hostler, told us the sad news. Jim's youngest son, a youth of sixteen, had been blown up by an explosion in a one-horse soda-pop factory up a nearby alley, and Jim was off for the day, arranging for the interment of the few fragments that had been recovered. We had never heard of this son, but we were full of sympathy, and when Jim returned we tried to tell him so in the shy manner of boys. He replied that it was God's deliberate act and will, and that he did not repine. The son, he added judicially, was not really bad, at least as sons went in an age of moral chaos, but nevertheless there was some worry in him, for now and then, like any other high-spirited colored boy, he got into trouble with the cops, and when that wasn't going on he wasted his substance on trashy yallah gals. Now he was far, far away, riding some cloud or rainbow, and hence safe from the hangman forever. He had even escaped, by the unusual manner of his death, the body-snatchers.

Two or three days later we saw a brisk-looking white man in a short yellow overcoat talking to Jim, and the day following, Jim again disappeared. We heard from Browny that the brisk-looking man was a lawyer and that the talk had been of damages. Another talk, he said, was proceeding downtown. Jim was gone a week, and then suddenly reappeared, but not to resume work. He showed up one morning in a stovepipe hat and a long-tailed black coat, carrying an ebony cane with a bone head in the shape of a horse with widely distended nostrils tinted red, and green gems for eyes. His right-hand coat pocket was bulging with at least a quarter's worth of peanuts, and he invited all his old colleagues to thrust in their paws and help themselves. In his other coat pocket he had half a dozen apples for horses he especially liked, including our pony Frank but not the trotter John, and in the hand unburdened by the cane he carried a two-pound bag of lump sugar. In all four pockets of his white waistcoat were rows of five-cent cigars, standing up like cartridges in a belt. He offered the cigars freely and recommended them as the best in West Baltimore.

He even offered one to Mr. Peter Reveille. His hip pockets were stuffed with chewing tobacco.

Such was Jim in the full tide of his bereavement. Mr. Peter Reveille told us that the lawyer had offered Jim $250, but that he had stuck out for $300, and got it. He let it be known that he had demanded the money in one-dollar bills, but where he kept them we didn't know until later. Some of the hostlers were of the opinion that he had sneaked into the stable loft by night and hidden them in the hay, and for a week or so a vain search for them went on. Browny insisted that they were in Jim's stovepipe hat. He knew, as all of us knew, that policemen always kept their valuables in their helmets; ergo, why not Jim? But this theory blew up when Jim dropped in, a week or so later, without his hat and complaining that two bad niggers from Boot Alley had knocked it off with clubs and run away with it. The hat was gone, but Jim continued in funds for a long while afterward—indeed, for fully a month. He visited the stable almost daily, and never failed to distribute cigars, peanuts, and chewing tobacco, with sugar and apples for the horses. He appeared, at different times, in no less than five hats, and was often mildly in liquor. But he never brought any liquor on the premises, and so the Reveilles, who had a large experience with the darker races, tolerated him patiently.

They knew that he would be back in his long boots and rubber apron soon or late, and he was. One morning early they found him at work, somewhat trembly and with a cut over his left eye, but otherwise as he had been in the days before wealth corrupted him. He had not been seen during the preceding week, and for a while his final adventures were unknown, for neither then nor thereafter did he ever mention them. But the other colored men gradually assembled and disgorged the story, and the cop on the beat helped out with a fact or two. It was really very simple. Jim, a decent widower, had been ganged and undone by the massed yallah gals of three alleys. They had all tackled him singly and failed, but when they tackled him in a body he succumbed.

The ensuing party raged for four days and four nights, with continuous music by banjos, mouth organs, and bones. It began in a little saloon that was the G.H.Q. of one of the alleys, but gradually spread over the whole block, and ended at last in a loft over an empty stable. There was no hint whatever of carnality; the thing was purely alcoholic. After the first few hours each of the yallah gals sent for her regular fellow, and beginning with the second day, all sorts of gate-crashers barged in. Thereafter there was a flow in and a flow out. Every hour or two some guest would collapse and roll home, and another would make the gate. Only Jim himself and a yallah gal named Mildred survived for more than forty-eight hours. Mildred, on the last day, was in the first stages of *mania à potu,* and the cop on the beat, looking in, ordered her off the job, but Jim was still going strong.

Alas, he didn't go long, for a little while later the saloonkeeper's son Otto came in to say that time was called on the party. Otto and his brother Hermann had been hauling booze for it for four days and four nights, and both were badly used up. Hermann, in fact, had had to be put to bed. But it wasn't fatigue that made Otto call time; it was the fact that Jim's last dollar bill had been devoured. The father of Otto and Hermann was known to be a determined man, with the cops always on his side, so no one questioned the fiat. One by one, they simply faded away, leaving only Jim. He rolled himself in his long-tailed coat and lay down to a prodigal's dreams. He slept all the rest of that day and all of the ensuing night to 5 A.M. Then he shuffled off to Reveille's stable and resumed his station in life.

It was not until long afterward that my brother and I learned where Jim had kept his fortune while it oozed away. Mr. Reveille, worming the story out of the blackamoors, told my father, who told it to a neighbor, Mr. Glaser, whose boy Harold, lurking about, overheard the telling and brought it to us. The money had been in the care and custody of the saloonkeeper all the while. He doled it out to Jim dollar by dollar, marking the score on a blackboard behind his bar. He charged Jim a dollar a day "interest" for keeping it. When the final orgies began, he charged a dollar for every day and a dollar for every night.

The Glaser boy reported that, in telling about this "interest," my father swore in a hair-raising manner. He had, in fact, little use for saloonkeepers. He would often say that while he knew and respected some upright men among them, only too many were disgraces to a humane and even noble profession.

William Saroyan

THE SUMMER OF THE BEAUTIFUL
WHITE HORSE

One day back there in the good old days when I was nine and the
world was full of every imaginable kind of magnificence, and life was
still a delightful and mysterious dream, my cousin Mourad, who was
considered crazy by everybody who knew him except me, came to my
house at four in the morning and woke me up by tapping on the
window of my room.

Aram, he said.

I jumped out of bed and looked out the window.

I couldn't believe what I saw.

It wasn't morning yet, but it was summer and with daybreak not
many minutes around the corner of the world it was light enough for
me to know I wasn't dreaming.

My cousin Mourad was sitting on a beautiful white horse.

I stuck my head out of the window and rubbed my eyes.

Yes, he said in Armenian. It's a horse. You're not dreaming. Make
it quick if you want to ride.

I knew my cousin Mourad enjoyed being alive more than anybody
else who had ever fallen into the world by mistake, but this was more
than even I could believe.

In the first place, my earliest memories had been memories of
horses and my first longings had been longings to ride.

This was the wonderful part.

In the second place, we were poor.

This was the part that wouldn't permit me to believe what I saw.

We were poor. We had no money. Our whole tribe was poverty-
stricken. Every branch of the Garoghlanian family was living in the
most amazing and comical poverty in the world. Nobody could understand where we ever got money enough to keep us with food in our
bellies, not even the old men of the family. Most important of all,

though, we were famous for our honesty. We had been famous for our honesty for something like eleven centuries, even when we had been the wealthiest family in what we liked to think was the world. We were proud first, honest next, and after that we believed in right and wrong. None of us would take advantage of anybody in the world, let alone steal.

Consequently, even though I could *see* the horse, so magnificent; even though I could *smell* it, so lovely; even though I could *hear* it breathing, so exciting; I couldn't *believe* the horse had anything to do with my cousin Mourad or with me or with any of the other members of our family, asleep or awake, because I *knew* my cousin Mourad couldn't have *bought* the horse, and if he couldn't have bought it he must have *stolen* it, and I refused to believe he had stolen it.

No member of the Garoghlanian family could be a thief.

I stared first at my cousin and then at the horse. There was a pious stillness and humor in each of them which on the one hand delighted me and on the other frightened me.

Mourad, I said, where did you steal this horse?

Leap out of the window, he said, if you want to ride.

It was true, then. He *had* stolen the horse. There was no question about it. He had come to invite me to ride or not, as I chose.

Well, it seemed to me stealing a horse for a ride was not the same thing as stealing something else, such as money. For all I knew, maybe it wasn't stealing at all. If you were crazy about horses the way my cousin Mourad and I were, it wasn't stealing. It wouldn't become stealing until we offered to sell the horse, which of course I knew we would never do.

Let me put on some clothes, I said.

All right, he said, but hurry.

I leaped into my clothes.

I jumped down to the yard from the window and leaped up onto the horse behind my cousin Mourad.

That year we lived at the edge of town, on Walnut Avenue. Behind our house was the country: vineyards, orchards, irrigation ditches, and country roads. In less than three minutes we were on Olive Avenue, and then the horse began to trot. The air was new and lovely to breathe. The feel of the horse running was wonderful. My cousin Mourad who was considered one of the craziest members of our family began to sing. I mean, he began to roar.

Every family has a crazy streak in it somewhere, and my cousin Mourad was considered the natural descendant of the crazy streak in our tribe. Before him was our uncle Khosrove, an enormous man with a powerful head of black hair and the largest mustache in the San Joaquin Valley, a man so furious in temper, so irritable, so impatient that he stopped anyone from talking by roaring, *It is no harm; pay no attention to it.*

That was all, no matter what anybody happened to be talking about. Once it was his own son Arak running eight blocks to the barber shop where his father was having his mustache trimmed to tell him their house was on fire. This man Khosrove sat up in the chair and roared, It is no harm; pay no attention to it. The barber said, But the boy says your house is on fire. So Khosrove roared, Enough, it is no harm, I say.

My cousin Mourad was considered the natural descendant of this man, although Mourad's father was Zorab, who was practical and nothing else. That's how it was in our tribe. A man could be the father of his son's flesh, but that did not mean that he was also the father of his spirit. The distribution of the various kinds of spirit of our tribe had been from the beginning capricious and vagrant.

We rode and my cousin Mourad sang. For all anybody knew we were still in the old country where, at least according to some of our neighbors, we belonged. We let the horse run as long as it felt like running.

At last my cousin Mourad said, Get down. I want to ride alone.

Will you let me ride alone? I said.

That is up to the horse, my cousin said. Get down.

The *horse* will let me ride, I said.

We shall see, he said. Don't forget that I have a way with a horse.

Well, I said, any way you have with a horse, I have also.

For the sake of your safety, he said, let us hope so. Get down.

All right, I said, but remember you've got to let me try to ride alone.

I got down and my cousin Mourad kicked his heels into the horse and shouted, *Vazire,* run. The horse stood on its hind legs, snorted, and burst into a fury of speed that was the loveliest thing I had ever seen. My cousin Mourad raced the horse across a field of dry grass to an irrigation ditch, crossed the ditch on the horse, and five minutes later returned, dripping wet.

The sun was coming up.

Now it's my turn to ride, I said.

My cousin Mourad got off the horse.

Ride, he said.

I leaped to the back of the horse and for a moment knew the awfulest fear imaginable. The horse did not move.

Kick into his muscles, my cousin Mourad said. What are you waiting for? We've got to take him back before everybody in the world is up and about.

I kicked into the muscles of the horse. Once again it reared and snorted. Then it began to run. I didn't know what to do. Instead of running across the field to the irrigation ditch the horse ran down the road to the vineyard of Dikran Halabian where it began to leap over vines. The horse leaped over seven vines before I fell. Then it continued running.

My cousin Mourad came running down the road.

I'm not worried about you, he shouted. We've got to get that horse. You go this way and I'll go this way. If you come upon him, be kindly. I'll be near.

I continued down the road and my cousin Mourad went across the field toward the irrigation ditch.

It took him half an hour to find the horse and bring him back.

All right, he said, jump on. The whole world is awake now.

What will we do? I said.

Well, he said, we'll either take him back or hide him until tomorrow morning.

He didn't sound worried and I knew he'd hide him and not take him back. Not for a while, at any rate.

Where will we hide him? I said.

I know a place, he said.

How long ago did you steal this horse? I said.

It suddenly dawned on me that he had been taking these early morning rides for some time and had come for me this morning only because he knew how much I longed to ride.

Who said anything about stealing a horse? he said.

Anyhow, I said, how long ago did you begin riding every morning?

Not until this morning, he said.

Are you telling the truth? I said.

Of course not, he said, but if we are found out, that's what you're to say. I don't want both of us to be liars. All you know is that we started riding this morning.

All right, I said.

He walked the horse quietly to the barn of a deserted vineyard which at one time had been the pride of a farmer named Fetvajian. There were some oats and dry alfalfa in the barn.

We began walking home.

It wasn't easy, he said, to get the horse to behave so nicely. At first it wanted to run wild, but, as I've told you, I have a way with a horse. I can get it to want to do anything *I* want it to do. Horses understand me.

How do you do it? I said.

I have an understanding with a horse, he said.

Yes, but what sort of an understanding? I said.

A simple and honest one, he said.

Well, I said, I wish I knew how to reach an understanding like that with a horse.

You're still a small boy, he said. When you get to be thirteen you'll know how to do it.

I went home and ate a hearty breakfast.

That afternoon my uncle Khosrove came to our house for coffee and cigarettes. He sat in the parlor, sipping and smoking and remembering the old country. Then another visitor arrived, a farmer named John Byro, an Assyrian who, out of loneliness, had learned to speak Armenian. My mother brought the lonely visitor coffee and tobacco and he rolled a cigarette and sipped and smoked, and then at last, sighing sadly, he said, My white horse which was stolen last month is still gone. I cannot understand it.

My uncle Khosrove became very irritated and shouted, It's no harm. What is the loss of a horse? Haven't we all lost the homeland? What is this crying over a horse?

That may be all right for you, a city dweller, to say, John Byro said, but what of my surrey? What good is a surrey without a horse?

Pay no attention to it, my uncle Khosrove roared.

I walked ten miles to get here, John Byro said.

You have legs, my uncle Khosrove shouted.

My left leg pains me, the farmer said.

Pay no attention to it, my uncle Khosrove roared.

That horse cost me sixty dollars, the farmer said.

I spit on money, my uncle Khosrove said.

He got up and stalked out of the house, slamming the screen door.
My mother explained.

He has a gentle heart, she said. It is simply that he is homesick
and such a large man.

The farmer went away and I ran over to my cousin Mourad's house.

He was sitting under a peach tree, trying to repair the hurt wing
of a young robin which could not fly. He was talking to the bird.

What is it? he said.

The farmer, John Byro, I said. He visited our house. He wants his
horse. You've had it a month. I want you to promise not to take it
back until I learn to ride.

It will take you *a year* to learn to ride, my cousin Mourad said.

We could keep the horse a year, I said.

My cousin Mourad leaped to his feet.

What? he roared. Are you inviting a member of the Garoghlanian
family to steal? The horse must go back to its true owner.

When? I said.

In six months at the latest, he said.

He threw the bird into the air. The bird tried hard, almost fell
twice, but at last flew away, high and straight.

Early every morning for two weeks my cousin Mourad and I took
the horse out of the barn of the deserted vineyard where we were
hiding it and rode it, and every morning the horse, when it was my
turn to ride alone, leaped over grape vines and small trees and threw
me and ran away. Nevertheless, I hoped in time to learn to ride the
way my cousin Mourad rode.

One morning on the way to Fetvajian's deserted vineyard we ran
into the farmer John Byro who was on his way to town.

Let me do the talking, my cousin Mourad said. I have a way with
farmers.

Good morning, John Byro, my cousin Mourad said to the farmer.

The farmer studied the horse eagerly.

Good morning, sons of my friends, he said. What is the name of
your horse?

My Heart, my cousin Mourad said in Armenian.

A lovely name, John Byro said, for a lovely horse. I could swear
it is the horse that was stolen from me many weeks ago. May I look
into its mouth?

Of course, Mourad said.

The farmer looked into the mouth of the horse.

Tooth for tooth, he said. I would swear it *is* my horse if I didn't know your parents. The fame of your family for honesty is well known to me. Yet the horse is the twin of my horse. A suspicious man would believe his eyes instead of his heart. Good day, my young friends.

Good day, John Byro, my cousin Mourad said.

Early the following morning we took the horse to John Byro's vine-yard and put it in the barn. The dogs followed us around without making a sound.

The dogs, I whispered to my cousin Mourad. I thought they would bark.

They would at somebody else, he said. I have a way with dogs.

My cousin Mourad put his arms around the horse, pressed his nose into the horse's nose, patted it, and then we went away.

That afternoon John Byro came to our house in his surrey and showed my mother the horse that had been stolen and returned.

I do not know what to think, he said. The horse is stronger than ever. Better-tempered, too. I thank God.

My uncle Khosrove, who was in the parlor, became irritated and shouted, Quiet, man, quiet. Your horse has been returned. Pay no attention to it.

James Thurber

THE NIGHT THE BED FELL

I suppose that the high-water mark of my youth in Columbus, Ohio, was the night the bed fell on my father. It makes a better recitation (unless, as some friends of mine have said, one has heard it five or six times) than it does a piece of writing, for it is almost necessary to throw furniture around, shake doors, and bark like a dog, to lend the proper atmosphere and verisimilitude to what is admittedly a somewhat incredible tale. Still, it did take place.

It happened, then, that my father had decided to sleep in the attic one night, to be away where he could think. My mother opposed the notion strongly because, she said, the old wooden bed up there was unsafe: it was wobbly and the heavy headboard would crash down on father's head in case the bed fell, and kill him. There was no dissuading him, however, and at a quarter past ten he closed the attic door behind him and went up the narrow twisting stairs. We later heard ominous creakings as he crawled into bed. Grandfather, who usually slept in the attic bed when he was with us, had disappeared some days before. (On these occasions he was usually gone six or eight days and returned growling and out of temper, with the news that the federal Union was run by a passel of blockheads and that the Army of the Potomac didn't have any more chance than a fiddler's bitch.)

We had visiting us at this time a nervous first cousin of mine named Briggs Beall, who believed that he was likely to cease breathing when he was asleep. It was his feeling that if he were not awakened every hour during the night, he might die of suffocation. He had been accustomed to setting an alarm clock to ring at intervals until morning, but I persuaded him to abandon this. He slept in my room and I told him that I was such a light sleeper that if anybody quit breathing in the same room with me, I would wake instantly. He tested me the first night—which I had suspected he would—by holding his breath after my regular breathing had convinced him I was asleep. I was not asleep, however, and called to him. This seemed to allay his fears a little, but he took the precaution of putting a glass of spirits of camphor on a little table at the head of his bed. In case I didn't arouse him until he was almost gone, he said, he would sniff the camphor, a powerful reviver. Briggs was not the only member of his family who had his crotchets. Old Aunt Melissa Beall (who could whistle like a man, with two fingers in her mouth) suffered under the premonition that she was destined to die on South High Street, because she had been born on South High Street and married on South High Street. Then there was Aunt Sarah Shoaf, who never went to bed at night without the fear that a burglar was going to get in and blow chloroform under her door through a tube. To avert this calamity—for she was in greater dread of anesthetics than of losing her household goods—she always piled her money, silverware, and other valuables in a neat stack just outside her bedroom, with a note reading: "This is all I have. Please take it and do not use your chloroform, as this is all I have." Aunt Gracie Shoaf also had a burglar phobia, but she met it with more fortitude. She was confident that burglars had been getting into her house every night for forty years. The fact that she never missed anything was to her no proof to the contrary. She always claimed that she scared them off before they could take anything, by throwing shoes down the hallway. When she went to bed she piled, where she could get at them handily, all the shoes there were about her house. Five minutes after she had turned off the light, she would sit up in bed and say "Hark!" Her husband, who had learned to ignore the whole situation as long ago as 1903, would either be sound asleep or pretend to be sound asleep. In either case he would not respond to her tugging and pulling, so that presently she would arise, tiptoe to the door, open it slightly and heave a shoe down the hall in one direction and its mate down the hall in the other direction. Some nights she threw them all, some nights only a couple of pair.

But I am straying from the remarkable incidents that took place during the night that the bed fell on father. By midnight we were all in bed. The layout of the rooms and the disposition of their occupants is important to an understanding of what later occurred. In the front room upstairs (just under father's attic bedroom) were my mother and my brother Herman, who sometimes sang in his sleep, usually "Marching Through Georgia" or "Onward, Christian Soldiers." Briggs Beall and myself were in a room adjoining this one. My brother Roy was in a room across the hall from ours. Our bull terrier, Rex, slept in the hall.

My bed was an army cot, one of those affairs which are made wide enough to sleep on comfortably only by putting up, flat with the middle section, the two sides which ordinarily hang down like the sideboards of a drop-leaf table. When these sides are up, it is perilous to roll too far toward the edge, for then the cot is likely to tip completely over, bringing the whole bed down on top of one with a tremendous banging crash. This, in fact, is precisely what happened, about two o'clock in the morning. (It was my mother who, in recalling the scene later, first referred to it as "the night the bed fell on your father.")

Always a deep sleeper, slow to arouse (I had lied to Briggs), I was at first unconscious of what had happened when the iron cot rolled me onto the floor and toppled over on me. It left me still warmly bundled up and unhurt, for the bed rested above me like a canopy. Hence I did not wake up, only reached the edge of consciousness and went back. The racket, however, instantly awakened my mother, in the next room, who came to the immediate conclusion that her worst dread was realized: the big wooden bed upstairs had fallen on father. She therefore screamed, "Let's go to your poor father!" It was this shout, rather than the noise of my cot falling, that awakened my brother Herman, in the same room with her. He thought that mother had become, for no apparent reason, hysterical. "You're all right, mamma!" he shouted, trying to calm her. They exchanged shout for shout for perhaps ten seconds: "Let's go to your poor father!" and "You're all right!" That woke up Briggs. By this time I was conscious of what was going on, in a vague way, but did not yet realize that I was under my bed instead of on it. Briggs, awakening in the midst of loud shouts of fear and apprehension, came to the quick conclusion that he was suffocating and that we were all trying to "bring him out." With a low moan, he grasped the glass of camphor at the head of his bed and instead of sniffing it poured it over himself. The room reeked of camphor. "Ugf, ahfg!" choked Briggs, like a drowning man, for he had almost succeeded in stopping his breath under the deluge of pungent spirits. He leaped out of bed and groped toward the open window, but he came up against one that was closed. With his hand,

he beat out the glass, and I could hear it crash and tinkle in the alley-
way below. It was at this juncture that I, in trying to get up, had the
uncanny sensation of feeling my bed above me! Foggy with sleep, I
now suspected, in my turn, that the whole uproar was being made in a
frantic endeavor to extricate me from what must be an unheard-of
and perilous situation. "Get me out of this!" I bawled. "Get me out!"
I think I had the nightmarish belief that I was entombed in a mine.
"Gugh!" gasped Briggs, floundering in his camphor.

By this time my mother, still shouting, pursued by Herman, still
shouting, was trying to open the door to the attic, in order to go up
and get my father's body out of the wreckage. The door was stuck,
however, and wouldn't yield. Her frantic pulls on it only added to
the general banging and confusion. Roy and the dog were now up,
the one shouting questions, the other barking.

Father, farthest away and soundest sleeper of all, had by this time
been awakened by the battering on the attic door. He decided that the
house was on fire. "I'm coming, I'm coming!" he wailed in a slow,
sleepy voice—it took him many minutes to regain full consciousness.
My mother, still believing he was caught under the bed, detected in
his "I'm coming!" the mournful, resigned note of one who is preparing to meet his Maker. "He's dying!" she shouted.

"I'm all right!" Briggs yelled, to reassure her. "I'm all right!" He
still believed that it was his own closeness to death that was worrying mother. I found at last the light switch in my room, unlocked the
door, and Briggs and I joined the others at the attic door. The dog,
who never did like Briggs, jumped for him—assuming that he was
the culprit in whatever was going on—and Roy had to throw Rex and
hold him. We could hear father crawling out of bed upstairs. Roy
pulled the attic door open, with a mighty jerk, and father came down
the stairs, sleepy and irritable but safe and sound. My mother began
to weep when she saw him. Rex began to howl. "What in the name
of God is going on here?" asked father.

The situation was finally put together like a gigantic jigsaw puzzle.
Father caught a cold from prowling around in his bare feet but there
were no other bad results. "I'm glad," said mother, who always looked
on the bright side of things, "that your grandfather wasn't here."

Ludwig Bemelmans

THE BALLET VISITS
THE SPLENDIDE'S MAGICIAN

The management of the Hotel Splendide, the luxurious establishment where I once worked as a busboy, a waiter, and eventually as an assistant maître d'hôtel in the banquet department, kept on file the addresses of a number of men who were magicians, fortune-tellers, or experts with cards. One of these entertainers frequently appeared at the end of the small dinner parties which were given in the private suites of the Splendide in the boom days, before the depression put an end to such pastimes and at last brought about the demise of the Splendide itself. Our entertainers had acclimated their acts to the elegance of the hotel, and the magicians, for example, instead of conjuring a simple white rabbit from their hats, cooked therein a soufflé Alaska or brought out a prize puppy with a rhinestone collar. When young girls were present, the magician pulled from their noses and out of corsages Cartier clips, bracelets, and brooches, which were presented to them with the compliments cf the host.

Among the best and most talented of our performers was Professor Maurice Gorylescu, a magician who did some palmistry on the side. He came to the hotel as often as two or three times a week. After coffee had been served, he would enter the private dining room, get people to write any number they wanted to on small bits of paper, and hold the paper to their foreheads. Then he would guess the numbers they had written down and add them up. The total would correspond to a sum he found on a dollar bill in the host's pocket. He did tricks with cards and coins, and he told people about the characteristics and the habits of dress and speech of friends long dead. He even delivered messages from them to the living.

At the end of his séances he would go into some vacant room nearby, sink into a chair, and sit for a while with his hand over his eyes. He always looked very tired. After about half an hour he would shake himself, drink a glass of water slowly, then eat something and go home.

Professor Gorylescu earned a good deal of money. His fee for a single performance was a flat hundred dollars, and he sometimes received that much again as a tip from a grateful host. But although he worked all during the season he spent everything he made and often asked for and received his fee in advance. All he earned went to women —to the support of a Rumanian wife in Bucharest, to an American one who lived somewhere in New Jersey, and to what must have been a considerable number of New York girls of all nationalities to whom he sent little gifts and flowers.

When he came to the hotel during the day, he would hang his cane on the doorknob outside the ballroom office, ask me for a cigarette, and after a while steal a look at the book in which the reservations for small dinners were recorded. Very casually, and while talking of other things, he would turn the leaves and say something like "Looks very nice for the next two months," and put the book back. It took only a few seconds, but in this time his trick mind had stored away all the names, addresses, dates, and telephone numbers in the book. He went home with this information, called up the prospective party-givers, and offered his services.

There was a strict rule that no one should be permitted to look at these reservations, certainly not Professor Gorylescu, but I liked him, and when I was on duty in the ballroom office I would pretend not to see him when he peeked in the book. I also gave him left-over *petits fours,* candies, and after-dinner mints, of which he was very fond. He stuffed them into his pockets without bothering to wrap them up. He would wave goodbye with his immense hands, ask me to visit him soon at his home, and suggest that I bring along some *marrons glacés,* pastry, nuts—anything like that—and then he would leave, a stooping, uncouth figure, bigger than our tallest doorman.

Maurice Gorylescu lived on one of the mediocre streets that run between Riverside Drive and West End Avenue. He had a room in one of the small marble mansions that are common in that neighborhood. The rooming house in which Gorylescu lived was outstanding even among the ornate buildings of that district. It was a sort of junior Frankenstein castle, bedecked with small turrets, loggias, and balconies. It faced the sidewalk across a kind of moat—an air shaft for the base ment windows—traversed by a granite bridge. The door was hung on heavy iron hinges that reached all the way across.

The character of this house was, moreover, complemented by the woman who rented its rooms, a Mrs. Houlberg. She stood guard much of the time at the window next to the moat, looking out over a sign that read "Vacancies." She always covered three-quarters of her face with her right hand, a long hand that lay diagonally across her face, the palm over her mouth, the nails of the fingers stopping under the right eye. It looked like a mask, and as if she always had a toothache.

Gorylescu lived on the top-floor front and answered to four short rings and one long one of a shrill bell that was in Mrs. Houlberg's entrance hall. Badly worn banisters led up four flights of stairs. From the balcony of his room one could see the time flash on and off in Jersey and the searchlights of a battleship in the Hudson. The room was large and newly painted in a wet, loud red, the shade of the inside of a watermelon. A spotty chartreuse velvet coverlet decorated a studio couch. Facing this was a chair, a piece of furniture such as you see in hotel lobbies or club cars, covered with striped muslin and padded with down. There was also a Sheraton highboy, which stood near a door that led into an adjoining room which was not his. From the ceiling hung a cheap bazaar lamp with carmine glass panes behind filigree panels. On shelves and on a table were the photographs of many women; in a box, tied together with ribbons in various colors, he kept packets of letters, and in a particular drawer of the highboy was a woman's garter, an old girdle, and various other disorderly trophies.

Gorylescu reclined on the studio bed most of the time when he was at home. He wore a Russian blouse that buttoned under the left ear, and he smoked through a cigarette holder a foot long. One of his eyes was smaller and lower down in his face than the other, and between them rose a retroussé nose, a trumpet of a nose, with cavernous nostrils. Frequently and with great ceremony he sounded it into an immense handkerchief. His cigar-colored skin was spotted as if with a bluish kind of buckshot, and when he was happy he hummed through his nose, mostly the melody of a song whose title was "Tu Sais."

At home he was almost constantly in the company of women. He made the acquaintance of some of them at parties where he had entertained. They brought him gifts, and if they were fat and old, he read their minds and told them things of the past and future. At other times he went looking for girls along Riverside Drive, humming through his nose, and dragging after him a heavy cane whose handle was hooked into his coat pocket.

He went to various other places to find girls. He picked them up at dance halls in Harlem, on the subway, on roller coasters. He easily became acquainted with them anywhere, and they came to his room willingly and took their chances with him. I always thought I might find one of them, dead and naked, behind the Japanese screen, where he kept a rowing machine on which he built himself up. For the space of time that I knew him, love, murder, and that man seemed to be close together and that room the inevitable theatre for it.

The Professor gave me a series of lectures during my visits to his room in which he detailed for me the routines and the mechanisms of his untidy passions. He insisted during these long *études* that the most important piece of strategy was to get the subject to remove her shoes. "Once the shoes are off, the battle is already half won," he would say. "Get a woman to walk around without shoes, without heels—she looks a fool, she feels a fool, she is a fool. Without her shoes, she is lost. Take the soft instep in your hand, caress her ankles, her calf, her knee—the rest is child's play. But remember, first off with the shoes." While he talked, he would scratch his cat, which was part Siamese. The lecture was followed by a display of the collection of photographs he himself had taken, as evidence of the soundness of his theories.

When the Russian Ballet came to town, Professor Gorylescu was not to be had for any parties at the hotel. He went to all the performances, matinées and evenings alike, and he hummed then the music of "Puppenfee," "L'Après-Midi d'un Faune," and the various *divertissements,* and was completely broke. One day he was in a state of the highest elation because he had invited a ballet dancer to tea. He wanted me to come too because she had a friend, who would be an extra girl for me; both of them were exquisite creatures, he assured me, and I was to bring some tea, *marrons glacés, petits fours,* and ladyfingers.

I came early and I brought everything. He darkened the room, lit a brass samovar, laid out some cigarettes, sliced some lemons, hid the rowing machine under the studio couch, and with the Japanese silk screen divided the room into two separate camps. On one side was the couch, on the other the great chair. He buttoned his Russian blouse, blew his nose frequently, and hummed as he walked up and down. He brushed the cat and put away a Spanish costume doll that might have made his couch crowded. He arranged the *petits fours* in saucers, and when the bell rang four times short and one long, he put a Chopin record on his victrola. "Remember about the shoes," he told me over his shoulder, "and always play Chopin for ballet dancers." He quickly surveyed the room once more, turned on the bazaar lamp, and, humming, opened the door—and then stopped humming suddenly. He had invited two of the dancers, but up the stairs came a bouquet of girls, more than a dozen of them.

All at once it was the month of May in the dimmed room. The lovely guests complimented the samovar, the cat, the music, and the view from the balcony, to which they had opened the door, letting much fresh air come in, which intensified the new mood. Gorylescu's voice became metallic with introductions; he ran downstairs to get more glasses for tea and came back breathing heavily. All the girls, without being asked, took their shoes off immediately, explaining that their feet hurt from dancing. They arranged the shoes in an orderly row, as one does on entering a Japanese house or a mosque, then sat down on the floor in a circle. One of them even removed her stockings and put some slices of lemon between her toes. "Ah-h-h," she said.

There started after this a bewildering and alien conversation, a remote, foggy ritual, like a Shinto ceremonial. It consisted of the telling of ballet stories, and seemed to me a high, wild flight into a world closed to the outsider. The stories were told over and over until every detail was correct. In all of these stories appeared Anna Pavlova, who was referred to as "Madame"—what Madame had said, what Madame had done, what she had thought, what she had worn, how she had danced. There was an atmosphere of furious backstage patriotism. The teller of each story swayed and danced with hands, shoulders, and face. Every word was illustrated; for anything mentioned—color, light, time, and person—there was a surprisingly expressive and fitting gesture. The talker was rewarded with applause, with requests for repetition of this or that part again and again, and there swept over the group of girls waves of intimate, fervent emotion.

The Professor served tea on his hands and knees and retired to the shadows of his room. He sat for a while in the great chair like a bird with a wounded wing, and then, with his sagging and cumbersome gait, he wandered around the group of innocents, who sat straight as so many candles, all with their shoes off. The room was alive with young heads and throats and flanks.

The Professor succeeded finally in putting his head into the lap of the tallest, the most racy of the nymphs. She quickly kissed him, said "Sh-h-h-h, daaaahrling," and then caressed his features, the terrible nose, the eyebrows, the corrugated temples, and the great hands, with the professional detachment of a masseuse, while she related an episode in Cairo during a performance of "Giselle" when the apparatus that carried Pavlova up out of her grave to her lover got stuck halfway, and how Madame had cursed and what she had said after the performance and to whom she had said it. An indignant fire burned in all the narrowed eyes of the disciples as she talked.

Suddenly one of them looked at her watch, remembered a rehearsal, and the girls got up and remembered us. They all had Russian names, but all of them were English, as most ballet dancers are; in their best accents, they said their adieus. With individual graces, they arranged their hair, slipped into their shoes, and thanked Maurice. Each one of them said "Daaaahrling" to us and to each other. It was Madame Pavlova's form of address and her pronunciation.

All the girls kissed us, and it was as if we all had grown up in the same garden, as if they were all our sisters. The Professor said a few mouthfuls of gallant compliments, and when they were gone he fished the rowing machine out from under the couch, without a word, and carried it in back of the Japanese screen. Together, we rearranged the room. The *marrons glacés* and the ladyfingers were all gone, but the cigarettes were still there.

AUTHORS AND TITLES

AMERICAN METHODIST WORSHIP

Recent titles in

AMERICAN METHODIST WORSHIP

Karen B. Westerfield Tucker

OXFORD
UNIVERSITY PRESS

2001

OXFORD
UNIVERSITY PRESS

Oxford   New York
Athens   Auckland   Bangkok   Bogotá   Bombay   Buenos Aires
Calcutta   Cape Town   Dar es Salaam   Delhi   Florence   Hong Kong
Istanbul   Karachi   Kuala Lumpur   Madras   Madrid   Melbourne
Mexico City   Nairobi   Paris   Shanghai   Singapore   Taipei   Tokyo   Toronto

and associated companies in
Berlin   Ibadan

Copyright © 2001 by Karen B. Westerfield Tucker

Published by Oxford University Press, Inc.,
198 Madison Avenue, New York, New York 10016

Oxford is a registered trademark of Oxford University Press.

All rights reserved. No part of this publication may be reproduced,
stored in a retrieval system, or transmitted, in any form or by any means,
electronic, mechanical, photocopying, recording, or otherwise,
without the prior permission of Oxford University Press.

Library of Congress Cataloging-in-Publication Data
Tucker, Karen B. Westerfield.
American Methodist worship / Karen B. Westerfield Tucker.
p.   cm.—(Religion in America series)
Includes bibliographical references and index.
ISBN 0-19-512698-X
1. Methodist Church—United States—Liturgy.   2. Public worship.
I. Title.   II. Religion in America series (Oxford University Press)
BX8337.T83   2000
264'.07'00973—dc21   99-049346

9 8 7 6 5 4 3 2 1

Printed in the United States of America
on acid-free paper

In memory of
Frank and Nellie Baker
Grady and Rowena Hardin

Methodist teachers and Christian exemplars

Acknowledgments

N O SCHOLAR EVER DOES her or his research in a vacuum. The professional and personal support of countless individuals has contributed to this project, but certain institutions and people should be named. The Louisville Institute for the Study of Protestantism and American Culture granted a summer stipend for research. Assistance was provided by library staff, archivists, and local church historians around the country, but special thanks should be given to library personnel at Drew University, Duke University, Emory University, Garrett-Evangelical Theological Seminary, the Library of Congress, Southern Methodist University, the University of North Carolina at Chapel Hill, Wesley Theological Seminary, the United Methodist Archives, the Illinois Great Rivers Annual Conference Archives, and Historic St. George's Church. Richard P. Heitzenrater offered advice and valuable information. Douglas R. Cullum obtained hard-to-find documents related to the Free Methodist Church. Lester Ruth provided helpful comments and graciously shared primary materials he had uncovered regarding early Methodist communion practices in stations. Russell E. Richey, Geoffrey Wainwright, and James F. White all gave a careful reading to the manuscript. I am grateful to Professor Harry Stout of Yale University for accepting this work into the series he edits, and to Cynthia Read, Theodore Calderara, Robert Milks, and Stacey Hamilton of Oxford University Press who collaborated in the publication of this book.

I benefited from the encouragement and support of colleagues and students at the Divinity School, Duke University. Fellow members of the Post-Reformation Historical Research Seminar of the North American Academy of Liturgy followed with interest the progress of the project. I particularly thank my husband Stuart and my son Benjamin for their patience and understanding during the more than a dozen years required to produce this study.

This book is dedicated to two Methodist couples whose partnered scholarship and ministry have both instructed and inspired.

Contents

Introduction

METHODISM, IT HAS OFTEN been asserted, is the quintessential American denomination. Yet the story of its worship life—an important descriptor for any religious body—has never been (fully) told. It may be that, as long as (international) liturgical scholarship limited itself to the study of service books, the texts of Methodism as a derivative branch of Anglicanism were not considered particularly interesting. In addition, liturgical historians and theologians, until recently, have hailed from Europe, where Methodism is proportionally quite small and therefore seen as a minor denomination—and hence not worthy of serious or sustained investigation. The development of a school of North American liturgical scholarship, and particularly the training of North American Protestant liturgical scholars, is now encouraging the study of largely heretofore overlooked Protestant liturgical traditions that have flourished on this side of the Atlantic. Historians of American culture, for their part, have generally shied away from dealing with the overtly theological dimensions of a people gathering to pray; even within Methodist studies, worship and its doctrinal implications have been largely neglected, save for the camp meeting and revivalism. Yet liturgists have now started to move "beyond the text" in an effort to understand the tacit and informal dimensions of worship practices in their social, cultural, and ecclesial settings. And students of domestic culture, as well now as exotic, have begun to set considerable store by ritual and cult as revelatory of a community's beliefs and development. Therefore, the time appears ripe for an examination of worship in the American Methodist tradition that will both make an insider's contribution to cultural history and provide for liturgiology the case study of a church that has always known its worship of God to be unconfined by written directions or prayers. This is what is attempted here.

At the outset, the phrase "American Methodist" used in this study must be clarified. The term here refers to those churches that considered themselves to be inheritors of the theology and practices of the eighteenth-century evangelical Anglican John Wesley, and as testimony to that affiliation, adopted "Methodist" or

"Wesleyan" as part of the denominational name. Not all of the denominations meeting that criterion receive mention, whether because of their small size (e.g., the Primitive Methodist Church in the U.S.A.) or their regional limitation (e.g., the Allegheny Wesleyan Methodist Connection); and, of those churches selected, more attention generally is given to the larger bodies. Yet this study intentionally finds a place for three African-American denominations and two Holiness churches whose stories and contributions are sometimes disregarded in favor of discussions concerning the three denominations that would in 1939 form the Methodist Church. The Methodist Church in 1968 united with the Evangelical United Brethren to form the United Methodist Church, but the inheritance from the Evangelical United Brethren is treated only insofar as it has a bearing on the "Methodist" liturgical trajectory after the date of merger.

American Methodism literally was born with the nation. Although Methodist meetings in Maryland and New York organized by lay men and women are attested from the 1760s onward, it was the formation in 1784 of the Methodist Episcopal Church that marked the beginning of Methodism's transition from a society within the Church of England to a separate denomination. As the nation matured, so did the denomination, with growing pains shared by both. Questions about the nature and practice of democracy in the early years of independence occasioned the creation of the nonepiscopal Methodist Protestant Church. Debates concerning the rights of African Americans and the holding of slaves divided both the nation and episcopal Methodism. In the late nineteenth and early twentieth centuries, technological and scientific advancement launched the nation into the mainstream of world affairs; Methodism struggled with maintaining an effective witness in a world that was redefining God and humanity. As the nation twice strove to recover from global warfare, Methodism, in part, healed itself from internal division and appealed for greater unity within Christendom. In the last three decades of the twentieth century, the United Methodist Church shared in the decline of the white Protestant establishment while simultaneously seeking to come to terms with the multicultural reality of the United States.

The shared historical phases of growth between the nation and Methodism have already been studied and documented. What has not been investigated is how Methodist liturgical expressions shaped and were shaped by the theological and ecclesial processes leading Methodism from society to mature denomination, and how the liturgy and the performance of worship were influenced by the ideals and developmental tensions within the nation as a whole. Did theological shifts internal and external to American Methodism, and the presence of other denominations and religions, have a bearing on worship? Are there indications that such factors as race, ethnicity, gender, region, economic standing, and modernization in their American forms contributed to liturgical change? Over the course of more than two hundred years, was the liturgy of Methodism—the worship of that quintessential American denomination—"Americanized"?

The focus of this book is not liturgical texts as such since studies already exist that expose the lineage of textual revision for the majority of "official" rites, at least for the larger denominations. Moreover, an examination limited to those texts oversimplifies the complexity of Methodist worship, for leaders of worship have always believed they had the flexibility and freedom to depart from the authorized ritual. Indeed, some characteristically Methodist worship services (e.g., the love feast, the watch night service, the camp meeting, family worship—and sometimes even Sunday morning) were organized without the benefit of a formally established text. Rather than simply chronicle the details of textual revision, therefore, this study looks behind and beyond the official liturgical texts to offer an exploration and analysis of the evolution of American Methodist worship, looking holistically at the ecclesial processes and influences (e.g., theological, liturgical, demographic, cultural, and social) that motivated Methodists to rethink or reorganize their theology and praxis of worship, and at the dogmatic topics and systematic questions thereby engaged. Thus, primary sources for the study, in addition to the authorized liturgical texts, include official ecclesiastical documents of other kinds; unofficial liturgical resources that were used by Methodists; and descriptions and accounts from individual Methodist diaries and journals, from church and secular newspapers, and from (selected) local church archives. Attention is also given to the nontextual matters of environment and performance.

Methods of various categories are employed that best facilitate the investigation and interpretation of a particular rite or liturgical event. In one category, liturgical texts are compared, analyzed, and criticized. Comparisons are made between the text, content, and structures of American Methodist liturgies, their liturgical antecedent (the *Urtext* in the Church of England's Prayer Book), their liturgical next of kin (the texts of British Methodism), and their liturgical contemporaries from other Christian traditions (both in North America and abroad). Internal analysis is rendered on specific rites in an effort to determine the rationale (where possible) for textual change, to interpret the overall theological intention, and to understand the significance of the liturgical structure. A second category of methods, borrowed from phenomenology, is employed to scrutinize the performance of the whole service of worship in context: words, objects, and actions. Descriptions from eyewitnesses are used where available; other accounts come from the detractors and critics of Methodism (e.g., Baptists regarding Methodist baptismal practice), and from Methodists who romanticize earlier periods within Methodist history. Unfortunately, Methodists have tended to focus on the results of worship (e.g., conversion, a new awareness of God) rather than the service itself, so documentation is scant, with the exception of accounts of camp meetings, revivals, and prayer meetings. Other methods allow concentration upon the theological or cultural assumptions governing or laden within the liturgical rite or event, and investigation of psychological and other functions. In sum, the goal is to paint for American Methodist worship as complete a picture as possible of its various forms, styles, settings, expressions, understandings, and dynamics. No other book, to my knowledge, has attempted to collect the liturgical wealth of American Methodism—or any other American Protestant tradition, for that matter—in such a comprehensive way.

The book is organized according to the several times and occasions of Methodist worship. The Lord's Day service, the basic unit of Methodist worship and that which liturgically links Methodism to the church catholic, occupies the first two chapters. The first chapter exposes the basic structural development of the word or "preaching" service, while the second explores the more detailed features of

Sunday worship and the contextualization of the Lord's Day within weekly, quarterly, and annual cycles. Despite some recovery of the connection between word and sacrament in the twentieth century, Methodists have generally understood the Lord's Supper almost to be an occasional service rather than an integral component of Sunday practice; thus the service of Holy Communion figures as a later and separate chapter. After the Lord's Day material comes, for contrast, chapter 3 on the largely unscripted and peculiarly Methodist "usages," whose emphases are integration into and maintenance within the denominational community. The sacraments of baptism (along with related questions concerning confirmation and church membership) and Eucharist, both markers of ecclesiastical identity and ritualized expressions of soteriology, constitute chapters 4 and 5. Hymns and music, hallmarks of the "singing Methodists" that pervade all aspects of worship, are then scrutinized as both theological statement and ecclesiological self-definition.

Chapters 7 and 8 concentrate on the occasional services of marriage and burial that reveal more concretely the interfacing of Methodist worship and the wider American ethos. Whereas the services of Sunday morning and the sacraments are distinctively Christian celebrations that define the nature of the church, weddings and funerals are also cultural rites that carry with them the Christian and non-Christian customs of time and place. To help set Methodist theology and practice in context, each of these two chapters includes important elements of social history surrounding these rites of passage. Chapter 9 looks at the liturgical articulation of the works of piety and mercy "expected" of the Methodist people. The material setting for worship and the changing configurations of the liturgical space are then addressed. Roles in the leadership of the various types of Methodist worship are the subject of chapter 11.

The final chapter—which is more than a mere "conclusion"—gains its special significance from the fact that it synthesizes the revisionary processes already examined and seeks to identify particular factors that have contributed to the evolution of Methodist worship as a whole.

AMERICAN METHODIST WORSHIP

A GENEALOGY OF AMERICAN METHODISM

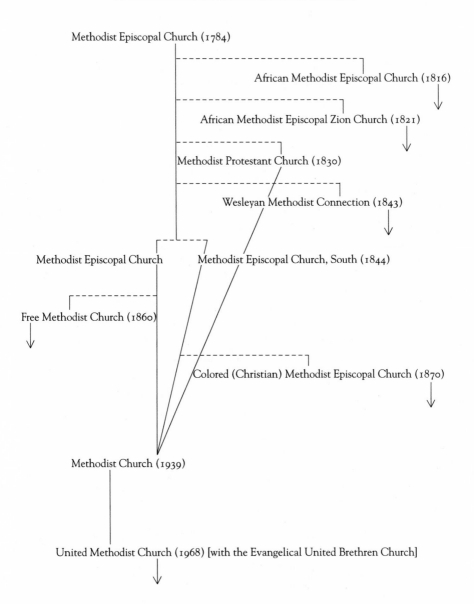

Methodist Episcopal Church (1784)

African Methodist Episcopal Church (1816)

African Methodist Episcopal Zion Church (1821)

Methodist Protestant Church (1830)

Wesleyan Methodist Connection (1843)

Methodist Episcopal Church

Methodist Episcopal Church, South (1844)

Free Methodist Church (1860)

Colored (Christian) Methodist Episcopal Church (1870)

Methodist Church (1939)

United Methodist Church (1968) [with the Evangelical United Brethren Church]

The Lord's Day
The Shape of Worship

IN 1932, REPRESENTATIVES OF THE Methodist Episcopal Church, in an effort to preserve the sanctity of Sunday as a day of worship and rest against the encroachment of secularizing tendencies, invoked the founding principles of the nation alongside the ecclesiastical practice of the Lord's Day. Appeal was made not only to the scriptural law and gospel; the Lord's Day was identified as "one of the first institutions planted on American soil," with its observance codified "in the second article of the Federal Constitution." The Methodists resolved to oppose all legislative efforts "to make the Lord's Day a holiday instead of a holy day. The church will not stand by and see the walls of the Lord's Day broken down."[1]

The juxtaposition—even on matters of worship—of agendas and traditions common to the denomination and the civil government reveals in Methodist thought an organic connection between the church and the nation that can be traced to the beginning of both institutions. Methodists, who before 1784 existed organizationally as a religious society under the general if distant jurisdiction of the Church of England, embraced the ideals of liberty of conscience and freedom of religious expression popular in colonial America. After the independence of the nation and the Methodist denomination, Methodists continued to uphold the value of freedom: for "spreading scriptural holiness throughout the land"; for reforming the nation; and for providing opportunities for worship in different liturgical styles. In the early years in particular, Methodists often pointed to the rise and development of the nation as a sign of God's work among a righteous people, though they were quick to admonish when correction seemed to be in order. This prophetic witness has remained a characteristic part of Methodism, and it has been held alongside an equally characteristic Methodist patriotism and nationalism. Yet at times that critical edge has been wittingly or unwittingly blunted as Methodism simultaneously sought to be faithful to God and relevant to the American people. From the mid-nineteenth century onward, as Methodism became more established and was identified by politician and church official alike as the most American of Protestant denominations, calls to accountability "under God" increasingly gave way (often grudgingly) to cultural conformity and accommodation. What might be called the Americanization of Methodism can be seen in all aspects of its life, and especially in the shape and content of its worship. The revisions made to Methodist Sunday worship throughout its history make this abundantly clear.

John Wesley's *Urtext*

Even John Wesley, Church of England priest and staunch Tory, had to concede in a letter dated September 10, 1784, that through "a very uncommon train of providences," the newly emancipated American people had been "disentangled" from the civil and ecclesiastical government of England. Because of their political freedom, Wesley allowed that the Methodists, "those poor sheep in the wilderness," likewise were set free to spread the gospel as an independent church, though Wesley assumed, as their founder, that he still would lead the fledgling denomination from England. One aspect of that freedom concerned liturgical expression: Methodists were now "at full liberty, simply to follow the scriptures and the primitive church."[2] The liberty so defined clearly implied certain norms for Christian worship.

Wesley's adherence to the classic Anglican triad of Scripture, Christian tradition, and reason as normative for doctrine underlay his instruction that Scripture and the primitive church should serve as sources for Methodist liturgical praxis. Self-defined as *homo unius libri*, Wesley insisted that Scripture was the supreme authority and definitive revelation in all matters, including the church's creedal and conciliar decisions. The standard and norm for Christian worship thus also was to be located in Scripture, though Wesley did not expect that the biblical text should provide the precise *ordo* or rubrics for worship. Scripture was the supreme rule; but valid, though subordinate, rules and forms could indeed "flow" from it.[3]

Christian tradition was for Wesley selectively vital; and of value to him, besides the English reformation, was especially ante-Nicene Christianity, a period that, in his day, had been the object of renewed interest. Numerous antiquarian works were reprinted, and accounts of early Christianity proliferated. Wesley recommended that the Methodist people familiarize themselves with the early church, and to encourage their reading he included selected primary and secondary materials, sometimes abridged, in the fifty volumes of his *Christian Library*. But while some churchmen looked to the literature of the ancients solely for fuel to stoke the fires of contemporary apologetics and polemics, Wesley also pursued a more pragmatic purpose. Because the first three Christian centuries represented for him the doctrine and practice of true, uncorrupted, scriptural Christianity, Wesley believed that the practices described in the apostolic writings and early church orders could provide suitable models for the renewal of the church. Wesley was not alone in the pursuit of what was perceived to be an unadulterated liturgical, spiritual, and ecclesiastical paradigm. He was, in fact, one among many who mined the riches of the early church for examples of liturgical *ordines*, prayer texts, descriptions of orders of ministry, and testimonies to holy Christian living; he also was acquainted with the products of these seventeenth- and eighteenth-century investigations.[4] Wesley's brief missionary sojourn in Georgia (1736–1737) afforded him an opportunity to experiment (albeit unsuccessfully) with ancient liturgical forms and practices, especially those disclosed in book 8 of the so-called *Apostolic Constitutions*. Even after his return to England he continued to regard America as a place where his ideals of primitive Christianity might thrive. Although his views on antiquity were nuanced as the years went by, Wesley never doubted that the Methodist work conformed to his (and others') conception of primitive practice, thus offering an alternative to the religious climate in America and in England.[5] Thus, Wesley's advice that the American Methodists employ the example of the primitive church to guide their new liberty came from a deep-seated desire that, in fact, had given impetus and shape to the Methodist movement as a whole.

Besides Scripture and tradition, reason was a necessary norm since, for Wesley, religion and reason were inextricably linked. Understood to be more than simply human thought or comprehension, reason was the perceiving of divine revelation through the agency of the Holy Spirit. Christian worship in particular was to be judged by conformity to Scripture and reason, and together these norms justified experiments in worship that varied from the liturgy of the Church of England, particularly where there was scriptural or apostolic precedent, or in matters judged to be adiaphora. In addition, the judicious use of reason coupled with Scripture led Wesley to conclude that there could be various styles or expressions of worship as long as the essentials of the faith were maintained and articulated. Modes of worship could not be dictated or prescribed, for rational human beings had a God-given right to worship as they were persuaded.[6]

Wesley the pragmatist added a fourth norm to the classical Anglican triad that strengthened his conclusion that Scripture and antiquity provided the best model for the American Methodists. Though not equal in authority to the other three criteria, the experiences of an individual and of the community were to be considered in making theological and practical assessments. The efficacy of worship, for example, could be judged by the resultant spiritual good: it proclaimed the gospel of salvation; it led to conversion and/or confession; it was truly edifying; and it inspired works of charity and mercy. Innovative practices in worship, therefore, could be evaluated not only in terms of their testimony to Scripture and tradition but also by the witness of the Spirit in human life.[7]

Lest the Americans be at a loss regarding his advice to follow the Scriptures and the primitive church, Wesley conveniently provided them with a model: a service book prepared in 1784 that was drawn from the 1662 *Book of Common Prayer*. Wesley's high regard for the Prayer Book was clear throughout his life, and he declared in the preface to *The Sunday Service of the Methodists in North America. With Other Occasional Services* that there was "no LITURGY in the World, either in ancient or modern language, which breathes more of a solid, scriptural, rational Piety, than the COMMON PRAYER of the CHURCH of ENGLAND."[8] This, however, did not mean Wesley regarded the Prayer Book as unalterable. During his American journey, Wesley confided in a diary entry for March 5, 1736, that he had "revised Common Prayer book." At the Methodist Conference of 1755 in Leeds, he openly criticized certain scripturally indefensible portions of the Prayer Book in the essay "Ought We to Separate from the Church of England?" And in his newly created service book, he felt free to edit the original, primarily by the deletion of long, redundant, and controversial texts, and by the omission of those things having "no valuable end" (e.g., the "so-called holy days"). But for Wesley, the Prayer Book, with all its imperfections, still contained language that was "not only pure, but strong and elegant in the highest degree."[9] By relying upon the perceived apostolicity of the Prayer Book of 1662, and by removing the extraneous material that obscured the purer elements, Wesley believed that he was giving the American Methodists the best liturgical document the church had to offer. The Americans, for their part, recognized Wesley's claim that their liturgy—and their church—was being organized according to the standards of primitive Christianity. Ezekiel Cooper wrote in his journal in 1788 that he was "from scripture & reason together with experience more than ever established in the Methodist principles as being apostolic."[10]

Wesley's service book, which was officially approved as the "prayer book" of the Methodist Episcopal Church at the constituting Christmas Conference of 1784 in Baltimore, contained services for baptism, marriage, Communion of the sick, burial, and ordination. But it was from the services for Sunday that the book took its name, indicating Wesley's preference that the Methodists gather for worship on the Lord's Day. Wesley's expectation was not entirely realistic, for in the early years, not all Methodists found it possible to assemble for Sunday worship, though they undoubtedly longed to do so. City stations and communities with a resident local preacher could expect a Sunday service. But the majority of Methodists were in societies located on circuits that might encompass hundreds of miles. The itinerant preacher responsible for a circuit would generally hold services in a given community only once in the course of two weeks, and rarely would that be on a Sunday.

Wesley provided orders of service for morning and evening prayer on the Lord's Day, and for the administration of the Lord's Supper that, following the Prayer Book tradition, included the sermon as part of the Ante-Communion. The Great Litany was to be prayed on Wednesdays and Fridays, and the Prayer for All Conditions of Men along with the General Thanksgiving were identified as the "Prayer and Thanksgiving to be used every Lord's Day." A table of proper lessons to be read at Sunday morning and evening prayer, and a listing of proper collects, epistles, and gospels to be read on Sundays and other particular days throughout the year were also included, but these had been substantially reduced from the Prayer Book model, since Wesley omitted the greater portion of the Anglican sanctoral while retaining from the temporal calendar Advent, Christmas, Good Friday, Easter, Ascension, Whitsunday, and Trinity. The number of psalms to be used was also decreased: in his "Select" psalter, which provided a thirty-day cycle of psalms for daily (not just Lord's Day) morning and evening prayer, Wesley deleted thirty-four psalms in their entirety and omitted sections of fifty-eight others, explaining only that he believed some psalms "highly improper for the mouths of a Christian Congregation." The language of some psalms was altered on account of Wesley's apparent preference at times for the style and syntax of the King James (Authorized) Version over that of the Coverdale version.

Unlike the Prayer Book, which stipulated that morning and evening prayer were to be said or sung daily, Wesley, by rubric, expected the services to be said (not sung) on the Lord's Day only. Wesley, in fact, made no rubrical addition allowing for congregational singing in any of his services, though it was expected that Methodist prayer would be accompanied with hymns, as is evident from the presence of *A Collection of Psalms and Hymns for the Lord's Day* that was sent along with the *Sunday Service*. Ideally, morning prayer each Sunday was to be concluded with the service of the Lord's Supper as long as it was presided over by a properly ordained elder (presbyter), but the reality in the new church was that the number of available elders was significantly smaller than the number of communities in need of one, and, in point of fact, American Methodists were as unaccustomed as Anglicans of the time to weekly Eucharist. Wesley's orders of morning and evening prayer were also significantly shortened from their Prayer Book form, in response, perhaps, to the long-standing concern among some Anglicans that the services were too lengthy. Some prayers were undoubtedly eliminated because they were considered inappropriate for the American context, such as the prayers for the royal family. Others were modified to reflect the new situation: the prayer for the King's Majesty was reformulated for the "Supreme Rulers."[11] Wesley's order for morning prayer took this shape:

Scripture sentences
Address ["Dearly beloved brethren, the Scripture moveth us, in sundry
    places. . . ."]
General Confession and Prayer for Forgiveness
The Lord's Prayer
Versicle and Response ["O Lord, open thou our lips. . . ."] with Gloria Patri
The Psalms with Gloria Patri
First Lesson
Te Deum
Second Lesson
Jubilate Deo
The Apostles' Creed
Introductory Dialogue ["The Lord be with you"] with Kyrie eleison
Collect of the Day
Collect for Peace
Collect for Grace
Prayer for the Supreme Rulers
Prayer of St. John Chrysostom
Apostolic Benediction ["The grace of our Lord Jesus Christ. . . ."]

Comparable changes were made to the Prayer Book order of evening prayer.

The Ante-Communion, or the service of Holy Communion up to the offertory, would have been inserted prior to the benediction on non-eucharistic Sundays, and had the following structure:

The Lord's Prayer
Collect for Purity

The Decalogue
Prayer for the Supreme Rulers [different from that in morning prayer]
Collect of the Day
Epistle Lesson
Gospel Lesson
Sermon

Wesley furnished no directions regarding the integration of morning prayer and the Ante-Communion, which is a surprising omission or oversight, given Wesley's assumption that morning prayer with the Lord's Supper service was to be the normative Sunday form. It seems unlikely that Wesley would have encouraged the customary Anglican practice of proceeding through the morning prayer and Communion liturgy as written, given his concern to avoid the "vain repetitions" that had been a criticism of the Prayer Book liturgy voiced from as early as the sixteenth century. Yet there is no evidence to support the possibility that the American Methodists omitted from the Ante-Communion those components that had already been used in the initial service of morning prayer.

The Methodist "Directory"

The *Sunday Service* as intended for American Methodists—another version first printed in 1786 was made available for Methodists in "His Majesty's Dominions"—went through five London-published editions during the years 1784–1790,[12] with revisions made to the services of baptism and communion by Wesley or perhaps by his assistant Thomas Coke, but with no marked changes in the services for Sunday. This suggests that, although for twenty years Methodists in America had employed a simple service of preaching, some members of the Methodist Episcopal Church found Wesley's liturgical plan basically suitable, appropriate, and useful, and indeed such seems to have been the case in the cities and towns as well as in some rural areas. Francis Asbury, who had been set apart as "superintendant" (renamed "bishop" in 1787) at the Christmas Conference, recorded in 1785 that during a visit to New York he "read prayers twice"; and Richard Whatcoat, elected bishop in 1800, observed while working with Asbury in South Carolina in 1790 that "Bror asbury Red the Morning Servis."[13] However, for most Methodists, particularly those in the less populated areas and the circuit riders who served them, Wesley's liturgy was not so successful. Thomas Haskins, one of the preachers present at the Christmas Conference, conceded in 1785 that though he made "a second attempt to read the morning service as abridged by Mr. Wesley," and the service was "most excellent in itself," ultimately it would not "be of much use among us—as a people."[14] The bound *Sunday Service* may have been regarded as a prohibitive expense for poor, illiterate communities for whom energetic preaching, extempore prayer, and lined-out hymn singing—and not liturgical prayer—were central. Many of the Methodists, especially the native-born Americans who had not been affiliated with the Church of England, found Wesley's prayer book and liturgical worship to be an alien and politically offensive imposition that neither reflected the essence of Methodist worship as they knew it nor aided the Methodist missionary impulse. Convinced that prayers were better said with the eyes shut, they felt their newfound freedom and their piety restricted by the Conference-approved *Sunday Service*, and they thus abandoned the book, believing that its use had never been made obligatory. Hints that official changes were in the wind came in December 1789, when a General Council of bishops and presiding elders meeting in Baltimore approved that "the exercise of public worship on the Lord's day, shall be singing, prayer, and reading the Holy Scriptures, with exhortation or reading a sermon, in the absence of a preacher."[15]

Soon after the death of their "venerable Father" in 1791, the American Methodists considered themselves at liberty to alter the liturgy that he had bequeathed to them. References to the Methodist "liturgy" or "prayer book" in the official *Discipline*, some of which had already been reworded or omitted, were completely struck from the *Discipline* in 1792. Morning and evening prayer services, the Litany, the psalter, the lectionary, and the propers disappeared and were replaced by a set of rubrics in a section of the *Discipline* headed "Of Public Worship," a presentation not unlike a Presbyterian directory of worship—and indeed some Methodists referred to this form as a directory of public worship. The rites of baptism, Lord's Supper, marriage, burial, and ordination from the *Sunday Service* were abbreviated, altered, and placed into a thirty-seven page section of the *Discipline* entitled "Sacramental Services, &c"; the nomenclature for the part containing the services would later be changed to "Ritual." The separation of the Eucharist from the pattern for regular Sunday morning worship and the transformation of the Sunday liturgy into largely an extempore service undoubtedly reflected the practice of Sunday worship for almost all Methodists. Yet by this method of revision, guidance for Methodist worship was essentially transferred from a prayer book to a piece of "canon law."

The replacement of Wesley's morning prayer service with a short paragraph of instructions may have actually, in the end, brought the Methodists into closer conformity with the ancient church their founder so admired. Morning prayer was now to consist of "singing, prayer, the reading of a chapter out of the Old Testament, and another out of the New, and preaching," a striking similarity (save for the singing) to the service of the word described in Justin Martyr's *First Apology*, chapter 67. The contents of the afternoon service were like those of the morning, though only one chapter from the Bible was to be read; encouragement for two readings in the afternoon was introduced with the 1804 *Discipline*. The evening service was to be observed simply with singing, prayer, and preaching. In the 1824 Methodist Episcopal *Discipline*, instructions for the use of the Lord's Prayer and the apostolic benediction (2 Corinthians 13:14) were added, with the former to be used "on all occasions of public worship in concluding the first prayer," and the latter at the dismissal. These basic components for worship on Sundays and other days were the acknowledged ingredients of authentic Methodist worship from the late eighteenth century into the second half of the nineteenth; and they continued to constitute the backbone for Methodist worship into the late twentieth century.

The Methodist leadership expected these minimal guidelines for the content of worship to be followed, since they were "given for the establishment of uniformity in public worship amongst us, on the Lord's-day." Nevertheless, some Methodist preachers felt at liberty to improve upon the rule. Jesse Lee claimed in 1810 that while preachers in towns and cities often adhered to the instructions, most others rarely obeyed them, preferring instead to read only one chapter of Scripture on Sabbath days, which was placed "either before or after the first prayer, and always before the preaching."[16] Methodist preachers clearly assumed that one Scripture lesson, usually not a full chapter and later often no more than a single verse, was sufficient to launch the main focus of the service: the sermon. For example, George Coles, writing of an afternoon service in New York City in 1841, reveals not only his simple order of service but also his use of the Scripture text:

> At 3 o'clock I began the service in Greene Street, and, after singing and prayer read the 147th Psalm, & after the second hymn took for my text the 20th verse of that Psalm and discoursed 1st on the sin of not acknowledging God as the author of all our blessing; 2ndly on the difference between pagan, Mahommedan, Jewish, Catholic, & Protestant nations; 3rd, on the word "judgments" in the text, which I suppose means the same as it does in the 119th Psalm; 4thly on the duty of praising the Lord, not only with our lips, but also in our lives.[17]

Similarly, Leonard Smith of Illinois describes morning worship from 1860:

> I arose about 5 ½ A.M. & paid my morning sacrifice to God. At the ringing of the second bell I repaired to the house of prayer to talk to the people on the Exercise of Godliness. I opened the exercise by singing the 297 Hymn to the tune Uxbridge after which I prayed. Then I read the morning lesson in the 4th Ephes. Then sang again the 570 Hymn to Boylston. Took my text from 1 Tim. 4:7. Closed by singing & prayer.[18]

Even before the revision of the *Sunday Service* in 1792, there had been a growing tension between the desire for a recognizable Methodist pattern of worship and freedom in liturgical expression. The adoption of Wesley's revision of the Anglican Articles of Religion in 1784 may have, in actuality, aided in sowing the seeds of this conflict, for Methodist Article 22 "Of the Rites and Ceremonies of Churches" recognized that differences in worship had always existed "according to the diversity of countries, times, and men's manners," yet required conformity to scripturally sound and commonly approved liturgical practices of the church lest order be broken and fragile consciences wounded. By 1789, the Council meeting in Baltimore had determined that it had the authority to "render the time and form of public worship, as similar as possible through all their congregations," and resolved that, where practicable, worship on the Lord's Day was to begin at 10 o'clock, and alternatively, if necessary, at 11 o'clock.[19] Uniformity in worship resurfaced as a topic at the meeting of the General Conference in 1824, where it was reported that the reading of Scripture, the Lord's Prayer, and the apostolic benediction were often omitted from public worship. Although neither the prayer nor the benediction had been previously identified in the *Discipline* as "requirements" for worship, the report presupposes their normativity for Methodist worship; ritual memory (from the office of morning prayer or from the general practice of the Methodist societies) may have encouraged the retention of the prayer and benediction, or perhaps they were used because of their status as scriptural forms. The legislative response to the report was to insist that the preachers "observe the order of worship" found in the section "Of Public Worship," again revealing certain assumptions, since many undoubtedly believed the section to contain only a list of components and not necessarily a sequence of items.[20] A follow-up report in 1832 saw improvement toward the goal of public worship as "uniform, Scriptural, and edifying,"[21] an accomplishment later reports show was short-lived. Methodists still felt at liberty to forgo the stated orders and improvise in worship, even though the assumptions of the denominational legislation were otherwise. In spite of repeated calls for uniformity in praxis, denominationally sanctioned worship orders for the Lord's Day were never *mandated* for the Methodist people.

Placed alongside the issues of uniformity and freedom in practice was another persistent yet related matter: the avoidance of a formalism in worship that potentially could stifle the Spirit. Formality, among other things, could be defined as rigidity in order (a risk when imposing uniform patterns), long and languid prayers, use of liturgical texts, and ostentatious attitudes and accoutrements. Simplicity was preferred, since the unadorned gospel message was best represented to plain folk by simple means. Methodists—even in 1850—would often look back nostalgically to earlier, simpler times and pine for the idealized bygone days:

> And we cannot believe that in a building which "for a long time had benches only with backs provided below," the congregation was either very large—very rich—very proud—or very showy. And as for the preachers, although Captain Webb, as a British officer, may have preached in his regimentals, a red coat on his back and an epaulet on his shoulder, he was neither stiff nor starched as many a Methodist preacher of our own times is. There was no strutting, self-conceited fop, dressed like a dancing master, dangling his cane as he walked to the house of God, to set his foot in that pulpit. There was no supercillious [sic] coxcomb to flounce and flutter, like a play actor before a starring [sic] audience. There was no Doctor of Divinity with "a wig full of learning," to talk to a listening congregation about things he did not understand, or if he did understand them, were not calculated to make his hearers wise unto salvation. There was no vindictive Laud with a heart full of bitterness and wrath against his brethren, to ascend that pulpit and announce, Methodist preachers are *"the* divinely instituted ministry"—*"the* divinely authorized expounders," &c. No! all these improvements in Methodism were reserved for future times. The preachers and people in those days acted under a conviction "Thou God seest me"; and when they assembled to worship, "they worshipped him in spirit and in truth."[22]

For some Methodists, what became identified as the revival style of hymn singing, ardent prayer, and fiery preaching that flourished on the frontier exemplified the basic and most fruitful means of winning souls. This often meant adopting a practical approach so that worship reached its commonly understood goal: the conversion of heart and mind, which often was dramatically confirmed by kinetic and vocal responses in the pew or at the altar rail. To obtain the sought end of worship, Methodists of the early nineteenth century and beyond willingly exhibited the liturgical pragmatism popularized by Presbyterian Charles Grandison Finney, whose "new measures" outlined in 1835 commended decency and orderliness in worship (1 Corinthians 14:40), but denied the need for any set forms or modes, noting that neither the apostles nor Jesus himself had used established liturgies.[23] The shape of Lord's Day worship, according to this thinking, was determined by the worship leader's assessment of the spiritual needs of the community, not by some prescribed order, though the general pattern was to progress from the "preliminaries" (e.g., singing, prayers, testimonies), to a "message," followed by an invitation to commitment. Methodist promotion of "new measures" in worship was the subject of criticism, both inside Methodism and outside, with one of the most notable critics being Mercersburg theologian John Williamson Nevin in *The Anxious Bench* (1843, 1844). Even so, simple, free, and locally derived styles of worship have always existed alongside the official *ordines* approved by the legislative bodies of Methodism. Some Wesleyan offshoots of the Methodist Episcopal Church, in fact, never produced official liturgical texts for Sunday worship. Hence, concerns about uniformity, formality, and freedom in worship persisted throughout the entire history of Methodism and in all its parts, and they continued to influence discussions about liturgical practice as well as official liturgical revisions in each generation.

The Establishment of Specified Orders for Morning Worship

The simple service of the word and in many cases the rubrics of 1792 (with the modifications of 1824) were maintained even as the Methodist Episcopal Church divided over issues as varied as race, denominational governance, slavery, and the Wesleyan doctrines of perfection and holiness, thereby giving birth to several new Methodist ecclesiastical bodies, including the African Methodist Episcopal Church (1816); the African Methodist Episcopal Zion Church (1821); the Methodist Protestant Church (1830, which divided in 1858 and was reunited in 1877); the Wesleyan Methodist Connection (1843); the Methodist Episcopal Church, South (1844); and the Free Methodist Church (1860). These new denominations continued or slightly altered the textual description of Sunday worship that they had inherited. The instructions were kept intact by the African Methodist Episcopal Church and the Methodist Episcopal Church, South, respectively the largest black and white denominations outside the Methodist Episcopal Church. The Methodist Protestants, in their first *Constitution and Discipline* of 1830, kept the intention of the 1792 rubric, but in the section on "Public Worship" gave the components a specific order for Lord's Day worship, described expectations of worship practice, and elaborated upon apparent problems of decorum (the first among the Methodist groups to do so in the section dealing with worship):

> The morning service on the Lord's day, shall consist of singing of a hymn, prayer, and reading a portion of the word of God; then singing another hymn, or part thereof, and preaching. After sermon, another hymn, or part of a hymn, shall be sung, an appropriate prayer addressed to the throne of grace, and the congregation dismissed with the apostolic benediction, while the preacher and congregation are yet kneeling.
>
> The afternoon and evening services shall consist of the same exercises, except reading portions of Scripture, which may be omitted.
>
> We recommend that no sermon exceed one hour; and that the minister be not tedious in conducting the other parts of divine worship. It is further recommended, that the Lord's prayer be repeated at the close of the first morning prayer.

During public worship, the congregation is expected to attend with becoming gravity, abstaining from all salutations of persons present, or coming in; and from gazing about, sleeping, smiling, whispering, and all other indecent behaviour. [It is expected of all who attend on our ministry, that they carefully avoid the too common practice of standing about the church doors before service, and of leaving the house before the congregation is regularly dismissed.]

While the minister is addressing the throne of grace, the whole congregation should meekly kneel before God; and during the singing of the first hymn, stand up with their faces towards the minister, and assist in this delightful part of divine worship. The verses of the second hymn should be read over by the minister, and then sung by the people while seated.

Although they did not alter the Methodist Episcopal Church's directions for worship, the Free Methodists, led by Benjamin Titus Roberts, nevertheless saw their departure in 1860 from the mother church as an opportunity to purge worship of what were perceived to be fashionable tendencies and worldly conformities and thus return to the power of godliness exhibited in early Methodism.[24] A century after their founding, Free Methodists still included virtually unchanged the prose directions for public worship they had inherited; but they had succumbed to the tendency of the other Methodists and reduced the amount of Scripture heard in worship.

These concerns about disorder and worldliness, arising in part from cultural, social, and economic changes within the Methodist constituency, reveal that much more was happening in Sunday worship than the simple rubrics would seem to indicate. As Methodism became firmly established as a denomination and an institution within the American society and settled in its own self-understanding, attention gradually shifted from ministry among the poor and lower class to the middle class and affluent, though ministry to the poor remained a part of Methodist work over the centuries. Fervent religious experience and evangelical zeal were tempered as many of the larger Methodist bodies sought social and theological "respectability," and styles of ministry changed with the dismounting of the itinerant. With the increased sophistication of Methodism's constituency came a desire for worship services that exhibited closer affinities to the more economically advantaged denominations, particularly the Protestant Episcopalians. The specified contents of the service became more numerous and, accordingly, the orders became longer and more complex. The narrative directions were replaced by an outline of worship elements. While for many congregations the new orders of worship were foreign to their own experience and practice (and would remain so), for others, particularly in the cities, what developed was likely a codification of what were perceived to be the most popular and representative practices. It is therefore significant that in 1864, four years after the Free Methodists separated themselves in order to restore a gospel simplicity to worship, the Methodist Episcopal Church made a few alterations to the section in the *Discipline* on "Public Worship": a "lesson" from Scripture of unspecified length was to be read rather than a "chapter," thereby potentially decreasing the amount of Scripture heard in the congregation; a doxology was to be sung at the end of the service before the benediction; and participation by the people in the various acts of worship was identified as an expectation.

Two years later, the Methodist Episcopal Church, South made a similar adjustment to the statement about its readings; in 1870, an outline order for the morning service was printed in the *Discipline* that followed the same structure as the 1830 Methodist Protestant, though it specified the use of two "lessons"; a separate rubric enjoined the saying of the Lord's Prayer in unison at the conclusion of the first prayer. The 1870 order would remain the standard for the Methodist Episcopal Church, South until 1905, and in 1880 it was made more widely available by the printing of the order and instructions from the *Discipline* in the final pages of the denomination's *New Hymn-Book*. The Colored (renamed "Christian" from 1956) Methodist Episcopal Church, which broke away in 1870 from the Methodist Episcopal Church, South, opted to follow the new worship pattern of the parent body.

As the printed orders for worship became more elaborate, they nevertheless kept the intention apparent in the 1792 directions and reinforced by revivalism: the service was directed toward the sermon and the yield that could be obtained from evangelical preaching. The order approved by the Methodist Episcopal Church in 1888 builds upon the previously established liturgical foundation and indicates that the prayer following the sermon might focus upon the appropriation of the message. The option of a responsive reading of Scripture is introduced:

Singing one of the hymns of our hymn-book, the people standing
Prayer, concluding with the Lord's Prayer, repeated by the congregation, the minister and people kneeling
The reading of a lesson from the Old Testament, and another from the New, either of which may be read responsively
The collection
Singing another of our hymns, the people sitting
Preaching
A short prayer for a blessing on the word
Singing, closing with a doxology, the people standing
The pronouncing of the apostolic benediction

This order was (directly or indirectly) imitated yet modified by the Methodist Protestants in 1892, who placed the collection immediately before the "sermon," did not include a final doxology (this was added in 1924), and elected not to designate a responsive reading of the Old and New Testament lessons. Instead, they placed an additional reading before the lessons: a responsive reading of a psalm or the Beatitudes, or a reading "in concert" of the Decalogue, all of which was to be concluded with the Gloria Patri. The Decalogue, which had been dropped from Wesley's Ante-Communion in 1792, was also introduced by the African Methodist Episcopal Church into their official order of public worship in the 1890s, where it was placed as the last reading before the sermon:

Voluntary by choir
Scripture Sentences: "I was glad" etc., according to the Ritual
Singing a hymn from our hymnal, after its announcement by the officiating minister
Prayer, minister and congregation kneeling

Voluntary by choir
Scripture lesson, minister and people reading alternately
Scripture lesson by minister
Singing
Reading of the Decalogue; minister leading, the people responding
Singing
Announcements
Preaching or Exhortation
The Lord's Prayer or an extempore prayer, the minister and congregation
    kneeling
Collecting Offerings
Doxology and Benediction

Methodist Protestants "officially" continued to use the 1892 order up to the time of their merger with the Methodist Episcopal Church and the Methodist Episcopal Church, South in 1939. The basic structure offered to the African Methodist Episcopal Church at the turn into the twentieth century continued, with some additions, down to the *Book of Worship* of 1984.

Not to be outdone in the area of liturgical innovation, the Methodist Episcopal Church adopted a new order in 1896, ignoring the caution voiced in 1892 by William McKinley and others that following the road toward increased ritualism would eventually lead to a decline in religion.[25] The 1896 service expanded that of 1888 by including options for choral and instrumental music and for the unison recitation of the Apostles' Creed immediately following the opening hymn as a statement of ecclesiological self-identity; these provisions had actually been proposed in 1888 by J. E. Wilson of South Carolina, but had been rejected in favor of the approved order.[26] In the 1896 outline, preaching is identified as the "sermon," announcements are to be given before the collection, and the reading of the Old and New Testament lessons is split by the singing of the Gloria Patri, with provision given for a responsive reading of the Old Testament lesson if it is from the Psalms. As with previous orders, the expectation was that this order would "establish uniformity in public worship," and to aid in such uniformity, approval was given to put the order in the people's hands by publishing it in that year's printing of the official hymnal. Such uniformity was to extend beyond the bounds of the Methodist Episcopal Church, however, for the 1896 text became the foundation of a liturgical if not yet political union between the two major branches of episcopal Methodism. Slightly revised and designated a "common order," it appeared in the Methodist Episcopal 1904 *Discipline*, in the 1906 Methodist Episcopal Church, South *Discipline*, in a shared hymnal published in 1905, and again (slightly adapted) in another shared hymnal in 1935. Both Methodist bodies agreed that emphasis ought still to be placed on the evangelistic quality of worship: a shared rubric in both churches' *Discipline* and in the hymnal instructed that "an invitation to come to Christ, or to unite with the Church, should be given when this [final] hymn is announced." The Methodist Episcopal Church, South officially maintained the "common" text throughout the ongoing discussions of reunion, though concern was expressed in 1934 that pastors in rural areas and villages had been unable "to develop the people for its use," and that pastors in the cities had discarded the order in favor of one of their own improvising.[27] The official adherence to the "common order" by the Methodist Episcopal Church, South stood in contrast to their ecclesiastical partner, which, in another innovative move, introduced (though not without debate) completely new orders of Lord's Day worship in 1932 that were believed to conserve "the noblest values of our rich evangelical heritage and speak the vital language of today."[28]

A Return to Wesley's *Ordo* and Instructions

The 1932 Methodist Episcopal *Discipline* offered two orders of worship for Sunday, and a third, "An Order for Morning or Evening Prayer," which was "adapted from the Sunday Service of John Wesley and suggested for occasional use." This was not the first time Methodists had turned their attention to recovering Wesley's previously abandoned *Sunday Service*, the use of which, it was sometimes claimed, had never been repealed in the *Discipline*. At the 1866 meeting of the General Conference of the Methodist Episcopal Church, South, the first following the war, the Conference approved a "memorial" (petition) by St. Francis Street Church in Mobile, Alabama, that Wesley's *Sunday Service* be restored and allowed for its optional use.[29] The Methodist Episcopal Church, South's book editor and editor of the volume was conveniently Thomas Osmond Summers, former pastor of St. Francis Street and chair of the Conference committee that had urged approbation of the memorial. Born in England, Summers had come to the United States in 1830 and distinguished himself by his scholarly interest in matters theological, liturgical, and literary; he eventually served as professor of systematic theology and dean of the theology faculty at Vanderbilt University until his death in 1882. Summers brought out the *The Sunday Service of the Methodist Episcopal Church, South* in 1867, which combined the denomination's current Ritual (services for the Lord's Supper, infant and adult baptism, marriage, burial, and ordination) with a new order for the reception of members and Wesley's Lord's Day services as published in 1786. Included from Wesley's *Sunday Service* were morning and evening prayer; the Litany; the table of proper lessons for Sunday morning and evening prayer and other particular days; and the substantial section of collects, epistles, and gospels to be used on Sundays throughout the year and at Nativity, Good Friday, and Ascension. Alterations and omissions from the Wesleyan original are evident; for example, at points the language of Wesley's work is brought into line with current denominational phraseology for historic Christian texts, and all Scripture translations now come from the preferred King James Version of the Bible.[30]

   Although it is impossible to ascertain the actual usage of the 1867 *Sunday Service* by local congregations, interest in Wesley's liturgy did not wane. Following the example of the Methodist Episcopal Church, South, the General Conference of the African Methodist Episcopal Church approved in 1880 the optional use of "Wesley's Prayer Book."[31] In 1891, Charles S. Harrower of the Methodist Episcopal Church first published *Select Psalms*, a book lacking the official sanction of the

General Conference, but carrying the "imprimatur" of Bishop Edward G. Andrews. Compiled in response to an apparent demand to "dignify and enrich" public worship, the book encouraged the use of a psalm with a concluding Gloria Patri in public worship—even though such a provision had not been specified in the Conference-approved service of 1888. The core of the book is Wesley's thirty-day cycle of psalms, translated throughout in the King James Version, and to which are joined "Selections of Psalms and Other Scriptures." Additional portions of Wesley's *Sunday Service* were printed alongside the current Methodist Episcopal Ritual: tables for proper lessons; the Decalogue with responses; the two ecumenical creeds; canticles, collects, versicles, and prayers from morning and evening prayer (supplemented with prayers proposed to the Protestant Episcopal General Convention of 1886); and outlines of the orders for morning and evening prayer.[32] Two years later, Harrower brought out a similar unofficial book, this time with full texts for a conflated service of morning and evening prayer, for the Litany, and for Sunday collects throughout the year (with stated epistle and gospel lessons), along with other enrichments. Neither the 1784 nor the 1786 *Sunday Service* was used directly as the source; instead, borrowings appear from the 1882 recension of Wesley's service made by the "English Wesleyans," and new material is imported (e.g., opening sentences as propers) from the 1892 *Book of Common Prayer* of the Protestant Episcopal Church in the U.S.A. No explanation is given for the preference of this revised text over Wesley's approved versions, though it may be significant that both of Harrower's books were published on the heels of the second ecumenical Methodist conference in 1891.[33] Another conflated service of morning and evening prayer was published in 1903, this one drawing directly from the 1784 service, though with some alteration, particularly the placement of the Prayer for the President from the American Prayer Book alongside Wesley's Prayer for Supreme Rulers, and the addition of two prayers (for Ministers of the Gospel and for All Conditions of Men) that Wesley had deleted.[34] Even though the 1903 version was closer to Wesley's original, it was Harrower's version of the "Wesley Sunday Service" that appeared in Methodist Episcopal bishop Wilbur Thirkield's *Service and Prayers for Church and Home* (1918, 1928).

The "Wesley" liturgical texts published by Summers, Harrower, and the anonymous editor of 1903 saw some usage in local church worship, as attested by Hugh D. Atchison, in 1927 the pastor of St. Luke's Methodist Episcopal Church in Dubuque, Iowa:

> Here and there we find Methodist Episcopal churches timidly trying to live up in some measure to our "great and good inheritance," by using some form of worship, based on the general outline of the *Sunday Service*. Saint Luke's Church of Dubuque . . . is one of these pioneer churches; and has used a greatly simplified form of this service for more than thirty years; and the results have been highly gratifying.[35]

The published services also prepared the ground for the production in 1930 of trial orders of worship by the Methodist Episcopal Church's Commission on Worship and Music, headed by Bishop Thirkield. Among the four services offered was an order for morning prayer (with rubrics indicating variations for evening) "adapted" from Wesley. Here portions of the historic Anglican office, as mediated by Harrower and the 1892 Prayer Book, were blended with Methodist assumptions of what was necessary for Sunday worship.[36] All four orders were framed in generally the same shape, and though they elaborated the previous "standard" form, they were now identified as following the psycho-spiritual-aesthetic sequence put forward by Congregationalists Von Ogden Vogt and Willard L. Sperry, who attempted to express how outer form articulated the inner experience of worship.[37] The commission believed that Vogt's progression—vision, humility, vitality (or exaltation), recollection, illumination, dedication, and peace—revealed the essential shape of the great historic liturgies, including the Prayer Book, though several components of the commission's "Wesley" service were jiggled so that they might fit Vogt's form. However, when the service was approved in 1932 as the "Order for Morning or Evening Prayer," the historic shape of Anglican morning prayer had been restored. The "Wesley" service was preceded in the *Discipline* of 1932 by two other orders, designated Order I and Order II. Order II was an abbreviation of the longer Order I, the latter taking the shape of the reconstructed and revised Wesleyan *ordo*, except for the location of the creed, which, in a departure also from Vogt's scheme, was placed earlier in the service rather than in the "illumination" section:

ORDER I	ORDER FOR MORNING OR
ORDER II (designated by *)	EVENING PRAYER ("Wesley" text)
*Prelude	Prelude
(Hymn, if a procession)	
*Call to Worship	Scripture Sentences
*(Hymn, if no procession)	Hymn
	Call to Confession
*Prayer (of Confession)	General Confession
*Silent Prayer	
Words of Assurance	Prayer for Pardon
*The Lord's Prayer	The Lord's Prayer
	Versicle
*Anthem or Chant (Venite or Te Deum)	Venite
Responsive Reading	Psalter
Gloria Patri	Gloria Patri
Affirmation of Faith, The Apostles' Creed, Or Other Affirmation	
*Lessons from the Old and New Testaments	Lesson from the Old Testament
	Te Deum [morning] or Magnificat [evening]
	Lesson from the New Testament
	Jubilate Deo [morning] or Nunc Dimittis [evening]
	Declaration of Faith (Apostles' Creed)

Prayer	Collect for Grace [morning] or Collect for Aid against all Perils and a Collect from the ordination liturgies [evening]
	Prayers, ending with the Apostolic Benediction
[Junior Sermon for children]	
Offertory	Offertory (an anthem may be sung)
[Junior Sermon, if not placed above]	
*Presentation of Offerings	Presentation of Offerings
Hymn	(Hymn, if sermon)
Sermon	(Sermon)
Prayer	(Prayer, if sermon)
*Hymn or Doxology	Hymn
*Silent Prayer	
*Benediction	Benediction
*Postlude	

These orders of 1932, along with the shared "common order" from the 1905 hymnal, formed the basis for discussion of a unified Methodist Church service made by a committee of representatives from the three Methodist bodies that were to reunite in 1939. In fact, the Methodist Episcopal Church, South virtually had already Order I from the 1932 revision, renumbered as Order II in their printing of the 1935 shared hymnal—though, in what may have been a typographical error or a liturgical experiment, the Gloria Patri was relocated to follow the Apostles' Creed, a change that would continue to influence the placement of the Gloria in local church worship. According to Nolan Harmon, a committee member and later a bishop, the chosen process in the development of the unified rite was to keep the basic texts of 1932 and to offer alternatives only when deemed necessary.[38] The result was the approval for the new Methodist Church of substantially the same four orders as had the official sanction of the Methodist Episcopal Church in 1932. The "Wesley" service remained the same. Order I was the same as in 1932, but now silent prayer followed the benediction, and, reflecting alterations already made to the order in the 1935 hymnal, the prayer after the lessons was now the "Pastoral Prayer," and an "Invitation to Christian Discipleship" appeared after the sermon prayer. The new Order III was virtually the old 1932 Order II, but with the designations of "Pastoral Prayer" and the "Invitation" as in Order I. The new Order II was a working over of the "common order":

Prelude
Call to Worship
Invocation
Hymn
Affirmation of Faith (Apostles' Creed)
Anthem
Responsive Reading
Gloria Patri

Lessons from the Holy Scriptures
The Silent Meditation
The Pastoral Prayer
The Lord's Prayer
The Offertory
Dedication of Offerings
Hymn
Sermon
Prayer
Invitation to Christian Discipleship
Hymn
Benediction
Postlude

This proliferation of orders for Sunday, begun in 1932 and continued in 1939, reached new heights with the publication in 1945 of the first official Methodist worship book since Wesley's *Sunday Service*, though its use was understood to be "optional and voluntary" in respect to the Methodist tradition of being "both liturgical and free." Three services each are provided for morning, for evening, and for morning or evening; the "Wesley" morning and evening service of 1939, now with the Collect for Peace, is continued; fifteen services are supplied reflecting the church year as well as ecclesiastical and civil occasions; and a morning and an evening service is offered for family or small group worship, thus justifying the title of the work as *The Book of Worship for Church and Home*. With the exception of one of the conflated morning and evening services that reproduces Order II of 1939 (the old "common" order), the rest are restatements or nuancings of 1939 Order I (following the shape of the reconstructed Wesleyan *ordo*). A theological and psychological rationale for Order I—and all of worship—is expressed, which still hints at the categories suggested by Vogt:

> An order of worship should move with unity and meaning. There is a fourfold aspect to an order of worship. Four attitudes of the devout worshipper are presented in ascending movements—adoration, confession, affirmation, and dedication. They imply the divinely descending movements of vision, pardon, illumination, and fruition.
>
> While this pattern allows for wide variety of content, it at the same time possesses such unity that, if it is generally followed by our churches, a Methodist will feel at home in any Methodist church. This is because the things we are most used to always come in the same order. For example, the Lord's Prayer, the Responsive Reading, and the Creed are always found in the same place, as are the Call to Worship and the Benediction.

I.   The Adoration of God

The congregation should be called to worship at the opening of every service by a hymn of praise and adoration.

Prelude
Call to Worship
Hymn

Invocation
Collect

II.   The Confession of Sin

If through our adoration we come to a vision of God, we naturally feel the need of confessing our sins.

Prayer of Confession
Silent Meditation
Words of Assurance
Prayer for Pardon or Words of Forgiveness
The Lord's Prayer

III.   The Affirmation of Faith

The experience of forgiveness should bring a mood of exaltation, in which we can affirm our faith through music, scripture, and creed, all moving toward the Pastoral Prayer.

Anthem
The Responsive Reading
Gloria Patri
Affirmation of Faith
The Lessons: Old Testament, New Testament
Pastoral Prayer

IV.   The Dedication of Life

All that follows the Pastoral Prayer, from Offertory to Benediction, should be in a mood of dedication, which is centralized in the Sermon. The goal of all worship is the dedication of ourselves, in the name of Christ, to his Church and Kingdom.

Offertory
Hymn
The Sermon
An Invitation to Christian Discipleship
Hymn
Silent Prayer
Benediction
Postlude

Not simply outlines (a separate outlined "Order of Worship" is provided), these services are richly developed with a variety of texts incorporated for prayer and praise. Many of these texts originate outside of Methodism in both denominational and ecumenical prayer collections; even a prayer from the 1940 *Union Prayerbook for Jewish Worship* is included, which serves as the invocation in the third evening service.

Users of the 1945 book may have found the presentation of multiple services to be unhelpful or unwieldy, for with the next liturgical revision approved twenty years later by the Methodist Church, only two services for Sunday with full texts were printed, with numerous seasonal and general aids for use as propers provided in separate sections. One service with full texts in the 1965 *Book of Worship* was an accurate reprinting of Wesley's 1784 morning prayer, which was placed in the concluding section of "Services in the Methodist Tradition." Wesley's actual service may have been included as a corrective to the newest variant services adapted from Wesley, such as those in *The John Wesley Prayer Book* (1956) and *The Wesley Orders of Common Prayer* (1957).[39] The other complete service, the standard form for Methodist worship, subtly reshuffled the components of the 1945 service and was given a new rationale: closer conformity to Wesley's order for morning prayer. The outline took this shape:

Prelude
Scripture Sentences, or Call to Worship
Hymn
Invocation
Call to Confession
General Confession
Prayer for Pardon or Words of Assurance
The Lord's Prayer
Versicle
Psalter or Other Act of Praise
Gloria Patri
Anthem
The Scripture Lessons
Affirmation of Faith
Doxology
Collect
Pastoral Prayer
Offertory with parish notices
Presentation of offering
Hymn
The Sermon
Invitation to Christian Discipleship
Hymn
Benediction
Postlude

The committee charged at the 1956 General Conference with developing new resources had sought to make Wesley's service more than a "museum piece" and so had offered a service "true to [the Methodist] heritage" and "historically and psychologically valid" that contained all the elements of "vital Christian worship: adoration, confession and forgiveness, praise and thanksgiving, proclamation of the Word, and dedication of life." The service carried the notice that it was an adaptation of Wesley's *Sunday Service* and that it was recommended for Lord's Day use; an abbreviated form of the service (in outline), without the Wesleyan identification, was also provided.[40] The standard service and the brief outline, along with other materials (but not Wesley's 1784 text), were then authorized for trial use from 1960 to 1964. Evidently the overt declaration of patterning the standard service upon the Wesleyan *ordo* proved problematic, for the heading was removed in the approved 1965 *Book of Worship*, and the explicit Wesleyan connections of the service were lost.

In many respects the 1965 *Book of Worship* was ill-timed: it appeared three years before the Methodist Church was to unite with the Evangelical United Brethren Church to constitute the United Methodist Church; and the work done did not take into account the liturgical research and ferment that had given rise to the Constitution on Sacred Liturgy (*Sacrosanctum Concilium*) and the subsequent ritual revision of the Second Vatican Council. Recognizing the problem, the United Methodist Church in 1970 established a committee to compose a series of alternate, yet unofficial rituals. This led to the issuance of a Service of Word and Table that established the normativity of a eucharistic shape for Lord's Day worship whether or not the Lord's Supper was celebrated. The service was fine-tuned from 1972 until 1984 when it was approved as the first *United* Methodist Lord's Day service.[41] The finalized text appeared in both the 1989 *United Methodist Hymnal* and the 1992 *United Methodist Book of Worship*:

Entrance
  Gathering
  Greeting and Hymn
  Opening Prayers and Praise
Proclamation and Response
  Prayer for Illumination
  Scripture
  Sermon
  Response to the Word
  Concerns and Prayers
  Confession, Pardon, and Peace
  Offering
Thanksgiving
  Prayer of Thanksgiving (or Great Thanksgiving at Holy Communion)
  Lord's Prayer
  (Breaking the Bread)
  (Giving the Bread and Cup)
Sending Forth
  Hymn or Song and Dismissal with Blessing
  Going Forth

The structure of the service did not rely on Wesley's morning prayer, but instead imitated the classical shape of the Sunday liturgy believed to be found in its primitive form in Justin Martyr, a pattern that had gained wide ecumenical acceptance as a paradigm for new forms of worship. Even though Word and Table lacked a structural indebtedness to Wesley, the framers of the rite acknowledged its conformity to the spirit of Wesley, in that, quite consciously, his descendants had simply followed the Scriptures and the primitive church as he had charged them to do in 1784.

Other Forms for Sunday Worship

Sunday Afternoon and Evening Worship

In 1792, when the Methodist Episcopal Church abandoned Wesley's orders for Sunday morning and evening in favor of a brief listing of components to be included in a service of worship, the Methodist leadership assumed that, where possible, their people would gather for worship on Sunday at times in addition to the morning hour. Samuel Seaman described the multiple gatherings that would have been typical in the nineteenth century for societies within city stations situated along the eastern seaboard, in this case a New York City congregation in the 1830s and 1840s:

> There were three sermons on the Lord's day, at 10:30 A.M., at 3 P.M., and in the evening at 6:30 in the winter, 7:30 in the summer, and 7 in the fall and spring. The afternoon congregations were at least as large as any. Sunday-school met at 9 A.M., and 1:30 P.M., and the children occupied the galleries with their teachers at both the morning and afternoon services, unless especially excused at the request of their parents. Week-evening services were half an hour later than those of Sunday, varying also with the season.[42]

For some Methodists, Lord's Day worship took place either in the afternoon or the evening on account of the distance between meetinghouses and the scarcity of ordained ministers. In remote areas, the main service of the week was not held on Sunday at all, or Lord's Day worship was presided over by a licensed local preacher or an approved exhorter, a role that, in later times, might also be assumed by the Sunday school superintendent. Afternoon worship was to include the same components as the morning service, though with a reduction in the amount of Scripture to be read; Methodist Protestants from their formation indicated that both afternoon and evening services were to be comparable to the morning service, except for the number of Scripture lessons. Although the Methodist Episcopal Church from 1864 to 1912 and the Methodist Episcopal Church, South from 1870 to the 1939 merger followed the Methodist Protestants in conforming the design of the evening service to that of the afternoon, many congregations of those denominations, as well as other Methodist bodies, continued to practice the instruction from the 1792 *Discipline* that "singing, prayer, and preaching" should comprise the evening service. Since the unchurched and unconverted were often the intended participants in the evening service, worship generally took on an evangelistic flavor. Many of the early Methodist preachers record in their diaries and journals the Scripture texts taken for the evening services and for other times of day, and note with pride the reaping of the harvest of new souls or their dismay at the coldness and hard-heartedness of their hearers.

In a move that may have reflected either the dwindling practice of multiple Sunday gatherings or the expectation that services at all hours should conform to the morning pattern, the Methodist Episcopal Church in 1912 eliminated from the disciplinary section "Order of Public Worship" all references to afternoon and evening worship; eight years earlier, the paragraph on afternoon and evening had been reduced to a simple footnote in the section. This omission is all the more striking in light of the concern that had been expressed in the popular periodicals of several Methodist denominations that the Sunday evening service was going the way of the afternoon service that had, in many congregations, largely disappeared. Indeed, some would argue, it was precisely the expectation that the evening service should be an imitation of the increasingly elaborate morning form that had contributed to its decline. A corrective would be to return to the uncomplicated, evangelistic service with a focus on persuasive preaching that had characterized Methodism of earlier days.[43] What should *not* be done, Congregational minister Washington Gladden first stated in 1898, was what some Methodist pastors and others had selected: to use various "devices" and other enhancements to attract persons to evening worship. Such amusements, said Gladden, inevitably led to the prostitution of worship.[44] Yet numerous Methodist congregations that had exercised their liturgical freedom in developing simple worship found that evening services no longer held the attraction they once did, though some, like Church Street Methodist Episcopal Church, South in Knoxville, reportedly had to turn crowds away during the years 1914–1915. Church Street's 7:30 P.M. evening service for Sunday, February 19, 1928—of prelude, hymn, prayer, anthem, announcements and offertory, sermon, hymn, benediction, and postlude—offered both simplicity and denominational integrity, for it was simultaneously a truncated version of the standard morning service and an expansion (by instrumental/choral music, notices, and offering) of the 1792 instructions.[45]

With an ever-increasing number of entertainments and diversions tempting Methodists, Sunday evening worship continued to decline, but it did not disappear. Evening gatherings were encouraged by the publication of worship aids from denominational presses and by the production of official liturgical texts: the 1932 Methodist Episcopal *Discipline* included the conflated "Wesley" morning and evening prayer, and the 1945 *Book of Worship* of the Methodist Church listed eight services for evening use (strangely, no special evening order was contained in the 1965 *Book of Worship*). The 1989 *United Methodist Hymnal* and the 1992 *Book of Worship* provided an evening service, but in a significant departure from the Methodist tradition, the service was no longer one with revival-type preaching, but more of a "cathedral"-style service of praise, prayer, and psalmody modeled on classical forms. Although some congregations used this order on Sunday nights, an increasingly popular Sunday evening form at the end of the twentieth century was the so-called "contemporary" service, based on principles that harkened back to Finney's "new measures." Drawing upon drama, the musical beat of the day, the latest in media and technology, and other cultural "entertainments" that certainly would have horrified earlier Methodists, these services, like the Methodist evening services of former days, often catered to the unchurched, now labeled "seekers." This freer, but planned, style of worship also made inroads into the Sunday morning order, as congregations experimented with forms that blended their regular pattern with the "contemporary" in an effort to be "seeker-sensitive."

Sunday School Worship

Methodist educational and fellowship ministries have also generated forms for Sunday worship. Methodists in England and America were at the forefront of what would become the Sunday school movement, and legislation supporting the Christian nurture and catechizing of children claimed a priority in the nascent Methodist Episcopal Church.[46] On account of a keen focus upon the organization and structure of the Sunday schools, and the proliferation of literature from denominational presses, Sunday school membership from all the branches of Methodism in 1866 allegedly was only slightly under that of the combined total from six other leading denominations.[47] Significantly, numerous scholars in Methodist Sunday schools had no other affiliation with the church; the inclusion of worship "exercises" with the gathering of the entire school was, in part, meant to encourage their—and the other children's—participation in the regular services. For Methodist members and their children, Sunday school worship sometimes served as the replacement for the worship associated with the Methodist class meeting which, by the mid-nineteeth century, was in decline. And, particularly for frontier or rural congregations, the Sunday school assembly, led by the Sunday school superintendent or other appointed lay leader, provided the primary opportunity for weekly worship, since a circuit-riding licensed or ordained preacher might only be able to lead worship once or twice a month.

Because no official guidelines were offered for Sunday school worship, the services varied according to location and context, and generally a truncated form of the congregation's regular service was followed, supplemented with prose and poetry from collections such as *The Sunday-School Speaker*, compiled in 1860 by Thomas O. Summers. Illinois clergyman Leonard Smith recorded in 1869 that he began his Sunday school with the reading of Scripture, singing, and prayer, followed by a "catechism lesson";[48] these components for opening worship are widely attested in other communities. As the regular Sunday morning service became more elaborate, so often did the Sunday school order, a development illustrated by the pattern used in the 1890s by Pisgah Church of Tazewell County, Virginia, which shows as well the popular custom of blending a service of worship with fellowship or business meeting, and the utilization of opening and closing forms:

Opening
    Bell Taps or Organ Voluntary, as signal for silence
    Singing
    Responsive Reading, school standing
    Prayer, closing with the Lord's Prayer in concert
    Calling of Roll
    Singing
The Lesson
    Teachers take charge of classes
    Recitation of the Lesson, including Catechism Lesson
    Warning Bell—five minutes
    Closing Bell—silence

Closing
  Singing
  Official Reports
  Review and application of lesson
  Announcements, including Church services
  Doxology. Dismission[49]

Additional components might include special speakers, a devotional or Bible study by the leader, recitations of Scripture or poems by the classes, the unison profession of a creed, special monetary offerings, reports on the health and welfare of members or neighbors with prayer on their behalf, and the celebration of special themes or days such as Bible Sunday, Rally Day, or Children's Day. Large churches cultivated well-organized orchestras and choirs that performed for the opening and closing gatherings and occasionally for the main Lord's Day service. Each church developed its assembly as it saw fit, stressing education, Christian formation, lay leadership, and the active participation of all present. Though Methodist Sunday schools were not restricted to denominational resources, Methodist publishers readily stepped in to fill a need: songs, responsive readings, and full "programs" for worship were available in the *Epworth Hymnal* (1885, 1891), *The Methodist Sunday School Hymnal* (1911), various versions of *The Cokesbury Hymnal* (first published in 1923 and in print for the rest of the twentieth century), and *The Abingdon Song Book* (1938); the Methodist Episcopal Church, South's *Superintendent's Guide* suggested themes and texts for devotions throughout the course of a year. Congregations that over time retained their Sunday school assembly because of custom or from the existential need of sharing a pastor with other congregations often kept the form parallel to the structure of the preaching service, while singing songs and hymns from what had become for them the "Sunday school hymnal." The assembly pattern used in the 1990s by Poplar Springs United Methodist Church of Sanford, North Carolina, demonstrates the fluidity between the two services:

SUNDAY SCHOOL	WORSHIP SERVICE
Gathering	Prelude
Greetings	Call to Worship
	Opening Prayer
	Hymn
	Affirmation of Faith
	Children's Time
Announcements	Concerns of the Congregation
Prayer	Morning Prayer and Lord's Prayer
	Offering
Hymn	Hymn of Preparation
Scripture Lesson	Scripture Readings
Lesson	
Offering	Sermon
	Closing Hymn
Dismissal	Benediction

Or a simple pattern reminiscent of early nineteenth-century practice might be retained, as was the custom in the late 1990s of Mt. Zion United Methodist Church in Hurdle Mills, North Carolina, which opened its Sunday school with a sequence of hymn singing, Scripture reading, and devotional reading, followed by supplicatory and intercessory prayer. When a congregation abandoned its assembly on account of changes in demographics, pedagogy, or leadership, beloved components of the school service sometimes migrated to the main Sunday worship service, creating a hybrid form with the expectation that worship would be simultaneously doxological, didactic, and koinonaic.

Efforts in the latter half of the nineteenth century and in the first two decades of the twentieth century to produce a uniform worship order for Methodist Sunday schools failed, perhaps on account of the greater concern to integrate children and youth into the primary corporate service. Inadvertently, the Sunday school assembly had become, for many children (and adults), a substitute for the preaching service, prompting Ohio Conference officials in 1875 to remark regarding the attendance of children from Methodist families at the main service that "either Methodist families have few children, or they put forth little effort to have them in their sanctuary."[50] Cries resounded through denominational newspapers to rectify this ongoing problem for the sake of the gospel and the future of the church.[51] Multiple solutions were proposed, including the collapsing of the Sunday school assembly and preaching service into a combined morning order of almost two hours duration, which would begin with opening exercises and Bible study directed by the Sunday school superintendent, and conclude with the pastor leading "appropriate services" and a short sermon.[52] But the decision reached by the Methodist Episcopal Church, at first unofficially and in 1932 officially, had, at its worst, the effect of further alienating children and youth from the primary service of the word. Utilizing the latest tools in the growing academic field of developmental psychology, and borrowing from the psychospiritual and liturgico-aesthetic work of Vogt, Sperry, and others, denominational leaders determined that *graded* Sunday school worship services were to be preferred over the multigenerational school gathering, since "difference in age, experience, capacities, and needs make necessary worship services that differ in purpose and content."[53] The intended outcome was twofold: to "train" children and youth for worship in the main congregation, and in doing so, to provide meaningful, appropriate, and well-constructed services that addressed life experiences and stimulated the religious imagination. Ideally, the Sunday school service and the preaching service, though distinct services of worship, were to be regarded as parts of a unified whole.[54] However, in some congregations, the age-specific service would become a "children's church" that youngsters attended as a substitute for all or part of the main service. In 1932, the Methodist Episcopal General Conference charged its agencies to produce appropriate age-level services for the Sunday school; and, along the same vein, it was also in 1932 that this denomination introduced into its official Sunday morning order the option of a "junior sermon," which persisted in Methodist worship under various titles. Books of age-specific worship resources continued to be published after the merger creating the Methodist Church, and among the most popular was a series written by Alice Anderson Bays, the centerpiece for which were talks on famous personages, works of art, or skills for Christian living.[55] Even though the services were designed for particular age groupings, Bays's order of service was nevertheless basically the same and hinted at the order used for the primary morning service:

Prelude
Call to Worship
Hymn
(variable sequence, consisting of one or more: Prayer, Scripture, Affirmation
    of Faith, Responsive Reading, Poem)
Story or Talk or Exposition of Painting/Sculpture
(Poem)
Prayer
Hymn
Benediction

Despite the availability of age-level resources, Sunday school services were often truncated versions of or variations upon the congregation's regular Sunday pattern, as evident from a 1964 worship service for the "junior department" of Glenmont Methodist Church in Wheaton, Maryland:

Hymn
Call to Worship
Silent Meditation
Prayer
The Lord's Prayer
Offering
Doxology
Presentation of Tithes and Gifts
Lesson from the Scriptures
Hymn
Benediction

The popularity of poetry, religious drama, paintings, sculpture, and other creative arts in the Sunday school encouraged their inclusion in the Lord's Day service, though actual usage was usually tempered by the congregation's sensibilities on such matters. Explorations during the 1940s and 1950s of the place of the arts in worship gave way in the 1960s and 1970s to experiments in worship with liturgical dance, sound recordings, film clips, and sacred clowning. These "innovations" were tested in non-Methodist congregations as well. Methodists widely produced "creative" orders of, or guidelines for, worship in print or in typescript: individuals, local churches, and even Methodist conference committees tried their hand.[56] Although much of what developed was ephemeral, it did actualize for many Methodists the long-held principle of liturgical freedom for Sunday worship.

Worship on the Lord's Day in a Methodist congregation may reproduce past or present official denominational services, it may be the product of a localized evolutionary process by which various worship patterns or components of worship are molded together to create a unique whole, it may combine the two previous types over the course of the year, or it may be highly variable in form. In spite of the wide range of structural possibilities, certain characteristics are predictable for much of Methodist worship. These worship elements conform not only to what is considered the essence of Protestant Christian worship but also to the foundational Methodist "directory" of 1792. To the basic components of prayer, reading of Scripture, preaching, and song may be added the rehearsal of creeds and the saying or singing of Psalms. The actual choice of texts and actions for any given service depends upon the particular emphasis for the day, whether that be determined locally or by conformity to wider theological, liturgical, and ecclesiastical agendas.

2

The Lord's Day

Ordinary and Propers

E VERY REGULAR SERVICE of Christian worship consists of both ordinary and propers: by the former is meant the invariable liturgical texts or acts of worship that are repeated each time the people gather; by the latter, the texts and acts that are variable and usually reflect the day or season of the church year. At first blush it might appear that Methodists had no ordinary as such until the twentieth century; that despite pushes for liturgical uniformity, the desire for liturgical free-dom and the evangelical fervor of the first hundred years obviated any invariable components of worship other than preaching. Yet clearly the Methodists have always had an ordinary, not of texts per se, but of standard components for worship as outlined in the Methodist "directory" of 1792, which was gradually expanded to include responsive psalmody and creeds though not in every congregation or denomination. Methodists also made use of propers tied to the Christian year, at first in a limited fashion and more fully as worship became more formalized. To the Christian calendar the Methodists added their own festival days and civic observances, blurring them in ways deemed appropriate for the most "American" of denominations. The ordinary and propers used in worship help define what it means to be Methodist on the Lord's Day.

The Contents of Lord's Day Worship

Prayer

Frequent and disciplined prayer in public and in private was, according to John Wesley, one of the fundamental and characteristic practices of the Methodists who were to carry out in all seriousness the Scripture mandate to pray—"to lift up their hearts to God"—without ceasing, and thereby exercise what was considered to be one of the instituted means of grace.[1] Wesley's revision of the Prayer Book therefore was intended to equip the American Methodists for what their self-definition charged them to do. The *Sunday Service* also recognized the radical departure that Methodists had made from the Prayer Book tradition when it allowed for the option of extemporary prayer in public worship,[2] though this rubric came not in Wesley's orders for morning and evening prayer, but in the service for the Lord's Supper. Wesley himself had no difficulty in combining written and extemporary forms of prayer on any liturgical occasion, though Methodists have often forgotten this fact.[3] The use of printed prayers on Sunday morning was not the favored practice of the majority of early American Methodists, who preferred the extemporary style over the reading of prayer texts; Methodists who worshiped in the large urban centers and utilized both types of prayer were, for a time, the exception. Thus the tension found early on concerning freedom or form in worship in general was borne out liturgically by the method of prayer used and theologically through the pneumatological presuppositions that undergirded the definitions of authentic prayer.

Extemporary prayer, valued by generations of Methodists as the best means of praying with the mind and the spirit (1 Corinthians 14:15; cf. Romans 8:15–16), admittedly could be subject to a variety of human weaknesses. In their 1798 commentary on the *Discipline*, Bishops Francis Asbury and Thomas Coke reinforced the caution they had received from Wesley against praying without intermission for more than eight to ten minutes and added their own warnings, which later Methodists would often reiterate since the advice apparently went unheeded:

> Scarcely any thing tends to damp divine service more than to be praying too long, and in a languid manner. Few things more tend to bring a congregation into a *formal* spirit. Sometimes indeed the minister is led within the vail in an unusual way, and may then justly give full vent to the holy flame. But on other occasions let the prayer be very fervent, and of moderate length. "When ye pray," says our Lord, "use not vain repetitions, as the heathen do: for they think that they shall be heard for their much speaking. Be not ye therefore like unto them." Matt. vi. 7,8.[4]

Writers of essays and pastoral aids over the next two hundred years recommended that those who were to pray in public should take stock of their own spiritual state, since indifference might breed formalism, malaise could discourage the prayers of persons in the pew, and personal confession could mask the intended purposes of corporate prayer. Equally dangerous was a style characterized by exaggerations in voice and mannerism, and the use of language or turns of phrase inappropriate to the place or time. Extemporary public prayer directed to the throne of grace ideally was to be sincere, heartfelt, comprehensive, clear, effective but unaffected, and brief.

Just as there were moves toward creating uniform liturgies for Lord's Day worship, similarly there were efforts, though initially more subtle ones, to endorse standard prayer texts. The instruction approved by the Methodist Episcopal Church in 1824 that the Lord's Prayer was to conclude the first prayer at all occasions of public worship effectively opened the door to the use of set prayers, though it was generally acknowledged that this preformulated prayer was unique in that it was prescribed as a form and model by the Lord himself. But which text of this Scripture-prayer was to be used? The differences in the synoptic texts were not lost on the

Methodists, and debates ensued from the late 1850s to the 1910s on the most appropriate text and translation, and whether or not the final doxology ought to be added.[5] During this period, unofficial prayer resources by Methodists appeared on the market alongside the reprints and revisions of parts of Wesley's *Sunday Service*. These publications included T. O. Summers's *The Golden Censer: An Essay on Prayer, with a Selection of Forms of Prayer, Designed to Aid in the Devotions of the Sanctuary, Family, and Closet* (1859), Charles LeVerne Roberts's *Divine Service: A Compilation of Collects and Psalms for Use in the Public Worship of God in the Methodist Episcopal Church* (1903), and Bishop Thirkield's *Service and Prayers for Church and Home* already mentioned (1918, 1928). The appearance of written prayer texts was unsettling to many Methodists. While Roberts's editorial note in *Divine Service* claimed that his collection responded to the cry "Back to Wesley" that reverberated through the Methodist Episcopal Church as a type of "liturgical movement," others feared that such interest in "ritualistic" prayers would force a departure from traditional Wesleyanism. Such concerns were well-founded, for as the momentum toward written prayers increased, the discipline and skills of praying extemporaneously or spontaneously in public worship declined, though they were best preserved within African-American Methodism. The changing attitudes of Methodists toward written prayers are substantiated by the presence of twenty-one pages of official but optional "Aids to Individual and Congregational Devotion" in the 1939 *Discipline* of the newly formed Methodist Church. The impetus toward printed prayers continued, with most American Methodist bodies since the 1950s placing prayer texts among their official worship resources. Usually the expected function of the prayer is specified (e.g., confession, intercession). The contents of the prayers reveal much about Methodist (or at least some Methodist) understandings on the pervasive theological and moral issues. For example, prayers articulating the concerns of the social gospel movement are rife in the 1930s and 1940s, with some, by such writers as the Baptist Walter Rauschenbusch, managing to find a place in books published in the 1980s and 1990s. Even the sources of the prayers spoke to Methodist assumptions about prayer and about Methodist ecclesial identity within the church catholic: the rediscovery of ancient texts and the ecumenical sharing of contemporary, multicultural resources invited the use of prayers ancient and modern, national and international.

Readings and Psalmody

The Articles of Religion sent to America by Wesley in 1784 have served as a constitutive and binding document for Methodist and Wesleyan churches. The fifth Article on the "sufficiency of the Holy Scriptures for salvation" sets forth the role of Scripture and delimits what is canonical (the Apocrypha is excluded). This statement reinforced Wesley's teaching that Scripture was the inspired and infallible word of God, which had supreme authority in the establishment of doctrine and in Christian life, though other subordinate authorities, such as reason, experience, and selected eras of the church's tradition might also be at work; a questionable modern interpretation claimed Wesley's norms for doctrinal authority were precisely fourfold (the "quadrilateral").[6] Exactly because the Scriptures were the paramount norm, the Bible was not to be revered at a distance but rather used with respect for its divinely appointed purposes: Methodists have always been charged to seek grace through searching the Scriptures corporately and privately by reading, hearing, and meditating on them. As Coke and Asbury noted in 1798, a "peculiar blessing" accompanied the public reading of the Scriptures, and so presiders at worship were to do all in their power to "lead the people to the love of the holy bible."[7]

The supplanting of the 1784 orders for morning and evening prayer by the rubrics of 1792 may, at first sight, suggest that the amount of Scripture potentially heard in the actual Methodist congregation was substantially reduced. In reality, the new rubrics may rather have been intended to increase the quantity of Scripture used in those assemblies that had already abandoned the *Sunday Service*. The instruction that a chapter be read from each testament was no stray thought. The proper lessons for morning and evening prayer that had come into the *Sunday Service* from the *Book of Common Prayer* were primarily readings of a complete chapter, though the lectionary for epistles and gospels—connected with the Communion service—did designate portions of chapters. Those who were familiar with Wesley's journal[8] and the preface to his *Explanatory Notes upon the Old Testament* (1765) would have recognized the use of two testamental chapters as the pattern for the daily private reading of the Scriptures that Wesley knew in his childhood and had recommended for all Christian people. Officially, at least, the designation of a minimum of two readings would remain unchanged in episcopal Methodism, though, as has already been noted, the term "lesson" would eventually replace "chapter." Other Methodist bodies called for unspecified readings or a single lesson, usually understood to be the text for the sermon, and thus better rubricized what was more generally Sunday practice in most of American Methodism.

In the second half of the nineteenth century, a growing hermeneutical shift away from the literal and historical reading of the Bible, which was generated by the development of critical approaches to the text,[9] provoked fears that the authority of Scripture—and hence the Christian faith as well as traditional Methodism—was under assault. Equally threatening were persons "exalted to high seats in the temple of wisdom and fame" who professed the infallibility of the "oracles of science" and who denied the validity of revealed truth and inspired Scripture.[10] Methodists rallied to support the "Bible cause" of their denominations and the American Bible Society (founded in 1816) by mobilizing efforts to circulate the sacred text to all who would receive it, thereby reinforcing the contention that "Protestantism and patriotism unite in pointing to the Holy Bible as the living genius, creative and conservative, of our civil as well as our ecclesiastical institutions."[11] Perhaps in response to the perceived undermining of scriptural authority, and coinciding with renewed interest in Wesley's forms for the Lord's Day, some Methodists began to look at developing a practical psalter that would encourage the use of more Scripture in corporate worship and, by allowing for responsive readings, the active participation of the people whose role was criticized as "nothing but patient waiting and hearing."[12] In 1865 was published an unofficial *Sabbath Psalter: A Selection of Psalms for Public and Family Worship*, compiled by Henry J. Fox, who offered fifty-three sets of psalms for morning and evening and, though intent upon avoiding "formalism" in worship, suggested that the psalm be used at the commencement of a service or following the first prayer. A memorial sent from the Genesee Conference to the Methodist Episcopal General Conference of 1868 to request the approval of a psalter began the series of petitions that would persist over the ensuing years in that denomination and others, though such strategies were seen by some as additional evidence of Methodism's sure movement toward ritualism. Meanwhile, collections of unauthorized responsive readings appeared, including those drawn from Wesley's Select Psalms and *Scripture Lessons arranged for Responsive Readings in Religious Services* (1889) by the Methodist Episcopal Church's publishing house, which, in a given reading, combined portions of psalms or other Scripture texts under a stated theme. The drive to approve a psalter eventually culminated, for the Methodist Episcopal Church and Methodist Episcopal Church, South, in the inclusion in the 1905 hymnal of two sets of conflated psalms for fifty-three Sundays of the year. Debates then followed about the propriety of tampering with holy writ to create a single reading from the conflation of multiple texts, the correctness of editing out theologically difficult passages from a single psalm, the placement of the psalms in other than canonical order, the translation of the text to be used, and, consequent to the First World War, the appropriateness for Christian worship of psalms praising a bellicose and vengeful God.[13] In the years since 1905, many Methodist bodies have placed either a psalter or a section of responsive readings in their hymnal or worship book.

Openness toward the use of a psalter coincided with another change: acceptance of the methods of biblical criticism and, with it, the raising of uncertainties about the authority of Scripture. Though cautions were put forward and claims made that some had gone too far in "using that liberty which Methodism has always allowed to its representatives,"[14] Methodists from the beginning of the twentieth century have explored and accepted new forms of scholarship with the intention that the church might more authentically address the times in which it ministered. In a statement that Methodists a century earlier would not have recognized, the bishops of the Methodist Episcopal Church, South in 1934 wrote that "scholarship has always found a friendly attitude in our Methodism, because life is the final test of truth."[15]

The incorporation of responsive psalmody into worship had the unintended result of depriving congregations of the fullness of Old Testament riches. Archie C. Murray of Baltimore expressed the problem to the Methodist Episcopal General Conference of 1912:

> Whereas the Responsive Reading of the Psalms—however excellent it might be if simply added to our rather brief form of worship—is far from being a sufficient substitute for the Old Testament Lesson of which it has deprived us;
>
> And whereas our Saviour, habitually quoting from the sacred Scriptures and referring to "Moses and the Prophets," the early sacred histories (as, e.g., "Kings") being then called "Former Prophets," certainly does not in any way countenance our Church's unfortunate reduction of the thirty-nine sacred books of the Old Testament Scriptures to the one book of Psalms—and neither do his Apostles.
>
> Now therefore we earnestly beg (thru you) the General Conference to restore the Old Testament Lesson by ordering that whenever any responsive reading is used, such

reading shall in no wise take the place of either of the two Bible Lessons to be read distinctly by the minister or leader.[16]

Although the issue raised by Murray was not immediately resolved, it did encourage long-term interest in the production of an Old Testament lectionary and eventually invited the specification of 110 Old Testament readings in the shared 1935 *Methodist Hymnal*. Interest in lectionary usage broadened, so that in the 1965 Methodist *Book of Worship* there was a single-year, Christian-calendar lectionary of three lessons (basically Old Testament, Epistle, and Gospel), a psalm, and an act of praise. Ecumenical involvement during the 1970s and 1980s by some of the Methodist branches in the Consultation on Common Texts (CCT) led to contributions by Methodist representatives toward the production of the three-year, three-lesson (plus psalm) Common and Revised Common lectionaries, with the results of those endeavors published in many of the Methodist service books produced in the late twentieth century. The frequency of lectionary usage in Methodist worship rose, but many congregations—and their preachers—still relied upon immediate divine inspiration or personal and pastoral agendas in the selection of Scripture for Sunday.

Preaching

Preaching always held a central place in Methodist worship and work, and was by most Methodists considered *the* essential component of a worship service. The primary intention of Methodist preaching was never exegetical accuracy, but rather the need to inflame stone-cold hearts and rekindle the lukewarm by the power of the gospel, through the agency of the Holy Spirit. Indeed, preachers from the first century of American Methodism would often boast that though their sermons (which "took" a Scripture text and elaborated upon it) or exhortations (testimonies or accounts of the faith not connected to a specific text) might not be erudite or systematic, they were effectual. Persuasive evangelical preaching has been so characteristic that it was once asserted that Methodists "get right into the heart, and there they stick, until they tear it all to pieces."[17] Englishwoman Isabella Lucy Bird Bishop would concede that among the most powerful sermons she heard in her mid-nineteenth-century visit to the United States were those from Methodist pulpits.[18] This evangelical emphasis can be traced to John Wesley, whose simple instruction in his Large Minutes (Question 36) that preaching "invite, convince, offer Christ, and build up" was repeated in successive editions of the *Discipline* and elaborated upon in Methodist preachers' own practical advice on homiletics:

> The design of preaching is to awaken sinners, and to bring them to Christ;—to urge believers to the attainment of holiness of heart and life;—to show sinners the turpitude of their hearts and sinfulness of their practice, and to bring them to the foot of the cross, stripped of self and of all self dependence;—to press the old Methodistical doctrines of justification by faith; the direct evidence from God, through faith in the merits of Christ, of the forgiveness of sin; and the adoption into his family. Nor are we to be ashamed of that unfashionable doctrine, Christian perfection: but we should point out clearly a travail of soul, not only for justification, but for sanctification, and the evi-

dence of it. The holier we are, the more fit we shall be both for this world and that reward which awaits us hereafter.[19]

Preachers were urged to be serious, to direct the message to the context or situation of the hearers, to speak the simple truth to the point and in understandable language, and "to have such a variety of subjects, thoughts, expressions, figures, arguments and illustrations as shall entertain and edify, instruct and benefit even the most refined and religious in [the] congregation."[20] Methodist itinerant preachers spoke to all classes, races, and language groups wherever and whenever there was need, in imitation of Wesley's own innovative and unrestricted preaching in domestic dwellings and in the open air. The urgency for proclaiming the gospel was such that both Wesley and Asbury preferred that itinerants be unmarried and thus unfettered, though that expectation disappeared in the early nineteenth century.

Methodist preachers often left detailed accounts of the desired spiritual awakening of souls that was manifested in response to their enthusiastic preaching; this popular genre of Methodist literature was published into the twentieth century. The early Methodists, in particular, would often comment that they had been "at liberty" when their preaching seemed to accomplish its intended goal—setting "at liberty" those enslaved to sin. Conversely, a preacher might comment, as did William Doub preaching on Revelation 22:14 in Hillsborough, North Carolina, that "I had not much liberty; but I hope some good was done."[21] The testimony of Thomas Rankin, who was sent to America by John Wesley, is representative of a fervent, charismatic style of preaching and worship that, after the Civil War, would be preserved particularly in the Holiness branches of Methodism:

At 4 o'clock I went to the chapel again. I preached from Rev. 3rd chapter, 8 verse. Towards the close of the sermon, I found an uncommon struggle in my breast; and in the twinkling of an eye, my soul was so filled with the power and love of God, that I could scarce get out my words. I scarce had spoken two sentences while under this amazing influence, before the very house seemed to shake, and all the people were overcome with the presence of the Lord God of Israel. Such a scene, my eyes saw, and ears heard; as I never was witness to before. Through the mercy and goodness of God, I had seen many glorious displays of the arm of the Lord, in the different parts of his vineyard, where his providence had called me to labour; but such a time as this I never, never beheld. Numbers were calling out aloud for mercy, and many were mightily praising God their Saviour; while others were in an agony, for full redemption in the blood of Jesus! Soon, very soon, my voice was drowned amidst the pleasing sounds of prayer and praise. Husbands were inviting their wives, to go to heaven with them; and parents calling upon their children to come to the Lord Jesus: And what was peculiarly affecting, I observed in the gallery (appropriated for the black people) almost every one of them upon their knees; some for themselves, and others for their distressed companions. In short, look where we would, all was wonder and amazement! As my strength was almost gone, I desired Brother Shadford to speak a few words to them. He attempted so to do, but was so overcome with the Divine presence, that he was obliged to sit down; and this was the case, both with him and myself, over and over again. We could only sit still and let the Lord do his work. For upwards of 2 hours the mighty pouring out of the spirit of God continued upon the congregation. As many of them had come from far, we with the greatest difficulty and the most earnest persuasions, got them to depart, between 7 and 8 o'clock in the evening. Some of them had to ride 10 and others 15 miles to their habitations. Such a day of the Son of Man, my eyes never beheld before. From the best accounts we could receive afterwards, upwards of 50 were awakened and brought to the knowledge of a pardoning God that day; beside many, who were enabled to witness that the blood of Jesus had cleansed them from all sin.[22]

The conversion of hearts and minds, or at least sound scriptural learning, was also expected from the other side of the pulpit. Methodists typically have judged the success or failure of preaching (and the preacher) by visible means, such as the number of persons gathered in praise, prayer, or distress at the "altar" after the sermon, or by the message's ability to move emotionally or to edify spiritually and sometimes even intellectually. So observed Mississippi native Maria Dyer Davies, writing in her late teens:

> December 29, 1850. Went to church to day, heard Mr. Massingale. Subject, analogy of the ancient races to the christian etc. Was not eloquent, but I felt built-up. Enjoyed it much & learned something too. . . .
> August 29, 1852. Sabbath-night. I have been to Plum Creek to-day. I did not *enjoy* the sermon. The minister was slow, discourse lengthy & somewhat common-place. I do not know though how many *were* benefitted by it. . . .
> April 21, 1853. Wednesday. We have been to church again, but I could not feel interested. Mr. Finley preached, was not in the spirit, thought his sermon not good. The church seemed cold.[23]

While, in principle, the goal and primacy of preaching have remained constant, the content and presentation of Methodist sermons have been affected by changes exterior to Methodism—such as shifting cultural presuppositions regarding rhetoric and public discourse, advancements in media technologies,[24] and the development of psychological disciplines—and interior, especially increased levels of education for clergy and laity, new or redirected theological and social emphases (raising concerns about neglected doctrinal issues), and the conception of the sermon as an element in liturgical worship. There have always been critics of lengthy sermons (one Captain Meredith Brock of Florida, it was said, took out his newspaper when he perceived sufficient time had elapsed).[25] But judging by actual practice and the written recommendations of "experts," Sunday morning sermons, over two hundred years, gradually decreased in duration from approximately one hour to (as brief as) ten minutes; brevity became the watchword as sound bites replaced oratory. Extemporary preaching, prepared for in advance by prayerful study and reflection, was repeatedly extolled as the preferred method of sermon delivery. Yet, over time, the utilization of sermon manuscripts became more accepted, though they were still condemned by some as too formal, mechanical, unnatural, and "not Methodist." The use of sermon manuscripts was encouraged not only by sophistication in academic study and the general decrease in oratorical skills but also by the intellectual demand in some quarters that sermons "make one think."

Even so, Methodist congregations in each generation have decried the decline in preaching from previous days, exposing a trend to replace spiritual subjects on Sunday morning with topics moral and psychological, and relegating the once central issue of conversion to occasional revival meetings. One remedy has been to focus upon the messenger rather than the message, giving rise first to the pulpit princes and, at the end of the twentieth century, to the marketability of televangelism. The practice of liturgical preaching, that is, the exposition of a biblical text that takes into account the context and content of the service as a whole, was first introduced to Methodists in the mid-twentieth century, and brought a new dimension and expectation, but did not establish itself as a feasible solution in uniting knowledge and vital piety.

The Apostles' Creed and Other Affirmations of Faith

When the Apostles' Creed appeared in 1896 as a standard component of the Methodist Episcopal Church's new order of public worship, it marked the first time since the abandonment of Wesley's orders for morning and evening prayer that a creed had officially been used for Methodist worship on occasions other than when the baptismal liturgy for adults was celebrated (where the creed in the interrogative mode served as the profession of faith prior to baptism). In spite of the limited usage of the Apostles' Creed prior to 1896, it had been the focus of ongoing controversy among all Methodist bodies. Debate had not been so much in regard to its doctrinal content and authority, but because of the single phrase "the holy catholic Church," which some took to indicate the Roman Catholic Church—an interpretation not unique to the Methodists but found among Protestants and Catholics alike. The Methodist Protestant Church, in addressing the issue, took the bold step of omitting the creed entirely from its liturgical formulations in 1830. To squelch misunderstandings, the Methodist Episcopal Church's General Conference in 1836 added an asterisk at the suspect phrase in the adult baptismal rite with the corresponding note reading "by holy catholic Church is meant the Church of God in general"; in 1864 this footnote formulation was altered to "the one universal Church of Christ" and was repeated in subsequent publications of the baptism service until 1932. The defining note, however, was not included when the creed appeared in the 1896 order for public worship and was added only in 1916. Even with the explanatory note, the matter was hardly resolved, as efforts were made at practically each succeeding quadrennial meeting of the General Conferences to have the phrase stricken from the creed. Indeed, the omission of the offending phrase was the solution taken by the Methodist Episcopal Church, South, which, from 1854 to 1910, used in its place "the Church of God" in the baptismal rite, though by 1905 the denomination had already officially restored the original terminology by its approval of the Sunday order published that year in the joint hymnal. The Free Methodists, considering that the theological assumptions undergirding "the holy catholic Church" were adequately covered by "the communion of saints," simply removed the first phrase in the baptism rite; the Wesleyan Methodists, on the other hand, omitted both phrases. African-American Methodist denominations addressed the problem by experimenting with many of these same solutions: in the twentieth century, the African Methodist Episcopal Church kept the original expression but added the sharp explanation "the Church Universal, and not the Papal Church of Rome." Methodist involvement in the ecumenical scene did not resolve this debate; one Methodist writer in the 1920s insisted that "catholic" and "Christian" could not be equated since the Catholic Church was essentially pagan.[26] Although worship resources produced by the largest Methodist bodies gradually restored "the holy catholic Church" to the creed, the phrase was still most often accompanied by an explanatory note.

Another clause from the Apostles' Creed, not found in the oldest forms of the symbol of faith but understood by later Christians to be part of the received text, was short-lived in Methodist usage. It appeared in the 1784 *Sunday Service*, but was deleted at one of the creed's three appearances in the 1786 edition, an omission that some scholars contend did not originate with Wesley. In the 1786 formulation, "he went down into hell" disappeared from the adult baptismal rite while "he descended into hell" was retained in the orders for morning and evening prayer. The discrepancy may be explained as an oversight, but by 1792 it made no practical difference since, with the dropping of morning and evening prayer, the baptismal formulation was the only version to remain. The omission of the phrase may be explained as an effort to remove a theologically volatile subject: the thirty-ninth Anglican Article affirming Christ's descent into hell had prompted debate within the Puritan wing and also among the founders of the Protestant Episcopal Church in America; it had not been included in Wesley's revision of the Articles. Only in the late twentieth century would United Methodists reintroduce the phrase, and then as part of the stated "ecumenical" version of the creed produced by the English Language Liturgical Consultation (ELLC).

Ecumenical awareness, particularly in the twentieth century, was a factor in efforts to establish a definitive text of the Apostles' Creed as a whole. When, for some Methodists, the Apostles' Creed became a normative part of the Sunday liturgy, a decision was required about the version of the creed to be used. Should it be a declarative variation of the baptismal interrogative, until then the only form of the creed still in Methodist usage? Should Wesley's formulation of the creed for the prayer services be restored, recognizing that Methodists had, in 1784, inherited from Wesley most of the variations in the wording of the creed found at different places in the Prayer Book? The form used for morning and evening prayer differed at several points from that in the baptismal liturgy, even when allowing for the interrogative address, though Wesley himself had attempted some textual reconciliation by modifying "resurrection of the flesh" to "resurrection of the body" in the baptismal formulation so that all three citations of the creed were in agreement on that matter. The version from Wesley's morning and evening prayer, the text also used in the Protestant Episcopal Church's daily offices of 1892, was the option selected in 1896 by the Methodist Episcopal Church, which nevertheless made some editorial modifications before printing the text in the *Discipline*. Though the Methodist Episcopal Church, South approved the creed for their Sunday order in 1906, a declarative version was not provided in their *Discipline;* one was available to congregations in the 1905 joint hymnal. Methodists now had two different versions of the creed, which then led to efforts to produce a single, uniform text.

The Protestant Episcopal Church's rites were a source for the official "discovery" by Methodists of the Nicene-Constantinopolitan Creed, since neither that creed nor the Athanasian Creed (which Wesley disliked because of its "damnatory" clauses) had found a place in Wesley's *Urtext*. Wesley had also omitted from his version of the Articles of Religion the eighth Anglican Article confessing belief in the three historic creeds. The Nicene Creed, which in the Prayer Book appeared as part of the Communion rite, undoubtedly had been deleted by Wesley not because of any doctrinal question (the first four Methodist Articles are virtually an abbreviated recasting of the Nicene formula), but to avoid the redundancy of two creeds in one liturgical performance, since the Communion order was expected to follow immediately after morning prayer. Because of the absence of the Nicene and Athanasian formulations in the first Methodist liturgy, the early Methodists had been accused of heterodoxy by their enemies, and in response had published sermons and treatises affirming the doctrine of the Trinity.[27] Nevertheless, neither the Nicene nor the Athanasian statements of faith was ever officially restored. Although the Nicene Creed may be found in some official worship books after 1945, its practical usage was limited among Methodists who preferred the shorter and theologically less demanding Apostles' Creed.

Methodists from the 1930s also created and used modern declarations of faith and Scripture statements, the latter being most often a catena of Scripture, from one canonical book or several, and loosely following the structure of the ecumenical creeds. The two most widely published modern declarations in Methodist resources have been the "Korean Creed," composed by Bishop Herbert Welch (with consultation from Korean Methodists and from representatives of the two largest branches of episcopal Methodism in America) and adopted in 1930 when the Korean Methodist Church became autonomous,[28] and the so-called "Modern Affirmation," which, at the request of Bishop Wilbur Thirkield, was drafted by Edwin Lewis of Drew Theological Seminary. Both of these creeds appeared in the 1932 ecumenically minded *Book of Common Worship for Use in the Several Communions of the Church of Christ*, edited by Thirkield and Congregational minister Oliver Huckel, and in the 1935 *Methodist Hymnal*.

Doxologies and Benedictions

Hymns and, in the second century of American Methodism, service music were normative for Methodist worship and, though these topics will have an entire chapter devoted to them, it is appropriate to mention here doxological ascriptions. Freestanding, single-stanza metrical doxologies of different meters were included in Methodist hymnals long before they became a specified component of the Methodist *ordo*. Two designated doxologies occur in the Methodist Episcopal hymnal of 1821, and nineteen may be found in the final pages of that denomination's 1849 hymnal; both hymnals contain the doxological conclusion shared between Thomas Ken's hymns for morning, evening, and midnight published in 1695: "Praise God, from whom all blessings flow." This stanza, found in most Methodist hymnals and typically set to the tune Old Hundredth,[29] came to be commonly known as *the* Doxology. Other short, trinitarian acclamations also served as conclusions for hymns, following the hymnic models offered by Charles Wesley and other hymn writers, and as independent musical praise that could appear at various points in the liturgy, though most often at either the beginning or end of the service. Methodists did not inherit metrical doxologies as a Christianizing resolution to metrical psalms, since Wesley had specified that the psalms and the concluding Lesser Doxology or Gloria Patri ("Glory be to the Father," etc.) were to be read. With the reintroduction of psalmody as an official and distinct component of the service almost a century after its excision in 1792, a sung Gloria Patri came into use along with a recommended tune by Charles Meineke.

A rubric in the 1824 *Discipline* of the Methodist Episcopal Church instructing that the apostolic benediction (2 Corinthians 13:14) be the sole form employed in dismissing the congregation from public worship was retained by that denomination until 1928; other Methodist denominations that fell heir to or adopted the prescription similarly relaxed their restrictions in the early twentieth century. The earlier effort toward liturgical uniformity actually, on the infrequent Communion Sundays, had led to variability in practice (which undoubtedly was also the case on other Sundays): the Communion service, which was typically tacked on at the end of the normal Sunday service, had its own benediction (Philippians 4:7), and despite calls for clarification about which benediction was to be used, no official statement seems to have been offered. One solution apparently was to sing the apostolic benediction at the conclusion of the Communion service, using a hymn text by John Newton ("May the grace of Christ our Saviour") found in numerous nineteenth-century Methodist hymnals under the subheading "apostolic benediction." The issue was put to rest first by the printing of optional scriptural benedictions (e.g., Numbers 6:24–26; Hebrews 13:20–21; 1 Timothy 1:17; Jude 1:24–25), and later by allowing (or at least not condemning) nonscriptural forms.

The Languages of Worship

The vocabulary and syntax of American English have evolved over the last two centuries, and Methodists have responded in different ways to the question of how this should affect the language of public worship. The replacement of some archaic Prayer Book forms with modern equivalents in the *Sunday Service* (e.g., "you" for the Old English nominative "ye," "are" [the present indicative plural of the verb "to be"] for "be," and the personal "who" for "which") opened the door for Methodists to keep abreast of common linguistic forms. Nowhere are renovations more evident than in the Lord's Prayer, though these may have come from Thomas Coke's hand rather than Wesley's, since the latter indicated in a June 20, 1789, letter to Walter Churchey that he preferred "which" to the 1784 use of "who art in heaven." Despite the apparent invitation to employ modern linguistic forms in worship, Methodists mostly have been conservative in their use of language; at the end of the twentieth century, many congregations within the Methodist family still considered the vocabulary and style of the King James Bible the most suitable for the reading of Scripture and the saying of prayers. Sometimes the alteration of a single word in a denomination's liturgical formulation was met with considerable discussion on linguistic and theological grounds, such as the request made in 1864 by a few members of the Methodist Episcopal Church to emend "Holy Ghost" to "Holy Spirit." The official change was approved only in 1916, and then the debate reopened when talks began that would lead to the merger of 1939. Although the recommending committee proposed the printing of both forms, among the descendants of that merger mention of the "Holy Ghost" was rarely heard in worship save in certain doxological ascriptions and hymns. The extent to which gender-inclusive liturgical language—for humans and for deity—ought to be used became a matter of debate, with the subject of God-language remaining unresolved at the end of the twentieth century.

American Methodism, while predominantly English speaking, has not been exclusively so, even from the earliest days. Asbury intentionally chose for companions in ministry Henry Boehm and other German speakers. Boehm recalled that in 1803 bilingual services took place at joint meetings between the Methodists and the United Brethren in Christ, with a single preacher speaking in both English and German alternately, or with two or more preachers working together to preach and provide simultaneous translation.[30] Throughout the nineteenth century, as immigrant communities established themselves, Methodists held services in German and Bohemian, Swedish, Danish, Norwegian, Italian, French, Portuguese, and Spanish, oftentimes conducted by ordained immigrant ministers who left their original ecclesiastical community to join with the Methodist cause, or by immigrant lay preachers who themselves had first heard the gospel from the Methodists. To aid in the Methodist work, the *Discipline* (with the order of public worship), hymnals, or other resource books were published by the church presses in these languages. The German-speaking community, the largest of the non-English immigrant groups, received the most sustained attention, with the first of a series of German Methodist hymnals published in 1839 (*Sammlung von geistlichen Liedern*); these hymnals in turn were used as part of the American Methodist missionary effort in Germany and other German-speaking countries.[31] Eventually, as these linguistically distinct populations became assimilated into the American melting pot, English became the primary liturgical language: in 1920, the Swedish Methodist Episcopal Church at Bishop Hill, Illinois, removed the ethnic designation from its name, and in 1922 services were held in English every other Sunday morning; by the 1950s, Swedish was used only for special occasions.[32] Attention of the Methodist bureaucracies then shifted to provide worship in the native tongue for indigenous Americans and for the more recent arrivals to American shores from Asia and Pacific regions. At the end of the twentieth century, official and unofficial worship resources for the United Methodist Church in the United States appeared in English (with prayers translated into English from other languages), Cherokee and other dialects of native American tribal groups, Spanish, Lao and a few languages of new Asian immigrants, and Korean.

Immigrant and indigenous peoples are distinguishable not only by their languages but also by the customs and cultural practices that shape their ethnic or racial identity. The inculturation of what may otherwise be construed as an "anglicized" style of Sunday worship has been permitted as long as the foundational doctrinal standards and the basic assumptions of Methodist worship have not been violated. Methodist worship, therefore, may take on a local color, not only by the language used but also by the customs integrated into weekly or occasional services. It is in the special services, such as those on the great occasions of the liturgical year, those demarcated as special Sundays of the ecclesiastical year of the denomination, or those significant to the local congregation, that the characteristic expressions of a community are most easily observed. An imported Swedish custom that, in 1997, had been in use at First United Methodist Church of Lindstrom, Minnesota, for seventy-five consecutive years, was the cradle-rocking service, held variously on "Children's Day" or Sunday school "Promotion Day." While lullabies were sung softly by a choir, each infant born within the last year was introduced to the congregation and then placed in a cradle to be rocked by several of the older children; in some years, this activity took the place of the sermon.[33] The 1992 *United Methodist Book of Worship*, in an effort to recognize the ethnic and racial diversity of the denomination and to encourage multicultural worship within a given congregation, included such services as an Hispanic Los Posadas ("Service of Shelter for the Holy Family") and rubrics for Tongsung Kido, a Korean practice of simultaneous vocal prayer by every person in the congregation on a common theme.

Sunday and the Annual Cycle

The Meaning and Observance of Sunday

Come, let us join with one accord
    In hymns around the throne;
This is the day our rising Lord
    Hath made and call'd his own.

This is the day which God hath blest
    The brightest of the seven,
Type of that everlasting rest
    The saints enjoy in heaven.

Then let us in his name sing on
    And hasten to that day
When our Redeemer shall come down,
    And shadows pass away.

Not one, but all our days below,
    Let us in hymns employ;
And, in our Lord rejoicing, go
    To his eternal joy.

This hymn by Charles Wesley, located in the section on "The Sabbath" in the 1849 *Hymns for the Use of the Methodist Episcopal Church* and in other Methodist collections, sets forth the multiple meanings of Sunday acknowledged historically by Methodists: the special but not the only day for worship, it is hallowed by God, recalls creation and the resurrection, requires release from earthly toil and responsibilities, and anticipates the eschatological day of the Lord that is the hope and desire of all believers. Each of these aspects has been present with varying degrees of intensity throughout the course of American Methodism, and the hymns in official and unofficial Methodist books, as they are organized under the headings of Sabbath, Lord's Day, or related themes, provide a window into the interpretations and emphases of a particular denomination at a certain time. However, it is the stress upon the Sabbath as the day of both worship and rest that had the most enduring impact upon the nation and the Methodist people—this in spite of the fact that many Methodists in the early period held their primary corporate worship service on a day other than Sunday. Methodists had no difficulty transferring the seventh-day legislation of the Decalogue to the first day of the week, a conclusion reinforced by the Sabbath theology of English Puritanism that had influenced Wesley and the nascent Methodist movement, and by the sabbatarian ethos of New England that permeated the religious life of the country. Required by their General Rules to avoid "profaning the day of the Lord,"[34] Methodists regarded keeping the Lord's Day as a duty, a delight, and a means of grace. No unessential labor or commerce was to be undertaken, and one was to avoid causing others to work. Private devotion and corporate worship were the duties at hand, yielding the dual blessings of spiritual renewal and physical rest. Personal and communal observance of the Lord's Day was therefore taken quite seriously: Bishop Asbury berated himself for riding his horse unnecessarily on the Sabbath, and in 1828, Bishop Joshua Soule was brought under investigation (and eventually cleared) when it was suspected he had preached a sermon suggesting that Christians were not constrained to keep the Sabbath since the law enjoining it had been abolished.[35]

From the mid-nineteenth century to the Second World War, Methodists remained concerned about preservation of the Lord's Day, but for them the issue shifted slightly from an internal focus upon the holy habits of the membership to the external (and sometimes internal) influences that threatened not only the maintenance of those habits, especially church attendance, but the central place of Christianity in American life as well. Also at stake, Methodists claimed, were the prosperity of the nation, the perpetuation of civil liberties, and social morality. Protection of a distinct and consecrated Lord's Day was incumbent "not only upon every true religionist and philanthropist, but every true patriot," since the Sabbath is "the bulwark of a vital Christianity, and a vital Christianity is the bulwark of the nation."[36] North Carolina's Sampson Circuit in 1866 approved a resolution that reveals at the local level the concern that resounded throughout all spheres of Methodism:

Whereas, we are positively commanded by Almighty God to remember the Sabbath Day to keep it Holy, Therefore Resolve that we, the members of this Quarterly Conference for Sampson Circuit do most respectfully and earnestly invite the attention of our people to the absolute necessity of a more constant and prayerful observance of the Holy Sabbath.

Resolved that visiting on this day for the purpose of transacting temperal [sic] business is also a violation of the Holy Day.

Resolved that the running of Railroad Trains, Steamboats, Stages, and Etc., on the various lines of travel except in cases of absolute necessity, is a violation of the command of God, and tends to the demoralization of our people in as much as it prevents tens of thousands from attendance upon divine worship and the proper influence of the Sabbath.

Resolved, that we call upon all Christians and good citizens to speak out earnestly and constantly against all desecration of the day of the Lord and appeal to all who are guilty of this sin to cease this violation.[37]

Each Methodist denomination organized committees, and national, ecumenical forums (e.g., the American Sabbath Union, the Sunday League of America, and the Lord's Day Alliance) were constituted to counter the decline in Sabbath observance that had become obvious in the years following the Civil War, and to address the attack on the Sabbath that was identified as taking shape largely under three principal forms. First, the relaxing of travel and commerce restrictions drew considerable attention. Church leaders issued appeals comparable to those of the Sampson Circuit for individuals to avoid unnecessary journeys and for the developing public transportation systems to cease or limit operation on the Lord's Day. Businesses or factories that opened on Sunday received condemnation for Sabbath desecration, as did saloons that served patrons, the postal system that transported and delivered mail, and the publishers and readers of Sunday newspapers. Second, the increasing American fixation with Sunday amusements—theater, moving pictures, dance, sports, family picnics, and other "evils of the age"—was disparaged. The day of rest was not to be reinterpreted as a day of mere recreation, since this attitude, it was feared, would force open the door even wider to the invasion of worldliness in the lives of Christians; this was a danger against which Methodists always had vehemently preached and published. And third, a growing Catholic and Protestant immigrant population from continental Europe, which allegedly ridiculed the "Puritan Sabbath," was fingered as a culprit for their use of Sunday for physical and mental enjoyment rather than for spiritual benefits.

The changing demands of the workforce eventually contributed to the relaxing or, in some cases, the disappearance of Methodist Sabbath restrictions. A related matter, in the years during and after the Second World War, was the increasing numbers of women in the workplace who, because of the demands of employment, found it difficult to maintain their customary role as the primary inculcators of Sunday observances. Another factor, simultaneously a cause and a manifestation of the phenomenon, was the gradual softening of polemics against worldliness which, by the middle of the twentieth century, had mostly vanished. "Votes to Put End to Amusement Ban" was the front page headline of the *New York Times* on May 18, 1924, when the Methodist Episcopal Church's General Conference produced the shocking decision to allow individual conscience in lieu of church legislation. Yet the General Rule against profanation remained on the disciplinary books, and some notion of Sabbath rest or limitations persisted in popular piety, most notably in the Holiness and African-American denominations. Hymns with an explicit rest motif still were sung, though their quantity declined in the largest Methodist bodies; the 1989 *United Methodist Hymnal* contained no hymn explicating the meaning of Sunday, whereas the 1996 *A. M. E. Zion Hymnal* preserved numerous Sabbath rest hymns.

While the recovery of the Lord's Day as the weekly day of resurrection—a product of the ecumenical rediscovery of early Christian theology and praxis—undergirded many of the late twentieth-century Methodist orders for Sunday worship, it generally did not, at least at the popular level, fill the theological void left by the turning away from a strong notion of Sabbath rest. This led, in some parts of Methodism, to a reduced commitment to Sunday as the normative day for worship, an attitude reinforced by the removal of governmental "blue laws" and the consequent changes in working patterns of church members, and also by the desire to reach newcomers at a time convenient for them. Arguments were made in some quarters that the move away from a normative Sunday was, in fact, a recovery of the earlier Methodist practice of holding corporate worship on any of the seven days of the week. Such a claim forgot that Sunday has *always* been the central and chiefly recognized day of worship and Sunday morning the preferred time for worship. Other days were utilized because the circuit-riding preachers could not be present in every community on Sunday, so it was a matter not of personal convenience, but of available leadership. Yet even as Sunday stood on the verge of losing its privileged standing, Easter as the annual day of resurrection, and the feasts and fasts born from the paschal mystery, found increased recognition.

The Annual Cycle

Methodists have never been without annual observances. Received from Wesley in 1784 was a temporal calendar for Sundays governed by readings and collects for the four Sundays of Advent, Sundays after Christmas, Sunday before Easter, Easter Day, Sundays after Easter, Sunday after Ascension, Whitsunday (Pentecost), Trinity Sunday, and Sundays after Trinity. This pattern conformed to the Prayer Book sequence of Sundays with a notable exception: though the Prayer Book readings and collects remained unchanged, the heading "Sundays after Christmas" was now used to locate the days previously designated as Sundays after Epiphany, the pre-Lenten Sundays of Septuagesima, Sexagesima, and Quinquagesima, and the first five Sundays of Lent. The absence of Lent and also Ash Wednesday may be explained as a consequence of Wesley's sensitivity to the series of objections that had been raised, primarily by the Puritans, regarding the scriptural legitimacy of a forty-day fast by Christians, and also, perhaps, by Wesley's desire to avoid the creation of a possible contradiction between his doctrine of Christian assurance and an extensive penitential season.[38] The omission of Epiphany is much more difficult to explain, given Wesley's knowledge of the feast's antiquity. But Wesley apparently was prepared to sacrifice for the sake of simplicity, brevity, and practicality any weekday "holy day (so-called)" that served no "valuable end." Of the thirty-three such holy days identified in the *Book of Common Prayer*, Wesley retains only the three christological "particular days" of Christmas, Good Friday, and Ascension; the sanctoral, including Wesley's beloved festival of All Saints' (so identified in his journal for November 1, 1767), found no place in the official Methodist annual cycle.[39]

Wesley's pared-back calendar undoubtedly was still more substantial than what many Methodists actually honored, especially those who had no history of association with the Church of England. But many of the days he designated were certainly familiar. Prior to the reception of the *Sunday Service*, Methodist Thomas

Rankin, in the years 1773 to 1776, made special mention in his diary of Christmas, Easter, and Whitsunday.[40] Freeborn Garrettson noted he observed "a solemn fast, being good Friday, the day on which the great Redeemer gave up his precious life."[41] Four years after Wesley's calendar was approved, Ezekiel Cooper recorded his concerns for the spiritual keeping of Thursday, December 25, 1788, and included the text he took for his evening sermon, which was the proper lesson indicated in the *Sunday Service* for morning prayer, not for evening:

> This being Christmas-day there were prayer meetings very early in the morning & preaching three times in the day. O what a pity this day is kept at all by many if they can't keep it better than they do! To my heart I was grieved to see & hear so much evil as I did among the people. In preaching my evening sermon I preached from His name Isa. 9.6. In my improvement I asked the congregation why they kept Christmas. Was it in remembrance of Christ's coming into the world? I then asked how they kept it. Was it in such a manner that they honoured or dishonoured the Son? I replyed that many of them kept it like Pagans or Turks whom one might think did it in contempt of Christ.

Although Wesley's provisions for a temporal cycle were laid aside in 1792, certain christological festal days continued to be recognized during the course of the year, and not only because of the perpetuation of cultural custom. In December 1792, Cooper commented again on Christmas, falling that year on a Tuesday; the pre-dawn service he described was apparently practiced by other preachers as well:

> This morning rose early, with a grateful heart. About sun rise we met at the preaching house where we had prayer. I read the second chapt. of Matthew and part of the first, and gave a lecture upon the nativity of our Lord. At N o'clock I preached to a full congregation, upon the occasion of the Festival.[42]

Cooper's final phrase provides a clue for the continuity of the liturgical observance of Christian days without the reinforcement of lectionary or collects. Embedded within the disciplinary section on the "matter and manner" of preaching was the counsel that originated from Wesley's Large Minutes, "always avail yourself of the great festivals, by preaching on the occasion." Although this instruction for the Methodist Episcopal Church would, in 1848, be transferred to the section on the conduct of preachers as a "smaller advice," it would endure until the 1939 merger; the Methodist Episcopal Church, South kept the provision in its *Discipline* until 1866, remarkably the same year in which approval was given for the republication of Wesley's *Sunday Service*. The seriousness with which the Methodist preachers were urged to approach at least the great days of Christmas, Good Friday, Easter, and Pentecost is evident from the 1798 commentary on Wesley's advice:

> Souls are of so much value, that we should improve every opportunity for their good. Shall the men of the world have carnal festivals on their birth-days, and shall we not commemorate the birth-day of our Lord? The primitive fathers of the church observed *the day*, which is *now* kept sacred by most of the churches of christendom. . . . Again, shall states and nations celebrate the day of liberation from slavery or oppression, or some other glorious event, from year to year? And shall *we* not celebrate by a holy

festival the crucifixion and resurrection of our Lord, and the mission of the Holy Spirit, to which we are indebted for blessings infinitely more valuable than any which the revolution of states can possibly afford?[43]

Throughout the nineteenth century, Methodists generally noticed a few Christian festal days in the course of the year, sometimes kept them with preaching, prayer, and song, and criticized persons (Methodist and otherwise) who used those days, especially Christmas, as an occasion to take "unusual liberties for self-indulgence and sinful associations."[44] But the feasts and fasts of the liturgical year generally never took hold either as the governing framework in Methodist conceptualizations of the yearly calendar or as holy days elevated beyond special days of prayer. As Coke and Asbury's 1798 commentary implies, a truncated liturgical year offered only one among several means of defining Methodist time: the annual cycle was shaped by an intricate interweaving of occasions common to the entire Christian Church, others particular to the denomination, and others yet again devoted to civic causes and commemorations. The various editions of the Methodist *Discipline* in the nineteenth century, for the most part, ignore the liturgical year, but readily make reference to the quarterly and yearly (and quadrennial) Conference gatherings that were, perhaps, the most prominent markers for the Methodist sense of annual time. These Conference meetings were not just business sessions and opportunities for fellowship; they were times for worship and prayer, the forms for which came not from prescribed orders of worship (except for Communion), but from the rich unwritten resources of the denomination coupled with favorite hymns.[45] Besides the Conferences, the *Discipline* from the second half of the nineteenth century also registered special denominational days to be emphasized in worship on Sundays or on other days of the week, or in the Sunday school. These days could promote a social issue, like Temperance Sunday, or the collection of a monetary offering for a particular cause, such as Children's Day, which, by the 1870s, was typically held on the second Sunday of June. Days with a focus upon intercessory prayer were encouraged, such as the Day of Prayer for Colleges; and for the sake of Christian unity, the Week of Prayer instituted by the Evangelical Alliance. Though it was not specified by the *Discipline*, General Conference reports clearly indicate that some Methodists at their general meetings aided the healing of the war-torn nation by participation in Decoration Day services at soldiers' graves.[46] Evidently, in some localities the activities of Children's Day and Decoration Day were combined into one Sunday evening observance.[47]

Other Methodist publications attest to the variety of days and seasons that might have been observed, with, of course, their actual performance determined by individual preference and community custom. The blurring of the three strands comprising Methodist time is best seen in the Methodist Episcopal Church's *Methodist Almanac* (retitled *The Methodist Yearbook* in 1880), which, on the cover of each annual issue, measured the number of years from the granting of American independence. The first issue of 1827, printed by T. R. Marvin of Boston, included among the monthly listings in calendrical sequence of "Observable Days, Aspects, &c." specific Methodist commemorations virtually comprising a type of Methodist sanctoral (e.g., Wesley's birth and death dates), national and local dates (e.g.,

Benjamin Franklin's birthday), and a temporal and sanctoral sequence otherwise unknown to Methodists (including Circumcision, Palm Sunday, Nativity of Mary, St. Stephen). The odd combination of materials suggests that an Anglican calendar of New England or some other source provided a template upon which were added Methodist references. Such a hunch may be confirmed by the "Advertisement" listed in the 1834 *Almanac*: the book, now produced by Methodist publishers in conformity with recommendations from the General Conference, was explicitly intended for more than the members and friends of the Methodist Episcopal Church. Even so, the 1834 issue reduced the liturgical calendar and redefined parts of it: December 25 is noted not for Christmas, but as a significant day in the founding of episcopal Methodism. After 1834, identification of days and seasons from the liturgical year come and go in no determinable pattern, but the Methodist and national aspects of the books remain strong, with some annual publications incorporating a separate chronological table of important Methodist events (e.g., 1842, 1858–1861). A table of "Festival Days, Holidays, Fasts, Etc." was printed in the editions of 1868 to 1872, which distinguished between the "national festivals" of New Year's Day, Washington's Birthday, and Independence Day, and the "religious festivals" of the annual Week of Prayer for Christian unity, prayer for colleges, Good Friday, Easter Sunday, Christmas, "and all Thanksgiving and Fast Days appointed by the National or State authorities." These days probably represent the simplest form of the calendar acknowledged by members of the Methodist Episcopal Church. Yet in 1873, the editor evidently returned to a template format (perhaps to secure a wider readership) by listing under a "Cycle of Time and Church Days" such occasions as Septuagesima, Ash Wednesday, and Corpus Christi; this table, under various headings and sometimes expanded, persisted to the final year of publication in 1933. Though Methodists would not have observed most of the days of this liturgical calendar, they certainly would have been aware of their existence simply through the use of the *Almanac* and had opportunity to become acquainted with the terminology of a more catholic liturgical year by reading the explanations that were sometimes added to the book.

The table of contents or subject headings in the official Methodist hymnals identify the expected usage of certain hymns and are thereby a good indicator of a church's "magisterial" conception of important days in the course of the year. Charles and John Wesley had published numerous hymn collections for days and seasons of the church year including Nativity, Easter, Ascension, and Whitsunday,[48] but few of those texts would find their place in American collections—a possible consequence of the removal in 1784 of the final clause from Wesley's instruction for preaching on the great festivals: "and singing the hymns, which you should take care to have in readiness." Nevertheless, Methodist hymnals have always included a repertoire of hymns for Christmas, Good Friday, Easter, Ascension, and Pentecost, though the specified headings differ by hymnal and denomination. Hymns for the New Year (and in some hymnals, hymns for the associated watch night service) are likewise universally present in varying quantities. Found in nineteenth-century hymn books are also hymns for denominational and local church occasions such as anniversaries of missionaries, Bible societies, and Sunday schools, and national events such as public fasts and general thanksgivings. Other hymns of thanksgiving for "our country" appear by the 1840s. The Methodist Episcopal Church, South's *A Collection of Hymns for Public, Social, and Domestic Worship* of 1847 offers twenty-eight hymns for "national solemnities," among which are two texts designated for the Fourth of July; their changed attitude toward the nation is reflected in the 1880 *New Hymn-Book*, which allows only three "national solemnity" hymns. Harvest hymns were added as an annual day of Thanksgiving evolved from a New England festival to a national day of celebration popular among a largely rural Methodism.

Methodists at the end of the nineteenth century were often attracted to the catechetical and devotional aspects—as well as the pageantry—of the liturgical year. This appeal, in part, grew out of a renewed interest in the Wesleyan liturgical heritage, which was made manifest by the reprinting of the *Sunday Service* and the publishing of derivative texts like Charles Harrower's book and thereby exposed a number of Methodists to the concept of a year shaped by the life of Christ. Attention to the Christian year was also construed as a remedy for the increasing secularization of the nation borne out by the decline in Sabbath piety evident in urban areas; the variety of forms and ceremonies accompanying festal celebrations could summon the interest of a distracted constituency. For the status-minded, the adoption of more elaborate services of worship, commonly associated with the so-called "liturgical" churches, could draw into the Methodist fold those who preferred that style of worship. Numerous explanations thus can be proffered for the elevation of christological festivals to a new importance. Some Methodists began to concede, as did Joseph Berry, editor of the *Epworth Herald* for Methodist Episcopal youth, that certain festal days were not to be regarded as cultural holidays with religious overtones or as days simply to be honored with prayer, but as, in fact, sacred days.[49] As might be expected, not all Methodists were enamored of this shift. Efforts were made to calm the anxieties of those who saw the promotion of Christian festal days as one more intrusion of formality and ritualism. In *A Treatise on the Lenten Season*, Bostwick Hawley argued that in addition to "giving some needed instruction to the people," "a judicious observance of these anniversaries would induce a reform in extreme ritualistic Churches."[50] Another writer who claimed that Methodism had "not rejected a moderate use . . . of commemorative days" and testified to the "almost universal" celebration of Christmas and Easter in churches in the eastern half of the country nevertheless insisted that caution be taken "lest in the ceremonial we lose sight of the spirit that underlies, and lest by a multiplication of days we return to what the Church found it necessary to abandon."[51]

What began as a reexamination of the values and benefits of a liturgical year led in the early twentieth century to a flurry of publications meant as homiletical and liturgical resources for local pastors and congregations. Even so, some were not convinced, finding "the white life of the Christian incomparably superior to what the ritualists call the 'liturgical colors.' "[52] True to the historic Methodist framework, Christian days were listed as special occasions in the calendar year alongside denominational days and civic commemorations. Charles Roberts's *Divine Service* of 1903, which kept Wesley's collects under their assigned Sunday and particular day headings, also added collects and responsive readings for the weekdays of Passion Week (the second week before Easter) and Holy Week, and for Thanksgiving Day, Missionary Day, national occasions, Children's Day, and Temperance Day. The 1905 joint *Methodist Hymnal* virtually reiterated Roberts's scheme for special days by providing responsive readings for Christmas, Palm Sunday, Good Friday, Easter, the Nation, Thanksgiving Day, Missions, Education, and Temperance and Moral Reform, and by accentuating the readings with hymns for those defined occasions and also for Advent, New Year, Holy Week ("Sufferings and Death"), Ascension, and Pentecost. Bishop Thirkield, in the 1918 *Service and Prayers for Church and Home*, expands the resources by providing prayers to accompany the responsive readings, ignoring Palm Sunday while adding Advent and the New Year. Besides these days, Methodists were often willing to experiment with innovative denominational and civic celebrations in the Sunday school,[53] some of which then crept into the Lord's Day service. The Sunday school observance held in a Grafton, West Virginia, Methodist Episcopal Church in May, 1907, to remember Anna Jarvis's mother, eventually, through Jarvis's own organizational efforts, blossomed into the churchly and national celebration—on Sunday—of Mother's Day.[54] In a Methodist-published book of 1916, Mother's Day stood along with Children's Day, Thanksgiving Day, Education Day, and Memorial Sunday as recommended special-day themes for Sunday worship.[55]

All but the Holiness wing of Methodism continued to promote, at least officially, a selection of ancient and modern annual celebrations; at the local level, the modern denominational and civic days often proved to be most popular. New Methodist days were proposed (e.g., Wesley [later Aldersgate] Day and All Methodist Church Sunday). In the spirit of maintaining the sanctity of the Lord's Day, petitions were put forward during the 1920s and 1930s for Methodist leaders to use their political clout in persuading the federal government to establish Good Friday as a legal holiday, but none were adopted.[56] A significant boost for observing Christian days and seasons in the churches came from the Federal Council of the Churches of Christ in America (later renamed the National Council of Churches), which, in 1935, claimed six Methodist denominations among its twenty-three member churches.[57] In that year, the Federal Council's Committee on Worship, chaired by Bishop Thirkield, began a study to produce a "Church Calendar Year" for use by "nonliturgical churches" that had "virtually no recognized calendar" and were "therefore subjected to sporadic influences." If churches, as part of their planning, were to employ an annual financial scheme, then "why not have a Christian Year for guidance in our daily devotions and public worship, for giving direction to our preaching and Bible reading, for the commemoration of historic days, seasons and personalities, and the general ordering of our varied program of work?"[58] The subcommittee charged with the task was convened by Methodist professor Fred Winslow Adams of Boston University School of Theology, who, in 1926, had claimed that Methodism was well placed to make a contribution to the revival of the theory and practice of worship.[59] The subcommittee's program was published in 1937 under the title *The Christian Year*, which contained the twofold agenda of revitalizing the recovered Christian year with contemporary and evangelical expressions, and providing another common basis for greater Christian unity. Not surprisingly, the work, in Methodist fashion, overlapped liturgical and civil—and now social (e.g., Race Relations Sunday) and ecumenical (e.g., Christian Unity Sunday)—occasions, yet conceived them as one whole system organized within a christological framework. The new liturgical season of Kingdomtide was also inaugurated, developed to emphasize the proclamation of the gospel in contemporary life (a theme of the social gospel movement) and to accommodate "modern days such as Labor Day and World Peace Day." This innovative season that divided up the long period after Pentecost would take hold more firmly among Methodists than any other Protestants and strongly influence Methodist preaching, teaching, and policy for at least the next two generations.[60]

The key Methodist role and presence in the Federal Council of Churches plan had a direct bearing on what Methodists would confirm as annual observances after 1940. For African-American Methodists, this is best seen by the defining structure of hymns in the official hymnals and by the responsive readings for "special days" that are supplied therein. A small number of notable, often "connectional," days are defined in the *Discipline*; for the African Methodist Episcopal Church in 1940, these included (Richard) Allen Day, Easter Day, Children's Day, and Endowment Day. Ties to the Federal Council's work are more clearly evident with the 1945 *Book of Worship* of the Methodist Church. Participating on the commission that would produce the book were Fred Winslow Adams and Oscar Thomas Olson, who replaced Bishop Thirkield in the chair of the Federal Council's Committee on Worship upon the latter's death in 1936. So it is not surprising that the book included a calendar, lectionary, aids for the Christian year, and fifteen orders of worship "Suggested for Festival Observances of the Christian Year" comprising Advent, Christmas, New Year, Epiphany, Lent, Good Friday, Easter, Whitsunday, Kingdomtide, Christian Unity, Memorial, Thanksgiving for "Harvest, Land, and Liberty," and Thanksgiving Day. Supplementing and reinforcing the official resources in the *Book of Worship* were articles in the Methodist periodical *The Pastor*, published from 1937 to 1956, which in its second decade regularly carried the features "Calendar" (offering homiletical and program resources), "Liturgy" and "Homiletics," and "Liturgical Question Box" (providing answers to queries about origins and practice).[61]

Resources for the annual liturgical-denominational-civil cycle continued to expand in the late twentieth century, even among the reticent Wesleyan and Free Methodists.[62] The largest Methodist body, the United Methodists, strove in its 1992 *Book of Worship* to maintain the historic blend of annual elements, but this book, unlike its 1965 predecessor, delineated between the different strands by providing separate headings, with the classic Christian year receiving obvious priority. In fact, it could be argued that two more categories made an appearance, though scantily represented and lumped under the subheading "other special days": pan-Methodist occasions (Aldersgate Day), and Protestant recognitions (Reformation Day). This format was not adopted by the last Methodist worship book to be produced in the twentieth century, that of the African Methodist Episcopal Zion Church (1996), which interwove the three basic strands while following the sequence of the liturgical year.

Being Methodist on the Lord's Day

Bishop George Foster Pierce of the Methodist Episcopal Church, South, concerned in the late 1860s for the preservation of a distinct Methodist identity in worship and elsewhere, inscribed these words in a letter: "Be Methodists out and out. Keep up all our peculiarities; preach like Methodists; sing like Methodists; pray like Methodists. There is nothing in Methodism to be ashamed of." But what peculiar Methodist identity was being advocated? Continuing his letter, Pierce advised the recipient:

> Train your children in the way they should go. Teach them to love Methodism; carry them with you to the house of God, to the class-meeting, to the love-feast; keep up your Sunday-school; buy books, give work, teach, hunt up the poor and neglected, bring the outcasts in. Pray for a revival. Lord, send now prosperity.[63]

For Pierce and others, proper Methodism was a continuation of a heritage of ritual simplicity, spiritual vitality, and ethical responsibility. Yet, as has already been seen, numerous Methodists came to regard their Wesleyan and American inheritance as something more complex than such a simple description would allow. Moves toward a stated and formal liturgical style were, in effect, a *retour aux sources*, a recovery of components from the earliest liturgical formulary of American Methodism. Evangelical outreach to the neighbor or community could not be divorced from concern for the spiritual well-being of the country and the world, so Methodism, from the beginning, saw itself as a key player in the establishment of a Christian nation under God, though different denominations as well as individuals were to choose disparate means to accomplish that end. The nation in turn, at least for a time, looked to Methodism as an advocate of the Christian moral values that had come to be interwoven with the national agenda. President Theodore Roosevelt, upon receiving a copy of the Methodist Episcopal Church's *Discipline* of 1908, was inspired to comment that not only do Methodists engage in the Lord's work and fight evil "with rugged strength and courage," they also "stand for and represent a peculiarly strong and virile type of American citizenship."[64]

By the 1930s, however, many Methodists had come to recognize along with other Protestants that the entanglement of Christianity with the wider American culture had compromised Christian identity as well as denominational particularity: "Instead of the church having Christianized civilization, they found that the civilization had captured the church."[65] Expanded use of the liturgical year, juxtaposed with the denominational and civil calendars, was one means many Methodist bodies employed to reclaim their distinctiveness as church. Participation in the growing ecumenical and liturgical movements enabled Methodists to contribute to a unified Christian engagement with nation and world, and it also allowed them, in concert with other Christian groups, to take stock of themselves and to reexamine what it meant to proclaim and worship the One whose kingdom is not of this world. At the end of the twentieth century, the always pragmatic Methodists continued to opt for a variety of solutions to the question of how to worship authentically both as the descendants of Wesley and as Christians who take seriously the multifaceted constituency that gathers or potentially gathers on the Lord's Day.

The uniform practice of Sunday worship was recurrently encouraged by some denominational authorities as the means by which a distinct and recognizable Methodist liturgical identity could be demonstrated in an increasingly pluriform American society, and as an insurance against inept worship leaders. But these causes for uniformity could not be separated from the broader concern that Methodists in all things be ordered as a people of the *Discipline*. When in 1792 Wesley's *Sunday Service* as a distinct book of worship was laid aside and its greatly abbreviated contents subsumed into the *Discipline*, Sunday worship became a component in a book of law for ordering Methodist life and work. Instructions for public worship were isolated in a section of the *Discipline* apart from the other (occasional, pastoral) offices and in a format comparable to other ecclesiastical legislation, suggesting a stronger legal status for the ordering of corporate worship on Sunday and other days of the week. This then raised a significant question: as part of Methodist law, were the rules governing public worship to be obeyed equally with the other contents of the *Discipline*? The question was difficult to answer definitively, since church leaders were not of one mind whether the rubrics after 1792 were intended to be an exact order or a mere listing of items that might be included in any sequence and combination. Many Methodists regarded the brevity of instructions as an expression of Methodism's genius to permit freedom of worship as local circumstances demanded. Yet numerous church leaders stressed that full obedience to church law required reasonable conformity to the stated plan for worship. Freeborn Garrettson, quoting St. Paul's direction to "walk by the same rule" (Philippians 3:16, KJV), contended in 1826 that the *Discipline* provided "standards or way-marks" necessary to "transmit our doctrines and usages to the generations following."[66]

Variety in local worship praxis, which included components heretofore unapproved, was already being exercised when official orders containing old and new components were drawn up by some denominations in the last decades of the nineteenth century. The argument persisted that worship leaders should conform to General Conference–approved "rules" for the sake of uniformity, yet concessions were sometimes made for a limited inculturation of the specified worship plan, as was proposed in 1894 regarding the Methodist Episcopal Church's order:

> The General Conference in its wisdom has not left our Church without a prescribed order of Sabbath worship. Paragraph 56 of the Discipline contains definite instructions upon this subject. The tendency, however, to substitute for the assigned order an arrangement peculiar to individual churches is certainly widespread. If the practice of the whole Church may be inferred from the customs which obtain in our own locality the order in the different churches varies widely. Some begin their worship with an anthem by the choir, some with a hymn, and some with the doxology. Some recite the Lord's Prayer, and some do not. Some read a responsive lesson from Wesley's *Select Psalms;* some read a psalm selected at random by the pastor; while some, perhaps a goodly proportion, read no responsive lesson at all. Some take the collection before

the sermon, and some afterward. In fact, it is hard to imagine a greater diversity than exists in the practice of a Church whose order of worship is so fully outlined in the Discipline. The attention of our younger ministers especially should be directed to this common neglect of the established rules. It is not here contended that the order prescribed is necessarily the best that could be devised; nor is it forgotten that the Discipline inserts the saving clause, "as far as possible," in its directions. Yet local alterations of the rules should not be capricious, injudicious, or unreasonable.[67]

Even Bishop Thomas B. Neely, who eventually in 1916 would dispute on legal grounds the changes made to the worship orders of the Methodist Episcopal Church, asserted that "the fair interpretation is that the order is what the General Conference wants and expects the Church to observe, but that, at the same time, the wording is not so ironclad that it will not bend where there is a real necessity." Neely then identified six principles for conducting public worship, the sixth of which states the case for denominational uniformity:

The form of service should be sufficiently fixed to maintain at least a fair degree of denominational uniformity, so that a member would know what to expect wherever he went; yet, at the same time, the order should be so flexible that it could be varied in minor matters when circumstances should indicate the necessity of some modification, by insertion or omission to meet the legitimate requirements of the occasion. These variations, however, would be exceptional. It is necessary to have some order of public worship, for no order to guide ministers and people leads to confusion and disorderliness of service instead of the orderliness which should characterize public worship. There is a judicious mean between the one extreme of a too ornate and overloaded liturgy and the other extreme of one so bald that, in its barrenness and coldness, it lacks the essential features of a scriptural and well-balanced service and therefore is measurably unprofitable. There is, however, something more important than a form of worship, and that is the fact of worship. The form has its value, but the spirit is more greatly needed. An order of worship is merely the skeleton. The skeleton is necessary, but it should be clothed upon the living body. Whatever may be the form, there must be the life. Where there is earnest spiritual life the Church can prosper with very little form. Where there is form without spiritual vitality the Church must fail.[68]

The opinion that the authorized orders should be "scrupulously and reverently observed" with an allowance for "variety within limits" continued to be expressed into the 1930s, as confirmed in the 1934 Episcopal Address at the General Conference of the Methodist Episcopal Church, South,[69] but this view was tempered by those who took a more stringent approach. For example, S. M. Merrill, in the 1908 edition of his *Digest of Methodist Law*, insisted that Methodist Episcopal churches refusing to use the 1905 "common" order should be considered guilty of "insubordination" and of "a breach of courtesy" toward their "sister" Methodist Episcopal Church, South.[70]

The tension between advocates of liturgical uniformity and those who supported the freedom of local expression was seemingly lessened in the Methodist Church by the disclaimer on the title page of the 1945 *Book of Worship* that it was "for voluntary and optional use," a move perhaps also meant to recognize, so soon after the 1939 merger, that ritual change within local congregations could not be accomplished quickly. With this statement, however, the relationship between liturgy and church law became ambiguous, especially since the Methodist Church's *Discipline* defined the services as "authorized." Claims were made that the *Discipline* bound persons to subscribe to the orders unchanged, but even the chairman of the commission that produced the book found it necessary to propose, ten years after publication, that the services "should be made official for required use."[71] Legal uncertainty may have been a deliberate means to mediate the conflict between uniformity and freedom, since an approved order for Sunday (in the 1965 *Book of Worship* described as the "usage of the Methodist Church") would provide a denominational standard, while still allowing for local liturgical expression. The legal standings and expectations again were not completely defined with the "official" *United Methodist Book of Worship* (1992), though the ordinal demanded that ordinands accept the denomination's "order, liturgy, doctrine, and discipline," a phrase church officials were hesitant to interpret. At the end of the twentieth century, Methodists of the United Methodist Church—and of the other denominations in the Methodist family—remained unclear about the legal standing of their approved Lord's Day orders of worship. Yet factions still clamored, for the sake of the liturgical identity and the theological integrity of the particular branch of Methodism, that the orders had to be followed to the letter; and others stressed that Methodism's legacy is not to require adherence to any form.

Distinctions have often been made between form and formalism, a qualification hinted at by Neely in his sixth principle. For a minority of Methodists, any stated form, official or otherwise, smacked of formalism and ritualism. Most, however, have been willing to concede the benefit of some logical, repeated order to worship. What has been feared is "the *meaningless* following of a form, or the following of a *meaningless* form,"[72] and the use of ceremonial or liturgical accoutrements that would preoccupy and distract both the worshiper and the worship leader. Cautions have always been raised that "our clear, sharp views of *spiritual, experimental,* and *practical* religion" must not "give place to magnificent cathedrals, 'loud-sounding organs,' operatic singing, and splendid rituals."[73] But Methodist angst heightened in the wake of the Oxford movement, as some of their nearest ecclesiastical kin, the Protestant Episcopalians, drifted in an Anglo-Catholic direction. This "Catholic" trend, perhaps indirectly, influenced the Methodist recovery of Anglican liturgical roots via Wesley, though those who favored this move were quick to reassure critics that Wesley's Lord's Day services "cannot be classed among ritualistic practices."[74] Contributing also to Methodist concern was the "peril of Romanism," increased by the influx of Roman Catholic immigrants. The seriousness of this issue during the late nineteenth century is spelled out in the *Discipline* of the African Methodist Episcopal Church, which includes an entire section "concerning ritualism." Although uniformity in practice was desired, and "the orderly repetition of the Decalogue, the Apostles' Creed, and the responsive reading of the Scriptures" commended, "any and all efforts that favor the introduction of ritualism in connection with our public service" was deprecated, since a "heavy and prosy ritualistic service" could stifle "spiritual interest."[75]

The engagement of some Methodists in the growing liturgical movement, the acceptance of more complex Sunday worship patterns, and an interest in aesthetics for worship led one writer in 1902 to ask cynically whether Methodists would have to choose "more liturgy or more life." A respondent countered that this was a false dichotomy, that more liturgy could, in fact, contribute to more spiritual life.[76] The bishops of the Methodist Episcopal Church, South echoed this sentiment, claiming that though "excessive ritualism cramps the soul and tends toward a mere form of godliness rather than the power thereof" and "sufficient liberty in worship for the guidance of the Spirit of God" must always be allowed, "the entire history of the Christian Church has demonstrated the value of a dignified ritual."[77] This view has been embraced as the majority of Methodist denominations continued along the road of liturgical renewal, while remaining sensitive to those who adhere to a free and flexible service; both types have been seen as equally Methodist.

In surveying the history of American Methodism, therefore, one must speak of Methodist liturgical *identities* despite recurrent efforts to mold practice into one unified, uniform pattern. Yet the differences between these identities are not sufficient to remove persistent family resemblances. Being Methodist on the Lord's Day means reading Scripture and preaching the good news of salvation and peace; singing hymns and, sometimes, psalms; offering prayer, often extempore, to thank, confess, and intercede; and graciously receiving the prevenient, justifying, or sanctifying grace that the triune God provides. Such characteristics are not, of course, exclusively Methodist. Indeed, it was never Wesley's expectation that Methodists and their worship should be substantively different from other "real Christians, of whatsoever denomination they be"; distinctions were to be made from "the unbelieving world, from all those whose minds or lives are not according to the gospel of Christ."[78] Nevertheless, Methodist Sunday worship does, in its underlying principles, exhibit a family trait: the appropriation, in some fashion, of what are perceived to be the liturgical guidelines and practices introduced by John Wesley for the people called Methodist. A wide range of interpretation has occurred here, because Methodist liturgical expression, even in its infancy, was multifaceted. The liturgical styles and the affective piety manifested already in eighteenth-century Methodism have virtually functioned as primitive paradigms for the worship of the past two centuries: evangelistic preaching, teaching, and hymn singing outside of church walls, which was deliberate but spontaneous; the unadorned, planned yet flexible preaching services in meetinghouse, chapel, domestic dwelling, or available sheltered space; the informal praise, prayer, and testimony service of the intimate class meeting, a later manifestation of which was the Sunday school opening exercise; and the formal, highly structured services for the Lord's Day, first from the *Book of Common Prayer*, and after 1784 from the *Sunday Service* and its recurrent appearance in adapted forms. These represent diverse, but ultimately not divergent, practices that have coexisted throughout the course of American Methodist history, with the formal service gaining prominence in the twentieth century.

While these various styles generally converge on the matter of worship's content and components, there have been differences—even within a particular style—on whether worship's predominant emphasis should be doxology, catechesis, conversion, or cultivation of the moral life. Wesley himself would not have made such sharp distinctions among these purposes, regarding them rather as strands in a single whole. Spiritual worship, claimed Wesley, "properly and directly consists in the knowledge and love of God, as manifested in the Son of his love, through the eternal Spirit. And this naturally leads to every heavenly temper, and to every good word and work."[79] The separation of the strands and the Wesleyan styles of worship selected to express them have contributed to the multiple liturgical profiles of American Methodism. Specific emphases have risen to prominence at certain times, and often the strands appear in combination, but like the worship styles that ritualize them, all four have been present from the rise of Methodism. The various configurations of strands and styles may be treated as separate Methodist liturgical identities. But they must not be seen as approaches complete unto themselves, for the sum of the strands and styles represents the fullness of the Methodist and the Christian life. Methodist Sunday worship is *both* simple and complex, informal and formal, free and fixed, evangelical and doxological.

3

The Great Festivals of the Methodists

A LTHOUGH WESLEY BELIEVED that Methodists should not be substantially different from other Christians, Methodists celebrated special services of worship that expressed and reinforced their denominational identity. These occasions were not delineated in Wesley's *Sunday Service* of 1784 or in subsequent recensions of that text. Rather, they developed independently from the Prayer Book tradition in response to Methodism's organizational and evangelistic concerns but were never regarded by church officials as a substitute for regular Lord's Day worship. Some of these worship services originated in Britain and were exported to the New World; others were honed from Methodist and a shared Protestant evangelical experience on American soil. No official or prescribed order was mandated, but over time, custom and expediency shaped paradigms that informally spread throughout Methodism. "These were our great festivals," commented Ohioan David Lewis on one peculiarly Methodist service. "Here we renewed our covenants with God and his people, obtained encouragement and strength in our souls, and rejoiced together in the salvation of God."[1] Though these "great festivals" would wane after Methodism's first century, they never were entirely lost, and some would find new life as the result of a renewed interest in the Wesleyan heritage. By these "great festivals" is meant in this chapter the whole range of love feasts, watch nights, services of covenant renewal, quarterly meetings, camp meetings, protracted meetings, and indoor revivals.

The Love Feast

The earliest Methodist missioners brought to America the love feast, a service devised intentionally to imitate early Christian praxis. From his reading of Scripture and Christian antiquity, Wesley knew of the ancient Christian agape or love feast, where "the Rich and the Poor feasted together at the same Table" and "they testified and confirmed their mutual Love and Kindness."[2] He may have been aware that love feasts had been revived by certain Separatists, Baptists, and Anabaptists during the sixteenth and seventeenth centuries. But it was Wesley's exposure to the Moravian renovation of the practice, at Savannah, Georgia, in 1737, and at the Moravian community of Herrnhut in 1738, that prompted his interest in its value as a means of bolstering Christian fellowship and reinforcing spiritual growth and accountability. The love feast became an integral component of the Fetter Lane Religious Society Wesley had helped to found in 1738, and after Wesley broke with Fetter Lane (which eventually would become the first Moravian congregation in England), the love feast continued among the Methodist societies, though in a manner distinct from Moravian practice. Attendance was mostly restricted: at first, to members of the gender-segregated and intimate Methodist bands,[3] because of the revelation of personal dispositions and the generation of intense emotion; and then gradually to the members of the small-group classes and the larger Methodist society who were in good standing. Earnest seekers not members of the society might sometimes be admitted with special permission. Status was authenticated by the presentation of a ticket or token distributed quarterly that bore the name of the owner or the authorizing person (and sometimes both), as well as the date or serial letter and the citation of a Scripture verse. Doorkeepers monitored admission and, to avoid outside accusations that these gatherings promoted orgiastic behavior (criticisms that nevertheless persisted), only the assistant or superintendent ministers directly responsible to Wesley could oversee the event. A highlight of the love feast was the symbolic communal meal:

> In order to increase in them a grateful sense of all His mercies, I desired that one evening in a quarter all the men in band, on a second, all the women, would meet; and on a third, both men and women together; that we might together "eat bread" (as the ancient Christians did) "with gladness and singleness of heart." At these *love-feasts* (so we termed them, retaining the name, as well as the thing, which was in use from the beginning) our food is only a little plain cake and water. But we seldom return from them without being fed, not only with "the meat which perisheth," but with "that which endureth to everlasting life."[4]

Exhortations, prayer, and almsgiving accompanied the meal, but the opportunity for personal testimony truly formed the heart of the fellowship. According to Frank Baker, all these components proceeded in a scheme that was "the normal order followed throughout Wesley's lifetime," a sequence that was customary, useful, and not required:

Hymn
Prayer
Grace (sung)
Bread distributed by stewards
Collection for the poor
Circulation of the loving-cup
Address by the presiding minister
Testimonies and verses of hymns
Spontaneous prayers and verses of hymns
Closing exhortation by the minister

Hymn
Benediction[5]

Among the hymns that were routinely sung was the five-section love feast hymn written by Charles Wesley and first published in *Hymns and Sacred Poems* (1740). The text of the first part, which contains echoes of the love feast's apostolic roots and its Methodist manifestation, crossed the Atlantic and has been handed down to generations of Methodists:

> Come, and let us sweetly join
> Christ to praise in hymns divine;
> Give we all with one accord
> Glory to our common Lord:
> Hands, and hearts, and voices raise,
> Sing as in the ancient days,
> Antedate the joys above,
> Celebrate the Feast of Love.
>
> Strive we, in affection strive:
> Let the purer flame revive,
> Such as in the martyrs glow'd,
> Dying champions for their God.
> We, like them, may live and love;
> Call'd we are their joys to prove;
> Saved with them from future wrath,
> Partners of like precious faith.
>
> Sing we then in Jesu's name,
> Now as yesterday the same,
> One in every age and place,
> Full for all of truth and grace.
> We, for Christ, our Master, stand
> Lights in a benighted land;
> We our dying Lord confess,
> We are Jesu's witnesses.
>
> Witnesses that Christ hath died,
> We with him are crucified:
> Christ hath burst the bands of death,
> We His quickening Spirit breathe.
> Christ is now gone up on high;
> (Thither all our wishes fly;)
> Sits at God's right hand above,
> There with Him we reign in love![6]

The first explicit witness of a Methodist love feast in America comes from the journal of Joseph Pilmore, who, along with Richard Boardman, had been sent by Wesley as a missionary. On Friday, March 23, 1770, Pilmore expressed the hope that through this "occonemy of the Methodists," the Philadelphians in attendance might be prepared "to eat bread togither in the kingdom of God." Two months later, on Sunday, May 13, he described an evening love feast in New York where "the Lord was remarkably present" and "we felt the softening power of the holy Ghost, and our Souls were disolved with love in the presence of the mighty God of Jacob."[7] From 1770 onward into the nineteenth century, accounts of love feasts increase in frequency, reflecting not only the proliferation of Methodist societies in America but also the occasion's overwhelming emotional and spiritual power, which moved participants to record the event in their diaries and journals. Services were expected to be no more than an hour and a half in duration, but because of the perceived presence of the convicting, justifying, and sanctifying Spirit of God, this rule was often violated. Technically the love feast could be observed anytime the authorized leader, defined after 1792 as the preacher in charge of a circuit, was present,[8] but the event regularly came to coincide with the quarterly visitation of the presiding elder; love feasts also were observed at the annual and quadrennial gatherings of the Methodist conferences. As in British Methodism, membership in the society was generally the prerequisite for attendance, and evidence (at first the class tickets, later love feast tickets) was expected to be shown. Laxity in this restriction caused a statement to be placed in the *Minutes* of the first Conference of the American Methodist societies held in 1773 at Philadelphia that persons should be admitted into the love feast only two or three times before they would be expected to become members of the society; the rule survived when the Methodist Episcopal Church was organized in 1784 and was kept by that church until 1864, whereas the Methodist Episcopal Church, South continued it until 1882. The desire that *all* who sought "to flee from the wrath to come" be formed in practical godliness and vital piety is clearly exhibited by the economic and racial diversity represented at the love feast of the eighteenth and early nineteenth centuries, an inclusivity that provoked Thomas Rankin to remark in 1774 that the devotion of the rich often paled to that of the poor of African descent.[9]

According to Nathan Bangs, the American service in the early years contained the same components as the British, though exhortations were sometimes absent from the love feast proper, and the sequence generally took a different shape: a hymn, prayer, the taking of bread and water, the relating of one's own "experience and enjoyment of divine things," almsgiving, singing, prayer, and the benediction.[10] Official stipulation of a collection for the poor to be made at the love feast is provided in the 1787 *Discipline*, though it quietly falls out by 1792. Yet almsgiving is listed in the suggested form for the love feast that first appears in the Methodist Episcopal Church, South's 1858 *Discipline*. This order basically follows Bangs's scheme, except for the inclusion after the opening prayer of a "short address, setting forth the nature and design of this institution," and, immediately before testimonies by the members, both the collection of the offering "whenever it is deemed necessary" and the reception of "candidates for church-fellowship" into the church. Almsgiving and membership components were dropped in 1866, and the outline as set forth from that date survived in the *Discipline* until 1938, the last book before merger.

Despite the "official" omission of the collection for the poor, it survived in practice and is mentioned in a description of an early twentieth-century love feast drawn from the childhood memories of Emory Stevens Bucke. Bucke also notes another variation from the suggested form: the reading of a Scripture lesson on the "bread of life" preceded the distribution of the bread, which then was followed by relevant commentary, testimonies, and hymn verses; the same actions came after a Scripture lesson on "the waters of mercy" and "never thirsting."[11] Pieces of Bucke's service meshed with the Methodist Episcopal Church, South's pattern in the service contained in the Methodist Church's *Book of Worship* of 1965; these are also joined by new elements:

A Hymn of Praise
The Scripture
Voluntary Prayers and the Lord's Prayer
An Address
A Hymn of Christian Fellowship
The Passing of the Bread [with the blessing "Blessed art thou, O Lord, God
  of the universe, who dost bring forth bread from the earth."]
Offering for the Poor
The Passing of the Cup [with the promise "Jesus Christ said, Whosoever
  drinketh of the water that I shall give him shall never thirst."]
A Thanksgiving in Unison
Testimonies
A Hymn of Thanksgiving
A Blessing

This is almost the same order provided in the 1992 *United Methodist Book of Worship*. The form suggested in the African Methodist Episcopal *Book of Worship* (1984), derived from a "primitive" ritual sequence proposed in *The Genius and Theory of Methodist Polity* (1885), by Bishop Henry Turner, preserves more of the simple shape described by Bangs, though the placement of the testimonies and the symbolic meal are reversed, and a Scripture lesson is added after the opening prayer. A rubric instructs that the love feast should be shared within a week before Communion is celebrated, a custom that Bucke noted as well. In this practice, the love feast functioned as a type of penitential or reconciliation rite based on Matthew 5:23–24. Bishop Turner offered the explanation: the love feast was a necessary preparation for Communion in that it allowed the people opportunity to "bury all bickerings, malice, envy and strife, and if any are not speaking, to get them to make up and start upon a new Christian career."[12]

The observance of the love feast declined as Methodism identified itself less as a connection of societies and more as a denomination. Nevertheless, the love feast survived to the end of the twentieth century, though for most Methodists its practice was more of a novelty or a memory of a precious peculiarity than a vital "feast of love" where "the love of God enkindles in the soul, it communicates from heart to heart, brethren are united in the closest bonds, God is felt to be gloriously present, heaven is begun on earth, and every heart responds to the sentiment."[13] During Methodism's first century in America, the love feast was looked to as an opportunity for fellowship and Christian nurture, where men and women, young and old, rich and poor could build one another up in Christian love; and the sharing of bread and water was a symbol of "the friendship existing between those persons who eat from the same dish & drink from the same bowl."[14] Sometimes the tense atmosphere sparked negativity, as the pastor of a Virginia church discovered in 1861, and the love feast itself then became an occasion for constructive reconciliation:

> Love Feast—a strange meeting for Love Feast—charges of enimity [sic] were made by the members against each other in very bitter terms and I bound them over to keep the peace. I found animosities had existed for years in this church and proposed the following covenant—1—Not to bear enemity [sic]. 2—To bridle the tongue. 3—To speak to each other. 4—To attend the means of grace. All present took the pledge on their knees except one man, who said he could not speak to a certain *brother*![15]

The relaxing of the qualifications for attendance, along with the cooling of Methodist fervor, proved in the end to have a part in the love feast's eventual decline. Although admission tickets continued to be issued despite calls within some denominations to curtail the practice, and the *Discipline* delineated who could properly attend, the restrictions for privacy often broke down, sometimes in response to accusations of exclusivism made both inside and outside Methodism. The selective nature of the gatherings, however, was not so much intended to be an obstacle (though in part there was a literal obstruction, since once the doors to the meeting were closed, no one was permitted to enter), but a pastoral design to provide an environment of trust where all—particularly women, whose public speaking in mixed company was discouraged socially—could express themselves freely, honestly, and equally.[16] The attraction of other Christians and non-Christians to these occasions, and the eventual opening of the doors to them, changed the essential character of the love feast to such an extent that for many its original usefulness was lost.

The Watch Night and the Renewal of the Covenant

Wesley knew from his sojourn at Herrnhut and from the Moravian Church's Constitution the custom of singing a verse at each hour of the night by those on the night watch,[17] and from his experience at Fetter Lane he probably was acquainted with the Moravian watch night service for New Year's Eve. But the direct origin of the Methodist watch night, according to Wesley, was the extended nighttime service of prayer, praise, and thanksgiving that developed around 1740 in the coal-mining community of Kingswood as a spiritual alternative to the evening tipple at the alehouse. At first hesitant to accept this innovation, Wesley eventually embraced it on account of its similarity to the vigils held in apostolic times and provided for in the Church of England's 1662 *Book of Common Prayer*, a point he made in countering his detractors who charged the Methodists of holding "midnight assemblies."[18] This "solemn season" soon spread beyond Kingswood to Bristol and Newcastle, and to London, where the first watch night was kept on April 9,

1742. The timing of what was apparently in the cities a monthly service was inherently practical, and the shape and content of the service determined to both glorify God and edify the people:

> We commonly choose for this solemn service the Friday night nearest the full moon, either before or after, that those of the congregation who live at a distance may have light to their several homes. The service begins at half an hour past eight and continues till a little after midnight. We have often found a peculiar blessing at these seasons. There is generally a deep awe upon the congregation, perhaps in some measure owing to the silence of the night; particularly in singing the hymn with which we commonly conclude:
>
> > Hearken to the solemn voice!
> > The awful midnight cry!
> > Waiting souls, rejoice, rejoice,
> > And feel the Bridegroom nigh.[19]

This hymn, a portion of the so-called "midnight hymn," was one of a number of hymns authored by Charles Wesley for use at the watch night, eleven of which were published independently as Hymns for the Watch-Night (1746); three years later, seven texts came out in the Hymns for New Year's Day (1749). One watch night hymn, "Come, let us anew our pleasures pursue" shares the first half line with a New Year hymn of the same meter, "Come, let us anew our journey pursue"; the latter hymn came to be used at watch nights on New Year's Eve, a practice that remained long after the decline—even in Wesley's lifetime—of the monthly gathering.

There is no firm evidence that American Methodists ever routinely observed a monthly watch night, but certainly in the eighteenth and early nineteenth centuries, the solemn occasion had not yet been relegated to the final evening of the year; and still into the late nineteenth century, members of the African Methodist Episcopal Church were encouraged to hold watch nights from 1:00 to 6:00 A.M. on Christmas morning in what was believed to be an imitation of ancient Christian practice.[20] According to oral and practical tradition, the service took place on various nights of the week, lasted several hours, and comprised preaching and exhortation (typically by different speakers), singing, and prayer. The watch night's characteristic length and contents encouraged Thomas Rankin to identify a comparable daytime service as a "watchafternoon," a designation apparently unique to Rankin.[21] True to its origins, Methodists in America saw the watch night as an alternative to worldly customs and amusements. In 1787 Asbury noted that "we had a watch night, and the gentry had a ball"; and in the 1798 commentary on the Discipline, after explaining that both Jesus and St. Paul spent all night in prayer, he asked, "And shall not the ministers and people of God in these days imitate such great examples? Shall the dissipated and profane revel and watch, night after night, in the service of Satan, and shall we think it too much to watch and pray sometimes for a few hours together?"[22] The Methodists even criticized less provocative nighttime behavior. In comparing the Methodist service with the cultural custom of ringing the church bell through the night to herald the new year, Ezekiel Cooper described the latter as "Satan's Watch Night."[23] Such Methodist piety, especially at the watch night on New Year's Eve, invited disruptions by those who were more attracted to unholy exploits. When a mob threatened on the last night of 1770, Pilmore concedes that "the terrors of the Lord made them afraid" and so they left the worshipers alone.[24] Other gatherings were not so fortunate: sneezing replaced singing when pepper was placed on a stove before a watch night in 1838.[25]

The expectation of every watch night was the outpouring of the manifold blessings of God. The themes of repentance (the conflict between darkness and light), readiness for the eschatological judgment, and watching and waiting all were intended to provoke a response of faith. These emphases were sometimes reinforced by the inclusion of other ritual acts at the watch night, such as the love feast, baptism, and reception into church membership.[26] But occasionally the intended benefits were slow in coming. At a New Jersey watch night around 1810, a remedy was made for a cool gathering:

> In the new Church, a "Watch Night" was held on New Year's Eve, but it was a dull time; about ten o'clock the elder brethren proposed to "break up and go home." The Class Leader, Brother Duer, cries, "No, brethren, that will not do, let us pray again." Sister Phebe Peters was called upon to pray; and in a short time during that pious woman's exercise, the power of the Highest fell upon the congregation; the house seemed to be filled with the Divine presence, and the members' hearts overflowed with love and joy. The meeting held until towards morning![27]

An exhorter's lack of skills changed the mood of another New Year's meeting:

> At 8 o'clock began the watchnight. I commenced the services by giving out, "Thou Judge of quick and dead," with as much solemnity of voice, attitude and look as I could command: it was well sung by a good choir, and numerous congregation in the old tune called "Aylesbury." After this I made a long prayer, and then gave out "Lo, he comes with clouds descending," which was well sung. I then preached a long sermon the 11th & 12th verses of the 20th Chapter of Revelation. After this we had singing and prayers, and some exhortation such as it was, for there was not a regular exhorter, nor a preacher of any kind, present besides myself. One of my *volunteer* exhorters made a very crooked piece of work of it; and his singing set the whole house in an uproar of laughter from which I found it rather difficult to recover them. I then dismissed them.[28]

Despite distractions, the New Year's watch night service progressed toward welcoming another year of the Lord. Some communities greeted it on their knees in prayer or sang "Come, let us anew our journey pursue" or another hymn. Others, noted Methodist Episcopal bishop Thomas Morris, renewed "the Christian's covenant to strive for 'a closer walk with God,'" and, kneeling, spent the minutes until midnight "confessing the sins of the past year, returning thanks to God for the blessings of life and grace perpetuated to them, and engaging with the Lord, each for himself, to be for Him the ensuing year, whether called to live and labor, or die and go to eternity."[29] To do this, many Methodists drew upon the resources that Wesley had provided for covenanting with God.

Wesley was not unique in promoting the renewal of one's personal covenant with God as an improvement in "practical divinity." He knew of covenant renewal from his mother and father, who, though convinced Anglicans, readily instilled in their son the language and concepts of Puritan covenant (federal) theology in which they had been nurtured by their own Dissenting parents. References to covenanting were also familiar to Wesley through his reading of Puritan devotional literature, selected writings from Laudian Anglicanism, and the Moravian Church's Constitution. So, it is not surprising that Wesley would freely employ covenantal language in his writing and, given his penchant for ritually expressing commitments to the Christian faith, develop a service of covenant renewal that usually concluded with the celebration of the Lord's Supper. Wesley's expectation was that the covenant service, like the love feast, would be a private, not public, event. Though some posit that a simple service was in practice by 1747 or 1748,[30] Wesley's journal entry for August 11, 1755, was the first to confirm that a service took place using the words of "that blessed man, Richard Alleine." The words referred to were the Puritan Richard Alleine's in *Vindiciae Pietatis: Or, A Vindication of Godliness* (1663), wherein lengthy directions for covenanting were followed by five brief instructions and a form of "solemn covenant" borrowed from Alleine's Puritan son-in-law Joseph Alleine (Joseph's material would also appear in the widely popular *An Alarme to Unconverted Sinners*, which appeared in 1671 after his death).[31] In 1753, Wesley published versions of both Alleine works in the *Christian Library*, but it was *Vindiciae Pietatis* that was subsequently used for the Methodist covenanting service, with the leaders drawing most often upon the *Christian Library* printing of Richard Alleine's text. To all or part of Alleine's directions and the covenant prayer might be joined exhortation, extemporary prayer, and hymns. By 1778 at least, a Charles Wesley hymn was commonly used at these services; the text soon became designated the "covenant hymn" and its use at covenant renewal a Methodist tradition:

> Come, let us use the grace Divine,
> And all with one accord
> In a perpetual covenant join
> Ourselves to Christ the Lord,
> Give ourselves up through Jesu's power
> His name to glorify,
> And promise in this sacred hour
> For God to live, and die.
>
> The covenant we this moment make
> Be ever kept in mind!
> We will no more our God forsake,
> Or cast His words behind;
> We never will throw off His fear,
> Who hears our solemn vow:
> And if Thou art well-pleased to hear,
> Come down, and meet us now!
>
> Thee, Father, Son, and Holy Ghost,
> Let all our hearts receive,
> Present with Thy celestial host

The peaceful answer give;
To each the covenant-blood apply
Which takes our sins away,
And register our names on high,
And keep us to that day![32]

The publishing in 1779 of a separate (and unapproved) text for the covenanting service by the Methodist itinerating preacher Thomas Lee may have provided the impetus for Wesley to bring out his own pamphlet, and in 1780 *Directions for Renewing Our Covenant with God* was printed. As might be expected, Wesley's *Directions* are virtually the directions and covenant prayer from *Vindiciae Pietatis*, though the first of Alleine's five directions is considerably abbreviated, and the rest of the text has been slightly reworked. The *Directions* went through approximately nineteen editions and formed the basis for later variations in the covenanting services that would develop in British Methodism.[33]

Apparently there was no printing of Wesley's *Directions* in America, and no direct American usage of Wesley's text can be confirmed. Even so, the Americans knew the practice of covenanting. From March to June 1786, Ezekiel Cooper twice records that covenants had been renewed.[34] The scant references available indicate that the short-lived covenant renewal soon was placed exclusively at the year's end watch night or, less frequently, on New Year's Day, and only hints are given about the shape and content of the service. Bishop Thomas Morris's reflections in 1852 (mentioned above) possibly suggest some familiarity with the language of Wesley's *Directions*; a fictionalized account of a watch night published in 1859 describes only the singing of the covenant hymn while the congregation knelt in the first minutes of the new year;[35] and Illinoisan Leonard Smith, in his journal for December 31, 1860, recorded that following "silent, secret prayer to God," "we concluded by shaking hands with all who had made a covenant with God." New Year's Eve watch nights, with ritual actions for covenant renewal sometimes conjoined, continued well into the twentieth century, though in some local congregations their character evolved from an entire evening of prayerful solemnity to a festival capped by prayer.[36] One Massachusetts pastor, frustrated with many from his congregation exchanging the traditional watch night for the glitter of the hotels and nightclubs, in 1938 experimented successfully with dancing and games in the church hall prior to midnight prayer in the pews.[37] The Methodist New Year's Eve watch night also sometimes expanded into an ecumenical, evangelistic service: in 1909, the Chicago Coliseum hosted over 12,000 in an evening of praise, prayer, appeal, and commitment.[38]

Perhaps in response to the increasing variety in practice, juxtaposed with the desire to reclaim Wesleyan liturgical traditions, the Methodist Church offered in the 1945 *Book of Worship* "The Order of Worship for Such as Would Enter into or Renew Their Covenant with God, for Use in a Watch-Night Service or on the First Sunday of the New Year." With the introduction of this service, the distinct (and officially unscripted) watch night service took second place to an ordered (and formal) covenant service, and thereby, wittingly or unwittingly, early American Methodist praxis was effectively reversed. The 1945 service did not reproduce one of the editions of Wesley's *Directions*, but rather borrowed from the British Methodist *Book of Offices* (1936) the order drawn up from the covenanting traditions of the various Methodist bodies that had recently merged in 1932.[39] What figured as the covenant prayer in the 1936 service was not a portion of the form of solemn covenant original to Joseph Alleine, but a segment from Richard Alleine's fourth direction reworked as a prayer. The sequence of the 1945 service varied slightly from the British service, but the 1936 order was restored for the service utilized in the 1965 *Book of Worship*:

Hymn ["Come, let us use the grace divine" or some other]
Collect for Purity ["Almighty God, unto whom all hearts are open"]
The Lord's Prayer [in unison]
Reading from John 15:1–8
Description of the New Covenant and Summons to Self Examination
Prayer of Adoration
Litany of Thanksgiving
Litany of Confession
Prayer of Confession [in unison]
Scriptural Absolution
Hymn
Introduction to a Renewal of the Covenant
Covenant Prayer [by the minister, then the people join in saying, "I am no longer my own, but thine. Put me to what thou wilt, rank me with whom thou wilt; put me to doing, put me to suffering; let me be employed for thee or laid aside for thee, exalted for thee or brought low for thee; let me be full, let me be empty; let me have all things, let me have nothing; I freely and heartily yield all things to thy pleasure and disposal. And now, O glorious and blessed God, Father, Son, and Holy Spirit, thou art mine, and I am thine. So be it. And the covenant which I have made on earth, let it be ratified in heaven. Amen."]
Introductory Dialogue [Sursum Corda]
Preface [brief]
Sanctus
Prayer of Consecration and the rest of Holy Communion or, if no Communion, a Hymn and Benediction

The 1984 African Methodist Episcopal *Book of Worship* also followed the 1936 British order, but inexplicably omitted the unison prayer of confession, the scriptural absolution, the introduction to a renewal of the covenant, and the covenant prayer. An intentional move away from the 1936 order back to Wesley's *Directions* occurred in the 1992 *United Methodist Book of Worship*, which presented, at the conclusion of the sequence normative for Sunday worship, selected directions for covenanting now briefly framed as invitation or prayer, and the 1780 covenant prayer abbreviated and reworked in contemporary language as the designated covenant prayer.[40] Rubrics indicated that the service could be used at times other than the New Year, but this recovery of the older tradition was tempered by the statement that ideally the service should be used only once annually.

The Quarterly Meeting

The love feast and, occasionally, the watch night and the renewal of the covenant converge in another peculiarly Methodist institution that David Lewis denoted as the "great festival": the quarterly meeting. Quarterly patterns were familiar in the British judicial system ("quarter days"), Anglicanism (e.g., ember days), other religious societies (most notably the Society of Friends), and in Methodism itself (e.g., the scheduled meetings of the band and general love feasts, and the issuance of tickets of membership). Inspired by such precedents, British Methodist John Bennet in 1748 developed a system of oversight whereby clusters or circuits of Methodist societies would join together four times a year to transact business. Bennet's method proved to be so beneficial that by the late 1750s the quarterly meeting became an established component of Methodist organization for monitoring both spiritual and temporal affairs.[41] Rules for ensuring the perpetuation of the quarterly meeting were written into the *Minutes* as one of the leadership responsibilities of Wesley's assistants, to whom also fell the duty of quarterly reports for each society's finances and membership, and "every remarkable conversion and remarkable death" (Large Minutes, Question 42). Because the assistant also had the task of overseeing watch nights and love feasts, it was convenient for him to plan these occasions of worship to coincide with the gathering of the society every three months. Early on, serious and sustained worship became synonymous with the quarterly meeting, and not just because of the peculiar Methodist rites, but on account of the numerous preaching services and prayer meetings that surrounded and interspersed the business sessions. The spiritual energy generated at these meetings often attracted persons not already affiliated with the Methodist societies, which required that distinctions be made between private and public events, a separation that was often difficult to maintain.

The quarterly meeting transplanted in American soil took root as a one-day event most often held on Tuesdays, but because of the distance between societies in rural areas (twenty to thirty miles was a common journey to meeting), and the desire expressed by persons in neighboring circuits to attend (some traveling upwards of fifty miles), the custom developed of holding two-day meetings on Saturday and Sunday. Jesse Lee further explained the rationale for the two-day format, which became the recommended procedure according to the 1780 American *Minutes*: slaves and the poor could come only on the Lord's Day; and the wealthy would not trouble themselves to come at any other time. "Shouting and praising God" could anticipate the meeting and the arrival of the preachers. On one occasion, the preachers found persons "on the ground crying for mercy, and others in extacies [*sic*] of joy." Lee recognized, in fact, that an extended meeting allowed greater opportunity to produce the affects of "lively religion":

> At a quarterly meeting held in Baltimore on the 8th and 9th of August, 1789, and during the following week, the kingdom of Satan suffered great loss. The first day of the quarterly meeting was profitable to numbers: many cried and wept bitterly for mercy, and some souls were born of God. Sunday, the second day, was most awful and glorious. In the love feast at eight in the morning, the society enjoyed a little Pentecost,

and dwelt as it were in the suburbs of heaven. The presence of God was awfully felt, while the people one after another feelingly declared *what God had done for their souls.*

In public preaching, the word was so accompanied by the energy of the holy Ghost, that there were few but felt its mighty power. Some of the greatest revilers of the work were constrained to tremble and weep. The congregation broke up on Sunday night very late, after many had been converted. Some were two, three or four hours on their knees, others were prostrate on the floor, most earnestly agonizing for mercy, till they could rejoice in God their Saviour. What power! What awe rested on the people![42]

Other Methodists would refer to the spiritual dynamism of these meetings with such epithets as "a glorious season," an "outpouring of grace," and "a melting time," which describe not only the intensity of the individual experience in both the public and private assemblies but more importantly the Christian unity and fellowship of the faithful expressed in the private, intimate gathering of the love feast. Meetinghouses, public buildings, barns, and even brush arbors and tents were used to shelter the crowds who assembled for public preaching services and for the services open only to Methodists with supporting documentation. The revival aspect of these meetings became so paramount that the business sessions led by the presiding elder on his quarterly visit as pastoral supervisor rarely find a mention in accounts other than the official record. Elizabeth Roe of Illinois refers in passing to the business-laden "quarterly conference"; but her interest is focused on the evangelistic quality of this meeting from the late 1820s, and on the contemporary reappropriation of the apostolic love feast:

The quarterly meeting commenced on Saturday, with preaching at twelve o'clock noon, and at early candle-light. This was the manner of giving out evening meetings, as there were but few people in Illinois at that early date who had clocks. The mantle clock was not in use then, and the old-fashioned ones with long wooden cases were difficult to move, and were left behind.

Brother [Peter] Cartwright preached at twelve o'clock, noon. The quarterly conference occupied the afternoon, and Brother Tartington preached at candle-light, and the service closed with a devotional prayer meeting. The preaching was food for my soul. I had not heard Brother Cartwright preach since I had been converted, except on this occasion.

Sabbath morning at nine o'clock we assembled without the tolling of a bell, in the upper room of the Court House, to enjoy a Love-feast. The room was filled, and the door closed, and oh! what a precious hour it was, as one after another arose to speak of the mercy of God; the love of a precious Savior shed abroad in their hearts; the victories they had gained since their last quarterly meeting or love-feast, and of the blessed hope of immortality and eternal life through Jesus Christ, our Lord. Many shouts of glory went up from hearts that were filled to the overflowing. The walls of the court house fairly rang with the melody. The house, for the present at least, seemed to be sacred on account of the presence of the Lord. It appeared to me something like the love-feast, or classmeeting the disciples enjoyed when doubting Thomas made one of their number, and our blessed Savior permitted him to put his finger into the wounds, and Thomas cried out, "My Lord, and my God!" I do not think there was a person in that house but who could say, "I know my Redeemer lives and intercedes for me; I shall see Him as He is. Praise the Lord for the hope set before us."

At eleven o'clock we had public service in the lower story—quite a large room—and it was filled, and every door and window was crowded with attentive hearers.

Father Cartwright discoursed, and seemed endowed with the power and demonstration of the Spirit of God. Some were awakened to a sense of their sins, and other were converted. It was a time long to be remembered, and will be remembered in glory.[43]

From the descriptions of Lee, Roe, and scores of other Methodists, a shape emerges for the two-day quarterly meeting that shows a tendency toward a common pattern, though not a fixed structure. A fast was expected on the Friday prior to quarterly meeting and was legislated in the *Discipline* beginning in 1792.[44] A preaching service around noon marked the beginning of the meeting on Saturday, which would be followed by the business session, sometimes held at the same time as another preaching service. The day would conclude with preaching and prayer meetings, and sometimes with a stated watch night or a service to renew one's covenant with God. The closed love feast most often began the Sunday phase, with a preaching service coming later in the morning and, if time and personnel allowed, also in the afternoon and evening.

Another consistent element of the quarterly meeting, though not as regular as the love feast, was the celebration of the Lord's Supper. By Methodist polity, the sacrament required the services of an ordained minister who, for many circuits, came only four times a year in the form of the presiding elder; baptisms and weddings, additional tasks of the ordained, were also performed.[45] Admission to the Lord's Supper was gained through proof of the quarterly ticket, and if one was not a Methodist, by examination of spiritual character. The placement of Communion in the course of the quarterly meeting could vary, with records indicating that it began the Sunday session, came immediately after or was blended with the Sunday love feast (with the collection of alms functioning as a type of linchpin), or followed a preaching service either on Saturday or Sunday.[46] The sacrament also might not be present at all, as apparently was the case for the meetings cited by Lee and Roe. Even though, for many Methodists, the quarterly meeting was the only chance to receive Communion, and they looked forward to the presence and power of God in the sacrament, for some the love feast proved to be the highlight of the meeting. Such elevated status undoubtedly is linked with the fact that the love feast was *the* Methodist occasion for communion with God and fellow Christians prior to the ordination of the first Methodist ministers in 1784, and its standing did not waver even after Methodists were permitted to receive the sacrament from the hands of their own clergy.

It has been said that the quarterly meeting, which intertwined the business of the circuit with the rituals that defined and formed the Methodist community, was the place where "Methodism was distinctively itself, most fully *church*."[47] Though the quarterly meeting as a forum for local church business endured into the twentieth century, its character as a unique opportunity for worship declined as preachers ceased to itinerate as in former days, as more ordained ministers were set apart for administration of the sacraments and the church's other rites, and as circuits were dismantled into single "station" churches or small "charges" of two or more. Some of the peculiar liturgical components of the quarterly meeting were preserved in another type of meeting, one unique to America that had developed alongside the quarterly plan and survived it when the quarterly meeting had outlived its original function: the camp meeting.

The Camp Meeting

Preaching in the open air characterized Methodism from almost the very beginning, and was a practice much criticized by Church of England clergy and others who deplored such irregularities. In England and America, Methodist services were held outside of church walls for two basic reasons: Anglican clergy were often unwilling to share their buildings with the Methodists; and the small structures available to the Methodist preachers frequently could not accommodate the crowds. To this twosome, the American Methodists, cognizant of the circumstances of a spreading population, added a third: the gospel was to be proclaimed in places where there were not yet established settlements. The Americans never had any qualms about praising God in "nature's temple," so when participants and observers at the quarterly meeting overflowed the designated room, the obvious solution was to move the public preaching services out-of-doors. Indeed, matters were sometimes so planned from the start. Because of the difficulty in finding lodgings near the meeting, many who came some distance, in any case, carried their own provisions with them and slept under the stars in makeshift beds on the ground or in a wagon. Therefore, even before the creation of the Methodist Episcopal Church, Methodists were already experiencing the setting as well as the revivalistic content of the camp meeting, which from the early 1800s would develop into an independent institution for worship, evangelism, and social exchange.

The camp meeting as a form thus did not arise ex nihilo in the revivalistic atmosphere that pervaded the nation in the phenomenon now identified as the Second Great Awakening. In addition to the Methodist outdoor preaching services and quarterly meetings, other antecedents, such as the Scottish Presbyterian eucharistic "sacramental seasons" and "holy fairs," and the outdoor preaching services of certain Separate Baptists in Virginia, bridged the gap between the two Awakenings.[48] Methodist outdoor meetings of more than two days' duration, at which participants intentionally camped together, were also held in Georgia and the Carolinas in the decade before the Presbyterian outdoor assemblies at Gasper River (1800) and Cane Ridge (1801) in Kentucky, which have been long credited as the first real camp meetings and as catalysts for the Second Awakening. No matter what denomination or site eventually is credited with the origination of the camp meeting, it is evident, despite the contentions of earlier historians,[49] that the Methodists did not adopt the camp meeting as an entirely new and innovative occasion for enthusiastic worship and the conversion of souls, but instead adapted and transformed what they had previously found successful at the quarterly meetings to the format of a residential protracted convocation that now was designated under a new name. The close relationship between the quarterly meeting and the camp meeting continued to be expressed, by some Methodists, through the practice of creating camp meetings out of regularly scheduled quarterly meetings. The connection between the two is explicity addressed in the *Discipline* of the Free Methodists by an instruction present from that denomination's inception and on into the first half of the twentieth century, which states that the holding of camp meetings "as the interests of the cause of God may require" is under the jurisdiction of the quarterly conference.[50] This juxtaposition of business and worship in quar-

terly and camp meetings thus concretely bore witness to the self-image of disciplined Christian life that Methodists codified, but did not explicitly articulate, in
their *Discipline*.[51]

Camp meetings have usually been associated with the American frontier, and
certainly Methodists found them to be a practical necessity and a spiritual boon
in the sparsely inhabited backwoods where hundreds and even thousands of worshipers flocked to the proceedings. But camp meetings were not an institution of
the frontier alone.[52] Bishop Francis Asbury and other Methodist leaders encouraged
open-air revivals across the nation: in the West and in the not-so-remote areas of
the eastern seaboard. The settled Methodists of city and town happily extended
their own familiar practices into the flexible camp meeting format because they
recognized, as did Asbury, its potential as a "battle ax and weapon of war" to
"break down walls of wickedness, part of hell, superstition, false doctrine."[53] For
similar reasons, other denominations, like the United Brethren, engaged in camp
meetings on the frontier and in settled regions during the first decades of the 1800s.
On occasion, Baptists and Presbyterians shared cooperatively in general or union
meetings with the Methodists, though at ecumenical "sacramental" meetings, the
Baptists separated themselves during the celebration of the Lord's Supper. Camp
meeting methods proved for some denominations to be divisive rather than upbuilding, and decisions were taken within certain groups, most notably those
within the Reformed tradition, to discard the practice soon after its implementa-
tion. However, the camp meeting as a vehicle for large-scale evangelical worship
continued to be cultivated throughout the nineteenth century by all the different
branches of Methodism. Methodist outdoor revival meetings could be found in
every region, in languages other than English (the Swedish "lager moten"), and
attended by whites, blacks, and native peoples, sometimes together and sometimes
apart.

The area for the camp meeting, which participants regularly denoted as hallowed
or sacred space, was arranged according to the expected components and anticipated outcome of the meeting. The earliest meeting places were loosely organized
near wood and water sources and pasturage, with a wagon bed or a hastily constructed platform used as an elevated stage for preaching and exhortation. Underbrush was cleared to create a grove for the worshipers, who, segregated by gender,
stood or sat on the ground, on logs, or on rough-hewn planks. The small tents
that surrounded the corporate worship area were constructed from assorted fabrics
to shelter families from the elements.

By the mid-1830s, as the camp meeting grew in popularity and size, so did the
complexity of the spatial design and the necessity of planning for what in some
places became an annual summertime event. On acreage set apart as campgrounds,
permanent structures were built, the most prominent being the pulpit or speakers'
stand, which evolved from a simple platform into a raised and roofed building
enclosed on three sides, which sometimes could accommodate the speaker and as
many as a dozen or more other persons. Two stands might be placed at opposite
ends of the ground, and large meetings could have even more, with prominence
given to the stand located, if the contours of the land allowed it, in a natural
amphitheater. Immediately in front of the preaching stand was an area, sometimes

enclosed, designated as the "altar." This straw-covered space could be open for standing and kneeling, or filled with one or more "mourners' benches" or "anxious benches," all set aside for those newly awakened to the bondage of sin and desiring deliverance, as well as for "backsliders" who again came seeking redemption. In some encampments, two tents, one for women, the other for men, or one large tent with partitions might be erected in the altar area, where an anticipating light would be kept burning day and night. Extending from the altar would be rows of benches separated by a wide aisle. The seating was most often in the open air, but over time a large tent might be supplied, or a shed or wooden pavilion ("tabernacle") constructed to house both pulpit and seating. The entire worship space could be configured as a circle, rectangle ("oblong square"), dodecagon, horseshoe, or other pattern, and around it might be the cooking fires that, along with candles and fire stands, provided illumination for the assembly. Behind each fire would be a tent, the occupants' wagon or carriage, and their horses. At popular meeting sites, larger "boarding" tents might be added, and eventually permanent cabins or cottages were built. As the facilities became more organized, each campground established regulations for participants and enforced policies devised to deal with "rowdies" and other outside disturbances; in some camps, police or guards were secured to monitor events. The *Camp Meeting Manual* (1854), by New York Methodist B. W. Gorham, and other guidebooks were published to expedite the increasingly complicated process of arranging and maintaining the camp meeting and grounds in "Methodist order." The growing sophistication of the camp meeting, evolving from a haphazard gathering of simple folk utilizing jerry-built and temporary structures to a planned summer "resort" of permanent constructions for a growing Methodist middle class, serves as an another indicator of Methodism's emergence into the cultural mainstream during the mid-nineteenth century.[54]

In comparison to the dramatic alteration of the camp meeting site, the content of the meeting changed very little, though the religious ecstasy the contents aroused gradually subsided except in gatherings sponsored by Methodism's Holiness churches. The essential ingredient of the assembly was evangelistic preaching, "more properly exhortations to repentance than illustrations of points of faith."[55] Often dozens of preachers, lay and clergy, would be on hand to lead three or more services each day, with some services scheduled simultaneously on different parts of the grounds. Prayer meetings, in families and other clusters (some gender-specific), were expected, and were as likely to lead to the altar as the preaching. Small groups sometimes formed spontaneously, "animated by the love of God, and attracted by the sympathetic groans of wounded sinners, whose piercing cries ascended to heaven," and so would remain in "petitions and intercessions to Almighty God, in behalf of themselves, and their mourning fellow creatures" throughout the day and night, if need demanded, to be rewarded when the "mourning penitents emerged into the liberties of the Gospel."[56] Songs and hymns filled the air, and could be taken from the denominational hymn books and special camp meeting songsters that were brought by the participants. If books were unavailable, the worship leader might sing the text line by line with the people responding in turn, thereby creating a "call and response" pattern. New tunes, some utilizing popular secular melodies, were also composed on site. Texts were improvised by using snippets of Scripture along with generous portions of "hallelujah," or by taking a familiar hymn text and adding to it an independent—and sometimes thematically unrelated—refrain or chorus (e.g., the Isaac Watts text "Come Ye that Love the Lord" with the refrain "We're Marching to Zion"). The theological themes of repentance, grace, forgiveness, and judgment abound in camp meeting songs, nuanced with images and metaphors that reflect the events of the camp meeting itself: pilgrimage to Canaan; warfare (encampment against the enemy; sinners slain in battle who emerge newly born); and the reunion of believers in heaven.[57]

The peculiar liturgical idioms of the Methodists adjusted well to the camp meeting format: closed love feasts were observed, most often when the gathering doubled as a quarterly meeting or was scheduled as part of an annual conference; every evening had the potential of being a watch night; and though a formal covenanting does not seem to have taken place, covenant language is employed recurrently to describe one's renewed promises to God. Also performed were the established Methodist rituals of baptism, the solemnization of marriage, and the reception of members, though formal rites of membership would not be introduced until the second half of the nineteenth century. The Lord's Supper, celebrated with a simple table placed in the altar area, was not always observed on the Lord's Day; frequently the sacrament was kept until the evening before or the day of departure. Other practices not uniquely Methodist also flourished at the camp meeting. The kinetic responses generated in reaction to the spiritual and emotional intensity of preaching services and the Methodist love feasts were equally abundant at the camp meeting, and were manifested in new and different forms. The shouting, barking, laughing, singing, jerking, falling, rolling, dancing, and running "exercises" that were distasteful to outsiders and condemned by them were, for the campers, visible evidence of the Spirit of God moving in their midst and thus essential signs of the spiritual life. Nathan Bangs and other Methodists found the physical eruptions objectionable and pleaded for reform, arguing that such a "spirit of pride, presumption, and bigotry, impatience of scriptural restraint and moderation . . . marred and disgraced the work of God."[58] Though the exercises were not usually prohibited, their appearance at meetings soon diminished. Concerning the jerks, a "very strange as well as disgusting exercise" where the individual rapidly whipped the head backward and forward, John Brooks of Tennessee commented that the practice "passed away in a few years, to the joy of all."[59]

The large assemblage of persons at the camp meetings offered opportunities for more than the provocation of religious enthusiasm and commitment. Camp meetings were convened during the War of 1812 and the Civil War, although the number of assemblies and attendance at them was reduced, and those held during the latter conflict sometimes became forums for promoting nationalistic agendas, effectively blurring the spiritual with the political, and the denomination with the nation. On one occasion, just before the final benediction at the 1861 Chicago District Camp Meeting, the congregation sang patriotic songs before a pulpit draped with the American flag. Following the benediction and the official closing of the camp meeting, speeches commending support for the Union were rendered by the same leaders who, days earlier, had led rallies for the kingdom of God. Tears ran down faces as the "Star Spangled Banner" was sung, moving the reporter to note that on that day, "the love of Christ and the love of our country met together. Religion and patriotism embraced each other."[60]

The co-opting of the camp meeting for the promotion of causes other than just the spiritual contributed to its decline in the years following the Civil War, as did population shifts, concerns about social respectability and status, and Methodism's increasing self-identification with the broader American society.[61] In their "Pastoral Address" at the 1880 General Conference of the Methodist Episcopal Church, the bishops identified the spiritual deficiences of those camp meetings "made a source of revenue mainly, or where luxurious ease and popular amusement are more largely patronized than prayer-meetings are." Equally troubling were Methodists who forsook Lord's Day worship in their local congregation for participation in these camp meetings and, by taking public transportation to them, desecrated the Sabbath.[62] Nevertheless, the camp meeting as an institution did not die, though many once-thriving campgrounds disappeared in the forests from which they had been carved. Methodism's Holiness branches nurtured the camp meeting, as did persons within the larger Methodist bodies, who challenged their churches not to neglect the old institution but to correct its inadequacies, in order to have "more of the old-fashioned power while we get more of the new style polish and culture" since " 'modern improvements' are no helps in bringing souls, soundly converted, into the kingdom of God."[63] Methodist periodicals, into the 1920s, regularly published calendars and advertisements for upcoming camp meetings, as well as descriptions of the good work accomplished at them. Numbers of twentieth-century assemblies maintained but modified the contents of the older gatherings. The Galesburg (Illinois) District Camp Meeting, held at Gilson on August 18–24, 1903, preserved in the daily program much of the arrangement of the meeting from former days, but also addressed contemporary needs, seen particularly by the stated involvement of children and youth and the demand for Bible study:

8:00	A.M.	Prayer Meeting
8:30	A.M.	Bible Reading
9:30	A.M.	Normal Bible Lesson
10:30	A.M.	PREACHING
2:30	P.M.	PREACHING
4:00	P.M.	Children's Meeting
[6:30	P.M.	YOUNG PEOPLE'S MEETING]
7:30	P.M.	Evangelistic Services[64]

In spite of the changes, the impression made at the camp meeting was still worthy of inscription in personal diaries: Hattie Womack Thornton recorded her thrill at the "wonderful testimonials" given at a 1912 camp meeting love feast presided over by missionary Elizabeth Claiborne.[65] Such experiences undoubtedly continued to be recounted when persons experienced spiritual awakening and nurture at one of the Methodist-related camp meetings that dotted the late twentieth-century American landscape.

Protracted Meetings and Indoor Revivals

In the more than two hundred years of American Methodism, numerous other experiments and forms of revival were engaged in by the ever-pragmatic Methodists, from elaborate assemblies with scores of preachers, to the "greatest liturgy in the world, short and scriptural and mighty powerful—'Amen,' "[66] each with the goal of converting the lost and edifying the faithful. Though ideally the spirit of revival would infuse Methodists throughout the year and be manifested by regular participation in "family, social, and public prayer, attended with a greatly quickened faith, and an increased love for all the services and ordinances of the sanctuary,"[67] observation taught that lukewarm preaching, laxity in observing the means of grace, and the distractions of life begat backsliders. Small group meetings of prayer and testimony were encouraged to keep faith and spiritual disciplines alive. Protracted meetings of prayer and praise led by local preachers followed up quarterly or camp meetings to ignite the fires of those who had not yet come to the altar, or to stoke the embers to full flame in those who had previously fallen away. Annual or more frequent indoor protracted meetings were held with fiery preaching by guest preachers, the singing of hymns calling for repentance and promising forgiveness, and concluding with an altar call to the railing that typically surrounded the pulpit and the Communion table. Numerous communities experienced a "town camp meeting" of several weeks' duration as the rural camp meeting declined and its methods became urbanized; the first such meeting in Winchester, Virginia, in 1869 drew a "large and attentive" congregation, and consisted of a prayer and experience meeting at 9 A.M., preaching by "prominent ministers" at 11:00 A.M. and 3:00 P.M., and an evening service.[68] Specially appointed Methodist evangelists might make an annual appearance in a local congregation for several days and nights of special services, and local "revival workers" were set apart to aid in the endeavor. In every decade, techniques and advice for the promotion of revivals were found in personal journals, periodical articles, and books on the subject, and though the methods varied (e.g., psychological analyses are proposed in the 1920s), the expected outcome remained constant.

A Peculiar Identity

The "great festivals" may be identified as the most characteristic worship services or settings of American Methodism, even though these services share affinities with non-Methodist, and even non-American, forms. Though not perhaps terribly original, Methodists were nonetheless highly adept at borrowing and reworking available resources to reinforce their Arminian claims that all persons, in every place, should be offered an opportunity, and indeed persuaded, to accept and embrace God's boundless love. Before 1784, the freestanding celebrations of the love feast, the watch night, and the renewal of the covenant, and the combination of services at the quarterly meeting were the places where Methodism was uniquely itself, where both insiders and outsiders recognized the distinctive Methodist presence, whether as an *ecclesiola in ecclesia* or as (functionally) an independent religious society. As Methodism developed after 1784, these services, joined by the worship marathon that was the camp meeting, continued for a time to be the principal and defining markers of the Methodist community, and as such, directly bore upon expectations for the normative Sunday worship pattern. In many respects, the great festivals were manifestations of a broader peculiarity that could be claimed to distinguish Methodism as a whole:

> There is a peculiarity of spirit that pervades and distinguishes the different denominations. The Episcopalians have their atmosphere. How antique and formal! The Presbyterians have theirs. How solemn, rigid and exact! "Decency and order" are their watchwords. The Baptists have theirs also. How damp, exclusive and denominational! The Methodist spirit or atmosphere is peculiar. It is a vital spirit. "Life and power" is a familiar note among us. What would pass for a meeting among others has little interest to a *live* Methodist, if it have not life, elasticity and power. It is a free spirit. "Liberty" is its watchword; liberty from sin, from bondage, body and soul; liberty to pray loud or low, to speak, to use all the gifts bestowed, whether "one talent" or "ten," whether among men or women; liberty for all, learned or unlearned, rich or poor, young converts or old ones; liberty to sing, whether by note or by rote, with the Spirit and with the understanding, to sing in the choir, or in the congregation; liberty for *all* to sing, "not one in ten only." Simplicity is characteristic of it; no affectation, no pompous, mechanical, or strained dignity. It is an *earnest* spirit."[69]

Wesley had drawn upon what he believed were ancient Christian principles in developing the love feast, watch night, and covenant renewal to articulate and sustain the unity of the Christian community—a unity ideally marked by the collapsing of distinctions of gender, race, and economic standing, since it was incumbent upon each and every redeemed sinner to testify to God's mercy and grace. "The very design of a love-feast," commented Wesley, "is a free and familiar conversation, in which every man, yea, and woman, has liberty to speak whatever may be to the glory of God."[70] Such intentions of social leveling, equality, and freedom were not restricted in the Methodist design to these special, intimate occasions, but found a concise expression there and also in the more public events of the quarterly meeting and camp meeting. The peculiar usages flourished in early Methodism, but not only because they provided a lively forum for mutual strengthening in the Christian faith. The undergirding egalitarian assumptions of these assemblies conformed well to the democratic sensibilities of the American Methodist membership; indeed, both the Methodist services and the political ideals of the young nation were themselves products of the Enlightenment's stress on the welfare of the individual. It was Methodism's democratic character as a people's movement that enabled the denomination's rapid growth in its first decades, despite the hierarchical structures set forth in its polity.[71] But as Methodists claimed a greater denominational—and bureaucratic—identity and transferred spiritual leadership more firmly into the hands of the ordained clergy, the liturgical opportunities devised for mutual care and accountability declined, and were over time redefined or reconfigured.

If "liberty" was the spirit, then "life, elasticity and power" were its signs and fruits. Methodists freely employed any available means to lead seekers to Christ and encourage their ongoing commitment, and found the flexible and temporally concentrated great festivals to be especially efficacious and edifying. A successful meeting was calculated by the numbers who experienced tangibly and dramatically the power of God and claimed it for themselves. Worship undeniably was oriented toward human ends, bearing out a theology that was informed both by evangelical concerns and by an Enlightenment optimism toward human capabilities. Although the great festivals were meant as occasional (quarterly or annual) supplements to the weekly Lord's Day service, the enthusiastic reception given to the style and content of the meetings virtually guaranteed that some communities would strive to replicate aspects of them on every Sunday morning. In addition to the evangelistic preaching that was already expected for Methodist worship, personal testimonies might also be included, as well as lengthy prayers by one or more individuals (but usually not women on Sunday morning!). And later, during the heyday of the camp meeting, assorted practices from that great festival, such as sustained altar prayer and the singing of camp meeting hymns, might be included in Sunday worship. It is therefore no surprise that Wesley's Lord's Day services were so short-lived, and that the American Methodist leadership had such difficulty trying to establish some modicum of uniformity in the practice of worship on the Lord's Day. The influence of the camp meeting and other revivals on Methodist Lord's Day worship was such that when specified orders were developed, they reflected the revival structure by the placement of the sermon near the conclusion of the service; Communion, when it was celebrated, was added on as the final event before departure, as at the camp meeting. But the adoption of the revival model for Sunday did have its drawbacks. Stress on the individual and his or her personal experience jeopardized the development of a strong ecclesial understanding of the gathering as a corporate body, even the body of Christ, where worship is done to the sole glory of God. This focus on the individual undoubtedly contributed to the privatization of religion in America, which one writer has labeled "American Gnosticism."[72] Revival worship also marginalized those deemed too young for an experience of conversion, a remedy for which was sought in the creation of general and age-level Sunday school worship assemblies and missionary society festivals.

Taken together, the great festivals comprised an entry rite into the Methodist community: the invitation came in exhortation and sermon; inquiries were addressed in prayer meeting, private conversation, and at the "altar"; admission was gained by the presentation of a ticket or token that was validated by sincerity of intention; integration came through ongoing participation in the peculiar services. Methodist understandings of baptism were strongly influenced by the conversion emphasis in the great festivals, since the love feast, watch night, and quarterly meeting were already in place when the Methodist Episcopal Church received its rites of baptism in 1784. Though Methodists have been ready to maintain the practice of infant baptism, the stress on a conversion experience—whether prior to baptism or as the "fulfillment" of a baptism received in infancy—began to strain against an understanding of baptism as itself a sacrament. This tension was not unique to American Methodism; it is already found in John Wesley.

4

The Rites of Christian Initiation

METHODISTS HAVE SPILLED MORE INK on the subject of Christian initiation than on any other worship-related topic. Treatises, tracts, and essays have been circulated widely as Methodists have sought to distinguish themselves from believer baptists (e.g, Baptists and Disciples of Christ), on the one hand, and from sacramentalists (particularly Anglo-Catholics), on the other. These apologias have had a greater benefit than simply the rebuttal of unacceptable theological positions: they have allowed Methodists to grapple with and hone their own particular definitions of baptism, membership, and most important, church. Although Methodists since 1784 have in principle adhered to the baptismal standards articulated in their Articles of Religion, the establishment of a firm statement about initiation has proven elusive precisely because of Methodism's inheritance both as a daughter of Anglicanism and as the religion of the warmed heart. Many of the recurrent controversies internal to American Methodism in this area owe their origin in large part to the seeming ambiguities inherent in the writings of John Wesley.

Baptism in Wesley's Sunday Service

The theology and practices of Christian initiation that Wesley favored at the end of his life and Wesley's perception of the theological and pastoral milieux in America at the conclusion of the Revolutionary War each appear to have guided his revision of the 1662 Book of Common Prayer initiatory rites. Retained in the Sunday Service were "The Ministration of Public Baptism of Infants to Be Used in the Church" (now simply entitled "The Ministration of Baptism of Infants") and "The Ministration of Baptism to Such As Are of Riper Years" (intended for children and adults who could respond for themselves). But both baptismal texts from the Prayer Book underwent significant alterations at Wesley's or other Methodist hands, first in 1784 and again in 1786; regarding the later edition, no definitive proof can be found determining whether it was Wesley or Thomas Coke who introduced the changes. Gone, certainly, already in 1784 was the entire office of confirmation, which Wesley in the 1755 essay "Ought We to Separate from the Church of England?" had declared to be one of the things in the Prayer Book he found indefensible.[1] Wesley's removal of confirmation may rest on several factors, none of which he explicitly delineates; he, in fact, said little about confirmation in a lifetime of sermons and other writings. Wesley believed that confirmation, as a distinct rite, could not be located either in Scripture or in apostolic sources, both of which were essential authorities for his liturgical praxis. The absence of scriptural precedent, the superstitious practices associated with confirmation, and its supposed superfluity had also encouraged long-standing opposition to the rite by the Puritans and other Dissenters (e.g., "An Admonition to the Parliament" of 1572, and the "Millenary Petition" of 1603), and Wesley was familiar with their arguments from his reading of history and from his acquaintance with ongoing debates regarding Prayer Book revision and the liturgical comprehension of dissenting groups. The general depreciation and neglect of the office in England and the unfamiliarity of the rite in America, since no bishop—the authorized administrator of confirmation in Anglicanism—had up to that date been found on American shores, may have each contributed to Wesley's decision. He also may have been unwilling to grant the Methodist "superintendant" episcopal status since, at the time the *Sunday Service* was written, he still understood Methodism to be operating within the broad framework of Anglicanism, and this was surely at the center of his objections to the use of the term "bishop" in American Methodist documents from 1787 onward. For Wesley, the rite of Christian initiation was *baptism*, and the two texts he bequeathed provided the starting point for subsequent Methodist practice, theology, and ritual revision.

The Administration of the Baptismal Rites

A cursory comparison of the first part of the 1784 baptismal texts with those in the 1662 Prayer Book immediately reveals a substantial reduction in the length of the opening rubrics, and therewith the removal of certain directions for performance. Among the materials lost are directions regarding the necessary preparation for participation in each respective rite. Similarly, instructions are removed about the location of the rite—both its whereabouts physically and its placement in the course of a broader service of worship (e.g., morning prayer). On the former, even Wesley's shortening of the title of the infant rite is telling: no longer is it stipulated that the rite will be "used in the Church" (interpreting the original title as an indicator of spatial location, rather than simply ecclesiastical status), and the condition of public administration is put in doubt, though "Public Baptism of Infants" is retained in the running heads at the top of each page. This does not suggest that Wesley was an advocate of private baptism in domestic dwellings, for in fact Wesley did not include the 1662 service for "The Ministration of Private Baptism of Children in Houses" among his services in 1784. Rather, it is more indicative of the laxity toward church baptism within Anglicanism in general, Wesley's own practice later in life, and his desire to offer an inculturated rite for the American situation. Early in his ministry, particularly while a missionary in Georgia, Wesley had scrupulously followed what he believed to be the Church of England's rule by requiring that infants and those of "riper years" be baptized in the church edifice. He encouraged the Methodists to receive baptism in their parish church, especially since only Anglican baptisms were officially registered, and technically, according to the sixty-eighth canon, no one requesting baptism could be refused. But when access to Anglican churches became limited because of Wesley's association with the Methodist movement (he himself was not assigned to a parish church), out of necessity Wesley resorted to baptism in Methodist preaching houses, the church buildings of Dissenters, secular buildings (including private homes), and the outdoors. Wesley anticipated that the American Methodists would have a comparable problem since only a few Methodist buildings had been constructed by 1784; besides, he could hardly allow the aspiration to spread the gospel and bring persons sacramentally into the Christian fold to be hampered by the requirement of a physical facility. Despite the elimination from the 1784 baptismal services of the Prayer Book's references to the building, Wesley's own practice shows that he expected baptism to be a public event in the presence of other Christians, and that it be a component within a larger service of worship either on the Lord's Day or a weekday.

The administrator of baptism in Wesley's rites was not a priest but a *minister*, whose exercising of sacramental authority is clarified within the 1784 ordination liturgies: baptism is normally the prerogative of the presbyter or elder, and hence also the "superintendant"; a deacon is permitted to baptize only "in the absence of the elder." No lay minister, except in dire emergencies, could rightfully have assumed the role of baptizer in Wesley's mind. An Anglican until his death, he concurred that the proper administrator within the Church of England was one who was *episcopally* ordained.[2] Consequently, a person baptized by an individual not within the apostolic succession lacked a valid baptism and was to be properly baptized if admission into the Church of England or to the other rites of the Church (e.g., the Lord's Supper or the burial office) was sought. Wesley's fierce adherence to this position in his early ministry, reinforced by his imitation of Non-Juror liturgical practices, landed him in dire straits in Georgia.[3] Though by 1738 he no longer insisted upon the "rebaptism" of Dissenters and regretted his previous stringency, throughout his ministry Wesley apparently continued to baptize those dissatisfied with "lay baptism."[4] Wesley's preference for episcopally ordained administration is evident from an introduction he prepared in 1756 for the publication of a "Treatise on Baptism," an abridgement of his father Samuel Wesley's *A Short Discourse of Baptism*, which had been appended to the larger *The Pious Communicant Rightly Prepar'd* (1700):

> The baptism—I ought to call it the "dipping"—of all Anabaptists, as much stress as ever they lay upon it, is no baptism at all. For they want episcopal administrators which are essential to Christian baptism. And indeed, this invalidates the baptism of all who have formally separated from our Church.[5]

Yet influenced by Edward Stillingfleet's *The Irenicum, a Weapon Salve for the Church's Wounds* (1659), Wesley was forced to concede in that same year of 1756 that though episcopal forms were "scriptural and apostolical," "neither Christ or

His Apostles prescribed any particular form of Church government," thus allowing for the recognition of nonepiscopal ordination and hence the validity of nonepiscopally administered baptisms.[6] Two years later in 1758, when the "Treatise" was published as the sixth section of the younger Wesley's *Preservative Against Unsettled Notions in Religion*, the introduction did not appear, and subsequent printings of the "Treatise" on both sides of the Atlantic never included it. The removal of the introduction was not intended as a silent permission for the Methodist lay preachers to baptize, since Wesley remained adamantly opposed to their doing so.[7] Wesley's own actions in 1784 of ordaining Richard Whatcoat and Thomas Vasey to the presbyterate, and appointing Thomas Coke as "Superintendant," doubtless provided in his own mind for a succession of American Methodist ministers who would dispense the sacrament.

All references to godparents and their role are struck from Wesley's two baptismal services, though a vestige remains in the infant rite where the "Friends of the Child" are charged to state the child's name when asked by the minister. This deletion pared back both services in terms of participation, local custom, and ritual text: godparents had been included in the infant rite from the inception of the first *Book of Common Prayer* in 1549; when the "riper years" rite was introduced in 1662, the place of godparents was retained following the model of the infant rite, though the newer rite added an address to the candidates. Wesley, with the tract "Serious Thoughts Concerning Godfathers and Godmothers" (1752, reprinted in 1758 in *Preservative Against Unsettled Notions in Religion*), had in fact acknowledged the expedient and apostolic, though nonscriptural, custom of selecting God-fearing baptismal sponsors to assist the newly baptized in the leading of a Christian life. Yet in this tract—and in the 1755 essay "Ought We to Separate"—Wesley doubted the appropriateness of the godparents' answers made on behalf of the infant, though "the compilers of our Liturgy inserted them because they were used in all the ancient Liturgies."[8] Generations of Puritans before Wesley had posed a comparable query and also challenged the exclusion of the parents in favor of the godparents; and both of these issues were being revisited in the ferment of unofficial liturgical revision during Wesley's day.[9] Thus it is not surprising that the proxy questions for the godparents were excised from the infant rite, and along with them all rubrics, addresses, and charges made to the sponsors in both rites. One consequence of this purging, however, was the loss of the symbol of faith from the infant rite. In the "riper years" service, Wesley kept the renunciation of Satan, profession in the form of the Apostles' Creed, and covenantal promise since the candidate was expected to make his or her own response.

Regarding the application of water, dipping (immersion) and pouring (affusion) had been specified in the 1662 Prayer Book, though for infants, pouring was advised only in cases when it could be certified that the child was weak. Of these two, Wesley's preference early in his ministry had been for immersion rather than the more common practice of affusion even for healthy infants; under the influence of the Non-Jurors, he believed immersion to be most consistent with the praxis of the early church and even adopted the revived patristic custom of triple immersion that had been specified in the 1549 *Book of Common Prayer*.[10] In conformity with the apostolic practice of immersion, Wesley kept the dipping of infants and those of riper years in his Prayer Book revision, but also indicated that pouring was feasible for older children and adults. However, the provision and conditions for infant affusion he excised, probably because he found the restrictions both problematic and widely disregarded: at least once, his own adherence to the rubrics had forced him to refuse baptismal pouring upon a healthy infant.[11] As a substitute, Wesley advised sprinkling (aspersion), an innovation among Anglicans, but known in England from the time of the interregnum in the seventeenth century when, in the briefly authorized *Directory for the Public Worship of God* (1644), the mode was specified along with pouring.

Wesley had come to believe that aspersion was appropriate within the range of meanings of *baptizo* and the intentions of the Lord himself, and presented it as a viable option in his 1751 publication of "Thoughts upon Infant Baptism. Extracted from a Late Writer." The anonymous "writer" has long been assumed to be the Anglican William Wall, and Wesley's "Thoughts" a condensation of Wall's *History of Infant Baptism* (1705), but large portions of the essay come from authors other than Wall or Wesley; Wesley's defense of the legitimacy of several baptismal modes appears to combine Wesley's own composition with material quoted from the sermon "Christian Baptism" by Congregationalist theologian and hymn writer Isaac Watts.[12] Wesley states, apparently in his own words:

> With regard to the mode of baptizing, I would only add, Christ no where, as far as I can find, requires *dipping*, but only *baptizing*: which word, many most eminent for learning and piety have declared, signifies to *pour on*, or *sprinkle*, as well as to *dip*. As our Lord has graciously given us a word of such extensive meaning, doubtless the parent or the person to be baptized, if he be adult, ought to choose which way he best approves. What God has left *indifferent*, it becomes not *man* to make necessary.

Biblical allusions also permitted sprinkling, which invited a particular theological interpretation of the baptismal act. Borrowing material original to Watts, Wesley further noted:

> Besides, pouring or sprinkling more naturally represents most of the spiritual blessings signified by baptism, (viz.) the sprinkling the blood of Christ on the conscience [1 Peter 1:2], or the pouring out of the Spirit on the person baptized [Acts 10:45–48], or sprinkling him with clean water [Hebrews 10:22; cf. Ezekiel 36:25], as an emblem of the influence of the Spirit; all which are the things signified in baptism as different representations of the cleansing away of the guilt or defilement of sin thereby.[13]

Because "God has left indifferent" the matter of mode, the mature Wesley did not insist on any particular form. Even if several persons were to be baptized at the same event, Wesley would typically administer the rite according to the mode requested.[14] Thus it may have been recognized that the identification of only two modes in the 1784 infant rite created an unnecessary limitation, and so the option of affusion was inserted into the 1786 edition of the *Sunday Service*.

In a strange but largely explainable circumstance, extant copies of the 1784 *Sunday Service* appear in two versions: some contain in the infant rite a rubric for postbaptismal signing with the cross and an accompanying statement; others do not. No usage of signation is found in any "riper years" text. Apparently the dual form of the infant rite resulted from an unresolved attempt at correction before the copies of the *Sunday Service* were sent to America—unbound, either from haste or to avoid the duty assessed for bound books. Examination of the books themselves reveals that the original printing did not include the signation; separately printed substitutes (cancels) with the signation were clearly a later addition, though not all of the books received the necessary readjustment.[15] Questions then must be raised about the originator of the correction, particularly in light of Wesley's comment in 1789 that "Dr. Coke made two or three little alterations in the Prayer-Book without my knowledge. I took particular care throughout to alter nothing merely for altering' sake."[16] Coke had overseen the printing of the work, but did a "little alteration" include omission of signation? In the late 1740s Wesley had himself identified "the superstitious use of the sign of the cross" as one of the abuses in the early church, and he knew from reading Puritan history and John Jones's *Free and Candid Disquisitions* (1749) the plea to make baptismal signation optional since many had scruples about it.[17] In spite of Wesley's familiarity with debates on the use of signation, the evidence points to Wesley as the source of the correction inserting signation into the infant rite. This raises the yet-unanswerable question why signation was dropped entirely from the "riper years" rite. For whatever reason, the subject was put entirely to rest in the next edition of the *Sunday Service* in 1786: signation is not present in either baptismal rite.

The Rite and Its Effects

Other emendations to the 1662 Prayer Book baptismal rites were made for the sake of linguistic modernization, brevity (e.g., the removal of the Gospel exhortation), and theological adjustment. Of considerable importance is Wesley's deletion of postbaptismal references to regeneration in the exhortation to thanksgiving and prayer found in both rites, and in the thanksgiving prayer of the infant rite, which expresses gratitude that "it hath pleased thee [to regenerate this Infant with thy Holy Spirit,] to receive *this Infant* for thine own *Child* by adoption, and to incorporate *him* into thy holy Church." Modification—deletion of "now" from "that being [now] born again"—was made to the thanksgiving prayer in the adult rite, a prayer Wesley surprisingly retained though it was virtually a repetition of the prayer for the Spirit that came earlier in the liturgy (and in which "now" did not appear in either the 1662 or 1784 form). To assume from these omissions that Wesley rejected a theology of baptismal regeneration is to ignore the testimony to the remission of sin(s) and regeneration that was retained in both rites before the imposition of water: in the address ("None can enter into the kingdom of God, except he be regenerate and born anew of water and of the Holy Ghost"); the first prayer, a collect based on the flood prayer in Luther's *Taufbüchlein* via Hermann von Wied's *Simplex ac Pia Deliberatio* ("didst sanctify water to the mystical washing away of sin"); the second prayer ("may receive remission of *his* sins by spiritual regeneration"); and in one of the blessings for the candidates that almost functions as a thanksgiving over the baptismal waters ("sanctify this water to the mystical washing away of sin"). Additionally, Wesley's revision of the twenty-seventh Anglican Article of Religion, "Of Baptism," annexed to the *Sunday Service* kept in its Methodist counterpart (Article Seventeen) the phrase that baptism is "also a sign of regeneration, or the new birth." The apparent inconsistency in Wesley's approach to baptismal regeneration in the rites and in his other writings has subsequently yielded great debates about his baptismal theology, particularly his understanding of the rite's efficacy. Wesley never intended to write on baptism as a theological systematician; rather, he addressed the subject of baptism as a committed Anglican priest vexed by persons who claimed the benefits of ritual baptism yet lacked the visible evidence of faith.

By including baptismal rites in the *Sunday Service*, Wesley maintained the Anglican doctrine that baptism is one of two dominically ordained sacraments of the Church that serves as "a sign, seal, pledge, and means of grace." Obligatory upon all for initiation into the Church, baptism was also to be understood as the *ordinary* means for salvation: "Indeed, where it cannot be had, the case is different, but extraordinary cases do not make void a standing rule." On the one hand, said Wesley, God expects persons to be washed in baptism, but on the other, God is not obliged to save only though the sacrament.[18]

The presentation of *two* baptismal services in 1784 bore witness to Wesley's conviction that neither age nor cognitive powers were factors in the eligibility to receive the sacrament. Though infants have yet to commit actual sin and lack the proficiency to confess faith or renounce "the devil and all his works," they are still proper recipients of baptism according to Wesley because they have been stained by original sin. For all guilty "children of wrath" the merits of the life and death of Jesus Christ are needed and applicable. Infants are capable of making a covenant or being bound by a covenant made for them by their parents or others—an everlasting gospel covenant, in direct succession to the covenant made between God and Abraham. Yet the sign of that Abrahamic covenant given to male infants or converts, circumcision, has been replaced, in the Christian dispensation, by the Lord's institution of baptism, which stands as a seal of the new covenant for both males and females. The continuity (or analogy) between circumcision and baptism is foreshadowed by the blessings and promises of the old covenant and realized by Christ's expectation that infants would come to him: they were to be counted with "the nations" (Matthew 28:19); and he demanded that their way not be hindered since to such as them belongs God's kingdom (Mark 10:13–16).[19]

That a baptismal connotation was assumed for the verses in Mark 10 is evident by the selection of the text as the prescribed Gospel lesson for the infant rite. Charles Wesley reinforced the baptismal connection with a hymn based on Mark 10:14 that was reproduced in several American Methodist hymnals:

> Jesus, kind, inviting Lord,
> We with joy obey thy word,
> And in earliest infancy
> Bring our little ones to thee.
>
> Born they are, as we, in sin;
> Make the unconscious lepers clean;
> Purchase of thy blood they are,—
> Save them by thy dying prayer.[20]

Thus in obedience to Christ's command, the Church throughout the ages, beginning with the designs of Christ himself and the baptism of "households" in the Acts of the Apostles, has baptized infants and children. In baptism, infants and all others who come to the font enter into a mystical union with Christ himself, and are admitted into the Church to "share in all its privileges and in all the promises Christ has made to it."[21]

A hymn written by Charles Wesley for use "At the Baptism of a Child" expresses precisely in relation to an *infant* the "way of salvation" (*via salutis*) that was open to all the human race such as it was set out in his brother John's prose writings:

> God of eternal truth and love,
> Vouchsafe the promised grace we claim,
> Thine own great ordinance approve,
> The child baptized into Thy name
> Partaker of Thy nature make,
> And give her all Thine image back.
>
> Born in the dregs of sin and time,
> These darkest, last, apostate days,
> Burden'd with *Adam's* curse and crime,
> Thou in Thy mercy's arms embrace,
> And wash out all her guilty load,
> And quench the brand in Jesus' blood.
>
> Father, if such Thy sovereign will,
> If Jesus *did* the rite enjoin,
> Annex Thy hallowing Spirit's seal,
> And let the grace attend the sign;
> The seed of endless life impart,
> Seize for Thy own our infant's heart.
>
> Answer on her Thy wisdom's end
> In present and eternal good;
> Whate'er Thou didst for man intend,
> Whate'er Thou hast on man bestow'd,
> Now to this favour'd babe be given,
> Pardon, and holiness, and heaven.
>
> In presence of Thy heavenly host
> Thyself we faithfully require;
> Come, Father, Son, and Holy Ghost,
> By blood, by water, and by fire,
> And fill up all Thy human shrine,
> And seal our souls for ever Thine.[22]

Since each succeeding generation is "burden'd with *Adam's* curse and crime," the benefits of Christ's onetime passion and death as well as his eternal pleading for sinful humanity provide the "promised grace" needed to restore the image of the Maker lost by the fall. By virtue of Christ's universal atonement, the Holy Spirit grants to all persons prevenient or preventing grace—a conscience that yearns for God—and only by an intentional rejection of this grace may it be lost. Because infants are still "born in the dregs of sin and time" and the "guilty load" must be "washed out," justifying or pardoning grace procured by the blood and righteousness of Christ is applied by the cleansing waters of baptism that "quench the brand." Justification is accomplished *by* God *for* the individual, resulting in a *relative* change. Simultaneously, sanctifying grace is bestowed that imparts "the seed of endless life": the newly baptized is regenerated, born again, born of the Spirit, thereby producing a *real*, though incomprehensible, change *in* the person. Granted "pardon" and born anew, the "favour'd babe" weathers the storms of temptation and grows in "holiness" toward "heaven" or glorification, which is perfection in love. Throughout the process of sanctification signs of faithfulness are to be utilized: these are works of mercy and works of piety, the latter also known as the instituted means of grace, which comprise prayer, receiving the Lord's Supper, searching the Scriptures, and fasting.[23] Should the child die before committing an actual sin, the Word of God assures that he or she is saved. But if the child should fall into and persist in actual sin, he or she would lose the "principle of grace" infused at baptism and so die spiritually.[24]

Infants brought to baptism are at the same time born again. Wesley understood, with the Church of England, that by the "hallowing Spirit" the "grace [did] attend the sign," and that God would "seize our infant's heart": "Our Church supposes that all who are baptized in their infancy are at the same time born again. And it is allowed that the whole office for the baptism of infants proceeds upon this supposition."[25] Though he avoided explanations of how sacraments work, preferring to trust that they do so, mysteriously, through the agency of the Holy Spirit, Wesley did reject what he understood to be the Roman Catholic doctrine of the sacramental effect *ex opere operato*, precisely because it could imply the efficacy of ritual performance apart from the working of the power of God. He affirmed with the Anglican Catechism of his day that a sacrament is "an outward and visible sign of an inward and spiritual grace, given unto us, ordained by Christ himself, as a means whereby we receive the same, and a pledge to assure us thereof."[26] This definition is essentially put forward in the twenty-fifth Anglican Article of Religion, and it survived in Wesley's editing of what became the sixteenth Methodist Article, though it was weakened by the removal of certain words:

> Sacraments ordained of Christ, are not only badges or tokens of Christian Men's Profession; but rather they are certain [sure witnesses, and effectual] Signs of Grace, and God's good Will towards us, by the which he doth work invisibly in us, and doth not only quicken, but also strengthen and confirm our faith in him. . . . And in such only as worthily receive the same, they have a wholesome effect or operation.

By his adherence to these statements, Wesley maintained the Augustinian differentiation between the external, material sign (*signum*) and the internal thing signified (*res*). Since they are not identical, the *signum* (baptism) and the *res* (new birth) are distinct; yet they are not separable, for both are needed to make a sacrament. In infant baptism, Wesley acknowledged that the *signum* and *res* are coinstantaneously imparted.

On the matter of infant baptismal regeneration, Wesley never wavered. Infant baptism was effectual and efficacious. But Wesley observed that persons baptized in infancy often appeared later to be more children of the devil than children of God—often as soon as the age of reason. To appeal to the new birth of one's baptism while living as a wretched sinner was to admit a false assurance of salvation and consign oneself to damnation. Hence, those who had lost the "principle of grace," who lacked the inward witness of the Spirit or had not manifested the Spirit's fruits, needed to be regenerated or "born anew" a second time, not through baptism if they had been validly baptized previously, but by the "circumcision of the heart." A conscious experience of saving grace, also termed by Wesley the "new birth," was necessary to restore the divine image that had been distorted or suppressed.[27] In the case of baptized backsliders, God's grace and mercy were constantly available for those who truly repented, that they might again be confident of their adoption as sons and daughters of God.

In effect, two new births, one sacramental and objective, and the other experiential and subjective, were necessary for most individuals baptized as infants. Though Wesley apparently did not regard the two births as unrelated, nevertheless he did not establish definitively the connection between the two; for example, the second new birth is never fully claimed to be a restoration or recovery of the grace bestowed in baptism.[28] Wesley's solution to the problem of postbaptismal sin may have unwittingly contributed to the diminution for later Methodists of any strong understanding of infant baptismal regeneration since, in practice, interest came to be focused more on the profession of personal assurance.

For the less frequent practice of adult baptism, Wesley held, as in infant baptism, that the *signum* and *res* are imparted simultaneously, but only if the candidate sincerely repented and believed in the gospel: "Baptism, administered to real penitents, is both a means and seal of pardon."[29] Baptismal regeneration was thus presumed to occur in adult candidates who presented no obstacle. Wesley, commenting upon the baptism of a "gentlewoman" in 1760, noted that "the peace she immediately found was a fresh proof that the outward sign, duly received, is always accompanied with the inward grace."[30] The expectation that the promised grace would accompany the sign to issue forth in regeneration is expressed in several stanzas of Charles Wesley's trinitarian hymn "At the Baptism of Adults":

> Father, in these reveal thy Son;
> In these for whom we seek thy face
> The hidden mystery make known,
> The inward, pure, baptizing grace.

> Jesus, with us thou always art;
> Effectuate now the sacred sign,
> The gift unspeakable impart,
> And bless the ordinance divine.

> Eternal Spirit, descend from high,
> Baptizer of our spirits thou!
> The sacramental seal apply,
> And witness with the water now!

O that the souls baptized therein
May now thy truth and mercy feel,
May rise, and wash away their sin—
Come, Holy Ghost, their pardon seal![31]

But Wesley also admitted that for adults the *signum* and *res* might not be imparted at the same moment, especially in cases where the person was not truly repentant or had already received assurance prior to the imposition of water.[32] Though the event of baptism itself might not be regenerational, it was certainly expected that the new birth would either precede or follow it. Baptism, then, could still be regarded as the rite of initiation into the Church, as a testimony to previous faith, and as a sign of God's ongoing work of grace in the life of the individual.

Theologically, Wesley appears to have held to both infant and adult baptismal regeneration throughout his life, though in the case of adult baptism the immediate, spiritual connection between the application of water and the new birth could not be guaranteed. The elimination of references to regeneration from certain postbaptismal statements and prayers in the 1784 rites thus cannot be interpreted as Wesley's rejection of a theology of regeneration, especially considering the retention of such language in the prebaptismal prayers.[33] While, as some have averred, the partial removal may have been prompted by Wesley's sensitivity to others' objections to the notion of regeneration or by his concern to emphasize the need for a subjective new birth,[34] a more plausible explanation is Wesley's unwillingness either to claim to know the mind of God or to suggest the sacrament's effect *ex opere operato*: prior to the imposition of water, one could speak assuredly of the promise of regeneration and pray for it; afterward, to insist that regeneration had inevitably occurred would improperly bind God or turn the sacrament into a human work.

The language of regeneration—particularly for infants—was more thoroughly eradicated from the 1786 edition of the *Sunday Service*, the responsibility for which has mostly been placed on Thomas Coke, with questions raised about Wesley's authorization of or involvement in the process. Removed from the first prayer and the relevant prayer for the candidates in each rite is the assertion that Christ sanctified water for the "mystical washing away of sin"; now, in the first prayer, water is sanctified "for this holy Sacrament." Both the second prayer (with "may receive remission of his sins by spiritual regeneration") and the prayer for the Spirit ("Give thy Holy Spirit . . . , that he may be born again, and be made an heir of everlasting salvation") disappear entirely from the infant rite; of these two, only the prayer for the Spirit is omitted for those of "riper years." Untouched in both rites is the statement in the opening exhortation that "None can enter into the kingdom of God, except he be regenerate and born anew of water and of the Holy Ghost," perhaps because it is a not-so-easily dismissed paraphrase of John 3:5.

The overall result of these alterations in the ritual texts of 1784 and 1786 was to set up a tension, and perhaps even a contradiction, between baptismal practice and Wesley's theology as articulated in the "Treatise on Baptism," the *Explanatory Notes Upon the New Testament*, and other sources. The ground was laid for subsequent controversies as the American Methodists sought to discern the mind or spirit of Wesley on the subject of baptism.

The Reception of Wesley's Baptismal Services

By 1784, the American Methodists for at least a dozen years had been longing to receive the sacraments from the hands of the Methodist preachers. Though Robert Strawbridge of Maryland had opted to administer both baptism and Communion without approval from either Wesley or the American leadership, most of the preachers waited impatiently for permission to assume a priestly role. Matters had come to a head at the 1779 Conference held in Fluvanna County, Virginia, and attended primarily by the southern preachers, where, after serious debate, a presbytery of three preachers was formed who ordained each other and then ordained the other preachers who were in agreement with the plan. Preachers in Virginia and North Carolina then administered the sacraments for a time, but because they feared a division among the Methodists and denunciation from Anglican friends, the decision was made to suspend sacramental privileges. Wesley's issuance of baptismal rites and the authorization of proper administrators thus came as a relief to a tense situation, though his sacramental services were a far cry from what the Fluvanna Conference had recommended and what had probably been practiced: the "ceremony," "according to our Lord's command," was to be "short and extempore," the proper modes were sprinkling or "plunging" as requested for either infants or adults, and signation was not to be employed.[35] The baptismal rites of the *Sunday Service* may have been duly received and adopted at the 1784 Christmas Conference, but among those ordained to sacramental ministry in Baltimore were men who had already performed another "Methodist rite."

Justification of "baby-sprinkling"—both subject and mode—consumed Methodist attention in the years before and after the creation of the Methodist Episcopal Church. When Baptists and others "haunted" the Methodists "like ghosts" "to persuade the people that they have never been baptized," countermeasures included general discourses and sermons on the topic (with prooftexting by use of Acts 2:36, Romans 5:18–19, and 1 Corinthians 7:14, as well as other texts).[36] In perhaps a concession to the Fluvanna "legislation," the 1784 *Discipline* (published in 1785) allowed for the recipient's or parents' preference of either immersion or sprinkling (Question 45), with pouring added in the edition published in 1786 (Question 43). Choice of mode was vigorously defended:

> After the last sermon I had to baptize two young men, one by pouring, the other by immersion. I went down to the water where I performed the ordinance, and having a mixed congregation, I was led to speak largely in vindication of baptizing both ways according to the desire of the people—insisting that the apostolic mood of baptizing could not be moved to be altogether one way or the other. I told them if any would shew me scripture to condemn any mood, I would then give it up. I found much satisfaction while speaking on the subject.[37]

Yet in a startling departure from Fluvanna's decision not to permit rebaptism, the 1784 *Discipline* (Question 46) and also the 1786 publication (Question 44) admit such a possibility in the instance where an individual baptized as an infant had scruples about the validity of his baptism, even after sustained argument to the contrary; this option was not continued from 1787 onward.

To aid the Methodist defense of infant baptism and the use of several "scriptural" modes, a seventy-one-page treatise was appended to the *Discipline* each year from 1790 to 1797. Written in 1788 by Moses Hemmenway, who was a Congregationalist minister stationed in Wells, Maine, and published under the title *A Discourse on the Nature and Subjects of Christian Baptism*, the lengthier original had been abridged for Methodist reading by book steward John Dickins. The extract both reinforced and expanded upon many of Wesley's arguments in the "Treatise on Baptism" and "Thoughts upon Infant Baptism": immersion was not the only scripturally valid mode; sprinkling best depicted the outpouring of the Spirit; infants were members of the "gospel church," inheritors of the Abrahamic promise, capable of making covenant, and eligible to receive the sign of the new covenant. Yet unlike Wesley's "Treatise," the newer work does not develop the doctrine of original sin as a factor legitimating infant baptism; the stress is upon infants as participants in the Abrahamic covenant and beneficiaries of Christ's adoption and inheritance. On the matter of rebaptism, Hemmenway provided the Methodists a firm statement that such an action was "utterly wrong" and without "precept or example." Bishop Francis Asbury, in 1797, echoed Hemmenway's position: "I consider that there was neither precept nor example in holy writ to justify our rebaptizing one who had been baptized in the name and form which Christ commanded in Matt. xxviii,19."[38] Notably absent from Hemmenway's treatise, other official documents of the time (besides the Articles of Religion), and personal records of the late eighteenth century is any sustained commentary on the issue of baptismal regeneration.

According to accounts in diaries and journals, adults and children under their care flocked to the Methodist deacons and elders for baptism. Methodist flexibility about mode may have been one factor; another was the circuit-riding system that brought the Methodist clergy into remote areas unfrequented by other ministers. The passage in 1787 of a restriction that forbade the reception of "a fee or present" for administering the sacrament also encouraged persons even from other ecclesiastical traditions to seek out Methodist officiants.[39] Printed under the section "On Baptism" in the *Discipline*, the restriction was altered from 1828 to prohibit the assessing of a "charge for administering baptism."[40]

The revised baptismal rites approved at the Conference of 1792 established texts that set the liturgical standard of baptismal praxis for the majority of Methodists well into the twentieth century. The 1784 and 1786 editions of the *Sunday Service* constituted the basic texts. The editing that was done (by yet-unknown hands, but certainly with the approval of Bishops Asbury and Coke) was by the omission of entire prayers or by the transference of prayers from one location within the rite to another. A rubric was introduced authorizing the substitution of a "suitable" exhortation in place of the opening address, which for both rites was the 1786 version of Wesley's text that contained the statement regarding regeneration from John 3:5 and the equation of baptism with membership in "Christ's holy Church." While thus allowing variety at one point, this new rubric of 1792 deleted the permission given in a 1786 rubric for the minister to omit prayers if constrained for time. Three legitimate modes were specified in the case of both infants and "those of riper years," with sprinkling now given priority. Also in both texts, another rubric suggesting the use of a closing extemporary prayer was substituted for the final prayer of thanksgiving and its preceding introduction, thus providing some flexibility, but regrettably removing explicit theological statements about the nature of baptism not elsewhere expressed, such as engrafting "into the body of Christ's Church" and burial "with Christ in his death."

Although American Methodist literature of the late eighteenth century does not dwell, as it would in the next century, on the issue of the baptismal regeneration of infants, the topic was nonetheless a pertinent issue, for the 1792 infant rite follows the 1786 edition in removing the prayers that substantially affirm regeneration. However, remnants are present, though the efficacy of what is prayed for may have been judged to be less immediate and more prolonged over time: in the opening prayer ("wash him and sanctify him with the Holy Ghost"); and in the blessings for the candidate, now located after the opening prayer (e.g., "may receive the fullness of thy grace"). A restoration made to the 1786 version of the infant rite, surprisingly not followed in that for "riper years," is the reinsertion of a petition in the final blessing for the candidates that God might sanctify the baptismal waters; instead of the 1784 formulation, the phraseology reworked in 1786 for the first prayer, "sanctify this water for this holy sacrament," is adopted. The 1792 infant rite, thus truncated and adjusted, took the following shape:

Opening Address ["Dearly beloved, forasmuch as all men are conceived and born in sin. . . ."]
Opening Prayer ["Almighty and everlasting God, who of thy great mercy didst save Noah and his family. . . ."]
Five Petitions for the Candidate ["O merciful God, grant that the old Adam. . . ."]; ["Grant that all carnal affections may die. . . ."]; ["Grant that he may have power and strength. . . ."]; ["Grant that whosoever is dedicated to thee. . . ."]; ["Almighty, ever-living God, whose most dearly-beloved Son Jesus Christ. . . ."]
Gospel Lesson [Mark 10:13–16]
Naming of the Child and Baptism in the Trinitarian Name
The Lord's Prayer
Extemporary Prayer

Because it was believed faith would be evident and repentance expressed in those of "riper years" coming to the font, the editors of 1792 had no reservations about retaining some of the prebaptismal language of regeneration for that rite. Restored to this rite, but in a new location, is the prayer for the Spirit that had been deleted in 1786. The collect based on Luther's flood prayer is omitted, perhaps to distinguish it from the infant rite. The former "second" prayer, a prayer with overt regeneration language, becomes in 1792 the opening prayer for the rite:

Opening Address ["Dearly beloved, forasmuch as all men are conceived and born in sin. . . ."]

Opening Prayer ["Almighty and immortal God, the aid of all that
  need. . . ."]
Prayer for the Spirit ["Almighty and everlasting God, heavenly Father, we
  give thee humble thanks. . . ."]
Gospel Lesson [John 3:1–8]
Address to the Candidates
Renunciation
Profession [including the interrogative form of the Apostles' Creed]
Five Petitions for the Candidates ["O merciful God, grant that the old
  Adam. . . ."]; ["Grant that all carnal affections may die. . . ."]; ["Grant that
  they may have power and strength. . . ."]; ["Grant that they being here
  dedicated. . . ."]; ["Almighty, ever-living God, whose most dearly-beloved
  Son Jesus Christ. . . ."]
Baptism in the Trinitarian Name
The Lord's Prayer
Extemporary Prayer

The 1792 rites may serve as a concise articulation of American Methodist baptismal—and liturgical—theology at the end of the eighteenth century. Brevity and
extemporaneity were important, but so was the authorization of a discernably
"Methodist" order of service that would unite the far-flung Methodist communities,
espouse Methodist doctrinal assumptions, and keep the Methodist preachers iden-
tifiably Methodist. Selection of a scripturally valid mode was deemed a matter
of personal conscience, with sprinkling considered the practice favored in the
"primitive churches in general."[41] Infants were arguably proper recipients of baptism, but the nature of the baptismal grace given was becoming more ambiguous
and the status of baptized infants in the church more questionable. The language
of baptismal regeneration was assuredly expressed for those of "riper years," while
Wesley's apparent certainty of infant regeneration was suppressed in favor of a
subjective "regeneration" in the years after the age of reason. Mode, the subjects
of baptism, the nature of baptism, and church membership: these four issues addressed directly or indirectly in 1792 would be continuing topics for discussion
during the next two centuries. Methodist theological positions in these areas would
not be crafted solely on the basis of an internal dogmatic framework; rather, Methodist views on baptism developed also in response to external stimuli, such as the
baptismal theology and practice of other denominations, the philosophical and
political notions of democratic egalitarianism present in American society, and the
social, anthropological, and (later) psychological understandings of children and
childhood.

The Mode and Subjects of Baptism

Throughout the nineteenth century, Methodist judgments about baptism were
voiced in a vast array of books, systematic theologies, tracts, hymns, sermons,
public forums and debates, and other media. The camp meeting in its heyday

provided an incomparable setting for disseminating partisan ideas, and in response to evangelical preaching and Methodist teaching on baptism, persons of all ages were baptized with the mode of their choice at a service typically held during the assembly's final hours. Camp meeting songsters frequently included versified polemics, though the texts were often more doggerel than poetry, as exemplified by a song from an 1807 collection by Virginia preacher Stith Mead:

> When Christ the Lord was here below,
> About the work he came to do,
> All righteousness by him was done;
> He even was baptis'd by John.
>
> This last old *Rite* he thus obey'd;
> From the strict path he never stray'd;
> And lo! the spirit in glory shed,
> Like water *pour'd* upon his head.
>
> A voice from God was heard to say,
> Upon that same accepted day,
> In thee, my Son, *I* am well pleas'd,
> Thou hast my threaten'd wrath appeas'd.
>
> Commission men to bear the news,
> To *Gentile worlds* and royal *Jews*,
> Baptizing all, both great and small,
> Whom God's most holy word doth call.
>
> The mode to us is told full well,
> By those on whom the spirit fell;
> Which brought to Peter's wond'ring eyes,
> How John the Baptist did baptize.
>
> In Acts the 11th, and 16th verse,
> This scripture truth you may rehearse;
> So let not this from bigots slip,
> That Baptism only means to dip.
>
> That infants then we may baptize,
> Who dares protest, when we premise?
> That Jesus took them in his arms,
> Inviting them to heav'nly charms.
>
> I bless the Lord that I was born,
> From PAGAN darkness to be torn,
> That e'er my parents for me vow'd,
> And gave my infant soul to God.
>
> Although from right I've err'd and stray'd,
> Yet when convinc'd I strove and pray'd,
> Until the Spirit was on me shed,
> Like water pour'd upon my head.

> I bless the Lord that I was found,
> To be baptiz'd on Christian ground:
> Not all the talk of artful men,
> Shall move me from my Brethren.[42]

Most of the burgeoning literature on baptismal topics by Methodists lacked the imprimatur of the General Conferences; it was simply the influential opinions expressed by authors who wrote in reaction to local and more widespread controversies. Conference-approved doctrinal assertions and practical prescriptions were, for the most part, conveyed in succinct paragraphs within the *Discipline*, by the identified baptismal hymns in the official hymnals, and in the summaries of denominational catechisms. The Methodist Episcopal Church, which had dropped the printing of the Hemmenway extract from the *Discipline* in 1797, provided again in 1814 a fuller authoritative statement on baptism with the publication of former Baptist preacher Peter Edwards's "A Short Method with the Baptists" in *A Collection of Interesting Tracts, Explaining Several Important Points of Scripture Doctrine*.[43] Edwards's essay, which was reprinted until 1825, emphasized the historic continuity of infant practice from the early church and challenged the "requirement" of an explicit New Testament warrant by arguing that if infants shouldn't be baptized, then, by similar reasoning, neither should women partake of the Lord's Supper. Three new documents were then introduced into the *Collection*: John Wesley's "Treatise on Baptism" and "Thoughts Upon Infant Baptism" (both unedited); and the brief "Remarks on Infant Baptism" by the English patristics scholar H. S. Boyd, which argued for the antiquity of infant baptism based on a reference to the baptism of Empress Eudoxia's "little children" in an oration by John Chrysostom. From 1861 until publication of the *Collection* ceased in 1892, a single baptismal essay was included by an anonymous (probably Methodist) nineteenth-century writer who defended the scriptural and historical basis for infant baptism, and promoted sprinkling and pouring as the most ancient modes.

The essays chosen to represent the official Methodist Episcopal position on baptism each accentuate the most prominent points of debate faced by all the Methodist denominations during the nineteenth century: proper mode(s) and subjects. Methodists defended aspersion and affusion against their Baptist and Campbellite (Disciples of Christ) accusers by arguing, as had Wesley, for the multiple meanings and practices associated with the verb *baptizo* in the New Testament. Preachers in the field, who generally lacked the necessary linguistic skills, depended upon the exegetical work of learned Methodists and other sympathizers to provide the various definitions of *baptizo* that could simultaneously persuade new converts to join the Methodist fold and debunk the ever-proselytizing immersionists. Methodist Protestant George Brown discovered while stationed at Connellsville, Pennsylvania, in the late 1840s that local debate hinged precisely on the "correct" interpretation of the relevant Greek verbs and nouns.[44]

Relentless antagonism from the exclusive immersionists created antipathy toward that mode, even in the first decades of the nineteenth century: New York minister George Coles confessed that one Sunday afternoon in 1832, following the baptism of "two grown persons and three infants," he "preached against *immersion*."[45] By midcentury, the Landmark movement within the Southern Baptist Convention, which claimed an uninterrupted succession of immersed believers back to the apostles, contributed to a further decline in the use of the mode among Methodists.[46] In an interesting countermove, some Methodist exegetes came to regard sprinkling and pouring—deemed variations of a single mode—as the most legitimate, scriptural forms. Aspersion and affusion were believed to represent best the spiritual cleansing coming from above and the descent of the Holy Spirit, and they could be "proven" to be the methods used by John the Baptist and the apostles (especially on the day of Pentecost). Immersion, in the Bible, was arguably more akin to destruction than salvation, and the suggestion that immersion baptism imitated or alluded to Jesus' death, burial, and resurrection (Romans 6:3–11, Colossians 2:11–12) was refuted as heresy and superstition;[47] indeed, the first prayer for the candidates, which petitioned God "that the old Adam . . . may be so buried," was dropped from both of the Methodist Episcopal Church's baptismal rites in 1864, though it was retained in other Methodist branches. The lack of strong Scripture proof for immersion was also combined with more practical concerns, including the frequent Methodist practice of baptism in family dwellings:

> Immersion is held to be antagonistic to pious thought, both in the candidate and spectators; it is imprudent, exposing health, and endangering life. Under some circumstances it is impossible, as with the dying and in desert places; is ofttimes inconvenient, and sometimes even indelicate; is useless, "much water" being of no avail, even for bodily cleansing, when the body is only wet, not washed; is in opposition to the Spirit's work, water tending to chill warmth and extinguish fire; contradicts the mode of *spiritual* baptism, that being invariably by a "shedding forth" or "pouring out;" it is unscriptural, the Bible nowhere, either by example or command, teaching it.[48]

In order to reflect these changing views, efforts were made from the second half of the nineteenth century to remove or limit the option of immersion, and to realign the order of the three modes for listing in the *Discipline* (within the rite itself, sprinkling came first; immersion was typically listed first in the general directions or elsewhere in the *Discipline*, at least until 1880 in the Methodist Episcopal Church).[49] Immersion never disappeared as an authorized mode, though by the turn into the twentieth century few Methodist candidates requested it, and some administrators, for reasons of conscience, refrained from offering it as an alternative.

Only occasionally did the issue arise whether the number of applications of water should correspond to the three Persons of the Godhead. The antiquity of "trine immersion" was known to the Methodists,[50] and apparently they had practiced both the single and the threefold forms since no restrictions appeared in any *Discipline*. But from the 1880s, efforts were made in some quarters to eliminate the threefold application, with claims that it was "highly improper, if not heterodoxical" since it denied the unity of the Godhead, and also that it was associated with "high ritualistic practices."[51] Nevertheless, no statement was added to any *Discipline* to address the propriety of either method.

Methodist writers in the nineteenth century, who unquestioningly held to the propriety of baptism upon profession of faith, were also adamant in their defense of infant baptism, reiterating but also expanding the arguments of covenant participation, baptismal supervention of circumcision, dominical "warrant," and apostolic practice "proven" by earlier generations. Yet these apologias were as much intended for the Methodists themselves as for their detractors since, not surprisingly, infant baptism was often neglected as a result of the ongoing stress by Methodists upon the necessity of personal conversion and profession, and the unrelenting criticism of the anti-pedobaptists. At the 1840 General Conference, members of the Methodist Episcopal Church were admonished to "give [their] infant offspring to God in holy baptism," and in 1850, a New York local preacher was reprimanded for refusing to be in attendance whenever infants were baptized.[52] An Ohio Conference report for 1875 acknowledged the continuing problem and offered explanations:

> Infant baptism is not generally practiced. Large circuits and stations report no children baptized. The highest number reported in any one charge was twenty-eight, and that charge having over five hundred members. It is observed also that of the members received into full connection a very large per cent received adult baptism, though large numbers of them were from the Sabbath-school and young people of the Church, which justifies the inference that for some time past there has been a decline in the sentiment and practice of our people as to the responsibility and value of infant baptism. It is suggested that even where the baptism of children is common there are erroneous and almost superstitious notions as to the value, nature, and obligation of infant baptism. That if a child is about to die it is very important to have it baptized, or that it is only a religious way of naming it. The pulpit and religious press should speak out on this subject; not dogmatically, but practically.[53]

To stem the decline in practice, an additional rationale for infant baptism was advanced, which was refined following the publication of Congregationalist Horace Bushnell's influential book *Christian Nurture* (1847): baptized infants, brought up under the care of the church and nurtured throughout childhood, would grow up confident in the Christian faith, and thus in later life exert a positive moral influence upon the larger society. A corollary of this viewpoint was that the demands of infant nurture would be reciprocally a beneficial religious stimulus to the child's parents; and parental responsibility for baptized infants would enhance the establishment of a Christian home.[54] Methodists, who had always been keenly aware of the power of infant baptism to influence the parents, now used as a strong justification for the practice the familial "sharing the benefits of religion."[55] The Methodist Episcopal Church in 1864 ritualized this view by introducing an address to the parents in the infant rite (adapted, in all probability, from the then-current Protestant Episcopal charge to sponsors) that delineated their duty "to see that he be taught, as soon as he shall be able to learn . . . all things which a Christian ought to know and believe to his soul's health, in order that he may be brought up to lead a virtuous and holy life." Most of the other Methodist branches followed suit, among them the Free Methodist Church, which in 1866, in its first major revision of the received infant rite, inserted a newly written prayer for the child and parents with the petition:

> We pray for these parents, that they may realize how great is the responsibility resting upon them, touching the proper training of those entrusted to their care: we beseech

thee to grant unto them the aid of thy Holy Spirit, that both by precept and example they may so lead *this child* in the narrow way of life, that both *parent* and *child* may come to the everlasting kingdom, which thou hast promised by Christ our Lord.

Hotly debated throughout the nineteenth century was the question whether the infants of unbaptized or unprofessed parents were eligible to receive baptism, a controversy fueled by the unacceptability to the Methodists of the Calvinist doctrines of election, limited atonement, and infant damnation. Some Methodists, against the Calvinists, applied a theology of universal atonement in such a way to baptism as to assert that "the child has a right to baptism, not in view of the faith of the parents, but in view of the *atonement* of Christ, since the same ground that entitles him to salvation, entitles him also to baptism."[56] This theological position deviated from Wesley's and changed the terms of the "rivalry" between baptism and the conversion experience that was expected later in life. Other arguments against the necessity of parental ecclesiastical status were based on belief in the call of Christ to *all* children, and the analogy between baptism and circumcision (the latter, in antiquity, given to some persons regardless of parentage). Though all infants were entitled to baptism, indiscriminate baptism was never advised. On the other side, those Methodists who insisted upon at least one believing parent ("belief" loosely defined as assent to the Christian faith even if not formalized by either baptism or active church membership) generally did so from an understanding of baptism's covenantal aspects or of baptism as the doorway to schooling in the Christian faith. The definition of baptism as an *ecclesiastical* ordinance also pressed for the necessity of a parent who was a church member, as did the parental vows introduced into the ritual of baptism. The moderating position actually appears to be the one most widely espoused and practiced in the second half of the nineteenth century: even though by Christ's redemption all infants were eligible for baptism, yet for the sake of the infants and the church, only those children should be baptized whose Christian care and nurture could be assured either within the family or the congregation.[57] This conclusion, though theologically articulated, may in reality reflect an underlying sociopolitical factor, namely, the democratic and Enlightenment guarantee of individual rights.

An equally persistent issue during the nineteenth century was rebaptism. Methodists generally agreed that since Campbellite and Mormon baptisms were not recognizably in conformity with historic Christian praxis by their employment of other than the triune Name, and were therefore invalid, persons with those backgrounds could legitimately be (re)baptized.[58] Baptisms by laity, though irregular, did not require rebaptism as long as they had been "seriously done" and "the subject, matter, and form, were according to the institution."[59] But there was less consensus regarding the handling of requests for rebaptism when an individual, baptized in infancy, later in life sincerely believed either his infant baptism or the mode by which baptism was performed to be inappropriate according to Scripture. This was particularly true for persons who, having been sprinkled as infants by Roman Catholic priests, then desired immersion as Protestants. Rebaptism was firmly rejected by many who contended that to rebaptize was to concede the necessity of a particular mode or the illegitimacy of infant baptism. Leonidas Rosser constructed his thesis for only one ritual baptism on the basis of the "proofs" for infant baptism: the impossibility of either annulling or supplanting previously made covenant obligations; the unrepeatability of circumcision; the permanence of God's promises and God's seal; and the irrevocability of future responsibilities and rewards.[60] Persistent demands for legislation against rebaptism from the 1840s eventually yielded such a statement for the Methodist Episcopal Church *Discipline* in 1868, with a comparable note added by the Methodist Protestant Church and the African Methodist Episcopal Church shortly afterward. Yet at the 1872 quadrennial meeting of the Methodist Episcopal Church's General Conference, Seba F. Wetherbee of the Maine Conference petitioned for an alteration of the statement against rebaptism in order to recognize personal conscience and choice on the matters of subject and mode. Wetherbee contended that the four-year-old rule was deterring parents from bringing their children to baptism and preventing adults who had been baptized as infants but now subscribed to immersion from joining the denomination.[61] Even though the Methodist Episcopal Church eventually succumbed to pressure and abandoned the statement against rebaptism in 1896 (the Methodist Protestant Church kept it until 1939; the African Methodist Episcopal Church maintained the restriction in their 1996 *Discipline*), denominational officials nonetheless made it clear that the removal of the rule did not constitute a silent approval of rebaptism.[62] Still, with the restrictions or without, Methodist practice of occasional rebaptism did not abate.

Methodists continued to produce books and essays focusing on the mode and subjects of baptism during the twentieth century, but not in the quantity of the preceding century. No new theses were put forward; old arguments basically were recast for a new audience who assumed that, for Methodists, aspersion, affusion, and immersion were the normative scriptural modes. Because Methodists were confident about their stand on modes and their refutation of exclusive immersionist claims, the meaning of baptism as burial and resurrection with Christ could now be utilized positively since Romans 6 had been "proven" not to be a warrant for immersion. The addition of a rubric urging the performance of the rites in the company of the congregation and in the church building in effect demonstrated, for many of the episcopal Methodist branches, the preference for sprinkling and pouring, since few buildings had baptisteries to accommodate either immersion or submersion.[63] The rubric, which first appeared in the 1932 Methodist Episcopal Church rites perhaps as the result of influences from both the ecumenical and liturgical movements, also signaled the desire to recover the ecclesial dimension of the sacrament that had been suppressed on account of geography (frontier individualism), political and social factors (privatization), and theological emphasis (the stress upon personal conversion).

The majority of Methodists adhered to the legitimacy of infant baptism, although, as will be seen, the nature, meaning, and formulation of the infant rite had moved further from its Wesleyan original. Some Methodist pastors, while continuing to baptize infants, argued for (and even practiced) a service of infant dedication in order where possible to defer baptism to a time when the rite would be more "spiritually meaningful." A challenge arose for the Methodist Church when, in 1968, it merged with the Evangelical United Brethren Church, which had inherited a rite of infant dedication from the Church of the United Brethren in Christ—a rite that had been introduced in 1945, only the year before official union with the Evangelical Church. Because the United Methodist Church did not envision the immediate production of a new worship book (the Methodist Church having brought out its *Book of Worship* in 1965), it regarded the worship services of the former denominations as authoritative. This meant that episcopal Methodism, for the first time, had a rite of infant dedication, though denominational officials were quick to claim the dedication service was best reserved only for former Evangelical United Brethren congregations. Although the 1992 *United Methodist Book of Worship* included no dedicatory service, creative pastors, on occasion, were known to fashion such a service. The Free Methodists, on the other hand, introduced in 1985 a new Service of Infant Dedication (an act allowed for by rubric since 1974) to stand alongside their rite of infant baptism.

The question of whether the parents of infants brought to baptism ought themselves to have been baptized remained unresolved in the first half of the twentieth century, and though in the remainder of the century the controversy persisted, several of the denominations gave a rubrical answer by stating in a preface to the infant rite the expectation that parents should be church members. Rebaptism continued to be requested by infant-baptized Methodists and persons coming from other Christian denominations, despite the presence of written and unwritten guidelines to the contrary. Though doubts about the validity of mode or subject were cited as the motivation for rebaptism, a concern increasingly articulated by persons baptized as infants was the absence of a cognitive or memorable experience of baptism. The recovery of "Wesley's" covenant service in the twentieth century in effect offered an opportunity for a "dry" public profession of faith in lieu of water baptism. The United Methodist Church's service for the reaffirmation of baptism, first proposed in 1976 and officially approved in 1984, and perhaps the African Methodist Episcopal Church's "Order for an Affirmation of the Baptismal Covenant" (though designed for infant-baptized children and youth making their first public profession) provided another ritual alternative.

The Nature and Meaning of Baptism

The nineteenth-century justification for the practice of infant baptism that was built upon a theology of implied or explicit universalism and a Bushnellian concept of Christian nurture (mediated largely through the work of Freeborn G. Hibbard)[64] signaled a significant shift away from a classical Wesleyan understanding of baptism's purpose, though both an Arminian denial of election and the notion of growth toward Christian perfection in love (*post* regeneration) had certainly been integral components of Wesley's *via salutis*. Members of the Methodist Church's commission charged in 1956 with the reformulation of baptismal and other rites to be placed in the 1965 *Book of Worship* recognized the implications of this shift:

> In preparing the Orders for the Methodists in America, Mr. Wesley carried over into the ritual for the administration of baptism two ideas from the Church of England which are foreign to our thinking. A comparison of our present order with the one

recommended by John Wesley reveals sharp divergencies. These differences in the main center around the teaching of total depravity and baptismal regeneration. Our present ritual bears marks of this conflict, and of the attempts of revisers to retain the form of the ritual for baptism while eliminating the offending elements in the content.

During this process of revision, the idea of baptism as a sacrament was watered down, if not lost altogether. In the main our ministers have acquiesced to the popular notion that baptism is nothing more than a dedication of the child to God by his parents. Indeed, some conceive of baptism as a social event where no Christian conviction is involved. It is looked upon as a mark of respectability in the community.[65]

Restrictive legislation prohibited tampering with the Articles of Religion received from Wesley, but liberal Methodists allowed themselves a certain latitude in interpreting the definitions of sacrament, baptism, and original sin found therein in the face of broader theological and cultural changes.

Though the baptismal rites as revised in 1792 remained virtually untouched by episcopal Methodism until the 1850s, the tenor of theological discussions in the first half of the nineteenth century hinted at what textual alterations would eventually be made. Methodists generally espoused a moderating position between what they perceived as theological extremes. In this they conformed to the example of English Methodist and systematician Richard Watson, whose influential *Theological Institutes* (1823), a longtime standard on both sides of the Atlantic, built upon yet went beyond the foundations laid by John Wesley. Regarding the sacraments, Methodists strove to chart a course between the Scylla of an "anti-scriptural" *ex opere operato* that made "the act of receiving a sacrament independent of true faith" and the Charybdis of a sentimental memorial that differs "not *essentially* from the other rites and ceremonies of religion." Positively, according to Watson, the sacraments were both signs and seals of the covenant: "To *every one* to whom the sign is exhibited a seal and pledge of the invisible grace is also given."[66]

But the relationship between the *signum* and the *res* continued to trouble the American Methodists, especially in regard to the sacrament of baptism and its connection to justification, regeneration, and sanctification. Methodists did not want to concede with the Quakers that the ritual of baptism was entirely expendable for it added nothing; neither did they view the sacrament as absolutely essential for the remission of sins and for salvation, as is evident from their criticism of Roman Catholics, Disciples, and "high-church" Tractarian Anglicans and Episcopalians. Yet they had inherited and even republished Wesley's "Treatise on Baptism" in which the *signum* and *res* still were argued to be imparted simultaneously in such a way that baptism figured as the "means and seal of pardon." Because they found Wesley's statements on baptismal regeneration difficult to accept (since they could not be "verified" by Scripture, reason, observation, or experience), and perhaps because they desired, consciously or unconsciously, to distinguish themselves further from Anglicanism, Methodists sought distance from Wesley on this point in theological discourses and in the ritual texts. When editor John Emory published in 1831 the first American edition of Wesley's works, he appended to the "Treatise" (following section 2.5) a disclaimer that Wesley's views on baptismal regeneration, "which we at this day should not prefer," were not his final opinions on the matter, but those of an earlier Wesley; a similar statement appeared after that date with printings of the "Treatise" within the *Collection of Interesting Tracts.* When critics such as Baptist James R. Graves argued that Methodism was guilty of "Romish" origins and "papist" practices because the expectation of baptismal regeneration was inherent in its baptismal liturgies and in the writings of its founder, some Methodist authors saw this as gross misinterpretation.[67] Others readily admitted to Wesley's regenerational statements, but noted that they were of "modified form" and "evangelical."[68]

Baptism was coming to be regarded less as a means of regeneration, and more as its sign, seal, or promise, in effect further separating the outward sign and the inward grace that Wesley considered distinct yet indivisible, but which he had conceded could, in some circumstances, be separated in time. The formulation in the seventeenth Article that baptism was a *"sign* of regeneration, or the new birth" became a proof text that the sign was to be "distinct and separate" from what was signified: in his commentary on the Articles first published in 1853, A. A. Jimeson would even state that the sign and what it signified "may exist without the other."[69] Caution was expressed lest baptism be viewed as synonymous with regeneration; the early church's metonymous designation of baptism by "the grace which it symbolizes" had, unfortunately, contributed to the error of "ascribing grace to the ordinance" itself.[70] That baptism was "to be regarded as emblematical, and not conditional, of the new birth"[71] the Methodist Episcopal Church, South taught in a 1861 catechism:

Q. What is baptism?
A. Baptism is a sign of the grace of God that makes us Christians.
Q. Does baptism make us Christians?
A. No; water cannot make us Christians: grace makes us Christians.
Q. Who works that grace in us to make us Christians?
A. The Holy Ghost.[72]

The distinction between *signum* and *res* was such that some Methodists would not only describe baptism and regeneration as two separate entities but also differentiate between a water baptism and a Spirit baptism, the former a shadow of the latter, which was the essential thing and necessary for salvation. The Methodist Episcopal Church, South reinforced this dichotomy in 1858 by removing from the infant rite references to the sanctifying of the baptismal waters and by including in their official hymnals of the mid-nineteenth century this hymn:

Rites change not, Lord, the heart,—
Undo the evil done,—
Or, with the uttered name, impart
The nature of thy Son.

To meet our desp'rate want,
There gushed a mystic flood:
O from His heart's o'erflowing font
Baptize this soul with blood!

> Be grace from Christ our Lord,
> And love from God supreme,
> By the communing Spirit poured
> In a perpetual stream.[73]

Yet water baptism was not construed to be an empty sign. T. O. Summers stressed that baptism's purposes were as a sign of God's mercy and grace, a ratification of the title to covenant blessings and a pledge toward the discharge of corresponding obligations, and an aid to sanctification.[74] Baptism was still described as a sacrament, but to avoid suggesting sacramental efficacy *ex opere operato*, the definition of the term *sacrament* was often reworked to emphasize its function as a sign of, or petition for, God's saving work and grace, but not as a *means* of grace. While these developments may perhaps be seen as the beginnings of a regrettable division between sign and reality, a benign interpretation at this point in the mid-nineteenth century might allow that the Methodist Episcopal Church, South feared the loss of God's freedom in granting the new birth; and, positively put, they wished to insist on the authentic interiority of the spiritual life.

Methodists were willing to concede that regeneration might accompany adult baptism if it was preceded by true repentance and faith. Generally it was believed that infants were not spiritually regenerated in baptism: the use of the term in reference to infants and children acknowledged only their new covenant relationship with God and the Church.[75] Indeed, given the argument sometimes advanced that infants, prior to baptism, were already beneficiaries of Christ's universal atonement (increasingly identified—incorrectly—as Wesley's doctrine of prevenient grace), any notion of infant regeneration was, in fact, redundant. But significant questions were thereby raised about the moral and spiritual status of infants and children, since, taken to its logical conclusion, this understanding of universal atonement undermined the doctrine of original sin—a doctrine already under attack by liberal theologies using social and philosophical concepts derived from the Darwinian theory of evolution.[76] Some authors held to both original sin and universal atonement, and related them in ways that avoided contradiction. Others claimed that children were born in a state of grace (defined as justification or simply as innocence) because *imputed* guilt had been cancelled, but their *inherited* corrupt nature required regeneration and sanctification after the committing of actual sin. One of the many variations on this position allowed (following Bushnell) that, with proper nurture, a child might never know sin, thereby suggesting that regeneration was unnecessary, a concession few Methodists were willing to admit. Without reconciling the tension between universal atonement and original sin, the Methodist Episcopal Church alone, in its 1856 *Discipline*, officially commended an understanding of the universal atonement related to infant baptism, though four years later the bishops nervously expressed concern about its theological implications regarding sin.[77] As if to remedy this problem, in 1864 the infant rite's opening address was revised to juxtapose the Wesleyan clause asserting that cleansing was needed from the sin in which all are conceived and born, and a new statement promoting the view that infants were redeemed by Christ's blood prior to water baptism. Additional alterations were made to the opening address (and other prayers) expressive of the shifting views: removed was the assertion that baptism granted to the child "that thing which by nature he cannot have" (a phrase retained in the adult rite), and distinguished as two actions were the baptism of water and that of the Holy Ghost.[78]

Infant baptism was no longer considered to bestow an immediate benefit other than establishing the covenant and granting a divine blessing. Instead, baptism anticipated spiritual fruition in the course of the individual's life. Both the Methodist Episcopal Church (from 1840) and the Methodist Episcopal Church, South (from 1844), in their respective paragraphs in the *Discipline* on the "Instruction of Children," speak of parents "dedicating" their children to the Lord in baptism. The Methodist Protestants had already defined baptism as dedication in their 1830 infant rite, both in an opening exhortation and in the prayer that followed:

> Almighty and most merciful God, Father of our spirits, Former of our bodies, Redeemer and Saviour of our souls, we thank thee that thou hast made it our privilege to dedicate our children to thy service, that they may be lively members of the church of Christ, and heirs of eternal life.

In 1864, the Methodist Episcopal Church, using the exalted language typical of the period, voiced in a new concluding prayer a comparable purpose for baptism whose benefits would unfold in the future:

> O God of infinite mercy, the Father of all the faithful seed, be pleased to grant unto this child an understanding mind and a sanctified heart. May thy providence lead him through the dangers, temptations, and ignorance of his youth, that he may never run into folly nor into the evils of an unbridled appetite. We pray thee so to order the course of his life, that by good education, by holy examples, and by thy restraining and renewing grace, he may be led to serve thee faithfully all his days, so that, when he has glorified thee in his generation, and has served the Church on earth, he may be received into thine eternal kingdom, through Jesus Christ our Lord.

Accordingly, many of the references to regeneration remaining in the infant rite were, in the liturgical revisions that occurred in some Methodist denominations from the 1850s to the 1880s, either removed entirely or understood proleptically; the more liturgically conservative African Methodist Episcopal Church would not alter the address and prayers from the 1792 form until the 1950s. Hints of adult baptismal regeneration likewise fall away from Methodist Episcopal and Methodist Episcopal, South rites, but the Free Methodists affirmed regeneration and original sin in their 1860 adult rite, as evident in the opening prayer ("that they, coming to thy holy baptism, may receive the inward baptism of the Holy Ghost") and in the opening address, the formulation of which did not change until the second half of the twentieth century:

> Dearly Beloved, Since all men are by nature sinners, and have nothing in themselves by which they can be delivered from the guilt and pollution of sin, and attain to that holiness without which no man can see the Lord, we invite you to join with us in fervent prayer for these persons, that they may have grace always to keep their Covenant with God, and that they may continually enjoy the washing of regeneration, and the renewing of the Holy Ghost.[79]

Though the Holiness and African-American Methodist churches refused to abandon a theology of original sin, and were (for a time) more hesitant to relinquish
some possibility of baptismal regeneration at least for adults, they, with the larger
Methodist bodies, generally devalued baptism as a sacrament.

Despite the alterations made to both infant and adult rites, certain members of
the two largest episcopal Methodisms were not satisfied that the work of revision
had gone far enough, especially those persons influenced by the liberal philosophical doctrines that permeated the scholarly and popular writings of numerous
Methodist theologians toward the end of the nineteenth century. Many Methodist
preachers were exposed to this literature (e.g., Miner Raymond's *Systematic Theology* [1877–1879], John Miley's *Systematic Theology* [1892, 1894], and Henry C.
Sheldon's *A System of Christian Doctrine* [1912]) as some of the titles appeared on
denominational reading lists required for ministerial licensing and on seminary
syllabi. As Robert Chiles has shown, a notable theological transition was underway
in American Methodism. In Wesley and eighteenth-century Methodism, primary
emphasis had been laid on the doctrines of revelation, original guilt and total
depravity, and grace; a subordinate place was accorded to the themes of human
reason, moral character, and free will. During the nineteenth and twentieth centuries, anthropological emphases were gradually elevated to a primary status, while
the theocentric was reduced to a secondary role. Though there were conservative
elements countervening these trends, the "liberal evangelicalism" of the late nineteenth century soon met the "evangelical liberalism" of the early twentieth century.[80] Thus, claims could be made that in Methodist teaching baptism was "a
public profession," used because "it is ordained by Christ—not because it can take
away sin, not because its administration is necessarily accompanied by the work
of the Holy Spirit."[81] Although representatives of the Methodist Episcopal Church,
South found the infant rite "a standing protest against Pelagianism on the one
hand, and Romish baptismal regeneration on the other, as well as so-called Zwing-
lianism," other members lobbied for changes to the infant rite of the Methodist
Episcopal Church, South, which had not made the extensive changes of its larger
sister church, arguing that "the ritual squints at the baptismal regeneration of
children, and implies their lost condition without conversion."[82] Sacramental efficacy thus waned while human positivism waxed.

Alterations to the baptismal rites in the first three decades of the twentieth
century reflect the agendas of the liberal theological discussions: the *social* gospel
proclaimed the evils of social sin (with an "Arian" Christology heralding Jesus as
a "young and fearless prophet") and, with the exception of the war years, the basic
goodness of the human condition was upheld. After years of petitions, the Methodist Episcopal Church, South in 1910 revised both its infant and adult rites: while
original sin was not denied, the human situation was regarded more optimistically;
and Jesus' invitation to little children replaced in the infant rite the implied reference to regeneration in John 3:5. The Methodist Episcopal Church's surgery was
far more radical. In 1916, all allusions to original sin and baptismal regeneration
were removed from the infant rite (Mark 10:13–15 and Matthew 28:19 replaced
John 3:5). The adult rite still spoke of sin, but only of actual sinning rather than
any natural depravity; and the citation from John 3 was reworked so that one is

not born of water and Spirit but simply born "anew." Objections were lodged that the revision abandoned the "old doctrinal teachings" and displayed "the new Anti-Methodistic theological drift."[83] Yet the 1916 revision functioned as a prelude to the more liberal emendations of 1932, which bear the influence of the personalist theo-philosophies advocated by Borden Parker Bowne and his students, particularly Albert C. Knudsen. Baptism now bestowed nothing (though perhaps a name, in the eyes of some persons); it simply served as a sign of the personal spiritual journey that would ideally ensue or continue after the ritual moment. Even the covenantal character of baptism was lost from the infant rite: the Order for Baptism of Children asserted that children are *entitled* to baptism because they are already members of the kingdom of God, thereby marking a drift toward Pelagianism that previous generations had striven to avoid. Baptism's only purpose was to launch the child's growth "in grace and in knowledge of the Lord Jesus Christ," and for this, the parents and the clergy took an active role; God played only a minor part. For adult baptism, the action centered on the candidate's personal confession of Jesus Christ as Lord and Savior and the acceptance of the "obligations" of the sacrament, namely, turning from sin (the historic renunciation of Satan and profession by the Apostles' Creed were eliminated in this revision) and endeavoring to "keep God's holy will and commandments."

The 1932 baptismal rites represent American Methodism's most extreme departure from its own heritage and from historic western Christianity. When the Methodist Protestants and the Methodist Episcopal Church, South merged with the Methodist Episcopal Church, the new Methodist Church's rites (in 1939, and again in the 1945 *Book of Worship*) largely followed the ritual text from the Methodist Episcopal Church. But in the baptismal rites, the more theologically conservative Methodist Episcopal Church, South carried greater influence and contributed a correction against possible accusations of Pelagianism (it was now asserted in the infant rite that all persons were recipients of saving grace), though in accordance with the current trend the doctrine of original sin remained muted. The subjective quality of all the baptismal rites still overshadowed any objective means of grace. This was the theological problem confronting those commission members who reported in 1960 that in the history of Methodist revision, "the idea of baptism as a sacrament was watered down, if not lost altogether," and upon which the bishops commented in that same year:

> Other Christians are asking us, and we might well ask ourselves, "Do your sacramental practices conform with your historic sacramental doctrines?" We recognize that The Methodist Church stands in an anomalous position in the eyes of other major Christian communions with respect to our current practice.[84]

The first three decades of the twentieth century had been characterized by a virtual literary lull on the topic of baptism; those books produced largely contained a rehashing of nineteenth-century themes. The 1940s saw renewed interest in baptismal issues, generated by Methodist ecumenical involvement, by rediscovery of Wesley, and by the recovery, through the liturgical movement, of earlier Christian practices. Also during this period, some of the churches that had maintained the eighteenth-century texts sought to provide an alternative "modern" form; in a display of pan-Methodist collegiality, the African Methodist Episcopal Church borrowed for its 1952 *Discipline* the Methodist Church's infant rite to stand alongside the older text (both rites, with some editorial emendations, would appear in the 1984 *Book of Worship*). Although Methodists, while never being unanimous in their assessment of the nature and meaning of the sacrament, had in the nineteenth century attained a general consensus on many issues, theological ferment in the twentieth century created a gulf of opinion that, by the century's end, had yet to be closed. Some Methodists continued to refute baptismal regeneration and the doctrine of original sin (both considered by Methodist church historian Robert Goodloe to be contrary to American democracy), oddly regarded baptism as a *"means* of grace which does not *confer* grace," and defined infant baptism as primarily "a dedication service with the parents assuming the responsibility of so instructing and leading the child that he will later confirm the stand taken by his parents."[85] In contrast to what was often labeled the "evangelical view" was the "sacramental," which emphasized the bestowal of objective divine grace over subjective profession, recognized the mysterious as well as the rational (a stress indebted to the recovery of patristic understandings of the sacrament), and combined the ecclesiastical with the personal. Ideally, both the "evangelical" and the "sacramental" views were to be respected, in conformity with the perceived intentions of Wesley himself. Such a via media was desired by the 1960 revisers. Yet in their rationale for restoring to baptism what they considered "its original and historic meaning as a sacrament,"[86] they employed, not the more traditional Augustinian arguments, but rather their more recent theological inheritance (e.g., the natural innocence of children, universal atonement, and a dominating subjective element). The infant rite, as published in the 1965 *Book of Worship*, defined baptism as "an outward and visible sign of the grace of the Lord Jesus Christ, through which grace we become partakers of his righteousness and heirs of life eternal," leaving open the relation between the *signum* and the *res*. For youth and adults, baptism of "water and the Holy Spirit" was rather more clearly seen as a restorative from sin since "all men have sinned and fallen short of the glory of God."

The baptismal rite of the United Methodist Church—first proposed in 1976, officially approved in 1988, and published in the 1992 *United Methodist Book of Worship*—moved further toward the recovery of baptism as sacrament while simultaneously retaining the element of personal faith (from parents and congregation, in the case of those who could not respond for themselves). Sharing in the ecumenical rediscovery of a patristic understanding, baptism was now seen as initiation into the paschal mystery of Christ's death and resurrection. A single but complex rite, with the theologically significant title of "baptismal covenant," suffices for every age group; the purpose of baptism is the same for all persons and, regardless of age, sin and evil are denounced (in a restored renunciation, though nowhere is original sin explicitly named) and Christ is professed (through the Apostles' Creed).[87] Efforts to reunite the *signum* and *res*, by use of the phraseology that "through the sacrament of baptism" we are "given new birth through water and the Spirit," met with great outcry from the evangelical wing of the denomination, which feared baptismal regeneration.[88] To clarify (or perhaps to equivocate), a denominational statement on baptism followed Wesley's contention (for adults) that the new birth might not coincide with the water bath.[89]

Though their liturgical texts may suggest a sacramental understanding of baptism, United Methodists, as well as other members of the Methodist family, did not fully resolve the quandary inherited from Wesley—to synthesize an objective baptismal grace with a personal profession of faith and a subjective experience of the Holy Spirit.

Baptism and Church Membership

Because Wesley had done away with confirmation, American Methodism received baptism as the sole ritual of initiation, though some Methodists opted to add laying on of hands and prayer in the practice of the baptismal rite, that, as Nathan Bangs suggested, "the blessing of the Holy Spirit [might] descend upon the subject of [the] holy ordinance."[90] But prior to 1784, Methodism's status as a religious society within the Church of England had necessitated a series of regulations for admission and membership independent of the sacrament of baptism, which was generally assumed to have been received, though was not mandated. This dual inheritance—both ecclesial and societary—would mire any prospects for consensus concerning the prerequisites of membership in the "Methodist Church."

The sacramental and the evangelistic were combined in the first official books of the Methodist Episcopal Church: through baptism, an infant or individual of "riper years" was "received into Christ's holy Church" and "made a lively member of the same"; and according to Question 16 in the *Discipline*, membership tickets were to be issued quarterly for regular admission to the "society" only after examination, a two-month trial period (after 1788, probation was set at six months),[91] and ongoing visible and active fulfillment of Christian duties, the neglect of which could bring expulsion. The new denomination, reflecting its sectarian origins, did not stipulate baptism as a prerequisite for membership, and those who argued against making it such pointed to the "one only condition" appertaining to membership in the still-binding General Rules of the United Societies: "a desire to flee from the wrath to come, to be saved from their sins." The absence of a baptismal requirement proved practically beneficial for Methodist communities served by unordained preachers, though it contributed to the confusion regarding the connection between baptism, conversion, and membership.

In the early years, the disparate official statements regarding church membership were commonly reconciled by identifying baptism with general membership in "Christ's holy Church," taking Philip's baptism of the Ethiopian eunuch into no particular church (Acts 8:35–39) as the scriptural precedent and justification. Denominational affiliation was granted following the period of probation, ideally with, but also without, baptism. After 1836, membership in a local Methodist Episcopal congregation was contingent upon prior baptism. A ruling in 1840 waived the probationary period only for members "in good standing in any other orthodox church" who sought affiliation with the Methodist Episcopal Church.

Methodist polity accorded well with the phenomenon of camp meeting and revival baptisms and with the regular practice of baptizing persons who had not yet experienced saving faith, but who were truly penitent: in both cases, individuals enrolled in a "class" to receive catechesis and nurture until their spiritual maturity warranted "full fellowship." When outsiders criticized "seekership and probation as both grossly unscriptural and highly pernicious," Methodists such as Illinois frontier preacher Peter Cartwright countered that it was the "safety-valve" of the Methodist Episcopal Church, since only sincere professors of religion, under the care of the church from the time of their baptism, should become members of the denomination or a congregation.[92] However, precisely which sincere professors were worthy of membership was debated among the Methodists in this period and later. While some insisted that evidence of the new birth was requisite (acknowledging that the thirteenth Article of Religion defined the church as a "congregation of faithful men"), others reiterated the societal "rule" that repentance and the desire for God's grace was sufficient.

During the first half of the nineteenth century, the vigorously defended practice of infant baptism was believed to initiate children into the invisible, catholic Church, but not to grant any formal association with either the denomination or the local congregation. Methodists generally did not attempt to untangle such an ecclesiastical conundrum (though there were constant calls for clarity, from both internal and external sources), preferring instead simply to juxtapose an affirmation of Christ's inclusion of children in the new covenant with the expectation that Methodist membership required evidence of vital piety. To motivate children toward personal faith and membership, Methodist preachers were obliged by the 1784 *Discipline* to catechize both baptized and unbaptized children. So guided, those youngsters who were deemed "truly awakened" could be admitted into societal membership. The educational requirements of the Methodist Episcopal Church expanded in 1824, with the organization of classes for children, and again in 1836 when the content of instruction for baptized children was specified to "embrace the nature of experimental religion, but also the nature, design, privileges and obligations of baptism." Whether the rights of baptism included access to the Lord's table was a subject of ongoing and heated discussion.[93]

Since, for many Methodists, introducing a baptized child into the invisible church and "yet not making him a member of any visible section of that Church" was ecclesiologically "absurd,"[94] more carefully delineated connections began to emerge in church legislation. The provision of the Methodist Episcopal Church in 1840, which permitted advising toward probationary status for "truly serious" children, was expanded in 1856 under the heading "Of Baptized Children" (Part 1, Ch. 2, §3) to supply a more definitive link between the baptized child and the visible church:

> Whenever they shall have attained an age sufficient to understand the obligations of religion, and shall give evidence of a desire to flee from the wrath to come, and to be saved from their sins, their names shall be enrolled in the list of probationers; and if they shall continue to give evidence of a principle and habit of piety, they may be admitted into full membership in our Church, on the recommendation of a leader with whom they have met at least six months in class, by publicly assenting before the

Church to the baptismal covenant, and also the usual questions on doctrines and discipline.

The Methodist Episcopal Church, South's *Discipline* in 1858 introduced a statement that went even further than that of its sister church by implying that baptized children already held probationary membership; following "a public profession of faith in Christ" and evidence "of a sincere and earnest determination" to live the Christian faith, the candidate would "be duly recognized as [a member] of the Church." Some critics denounced the change, fearing that both infant baptismal regeneration and religious formalism were on the rise.[95] Certainly the former was not a danger, and in fact, both denominational statements more strongly reflect the current positive views of childhood, a theology of Christian nurture, and the growing assumption that infants before baptism were, by Christ's atonement, already citizens of God's kingdom.

Repeated requests to produce an approved service for the reception of probationers yielded for the Methodist Episcopal Church in 1864 a "Form for Receiving Persons into the Church After Probation," an order later borrowed, with some modifications, by the African Methodist denominations. The Methodist Episcopal Church, South, which in 1866 had rescinded entirely the obligation of a probationary period, produced in 1870 the "Form of the Reception and Recognition of Church-Members." Each rite began with an ecclesiastical definition, establishing the nature and work of the Church, as well as the general and local obligations of its members. The membership language of the respective denominational *Discipline* was restated in the service, both in the form of an address and in one of the questions to the candidate. In fact, the Methodist Episcopal Church's rite functioned more as a legal transaction than an act of worship, since the ritual action revolved around the minister, the congregation, and the candidate, and prayer (extemporary) was stipulated only in a final rubric. Perhaps in reaction, the 1870 rite provided two formulaic prayers and the Lord's Prayer. Profession of the necessary spiritual prerequisites was required in both services, with the Methodist Episcopal Church insisting upon "saving faith," and the Methodist Episcopal Church, South employing the language of the "one only condition." The baptismal covenant was ratified and confirmed (T. O. Summers even likened the new service to confirmation,[96] and indeed some turns of phrase were drawn from Anglican confirmation orders), and then the candidate agreed to abide by the discipline and life of the denomination, and to support it materially. The Methodist Episcopal Church required assent to its doctrine by asking, "Do you believe in the doctrines of Holy Scripture, as set forth in the Articles of Religion?"—a subscription some found contrary to the Wesleyan tradition.[97] The phraseology of the rites clearly indicates that their completion bestowed a membership status not previously found in baptism, and for which the extension of the "right hand of fellowship" was the culminating ritual action. This procedure beyond baptism was similarly accentuated by the Methodist Protestant "Form of Reception" first produced in 1868 in which candidates submitted themselves to a new and distinct membership covenant.

Even with formal rituals in hand for some of the denominations by the late nineteenth century, the theological and practical interconnections between baptism, conversion, and membership remained unclear. Methodists concurred that through baptism the young were brought into an intentional nurturing affiliation with the visible church, though the precise nature of that association was disputed. Children typically were not eligible to qualify as full members until at least the age of accountability, with the targeting of early adolescence for solicitation of spiritual commitments supported by research in the new field of developmental psychology. Different criteria were proposed as prequisites for full membership no matter what age: evidence of regeneration, unfeigned repentance, public assent to the essentials of the Christian faith, and completion of a prescribed course of catechesis.[98] The Holiness branches of Methodism expressed more confidence in their criterion: "Church members should be real Christians—truly pious—converted persons."[99] Disqualifications from either potential or active membership were also topics of discussion, with "nonscriptural" divorce often heading the list.

Probationary status for baptized adults and children continued as an operative category for most denominations. The Methodist Episcopal Church, apparently impressed by an earlier Methodist Protestant form, utilized from 1896 until the 1939 merger (and then as the Methodist Church until 1964) an official "Form for Receiving Persons into the Church as Probationers" (altered to "Preparatory Members" in 1916) that effectively enrolled the baptized as catechumens. Candidates professed their "earnest desire to be saved from sin," and their intention "to give reverent attendance upon the appointed means of grace in the ministry of the word, and in the private and public worship of God." Formal instruction then followed in anticipation of future membership commitments. Baptized children were not expected to participate in the rite after 1912, as the *Discipline* from that year conferred probationary membership with the reception of baptism, but as before they were still to be the recipients of formal catechesis in the Sunday school and in special classes. To aid children on their journey toward reception as full members, the suggestion was offered in 1929 to "grade" church membership with four distinct ritual markers in infancy (baptism), the "junior period," middle adolescence, and young adulthood.[100]

In deference to the distinct needs and contributions of children, a separate membership rite was developed for them, in 1914 by the Methodist Episcopal Church, South, and two years later by the Methodist Episcopal Church; other Methodist bodies would develop comparable services in the second half of the twentieth century. Suppositions were shared between the episcopal Methodist rites, such as the necessity of public and personal appropriation of membership privileges and duties. An ecclesiastical self-definition along with the location of membership were more strongly articulated in the rite of the Methodist Episcopal Church, South ("Is it your sincere desire, of your own free will and accord, to continue as a member of the Church of Christ, in the communion of the Methodist Episcopal Church, South?"), and the same body uniquely insisted that parental nurturing responsibilities continued after child membership; the latter, but not the former, component survived when the Methodist Church revamped the rite of the Church, South as its new text. The Methodist Episcopal Church's children's membership rite had been abandoned in 1932, leaving only a general rite as the sole order for membership. In a shift of tone, following modifications approved in 1916 and again in 1932, the Methodist Episcopal rite no longer inquired about "saving faith," but asked the candidate to "confess Jesus Christ as Lord and Savior."

New in 1932 to the Methodist Episcopal Church's "Order for Receiving Persons into the Church" (itself a revealing title) was the laying on of hands accompanied by the blessing, "The Lord defend thee with his heavenly grace and by his Spirit confirm thee in the faith and fellowship of all true disciples of Jesus Christ." Words and actions hinted at a rite of confirmation, as had the optional laying on of hands in the baptismal rites of the Methodist Episcopal Church, South, first recommended in 1866. Churchly literature labeling the membership rites as "confirmation" was common from the 1930s. Even the African Methodist Episcopal Church, in outlining the contents of the worship materials in the 1940 *Discipline*, identified its rite of reception of members with confirmation, though the rite itself made no such association (and the denomination, by the end of the twentieth century, had not produced a service of worship so specifically identified). The Methodist Church in 1965 promulgated an "Order of Confirmation and Reception into the Church," using a title that was claimed to "restore the Sacrament of Baptism to its traditional meaning as a sign and seal of inclusion in Christ's holy Church," and defining confirmation as a renewal of baptismal vows and an active assumption of membership's responsibilities and privileges.[101] Another stated intention was to represent the "historic" office of confirmation, with "historic" defined as the rite separate from baptism that began to emerge in the western church in the fifth century, and that was practiced as baptismal reaffirmation and the culmination of concentrated catechesis by continental Protestants and their descendants. Profession and membership (human work) were the rite's primary purpose. Only secondarily was it conceived as an imbuing of the candidate with the Holy Spirit through the laying on of hands (divine action)—the function of the earlier postbaptismal acts from which "confirmation" developed.

Recovery of a unified sacramental initiation rite (water bath, invocation of the Holy Spirit and laying on of hands ["confirmation"], first Communion) using fourth-century models was the goal of the United Methodist Church's revisionary work from the 1970s through the 1990s, and the desire at the end of the twentieth century of other Christian churches as well. Following the design of earliest Christian praxis and the continuing custom of the Orthodox, the intention was to complete Christian initiation for children and adults at one event. Yet the rites reflecting the normative practice of adult initiation in the early church proved insufficient for the pedobaptist and personal-profession-requiring United Methodists: laying on of hands (designated "confirmation") might accompany baptism, but there was still the expectation that a person baptized in childhood would later make public profession, at which time denominational loyalty would also be vowed. While the rite implies that a child at baptism becomes a member of Christ's church universal and local, the denomination was more reticent to establish legislation to that effect.

At the end of the twentieth century, Methodist polity and baptismal practice assume that baptism is not sufficient completely to establish church membership. Categories of probationary, preparatory, or "junior" membership are still used by some denominations for baptized adults on trial or for baptized children. Baptism's ability to grant some status of membership is put further in doubt when even unbaptized children under the care of a congregation may be ranked as preparatory *members*. To add to the confusion: the classification of "constituent" may be used for all nonmembers of a congregation, whether they be baptized or unbaptized, young adults or the elderly. Methodism's hesitation to tie firmly together baptism and church membership undoubtedly stems in part from its origins as an evangelical society that regarded personal appropriation of the saving work of God in Christ as superior to the sacramental application of water. But the problem is not unique to Methodists: it has been an issue throughout the history of Christendom, but particularly after the establishment of infant baptism as the predominant practice in the making of Christians.

The Unresolved Tension

A tension occurs whenever the church both baptizes infants and expects personal faith of its members. This tension was played out in Wesley's theology as he strove to hold in tandem both the grace that precedes all human response and the necessity of saving faith confessed and lived out. One solution would have been to adopt a believer baptist stance; but Wesley, as an Anglican, affirmed the giving of baptism to infants as a needed and effective remedy for the original sin that tainted each individual from the womb. The unresolved tensions found in Wesley between infant baptism and the experience of the new birth took on a new shape for the American Methodists. On the one hand, insofar as Methodism retained its character as a movement within the evangelical revival, it kept individual religion to the fore. On the other hand, however, Methodism sought to provide an ecclesial framework for the largest possible proportion of the population, which, with the changed evaluation of childhood in the general culture, led it to redefine the meaning and effect of infant baptism away from remission of sin and regeneration toward a pedagogy of goodness. Though Methodists have continuously experimented with different theological and practical solutions to the problem of representing in Christian initiation both God's objective gift of salvation and the subjective human response, no single satisfactory answer has been found.

The Methodist Church's bishops realized in 1960 that Methodism sometimes stood in an "anomalous position" with respect to the church catholic on the matter of the sacraments. Their episcopal successors in the United Methodist Church were concerned to place Methodism more squarely within the broader Christian tradition. The method employed in their response to the World Council of Churches' text of 1982 on *Baptism, Eucharist and Ministry* seems to imply that the various positions on baptism held by different groups within United Methodism ensure that the denomination as a whole manages to do justice to all the various features that a fully Christian understanding demands.

In both the Wesleyan heritage and contemporary theology and practice of Methodists, baptism appears to be regarded from three differing perspectives. First, the traditional Wesleyan interpretation of infant baptism emphasizes very personally such doctrines as original sin, universal atonement, and prevenient grace. Second, the more churchly emphasis is based upon a covenant theology and corporate fellowship in Christ. Third, some United Methodists accept the presuppositions underlying believer's baptism only, interpreting it in clearly voluntaristic terms. In fact, John Wesley's own teachings can be construed to support each of the three positions as conditioned by varying stages of the denomination's life in America.

It is observed that United Methodism can be recognized as both a church and a movement. We emphasize at the same time both the objective and subjective aspects of the gospel, both the ecclesial and the personal. This stance is not one of theological indifference, but an understanding of how divine action and personal human response come together. Therefore, it is incumbent on our church to recognize the regularity and validity of baptismal rites in other Christian churches, and to include a variety of baptismal modes in our own.[102]

Thus, Methodism at the end of the twentieth century appeared almost as a microcosm embracing many of the understandings and practices that figure unreconciled in historic Christianity.

5

The Lord's Supper

"I ALSO ADVISE THE elders to administer the supper of the Lord on every Lord's day." In this way, John Wesley, in his letter of September 10, 1784, to "Dr. Coke, Mr. Asbury, and our Brethren in North-America," established a christological linkage between the sacrament and Sunday, and therewith his preference for Methodist liturgical praxis. What Wesley urged upon the Americans was not new for Methodists, though the provision for distinctively Methodist celebrants at Communion was an innovation—and an arrangement not approved by the majority of Anglican clergy on either side of the Atlantic, including Wesley's own brother Charles, who chided his sibling in prose and in verse.[1] From the earliest days of the Methodist movement in Britain, John Wesley had encouraged not just frequent Communion, but *constant* Communion, in imitation of what he believed to be attested in Scripture (Matthew 6:11; Acts 2:46) and in apostolic practice.[2] Wesley's own habit, since the age of twenty-two, had been to partake of the sacrament at least weekly, and while at Oxford he invited his students and members of the Holy Club to observe the rubric in the Prayer Book (1662) that at cathedral and collegiate churches the sacrament was to be received "every Sunday at the least" unless there be "a reasonable cause to the contrary."[3] Regular reception of the Lord's Supper was also emphasized in the religious society at Fetter Lane in which Wesley participated after his return to England from America, though when the Moravian Philip Henry Molther began to teach that the sacrament should be limited to those who had full assurance of faith, the Methodists, who disagreed with Molther, departed to form their own distinct society in 1740. Four years later, Wesley directed members of the Methodist "Band Societies" "to be at church, and at the Lord's table, every week."[4] This was doubtless a difficult requirement, given much Anglican antipathy toward the Methodists, as well as the custom of many rural and urban parishes of offering the sacrament only thrice yearly, and then only as a concession to the Anglican canon of 1604 and the Prayer Book's requirement that parishioners communicate a minimum of three times a year (including Easter). To address the expectation that qualified Methodists would receive the sacrament, and to accommodate the scores of hungering souls who desired "the office of love," Wesley encouraged sickroom reception (permitted by canon law), and consented, over time, to have the Supper celebrated at Methodist gatherings when the preacher was an ordained Anglican priest. At those assemblies hymns would be sung, particularly those from the doctrinally articulate collection of *Hymns on the Lord's Supper* (1745).

The Eucharist was thus an intrinsic part of the evangelical Wesleyan revival. Wesley recognized that in America "for some hundred miles together there is none either to baptize or to administer the Lord's supper,"[5] and that the Methodists longed for the sacraments from their own preachers—a privilege debated from 1772 and a matter that came to a head with the southern preachers' decisions at the Fluvanna Conference in 1779.[6] For these reasons (along with the inaction of the bishop of London, whose jurisdiction included oversight of the colonies) Wesley was finally moved to take into his own hands the irregular task of setting some men apart as Methodist presbyters. But the sacrament that had been the vital core of Wesley's ministry and mission in Britain was, in America, an occasional— though still desired—devotion even after Wesley's bold initiative, owing to the geographical spread of the population, the expectation of an itinerant ministry, and the dearth of authorized ministers, who might appear in a given community only quarterly (a meager sum of twelve or thirteen elders was selected at the 1784 Christmas Conference to serve with "Superintendant" Thomas Coke and the already-ordained Richard Whatcoat and Thomas Vasey in the United States, Nova Scotia, and Antigua). Wesley's ideal that the elders would celebrate and the people receive the Lord's Supper every Lord's Day was never realized in practice for the entirety of American Methodism, although congregations at various times and places strove to adhere to the intention of Wesley's advice. Weekly Eucharist may not have survived the transposition to America, but Wesley's eucharistic rite did; and of all the orders in the *Sunday Service* for local use, it was to remain for two centuries the closest to Wesley's original in form and in substance.

The Reception of Wesley's *Ordo*: 1784–1792

In providing in the *Sunday Service* a eucharistic liturgy for use "every Lord's day," Wesley started with the Prayer Book's "Order for the Administration of the Lord's Supper or Holy Communion," in which the Communion liturgy proper was preceded by an Ante-Communion (Lord's Prayer, Collect for Purity, Decalogue with the response "Lord, have mercy upon us, and incline our hearts to keep this law," two Collects for the King, Collect of the Day, Epistle Lesson, Gospel Lesson, Nicene Creed, rubric for Notices, Sermon). Overall, the order received from Wesley a conservative revision despite his stated design to shorten the length of the Lord's Day service.[7] The content of the prayers was largely left unchanged; in the Prayer of Consecration, only a redundant "one" was omitted ("by his one oblation of himself once offered"):

Almighty God, our heavenly Father, who, of thy tender mercy, didst give thine only Son Jesus Christ to suffer death upon the cross for our redemption; who made there (by his oblation of himself once offered) a full, perfect, and sufficient sacrifice, oblation, and satisfaction for the sins of the whole world; and did institute, and in his holy Gospel command us to continue, a perpetual memory of that his precious death until his coming again; hear us, O merciful Father, we most humbly beseech thee, and grant that we, receiving these thy creatures of bread and wine, according to thy Son our Saviour Jesus Christ's holy institution, in remembrance of his death and passion, may be partakers of his most blessed Body and Blood: who, in the same night that he was betrayed took bread; and when he had given thanks, he brake it; and gave it to his disciples, saying, Take, eat; this is my Body which is given for you; do this in remembrance of me. Likewise after Supper he took the cup; and when he had given thanks, he gave it to them, saying, Drink ye all of this; for this is my Blood of the New Testament, which is shed for you, and for many, for the remission of sins: Do this as oft as ye shall drink it, in remembrance of me.

Where alternate prayers were provided in the Prayer Book, Wesley removed one of the options, thereby reducing the length of the printed text but not the performance. To avoid redundancy, the Nicene Creed was dropped from the Ante-Communion, since the Apostles' Creed appeared in the preceding order of morning prayer; yet surprisingly the Lord's Prayer, which would have been said as part of the morning office, was retained in the Ante-Communion as a presidential prayer and in the Communion rite proper as a prayer of the elder and people after the partaking of the bread and wine. Adjustments throughout the rite were made for the American context by reworking references to the king and his realm (changes were made once again in the 1786 edition) and to ministerial offices (removing the nomenclature of bishop, priest, curate), and by the excision of rubrics that bespoke a settled and established ministry. No real attempt was made to abbreviate the listing of offertory sentences: the sole sentence to disappear was taken from the Puritan-detested apocryphal book of Tobit; yet another sentence from Tobit (4:8–9) was retained among the nineteen remaining sentences until it was deleted in the 1786 edition. Wesley's expectation of a weekly Eucharist is hinted at by the removal of the post-offertory rubric ("when there is Communion"), the rubric requiring announcement of the next Communion celebration (and with it the three exhortations), and the collects at the end of the rite to be said following the offertory "when there is no communion."

Since the bulk of the revision was accomplished by deletion rather than disruption, the basic shape of Wesley's service after the Ante-Communion was still that of the Prayer Book:

Offertory Sentences
Collection of Alms [during the reading of the sentences]
Prayer for Christ's Church Militant ["Almighty and everliving God, who by thy holy Apostle. . . ."]
Invitation ["Ye that do truly and earnestly repent of your sins. . . ."]
General Confession [made by the minister on behalf of the people; "Almighty God, Father of our Lord Jesus Christ, Maker of all things, Judge of all men. . . ."]

Prayer for Forgiveness

Comfortable Words

Sursum Corda ["Lift up your hearts. . . ."]

Common Preface ["It is very meet, right, and our bounden duty. . . ." to be followed by a Proper Preface on Christmas Day, Easter Day, Ascension Day, Whitsunday, and the Feast of Trinity]

Sanctus ["Therefore with Angels and Archangels. . . ."]

Prayer of Humble Access ["We do not presume to come to this thy Table. . . ."]

Prayer of Consecration ["Almighty God, our heavenly Father, who, of thy tender mercy didst give thine only Son Jesus Christ. . . ."]

Communion of the Ministers

Communion of the People

The Lord's Prayer

Post-communion Prayer ["O Lord and heavenly Father, we thy humble servants desire thy Fatherly goodness. . . ."]

Gloria in excelsis [to be said]

Extemporary Prayer [optional]

Benediction [Philippians 4:7 with trinitarian blessing]

Wesley did introduce some new material, giving a subtle distinction to the Methodist service that reflected his own theological and liturgical preferences. He turned the absolution after the General Confession from a pronouncement of divine pardon, whether understood in a declaratory or a performative way, into a prayer for forgiveness on behalf of all the penitent; comparable changes were also made to the absolution in the morning and evening offices.[8] Many of the rubrics identifying postures during the liturgy were eliminated, particularly the "all meekly kneeling" during reception, which some felt intimated eucharistic adoration (though most Methodists had opted to kneel and would continue to do so).[9] Instructions were added that the people should stand during the Comfortable Words and kneel at the Prayer of Humble Access. Contrary to the Prayer Book, but in line with other eighteenth-century revisions,[10] Wesley advised that should the consecrated elements be spent before all had received, the entire Prayer of Consecration was to be repeated and not simply the Words of Institution. The absence of the manual acts from the Prayer of Consecration in some copies of the *Sunday Service* demonstrated not a Wesleyan innovation but an unauthorized Coke variation, since later editions included the directions. The service ended with the option of the characteristically Methodist practice of extemporary prayer. Mention of another Methodist custom is notably absent: nowhere did Wesley provide rubrically for the singing of hymns. Even with Wesley's alterations, the 1784 Lord's Supper service was closer to the 1662 Prayer Book than would be the 1789 Communion rite of the American Protestant Episcopal Church, which drew upon the 1764 Scottish Communion liturgy as its base.[11]

The *Sunday Service* also included the Prayer Book's order for the Communion of sick, and kept the collect, the lessons from Hebrews 12:5–6 and John 5:24, and the rubrics indicating that the service was to continue at the Invitation and that the ministers were to receive first. However, absent entirely from Wesley's revision was the Prayer Book's prior service "for the visitation of the sick," perhaps because the Methodist "essentials" of prayer, Scripture, and hymn had worked remarkably well for improvised bedside worship.

Wesley's eucharistic theology was passed on to the American Methodists primarily through his resources for public prayer, namely, the revised Lord's Supper service itself and the nine Wesleyan Communion hymns that were included under the category "sacramental" in *A Pocket Hymn Book Designed as a Constant Companion for the Pious* (1785?) published in America.[12] The richest theological statement by the Wesleys on the sacrament, the collection of 166 *Hymns on the Lord's Supper* inspired by the structure and content of Daniel Brevint's *Christian Sacrament and Sacrifice* (1673), appears not to have been at all widely used in America in spite of the fact that the book went through nine British printings by 1786;[13] and neither the large *Collection of Hymns for the Use of the People Called Methodists* (1780), nor the *Collection of Psalms and Hymns for the Lord's Day* (1784), which was sent along with the *Sunday Service*, had a section designated for sacramental hymns, although the former contained four hymns from the *Hymns on the Lord's Supper* in the section "For Believers Saved" and three elsewhere. The received *lex orandi* was supplemented with overt doctrinal statements on the sacrament found in the twenty-four abridged Articles of Religion, and by incidental references in Wesley's *Explanatory Notes upon the New Testament* and his Standard Sermons, both of which were considered measures of Methodist doctrine before and after the Christmas Conference.

Like other Christians of his day, Wesley regarded the Supper as a perpetual commemoration of Christ's death and passion observed in obedience to his "gracious word" in the holy Gospel.[14] But this "precious legacy" bequeathed in the "death-recording rite" Wesley understood as a dynamic remembrance (*anamnesis*) of Christ's saving work, for at the table the believer is transported back to the foot of the cross while simultaneously receiving in the present the benefits of the passion:

> Who thus our Faith employ
> His Sufferings to record,
> Ev'n now we mournfully enjoy
> Communion with our Lord;
> As tho' we every one
> Beneath his Cross had stood,
> And seen him heave, and heard him groan,
> And felt his gushing Blood.
>
> O God! 'tis finish'd now!
> The Mortal Pang is past!
> By Faith his Head we see Him bow,
> And hear Him breathe his last!
> We too with Him are Dead,
> And shall with Him arise,

> The Cross on which He bows his Head,
> Shall lift us to the Skies. (*HLS* #4:3–4)

For those who repent of their sins and draw near with faith, the sacrament is efficacious, conveying the promised "antidote for sin" and "feeding our souls." The "cup of blessings" that imparts Christ's blood and the bread that is his "mystic body" "cheer each languid heart [with] the grace which sure salvation brings":

> Author of our Salvation, Thee
> With lowly thankful Hearts we praise,
> Author of this great Mystery,
> Figure and Means of Saving Grace.
>
> The sacred, true, effectual Sign,
> Thy Body and thy Blood it shews,
> The glorious Instrument Divine
> Thy Mercy and thy Strength bestows.
>
> We see the Blood that seals our Peace,
> Thy Pard'ning Mercy we receive:
> The Bread doth visibly express
> The Strength thro' which our Spirits live.
> (*HLS* #28:1–3)

In the sacrament Jesus "meets his followers" by his "special presence," a definition-defying real presence not explicable by the doctrine of transubstantiation (which is "repugnant to the plain words of Scripture, overthroweth the nature of a sacrament, and hath given occasion to many superstitions" [eighteenth Article of Religion]). Communicants at the table are also assured that they will "meet [him] in the skies" to "banquet with our Lord in heaven"; meanwhile, they find their "heaven on earth begun" by the union of the worship "below" with that of "the Church triumphant in thy love" since "the kingdoms are but one."[15] Because the "Son of God and Man" enjoined "all who truly bear the bleeding Saviour's name" to attend the "eucharistic feast" and thereby receive "pardon and holiness and heaven," the Christian should partake regularly and willingly.

That Christ's sole oblation at Calvary was sufficient satisfaction for the sins of the whole world was confirmed in the eucharistic rite and in the twentieth Article of Religion. Yet for Wesley, along with other Anglicans of the seventeenth and eighteenth centuries whose theology drew upon the content of the Epistle to the Hebrews, the sacrifice is perpetually presented by Christ, who is both the great high priest and the eternal victim, in order that his followers may receive its benefits afresh:

> Rivers of Salvation still
> Along the Desert roll,
> Rivers to refresh and heal
> The fainting sinsick Soul;
> Still the Fountain of thy Blood

Stands for Sinners open'd wide,
Now, e'en now, my Lord, and God,
I wash me in thy Side. (HLS #27:3)

To Christ's offering his people are to join their own sacrifice of praise and thanksgiving, and resign their souls and bodies to his "blessed service" that "every thought and word might proclaim" the goodness of God.[16]

Wesley's resources for the Lord's Supper were assimilated by the American Methodists, whose expectations and understandings of Communion had already been shaped in part by the discipline and rules of the Methodist society. The sacrament, acknowledged by Methodists to be a means of grace instituted by Christ, was to be received only after an individual had made a careful review of both heart and motive. This examination was aided by the spiritual accountability required within one's assigned band or class. Wesley had no need to include rubrics or exhortations in the *Sunday Service* defining qualified communicants, since the Methodist system effectively provided the means for fencing the table. Tickets or tokens, such as those by then used for the love feast, were distributed quarterly to identify and admit persons deemed sincere in their intentions. The love of neighbor that was required of every communicant included one very particular manifestation of Wesley's "social holiness": the first American *Discipline* (and the only *Discipline* to do so) forbade the communicating of any slaveholder who refused to manumit his slaves according to the plan devised by the church (Question 42.5). Yet the Methodists were not exclusionary; they willingly offered hospitality to persons not of their own church who desired to partake of Communion administered by the Methodist elder, but asked that such individuals subject themselves to the same evaluative criteria as the members. Approval was obtained from the minister or other designated leader, but in some places the congregation evidently had opportunity to voice objections.[17] Such care toward admission was especially practiced at the more private Lord's Supper services held at bedside and at the quarterly meeting (often in tandem with the love feast). During large public gatherings that were not as easily monitored, Methodist elders often preached a "sacramental" or "preparatory" sermon prior to administration as a means of delineating who were proper communicants. In both settings, private and public, Methodists at the Supper of the Lord experienced the power and love of God that, on one occasion in Baltimore, was described as "a sword piercing through many hearts & cordials to others."[18]

Prior to 1784, the quarterly meeting had sometimes been used by Methodists as a eucharistic occasion, with the sacrament presided over by sympathetic Anglican clergy or by their own (unauthorized) preachers.[19] After 1784, when presidency at the table was emphatically restricted to the elder alone in accordance with Wesley's plan, Communion at the quarterly "great festival" became the common pattern, as evident from Thomas Ware's matter-of-fact comment that "the administration of the ordinances at our quarterly meetings was singularly owned of God."[20] Recognition of the impracticality of weekly observances when the elders were so few was registered by the Americans' willingness to tamper with a foundational Wesleyan document. Whereas in 1791 the *Discipline* reprinted the Band Society direction—"to be at church, and at the Lord's table, every week"—as Wesley had promulgated it in 1744, one year later in 1792 (and after Wesley's death) the line in the *Discipline* now more accurately read, "to be at church, and at the Lord's table, at every opportunity." This alteration and the other changes approved in 1792 were not intended to belittle the sacrament or suggest a diminished eucharistic piety.[21] On the contrary, the people who had clamored for the Lord's Supper continued to hold it in high esteem, since there they expected to meet the "Master of the feast" and fellowship as brothers and sisters in Christ. The requirement that Methodists receive "at every opportunity," which for many came quarterly, meant that Methodists at the least partook more frequently than had been the custom in the great majority of Anglican parishes.

In the setting of the quarterly meeting, the Lord's Supper service proper could be attached to the end of a service of song, prayer, Scripture, and preaching or exhortation (which was the sequence of the "ceremony" detailed by the Fluvanna preachers),[22] or it could be directly preceded or followed by a love feast, or it could exist autonomously. Indications are that Wesley's Ante-Communion may have gotten little usage, and the Communion service proper often began with the collection of alms. It is therefore not surprising that, with the revision of the Lord's Supper rite in 1792, the material preliminary to the offertory sentences in Wesley's 1784 service was jettisoned, with only the Collect for Purity surviving in a new location after the Prayer for Forgiveness. Removal of the direct textual association between the sermon and the Lord's Supper, and the subsequent relegation of the Communion service to the separate section of the *Discipline* on "Sacramental Services, &c.," attested in print to what was already the case in practice—that the Supper of the Lord was not administered on every Lord's Day. Yet it also left in doubt the continuation of the historic conjoining of word and sacrament since nowhere was it explicitly stated that a sermon must accompany Communion and, according to the *Discipline* (section "Of Public Worship"), the reading of Scripture lessons need not be done on Communion days. Another clear linkage between word and sacrament was lost with the deletion in 1792 of Wesley's brief rite for communing the sick.

In their revision of Wesley's revision, the Americans continued his process of reducing the length of the service. The offertory sentences were reduced by four. Removed from the order were the Prayer for Christ's Church Militant, the Comfortable Words, the Sursum Corda, all references to the proper prefaces (and with it direct acknowledgment of the church year), and the rubric for kneeling at the Prayer of Humble Access. Adjustments were made to the manual acts and to the rubrics and words at the distribution. For the latter, the words "body and soul" in "preserve thy body and soul unto everlasting life" were reversed, perhaps to reinforce the eighteenth Article's teaching that "the body of Christ is given, taken, and eaten in the supper, only after an heavenly and spiritual manner." The order approved in 1792 would remain virtually untouched for approximately the next half century:

Offertory Sentences
Collection of Alms [during the reading of the sentences]
Invitation
General Confession
Prayer for Forgiveness
Collect for Purity
Common Preface
Sanctus
Prayer of Humble Access
Prayer of Consecration with manual acts
Communion of the Ministers
Communion of the People
The Lord's Prayer
Post-communion Prayer
Gloria in excelsis
Extemporary Prayer
Benediction

Church leaders in 1792 also introduced a new provision that would substantially impact eucharistic practice and theology in later Methodism. A rubric was added at the conclusion of the Lord's Supper rite, reading, "If the Elder be straitened for time, he may omit any part of the service except the prayer of Consecration."[23] The new rubric supported the liturgical liberty desired by ministers and people, but it also invited a lack of ritual uniformity across the denomination and led to the corruption of the rite's integrity in two different manners. Most drastically, some elders soon felt free to substitute material of their own composing even at the cost of the Prayer of Consecration itself. Although the Methodist Episcopal Church would introduce legislation in 1824 requiring that "in administering the ordinances" the "form of discipline invariably be used," the continuance of the 1792 rubric with the rite (even into the twentieth century) had the end result of perpetuating the problem. On this matter, Freeborn Garrettson remarked in 1826:

> But I have been astonished to see some of our brethren in the ministry, especially the young, laying aside such beautiful and expressive compositions, and marrying, baptizing, and even administering the Lord's supper, extemporaneously. I am sorry to lose a single sentence or even word of our sacramental forms. To be a lovely people, a prosperous people, a united people, a people gathering in an abundant harvest, we must be a holy, inoffensive people, following all the usages of the church, as transmitted to us by the venerable Mr. Wesley. I say Mr. Wesley; for we all know that the Bible was his standard.[24]

Less blatantly, even when the 1792 text was not replaced by free compositions, the rubric's isolation of the Prayer of Consecration yielded problems of reductionism. Among some elders it encouraged a minimalist approach to observance of the sacrament, for on occasion, the sacrament might consist solely of a hymn, the Prayer of Consecration, and the distribution.[25]

The Rite and Its Interpretation

1792–1968

The Methodist Episcopal Communion rite of 1792 was taken up without alteration in the respective *Discipline* of the African Methodist Episcopal Church, the African Methodist Episcopal Zion Church, and the Methodist Episcopal Church, South. Other Methodists in the first decades of the nineteenth century perpetuated the custom of reducing the length of the foundational text. The "United Societies of the People commonly called Methodists" (later the Union Methodists), who broke in 1801 from St. George's Church, Philadelphia, proposed a rite consisting of the 1792 components of Offertory Sentences, Invitation, Prayer of Humble Access, Prayer of Consecration (with manual acts), Words at the distribution, Lord's Prayer, and Benediction.[26] A comparable pattern was set out in the first *Discipline* (1843) of the Wesleyan Methodist Connection of America, with offertory sentences and a collection for the poor, the Invitation, a general prayer by the minister (created by fusing the first part of the General Confession with the Common Preface, Sanctus, and Prayer of Humble Access), Prayer of Consecration (without manual acts), the Words at the distribution, the Lord's Prayer, a rubric allowing for the option of extemporary prayer, and a benediction. Two years later, the Wesleyans severely truncated the ritual text, although they added a rubric designating a hymn between the sentences at the giving of alms and the Invitation: the specified texts for the general prayer and the Prayer of Consecration were replaced by a single rubric calling for a general prayer "in the name of all those who are minded to receive the holy sacrament," which was then followed by the Words at the distribution, and the Lord's Prayer. At the end of the century the 1845 Wesleyan Methodist pattern remained, although the offertory sentences had been replaced with the reading of selected scriptural warrants for the sacrament (Matthew 26: 26–29; 1 Corinthians 10:16, 17; 1 Corinthians 11:23–29), and the specific instruction for almsgiving had been deleted.

The Methodist Protestant Church in 1830 compressed the 1792 rite but also introduced new material, for example inserting into the text several Scripture sentences to be said first at the distribution of the bread and then at the cup, and including a rubric for hymn singing at the distribution in order to record the already extant practice. After beginning the service with an "appropriate discourse," the collection of alms (with offertory sentences), and the preparation of the table, the Methodist Protestant minister gave a general introduction (newly composed) and then led into a long prayer. The first three paragraphs contain material drawn from various parts of the 1792 eucharistic rite,[27] from Scripture (e.g., Romans 3:23), and from an unexpected source in the second paragraph: the General Confession from Wesley's (and the Episcopal) morning and evening prayer ("Almighty and most merciful Father, we have erred and strayed from thy ways. . . ."). The fourth paragraph adds two further ingredients in this pastiche, namely, pietistic turns of phrase (e.g., "melted into tenderness") and long scriptural quotations (Isaiah 53:4–5) that help to create the flavor of extemporary prayer. Particularly interesting here is the explicit invocation of the Holy Spirit, which, except for the Collect for Purity, was not otherwise present in Wesley's rite:

> Grant unto us, O our heavenly Father, the effectual assistance of thy holy Spirit, that while we partake of these thy creatures of bread and wine, according to thy Son our Saviour's holy institution, in grateful remembrance of his death and passion, that our hearts may be penetrated with unfeigned love and gratitude for the unspeakable gift of thy Son, in the redemption and salvation of our souls. May we be melted into tenderness on account of the great love wherewith Christ hath loved us, and given himself for us. May we ever remember his agony and bloody sweat in the garden of Gethsemane; his cruel mockings and scourgings in Pilate's hall; and his ignominious death on the cross. Surely he hath borne our griefs, and carried our sorrows; he was wounded for our transgressions, he was bruised for our iniquities, the chastisement of our peace was upon him, and by his stripes we are healed. May we have redemption through his blood which was shed for the remission of our sins; and, being justified by faith in him, may be filled with love, have grace to keep all thy commandments, and show forth the Lord's death till he come. And finally, be brought, with all the Israel of God, to inherit eternal life, through the merits and mediation of our Lord and Saviour Jesus Christ.

The pneumatological reference in this prayer could be complemented with the singing of a hymnic epiclesis by Charles Wesley, which found a place in Methodist Protestant and other Methodist hymnals in the section on the Lord's Supper:

> Come, thou everlasting Spirit,
>   Bring to every thankful mind,
> All the Saviour's dying merit,
>   All his sufferings for mankind:
> True recorder of his passion,
>   Now the living fire impart,
> Now reveal his great salvation,
>   Preach his gospel to our heart.
>
> Come, thou Witness of his dying;
>   Come, Remembrancer divine!
> Let us feel thy power, applying
>   Christ to every soul—and mine!
> Let us groan thine inward groaning,
>   Look on him we pierced and grieve,
> All receive the grace atoning,
>   All the sprinkled blood receive.[28]

Methodists in the first half of the nineteenth century may have been impelled to spread "scriptural holiness throughout the land," but many were equally concerned to fulfill the Lord's command to "Do this in remembrance of me." A minister forced by circumstances to miss the sacrament celebrated at the conference of preachers confessed remorse "that I should so lightly esteem the ordinance of the Lord."[29] That the desire for the Lord's Supper remained among the laity even after the rite was reduced in length and content is attested by the sacramental celebrations held for the sick and imprisoned, and the preaching of "profitable" sermons on the subject of the Eucharist.[30] One elder noted that he usually carried a small flask of wine among his saddlebags in order to communicate persons in the remote regions of his circuit who hungered for the sacrament but found it difficult to attend the quarterly gatherings.[31]

Building upon the foundation of sacramental theology laid by John Wesley, Methodists, in their theological discourses upon and hymnic statements about the Eucharist during this period and beyond, accentuated the *koinonia* between believers and Christ, the communion and unity expressed among the participants while meeting around the table, the fellowship of love that transcended time and space, and the anticipation of supping with Christ and the saints in the kingdom of glory. Special emphasis was placed upon the atoning sacrifice as (contrary to Calvinist doctrine) beneficial to all humankind, for which the grateful response should be praise and thanksgiving. The Supper was identified as the successor to the Jewish Passover (comparable to baptism's replacement of circumcision), but it was not to be understood only as a commemoration of Jesus' dying love in a historical sense. As a representation of Christ's vicarious and propitiatory sacrifice for the sins of the whole world, the rite (by God's own design) set the meritorious passion and death mentally and sensibly before faithful and sincere penitents.[32]

> O Thou eternal victim slain,
> A sacrifice for guilty man,
> By the eternal Spirit made
> An offering in the sinner's stead,
> Our everlasting Priest art thou,
> And plead'st thy death for sinners now!
>
> Thy offering still continues new,
> Thy vesture keeps its bloody hue;
> Thou stand'st the ever-slaughter'd Lamb,
> Thy priesthood still remains the same;
> Thy years, O God, can never fail,
> Thy goodness is unchangeable.
>
> O that our faith may never move,
> But stand unshaken as thy love:
> Sure evidence of things unseen,
> Now let it pass the years between,
> And view thee bleeding on the tree,
> My God who dies for me, for me![33]

The Lord's Supper, a meal actively claiming the grace of the "Victim Divine,"[34] was therefore to be understood as a covenant rite that, on God's side, is "the visible token and pledge of a covenant of mercy in the blood of Christ." For those who partake, the sacrament is a sign and a seal of God's promises, "a visible acknowledgement of this covenant so ratified by the sacrifice of Christ, and an act of entire faith in its truth and efficacy in order to the remission of sins, and the conferring of all other spiritual benefits."[35] The bread and wine thus are emblems of Christ's redeeming love that, by faith, are taken and eaten as spiritual sustenance.[36]

> The Father gives the Son;
> The Son his flesh and blood:
> The Spirit applies, and faith puts on
> The righteousness of God.[37]

Richard Allen, founder and bishop of the African Methodist Episcopal Church, expressed these theological concepts in the language of devotion, borrowing phrases from the liturgy and the Articles:

> I believe, that Thou hast instituted and ordained holy mysteries, as pledges of thy love, and for a continual commemoration of Thy death; that Thou hast not only given Thyself to die for me, but to be my spiritual food and sustenance in that holy sacrament to my great and endless comfort. O may I frequently approach Thy altar with humility and devotion, and work in me all those holy and heavenly affections, which become the remembrance of a crucified Saviour.[38]

The fundamental theological themes and emphases of the first half of the century were continued and reinforced in the second, though by the mid-1850s, the content of books and manuals on the Lord's Supper was nuanced to address a growing neglect of the sacrament that church leaders deemed "inconsistent with growth in grace and a life of piety."[39] Writers in this period expressed concern that on "sacrament sabbaths," members sometimes would leave the church before the eucharistic rite began or "sat aside while the blessed ordinance of the Lord's Supper was being dispensed."[40] The decline in attendance was attributed to multiple causes. The somber Supper proved less attractive than the more restricted and visibly evangelical love feast. On account of Baptist influence and, toward the end of the century, because of questions raised concerning the original sinfulness of humanity and the atonement as the indispensable means of salvation, some Methodists had come to regard the Supper as a memorial and fellowship meal rather than as a necessary and efficacious sacrament for the remission of sin. An extreme position occasionally taken was an entire rejection of the Supper as an example of Romish "sacramental religionism." Concerns about the spiritual and moral disposition of the celebrant caused some donatistic Methodists to abstain from the sacrament, despite arguments to the contrary.[41] Among the more biblically literal and spiritually serious, the sacrament was avoided lest it be approached without proper preparations (among these reconciliation with one's neighbor, i.e., Matthew 5:23–24) or taken unworthily (1 Corinthians 11:27–29). The primary reason given for the decline was the general disregard for reception as a Christian duty. In providing a remedy for this problem, membership manuals and catechisms repeated the obligation to partake and the implications of laxity: "No one can be excused from this duty which we all owe to the Lord Jesus. It is as plainly enjoined as is prayer or praise. To neglect it is not only to disobey Christ, but to slight his dying request."[42] Following a practice observed by the Methodist Protestants since 1830, the Methodist Episcopal Church, in 1864, approved a disciplinary solution by bringing to trial any member who habitually neglected the sacrament and the other means of grace, with expulsion from the church the alternative of last resort.[43]

A theological and historical study by Samuel Luckey, *The Lord's Supper* (1859), was designed with the stated purposes of encouraging covenant responsibility and invigorating sacramental participation. In successive chapters, Luckey considered the Supper as memorial, passover, Eucharist, Communion, and sacrament, and under each thematic heading noted an appropriate Christian behavior or response. To understand the ordinance as a memorial, said Luckey, is to discern that it is based upon the historical fact of the atonement. Not only is there the confirmatory witness of Christ's passion and death in Scripture; there is also the corroboratory and incontestable evidence of its truth by the endurance of the sacramental practice from the time of its institution. Each individual who partakes of the sacrament contributes toward the unbroken succession of testimony to Christ's sacrifice and its benefits. Conversely, a Christian who disregards the sacramental privilege risks disrupting the continuity of proclamation and denies the validity of the atonement.[44] Luckey then placed this interpretation of memorial in the broader context of the other themes. Against the backdrop of the theological discussions of his day, he cautioned against focusing solely upon an understanding of the Supper as a memorial that would deny its full purpose as a sacrament and thus encourage the communicant to regard the service as a mere, empty form. "Our views must penetrate deeper than this into the sacred mystery in order to derive all the benefit from it which it was designed to convey to those who meekly receive it in a right manner."[45]

Perhaps because Methodist theological reflection directed upon the sacrament in the second half of the century was largely consistent with what had come before, few changes were made to the eucharistic rites during this period. The Methodist Protestants, who at this time abbreviated their former eucharistic prayer and then concluded it with the Lord's Prayer and Wesley's Invitation, were the only denomination to introduce substantial new material. For several years they experimented with an alternative reading of either the Decalogue or the Beatitudes after the collection of alms, eventually settling upon the reading of Isaiah 53:(1–3) 4–10 and the rehearsal of the Apostles' Creed in that location. The Free Methodists, who had taken over the Methodist Episcopal rite verbatim, eventually dropped the opening offertory sentences, thus beginning the rite with the Invitation. The first alterations made to Methodist Episcopal Church, South's rite came in 1854, of which the most significant was the removal of the rubrics for the manual acts that had been judged by some to be "a mimicry of our Saviour's sacrifice—the offering of him as an unbloody sacrifice upon the altar."[46] (Despite requests for their excision, the Methodist Episcopal Church would keep the instructions, though they were altered.) Further revisions were approved by the Church, South in 1870, including the relocation of the Lord's Prayer following the Prayer of Consecration and the communication of the ministers, and the introduction of a rubric officially inviting the congregation to sing a hymn during the distribution; the 1870 order would be the form of the eucharistic rite adopted by the Colored (Christian) Methodist Episcopal Church.

Several of the alterations suggested or approved for the Methodist Episcopal Church's rite adumbrate later textual revisions and theological shifts related to the Lord's Supper, as well as the increasing tendency (at least officially) toward liturgical formality and elaboration in that denomination. For one quadrennium only (1864–1868), the phrase from the Prayer of Consecration, "receiving these thy creatures of bread and wine, according to thy Son our Saviour Jesus Christ's holy institution, in remembrance of his death and passion," was shortened to "receiving these memorials of the sufferings and death of our Saviour Jesus Christ." The reversion to the older form in 1868 indicates that the denomination was neither ready to strike at what they believed was the heart of the sacramental rite, nor willing as a body to continue a move in a direction of what might be construed as memorialism. They *were* disposed to introduce new phraseology further reinforcing that the benefits to be received from the sacrament were purely spiritual: with the textual revision authorized in 1864, the Prayer of Humble Access no longer petitioned that after reception "our sinful souls and bodies may be made clean"; instead, the request was a more general "that we may live and grow thereby." An unusual move was the relocation in 1864 of the Common Preface and Sanctus to a place immediately before the distribution, where it apparently was meant to function as a corporate "outburst of thanksgiving and praise" in anticipation of reception.[47] New rubrics specified that the Invitation, the Confession, and the Prayer of Consecration were not to be omitted even if the minister was "straitened for time" (1864); that the Gloria in excelsis could be said or sung (1868);[48] and, that, at a minimum, the Confession, the Prayer of Consecration, the words at the distribution, the Lord's Prayer, an extemporary supplication, and the Benediction were to be employed when communing the sick (1884). Despite instructions in the *Discipline* mandating that the Communion rite as approved be used verbatim, numerous Methodist Episcopal ministers (and those of other Methodist denominations with a similar rule) nevertheless felt at liberty to offer their own formulations and prayers as substitutes.

No effort was made by any of the denominations to ensure that preaching accompanied the sacrament. By the last decades of the nineteenth century, a practice on Communion Sundays, even in "station" churches with a single Sunday service, was to omit preaching to save time. In some congregations, this meant that the Lord's Supper rite alone was utilized for the order of the day, with the addition of opening and closing hymns. One author acknowledged that elimination of the sermon was contributing to the decline in worship attendance on Communion days, since would-be communicants who regarded the sermon as the essential component for every service of worship absented themselves, and those not inclined or prepared to commune stayed away since they could not participate.[49] To avoid either constriction of the Sunday morning preaching service or overly lengthy services with preaching and Communion, some time-conscious Methodists opted to move the observance of Communion to an afternoon or evening service, borrowing a pattern of some quarterly meetings, or, where feasible, to offer Communion in an early-morning chapel service. Thus what had already been construed as an occasional service became, wittingly or unwittingly, an irregular, special service.

The eucharistic rites for most of the Methodist denominations received only minor emendations from the 1880s to the 1960s, and the revisions were typically done by the relocation or removal of material, with the text of the African Methodist Episcopal Church being the least altered overall and the most consistent with what had been produced in 1792. Not so the Methodist Episcopal Church, which would again tamper with its service in 1916 and in 1932 sanction a significantly changed order that, nevertheless, for the first time since 1792 combined word and sacrament in a unified rite. Usage of the full text as printed was stated as the preferred practice, though the deletion of the Ante-Communion remained an option. The production of "an entire service for all instead of an addendum at which people may stay or go as they please," with a ritual form that permitted "the laity to have a larger participation in our services," required the "omission of some phrases which had become endeared through much repetition" and their replacement with "those of contemporary vitality which will become sanctified by use."[50] Practical considerations were conjoined with others ecclesiastical and more academic: members of the revision commission, in the spirit of the ecumenical and liturgical movements, confessed to having consulted the rituals of other Methodist and Evangelical churches; and recent studies in early Christian praxis, psychology, anthropology (especially the phenomenological approach), and comparative religions undergirded the revisers' stress on the desirability of ritual form, and on the historical and theological appropriateness of an integrated service of word and sacrament that valued active congregational involvement.[51]

A few refinements were made to the 1932 order at the General Conference of 1936, and it was the 1936 rite that would carry over into the 1939 merger:

Hymn [Heber's "Holy, holy, holy" is designated]
Litany ["God is a Spirit. . . . God is Light. . . . God is Power. . . . God is Love. . . ."]
Gloria Patri [said or sung]
Collect for Purity [in unison]
The Lord's Prayer
The Decalogue [litany] and/or the Summary of the Law [both optional]
The Beatitudes [two forms, both litanies, both optional]
Epistle
Gospel
Apostles' Creed or other "authorized" Affirmation of Faith
Sermon or Communion Meditation
Hymn [with the preparation of the altar]
Collection of Alms with Scripture Sentences [four sets of five sentences]
Ascription of Praise [1 Chronicles 29:14, said or sung]
Scriptural Thanksgiving [1 Chronicles 29:11]
Invitation
General Confession [by the minister and people together]
Prayer for Forgiveness
Comfortable Words

Sursum Corda
Common Preface ["It is very meet, right. . . ."]
Sanctus [said or sung]
Prayer of Consecration
Prayer of Humble Access
Communion of the Ministers
Communion of the People
Post-communion Prayer
Gloria in excelsis [said or sung]
Benediction [Philippians 4:7 with trinitarian blessing]

Structurally, with its inclusion of an Ante-Communion, the rite represented an approximate return to the historic 1784 pattern, though in the Communion section, the Prayer of Humble Access was repositioned after the Prayer of Consecration. The reinstatement of the Decalogue came after decades of requests for its return for use as an act of Communion preparation and confession;[52] the repeated response was the one Methodists had known prior to 1792. Continuing an alteration made in 1916 (1910 in the Methodist Episcopal Church, South), the laity joined the minister in praying the General Confession. Yet even as Methodism's liturgical past was reclaimed and many of its beloved usages were continued or "modernized," other accepted goals of the 1932 revision were put forth, including the selective reception of ecumenical liturgical resources and the promotion of "contemporary vitality." Now extending the Decalogue, or substituting for it, was the Summary of the Law, familiar in that location to American Episcopalians since 1789.[53] An option in place of or in addition to the Decalogue was the reading of the Beatitudes as a litany, which, though new to the Methodist Episcopal Church, had been regarded as an appropriate substitution for the "old" law in certain English-language liturgies since the seventeenth century and was included in the worship of Americans from some Reformed traditions.[54] The new opening litany (four Old and New Testament sentences alternating with the refrain "Glory be to God on high") appears to have been modeled after the first part of a "Service of Preparation for Holy Communion" printed in a collection of ecumenical and experimental liturgical resources contrived to enrich devotional experiences and "clothe with the dignity of liturgical form thoughts that express the religious needs of modern life."[55]

Attention to contemporary expression was not only achieved by the importation of recently composed texts. Historic components were reworked in 1932 to eliminate "words and forms which have become unmeaningful to the present generation."[56] Among the antiquated and now theologically suspect were phrases that enforced an understanding of the Supper as an objective means of grace and an efficacious sacrament and that defined God as a sovereign, yet merciful, judge who demanded satisfaction for human sin. Lord's Supper hymns specified in hymnals and popular literature produced by many of the Methodist bodies had already emphasized the Supper as a memorial meal, an opportunity for self-dedication to moral duties and spiritual improvement, and a symbol of union with Christ and of the unity among believers;[57] now the prevailing view was to be expressed in ritual language. Thus, "provoking most justly thy wrath and indignation against us" was eliminated from the General Confession as inconsistent with a view of a benevolent and beneficent God. The institution and command in the Prayer of Consecration was no longer "to continue a perpetual memory of his precious death until his coming again," but "to continue this memorial of his precious death." Communicants now partook "of the divine nature through him" rather than "of his most blessed body and blood," according to the Prayer of Consecration. Similarly, the reference to "eating the flesh" and "drinking his blood" was altered in the Prayer of Humble Access to "these memorials of Thy Son Jesus Christ" by which one is now "filled with the fullness of his life."

Church politics prior to the 1939 merger determined that the Methodist Episcopal rite would continue in the new Methodist Church, though as a concession to the Methodist Protestants, the responsive reading from Isaiah 53:1–10 was added following the Beatitudes. The rite of the former Methodist Episcopal Church, South was kept as an alternative order, not only because of dissatisfaction with the Methodist Episcopal service but also to avoid the expense of producing a new hymnal (the Communion order of the Methodist Episcopal Church, South was contained in that denomination's printing of the joint 1935 *Methodist Hymnal*). The two official Communion rites available to ministers and congregations of the Methodist Church in 1939, and again in the 1945 *Book of Worship* (with optional proper prefaces and lectionary added for both forms),[58] demonstrated the diversity and confusion that existed regarding the theology and practice of the sacrament: the one unified rite of word and Supper suggested a memorialist stance, while the separate rite for the Supper preserved historic Methodist sacramental language. These discrepancies did not go unnoticed, and debates between "Zwinglians" and the "sacramentalists" ensued in Methodist organs, principally the *Advocate* and *The Pastor*.

Born from this literary activity in 1946 was the Brotherhood of St. Luke (redesignated the Order of St. Luke two years later), founded for the purposes of studying the liturgies of the church catholic, cultivating within Methodism the liturgical renewal that was engaging other churches, and encouraging the faithful and informed practice of the sacraments. Members of this organization, through *The Pastor* and their own periodical, *The Versicle*, introduced Methodists to liturgical scholarship of the East and West (e.g., Dom Gregory Dix and *The Shape of the Liturgy*), and the ritual revisions under discussion in other churches during the 1950s and 1960s. Essays and advice columns by Romey P. Marshall, William Esler Slocum, Paul S. Sanders, and W. Maynard French, among others, exposed the history and theology of Holy Communion and other Methodist rites, and offered suggestions on the administration of the current services—for which they were sometimes accused of "un-Methodist" formalism and ritualism. In light of current scholarship, members of the Order and their sympathizers attempted a recovery of both the early church and Wesley. They stressed that the Lord's Supper was a "thanksgiving," but also an objective sacrament at which Christ is present through the power of the Holy Spirit to sanctify his people, and where believers join their sacrifice of praise and work with his and are thereby empowered to live a life of prayer and service.[59] Romey Marshall, at the request of the African Methodist

Episcopal Zion Church, drafted a new order for communion sensitive to the agenda of renewal, and although that denomination would not adopt the service, the Methodist Church would include some of the proposals in their next revision of the rite.[60]

The members of the Order of St. Luke constituted only a small minority within the Methodist Church. Yet their desire for a normative, unified rite that preserved the understanding of the Supper as Eucharist, sacrament, memorial, and Communion reiterated the emphases of liturgical renewal under discussion by other Protestant denominations. These deliberations within the wider church, and internal efforts—even by the bishops[61]—to elevate the place of the sacraments in practice, did not escape the notice of the committee that had been charged in 1956 with the Methodist Church's liturgical revision. A single and complete order of word and sacrament attentive to the Wesleyan heritage and the "psychological stages in the experience of corporate worship" was put forward in 1960, with a variant text provided at the Prayer of Consecration and at the Prayer of Humble Access in recognition that "the words 'so to eat his flesh and to drink his blood' are an offense to some of our people, while they are inspiration and power to others."[62] Final approval in 1964 was given, however, to two rites, one word and sacrament, the other sacrament only in a "brief form," with no alternative prayers within either rite. The sequence of the full rite had been drastically altered as a result of the intention to integrate the distinct parts of word and of sacrament (which, at the time, were identified as the liturgy of the catechumens and the liturgy of the faithful) into a cohesive whole. New material (e.g., the Prayer for the Whole State of Christ's Church in the form of a litany) stood alongside an altered Gloria, Prayer of Confession, and Prayer of Humble Access:

Scripture Sentences
Call to Prayer
Collect for Purity
The Lord's Prayer
Gloria in excelsis [said or sung]
Invitation
General Confession
Prayer for Forgiveness
Comfortable Words
Pastoral Prayer or Prayer for the Whole State of Christ's Church
Lesson(s) [with an anthem or hymn between the Epistle and Gospel if two
    lessons are used]
Apostles' Creed or other Affirmation of Faith
Sermon
Notices
Hymn
Offertory with dedication
Rubric indicating the option of a collection of alms
Sursum Corda

Common Preface [with option of adding a Proper Preface for Christmas,
  Epiphany, Easter, and Pentecost]
Sanctus [said or sung]
Prayer of Consecration
Prayer of Humble Access
Agnus Dei [said or sung]
Communion of the Ministers
Communion of the People [with the optional singing of hymns]
The Peace
Post-communion Prayer
Hymn
Benediction

For those who wished to continue the familiar shape of the Methodist liturgy, the brief form was the only recourse, and even then the Sursum Corda, Common Preface, Sanctus, and Gloria were missing.[63] For Methodists and non-Methodists concerned for liturgical renewal, both forms were inadequate in structure and in content. Episcopal liturgist Massey Shepherd (who spearheaded the efforts of the Consultation on Church Union to produce a model service in 1968 and was its principal writer), in correspondence with Order of St. Luke member Lawrence Snow, criticized the Methodist liturgical conservatism:

> I am sorry to see the Methodists being so traditional and conventional, instead of pioneering in the light of current liturgical developments—such as, e.g., the rite of South India or Taizé. . . . I share your comments on the proposed Methodist rite. I could make others—such as the unhappy position of the Lord's Prayer, for example. But I shall refrain, because my main concern is that the revision seems to be made too narrowly within the compass of the Prayer Book tradition, and is not sufficiently oriented towards the ecumenical dimensions of liturgical revision that now are so important.[64]

Only in the next decade would Shepherd's aspirations for the Methodist eucharistic liturgy become a possibility within one of the Methodist denominations.

1968–1996

Given that the Methodist Church had just completed a liturgical revision, the newly created United Methodist Church in 1968 elected not to formulate new orders for Communion, but instead authorized for use the four rites that it had inherited: the full and brief services of the Methodist Church, and the "regular" and brief forms of the Evangelical United Brethren Church. The latter's regular order, designed as a "unit complete in itself," was considered by that denomination to be historic, catholic, and evangelical, and as such, it shared affinities with the Methodist Church's rites of 1945 and 1965, and more broadly with the Prayer Book tradition as well as the Reformed tradition:

Processional Hymn or Call to Worship
Collect for Purity

The Lord's Prayer
Responsive Psalm [95, 96, or 100]
Gloria Patri
Epistle Lesson from 1 Corinthians 10:16–21
Hymn of Adoration [Heber's "Holy, holy, holy" suggested]
Gospel Lesson from Luke 22:14–19
Apostles' Creed
Sermon
Prayer for the Church
Anthem
Offertory
Communion Hymn
Examination of Conscience [the Beatitudes with responses, or the Decalogue
    with responses, or Kyrie]
General Confession [from the Prayer Book daily office]
Words of Assurance
Sursum Corda
Common Preface ["It is very meet, right. . . ."]
Sanctus
Prayer of Humble Access
Prayer of Consecration [from the first part of the Methodist prayer, adapted
    to include an invocation of the Word and Holy Spirit comparable to the
    1549 Prayer Book]
Words of Institution [quotation of 1 Corinthians 11:23–26]
Communion of the Ministers
Invitation
Communion of the People
Post-communion Prayer [two forms]
Gloria in excelsis [as a responsive reading]
Benediction [Philippians 4:7 with trinitarian blessing]

Despite the strong similarities of the rites contributed by the predecessor denominations, what would become the distinctively United Methodist rite did not develop from a coalescing of those two services. The new rite would not depend directly upon the liturgical traditions of the merged churches, but would, like other eucharistic revisions of the 1960s and 1970s, look to a ritual paradigm that antedated both Protestantism and the split between the churches of the East and West: a sequence of word and sacrament as found in the *First Apology* of Justin Martyr (chapter 67) and hinted at in Luke 24:13–35; and a eucharistic prayer or anaphora that imitated, in particular, the prayer in the so-called *Apostolic Tradition* attributed to Hippolytus, and also the anaphoral construction of West Syrian/Antiochene models.[65] For Methodists, this signaled the first radical departure from the Lord's Supper texts received from John Wesley. Yet, as the revisers noted, the new formulation bore out "Wesley's admonition that our worship 'follow the Scriptures and the primitive Church' while at the same time speaking to the condition of contemporary United Methodists." The revised ritual text represented "an attempt to incorporate both the historic and ecumenical witness of the church and also the distinctive gifts that our United Methodist heritage enables us to contribute to the universal church."[66]

The service first introduced to United Methodists in the spring of 1972 as an unofficial alternate text (later to be called Supplemental Worship Resources 1) was the culmination of eight drafts, the first of which was put before the Alternate Rituals Committee in February 1971.[67] Among the matters debated had been whether to include the Kyrie and the Gloria in excelsis (the former was dropped, the latter kept as an optional act of praise), and which affirmation of faith should be used (Nicene Creed, Apostles' Creed, or the United Church of Canada's statement—the latter was taken up in the 1972 text, but a rubric allowed the option of other affirmations).[68] The 1972 rite introduced several new components, including an epicletic prayer for illumination borrowed from the Reformed tradition, the sharing of the peace, and the distinct ritual action of the fraction in order to represent fully the ancient four-action shape of the liturgy delineated by Dom Gregory Dix (offertory, thanksgiving, breaking of the bread, distribution):

Greeting
Hymn of Praise
Confession and Pardon
Act of Praise
Prayer for Illumination
Scripture Lessons [interspersed with psalms, canticles, anthems or hymns]
Sermon
Affirmation of Faith
Prayer for Others
Invitation and Peace
The Offering
Thanksgiving
The Breaking of Bread and Taking of the Cup
The Giving
Prayer after Receiving
Hymn or Doxological Stanza
Benediction

Although the 1972 rite would be revised in 1981 and again in 1984, the order remained relatively stable, with the only significant structural change the reconfiguration of the confession and pardon sequence as a response to the sermon and a preparation for the sacrament. In its original place was inserted an opening prayer that might be a prayer of the day, although the confession and pardon might still take place at that point if not used after the sermon. Eventually the Collect for Purity was specified as the opening prayer, though with the option of other prayers. Attempts throughout the process to restore the cherished Prayer of Humble Access failed.

The classic West Syrian/Antiochene shape of the new eucharistic prayer and its emphasis on *eucharistia* posed no significant problems for the revision process. Thanksgiving for God's works and not (primarily) remorse for human sinfulness

was the focus, accentuating a tone of jubilant Easter resurrection and not penitential Good Friday. Dilemmas were faced as the committee strove to define and
articulate in prayer the active role of the Holy Spirit in the sacrament, the nature
of Christ's sacrifice and presence, and the recognition that Christians participate
not only in the new dispensation but in the full scope of God's salvation history,
from creation to eschatological fulfillment. Regarding the latter, the decision was
made early in the process to forgo proper prefaces in favor of complete, distinct
prayers for special seasons and occasions—an unusual solution, one shared with
Ethiopian anaphoras and certain Gallican mass-books—which allowed expression
of thanks for God's saving works of the old and new covenants. The basic prayer
of 1972, reached by compromise and consensus, met the goals of appealing to and
directing the liturgical and theological sensibilities of United Methodists, for the
optional text eventually sold over two and a half million copies:

> The Lord is with you.
> *And with you also*
> Lift up your hearts.
> *We lift them up to the Lord.*
> Let us give thanks to the Lord our God.
> *It is right to give him thanks and praise.*
> Father, it is right that we should always and
>   everywhere give you thanks and praise.
>   Only you are God.
>   You created all things and called them good.
>   You made us in your own image.
>   Even when we rebelled against your love,
>   you did not desert us.
>   You delivered us from captivity,
>   made covenant to be our God and King,
>   and spoke to us through your prophets.
> Therefore, we join the entire company of heaven
>   and all your people now on earth
>   in worshiping and glorifying you:
> *Holy, holy, holy Lord, God of power and might,*
> *heaven and earth are full of your glory.*
>   *Hosanna in the highest.*
> *Blessed is he who comes in the name of the Lord.*
>   *Hosanna in the highest.*
> We thank you, Father,
>   that you loved the world so much
>   you sent your only Son to be our Savior.
> The Lord of all life came to live among us.
>   He healed and taught men,
>   ate with sinners,
>   and won for you a new people by water and the Spirit.
> We saw his glory.

Yet he humbled himself in obedience to your will,
    freely accepting death on a cross.
By dying, he freed us from unending death;
    by rising from the dead, he gave us everlasting life.
On the night in which he gave himself up for us,
    the Lord Jesus took bread.
After giving you thanks,
    he broke the bread,
    gave it to his disciples, and said:
Take, eat; this is my body which is given for you.
When the supper was over,
    he took the cup.
Again he returned thanks to you,
    gave the cup to his disciples, and said:
Drink from this, all of you,
    this is the cup of the new covenant in my blood,
    poured out for you and many,
    for the forgiveness of sins.
When we eat this bread and drink this cup,
    we experience anew the presence of the Lord Jesus
        Christ
    and look forward to his coming in final victory.
Christ has died,
Christ is risen,
Christ will come again.
We remember and proclaim, Heavenly Father,
    what your Son has done for us
    in his life and death,
    in his resurrection and ascension.
Accept our sacrifice of praise and thanksgiving,
    in union with Christ's offering for us,
    as a reasonable and holy surrender of ourselves.
Send the power of your Holy Spirit on us,
    gathered here out of love for you,
    and on these gifts.
Help us know
    in the breaking of this bread
    and the drinking of this wine
    the presence of Christ
    who gave his body and blood for mankind.
Make us one with Christ,
    one with each other,
    and one in service to all mankind.
Through your Son Jesus Christ,
    with the Holy Spirit in your Holy Church,
    all glory and honor is yours, Father. Amen.

By the time the basic "Great Thanksgiving," as part of an entire service of "Word and Table," was officially sanctioned in 1984, it had been revised with attention to inclusive language, and musical settings had been scored for the congregational responses. Theologically, the text had become more bold in interpreting Christ's presence ("Make them [the bread and wine] be for us the body and blood of Christ") and explicating the sacrament's redemptive and ethical aspects ("that we may be for the world the body of Christ, redeemed by his blood").[69] The principal text became the model for dozens of eucharistic prayers crafted for use at weddings, funerals, and the various seasons and festivals of the Christian year, thereby allowing for a breadth of theological and euchological expression not permissible by the constraints of a single prayer.

According to the *United Methodist Hymnal* (1989) and the *Book of Worship* (1992), the previously approved basic pattern of Word and Table was expected to govern the order of service on Communion and non-Communion Sundays (the Great Thanksgiving being replaced by a general prayer of thanksgiving). Yet United Methodist leaders recognized (aided by letters expressing reservations about the new text) that ritual customs and theological understandings are not easily uprooted. The complete order of Word and Table was given priority in both books (Service 1), but was followed by a series of services in which the Communion portion of the rite alone appears, allowing the new Communion text to be appended to a congregation's usual Sunday morning liturgy or an abbreviation of it. Service 2 comprised the Invitation, Confession and Pardon, Peace, Offertory, and the basic Great Thanksgiving. Designed for flexibility and freedom, Service 3 included from the basic Great Thanksgiving only the congregational responses and the transitional statements preceding them, so that an alternate eucharistic prayer or an extemporary formulation might be offered. Newly created for the 1989 hymnal and designated as Service 4 was a sacrament-only service conflating and re-ordering the former Methodist and Evangelical United Brethren Communion rites; from the latter came an introductory dialogue and an epiclesis ("bless and sanctify with thy Word and Holy Spirit these thy gifts of bread and wine") not found in the former Methodist rite. Service 4 was expanded in the *Book of Worship* to a service of word and sacrament, again blending components from the predecessor denominations.[70] A brief service for use with the sick and homebound was included in the *Book of Worship* as Service 5. These multiple options for the Lord's Supper offered in the official resources fulfilled the United Methodist desire for flexibility and variety. But the 1992 *Book of Worship* also stands as testimony to the diversity of Lord's Supper practices that have existed within American Methodism from the beginning despite repeated calls for ritual uniformity.

Although it may not have been a dominant factor in the decision to preserve the historic Methodist (and Evangelical United Brethren) Communion rite in the 1989 and 1992 books of the United Methodist Church, the continuation of some vestige of the older form has enabled that denomination to maintain a ritual linkage with the wider American Methodist family. The other Methodist denominations, cognizant of the liturgical changes elsewhere, elected to keep relatively close to their ritual inheritance. The African Methodist Episcopal Church's service of "The Word of God and Celebration of the Holy Communion," first published in 1980 and showing resemblances to the patterns of other revised rites, contained new prayers and modernizations of the older ones, but also maintained separately the church's "traditional" Communion service.[71] No new Lord's Supper text or revision of the old was taken up by the African Methodist Episcopal Zion Church in their 1996 *Book of Worship*, although the sacramental rite was now preceded by a word service. As dialogues to reunite the Methodist family continued at the end of the twentieth century, the shared text for the Lord's Supper potentially offered a key to an even more substantial communion.

Admission to the Table

Methodists have never been able to establish a consensus about the conditions necessary for admission to the Lord's Supper. Disputes with other Christians and internal theological shifts have only added to the uncertainty of the issue, which, it may be surmised, originates from the absence of a definitive statement about proper communicants in Wesley's *ordo* for the Lord's Supper. Instead of a rubric, the American Methodists fell heir to several assumptions based upon the content of the *Sunday Service* and British Methodist praxis. Some of these suppositions were not easily translated into the new context; others were readily appropriated and, over time, acquired a range of interpretations.

No service of confirmation finds a place in the *Sunday Service*, bearing out Wesley's contention in his *Treatise on Baptism* that, following the example of the ante-Nicene church, baptism suffices for initiation into Christ's church and membership in the same. Access to the table, therefore, was granted by baptism alone, and not through a pair of formal rites, as had been the historic and expected Anglican practice. Acting upon this view, Wesley and other Anglican clergy sympathetic to the Methodist cause baptized those who desired to affiliate with the Methodist societies but had not yet received the sacrament (e.g., Quakers and Baptist sympathizers) and permitted their communion without confirmation. Yet these persons and those already baptized (confirmed or not) did not automatically gain admission to Methodist Communions, for entry was allowed only to those society members and visitors who held the requisite ticket signifying successful examination of their moral character and their spiritual seriousness. The Invitation contained in the Prayer Book Communion rite, which would have been addressed only to baptized and (ideally) confirmed Anglicans, reinforced for Methodist participants the scrutiny they had already undergone preparatory to the rite:

> Ye that do truly and earnestly repent of your sins, and are in love and charity with your neighbours, and intend to lead a new life, following the commandments of God, and walking from henceforth in his holy ways; draw near with faith, and take this holy Sacrament to your comfort.

Methodists heard the Invitation not only as demanding but also as generous: those baptized who had not yet come to a full assurance of saving faith, but who knew their "utter sinfulness and helplessness" and could sincerely profess to be striving toward holiness, were welcomed to the table. Thus, the sacrament could be a *confirming* ordinance for the assured, and as Scripture and experience authenticated, a *converting* ordinance for those yet "*unconverted*, who had *not* yet 'received the Holy Ghost,' who (in the full sense of the word) were not *believers*." To every soul who expressed at least a modicum of faith, God would convey through the sacrament preventing, justifying, or sanctifying grace depending on the stage of each individual's spiritual maturity.[72] Wesley's belief that there were degrees of faith had caused the rift with Molther and the Fetter Lane Moravians who advocated "stillness," meaning one should be still and abstain from any outward work, including the means of grace, until true faith was obtained.[73] Wesley's view was equally disconcerting to Scots Presbyterians and others who feared the Methodists allowed "all promiscuously to come to the Lord's table."[74] Such accusations were unwarranted, for the discipline surrounding Methodist Communions, in fact, did not suffer all comers.[75] The tenor of Wesley's policy was to encourage people, at whatever stage in the life of redemption, to come regularly to the Lord's table—provided they showed evidence, as with membership in the Methodist societies in general, of their "desire to flee from the wrath to come, to be saved from their sins."

The American Methodists, even with their strong affirmations of freedom and liberty, could not countenance a totally unrestricted table, and so, after the revision of 1792, continued in their disciplinary rules the condition of examination or careful monitoring. It was not until 1858 that the Methodist Episcopal Church, South dropped the stipulation introduced in 1792 that "no person shall be admitted to the Lord's Supper among us who is guilty of any practice for which we would exclude a member of our Church." The Methodist Episcopal Church kept the prohibition until 1892. As late as 1996 the *Discipline* of the African Methodist Episcopal Church retained the regulation; and only in 1976 did it remove the even more precise qualification that first appeared in 1786 and had persisted in that denomination with only slight verbal changes, but which had earlier disappeared from other Methodist bodies: "Let no person who is not a member of our Society be admitted to the Supper without examination and some tokens given by an Elder or a Deacon."[76] The Free Methodists, in the latter half of the twentieth century, maintained in print that persons who were immoral or engaging in disreputable practices ought to be fenced from the table until penitence was made. They also held up a provision found in early Free Methodist legislation that drew upon the requirements of repentance, neighborly charity, and holiness of life stated in the rite: "All persons properly included in the general invitation may be allowed to partake of the Lord's Supper among us."

In practice, most Methodist churches in the nineteenth century saw the "Ye that do truly and earnestly repent" as a sufficient safeguard when ministers and church leaders carefully judged worthy communicants by that standard and by the fundamental doctrines of the Christian faith defined in the Articles of Religion. Room was thereby left open, following Wesley's design (though not using his phrase "converting ordinance"), to admit those earnest seekers who were not yet completely convinced of their acceptance with God. Thus a young, weeping penitent could receive permission from Bishop McKendree to approach the table:

Hurrying to the table she fell upon her knees and cried aloud to God. With streaming eyes the Bishop administered the bread; and just as her lips tasted the wine of the sacramental cup, pardon was communicated, and heaven sprung up in her heart. Instantly she rose to her feet, and her face shining like that of an angel, while, with an eloquence that went to every heart, she told the simple story of the cross, and the wondrous power of Christ to save. All seemed to partake of the common joy of that renewed spirit.[77]

By that same interpretation, an ex-governor of Maryland surrendering himself to Christ could receive Communion for the first time as "an open declaration of his Christian purpose and faith."[78] Conversely, a woman not a Methodist, whose opinions on the divinity of Christ suggested Arianism, could be barred from communing with their fellowship, or a class leader unreconciled with his neighbor could fence himself.[79] Those persons who were already communicants were expected to have prepared themselves for reception by prayer, introspection, and repentance, and ideally, by fasting on the Friday beforehand.[80] By 1884, the African Methodist Episcopal Zion Church had stipulated another act of preparation on the Friday before the sacrament: according to their disciplinary article "Of the Lord's Supper," on Friday evening "every pastor in charge of a circuit or station" was to examine "the members of the society in general class" to see "how their souls [were] prospering."

The Invitation provided a viable and valuable guideline for admission, but stripped from its original Prayer Book context, it had lost the fundamental assumption and safeguard that underlay it. No longer could it be presupposed that those who heard the summons had previously been baptized. Elders, following the lead of numerous Methodist writers, in general expected baptism to have taken place prior to the Lord's Supper and for communicants to have some degree of faith, but made exceptions if circumstances (such as the desire for immersion) had prevented an individual from previously receiving the baptismal washing.[81] A deliberate or voluntary neglect of baptism, however, usually kept one from the table.[82] Some elders also recognized that at larger gatherings, where the normal strictures of the Methodist system could not be fully employed, or when, by the late nineteenth century, the procedures for examination had mostly broken down, a self-administered test of "Ye that do truly" might include the unbaptized. Efforts during the mid-nineteenth century to establish a disciplinary rule delineating baptism as a precondition failed,[83] primarily because Methodists, in polemical debates with the Baptists at that time, were reluctant to concede either the necessity of baptism prior to Communion or the validity of a restricted, "close" Communion. Thus carefully balanced statements also appeared in the literature:

> Though, therefore, it is lawful, as a matter of Church order, that Baptism precede the use of the Lord's Supper, the same as in the dispensation of shadows circumcision usually preceded the passover; yet neither Baptism nor any other Church ordinance is a necessary prerequisite to the Eucharist, and, therefore, not of the communion of Christians with their Lord at his table. The only positive requisite to this communion relates to and involves character rather than forms or ceremonies, and consists of sincere penitence and faith in Christ, or that righteousness which is by faith in Christ.[84]

Baptists contended, on a basis of Scripture and church history, that baptism indispensably preceded the Lord's Supper; to invert the order, as Methodist permissiveness allowed by admitting the "unregenerate" to the table, was to "pervert the Supper and sin a daring sin against Christ." Countering what they perceived to be Baptist exclusivism, Methodists offered their own scriptural "proofs" negatively put: for example, the disciples had not been baptized before they ate in the upper room, the Great Commission came only after the Supper had been instituted, and nowhere did Christ either command baptism to precede the Eucharist or establish any priority of order (each sacrament thus having its own nature and design).[85] Against the Baptist understanding that baptism as initiation into church membership made one eligible for the Supper, many Methodists argued that active faith was the integral ingredient, and not necessarily baptism. With such an interpretation they could also answer Baptist challenges that, by virtue of their baptism, infants logically had a right to Communion. Although in 1826 Freeborn Garrettson had hinted, based on early Christian praxis, that "little children" could receive the Eucharist,[86] Methodists had generally followed the advice contained in the "Extract on the Nature and Subjects of Christian Baptism" appended to the *Discipline* from 1790 to 1797, which reflected Wesley's own practice: children became eligible when they could "understand the nature and design of the Lord's Supper" and had a "measure of knowledge and faith" to discern the Lord's body.[87] But in the heat of controversy with the Baptists, new (and questionable) rationales were now given for excluding infants and children. An infant could participate in a passive ordinance (baptism), but was incapable of an active ordinance (Communion).[88] Because Jewish children circumcised in infancy could not participate in the Passover until they understood its significance (the age of twelve "according to Luke 2:41–42"), by analogy, baptized Christian children could not partake until they had the proper spirit and understanding.[89] Baptism did not automatically bestow church privileges: just as women, who had been baptized, were prohibited from holding church or ministerial offices, so, by the same reasoning, infants were not entitled to Communion.[90]

Methodists, to Baptist minds, were guilty of theological inconsistencies on these matters, though these paled in comparison to those that surfaced during disputations on the related subject of open versus "close" Communion. Methodist rhetoric and literature criticized as unscriptural and unpastoral the Baptist contention that only *immersion* baptism made one fit for the table: "the Master made no such distinction" regarding mode, and "his disciples did not teach it, nor enjoin on others to preach it";[91] and an insistence upon immersion denied the possibility of Communion to the sick or dying not previously baptized.[92] Likewise, such a requirement fostered a sectarian spirit, consequently promoting bigotry and intolerance, denying religious liberty, and hindering the Christian unity and cooperation that John 17:21 records was prayed for by the Savior:

> When the table is spread, by any one denomination, and the bread and wine is placed thereon, it is emphatically *the table of the Lord*, and not the table of *that particular denomination*. The duty of the administrator is to invite all orthodox Christians who are in good standing in their respective Churches—as the Methodists *invariably do*—to join in the commemoration of the death and sufferings of Christ; and he is not at

liberty to withhold the sacred elements from such, or order them to stand aside, as the Baptists do on all occasions.[93]

To these accusations Baptists retorted with their own charges of exclusivism, by condemning Methodists whose supposed liberality was compromised by their harassment of Baptists unwilling to accept Methodist invitations to the table, and by pointing to the Methodists' own strict disciplinary laws and regulations, especially those associated with admission to the love feast.[94] On the latter, Methodists defended their polity by drawing a distinction between the Lord's Supper as a "divinely instituted means of grace designed equally for all Christians of every Church" and the love feast as "a prudential means adopted by us, and designed exclusively for us, and those of our friends whom we may choose to invite."[95]

By the turn into the twentieth century and Methodism's establishment as a "national" religion, Methodist practice generally was to recognize baptism as the proper antecedent to the Lord's Supper, and to acknowledge the Invitation, taken literally, as the standard for self-examination. For this reason, the newsletter of a Durham, North Carolina, church would give notice for Communion, expecting its membership to engage in the time-honored practice of sacramental preparation:

> The Communion Table will be spread at both the morning and evening services next Sunday so that the entire congregation may have the advantages afforded by it. Members should examine their hearts and see that all malice and envy and uncleanness are put out of them, and be sure that they are in love and charity with all men. It should be a time of consecration and devotion on the part of every one of us. Turn to First Corinthians, 11th chapter and 23d verse, and read to the end of the chapter.[96]

But Methodists would also practice open Communion, now defined not only to mean that Christians in good standing from other congregations and churches were welcome (the usual understanding of "open" Communion, and the one used in the Baptist debates), but that any individual who could answer the Invitation could partake. "It is not in the spirit of Christ to reckon rigid conformity to ecclesiastical propriety above the dictates of Christian cordiality," claimed Methodist theologian Henry Clay Sheldon.[97] Aided by a theological liberalism that elevated personal experience, held an optimistic view of the human condition, promoted the ideals of democracy, and advocated a social gospel, many Methodists soon took such notions as "Christian cordiality" to refer to an indiscriminate admission to the table; any who so desired could come since "God does not arbitrarily require faith as a previous condition to be met before he is willing to save."[98] Newly published studies on the theology of John Wesley and the history of Methodism complemented this view, perhaps unintentionally, by recounting Wesley's understanding of Communion as a "converting ordinance" yet without relating it precisely to the original controversy over "stillness," and without taking into consideration that by their own time a shift in meaning had occurred so that "unconverted" generally no longer referred primarily to the "unawakened" or "unassured" baptized but to those altogether without religion. Concerns about the psychological damage rendered to people by their exclusion from the table, and the limitations to evangelization imposed by barring access to the "altar rail"—the customary place of prayer, repentance, and surrender—may each also have contributed to a redefining of "open" Communion.

At the end of the twentieth century, the only official standard for admission remained the invitation to Communion within the eucharistic rite. Efforts to mandate a baptismal prerequisite continued to fail, because the broad definition of open Communion was deemed normative by many. Much depended upon local custom and pastoral discretion to determine which, if any, preconditions existed for admission to the table.

The Frequency of Reception

Communion every Lord's Day was an impossibility from the outset in America, but denominational leaders expected opportunities to be made for regular reception. Congregations were enjoined to attend the means of grace and were sometimes encouraged through the public reading of Wesley's sermon on "Constant Communion."[99] Although the elders had the authority to celebrate Communion at any gathering of Methodists, many appeared content to offer the sacrament when requested, occasionally at certain festivals (e.g., Christmas Day or Eve), or at the time it normally was expected. For many Methodists, the quarterly gathering of the societies (and later, churches) on a circuit for business, worship, and fellowship provided the ordinary and sole occasion for Communion. In some of the larger city appointments, the custom established early was that of monthly Communion. A widespread pattern was for a given Sunday of the month to be marked by a sacramental service for at least one of the societies. Thus the societies in New York City, in the 1790s, held the sacrament at "old church" on the first Sunday of the month, and at "new church" on the second Sunday; by 1816, the sacrament was administered at John Street, Two Mile Stone, and Asbury African on the first Sunday, at Zion African on the second Sunday, Second Street and Duane Street on the third, and at Fourth Street and Greenwich on the fourth Sunday.[100] An appointment plan for preachers on the "New York Circuit" supplied for May 1831 through June 1832 shows an adjustment to the older configuration: all of the churches except for two received the sacrament on the second Sunday of the month; the two exceptions held Communion at one of the afternoon services during the month.[101] The rhythm of quarterly Communions in circuits and "at least once a month in stations" was the officially stated instruction of the Methodist Protestant Church throughout its history.

Some popular writers on the sacrament, such as British Methodist Adam Clarke, whose work was widely read in America, commended reception once a month or once every six weeks as "the proper mean"; he considered weekly "too frequent" and quarterly "too seldom."[102] James Porter, writing in the 1850s, assumed the ordinance to be "usually administered in our regular stations the first Sabbath in each month."[103] Nevertheless, as churches grew from locations on a circuit to congregations with their own resident minister, the ingrained quarterly pattern was preferred both by pastor and people. Certain leaders of the Methodist Episcopal

Church lamented that its constituents might not be supplied with the sacrament as often as desirable—an argument that would eventually be used to permit pastors other than elders to preside at the table under limited circumstances.[104] A proposal was made in 1888 to see that, where possible, the Supper was observed once every two months, but despite such efforts, no formal legislation on frequency was ever established by that denomination, even though it implemented and maintained the regulation that members could be brought to trial for neglecting the sacrament.[105] The Methodist Episcopal Church, South, however, followed the lead of Thomas O. Summers, who in 1859 had claimed that "according to our standard authors, and the heretofore almost universal usage of Methodism, the communion should be celebrated at least once a month in every congregation where it can conveniently be done."[106] Summers's assessment was the substance of the rule adopted by his denomination in 1870, which also acknowledged that in places where monthly Communion was impracticable, the sacrament ought instead be held at every quarterly meeting. Efforts failed in that same year to require each quarterly conference to record the number of eucharistic celebrations for that quarter, but just such a prescription was approved in 1922. The "Complete Quarterly Conference Record Book" used by the Buckhorn Charge in the Illinois Conference of the Methodist Episcopal Church, South, if accurately kept, may speak more to the realities of Communion frequency (or infrequency) particularly in the rural areas where Methodism was strongest: for 1922–1923, 1923–1924, and the first three quarters of 1924–1925 (the record for the fourth quarter is missing), the question about sacramental administration was either left blank or answered "no"; Communion was celebrated in three of the four quarters of 1936–1937, only one quarter in 1937–1938, and in each of the first three quarters and twice in the fourth of 1938–1939.[107]

Legislation or not, the annual schedule for the Eucharist was mostly determined locally by pastors, who often were hesitant either to lengthen the service by adding Communion or to shorten the sermon to accommodate it, and by congregations, which might be indifferent to the sacrament or worried that too frequent reception could render Communion less "special." External influences, such as the practices of churches representing other Christian denominations, were also a factor, positively or negatively. Within Methodism as a whole, therefore, the frequency with which the sacrament was received was highly variable: a monthly observance could be held in one of the larger churches in the South, or an annual celebration might be deemed sufficient. Such variability characterized Methodism even at the end of the twentieth century, in spite of the push begun in the early part of the century and continued throughout it for Methodists to hold more frequent celebrations, and ideally to emulate the weekly observances of ancient Christians, the Methodists of Wesley's day, and (increasingly) other Protestant churches in North America. The United Methodist Church designed its Service of Word and Table to be used weekly for word and sacrament, but this intention was followed only in a small minority of congregations.

The Elements for Communion and the Method of Reception

The manual acts accompanying the Prayer of Consecration and the rubric following that prayer in the eucharistic rite of 1792 together identify what Methodists
expected at the distribution of the sacrament whether kneeling, standing, or sitting: to receive in the hand a portion of the bread that had been broken by the
elder and upon which his hands had been laid, and to be given a cup of wine
similarly blessed. No instructions specified the type of bread or wine to be used.
For the first half of the nineteenth century at the least, the *Discipline* of most
Methodist denominations assigned the procurement of the elements to the circuit
steward, who, presumably, contributed from the foodstuffs at hand or arranged for
special items. Grape wine was difficult to acquire and expensive, so often the
steward resorted to purchasing the only available "wine," which might be grape
wine diluted with distilled liquor, a locally produced wine made from other fruits,
or an alcoholic concoction containing no wine. The varieties of substances brought
to the sacrament, and the ever-present desire among some Methodists for uniformity of practice, undoubtedly reinforced the opinion among some that the only
suitable elements were those that conformed to what the Lord himself had used.
So wrote W. P. Strickland in 1851:

> If it is clear that the *bread* used by him on that occasion was *unleavened*, and the *wine*
> unmixed and *unadulterated*, we should follow his example, as far as we can, to the
> letter. How often have we been pained by receiving at the Lord's table bread raised
> with yeast, salaeratus, or salt, or shortened with lard or butter, while what was called
> wine resembled vinegar mingled with myrrh, more than the pure juice of the grape![108]

Concerned for the quality of the sacramental element, the Methodist Episcopal
Church in the early 1860s recommended the use of a locally produced and pure
grape wine.[109] Consideration was given to the uniform use of unleavened bread,
though no official legislation on the matter was ever enacted by any Methodist
body, since many evidently concurred with Thomas O. Summers's assessment that
"the element in this case is not so clearly defined as to restrict it absolutely to
wheaten bread, leavened or unleavened."[110] Even so, circuit, and later, Communion stewards often opted to use "unseasoned" bread.[111]

The contents of the cup also attracted considerable attention as questions were
raised regarding the kind of wine Jesus would have used at the Last Supper. This
inquiry by Methodists, Presbyterians, Congregationalists, and others (including
Baptists) was spurred on by involvement in the cause of temperance, an issue
Methodists had addressed in legislation from their founding,[112] and a subject that
had provoked numerous articles in Methodist periodicals from the 1820s. At stake
for many was whether or not Jesus had commanded his followers to imbibe an
intoxicant. An article by Congregationalist and biblical exegete Moses Stuart published in the October 1835 issue of the *Methodist Magazine and Quarterly Review*
that questioned the use of fermented wine for the sacrament opened the gate to
a flood of essays and statements by Methodists and non-Methodists in Methodist
publications throughout the course of the century. Some Methodists, concurring
with Stuart's points in his essay and the assumptions of the "two-wine theory" in

his publication *Scriptural View of the Wine-Question* (1848), sought to demonstrate by scriptural and historical evidence that both fermented and unfermented wines were to be found throughout the ancient world and in the Bible, and that a nonalcoholic drink had been on the table in the upper room. Such was the intention of the lengthy study *Oinos: A Discussion of the Bible Wine Question* (1883) by New Hampshire Methodist Leon C. Field, who concluded that Jesus had not made fermented wine from water at Cana, and neither had he commended nor himself used alcoholic substances.[113] Arguments setting forth Jesus' use of unfermented wine were readily embraced at the local level, as evident from Illinois preacher Leonard Smith's comments regarding the miracle at Cana:

> Jesus made wine out of water. Perhaps as the water was drawn from the vessels it was made wine. That wine was evidently sweet wine, the unfermented juice of the grape. . . . Christ would not use any but new wine. Would he have if the people were intoxicated given them new wine to make them drunker? Blasphemy. Certainly the wine used was a new sweet wine. No where was any other wine used.[114]

Theological and social concerns were also translated into liturgical practice. With the first edition of their *Discipline*, the Wesleyan Methodist Connection included a rubric with the Lord's Supper rite instructing that "unfermented wine only should be used at the sacrament." At the same time that the General Conference of the Methodist Episcopal Church was advocating a pure grape wine for the sacrament, some ministers from that denomination were already electing to substitute water, wine diluted with water, or an unfermented grape juice, usually without repercussions from their respective judicatories.[115] Indeed, some Methodist Episcopal annual conferences, in the late 1860s and early 1870s, resolved through their temperance committees to discourage any use of alcohol, even at Communion. The denomination took heed of these strong feelings, and in 1872 approved the General Conference Committee on Temperance report that recommended unfermented wine be given at the sacrament.[116]

By 1874, an anonymous article in the *Western Christian Advocate* boasted that numerous churches in and around New York and Philadelphia had "banished the alcoholic cup from the Lord's table" since they had determined, in an interesting moral comparison, "that the Bible no more sanctions the use of intoxicants at the Lord's table than it does American slavery." To encourage others to follow suit, a recipe for an unfermented raisin wine was appended.[117] Commercially produced unfermented grape juice was also becoming available as a direct result of Louis Pasteur's experiments in the 1850s with regulating the fermentation process. The former Wesleyan Methodist preacher Thomas Bramwell Welch, whose own concern against serving alcohol at the sacrament had in 1869 motivated him as a trained physician and dentist to produce "Dr. Welch's Unfermented Wine," began to find his fellow Methodists receptive to the new product when, beginning in 1875, Methodist publications were targeted for advertising.[118]

Over the years 1872 to 1916, the Methodist Episcopal Church's recommendation of unfermented wine for the sacrament slowly evolved into a mandate that the "pure, unfermented juice of the grape" be used.[119] The Free Methodists moved more quickly and had by the mid-1870s instructed stewards to offer the unfermented juice of the grape and "in no case" to use "intoxicating wine." Petitions came before the general bodies of the Methodist Protestant Church and Methodist Episcopal Church, South, but no churchwide legislation was ever enacted, leaving room for both wine and juice usage—sometimes within the same service of worship. Many remained convinced as did Thomas O. Summers, and even members of the denominations with written policies, that the two-wine theory was nonsense, that what the Lord blessed in the cup was clearly defined as wine, and that to emend arbitrarily the Savior's instruction would ultimately cause more damage than good. "It would be better not to pretend to celebrate the Lord's-supper than to do it with water, unfermented grape or raisin juice, or any other slop," insisted Summers. "Get the pure, fermented, generous juice, 'the blood of the grape,' and if possible let it be red, as best setting forth the thing signified."[120] Although by the turn into the twentieth century many Methodists were using or experimenting with an unfermented juice, others adhered adamantly to what they believed the Lord himself had instituted and was shared with other Christians throughout the world.

The scientific advancements that led to the production of unfermenting juice for the Communion cup also triggered concerns about the cup itself—and again debates among Methodists. The discovery by investigators in the new field of microbiology that germs were the culprit behind illness and disease provided the incentive for a widespread campaign toward improvements in health and sanitation, among which was included the elimination of the common drinking cup in public places. By the late 1880s, members of the medical community and Protestant Christians of various denominations were asking whether sipping from the Communion chalice could also be a source of contagion. One physician in 1887 suggested the method of intinction (the "bread so prepared that it may be dipped in the cup of wine") as a substitute for placing the lips on the "poisoned chalice."[121] Over the next two decades, Methodist writers offered other alternatives: glass siphons or straws, grape-shaped capsules filled with wine or juice, individual spoons, individual communion cups, and the omission of the wine altogether (though such risked violating the nineteenth Article of Religion). Of these options, the individual cup seemed the most attractive, practical, and "convenient," and by the mid-1890s it was being used at Methodist sacramental celebrations. During their November 1895 meeting, the Board of Stewards of the Tryon Street Methodist Episcopal Church, South in Charlotte, North Carolina, officially approved individual cups for communion, having found them to be "cleanlier" and one means of encouraging the communion of persons who had previously stayed away.[122] Increasing numbers of Methodists began to introduce individual glass cups to their services in the years following, often filled with Welch's grape juice.[123]

Methodist enthusiasm for individual cups was far from unanimous in the 1890s and the following decade. Here a firm distinction was made between a personal receptacle and several cups that each might be used to serve dozens of communicants (including the custom, even in smaller congregations, of giving one cup to men and another to women). Arguments were proffered that before any consideration should be given to abandoning the historic and universal Christian custom, proof was needed that irrefutably identified the chalice as the source of a communicant's illness. Questions were posed, tongue in cheek, whether capitulation to the "morbidly sensitive" also required purification of the baptismal water after each act of sprinkling, or limitations upon Christian charitable acts toward the sick, the dying, and the dead. Debates raged regarding the legality of a congregation or pastor introducing the "saloon method" to the sacramental service without the prior approval of the denomination's legislative body. But most important, opponents of individual cups registered fear that departure from the common cup significantly altered the intended and essential meaning of the sacrament itself: as a sign of the union between Christ and believers, and an expression of the equality and lack of distinction among those who are one body in Christ. Thus, many Methodists shared the sentiment of J. M. Buckley, editor of the New York *Christian Advocate*, who described the individual cup "as one of the most inconsistent and repugnant innovations ever foisted upon any part of the Christian Church."[124]

The voices opposing the innovation, however, very quickly became the minority. Proponents of the new device appealed effectively to the emotionalism of the health issue, as well as to Scripture, the "essentials" of tradition, and the individualism by then a key component of Methodist spirituality and of American democracy. It was pointed out that Jesus had not mandated the use of the common cup, and neither had his church at any time fixed the number of cups to be used. Individual cups, it was suggested, might have been used at the Last Supper to contain the sacramental drink, since what was believed to be the custom at the Passover meal—captured in Leonardo da Vinci's artistic rendering of the event— supported such a claim. Even if Jesus had used a common cup, what mattered was the significance of the action and not its precise imitation. At issue was not *how* the sacrament was taken, but that it *was* taken in remembrance of him. Multiple modes (as with baptism) were therefore not only justifiable liturgically, but were also a sign of the reasonable Christian liberty in nonessentials that purportedly was a hallmark of Methodism. In addition, Jesus had not specifically identified the Supper as a symbol of unity or a vehicle of fellowship in the words of institution; hence, those meanings could be construed as secondary interpretations. The primary understanding of the sacrament was of the communion between the individual believer and the divine, which was best represented by the individual cup: "He takes that little cup in his hand, filled from the common wine, and, forgetful of all but the sacrifice of the cross, he enters into undisturbed fellowship with Jesus."[125] If an expression of unity was desired within the congregation, it could be achieved by the simultaneous eating of the bread and then the unison drinking of the individual cups.

Petitions requesting official approval of individual Communion cups that were presented at the General Conferences of 1900, 1904, 1908, and 1912 by members of the Methodist Episcopal Church did not yield the desired legislation. The *Discipline* of most other Methodist bodies likewise did not establish an official policy. The Free Methodists, however, introduced a rubric in 1915 (still present in their

1995 *Discipline*) recommending the use of individual cups "whenever practicable." For many Methodists, no approval also meant no prohibition, and the use of personal cups flourished throughout the twentieth century, encouraged by advertisements for individual Communion services published in denominational papers and church supply catalogs. The Methodist Episcopal Church made no correction to its rubrical manual acts (altered in 1864) to account for the change taking place: the "cup" and the plate of bread were still to be taken into the hand; but now for the bread there typically was no formal fraction, since, to avoid "handling food unnecessarily," the bread was precut into small pieces and the communicant permitted "to help himself."[126] To include the new method the African Methodist Episcopal and the African Methodist Episcopal Zion Church did not need to modify their manual acts, which had kept the language of 1792, for they conveniently contained the instruction for the presider to lay the hand "upon all the vessels which contain the wine." At the creation of the Methodist Church in 1939, the manual acts were removed entirely from the Communion rite (perhaps as a concession to the two denominations that had previously dropped them), but reference to a singular cup continued in other rubrics; in the 1965 rite the manual acts were restored.

Throughout the twentieth century, various elements and methods of reception were thus possible within any given Methodist congregation, depending upon local traditions and the assertiveness of pastoral leadership. Different combinations of forms could be employed in services throughout the year or even on a specific occasion. Grape juice generally was offered, and efforts to restore widespread use of fermented wine (for theological, liturgical, and ecumenical reasons) were largely unsuccessful: a rubric introduced in the 1984 *Book of Worship* of the African Methodist Episcopal Church authorized both "wine and the unfermented juice of the vine"; the rubrical designation "wine" in the United Methodist rite approved in 1988 was understood to comprehend both fermented and unfermented substances. Bread leavened and unleavened (including wafers and matzoth) could be placed on a plate or basket; the African Methodist Episcopal Church from 1961 narrowed the choice by stipulating unleavened bread. Experimental liturgies, particularly during the 1960s and 1970s, saw the consumption of a wide range of questionable elements, but these never supplanted the more common forms. Continuing fears of infectious diseases kept most Methodists away from the common cup though some sought its restoration, applying the same rationales put forward for the reintroduction of wine. The mode of intinction, the growing popularity of which Romey Marshall linked to the practice of chaplains during the Second World War, was regarded as a suitable compromise in spite of the fact that it did not satisfy the Lord's command to "drink this."[127] Communion could be received in the pews, at the railing, at the altar, or at serving stations scattered around the worship space. Another method ridiculed as "cafeteria" Communion, whereby communicants served themselves from tables placed in the chancel, was not widely accepted, particularly since its detractors insisted that according to Jesus' precedent and Methodist custom, the elements should be given into the hand and not selfishly taken.[128]

What Means Communion?

Methodism arguably became a separate denomination in response to the strong desire of the Methodist societies to receive the sacraments. Yet within a century, the Lord's Supper was largely perceived as a respected but occasional interruption to the Sunday morning preaching service. Ironically, while Methodists were beginning to understand themselves more confidently as church rather than as religious society, enthusiasm for both administration and reception generally waned. Each *Discipline* continued to describe the Eucharist in sacramental terms as a divinely initiated and effective means of grace, and as an instrument for the upbuilding of the community of saints. With some exceptions, the contents of the approved Lord's Supper rite remained relatively close to Wesley's original. But the prevailing Enlightenment rationality that permeated society and church—when added to Methodism's evangelical accent on inward holiness and the validity of individual experience—encouraged the reasonable explanation that the Supper was a simple memorial meal observed in obedience to Christ's command whereby each person (perhaps fearfully) confronted God and was inspired for moral living. Emphasis upon the welfare and faith of the individual and a diminished sense of the communion of the community was reinforced by the decline in references to the body of Christ in liturgical texts,[129] by sensitivities about fermented wine and the germ-laden common cup, and by the relaxing, within many Methodist denominations, of requirements that restricted access to the table. The dismantling of fences to the table may also have been motivated by a keen sense of democratic idealism, urged on by theological and social perspectives that blurred Christian values with the work and destiny of the nation.

Recovery of Wesley's interpretation of eucharistic theology and praxis, while sought by some in the nineteenth century, received more attention in the succeeding century with encouragement from the ecumenical, liturgical, and Wesleyan-revival movements. Even so, the newer "inheritance" of an infrequent, individualized Communion focusing on personal piety dominated Methodist conceptions and practice during the twentieth century. In fact, a commonly used source for Wesleyan eucharistic theology throughout the nineteenth century— selections from the *Hymns on the Lord's Supper* included in official hymnals—was inexplicably excluded from the specified Lord's Supper hymns in the joint hymnals of 1905 and 1935. After two generations when no Wesleyan eucharistic hymns were identified as such, the Methodist Church's 1965 hymnal included three among the Lord's Supper hymns, but then the United Methodist Church's 1989 hymnal reduced the number to two.[130] The modest restoration of Wesleyan eucharistic hymnody in the second half of the twentieth century by some denominations, along with their efforts to promote a practice of word and sacrament and to express more effectively an ecclesial understanding of the corporate worship of the body of Christ, provoked tensions not only within the denominations but also in local congregations as questions were raised about whether or not a uniform American Methodist theology and practice of the sacrament was possible—a question that was continually asked by their spiritual ancestors.

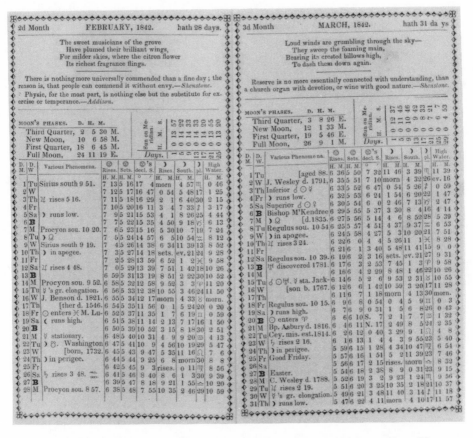

The sweet musicians of the grove
Have plumed their brilliant wings,
For milder skies, where the citron flower
Its richest fragrance flings.

There is nothing more universally commended than a fine day ; the reason is, that people can commend it without envy.—*Shenstone*.

Physic, for the most part, is nothing else but the substitute for exercise or temperance.—*Addison*.

MOON'S PHASES. D. H. M.
Third Quarter, 2 5 30 M.
New Moon,   10 6 58 M.
First Quarter, 18 6 45 M.
Full Moon,   24 11 19 E.

D.M.	D.W.	Various Phenomena.
1	Tu	Sirius south 9 51.
2	W	
3	Th	♃ rises 5 16.
4	Fr	
5	Sa	) runs low.
6	B	
7	M	Procyon sou. 10 26.
8	Tu	) ☌
9	W	Sirius south 9 19.
10	Th	) in apogee.
11	Fr	
12	Sa	♃ rises 4 48.
13	B	
14	M	Procyon sou. 9 52.
15	Tu	♀'s gr. elongation.
16	W	J. Benson d. 1821.
17	Th	[ther d. 1546.
18	Fr	☉ enters ♓ M. Lu-
19	Sa	(runs high.
20	B	
21	M	☿ stationary.
22	Tu	) ☉. Washington
23	W	[born, 1732.
24	Th	) in perigee.
25	Fr	
26	Sa	♄ rises 3 48.
27	B	
28	M	Procyon sou. 8 57.

Loud winds are grumbling through the sky—
They sweep the foaming main,
Bearing its crested billows high,
To dash them down again.

Reserve is no more essentially connected with understanding, than a church organ with devotion, or wine with good nature.—*Shenstone*.

MOON'S PHASES. D. H. M.
Third Quarter, 3 8 26 E.
New Moon,   12 1 33 M.
First Quarter, 19 5 46 E.
Full Moon,   26 9 1 M.

D.M.	D.W.	Various Phenomena.
1	Tu	[aged 88.
2	W	J. Wesley d. 1791.
3	Th	Inferior ☌ ☉ ☿
4	Fr	) runs low.
5	Sa	Superior ☌ ☉ ♀
6	B	Bishop M'Kendree
7	M	) ☌ [d.1835.
8	Tu	Regulus sou. 10 54
9	W	) in apogee.
10	Th	♃ rises 3 24.
11	Fr	
12	Sa	Regulus sou. 10 39.
13	B	♅ discovered 1781.
14	M	
15	Tu	☌ ☉♅. ♄ sta. Jack-
16	W	[son b. 1767.
17	Th	
18	Fr	Regulus sou. 10 15.
19	Sa	) runs high.
20	B	☉ enters ♈
21	M	Bp. Asbury d. 1816.
22	Tu	Cey. mis. est.1814.
23	W	♄ rises 2 16.
24	Th	) in perigee.
25	Fr	Good Friday.
26	Sa	
27	B	Easter.
28	M	C. Wesley d. 1788.
29	Tu	♃ rises 2 19.
30	W	☿'s gr. elongation.
31	Th	) runs low.

Opening from *The Methodist Almanac, for the Year of Our Lord and Saviour Jesus Christ, 1842* (1841).

Plan of a camp meeting near Washington in 1806 drawn by architect Benjamin Henry Latrobe; reproduced from Talbot Hamlin, *Benjamin Henry Latrobe* (1955).

Old Bethel Camp Meeting.

FOR 1868, AUGUST 12th, AND 20th, INCLUSIVE.

REGULATIONS.

All persons Encamping or Worshipping on this Ground, will be expected to observe the following regulations:—

1st. All Tents are to be located with the consent, and under the direction of the Managers.

2d. Nothing will be exposed for Sale, by placard or otherwise, except it is authorized at a Regular Meeting of the Managers.

3d. No *food* or refreshments of any kind, will be sold on the Sabbath, except those furnished at the Boarding Tents, and at the Stand at the head of the Ground, which will be allowed to Sell, from 12½ to 2 P. M. then to be closed until supper-time, when one hour is allowed for the Sale of Bread and Cakes, then to be closed until Monday morning.

4th. No *controversy* on Religion or Politics, will be allowed on the Ground.

5th. All *washing* about the Wells, is strictly prohibited.

6th. No *smoking* of Tobacco within the circle formed by the Tents, will be allowed at any time.

7th. *Work* of every kind must be suspended during Religious Services at the Stand.

8th. No *walking* or *talking* during Service at the Stand.

9th. But *one person* will be allowed to occupy a Tent, during Service at the Stand, except those in care of the Sick, or of Infants.

10th. A *light* must be kept in the front part of every Tent during the night.

11th. The boarding Tents are to be regulated by the ringing of the Bell at the head of the Stand, no small bells to be rung.

Breakfast at	6 o'clock,
Dinner	12½ "
Supper	6 "

THE SPECIAL ORDER FOR EACH DAY.

The Bell will be Rung as a Signal—

At 5 A. M., for Rising,	At 10 A. M., for Preaching.
" 6½ " " Family Prayer.	" 2½ P. M., " "
" 8 " " Prayer Meeting at Stand,	" 7 " " "

At 10 P. M. the close of all Religious Services, and for clearing the Ground.

The Places designated for retirement, are as follows:—For FEMALES, on the right and left of the Stand. For MALES, in front of the Stand.

BY ORDER OF THE MANAGERS.

J. LEWIS, P. E.

M. C. STOKES, Preacher in Charge.

Regulations for a New Jersey camp meeting; reproduced from Hazel Simpson, *The History of Bethel Methodist Episcopal Church* (1945).

sin; and grant that *this Child*, now to be baptized, may receive the fulness of thy grace, and ever remain in the number of thy faithful and elect children, through Jesus Christ our Lord. *Amen.*

Then the Minister shall take the Child into his Hands, and say to the Friends of the Child,

Name this Child.

And then, naming it after them, he shall dip it in the Water, or sprinkle it therewith, saying,

N. I baptize thee, In the Name of the Father, and of the Son, and of the Holy Ghost. *Amen.*

Then the Minister shall say,

WE receive this Child into the Congregation of Christ's flock, and * sign him with the sign of the Cross; in token that hereafter *he* shall not be ashamed to confess the faith of Christ crucified, and manfully to fight under his banner against sin, the world and the devil; and to continue Christ's faithful soldier and servant unto his life's end. *Amen.*

* *Here the Minister shall make a Cross upon the Child's Forehead.*

Then shall the Minister say,

SEeing now, dearly beloved brethren, that *this Child is* grafted into the body of Christ's Church, let us give thanks unto Almighty God for these benefits, and with one accord make our prayers unto him, that *this Child* may lead the rest of *his life* according to this beginning.

Then shall be said, all kneeling,

OUR Father, who art in heaven, Hallowed be thy Name; Thy kingdom come; Thy will be done on earth, as it is in heaven: Give us this day our daily bread; and forgive us our trespasses,

passes, as we forgive them that trespass against us; And lead us not into temptation; But deliver us from evil. *Amen.*

Then shall the Minister say,

WE yield thee hearty thanks, most merciful Father, that it hath pleased thee to receive *this Infant* for thine own *Child* by adoption, and to incorporate *him* into thy holy Church. And humbly we beseech thee to grant, that *he*, being dead unto sin, and living unto righteousness, and being buried with Christ in his death, may crucify the old man, and utterly abolish the whole body of sin; and that, as *he is* made *partaker* of the death of thy Son, *he* may also be *partaker* of his resurrection; so that finally, with the residue of thy holy Church, *he* may be *an inheritor* of thine everlasting kingdom, through Christ our Lord. *Amen.*

The Ministration of BAPTISM to such as are of RIPER YEARS.

The Minister shall say,

DEarly beloved, forasmuch as all men are conceived and born in sin (and that which is born of the flesh is flesh, and they that are in the flesh cannot please God, but live in sin, committing many actual transgressions); and that our Saviour Christ faith, None can enter into the kingdom of God, except he be regenerate and born anew of water and of the Holy Ghost; I beseech you to call upon God the Father, through our Lord Jesus Christ, that of his bounteous goodness he will grant to *these Persons,* that which by nature *they* cannot have; that *they* may be baptized with Water and the Holy Ghost, and received into Christ's holy Church, and be made lively *members* of the same.

Then

Baptismal text from John Wesley's *The Sunday Service of the Methodists in North America* (1784) that includes the signing with the cross in the infant rite.

Quarterly tickets used by the Methodist Episcopal Church, courtesy of the Archives, Center for Methodist Studies at Bridwell Library, Perkins School of Theology, Southern Methodist University.

A Christian Methodist Episcopal Church elder presides at communion in 1998; reprinted from *The Christian Index* by permission of the publisher.

Advertisements for communion ware in the *Northwestern Christian Advocate* (1912).

A church youth orchestra of the 1930s; reprinted from Mildred Morse McEwen, *First United Methodist Church, Charlotte, North Carolina* (1983), with permission.

A church decorated for a wedding in 1918; reprinted from Wyatt Brown, ed., *Early Methodism in Greenville, North Carolina, and a History of the Jarvis Memorial United Methodist Church* (1978), with permission.

One of the few octagonal buildings constructed in America for Methodist worship, McBee Church of Conestee, South Carolina, was designed in the 1840s by John Adams, a local wheelwright; photograph by Fred Rollison, reproduced courtesy of the Greenville News-Piedmont Company.

An artist's rendering in *Frank Leslie's Illustrated Newspaper* (vol. 53, 2 Sept. 1882) of Margaret Van Cott exhorting at a camp meeting at Neelytown, New York.

6

The Music of Methodist Worship

METHODISTS HAVE ALWAYS considered themselves to be a singing people. Even before they received the 1784 *Sunday Service*, American Methodists were using books and pamphlets containing evangelical hymns, thanks in large part to the prolific output of hymn writer Charles Wesley and the publishing enterprise of his brother John. American publishers prior to 1784 reprinted a few of the Wesley hymn collections, usually at the request of particular Methodist societies. Among the most frequently reproduced were *A Collection of Psalms and Hymns* (1741), *Hymns for Those That Seek, and Those That Have, Redemption in the Blood of Jesus Christ* (1747), and *Hymns and Spiritual Songs* (1753), all three of which were brought out in 1773 by New Jersey printer Isaac Collins, and in 1781 by Philadelphian Melchior Steiner. John Wesley's *Collection of Psalms and Hymns* (1737), published in Charleston, South Carolina, and issued for the Anglican community in Georgia while Wesley was a missionary there, apparently never saw a second printing as a distinct collection.[1] Although no direct reference was made to cantillation in the *Sunday Service*, Wesley's expectation that Methodists would sing in worship was clear, for his *A Collection of Psalms and Hymns for the Lord's Day* (1784), a slightly abridged version of the 1741 *Collection of Psalms and Hymns*, was sent along with his Prayer Book revision. That the Methodists would defer to the Wesleyan collections was stated officially in the May 1784 *Minutes* of the preachers by their design to "keep close to Mr. Wesley's tunes and hymns."[2]

Public worship, as well as private, family, and social worship, would not have been considered *Methodist* unless accompanied with song. What prayer books were for some Christians, the hymn books were for generations of Methodists: a source for praise, prayer, devotional meditation, and doctrine. Hence, the arrangement of hymns or songs in official collections reveals much about the expectation of their use and more broadly identifies an editor's or a church's theological, liturgical, and ecclesiological principles. Likewise, Methodist preferences for certain types of song, and the manner deemed appropriate for their performance, expose essential aspects of Methodist self-identity. In the more than two hundred years of Methodist music in America, several tendencies or trends are evident, some of which stand in tension with one another.

Expressions of "Experimental and Practical Divinity"

The contents of "official" hymnals produced by American Methodists from 1784 through the 1830s imitated, at least partially, the design of the 1780 *Collection of Hymns for the Use of the People Called Methodists*, what John Wesley described in the preface to the work as "a little body of experimental and practical divinity." In the 1780 *Collection*, which was often referred to as the "Large Hymn Book," the entire sequence of hymns followed the shape of the Wesleyan *via salutis* and was thereby organized "according to the experience of real Christians," beginning with an invitation to repentance, and concluding with integration into the community of faith.[3] The earliest American hymn books exposed the *via salutis* under various headings by a substantial proportion of hymns that were given priority through their placement at the front of the collections. By this method, basic Methodist claims about the mercy, redemption, and salvation made available by Christ's universal atonement were outlined somewhat systematically, and the evangelical and evangelistic emphases characteristic of the classical Methodist movement were maintained. These hymns were followed by or interspersed with texts falling under various categories: some headings were ecclesiastical or liturgical and indicated hymns meant for Methodists as a worshiping church; other headings designated verse to be used at the "peculiar" Methodist services. Thus the pocket-sized books of hymns were intended simultaneously to stimulate growth toward personal holiness and to provide a resource for singing at the multiple settings expected for worship. The *Pocket Hymn-Book, Designed as a Constant Companion for the Pious* (1790), which carried the imprimatur of Bishops Asbury and Coke and an introductory letter requesting Methodists to purchase no hymn books without the bishops' signature, utilized a basic format that was adjusted and expanded in later editions and in other Methodist hymnals, such as the *Collection of Hymns for the Use of the Methodist Episcopal Church* (1821):

1790	1821
Awakening and Inviting	Awakening and Inviting
Penitential	Penitential
Petition	Describing Formal Religion
Rejoicing	On Backsliding
Praise	Prayer and Intercession
Trusting in Providence	Prayer and Watchfulness
Suffering	Watchnight
Funeral	Justification by Faith
Fellowship	Goodness of God in Redemption
Backsliding	The Attributes of God
Nativity	Sacramental: The Lord's Supper
New-Year	Sacramental: Baptism

Good-Friday
Praise
Morning and Evening
Sacramental
Parting
Christmas Hymn
Baptism
Class-Meeting

Rejoicing and Praise
For Full Redemption
Trusting in Grace and Providence
The Christian's Warfare
Christian Fellowship
Pastoral
On the Spread of the Gospel
Christmas
New-Year
Family Worship: Morning and Evening
Family Worship: Parents and Masters
Birthday
Resurrection
For the Sabbath
Reading the Scriptures
Prospect of Heaven
Funeral Hymns
Describing Judgment
Dismission
Additional Hymns
Doxologies

The hymns were evangelistic and addressed sinful humanity's need for saving grace, but the purpose of the hymn books was not to encourage an individual piety divorced from a corporate expression of faith. The triune God remained the subject of the hymns and the recipient of praise and thanksgiving. The condition and decision of the individual was set within a broader context, whether it be those mourning for redemption, the newly awakened, or those striving for Christian perfection. Growth in personal holiness was inextricably linked with social holiness,[4] and this fundamental Wesleyan concept permeated the hymns of Charles Wesley that, by sheer numbers, dominated each approved Methodist collection produced in the first half of the nineteenth century. To the hymns of Charles Wesley were joined those by other notable English and evangelical poets, among them the Independent (Congregationalist) Isaac Watts, whose achievements in promoting metrical scriptural paraphrases for Christian worship inspired the poetry and the praxis of the Wesleys.[5]

As a people striving toward holiness, Methodists of the late eighteenth century and the first three decades of the nineteenth generally sought to distinguish themselves from the world around them. The theological content of their hymns made this clear and their performance of sacred song was to testify further to that fact. Into the first *Discipline* (Question 57) the American Methodists inserted their adaptation of the answers to the question "How shall we guard against formality in singing?" taken from Wesley's Large Minutes (Question 39):

1. By choosing such hymns as are proper for the congregation. 2. By not singing too much at once; seldom more than five or six verses. 3. By suiting the tune to the words. 4. By often stopping short, and asking the people, 'Now! Do you know what you said

last? Did you speak no more than you felt?' 5. Do not suffer the people to sing too slow. This naturally tends to formality, and is brought in by them who have either very strong or very weak voices. 6. In every large society let them learn to sing: and let them always learn our tunes first. 7. Let the women constantly sing their parts alone. Let no man sing with them, unless he understands the notes, and sings the bass as it is pricked down [in 1788 changed to "as it is composed"] in the tune-book. 8. Introduce no new tunes till they are perfect in the old. 9. Recommend our tune-book everywhere. And if you cannot sing yourself, choose a person or two at each place to pitch the tune for you. 10. Exhort every person in the congregation to sing, not one in ten only. 11. If a preacher be present, let no singer give out the words. 12. When the singers would teach a tune to the congregation, they must sing only the tenor.

Methodist singing thus was decidedly congregational. In corporate worship, efforts were to be made to ensure the greatest possible level of participation. "Few things can be more pleasing to the Lord," commented Bishops Asbury and Coke in 1798 on this section of the *Discipline*, "than a congregation, with one heart and one voice, praising his holy name."[6] To that end, choirs, ensembles, and soloists were discouraged, though not prohibited, since skilled choristers could, ideally, bolster congregational singing; the twelfth "answer" itself suggests the presence of music specialists within a congregation, which could be, as in some British Methodist chapels, a precentor or designated song leader. Wesley had removed from the Prayer Book references to anthems and other service music sung by clerk and choir, thereby indicating his strong preference for "hearing the whole congregation . . . 'sing with the spirit and the understanding also' " rather than listening to a few who "kept [the singing] to themselves, and quite shut out the congregation."[7] Yet the American Methodists did not number among their instructions for singing an explicit restriction against the singing of anthems. Neither had they included the statement from the Large Minutes to "let no organ be placed anywhere," possibly since such a regulation was largely unnecessary in the American context.[8] Perhaps the overall orientation toward congregational singing was deemed sufficient to warrant an openness to a limited offering of other musical contributions.

By 1792 the regulations on singing attained a form, under the general heading "Of the Spirit and Truth of Singing," that would survive, with a few alterations, in the Methodist Episcopal Church until 1856 and in the African Methodist Episcopal Church until 1885.[9] Three new rules had been added to define further the acceptable content and style of Methodist song. As a means of restricting questionable texts or doggerel verse and at the same time encouraging uniformity in practice, Methodist leaders were enjoined to "sing no hymns of your own composing." This rule, which from 1784 had been under the question on "smaller advices relative to preaching" and was moved in 1787 to the section on singing, was often ignored, as evident from the number of hymn books that were privately published, such as the one produced in 1807 by Stith Mead and containing his baptismal hymn. Related to this instruction was the recommendation new in 1792 for Methodists "not to attend the singing schools which are not under our direction."[10] Music literacy was encouraged, but not under the guidance of singing masters who might overly encourage currently popular musical forms, thus prompting the third restriction: "The preachers are desired not to encourage the singing of fuge-tunes [sic] in our congregations." An additional note (which soon became a rule in its own right) explained that although the use of fugue tunes was neither sinful nor improper for private settings, such musical arrangements were not suitable for corporate worship "because public singing is a part of divine worship in which all the congregation ought to join." According to Jesse Lee, preachers especially in the northern states had been guilty of introducing or allowing fugue tunes in the congregation, wherewith the younger people who understood the musical form sang out, and the old saints fell silent.[11] Fugue tunes not only jeopardized effective congregational singing, they also obstructed the hearing of a melody wherein, many Methodists believed, was the natural power of music to move the passions.[12] With "four parts all going at one time, and each part on different words," fugal arrangements similarly impeded the clear declamation of the text, which led Ezekiel Cooper to conclude that the "new mood of singing" was "instituted more to please the ear, than anything else."[13]

The selection of appropriate tunes, therefore, was as critical for Methodist worship as was the choice of words. Books of hymn tunes were published independently from collections of hymn texts, and Methodists borrowed freely from John Wesley's published collections of tunes,[14] and from books by American or other British compilers. Tune books could use round-note or shape-note systems, typically were designed with one stanza of a hymn text underlaid, and were often produced in an oblong format with the spine on the short end ("end-openers"). The collections were usually organized by meter, with the most frequently used meters (common, long, and short) at the front of the book, and a variety of "particular" meters coming next. Some of these books contained a brief section introducing the rudiments of music theory to further the cause of music literacy. Printed materials, however, were not the sole source of music. Orally transmitted "folk" and original melodies were a significant part of a core repertoire, especially in the more remote, rural areas.

Because of the diversity of tunes, questions soon were raised by some in the Methodist leadership about tune resources to be standardized for Methodist use. From 1808 to 1820, for example, the Methodist Episcopal Church discussed whether to adopt officially a succession of tune books prepared by James Evans of New York that were aligned with the Methodist hymnals, and although never authorized, Evans's books saw wide use among the Methodists.[15] The first approved tune book for the Methodist Episcopal Church came as the result of the General Conference's action in 1820, and in 1822 *The Methodist Harmonist* was published. After several reprintings of the 1822 book, the General Conference in 1832 authorized a revised and improved version of *The Methodist Harmonist* (1833) with "a selection of anthems, pieces, and sentences," thereby attesting (at least officially) to an increasing openness toward new forms. Other tune books were then issued by the Methodist Episcopal Church's book agents, who, under a ruling of the 1820 General Conference, could bring out new materials approved by the Book Committee without the formal action of the General Conference (hence they were "official" but not "authorized"). Among them was *The Harmonist* (1837), designed, as stated in the preface, to "suit the taste of the different sections of the country." As an accommodation to persons "very partial to them," a number of fugue tunes were printed despite the restrictions against them still listed in the *Discipline*. Even though the Methodist Episcopal Church had standard and quasi-official tune books and expected its members to use them, pastors and people still felt at liberty to employ whatever best suited their musical tastes and spiritual needs. Reckoned among the ready alternatives were the large supply of camp meeting songsters and the growing number of song books for Sunday schools.

With or without tune books, the custom during this period in many Methodist congregations, large and small, was to "line" the hymns, a type of performance practice urged for the cantillation of psalms in the Presbyterian *Westminster Directory* (1644). The common method was for one or two lines of a stanza to be said or sung by the preacher, his appointee, or a song leader, and when the congregation had sung them, to read out the next one or two lines. Methodist Protestant ministers, for the second hymn of the service, were specifically advised by their *Discipline* to read out all the verses before the people sang the hymn while seated (the first hymn would have been sung while standing). Another and older practice, the so-called "old way of singing," called for a rapid, chantlike presentation of a line of the text, followed by the congregation slowly singing the text to a familiar tune with ornamentations added to the melody; there may be evidence for this style at the worship of black Methodists attending Philadelphia's "Mother Bethel" in 1811.[16] The lining out of hymns took into account the illiterate and the poor who could not afford a hymn book, but also risked unintended improvisation upon the standard tunes if the precentor was not a proficient musician. Since the method was meant to encourage melody making by all worshipers, the Ohio Annual Conference, in 1834, went so far as to approve a resolution instructing that hymns were always to be lined out in public worship.[17]

The Ohio legislation of 1834 came in response to a decline in congregational singing, a problem precipitated by the development of church choirs that emerged under the impetus of the singing schools—the schools themselves having the intended purpose of replacing singing by rote (especially lined-out hymns) with singing by note. Trained singers in quartets or choirs might offer an anthem and one or more hymns during Sunday worship; in some urban congregations during the 1830s, choirs and paid vocalists displaced congregational singing altogether. The admission of choirs to corporate worship had been and remained controversial, with congregations sometimes divided over their usefulness. The presence and placement of a choir were issues, as was the choir's membership: although persons might be good singers, they might lack the piety expected of worship leaders; in other words, they might have the form but not the power of godliness. "Unconverted singers are more like porcupines than the 'sheep of Christ's fold,' " lamented Methodist Episcopal minister George Coles after spending an evening trying to improve the singing of his congregation.[18] Responding to and also anticipating problems with singers in the Sunday choir, the African Methodist Episcopal Church by 1840 had added to its directions "Of the Spirit and Truth of Singing" the instruction that "no person or persons shall be allowed to sing in our choir, who will not be subject to our authority."[19]

The instrumental accompaniment of congregational singing and the instrumental introduction of a melody in lieu of a vocalized lining out were also controversial subjects. Although evangelical chapels in England sometimes used a bass viol (cello) to accompany voices in worship, many Methodists during this period showed a resistance to the practice, instead preferring a cappella singing. Upon learning that a Methodist Episcopal congregation near Detroit had allowed a bass viol into worship, preacher James Gilruth resolved to "break up this or break down in attempting it."[20] Conversely, as might be expected, advocates of refined or "better" music urged the use of instruments. Thus even by the first decades of the nineteenth century, Methodists were not of one mind regarding the substance and performance of song in Methodist worship.

To Remain a "Peculiar" People?

As early as 1837, a new system began to be displayed for organizing the hymnic contents of authorized hymnals. Not that the arrangement primarily according to the *via salutis* disappeared: as the churches moved toward the new method, the older format was abbreviated to comprise a section of the new design; and some churches issued supplemental hymnals that retained the familiar pattern in the overall framework. The new dogmatic scheme, which shows an organic connection to the previous forms, was, like its predecessor, judged to correspond with the progress and importance of the Christian life. But now the organization of the hymns also reveals a desire for serious theological reflection, an awareness of Protestant scholasticism and a heightened ecclesiastical self-understanding. Hymnals were to function as primers of systematic theology, not only for congregations, but also for the training of pastors.[21] Specified liturgical usages appear alongside the devotional; hymns for the Christian seasons are subsumed under their dogmatic heading. One of the most detailed configurations set forth was that by Thomas H. Stockton for the *Hymn Book of the Methodist Protestant Church* (1837), whose sophisticated theological system began with God and then developed the economy of salvation over the course of 725 hymns by a wide range of authors. This was followed by a separate section identified as "Miscellany," which included those subjects not easily ordered under the previous scheme. All together the entire book was conceived for the purposes of public, social, family, and private worship:

Existence of God
Character of God
   Unity of God
      General Attributes
      Special Attributes (Eternity, Independency, Immutability, Spirituality,
         Omnipresence, Omniscience, Omnipotence, Wisdom, Holiness, Justice, Goodness, Truth, Faithfulness, Mercy, Love)
   Trinity
Relations of God
   Maker

Preserver
Sovereign
Works of God
  Creation
  Providence
  Redemption
    Love of the Father
    Mediation of Christ (Character, Promise, Types, Birth, Life, Death, Resurrection, Ascension, Intercession, Reign, Second Coming, Offices, Titles)
    Dispensation of the Spirit (Promise, Descent, Operations, Prayer, Addresses)
    Institution of the Church (Church, Bible, Ministry, Sabbath)
    Public Worship (Assembling, Before Sermon, Praise, Prayer, After Sermon, Dismission)
    Social Worship (Prayer Meeting, Class Meeting, Love Feast)
    The Ordinances (Baptism, Lord's Supper)
    Admission to Membership (Application, Welcome)
    Houses of Worship (Foundation, Dedication)
    Times of Declension
    Times of Revival
    The Millennium
Process of Salvation
  Introductory
  Sin
    Original
    Universal
    Destructive (In Life, In Death, In the Judgment, In Hell)
  Repentance (Conviction, Contrition, Confession, Reformation)
  Faith (Nature, Prayer for Faith, Exercise of Faith)
  Justification (Sought, Found)
  Regeneration
  Adoption
  Witness of the Spirit
  Graces of the Spirit (Beatitudes, Confidence, Courage, Fear, Godliness, Gratitude, Hope, Humility, Joy, Love, Mind of Christ, Resignation, Wisdom)
  Sanctification
  Triumph in Death
  Glory in the Resurrection
  Approval in the Judgment
  Immortality in Heaven
    Miscellany
Personal and Domestic Duties
  Private Devotion (Retirement, Reading the Scriptures, Watchfulness, Prayer, Praise, Morning, Noon, Evening, Midnight)

For Parents and Masters
Family Worship (Morning, Evening, Morning or Evening)
Emblems Of Christian Life
　A Pilgrimage
　A Race
　A Warfare
Affliction
　Poverty
　Persecution
　Temptation
　Sickness
　Bereavement
The Backslider
　Penitent
　Restored
Special Occasions
　Fast-Day
　Funerals
　Watch-Night
　New-Year
　Meetings for the Poor
　Missionary Meetings
　Sabbath School Meetings
Hymns Not in the Plan
Doxologies

Ten years later, the Methodist Episcopal Church, South issued its first hymnal, *A Collection of Hymns for Public, Social, and Domestic Worship* (1847), organized under a simpler plan, but one that nevertheless demonstrated the ecclesiastical status and priorities of the new denomination, the book's expected uses, and the willingness of some Methodists to blur national and Christian identity:

Part I: Public Worship

Being and Perfections of God
Mediation of Christ
Offices of the Holy Ghost
Institutions of Christianity
　　The Church
　　The Ministry
　　Baptism
　　The Lord's Supper
　　The Sabbath
The Gospel Call
Penitential Exercises
Christian Experience
　　Justification and the New Birth

Entire Sanctification and Perfect Love
Duties and Trials
Death and the Future State
Special Occasions
Missions
Bible
Erection of Churches
Education of Youth
The Seasons
National Solemnities
On a Voyage

Part II: Social Worship

Communion of Saints
Prayer

Part III: Domestic Worship

The Family
The Closet

Benedictions and Doxologies

Other Methodist denominations during this period (and beyond) adopted methods of organization for their authorized hymnals similar to that of the 1847 book, although the configuration of the scheme could vary (especially the location of the slowly shrinking group of *via salutis* hymns), and new categories could be added. For example, the authorized *Hymns for the Use of the Methodist Episcopal Church* (1849) framed the dogmatic structure of that book's contents with hymns designated for "worship," beginning with a general heading "Introductory to Worship" and concluding with hymns specified for the "Close of Worship." Even the *Collection of Hymns for the Use of the Wesleyan Methodist Connection in America* (New Edition, 1845), organized primarily according to an expanded *via salutis* pattern by compiler Cyrus Prindle, shows influences of the new organizational methodology: the categories "Attributes of God," "Trinity," "Fall of Man," "Depravity," and "Christ, Atonement, &c" precede the older opening headings of "Awakening and Inviting" and "Penitential."[22]

During this period, Methodists continued to sing many of the British evangelical hymns of their ancestors, although the number of texts by the Wesleys, Watts, Doddridge, and others gradually declined in favor of new or newly discovered hymns by American and English poets. Selected hymns, songs with refrains, and choruses for the camp meeting, the revival, and the prayer meeting, previously published individually in separate songsters or in composite volumes, now, by popular demand and for reasons of marketing, started to come into official denominational books. Favorite Sunday school hymns likewise found a place; and in return, the Sunday school hymnals inherited many of the beloved *via salutis* hymns that were being displaced from the authorized hymnals. The general intention was to publish official books that would, in one discrete volume, represent the multiple purposes of sacred verse: doxological, evangelical, penitential, catechetical, and devotional. To meet the needs of their members and constituents who did not speak English, Methodist publishers produced translations of the authorized book or new collections that could be used for North American congregations or for mission abroad (e.g., *Deutsches Gesangbuch der Bischöflichen Methodisten-Kirche* [1865]). Methodist ministry with Native American congregations was aided through the publication by church book concerns of hymnals attentive to cultural particularities, such as *Indian Melodies* (1845) by Narragansett (Brotherton) compiler Thomas Commuck. Despite a positive reception to recommendations made in 1864 and 1868 from the North Indiana Conference that the Methodist Episcopal Church print their hymnal in braille, such a publication was not deemed financially feasible at that time.[23]

Numerous hymn and song texts introduced into the authorized hymnals were of irregular or unusual meters, which required the publication of appropriate tunes to accompany them. For this reason, and because of the diversity of Methodist musical tastes, many of the larger denominations responded with official and unofficial tune books devised to prevent their members from deferring to non-Methodist resources and to secure a greater uniformity in practice. Tune books were often cross-referenced with the authorized hymnals, but in response to demand, denominational book agents from the mid-1850s began issuing unofficial single volumes, bound on the long edge, that combined both texts and tunes.[24] Some of these books, such as *Hymns for the Use of the Methodist Episcopal Church. With Tunes for Congregational Worship* (1857), were printed so that on the left-hand page were tunes organized by meter, interlined with the first stanza of a suitable hymn text, and on the right-hand page were entire hymn texts for the representative stanzas and other hymns of like meter. Other collections placed tunes at the top of each page with texts of the same meter below (e.g., L. C. Everett, *The Wesleyan Hymn and Tune Book; Comprising the Entire Collection of Hymns in the Hymn-Book of the Methodist Episcopal Church, South, with Appropriate Music Adapted to Each Hymn* [1860]). Anthems, quartets, octets, and other set pieces could be added in a separate section.

The types of tunes used in these collections were subject to debate. Methodists sympathetic to the music reform movement spearheaded by Thomas Hastings, Lowell Mason, and others, preferred "refined" tunes based upon or inspired by European musical sources (e.g., chorales, oratorios, opera, symphonic works) to "crude" American folk melodies and ballads. But in this period, melodies originating from "secular" sources were considered by many to be of lesser value (if articles in Methodist weeklies are an accurate measure) than those simple and suitable tunes that "addressed the heart rather than the sense" and were "distinguished from the platitudes of worldly sentiment [and] identified with immortal truths."[25] Some Methodists were not satisfied with the direction of their official hymnody, text and tune, and nostalgically longed for the old hymns, especially those that bespoke an Arminian free salvation. "The songs of the day may please the ear by their new dress, but they lack that soul and depth that exists in the old ones," observed Leonard Smith of Illinois.[26]

Dissatisfaction was also voiced by those who deplored the continuing decline in congregational singing and the increasing use of musical instruments in corporate worship: "Organs, choirs, and promiscuous sittings have pretty well petrified Methodism in our cities and large towns. Oh, that Methodists were content to be a peculiar people. As we assimilate, our hold on the masses relaxes."[27] The demise of Methodist peculiarities was not the only cause of consternation. Of concern was the integrity of worship itself. Those who did not find the organ objectionable, believing it to be "appropriate to the sanctuary" and "never desecrated to profane uses," decried the inclusion of a "promiscuous mingling together of flutes, clarinets, and fiddles" that secularized the sacred event.[28] The surrender of singing to only a few compromised worship's power and purpose:

> We doubt whether it would be erroneous to say that singing is not only an important part of divine *worship*, but *the most* important part. It unites prayer and praise, and, indeed, all the affections and acts of the soul which are involved in worship, and its devotional expression is more earnest, and fervent, and sublime, than the ordinary form of prayer, or, indeed, any other devotional act. It is the *ecstasy* of devotion, rising higher, uttering itself more rapturously, or more importunately, than any other religious exercise. It has, or at least is adapted to have, more of the *communion* of religious worship, than any other devotional form. In prayer the multitudes listen to, or quietly, if not passively, follow the preacher; in singing it is designed that they should openly unite, each taking an active part, each speaking for *himself*, and for the *whole*. What other act of public worship is so exalted, and should be so grand and so rapturous?[29]

A petition from Urbana, Ohio, sent to the 1840 General Conference of the Methodist Episcopal Church requested action regarding choirs that "sit apart from the great body of the church," "wholly govern the singing," and introduce "such tunes as our members cannot sing." Denominational leaders did not enact new regulations; rather, they urged reinforcement of the already-present rules in the *Discipline* extolling the singing of all persons in the congregation.[30] The Pastoral Address delivered on the occasion of the Methodist Episcopal Church, South's 1846 General Conference advised against instrumental music in worship (as contrary to "primitive usage") and choirs supplanting the congregation's song, yet no formal action was taken then or later at the General Conference of 1874 when the topic was again broached in that year's Pastoral Address.[31] Disputes persisted at the local level, however. Congregations embroiled in controversy sometimes split over musical issues such as whether or not to install an organ—the organ, like a choir, symbolizing formality (and consequently for some, a decline in spirituality) in worship.[32] Concerns about protecting the apostolic and Wesleyan primacy of congregational singing continued to be voiced, but in the majority of Methodist denominations, the momentum toward use of choirs and instruments in corporate worship could not be disrupted.

The more conservative Holiness denominations, fearing Methodism's acculturation, made music in worship a constitutive concern, and addressed the subject through official legislation. The Wesleyan Methodists in their first *Discipline* recommended both the lining out of hymns and the elimination of instrumental music. Free Methodist D. F. Newton opined that instruments and choirs obstructed a return to primitive Christianity, for they were "clogs to the wheels of salvation and greatly retard[ed] millennial glory."[33] Acknowledging the complaints of Newton and others, the Free Methodists included specific restrictions in their *Discipline* and kept them through the first third of the twentieth century: under the heading "Of the Spirit and Truth of Singing" was entered "in no case let there be instrumental music or choir singing in our public worship."

Increasing Diversity: Methodist and Musical

The 1878 *Hymnal of the Methodist Episcopal Church*, the first authorized hymn book for that denomination that was published in two versions, one with text only and the other with texts and tunes, virtually gives an official endorsement to the disputed changes in Methodist musical praxis. Included in the "Preface to the Hymnal with Tunes" were the suggestions that "there should be a choir or a precentor, and an organ, if possible, to lead the people," and that these supports to congregational song were best situated "in front of the congregation." Four years later, Methodist Episcopal Church, South book agent and theologian Thomas O. Summers defended both organs and choirs rightfully used in worship, and even composed the hymn "Praise Him with Organs" for the inauguration of a new organ at McKendree Church in Nashville.[34] Choirs had become fixtures in numerous Methodist churches and an expected component of Sunday and certain occasional services (e.g., revivals), so new debates focused upon such matters as the vesting of choristers and female singers wearing hats for worship. Children and youth were constituted into "junior" choirs and made appearances in worship. Organs or pianos mainly accompanied singing and sounded solo works in those churches that used instruments, and by 1900 Wesleyan Methodist congregations also figured among them. Other instruments were also used in increasing variety during this period. New inventions such as the reed organ and the "vocalion" were promoted as economical substitutes for larger keyboard instruments.[35] Woodwinds and strings, formed into chamber groups or orchestras primarily associated with the Sunday school, occasionally played in corporate worship; their offerings could be selected from musical arrangements produced by Methodist publishing houses. Hesitations were at first expressed about the use of brass, however, even within congregations accepting of other instruments: in 1885, a dispute erupted in a North Carolina church about the place of a cornet in worship, which was resolved when the pastor confirmed the instrument's suitability for "enriching" worship.[36] Only the Free Methodists would maintain their musical restrictions for the majority of this period; even after choirs and instruments were permitted, their use was qualified and limited.[37]

Nevertheless, vigilance was urged lest instrumental music, choral singing, or solo monopolize worship or turn it into a concert. Enthusiastic and robust hymn singing was ever encouraged as "the people's liturgy" to be participated in fully with heart and voice,[38] and the blame for its decline was inevitably placed on the musical interlopers. "Whatever keeps the people from singing keeps them from worshipping God, and thus destroys the vital power of the church," warned African Methodist

Episcopal bishop Henry Turner.[39] The reintroduction of lining the hymns, which had fallen into disuse, was recommended—by rubric in the African Methodist Episcopal Church—as was the careful and devotional reading out of hymn texts from the pulpit prior to their cantillation by congregation or choir.[40]

Choirs and instruments were not the only culprits to be blamed for hushing congregational song. Some Methodists criticized the contents of the authorized hymnals themselves, but for various reasons. The official hymnals continued, with some adjustments, the organizational pattern of the previous period which employed a dogmatic outline and framed the hymns according to the occasions of worship. The Methodist Episcopal Church's movement toward more formal and definitive patterns for Sunday corporate worship in the late nineteenth century was expressed in its 1878 hymnal, a collection that both the Wesleyan Methodist Connection and the African Methodist Episcopal Zion Church would eventually adopt as their own. The book began with hymns under the category of "Worship" consisting of general praise hymns and hymns for "Sabbath" and "Morning and Evening"; the total number of hymns under "Worship" was 117 (out of 1,117), almost double the 63 (of the total 1,129) in the 1849 book. Efforts to incorporate service music more broadly in worship was indicated by a new category, "Occasional Pieces and Chants," added at the end of the dogmatic scheme in the version of the 1878 hymnal with tunes. This or a comparable heading would subsequently be listed in other authorized denominational hymnals published with tunes, save (at least for a while) for those of the Holiness churches. The presentation of service music was not entirely new: separate listings of doxologies had already appeared in earlier authorized books; and because of their "frequent use in our churches" (according to the publisher's notice), six psalms in the style of Anglican chant had been included in the appendix of the unofficial *New Hymn and Tune Book: An Offering of Praise for the Methodist Episcopal Church* (1867), edited by popular evangelist and song book compiler Philip Phillips. But the 1878 book marked a turning point for the contents of future authorized hymnals, and two years later another milestone was reached with the first placement of liturgical texts (an order for public worship; baptism and membership rites) into an official hymnal—*The New Hymn-Book* of the Methodist Episcopal Church, South. For some, these changes, along with the appearance of hymns representing the treasury of the ages, particularly translations of Greek, Latin, and German hymns, marked progress in Methodist spirituality and liturgical respectability. For others, they signaled a loss of the vigors of historic Methodist "experimental" religion and represented unwelcome innovations that kept persons from active vocal participation in worship.

The economic, social, theological, and spiritual diversity now characteristic of the Methodist membership was reflected in its preferences for texts and tunes. Multiple opinions were voiced in periodicals and legislative proposals about music's purposes and performance. The view that Methodist worship music should be a cultivated expression of the sacred arts was countered with the proposition that the words and music popular with the people ought to be the norm for both worship and denominational hymnals. Even so, claims were made that limits ought to be applied to the wholesale adoption into church music of "worldly" musical forms (e.g., secular patriotic songs reflecting a rampant nationalism, and jazz)[41] or those songs that, in violation of the long-standing General Rules, "did not tend to the knowledge or love of God." Concerns that hymns of doctrinal depth (e.g., the Wesley hymns) form the core repertoire, rather than popular but theologically bankrupt "ditties," were met with the argument that the salvation of souls could be accomplished only with recently composed songs of sound sentiment and fervent devotion, and for that reason denominational hymn books were rarely used at revivals. Texts deliberately written to articulate the theological emphases of liberalism and modernism contributed to the downplaying of hymns explicitly addressing sin and its penalties, and gave rise to the category of social gospel hymns. The ministries of social welfare promoted by the churches and engaged in by deaconesses, members of the Women's Christian Temperance Union, and other social reformers, also gave impetus to the inclusion of new types of hymn texts. In reaction, Methodist evangelicals lauded the gospel hymns of the urban revival that, in simple words and melodies, and with predictable harmonies, expressed the heartfelt yearning of the individual soul for God, though the gospel hymn's stress upon personal, autonomous religion and freedom of choice accentuated, perhaps unwittingly, one of the basic tenets of liberalism. Methodists actively contributed to the gospel genre,[42] with texts and tunes composed in both the "white" and "black" style: selections from the work of Fanny Crosby ("Blessed Assurance, Jesus is Mine"), Ira D. Sankey (the tunes "Tell It Out" and "Sankey"), and Charles Albert Tindley ("We'll Understand It Better By and By") made their way into the authorized hymnals and were still sung at the end of the twentieth century.

As in former days, those dissatisfied with the new authorized books turned elsewhere, sometimes to the previously authorized books already owned and kept (for both financial and emotional reasons), and often to the unofficial collections also produced by denominational presses. The *Cokesbury Hymnal*, later renamed the *Cokesbury Worship Hymnal*, was, as stated in the 1923 edition, "an attempt to bring back the old hymns and tunes that people *love* to sing" in an effort to remedy entire defection from Methodist publications. A few hymnal editorial committees for the denominationally approved books endeavored to address the pluralities of their constituency and growing ecumenical activity while maintaining the trajectory already established, that the primary (but not exclusive) use of the hymnal was for public worship. Nowhere was this better seen than in the 1935 pan-Methodist hymnal, assembled on the verge of the merger between the two largest episcopal Methodisms and the Methodist Protestant Church.[43] According to the preface, the commission charged with the book's preparation "constantly held in mind the perpetuation of the Wesley tradition, the varied desires of the Church, the different ages of Church members, the continued value of evangelism, and the emphasis upon the application of the gospel to everyday life."[44] In response to complaints about the difficulty of following text and notation when located in different places on a page, as many stanzas as possible of any given hymn were interlined between the musical staves. The texts and tunes chosen reflected diverse theological interests and musical styles, although traditional evangelical emphases such as repentance were downplayed (only four hymns so identified), and the subject of death (with only three suggested hymns) is jettisoned in favor of hymns anticipating the bliss of eternal life. The general organizational headings of the book maintained a continuity with previous dogmatic plans, and added headings expressive of the new theological and liturgical trends:

Worship
God
Jesus Christ
The Holy Spirit
The Gospel
The Christian Life
The Living Church
The Christian Home and Family
Hymns for Children
The Kingdom of God
The Eternal Life
Special Seasons and Services
Ritual Music for the Holy Communion
Ancient Hymns and Canticles
Ritual and Responsive Readings

In their 1957 hymnal, the African Methodist Episcopal Zion Church took up this same structure and added two new general categories with a few representative hymns that conveyed the church's commitments to the past ("The Wesley Graces") and the present ("Youth"). Virtually the same subheadings were adopted as in the 1935 book, but with some specialties ("Spirituals") that defined the hymnal as a worship resource for African Americans proud of their distinct musical heritage. The diversity within that denomination was likewise expressed in its hymns: selections by African-American poets and composers were interspersed with texts and tunes both ancient and modern, many of them unknown in the 1935 pan-Methodist book. The distance Methodist music and hymnals had come from 1784 is evident in a series of instructions delineated in the Address by the Zion bishops printed at the front of the hymnal; yet therein are echoes reminiscent of the historic "Of the Spirit and Truth of Singing":

2. Let all provide themselves with books. Every member should have his hymn book.
3. Let all sing.
4. The minister must take and express deep and constant interest in congregational singing. We must redeem it from the failure into which it has drifted by the choir and chorus emphasis.
5. The choristers, directors of choirs, and ministers of music, must do the same.
6. There should be a choir, or a precentor and organ if possible to lead the people. The best arrangement is to have the choir and organ in front of the congregation.

7. Frequent gatherings of the congregation in praise meetings and for instruction and practice in learning new hymns are most desirable. For the sake of variety and freshness, the pastor and chorister should make unyielding efforts to have the congregation learn new tunes.

8. This book should be the standard book of the Church School as well as of the congregation and should be constantly used in the social meetings as well.

New Songs and Sounds

Methodist music in the latter half of the twentieth century maintained a few continuities with its early roots, particularly the emphasis upon active congregational singing. Hymnal organization based primarily upon the *via salutis* disappeared, but the original Methodist pattern, identified under various names, remained in fragmentary form imbedded within a larger dogmatic structure. The dogmatic schemes for the church hymnals varied; likewise did the placement of the *via salutis* material, and the location for the increasing number of hymns specified for seasons and occasions in the Christian liturgical calendar, which were prompted, in part, from the ecumenical and liturgical movements (these latter are located under a separate general heading within the hymnals for the Methodist Church [1965] and the African Methodist Episcopal Zion Church [1996]). The *African Methodist Episcopal Church Hymnal* (1984) ordered its hymns and resources roughly according to the pattern laid out in 1935, and the joint hymnal of the Wesleyan Church[45] and the Free Methodists (*Hymns of Faith and Life* [1976]) used six general categories ("The Worship of God," "The Christian Life," "The Living Church," "The Nation," "Service Music," and "Rituals"); both books situate hymns addressing the way of salvation under the heading "The Christian Life." The *Methodist Hymnal* (1965) anticipated the location to be selected in its successor of 1989 by placing hymns on the Christian life as the final heading under the overarching category "The Gospel and Christian Experience," which also included hymns on the Persons and the Unity of the Trinity. A five-part creedal structure governed the ordering of hymns in the *United Methodist Hymnal* (1989):

General Services
Hymns, Canticles & Acts of Worship
   The Glory of the Triune God
   The Grace of Jesus Christ
   The Power of the Holy Spirit
   The Community of Faith
   A New Heaven and a New Earth
Psalter
Other General Services & Acts of Worship

Here the *via salutis* was set out under the pneumatological article ("In Praise of the Holy Spirit," "Prevenient Grace," "Justifying Grace," "Sanctifying and Perfecting Grace"), and a significant number of hymns for liturgical times and rites were lodged under ecclesiology. Thus at the end of the twentieth century, a new governing framework based upon a liturgical structure had emerged. While it still incorporated the older devotional scheme, no longer did it do so under categories descriptive of the "experience of real Christians," but rather using headings believed to encapsulate the essentials of Wesley's (and Wesleyan) soteriology.

The diversity characteristic of hymnals produced in the first half of the twentieth century continued in the second half, with the Methodist and later the United Methodist Church the most deliberate about introducing texts concerning the contemporary ecumenical issues of social justice, environmental stewardship, the discipleship and witness of women, and Christian unity. Recognizing its multicultural constituency, the United Methodist Church oversaw the production of separate hymnals for racial and ethnic groups (e.g., African American, Native American, Korean, Hispanic), many of whom expressed distinct linguistic and musical preferences; representative hymns and songs from these groups appeared in the 1989 book. Tunes in compositional styles familiar to nineteenth- and early twentieth-century Methodists still predominated during this period for all the Methodist denominations, since such musical harmonies were construed by many as definitive of proper church music. Musical settings heretofore unfamiliar were also introduced, based upon the assumption that spreading the gospel in a modern age required the singing of new types of songs. Arrangements of blues, pop-gospel, 1960s folk, Taizé worship music, and even plainchant could be found in some Methodist hymnals. Thus, a Charles Wesley text might be located adjacent to a contemporary gospel song, and a Lutheran chorale placed near a text by United Methodist Jane Marshall. Patriotic texts coexisted in the same book with new Christian songs written by Methodist poets and composers from outside the bounds of North America, and who resided in regions once served by missionaries from the United States.

The technology that allowed quick access to new songs from around the world caused Methodists at the end of the twentieth century to revisit a problem of former days: how to establish a definitive corpus of Methodist music. When a congregation opted to use texts for songs and choruses splashed upon a wall by an overhead projector, there were no limits (after securing proper copyright permission) to what they might sing. Denominational theological distinctions evident through hymnody—especially as conveyed by the organizational arrangements of an authorized hymnal—thus were no longer possible as books were laid aside. Another problem once again was what constituted proper congregational song and the appropriate musical accompaniment to that song. The search for texts strong in theological substance while personally engaging became particularly relevant given the easy access to new music that had stood neither the test of time nor the rigors of an editorial committee. Determination of appropriate instruments was left to local congregations, who could choose anything from alto saxophone to zither. Technology also brought the possibility of prerecorded music. With all these innumerable options for multiple forms of media, some Methodists nevertheless elected to reclaim part of their simple past by restoring the role of the song leader.

Tendencies and Trends

As attested in the evolving methods for the organization of hymnals in all the Methodist denominations, the tendency has been for Methodists to move from a structure reproducing the individual and corporate way of salvation, to a dogmatic pattern, and then (for United Methodists) to a liturgical framework. Such a process is not unique to the Methodist family: in general, newly formed churches tend to organize their hymnals either alphabetically by first line or by following a scheme stressing a particular piety and devotion; churches then move to a dogmatic system following either the sequence of biblical revelation or a theological understanding of God, church, and world; and finally employ a liturgical pattern designed according to the liturgical calendar or the shape of the liturgy itself. But Methodists have not abandoned the oldest pattern, the devotional system, as they moved on to other structures. The *via salutis* remained for Methodists an accurate description of the Christian life, as well as a connection with their theological and hymnological roots. To a certain degree, retention of the *via salutis* has allowed Methodists to preserve something of their original identity as an *ecclesiola in ecclesia*—a religious society within the greater church—as they became institutionalized and bureaucratized as denominations.

As hymnal organization was transformed from a devotional to a dogmatic format, and as worship for the larger Methodist bodies became more formal and elaborate, another shift occurred, particularly at the end of the nineteenth century: evangelical hymn texts that interwove individual and corporate piety were supplanted by a new type of "gospel" text that dwelt upon the personal religious faith of the autonomous individual. Precisely at a time when many of the churches were striving to invite denominational unity through the placement of orders of worship into the hymnals, there occurred a decline in hymns (among them the Wesley hymns) articulating the church as the body of Christ, and worship as the praise of the entire company of believers. The American emphasis upon the rights and dignity of the individual was being played out in Methodist hymnody as elsewhere in Methodist theology and practice. Then, with the rise of the American social conscience in the twentieth century, and the liturgical movement's accent upon *leitourgia* as the worship and work of all the faithful, hymns bespeaking the community's *diakonia* and doxology began to be added alongside the old gospel favorites. Thus twentieth-century hymnals such as the United Methodist 1989 book may address the diverse preferences of its users through different types of hymns, but also juxtapose contradictory theologies about the relationship between the individual and the church.

Hymnals and music practice also show the tendency, seen elsewhere, of Methodists over time to accommodate to the broader culture. Methodists have done so at different rates, with some embracing acculturation as a positive method for ensuring relevance and meeting current needs, and others reluctantly conceding the adoption of popular styles and modes. The Methodist Episcopal Church has been the most ready to assimilate cultural forms; the Free Methodists, as might be expected, have been more resistant. Even before the Free Methodists had permitted the use of choirs and instruments in their worship, the successor of the Methodist

Episcopal Church, the Methodist Church, had provided in its *Book of Worship* (1945) orders for the "Recognition of Choristers" and the "Dedication of an Organ." What new songs Methodist denominations sing and how they render praise and prayer are thus inextricably linked to their theological self-understanding, and especially their perception of the relationship between persons of faith and the world that God sent his Son to save.

7

The Solemnization of Christian Marriage

T HE FOREGOING ACCOUNTS of Sunday worship, the peculiar services, the sac- raments, and music have reinforced the initial proposition that changes in the shape and content of Methodist worship reveal a process of "Americanization," in other words, a tendency gradually to abandon countercultural distinctions and accommodate certain views and practices of the larger American society. The trend already evident in Methodist music and within the "ecclesiastical" rites, those distinctively Christian celebrations that essentially define the nature of the church, is even more apparent in the Methodist public rituals for life-cycle events. Because marriage and, similarly, burial are not unique to the church and are indeed com- mon to every society and culture, they to a greater extent blend features from the general culture with the specifically liturgical. No liturgy in fact is void of local cultural color; and the localization of a church's liturgy may testify to the incar- national nature of Christian worship. These "occasional" rites tend to be more open to the vox populi than others, and textual modifications are often the result of changes in or influences from the practice of the wider society. Yet at the same time, participants in these rites often show the inclination to adhere to the "tra- dition," whether it be expressed by words, actions, or gestures.

The marriage rites and the accompanying official legislation related to marriage purported to define for Methodists the nature and purpose of a Christian marriage. Amendments to older forms and policies were brought on by theological shifts, themselves influenced, at least in part, by changes in the society at large regarding the status of women, the meaning and function of marriage and family, and the customs and ceremonies considered "essential" for a wedding. Because Methodist ministers were called upon, as sometimes the only legally authorized officiants available, to preside at the nuptials of persons unfamiliar to them or to the church, the specific language of the Christian marriage rite soon became connected with the general marital vocabulary of the supposedly Christian nation, contributing further to the blurring between the churchly and the civil.

Wesley's Marriage Restrictions and Rite, and Their Reception

John Wesley's first publication on the subject of marriage was *Thoughts on Marriage and a Single Life* (1743), wherein he asserted that although marriage should not be despised, for it was ordained by God, continence, or the celibate state, was preferable for believers since it was God's special gift for the redeemed.[1] Wesley recognized the virtue of Christian companionship and he himself blessed marital unions, but throughout his life he advocated the superiority of the single life for Christians, mostly from the fear that some would substitute preoccupation with a spouse for attention to godly living.[2] As a means of protecting Christian discipline for those who chose to marry, Wesley urged the avoidance of marriage with unbelievers and the acquisition of parental consent to the marriage. That some American Methodists took Wesley's instruction to heart is evident from a homemade notebook fashioned by Elizabeth Smith and given to preacher Philip Gatch before their marriage in 1778; the first entry reads, "Believers to Marry with Unbelievers is not Lawful," followed by citations from Genesis 6:1–2, Deuteronomy 7:3, and 2 Corinthians 6:14.[3]

Concern that such advice was frequently overlooked on both sides of the Atlantic prompted the Methodists to enact relevant legislation in the Large Minutes, which the Americans subsequently integrated almost verbatim into their first *Discipline*:

> Q. 20 Do we observe any Evil which has lately prevailed among our Societies?
>
> A. Many of our Members have married with unawakened Persons. This has had fatal Effects. They had either a Cross for Life, or turned back to Perdition.
>
> Q. 21 What can be done to put a Stop to this?
>
> A. 1. Let every Preacher publickly inforce the Apostle's Caution, *Be not unequally yoked with Unbelievers.* 2. Let him openly declare, whoever does this will be expelled the Society. 3. When any such is expelled, let a suitable Exhortation be subjoined. And 4. Let all be exhorted to take no Step in so weighty a Matter without advising with the most serious of their Brethren.
>
> Q. 22 Ought any Woman to marry without the Consent of her Parents?
>
> A. In general, she ought not. Yet there may be an Exception. For if, 1. A Woman be under a necessity of marrying: If, 2. Her Parents absolutely refuse to let her marry any Christian: then she may, nay, ought to, marry without their Consent. Yet even then a Methodist-Preacher ought not to marry her.

During the period 1784 to 1788, the preachers meeting in conference mollified the language regarding the consequences of marriage with an unawakened individual. Whereas in 1784 marriage with such a person had "fatal effects" and resulted in a "cross for life," by 1788 these marriages had "bad effects" whereby the believer was "hindered for life." The 1792 *Discipline* retained the phraseology of the 1788 *Discipline* and added a note defining what was meant by the "unawak-

ened": "one whom we could not in conscience admit into society." Members like
"Sister S. B.," who opted to marry the unawakened, received the promised pun-
ishment of expulsion. "It went right hard with some of her friends," confided
Ezekiel Cooper to his journal, "but I must enforce the rules."[4]

The regulation relating to parental consent received minor editorial changes
between 1784 and 1792, though no addition was made specifying the age below
which consent was required, perhaps because Methodists preferred consent in all
cases and, besides, the legal age varied by state.[5] One editorial change in 1788
cleared up the ambiguous last sentence of the rule, which stated that "a Methodist-
Preacher ought not to marry her [a woman not receiving consent]." Certainly,
before the Christmas Conference of 1784, the understanding of the rule in the
Large Minutes was that a Methodist preacher should not himself marry a woman
without parental consent. That such was the case is revealed in a letter of May
18, 1784, from Irishman Robert Lindsay addressed to his former countryman and
fellow Methodist preacher Edward Dromgoole, who at that time was serving in
Virginia:

> Well, I have at last taken courage, and on the 6th inst. [of this month] ventured into
> the holy state of matrimony! . . . But—O pity me! In securing the possession of my
> dear companion, I have step'd aside from the Minutes of Conference which forbids a
> Methodist preacher to marry a woman without the consent of her parents. Here I stand
> exposed to any penalty my Brethren shall think fit to inflict upon me. But, I hope for
> a favourable issue. We dearly loved each other, and were determin'd to sink or swim
> together. Each of us ventured much, but I hope to find more lenity from my Brethren
> than She is ever likely to find from her friends.[6]

But after 1784 some uncertainty seems to have arisen whether the rule meant
rather that an ordained Methodist preacher could not officiate at the wedding of
a woman who had not received parental consent. By the alteration of the text to
read, "yet even then a Methodist-Preacher ought not to be married to her," the
intent was clarified.[7]

Other proscriptions related to marriage came via Wesley to the American Methodists, but these were received through the rubrics and ritual text of "The Form
of Solemnization of Matrimony," revised from the marriage liturgy of the 1662
Prayer Book and incorporated in the 1784 *Sunday Service*. Wesley retained the
opening rubric of the Prayer Book rite requiring the publication of banns, by which
impediments to marriage such as consanguinity and legal betrothal to another
could be revealed and investigated. Banns were to be read "in the congregation"
over a period of three Sundays at an unspecified point "in the time of divine
service," thereby satisfying the legal prerequisite for appropriate public notification,
and also discouraging clandestine, hasty, or by Methodist standards, inappropriate,
marriages. Surprisingly, Wesley did not recognize by rubric the use of marriage
licenses obtained from the civil magistrate that were becoming more popular than
the public reading of the banns. The matter was redressed in the 1786 and subsequent editions of the *Sunday Service* by the provision that banns could be omitted
if "a license be procured from the proper authority." Further flexibility was granted
in the 1792 revision through the allowance that banns need not be read if the

couple were "otherwise qualified according to law." Even if a license had been sought, the fourth public reading of the banns was preserved in the marriage rite, directed first to those gathered ("if any can show any just cause. . . ."), and then to the couple:

> I Require and charge you both (as you will answer at the dreadful day of judgment, when the secrets of all hearts shall be disclosed) that if either of you know any impediment why you may not be lawfully joined together in Matrimony, you do now confess it. For be ye well assured, that so many as are coupled together otherwise than God's Word doth allow, are not joined together by God, neither is their Matrimony lawful.

After the final reading of the banns, the requisite verbal consent of the couple before witnesses was to be rendered. Inquiry was made whether each partner gave uncoerced, free, and mutual consent—what had long been recognized as constituting the legal essence of marriage. Wesley preserved the Prayer Book's interrogative ("Wilt thou have") in which the questions for the bride and groom were parallel except for the additional pledge by the former to obedience and service ("Wilt thou obey him, serve him, love, honour, and keep him, in sickness and in health"); the simple response remained in each case "I will." But Wesley omitted a second form of consent that followed the couple's action, that by the woman's father or his representative. Perhaps Wesley found it unnecessary ritually to solicit parental consent ("Who giveth this Woman to be married to this Man?"), since presumably Methodists were already obligated to obtain such permission. But other factors may have motivated him as well: the absence of fathers at weddings; the superfluity of the custom; his view of women as spiritual equals to men; and his disdain for the practice of exchanging human beings as property.[8] Thus, in Wesley's (and the 1792) rite, the respective interrogatives ("Wilt thou have") were immediately succeeded by an active form of consent with each word spoken aloud by the couple, in which the woman, as in the previous question, vows also obedience to her husband: "to have and to hold, from this day forward, for better for worse, for richer for poorer, in sickness and in health, to love, cherish, and to obey, till death us do part."

The purposes and results of marriage had been expressed in the opening exhortation (which repeated the Prayer Book text in its entirety), and they would be implied in the prayers following the active consent by the couple. Wesley could easily concur with the interpretation in the exhortation that marriage was "an honourable estate, instituted of God," since he believed that "Christ does not take away human Society, but sanctif[ies] it."[9] He retained the classical western ordering for the reasons of marriage, which defined marriage first as a medium for the production of children and their nurture in the love and fear of God. The other causes construed marriage as a remedy against sins such as lust and fornication, and as a means of providing mutual comfort and help. In spite of the placement of procreation as the primary purpose of marriage in the opening exhortation within the Methodist rite, Wesley's writings on marriage tended to focus on mutuality and the covenantal aspects of marriage (both strong Puritan themes), especially the respective duties of the partners; the omission from Wesley's revision of the final statement on marital duties that had concluded the 1662 rite was probably for the sake of brevity. Husbands and wives were regarded by Wesley as the "nearest relations" who had been joined by God in an unbreakable bond of mutual faith in which they were to love each other for better or worse.[10] Prayers were offered in the rite that the couple might, as did Isaac and Rebecca, "surely perform and keep the vow and covenant betwixt them made," and the knitting together of a man and woman, in its purest form, was a sign of "the mystical union that is betwixt Christ and his Church." God's blessing was invoked that the newly married might, as Christians, "obey thy will," "be in safety under thy protection," and "abide in thy love unto their lives' end."

Wesley's emphasis upon companionship, as well as late eighteenth-century squeamishness about indelicate discussions of sexuality, may have prompted the leaders of the Methodist Episcopal Church to subject the rite to surgery by an editor's pen in 1792. Gone is the warning in the opening exhortation against entering marriage "lightly, or wantonly, to satisfy men's carnal lusts and appetites, like brute beasts that have no understanding," as well as the reference to the three causes for which matrimony was ordained. The Methodist Episcopal revision of the exhortation was similar to the one made in the marriage rite of the Protestant Episcopal Prayer Book of 1789, particularly in the omission of the causes for marriage, although the Methodist emendation retained the christological references that were struck from the Prayer Book. Again like the Episcopalian change, the 1792 revision also deleted the prayer for childbearing ("O Merciful Lord and heavenly Father, by whose gracious gift mankind is increased").[11] Some editorial adjustments were made within retained texts, for example, the replacement of references to the couple as God's "servants" with the phrase, "this man and this woman." Such a change suggests that lack of specificity regarding the theological convictions of the couple was necessary given the fact that itinerating Methodist ministers might not, in a short period of time, be able to ascertain the couple's beliefs. Thus the 1792 rite assumed a structure similar to but abbreviated from the 1784 service:

Instructions about public notification prior to marriage
Banns formulary
Rubric about the day and time of marriage, position of couple [man on the right hand, woman on the left]
Introduction and exhortation ["Dearly beloved, we are gathered together here. . . ."]
Final publication of the banns
Declaration of intention and consent
Marriage vow
Prayer ["O Eternal God, Creator and Preserver. . . ."]
"Those whom God hath joined together. . . ."
Pronouncement of marriage ["Forasmuch as M. and N. . . ."]
Blessing ["God the Father, God the Son. . . ."]
The Lord's Prayer
Prayer ["O God of Abraham, God of Isaac. . . ."]

Prayer ["O God, who by thy mighty power hast made. . . ."]
Blessing ["Almighty God, who at the beginning. . . ."]

Notably absent from this order, and from Wesley's *Urtext* as well, is any mention of the wedding ring. By deleting explicit reference to the ring, though without prohibiting its use, Wesley may have been expressing sensitivity to historic and contemporary objections made by Puritans and Presbyterians who questioned the ring's identification as a sacramental sign, its lack of scriptural warrant, and its association with idolatry and superstition. Elimination of the ring also removed a long-standing symbol of bride purchase, and it conformed to Methodist regulations, stated in the 1744 "Directions Given to the Band Societies" and in the General Rules, that "needless ornaments" and "gold and costly apparel" should not be worn. The wearing of fancy dress, it was believed, engendered pride, vanity, anger, and lust, and marred the inward ornamentation through which God was glorified by a meek and quiet spirit. Needless ornaments defrauded God, who had entrusted "worldly goods" to faithful stewardship, especially service of the poor.[12] Nowhere did Wesley specifically mention wedding rings under the categories of rings or gold, but as most of his advice was directed toward women's apparel, it is possible to assume that wedding rings were included in the rules for the Methodist Societies—restrictions that the Americans added to the first edition of their *Discipline* (1784, Question 18, A.4): "Give no Ticket to any that wear High-Heads, enormous Bonnets, Ruffles or Rings."

Although the 1784 marriage rite did not specify the officiant of the marriage service beyond the term "minister," the *Discipline* (1784) explained that both elders and deacons were empowered to solemnize matrimony. Unordained preachers were not allowed such privileges, a factor important for both ecclesiastical and civil interpretations of the legality of marriage. A slight but significant variation, that the deacon should "perform the office of Matrimony in the Absence of the Elder," was printed in the 1787 *Discipline* (and remained as the Methodist Episcopal Church's polity until 1860 when unrestricted authority for solemnization was returned to the deacon). Yet at a time when the solemnization of matrimony was thus becoming tied primarily to the "sacramental" office of the elder, curiously the marriage rite was being further purged of references to the ecclesial setting of the rite: in 1792, the phrase within the opening exhortation "in the face of this congregation" was replaced by "in the presence of these witnesses." Nevertheless, accounts in personal diaries and journals suggest that many weddings still were conducted in a congregational context, before or after a scheduled occasion for corporate worship, and particularly at the time of the quarterly meeting when an elder was guaranteed to be present.

Wesley had excised the rubric delineating the "accustomed duty" due to the priest and clerk for their presence at the marriage rite, yet the American Methodists were compelled to legislate (1784 *Discipline*, Question 48) against the solicitation or reception of marriage fees. It became clear that additional, more precise, provisions were needed on the matter of receiving marriage fees (it was still not permissible to make a charge), and in 1792 regulations were established to avoid financially related jealousies and to maintain equitable remuneration among the ministers and preachers, particularly those within the same circuit.[13] By 1804, ministers were permitted to accept—and keep for themselves without making report—fees that they were offered, and they eagerly anticipated the money and goods from friends and strangers that would supplement their meager income.

Changing Perceptions of Marriage

The changes in agricultural and industrial technologies, economic patterns and systems, demographics, and social structures that had an impact on North American society were felt with varying intensities at different times in different regions. The South, for example, generally addressed the issues stemming from urbanization and industrialization at a much later time than did the North. One consequence of these shifts, again with regional and temporal variations, was trends leading toward the reformulation of gender roles, definitions and responsibilities, and the alteration of family structures and values. Two quite different views of women and their relationship to society resulted; editorials and articles in Methodist periodical literature bear witness that national discussions outside of the Methodist family were taking place inside as well. In the first line of thinking, women came to be more strongly connected with sex-specific virtues such as altruism, self-sacrifice, and humility, associations encouraged particularly but not exclusively by evangelicals in the South. Women's roles as mother, religious nurturer, moral exemplar (spiritually "superior" to her husband), and the enabler of family religion were exalted; the ideology of domesticity formed the foundation for a definition of womanhood. These attributions may have been intended to enforce perceived biblical precedents for gender roles and preserve patriarchal control and authority; they provided a means for maintaining stability and the social order as developments in industry and agriculture removed men from the domestic sphere. Nevertheless, the stress on domesticity also had the practical result of providing more power for women within the contexts of the household and of the marriage itself. The second approach, also with temporal and regional variations, took the form of a reaction to the rigid delineation of specific gender roles and ideologies. This response sought, instead, to check or abolish sex-specific limitations. As women gradually shifted from producers to consumers, they found purpose and meaning (and for some, religious expression) outside the home: the moral exemplars of the home became the moral exemplars of the nation. Involvement in religious revival (such as Finneyite revivalism and the Holiness movement in which women played prominent roles), social reform (particularly the movements for temperance, abolition, education, suffrage, and women's rights), and creative endeavors (e.g., literature focused primarily upon a female readership) issued forth from the desire of women to better themselves as well as society.

Changing views toward women and their roles during the 1800s had an impact upon Methodist marriages, and upon the approaches taken toward marriage advice printed in denominational publications.[14] Yet the basic theology of marriage—as a holy covenant instituted and blessed of God, and characterized by mutual love and care—remained relatively stable. Marriage ideally ministered both to God and to the pair: "May the God of heaven bless and sanctify our union for the promotion of his glory and our spiritual and eternal good" was the prayer of preacher Thomas Morrell on his wedding day in 1802.[15] Couples were to take seriously the wedding service and the lifelong commitment before God that it inaugurated, for "next to personal piety," no other action was "more important or imperative."[16] Thus wrote Robert Taylor in his diary for 1879:

> This has been a memorable day in my history—I was united in holy wedlock to Cousin Emma Taylor by the Rev. John Williams about 9 P.M. at Cousin Martha's residence, some twenty-five friends and relatives present to witness the ceremony. I feel that I have indeed taken an important and responsible step. My prayer is that heaven may assist me that I may be able to honor the relation which I now occupy as husband and that I may prove indeed a blessing and a suitable companion to her to whom I have linked my destiny for life.[17]

The expectations of marriage, utilizing imagery within the marriage rite itself, were detailed in a wedding hymn by evangelical Anglican and (Calvinistic) Methodist sympathizer John Berridge, whose text, from 1802, was published in various Methodist hymnals throughout the century and was included in the 1905 joint hymnal between the Methodist Episcopal Church and the Methodist Episcopal Church, South:

> Since Jesus freely did appear
> To grace a marriage-feast;
> O Lord, we ask thy presence here,
> To make a wedding guest.
>
> Upon the bridal pair look down,
> Who now have plighted hands;
> Their union with thy favor crown,
> And bless the nuptial bands.
>
> With gifts of grace their hearts endow,
> Of all rich dowries best!
> Their substance bless, and peace bestow,
> To sweeten all the rest.
>
> In purest love their souls unite,
> That they with Christian care,
> May make their domestic burdens light,
> By taking each their share.
>
> True helpers may they prove indeed,
> In pray'r, and faith, and hope;
> And see, with joy, a godly seed,
> To build their household up:
>
> As Isaac and Rebecca, give
> A pattern chaste and kind;

So may this marry'd couple live,
And die in friendship join'd.

On ev'ry soul assembled here,
O make thy face to shine,
Thy goodness more our hearts can cheer
Than richest food or wine.[18]

Yet despite such pervasive talk of mutuality and equality, gender distinctions, culturally and theologically driven, persisted within Methodist marriages.

Because the opening exhortation of the rite provided concisely the scriptural warrant for God's and the church's association with marriage (Genesis 2:20–25; John 2:1–11; Ephesians 5:22–25; Hebrews 13:4), all the episcopal Methodist denominations and the Free Methodists kept it throughout the nineteenth century and did not tamper with it except for a few minor editorial emendations (e.g., replacement of the archaic "betwixt"). In the Wesleyan Methodist marriage rite of 1892, the exhortation was greatly abbreviated, but it continued to stress that marriage was "an honorable estate, instituted of God in the time of man's innocency, and should not be entered upon unadvisedly or lightly." The Methodist Protestants, however, from 1830 to 1870, substituted an alternative to the older formulary in the form of an address that delineated at length the shared interests and responsibilities of the couple, perhaps in accordance with the new denomination's emphasis upon mutual rights in church governance. The sole mention of marriage as part of the divine economy for humanity was an oblique reference to the "principles and rules of conduct" furnished by the "word of God." But marriage was not to be regarded as just a human institution: the couple was advised to "constantly seek the protection and assisting grace of God, to enable them faithfully and mutually to discharge the numerous and important duties required"; and the only prayer in the rite, given before the pronouncement of marriage, asked God to bless, guide, and protect the couple.

There were limits to the Methodist Protestant definition of mutual rights. True, the opening statement appeared to assume a relative equality within the marriage, and the only "vow" in the rite, the interrogative of consent that required the brief reply "I will," had removed the stipulation that the woman was to serve her husband; nevertheless, she still promised to obey him.[19] The Methodist Episcopal Church in 1864 was the first to excise completely both references to obedience and service, undoubtedly in response to evolving perceptions about women in church and society, but also perhaps because of the spiritual constraints that might be imposed upon a wife whose husband was at odds with the mission and ministry of the church. Given how families were sometimes divided over the issue of slavery, and how women were often active in the abolition campaign, it is possible that the denomination, attentive to these concerns during the war years, chose to delete language that could possibly bind a woman to act in ways that were incompatible with her own political and moral beliefs. Although the proposed order sent to delegates in advance of the 1864 General Conference deleted only "serve" and not "obey," the rite presented at the time of the Conference, and recorded in the

Journal, omitted both terms. A related alteration, also granting conceptual and textual symmetry, was made in the pronouncement of marriage of *husband* (not "man") and wife.[20] No official explanations were given. As an anonymous reviewer of the 1864 Ritual noted, "the promise to obey on the part of the bride is quietly omitted." The same reviewer then pleaded that the marriage rite, as emended, be used uniformly and intelligently:

> And now that we have this suitable form, let it be always used, and always in the Church. Our ministry have, we fear, sadly concurred to demoralize the public mind by not discountenancing slight, thoughtless, and too little solemn performance of this rite, tending to reduce it to a mere civil contract which an alderman can mediate with a few trifling words. We fear that our people have too slight a conscience, because our ministry have thought too little deeply on the subject. We hope this ancient and yet renovated form will be ever used with an earnest view to an impressive effect.[21]

Not surprisingly, the deletion did not meet with unanimous approval, for the authority and instruction of Scripture appeared to be undermined:

> By all means let there be harmony between the mandates of the great Legislator, God, and the requirements of his Church. Therefore, let one of two things be done: let the word "obey" still find a place in the marriage ceremony, it cannot be out of place there if it be in place in the sacred record; or let God's word, which enjoins the duty, be so modified that the objectionable word may no longer be found there to be a source of annoyance to any. In a word, let the whims and fancies of men and women henceforth constitute their law, and let the Church inform them that the Bible is a dead-letter, and the necessity of all appeal to it no longer required.[22]

A resolution submitted to the 1868 General Conference requested "the restoration of certain words to the Marriage Ritual";[23] however, no words were reintroduced.

The absence of the obedience language in the Methodist Episcopal rite appears to have encouraged other Methodists to make similar, at first unauthorized, emendations in performance. Evidently because of such practice among ministers of the Methodist Episcopal Church, South, Thomas O. Summers stressed that "ministers who are so foolish as to omit the words 'obey him and serve him,' at the request of a weak woman, deserve severe censure."[24] Only in 1930 did the Methodist Episcopal Church, South delete the two words entirely from the rite.[25] The African Methodist Episcopal Church, the last to remove the language, kept both expectations in its rite until 1960, thereafter dropping "obey" from the normative rite, and both terms from an "optional" text (based upon the Methodist Church's 1945 service). In the normative rite published in the African Methodist Episcopal *Discipline* through 1996, the woman continued her promise to serve, although couples were offered one optional text without the term, and another option in that church's 1984 *Book of Worship* where both individuals vowed service to the other. The Wesleyan Methodists, who apparently never required obedience or service by their authorized text, resolved the matter of gender parity by the asking of single question addressed to both persons.

At the end of the nineteenth century, it was the introductory statement to the rite that bore the primary burden of articulating liturgically Methodist views of the purpose of marriage. For the sake of expediency and simplicity, the concluding prayers of the 1792 service had been dropped officially or unofficially from many of the formal texts, with Methodist presiders taking the liberty of substituting extemporary prayer. The Methodist Episcopal Church, South (in 1854) and, hence, the Colored (Christian) Methodist Episcopal Church (their text being derived from the South rite) were the only episcopal Methodist bodies to have omitted all the texts following the first benediction ("God the Father, God the Son"), except for the Lord's Prayer, which was repositioned before the prayer "O eternal God." The Methodist Episcopal Church, in 1864, removed from the concluding prayers the historic nuptial blessing, "O God, who by thy mighty power," probably on account of its restrictive definition of marriage duties (including obedience) for the wife and its virtual restatement of the opening exhortation, but possibly because the language therein implied a sacramental view of marriage. In that same revision, the Lord's Prayer was relocated to end the service,[26] and a rubric was added prior to the Our Father formalizing the use of extemporary prayer. The benediction "Almighty God, who at the beginning," which had been slightly modified in 1864, and another prayer for blessing upon the couple, "O God of Abraham," were eventually removed from the Methodist Episcopal rite in 1916. With the striking out of these texts, and the deletion of the reference to the marriage of Isaac and Rebecca from the prayer "O eternal God" (apparently because some believed that the marriage of the biblical pair was not characterized by true faithfulness),[27] most of the Old Testament references to marriage were lost from the rite.[28] Only within the African Methodist Episcopal Church would these prayers be kept inviolate into the second half of the twentieth century.

By the early twentieth century, many women had rejected the limitations of the "prescribed" gender role and sought employment outside the home, completed a college education, or pursued a professional career. Some women elected to delay marriage until later in life, while others, no longer concurring with the assumptions of male superiority and female submission in marriage, abstained entirely from marriage. The redefining of women's roles created a crisis in terms of ecclesiology (e.g., the membership and voting rights of women in the church, the licensing of women to preach, and the ordination of women) and sociology (the demise of the traditional understanding of the family). Civil divorce legislation within the individual states, which began to proliferate in the late nineteenth century, was met with accusations of "individualism" and "socialism," reactions comparable to those voiced regarding women's increasing opportunities and independence.[29] For the Methodists, rising rates of divorce resulted in efforts to establish, internally, official statements and policies on divorce and, externally, resolutions to promote uniform national marriage and divorce laws. Even the practices of polygamy in Mormon Utah and in the overseas mission field were topics for discussion. Concerns were expressed to preserve the human, "divine," civil, and "religious" institution of marriage, since also at stake was the family, the "foundation" of church and state.[30]

The Methodist Episcopal Church was the only Methodist denomination in the early twentieth century to alter significantly its marriage rite. In 1916, and again in 1932, the denomination dropped Scripture references from the historic text, thereby risking that the church's theology of marriage as expressed in the rite be seen as abandoning scriptural norms. At the same time, the former emphasis upon the godly covenant and companionship of the couple assumed a secondary place to a new accent upon the preservation and perpetuation of the family. The reference to Hebrews 13:4 in the opening exhortation that stated marriage is "commended of St. Paul to be honorable among all men" was omitted in 1916 because, conforming to the principles of biblical criticism, the revising commission felt compelled to use the version or translation that, in their judgment, "most truly represented the Scriptures in the original." As commission member and Methodist Episcopal theologian Harris Franklin Rall, professor at Garrett Biblical Institute, explained:

> In our marriage service there is a statement which says that St. Paul commends marriage to be honorable among all men. Any scholar will tell you that that is a palpable mistranslation which does violence to the Word of God. That word does not say that marriage is honorable. It is in the form, not of a declaration, but of an injunction, which, properly translated, is: "Let marriage be had in honor among all, and let the bed be undefiled." We cannot, therefore, in justice to our loyalty to the Word of God, make any other recommendation.[31]

The opening exhortation was again altered in 1932 by removal of allusions to the first marriage in Eden and the "mystical union" of Ephesians 5 (the latter was restored in the Methodist Church's rites of 1939 and 1945). Support for the waning institution of the family was intended by the addition of "the family is the foundation of human fellowship" following the Cana reference (the insertion survived only seven years), and the introduction of a new sociotheological statement as the charge to the couple:

> I charge you both, as you stand in the presence of God, to remember that love and loyalty alone will avail as the foundation of a happy and enduring home. If the solemn vows which you are about to make be kept inviolate, and if steadfastly you seek to do the will of your Heavenly Father, your life will be full of peace and joy, and the home which you are establishing will abide through every vicissitude.

Even though at the time of merger in 1939 both the Methodist Protestant Church and the Methodist Episcopal Church, South retained the greater part of the older form for the charge to the couple, modified versions of the 1932 Methodist Episcopal statement persisted in the rites produced for the Methodist Church in 1939 and 1945, and were coupled with the phrase, "no other human ties are more tender, no other vows more sacred than those you now assume."[32] The human and familial aspects of marriage were also expressed in a new concluding sentence added in 1939 to the historic "O eternal God" prayer, which asked God to "look graciously upon them, that they may love, honor, and cherish each other, and so live together in faithfulness and patience, and wisdom and true godliness, that their home may be a haven of blessing and a place of peace."[33]

While the extension to the prayer "O eternal God" remained in the Methodist Church's 1965 *Book of Worship*, the revised charge to the couple did not and was abandoned in favor of a charge that conflated the historic and contemporary versions. Marriage was again explicitly defined early in the ritual text as a "holy covenant" testified to by the "pledge of faith." If the vows were "kept inviolate, as God's Word demands" and the couple "steadfastly endeavored" to do God's will, God would "bless the marriage, grant fulfillment in it, and establish the home in peace." References to the covenantal aspects of marriage, as well as the familial, were entered into the Free Methodist Church's revision of the marriage rite in 1955, which, in part, found its inspiration from the Methodist Church's 1945 text. At the Free Methodist service, the couple was reminded that the marriage covenant was "more than a legal contract, being a bond of union made in heaven, into which you enter discreetly and reverently."

Methodist marriage rites at the end of the twentieth century kept or restored the scriptural warrants for Christian marriage, and spoke strongly of marriage as God's gift and a covenant intended to imitate God's covenant with humankind; the domestic references were largely incidental. The introductory statement in the Free Methodist rite supplied from 1969 identified marriage as God's creation "for the blessing [later, "well-being"] of mankind," which was "protected [later, "safeguarded"] by the laws of Moses, affirmed by the words of the prophets, and hallowed by the teachings of our Lord Jesus Christ." The revised United Methodist rite (1992) claimed "the covenant of marriage was established by God, who created us male and female for each other," and located the marriage covenant within the context of the baptismal covenant and its demands of Christian discipleship. The concept of covenant was integral for the series of United Methodist services of "Christian" marriage: within the "Service for the Recognition or the Blessing of a Civil Marriage," a text new to Methodists, an overt distinction was made between the "solemn contract" made by those "married by the law of the state," and the marriage covenant declared "before the witness of the Church."

Qualifications for Marriage

The rubric mandating the reading of the banns (unless legal conditions had been met otherwise) and the formulation for proclaiming the banns gradually fell out of most of the Methodist marriage texts. The Methodist Protestants and the Wesleyans never included them. The Methodist Episcopal Church, South eliminated them in 1854, and the Methodist Episcopal Church followed suit ten years later. The African Methodist Episcopal Church continuously preserved both rubric and formulary in their normative marriage text through to the 1996 Discipline, and the Free Methodists (of North America), who originally made no mention of them, introduced them in 1979, apparently out of respect for the legal requirements of some Canadian members. When banns-related material was removed, several of the denominations substituted a statement regarding the legal prerequisites for marriage ("having been qualified according to law"), thereby confirming that the regulation of marriage was the prerogative of the state, largely through the issuance of a license. Yet Methodists throughout maintained their own criteria that determined whether or not one of their ministers could properly solemnize matrimony. Some ministers overlooked or dismissed ecclesiastical restrictions, prompting the comment in a widely read book on the ministerial office published in 1923 that "he is no true minister of Jesus Christ who performs the marriage ceremony 'for anyone who can secure a license.' "[34] Possibly as a reaction against such laxity, the opening rubric within the 1939 marriage rite of the Methodist Church was formulated to state explicitly that the church had its own preconditions beyond civil regulations: persons to be married were to be qualified "according to the law of the state and the standards of the Church."[35] The Methodists' ongoing interest in "appropriate" marriages reflected a desire to maintain and reinforce moral, ecclesiastical, and biblical standards in a rapidly changing world.

Regulations Regarding Marriage with the "Unawakened"

Marriage with unbelievers continued to be discussed at General Conference meetings after 1792, and in particular the prescribed consequence for such marriages, namely, expulsion. At the request of the membership, a more thorough explication was approved at the 1796 General Conference of the Methodist Episcopal Church to accompany the previous legislation:

> We do not prohibit our people from marrying persons who are not of our society, provided such persons have the form, and are seeking the power of godliness; but if they marry persons who do not come up to this description, we shall be obliged to purge our society of them. And even in a doubtful case, the member of our society shall be put back upon trial.
>
> N.B. We are well assured, that few things have been more pernicious to the work of God than the marriage of the children of God with the children of this world. We therefore think ourselves obliged to bear our testimony, both in doctrine and discipline, against so great an evil. But as our former minute on this subject was not clear, we have added this explication, hoping that thereby the preachers who have the oversight of circuits will be easily enabled to determine on every point which may come before them, to the satisfaction of the truly pious, and to the prevention of a practice so exceedingly injurious to vital religion.[36]

Attempts to lessen the severity of the punishment proved unsuccessful at the 1800 General Conference, but prevailed four years later when the requirement of expulsion was replaced with the provision to put individuals "back on trial for six months" accompanied with a "suitable exhortation." Evidently some ministers feared that expulsion (especially when the non-Methodist partner was of "excellent moral conduct") drove offended families away from the church; a "merciful and conciliatory reproof" instead was deemed sufficient.[37] Other alterations in 1804 contributed to an overall effect of softening the restriction: the title of the disciplinary section was switched from "On Unlawful Marriages" to "Of Marriage" (a title that was retained in the Methodist Episcopal Church until 1864 when it became "Rules Relating to Marriage"); and the *prohibition* of marriage with unbelievers was tempered to a *discouragement*. The General Conference in 1808 rejected an amendment proposed by Jesse Lee to deny reception of the Lord's Supper and participation in the love feast to those on trial for unlawful marriages.[38]

The rule that Methodists who married unbelievers would be placed on trial was omitted in 1836 from the Methodist Episcopal Church's section of the *Discipline* on marriage. As a result, the regulation against marriage with the unawakened became nothing stronger than a statement discouraging such unions, although the church member was still reminded that such marriages produced "bad effects" and were contrary to St. Paul's advice in 2 Corinthians 6:14. These guidelines, consisting of the material adopted in 1784 and the addition of 1796 without references to expulsion and placement on trial, survived, with minor alterations, until that Church's *Discipline* of 1928. Then it assumed an entirely new form—a series of recommendations, including a provision for premarital education and counseling—that lasted until 1939. Even though the marriage restrictions had gradually been moderated, they remained important enough for the life of the church that they were mentioned in popular literature and in booklets used for the preparation of persons for church membership.[39] Bishop Thomas Morris was compelled to remark on them in his *Miscellany*, wherein he deplored the marriage between a "practical Christian" and an unawakened sinner as "inconsistent," "inconvenient," "unfavorable to happiness," and "dangerous."[40] The same point was made by the story of Louisa:

> When she was about eighteen years of age, she became the object of particular attention on the part of a young man, who had recently set up in business in the place as a merchant. He was a young man of fine personal appearance, and of prepossessing manners, but he had not the fear of God before his eyes. He heeded not the Sabbath-day, and he dealt out the liquid poison that carried desolation and woe to many families in the community. It was with deep regret that some of the friends of Irvin saw his marked attention to Louisa. They feared that she might form a connection that would be fatal to her Christian character. But they knew not the strength of her Christian principles. She was not one of those that "help the ungodly, and love them that hate the Lord." 2 Chron. xix, 2. She declined an alliance with him, notwithstanding the temporal advantages held out by the proposed connection. This was an occasion of surprise to many, and of joy to the faithful few.[41]

Although the Methodist Protestants never adopted the marriage instructions, and the Methodist Episcopal Church, South discontinued them in 1866 with their first *Discipline* produced after the disruption of the Civil War, the Methodist Episcopal Church was not alone in its retention of the regulations. When finally the Methodist Episcopal Church abandoned them in 1939 (not to be introduced into either the Methodist or United Methodist denominations), they endured in various configurations within the Holiness and African-American denominations, save for the Colored (Christian) Methodist Episcopal Church, which had not inherited them. The last decade of the twentieth century still saw the rules printed in more than one *Discipline* of the Methodist family, and in terms directly tied to the instruction contained in the first *Discipline* published in 1785.

The Requirement of Parental Consent

Even though women had assumed a predominant role in choosing a partner, the expectation that a Methodist woman should receive parental consent prior to marriage was retained throughout the nineteenth century in the respective *Discipline* of the Methodist Episcopal Church, the African Methodist Episcopal Church, and the Free Methodist Church.[42] Parental control in spouse selection generally took the form of a veto, and parents who objected to a daughter's choice typically resorted to relocating their entire family or to sending the daughter away from home.[43] For those churches that kept it, the requirement seems to have been taken seriously by some ministers, if the recollections made in 1875 by a "regular contributor" to one Methodist periodical be accurate:

> "We sent for you to marry us," said the lady, decisively. The book was opened and the words read: "Dearly Beloved—We are assembled here in the presence of" when there was a sudden and furious ringing of the door-bell. Then it was opened and some one tried the door of the parlor, which, to my surprise, had been locked.
>
> "If any minister is marrying a couple in this room," screamed a voice from without, "I forbid the ceremony." There was an awkward pause.
>
> "Go on," said the lady, in a commanding tone; "we are of age—pronounce us man and wife."
>
> I refused until I could find out what the objection was; the woman entreated, her lady friend grew white with fear; the noise outside kept waning, and the expectant groom was motionless and indifferent.
>
> "It is only the father," said the lady, "and he says the young man is weak minded, because—because—he wants to marry me. He has persecuted the young man terribly, but he shall do so no longer, for the young man is of age, and we shall yet get married, and I shall protect him."
>
> Sure enough they were afterwards married, but not by Yours, truly.[44]

The most serious of the Methodist denominations in enforcing the rule were the Free Methodists, who added a stricter stipulation to their *Discipline* soon after their founding, which prohibited their ministers from officiating at the marriage of any person under eighteen unless the parents or guardians were present or had given written consent; two witnesses who knew the "contracting parties" also needed to attend. At the end of the twentieth century, the same regulation instructed Free Methodist pastors. The African Methodist Episcopal Church was the only other denomination to persist in recording the consent advice (the Methodist Episcopal Church removing theirs in 1928), but they had altered it so that women *and men* generally were to receive approval before the minister could appropriately preside.

Even when parental sanction did not appear as a requirement in the *Discipline*, "formal" consent was obtained by the social convention of the man asking the woman's father for permission. A ritualized form of consent—the giving away of the bride—appeared in some Methodist weddings long before the question and answer with accompanying action was officially inserted into some of the authorized marriage texts in the twentieth century. Although it was 1916 before the giving of the bride was printed in the Methodist Episcopal Church's Ritual, and 1924 when the Methodist Protestants did the same, handwritten entries in personally owned books disclose that the practice certainly preceded codification in the liturgical text, even as early as the mid-1800s.[45] Comments by T. O. Summers in 1873 reveal that although the Methodist Episcopal Church, South had not officially placed the giving of the woman within the official text of the marriage rite, its use was implied, "but not formally prescribed, because it was considered complex and unnecessary."[46] Despite ecclesiastical sensitivities to gender equality, brides were given by their fathers at Methodist weddings in the 1990s, more from social custom than any real understanding of the original intention of the ritual act. As an option, some couples had both sets of parents "give them away" or, according to the approved United Methodist rite (in a subtle act of consent), offer their blessing upon the creation of the new family.

Divorce Regulations

Methodists in general tended to believe that the escalating rate of divorce throughout the 1800s was provoked by growing female independence, male employment away from the home, and worldly distractions that usurped the primacy of the family. All of the Methodist denominations responded to the seriousness of the problem by addressing the subject in popular prose and in legislation. The bishops of the Methodist Episcopal Church, South called upon that body to recognize the threat to marriage and the family:

> We have lived to see the divinely ordered *Institution of Marriage* seriously endangered by the readiness with which divorces are granted by many of the State legislatures and courts, so that a very large per cent of marriages are being annulled annually. The true marriage relation strengthens the State and the Church. . . . All should be done that can be to sustain the primal institution of God and to avert the low estimate of it now taking possession of the public mind. Action is advisable looking in the direction already taken by some of the Churches—the forbidding the celebration of the rites of matrimony by their ministers between parties where either has been previously divorced, excepting for the one scriptural cause, as in Matt. v. 32 and xix.[47]

By the late nineteenth century, each Methodist body defined its position on divorce through legislation, and sometimes with rubrics preceding the marriage rite. Methodists uniformly disapproved of divorce, but made allowance for the "one scriptural cause"—adultery. Within some of the denominations, persons divorced on other than "scriptural" grounds could be placed on church trial or expelled, and those previously divorced were restricted from membership. The African Methodist Episcopal Zion Church recognized in its polity the inhumane circumstances sometimes imposed by the institution of slavery by allowing an individual with two or more living spouses to be admitted into church membership as long as there was "not the least prospect of being together again in this life." Scriptural precepts also governed remarriage. Pastors were usually permitted to officiate at the remarriage of the party innocent of marital infidelity, or of divorced parties seeking reunion, but themselves risked trial on charges of immorality or, at the extreme, defrocking if they joined in marriage one who had not been "scripturally" divorced.

These policies were continued by all the churches into the first half of the twentieth century. Even the usually liberal Methodist Episcopal Church perpetuated its previous stance and elaborated upon it: the Church's 1928 statement coupled with cases of adultery the provision for the "full moral equivalent" of adultery, which, in the 1932 *Discipline*, was interpreted as "other vicious conditions which through mental or physical cruelty or physical peril invalidated the marriage vow." Yet a possible relaxation of standards was hinted at in 1932 by that church's dropping of the phrase from the charge to the couple declaring the marriage un-lawful if the couple was united "otherwise than God's Word doth allow." The statement on marriage of divorced persons established in 1932 was retained by the Methodist Church in 1939 along with the provision for charges of maladministra-tion when the church's standards were violated.

The second half of the twentieth century saw a variety of Methodist responses to divorce. The African-American Methodists generally kept intact their legisla-tion of earlier generations, including the expulsion from membership of divorced members who remarried and the charges against the minister for officiating, though in practice the rules were often ignored. The spirit of the previous law was retained by the Free Methodists in their approved statement of 1985, but the church's efforts to promote penitence, redemption, and wholeness were also now men-tioned. The United Methodist Church invited controversy by the publication in 1976 of "Rituals with the Divorced" as a component of the larger work *Ritual in a New Day* published as an unofficial resource by the denomination's Section on Worship. A greater tolerance toward divorce and remarriage had been expressed in the 1976 *Discipline* (¶71C, "where the partners are, even after thoughtful con-sideration and counsel, estranged beyond reconciliation, we recognize divorce and the right of divorced persons to remarry"), and church leaders were offered the new resource to aid individuals and congregations in coming to terms with and providing a Christian response to societal reality. But United Methodists were not unanimous about the change in stance on the subject, and the four brief rituals for use with the divorced, one of which accentuated the new freedom of the couple rather than the need for repentance or healing, were as salt in a wound. With debate fired by the secular press, volume editor H. Grady Hardin and the United Methodist weeklies received numerous letters of complaint. The rituals died a quiet death; the United Methodist *Book of Worship* (1992) contained no "divorce ritual," but only a prayer and suggested Scripture readings for "ministry with persons going through divorce" in the section on Healing Services and Prayer.

The Wedding Celebration

Until roughly the middle of the nineteenth century, Methodist weddings were generally characterized by simplicity, austerity, and an attention to Christian ex-pression. Methodist preachers of this period railed against many popular social wedding practices as being contrary to Christian values. Drinking and dancing, both of which were disapproved of in the General Rules, especially drew the ire of the preachers.[48] Overindulgence in the wedding festivities—which could last late into the evening—was rebuked, especially if it interfered with attendance at worship, prayer, or the meeting of the class.[49] Some Methodist ministers were exceedingly scrupulous lest they conform to worldly conceits:

> Tusd eveing I joined in matrimony Rev Henry Colclazer & sister Aseneth True. Their Deportment on the occasion was calm & dignified—After the ceremony was over a supper in hand was served round—A certain Mrs—Requested me to be seated by the

bride To which I pled an excuse—That I wished not to conform to vain ceremonies of this world.[50]

In contrast with weddings that engaged the prevailing social customs, Methodist weddings of the especially devout might incorporate the singing of hymns, lengthy extemporary prayer, exhortations or testimonies, and even the observance of the Lord's Supper. Catherine Livingston, married to Freeborn Garrettson at Rhinebeck, New York, in 1793, recorded in her diary that they partook of Holy Communion after the wedding ceremony and then sang the "Covenant Hymn."[51] Because weddings were often performed in conjunction with other religious meetings and services of worship, conversions could sometimes occur during the nuptials, as happened at the marriage of John B. Matthias to Sarah Jarvis when two people were "awakened,"[52] or could arise immediately afterward. E. F. Newell recalled the spiritual intensity that surrounded his wedding in 1810:

Having been appointed to travel on Norridgewock circuit, Me., on my way to my appointment I called at Sidney, at which time we were published. I was then absent on my circuit near 4 months ere I returned. Then I visited Sidney on a Quarterly meeting occasion and we were married in the following manner, or style:—At the close of the afternoon sermon I rose and informed the people of our intention and gave some reasons for our wishing to be married in public. I then kneeled and prayed, and while praying a broken hearted sinner cried aloud for mercy. When I rose I went and took Fanny Butterfield by the hand—we stepped forward, and our beloved Bro. Gideon Wells, Esq., in a most solemn and impressive manner, performed the ceremony, and proclaimed us lawfully married husband and wife, agreeable to the laws of the State and the written Word of God. He then gave us good advice and Elder O. Beal followed with a most appropriate and affecting prayer.

The loud sighings for mercy continued through the ceremony; but this did not disturb us in the least, for we had been fasting and praying, (although unknown to each other,) that our God, in whom we trusted, would give us, on the occasion, some public token of his favor,—or if displeased with the step, rather let us die in the presence of the congregation than sin against his holy will! To us, this was a token of favor—an answer to our prayers. After the ceremony I went and assisted in spreading the sacramental board on the green in the door yard, (for the meeting was held in a private house,) leaving Fanny in the midst of her young female friends and acquaintances, who were pleasantly congratulating her on having changed her name; she replied, truly, I have a new name, but it is only for a season; but if you will comply with the conditions of salvation you may each and all of you have a new name, a name glorious and enduring, even the new name of Jesus! Many wept while she exhorted. We then renewed our covenant with God at the Sacramental board, and the gentle dews of heaven watered our hearts while we bowed prostrate before our blessed and adorable Redeemer. Thus we were married with as little ceremony as possible, according to our desire.[53]

In another instance, a man converted at a Methodist preaching service who was thereafter determined to live a new life professed that he had never legally married the mother of his children. Immediately he and his common-law wife were married in the assembly, and that being done, the entire family was baptized.[54]

Many of the Methodist bodies approved legislation that required officiants to solemnize matrimony according to the approved ritual text—for both civil and ecclesiastical reasons. Formal enforcement of the rite only fueled the controversies with some opponents of Methodism, who accused the Methodists of capitulating to popery, given the fact that the episcopal Methodist marriage services shared structural and linguistic similarities with the liturgy of the "Romish Church."[55] Yet the repetition of statements in church law and elsewhere that ministers should perform the authorized marriage service provides further evidence for what is also borne out in the few narrative descriptions of Methodist weddings available: Methodists did not always do it "by the book." In actual practice, rubrics did not limit what Methodist weddings could include. For example, women married according to the Methodist rites sometimes conformed to social custom and not rubrical direction by receiving wedding rings, since the rites themselves did not direct such until the action and accompanying pledge were introduced as an optional component, first in the Methodist Episcopal Church's service of 1864, and two years later in the Methodist Episcopal Church, South. Following social convention, a single ring was given; only from the 1930s onward did the texts begin to allow for a double-ring ceremony.

Although usage of a wedding ring was provided for in the liturgical text produced in 1864, the Methodist Episcopal Church's *Discipline* had not been purged of its regulations regarding dress. While penalties for indiscretion in apparel had been eliminated in 1856, a charge was instituted to discourage "superfluity in dress" and to exhort the people to observe the precepts outlined in 1 Timothy 2:9 (in which gold is explicitly discountenanced). Yet as members of the Methodist Episcopal Church (as well as other Methodist denominations) became more concerned with respectability, more affluent and individualistic, and more accepting of their cultural milieu in the latter part of the nineteenth century, the desire to conform to what had come to be regarded as antiquarian regulations lessened, and the questionable legislation was modified and eventually removed.[56] Nevertheless, a mostly ignored vestige of the concern for attire remained with all the Methodist denominations into the late twentieth century through the continuous reprinting in the *Discipline* of the General Rules, a part of which advised persons to refrain from "the putting on of gold and costly apparel" as "evidence of their desire of salvation." The Holiness denominations persevered in their restrictions about dress in obedience to the General Rules, though some of their members, along with other Methodists, apparently used wedding rings and special clothing for the nuptial celebration. The Free Methodist Church in 1874 approved a resolution declaring that the rule against gold referred to gold wedding rings; in 1939 and again in 1943 the rule was interpreted more broadly to apply to any finger ring. These explanations of the General Rule were deleted in 1951.

By the late nineteenth and early twentieth centuries, Methodist weddings and related festivities were no longer simple affairs, and they had embraced many of the "vain ceremonies" that earlier Methodists had shunned. Yet some distinctions from the practices of the wider society were still present, as drinking and dancing still garnered disapproval, and wedding homilies might be preached and Christian counsel given (though not specified by rubric):

Today I solemnized the marriage of Adam Beck and Clara Peterman. The ceremony was nice and pleasing to all, text Ruth 4:13. The crowd was a mixture of Christians and non-Christians.

The brother of the bride insisted to dance and said he would leave if they would not dance. He is the only relative she has (they being orphans). So she had to allow it. Neither bride and groom nor any of my people danced. We enjoyed ourselves in another room. The others did not dance much. The good spirit was prevailing. I received $5.—from the groom—There were only 3 or 4 reckless boys there, but were hardly noticed by the large crowd.[57]

Weddings could take place in several locations: at the parsonage, the bride's home, the home of the bride's parents, and, less often, at the church. With the decline of the quarterly meeting and the camp meeting, those occasions only infrequently served as matrimonial venues. Weddings in this period were private affairs, more so than those of the earlier years when the infrequent appearance of the qualified minister often thrust the wedding into the public and congregational arena. Marriage ceremonies, as formerly, could be held at any time of day, any day of the week, though questions were raised in the 1870s about the legality of Sunday weddings, since contracts drawn on the Sabbath were considered illegal.[58]

The blurring of the civil and the sacred continued in the second half of the twentieth century, as the "church wedding" became socially desirable for the exchanging of vows. Books and essays detailing the "formal" wedding with its proper protocols and choreography (often requiring a wedding director or master of ceremonies) appeared as denominational publications. Just as some Methodists were open to the "enrichment" of worship on Sunday morning, so too were they willing to embellish the wedding service, although the actual structure and content of several printed denominational ritual texts varied very little. Music was intentionally integrated into the service in the form of preludes and postludes, processionals and recessionals, solos and anthems, and hymns. Candle-lighting ceremonies—and, thanks to the enterprising floral industry, the use of the wedding candle—became popular accoutrements. Pastors might be compelled to offer a wedding address, and upon request could serve the Lord's Supper, sometimes to the couple alone. On the matter of Communion, a companion volume to the 1965 *Book of Worship* of the Methodist Church instructed that it should not be celebrated at the wedding service, lest it be exploited for sentimental or aesthetic reasons.[59]

At least from the 1950s, some Methodist pastors had begun to reconceive the wedding as a service of worship, and structured the event in imitation of Sunday morning. In 1955, J. Bernard Dryfield laid out his design for weddings incorporating worship elements familiar to members of the Methodist Church in Philippi, West Virginia, where he served:

Prelude
Invocation (response if choir is used)
Hymn
The Responsive Reading
The Gloria Patri
Hymn

The Sermon
Solo
The Marriage Ceremony
Hymn
Benediction
Recessional[60]

A little over thirty years later, the United Methodist Church authorized a ritual text for marriage designed to follow the structure of the basic pattern of worship approved for that denomination. The opening exhortation and the declaration of intention by the couple preceded the reading of Scripture, the sermon, and the intercessory prayer; the marriage vow, the blessing and exchange of rings, the declaration of marriage, and the nuptial blessing came as a response to the word. Optional Communion could be celebrated with a specially composed nuptial "Great Thanksgiving." This marriage service showed a deliberate attempt to counteract cultural concessions previously made, and again define "Christian marriage"—the very title of the service—distinctly and uniquely.

The "Order for the Reaffirmation of the Marriage Covenant" and the "Marriage Anniversary Prayers" provided in the 1992 *Book of Worship* of the United Methodist Church were not the first attempt by Methodists to give liturgical expression to such matters, though they were the first formally approved ritual texts to do so. Reminders of the important day in the life of the couple were observed at least by the mid-1800s in the form of golden wedding anniversary celebrations, and these were often recapitulated in announcements or notices made in Methodist newspapers. Prayers by area clergy, hymns, the renewal of wedding vows, and a benediction could be used to mark a marital union sustained for half a century. At the festivities honoring James and Elizabeth Pyle Atwood of Pennsylvania in 1862, a short address was given, "reciting a few facts of their former history, their piety, and persevering honest industry, which had been crowned with such abundant success, showing the contrast between the good and the careless or vicious in the evening of life."[61] An account from 1906 described the anniversary of Daniel and Elizabeth Helms of Indiana:

> After the dinner all gathered to listen to the wedding ceremony, in which the vows of a half-century ago were reaffirmed. Gifts of gold, as a reminder of the day, were presented. Letters of congratulation from different States were read. At night the general public came, bringing tokens of love and esteem. Before their departure "Nearer, my God, to Thee," was sung, earnest prayer was offered, and with "Praise God, from whom all blessings flow," the day closed.[62]

Through these informal rituals, the centrality of marriage for family life was proclaimed, and the sacrality of the marriage covenant was affirmed.

The Rite of the People and the Church

While the marriage rites produced after 1792 are characterized by a reduction in the liturgical materials that had been inherited from Wesley's *Sunday Service*, they are also marked by the inclusion of new formulations, the reinstatement of liturgical components that had originally been purged by Wesley from the 1662 rite, and, in some revisions, the optional usage of some traditional portions of the rite (e.g., the charge to the couple and the marriage vow). In general, the number of prayers or statements was not increased. Rather, material that elaborated upon the nature of Christian marriage was substantially reduced overall from the amount initially included in the Wesley *Urtext*, and what was retained was often modified; an exception to this reduction might be the United Methodist rite, which defined marriage primarily through a series of prayers rather than with a lengthy declarative statement. Alterations or additions in individual ritual texts were sometimes clearly borrowed, and the most frequent sources were the liturgy of the Protestant Episcopal Church and the rites of different members of the Methodist family, but typically the Methodist Episcopal and, later, the Methodist Church. Other materials, and the entirety of the earliest Methodist Protestant rite, were apparently generated from within the committee responsible for revision. Many of the insertions addressed the milieu in which Methodism found itself, either as an affirmation of changes in theological and cultural perceptions or in reaction against them. Movements toward the social and political rights of women may have encouraged the expression of the equality of husband and wife within the marriage rite by the deletion of the language of obedience and service, and eventually by the provision for the giving of two wedding rings, thereby obscuring the old association of the ring with bride purchase. The giving of the bride, which contradicted a positive view of the equality of the woman, came into the rite not because of a growing conservatism toward the inclusion of older ritual practices per se, but more likely because of popular praxis and the increasing desire of Methodists to be socially and ritually respectable. Liberalizing movements in society at large also provoked a concern on the part of the churches for the survival of the institution of the family and traditional family structures, and those concerns came to be voiced in many of the rites. Yet at the same time, the polity of many of the Methodist denominations had itself become liberalized as evidenced by the discarding of former marriage restrictions and an increasing openness toward the remarriage of divorced individuals.

Even though many of the new additions to the rite were related to specific actions by the couple, the clericalization of the marriage rite that began with Wesley's revision continued in subsequent American Methodist versions of the rite or its substitutes. Only the Lord's Prayer was occasionally recited by the gathered community in the course of the liturgy, though hymns (not specified by rubric) may have been sung. Yet, in many respects, the marriage rite had become the rite of the people: Wesley's rite, from which many popular practices had been deleted, had been transformed into one that permitted—and even welcomed—associated cultural customs. In the second half of the twentieth century, with a renewed sense among many Methodists of the service of Christian marriage as an act of worship, the blessing of the covenant of marriage became not only the rite of the people replete with their cultural expressions but also (as the earliest Methodists knew) the people's "work" before God as well.

8

Methodist Funerals

COMPARED TO METHODIST MARRIAGE services, American Methodist funerals overall tended to be slower to exhibit change in text and general performance, undoubtedly reflecting the human need for stability and familiarity at the time of death. Yet such textual conservatism masks the significant adjustments made to popular Methodist (and more broadly Christian) understandings of death, resurrection, and eschatology. Therefore, because funerals—like weddings—intertwine ecclesiastical and social aspects, examination of them requires attention to the circumstances in which rite and practice develop. The issues in the wider society that sparked conflict or required accommodation, the theological and conceptual shifts that occurred inside and outside the church, and the regional and local customs brought by the people to the Methodist gatherings—all these must be considered. Many of the same factors that precipitated modifications in the perceptions about women and their roles during the nineteenth and twentieth centuries—industrialization, urbanization, increased mobility of populations, and transitions in family patterns and structures—were also operative in transforming views of dying and death. Additional elements were also influential, among them advancements in science and medicine (resulting in a gradual rise in life expectancy and a decline in infant mortality), technological progress (particularly in transportation and communication), the increasing secularization of American society, and what may be identified as the construction of new cosmological systems (e.g., scientific naturalism and religious liberalism).[1]

The emphasis upon individualism and rationalism that defined much of western thought in the eighteenth century contributed to the reconceptualization of the pre-Reformation understanding that a continuum existed between the living and the dead, a communion that had been manifested liturgically by masses, offices, and prayers for the dead (encouraged by the doctrine of purgatory), and by the invocation of the saints. The belief that earthly life served solely as a prelude for death and eternal life was slowly being eroded by an attachment to the material world, and with it an uncertainty about what, if anything, came after death. Anxiety about the nature of death created a discomfort toward bodily decomposition and contact with the deceased, leading to the increased use of coffins, the establishment of professional morticians, and the commercialization of funerals. In America as in England, the preaching of funeral sermons, which typically included a eulogy, became more prevalent in response to the stress upon the individuality of the deceased and the importance of the immediate family. The family, or the executor of the will, increasingly took over from the individual at his or her impending death the responsibilities for funeral arrangements, thereby replacing a focus upon one's own death with attention to the death of another.[2] Mourning was dramatized by the use of distinctive apparel and appurtenances: among these figured funereal decorations hung on the deceased's home; horses, coaches, and mourners swathed in black; and rings, scarves, and gloves given by family members as mementos of the dead.

Questions regarding the nature of death, the dead, and the hereafter continued to be raised in the antebellum period, and the ways in which these queries were answered contributed to the growing expectation that death should be tamed or beautified. As before, energies were still to be concentrated upon maintaining connections with the deceased, thereby reducing the social distance between the living and the dead, but now in a context that tried to deny the harsher realities of death.[3] This redefined contact between survivors and the departed generally was mediated through the investment of personal attention and financial resources.

During the last half of the nineteenth century and into the twentieth century, commitment to the care of the dead was accomplished in a variety of ways, with the preservation and the display of the body after death becoming special interests. Coffins—containers characterized by a tapering from the shoulder area— were superseded by rectangular, decorated, and aesthetically pleasing caskets capable of providing "protection" for the precious occupant. Embalming had been utilized during the Civil War as a practical method for preserving soldiers' bodies for distant burial and became popularized by the slain President Lincoln's funeral cortège, which traveled to various sites across the nation prior to the burial: it now came to be seen as a means by which the dead could be honored, and it allowed for the deceased to be gazed upon for an extended period after death, since physical appearance could be improved by advances in restorative techniques. Viewing of the remains became an important component of the social rituals associated with death, although the practice was frequently objected to on psychological and theological grounds. Because cremation compromised the popular desire to maintain physical contact with the deceased, it was not widely selected as a means of disposal in this period; however, by the end of the twentieth century, cremation was regarded as both economically and ecologically advantageous.

Although in rural areas the extended family took primary responsibility for the washing and dressing of the body, urban citizens often turned to funeral professionals for assistance, given that their families were frequently removed by distance. Domestic dwellings continued, as in former days, to constitute the primary setting for funerals in both rural and urban areas. However, small, one-family dwellings in cities often could not contain the equipment for embalming, the casket, or the funeral, and so the funeral home more often became the locus for events surrounding the last rites.[4] Mourning practices also became more stylized and elaborate, with variations according to geographic area and social class: guidelines were provided for mourning garb, the period of mourning, and types of accoutrements to be used.[5] The landscaped "rural cemetery," available to the general public, provided a personalized, beautiful, and consoling meeting place for the living and the dead. Literary works of the second half of the nineteenth century addressed the linkage between the living and the dead, stressing that the bereaved would be reunited with their loved ones either before or after their own deaths. Graphic details of the afterlife painted in popular consolation literature (often authored by women and clergy) produced a picture of the habitation of the dead not unlike the world of the living. The assurances of popular literature and the movement promoting scientific naturalism assisted in their respective and opposite ways the general notion that death was no longer to be feared: for scientific naturalism death was merely a "natural event," while according to popular literature it was also a time for blissful sleep or the entry upon a familiar afterlife.

By the second half of the twentieth century, death was taboo, and a reality to be avoided psychologically and physically; this interpretation had become possible in part through the advances of medicine that removed death from the home to the hospital and located it largely in one segment of the population: the elderly. Undertakers, who represented a specialized profession and made available a specialized facility, the funeral home, became the "ministers of death," locating death conveniently in a restricted, specialized sphere. Another manifestation of the disassociation from death was the development of the so-called Memorial Park, begun in the 1920s: ground-level plaques (rather than headstones, for ease in keeping the parklike grounds), statuary, and the option for "perpetual care" defined the new strategy. Death had become unnamable, and the care of the dead was often left in the hands of strangers. In reaction, hospice and thanatological programs arose with the explicit purpose of humanizing the process of dying, and reclaiming death as a part of life.

From the eighteenth century onward, Methodist responses to the changing views of dying and death wrought by social and cultural forces demonstrate once again what has already been documented elsewhere, namely, a gradual transition from a countercultural stance to one more willing to accommodate popular secular assumptions. The earliest approach, which never in fact entirely disappeared, was to regard the events surrounding death primarily as occasions to stress religious conversion, thereby perpetuating the older position that defined the purpose of life as preparation for death. Around the last quarter of the nineteenth century, however, consolation of the bereaved became the primary duty expected of clergy, family, and friends when confronted by death. By the end of the twentieth century, the largest Methodist denomination had moved to redefine the funeral by placing Christian death back within the entirety of the saving work of Christ summarized in the paschal mystery of his death and resurrection. Conversion, consolation, and conformity to Christ: these are the principal conceptual approaches to rituals surrounding death taken up by Methodists in the course of over two hundred years of ministry.

Conversion

At the 1784 Christmas Conference, members of the newly formed Methodist Episcopal Church showed themselves to be Wesley's "Sons in the Gospel" by accepting
from their "venerable Father" a liturgy, disciplinary rules derived from the Large
Minutes, and the doctrinal standards contained in his sermons and New Testament
notes. In the *Sunday Service* they received a revised and abbreviated version of the
Prayer Book's "Order for the Burial of the Dead" that provided an alternative to
the two forms for burial already practiced by the unordained preachers: either an
exhortation and a concluding prayer as Wesley had advised in 1755,[6] or Scripture
readings and prayers taken from the Prayer Book rite that might be added to an
exhortation or stand separately.[7] Whatever the form, hymn singing normally accompanied Methodist funerals. Lay preachers in America had always been expected to deliver funeral sermons, but their enthusiasm for doing so was qualified
in 1777 by an American-generated proscription restricting sermons to the case of
"those who we have reason to think died in the fear and favour of God."[8] The
only other regulation related to funerals was imposed in 1784, and again this did
not come from Wesley or the Large Minutes. As also with baptism and marriage,
fees were not to be charged or received for burial since the aim was to "save souls
and not to enrich ourselves."[9] Thus by 1784, the American Methodists had developed their own funeral praxis somewhat independent of their English kin. Their
indebtedness to Wesley, therefore, was not so much in ritual performance per se,
but in the theology articulated within the doctrinal standards that undergirded the
Methodist approach to dying and death.

In Wesley's view, death was paradoxically both a punishment and a promise,
although he generally placed the emphasis upon the latter. To begin with the
penalty: death constituted more than the natural completion of life processes;
temporal death, spiritual death, and eternal death were the consequences of the
lingering sin of Adam's fall.[10] Therefore, death was deemed a penalty rather than
a divinely ordained means to increase dissatisfaction with the earthly and material.
Although godly and ungodly alike experienced consternation at the inevitability
of death, Wesley believed that the Christian should not fear but strive to affirm
that "to die is gain" and welcome the "lovely appearance of death."[11] To accentuate
that end, he perpetuated the late medieval tradition of the *ars moriendi* by affirming
that death, in addition to being the result of sin, was also for faithful Christians
the promise of the cure of sin and an "entrance into a far more desirable country."[12]
Thus, an ideal or "comfortable" death was characterized by "a calm passage out of
life, full of even, rational peace and joy."[13] By painting a positive and evangelical
picture of death utilizing biblical material and traditional Christian affirmations
and interpretations, Wesley directly addressed the uncertainties about death characteristic of his day.

Decisions made during life were therefore inseparably connected to what came
after life. Upon death, according to Wesley, the souls of the deceased would enter
an intermediate, penultimate state in which they would remain until reunited with
the body at the resurrection of the dead. In that state variously identified as "the
ante-chamber of heaven," "Abraham's bosom," and "paradise," the faithful dead

would gain a foretaste of heaven, converse with the saints of all ages, and be "perfected" and "ripened" for the heavenly realm. For the wicked, the intermediate state was a foretaste of unavoidable hell.[14] Wesley rejected the Roman Catholic conception of purgatory as he understood it: not only did he condemn the doctrine as without scriptural warrant and "repugnant to the Word of God" (as per the Articles of Religion), he also opined that a believer who died penitent had no need for purification from earlier wickedness in a "purging fire near hell."[15] Wesleyan funeral hymns looked toward an immediate reunion in soul with the brothers and sisters who had died in Christ. Thus in the third stanza of "Rejoice for a brother deceased":

> There all the ship's company meet,
> Who sailed with the Saviour beneath;
> With shouting each other they greet,
> And triumph o'er trouble and death:
> The voyage of life's at an end,
> The mortal affliction is past;
> The age that in heaven they spend
> For ever and ever shall last.[16]

The resurrection to eternal life, "both the Fountain and the Object of our Faith," was not guaranteed to all humanity, but only to the saints in Christ who would rise "in due season"; the notion of unconditional universal salvation was, for Wesley, unsupportable by either Scripture or sound reason.[17] In Wesley's thought, the general resurrection of the dead would be followed by the judgment at which all individuals would be held accountable. Eternal punishment, as a consequence of original sin, was the future prospect for those who did not in their earthly life acknowledge their alienation by sin, earnestly repent, and seek or appropriate God's redeeming and perfecting love though faith in Jesus Christ. Conversely, for those who followed the *via salutis*, the eschatological goal (namely, salvation to eternal life and the transformation or restoration of sinful humanity into the *imago dei*) that had been anticipated and (in part) attained in earthly life was achieved. Nowhere are Wesley's views on the last things better summarized than in the hymns on the subject, especially those in the section "Describing Judgment" in the 1780 *A Collection of Hymns for the Use of the People Called Methodists*: according to the hymn "The great archangel's trump shall sound," sinners on that dreadful day "shall lift their guilty head and shrink to see a yawning hell," and the faithful "shall stand in Jesu's righteousness" and "smile to see a burning world."[18] Several of the hymns found in the *Collection* that address eschatological and funerary themes came from an independent pamphlet of *Funeral Hymns*, first published by the Wesleys in 1746; such Wesleyan perspectives in verse were also contained in a second pamphlet of forty-three *Funeral Hymns* (1759), and in forty hymns from *Preparation for Death, in Several Hymns* (1772).

Since the death of a Christian anticipated his or her entry into the "everlasting habitations," the response of the dying and the bereaved was not to be grief but joy. As a young man, Wesley emphasized, even at funerals, the inappropriateness of grief, and encouraged patience and resoluteness instead. Following the deaths of his sister's children, he wrote to her that their passing was "a great instance of the goodness of God towards you," since now "you have nothing to do but to serve our Lord without carefulness and without distraction, till you are sanctified in body, soul, and spirit."[19] Wesley modified the extremity of his position with age and experience, although he clearly preferred that Christians meet the death of a loved one and their own deaths with an acceptance of the mercy and grace of God.

The funeral of a devout Christian, like eyewitness and written accounts of the last days and "happy" deaths of the faithful, was recognized by Wesley and the early Methodists as a source of continuing inspiration and a powerful instrument for convincing or converting unbelievers. Funerals or the events surrounding interment were regarded as occasions for evangelism. Wesley urged his preachers and other leaders of the Methodist societies to "improve" the opportunities accorded at funerals when "the windows of heaven are open" that the burial of the dead might prove to be "a blessing for many."[20] To accentuate Christian testimony, Wesley enjoined moderation at funerals, preferring neither the "stupid, senseless Pageantry" associated with the custom of lying in state nor the starkness of Scottish funerals.[21] Simplicity with decorum was the standard for the Methodists, who often expressed the wish to be buried as "plain Christians" at a solemn occasion where tears of sorrow would intermingle with tears of joy. There seems to be no evidence to support the claim that early Methodist funerals were eucharistic occasions.[22]

Wesley's revision of the burial office conformed to his perspectives on Christian eschatology and thus constituted a distinct shift in emphasis from the theology espoused in the Prayer Book's rite. Wesley deleted phrases (from the Collect) and entire prayers (the Committal and the Prayer of Thanksgiving) apparently because they were too confident in naming the eternal destiny of every individual who might receive the last rite.[23] Challenges to the presumption that all who died departed "in sure and certain hope of the resurrection to eternal life," as stated in the Committal, had already been made by the Puritans and others before Wesley. Similarly, objections had previously been raised about the Prayer of Thanksgiving (even by Wesley himself in 1755),[24] and in particular regarding the truthfulness of the phrase "We give thee hearty thanks, for that it hath pleased thee to deliver this our brother out of the miseries of this sinful world." With Wesley's omission of these references, no longer was the dead individual the focus of the liturgy, even though the funeral remained the occasion for gathering to remember the departed and for returning the body to the earth: there was neither scrutiny regarding the person's faith nor identification of his or her character—indeed, the deceased remained nameless. Intentionally or unintentionally, Wesley's burial liturgy was a "generic" commendation; specificity, when warranted, could be articulated in the funeral sermon, though such was not identified by rubric within the rite. The attention in Wesley's burial rite, in keeping with the Methodist stress upon an evangelical witness at the time of death, was placed upon the faithfulness of the community gathered, who, through hearing the word of God and singing hymns of faith and hope, were called to accountability before God and each other.

The 1784 burial service was basically an extended reading of Scripture, since Wesley left virtually untouched the Prayer Book material drawn directly from holy writ. The exact location for performing the first part of the rite with its sentences and readings was undefined in order to adjust to the various circumstances of the American situation; the second part was specified to take place "at the grave":

Scripture Sentences [said when the minister meets and goes before the corpse]
   John 11:25–26
   Job 19:25–27
   1 Timothy 6:7; Job 1:21
Psalm 90
1 Corinthians 15:20–58
Sentences at the Grave [when the corpse is laid in the earth]
   Job 14:1–2
   Media vita ["In the midst of life. . . ."]
Revelation 14:13
Kyrie eleison
The Lord's Prayer
Collect ["O Merciful God, the Father of our Lord Jesus Christ, who is the resurrection and the life. . . ."]
Apostolic Benediction [2 Corinthians 13:14]

The two exceptions to the explicit biblical content were the Collect (though it quotes John 11:25–26) and *Media vita*, the latter consisting of a series of sentences:

In the midst of life we are in death; of whom may we seek for succour, but of thee, O Lord, who for our sins art justly displeased?

Yet, O Lord God most holy, O Lord most mighty, O holy and most merciful Saviour, deliver us not into the bitter pains of eternal death.

Thou knowest, Lord, the secrets of our hearts: shut not thy merciful ears to our prayers; but spare us, Lord most holy, O God most mighty, O holy and merciful Saviour, thou most worthy Judge eternal, suffer us not at our last hour for any pains of death to fall from thee.

Wesley's inclusion of this text kept alive a long-standing tradition of the western church, which was usually traced (probably falsely) to Notker (d. 912), a monk of St. Gall. During the Middle Ages, *Media vita* had been widely popular throughout Europe, particularly in Germany; Luther's German paraphrase of the Latin was a source for Miles Coverdale's English metrical version, which in part inspired the translation placed in the funeral liturgy of the 1549 *Book of Common Prayer*.[25] Wesley, in writing about spiritual and physical death, would on occasion illustrate his thesis by alluding to the familiar *Media vita*.[26] Because of his interest in primitive liturgical practice and in the Christian East, Wesley may have found the echo of the *Trisagion* preserved in the sentences—"O Lord God most holy, O Lord most mighty, O holy and most merciful Saviour"—to be an important link with Christian antiquity. Hence *Media vita* was retained in his revision and continued in some Methodist burial liturgies into the late twentieth century.

Journals of the ordained ministers indicate that they found Wesley's 1784 burial rite suitable for their use, but how consistently they followed its order and content is unknown, since notations record only ambiguous phrases such as "read the burial service" and "performed the funeral rites."[27] No explicit regulations excluded the unordained from officiating other than, perhaps, the use of the term "minister" in the ritual text. A limitation may have been implicit in the rule approved in 1787 forbidding lay preachers from reading the "Liturgy" unless they had written direction from a bishop or elder. With the rescinding of this provision by the first General Conference of the Methodist Episcopal Church in 1792, there were no official obstacles to lay leadership of the burial rite, since overt prohibitions were stated only for the celebrations of the Eucharist, baptism, and matrimony. Despite the absence of restrictions, the Methodist people soon showed a decided preference for either the elder or the deacon to preside at the rites or preach a funeral sermon for their beloved dead. If an ordained Methodist was on hand when a member of a non-Methodist denomination died who had no clergyman for that denomination nearby, the Methodist might be called upon to lead or assist in any part of those obsequies.

The General Conference in 1792 abbreviated Wesley's burial liturgy by the removal of the readings from Psalm 90 and 1 Corinthians 15. Not only was the amount of scriptural material reduced, but the rite moved quickly from the meeting of the corpse to the gathering at the grave: the 1792 rite was essentially a graveside service. Some Methodist funerals, therefore, entirely took place where the body was laid to rest, with a sermon sometimes added to all or a portion of the approved rite. Alternatively, an additional service supplementing the graveside component could be held in the preaching house, the home of the deceased, or other setting, with a sermon (if requested) often constituting the centerpiece. The order followed might be that expected for the community's Sunday worship, another familiar pattern, or an improvised arrangement judged best for the occasion. Such a service could fall immediately before or after interment (the deceased's remains were typically present in the former event), but in cases where a preacher was unavailable, the additional service came days or weeks after burial. Graveside and other funerary services took place during the day or early evening, and on any day of the week, and in the decades after 1792 (as before) often drew substantial numbers in attendance on account of the anticipated revival atmosphere. There are also examples of evangelistic funeral sermons preached before an individual's last breath: after having premonitions about his own impending death, Edmund Henley in 1808 gathered his friends and acquaintances at a stand in the graveyard and preached his own funeral sermon.[28] Thus the rubric stating "the following or some other solemn Service shall be used" that began the Methodist Episcopal burial rite from 1792 until 1852 codified the freedom and variety in liturgical expression Methodists were accustomed to at the time of death. Yet overlapping with the rubric for flexibility was the legislation first placed in the Methodist Episcopal *Discipline* in 1824 requiring the consistent and uniform use of the church's authorized rite—a rule that denomination carried until 1912. The Methodist Episcopal Church, South's rubric for ritual liberty was dropped in 1858, for according to Bishop Joshua Soule, who "regretted the existence of that rubric," "the service is often reduced to—I do not know what."[29]

Despite the variability in practice, Methodist funerals ideally were to be characterized by simplicity and proper decorum. Popular customs such as decorating coaches, wearing fancy hatbands, and giving mementos were discouraged as prideful vanities; the distribution and consumption of spirituous liquors at funerals was thoroughly condemned. The Wesleyan Methodists, from the outset, legislated the countercultural austerity desired for their funerals by listing under the section on "Dress and Furniture" in the *Discipline* a note stipulating "we disapprove of Christians changing their apparel in mourning for the dead." The plainness—and cost— of Methodist funerals is reflected in a sexton's fee list dated 1837 for the church at Schenectady, New York:

Ringing bell	$ .62½
Hearse and cloth, horse and driver	1.75
For digging graves from the first of April until November 20th	
Single coffin	.75
Double coffin	1.00
For child under 12 years, single	.50
For child under 12 years, double	.75
For digging graves from November 20th to April 1st	
Single	1.50
Double	1.75
For children under 12, single	1.00
For children under 12, double	1.25
For inviting bearers	.50
For attending funerals and filling up graves	.75
For inviting people in general and the bearers	1.00[30]

Solemn yet joyful hymn singing as the body was carried in procession or placed in the grave was recognized as the most appropriate decoration for Methodist funerals. Christian song also proved beneficial in uniting persons of different social backgrounds, racial groups, and ecclesiastical traditions who might attend or participate in the same funeral. William Colbert recorded in 1805 the hymns sung at a Philadelphia funeral attended by Methodist Episcopal and Protestant Episcopal ministers of different races:

In the afternoon attended the funeral of Charles Boston a Black man, who was inered [*sic*] between the old and new walls of Bethel Church. A great multitude attended the funeral, which was conducted with a great degree of solemnity. Absolom Jones, Richard Allen, and James Champion walked before, James Smith, Jeffry Bula and myself followed. The singers followed us, and the bearers them. The hymns sung were "Rejoice for a brother disceased—Hark from the tombs, and My God my heart with Love inflame." This was ended in the house. I then delivered a short oration, and we went to the grave singing "a solemn March we make." At the grave Absolom Jones, the African Minister of the Episcopal Church, with a very audible voice went through the

Form of the burial of the dead. We then returnd from the grave singing a Hymn very applicable to the accation and left the place.[31]

Although Methodists debated the use in church worship of formal part singing and fugue tunes, Methodist tune books by the 1830s incorporated funeral anthems in those musical settings that may have been intended for domestic funerals and burials not in a churchyard; such may have been the motivation behind the choice of words "for Particular Occasions" used in the titles of the tune books. The *Methodist Harmonist* (1831) contained two hymn anthems written for part singing, Barton's "The Dying Christian," and "The Dying Christian's Happy End"; the former text proclaimed the Wesleyan view of death as ultimately promise and goal:

> Vital spark of heavenly flame,
> Quit, O quit this mortal frame;
> Trembling, hoping, ling'ring, flying,
> O the pain, the bliss of dying.
> Cease, fond nature, cease thy strife,
> And let me languish into life.

An expanded version of "The Dying Christian" (utilizing the language of 1 Corinthians 15:54–55) was included in *The Harmonist* (1841) and set to a fugue tune. Several other anthems suitable for funerals appeared in the 1841 book, among them William Billings' homophonic "Funeral Anthem" with the text of Revelation 14:13 taken from the burial liturgy.

As the Methodist family divided in the first half of the nineteenth century, they kept in their burial liturgies the scriptural witness to the frailty of human life juxtaposed with the hope for believers obtained by Christ's victory over the grave. For all but one denomination, some version of Wesley's rite, as altered in 1792, proved adequate in conveying that message of repentance and trust. The Methodist Protestants reconfigured the burial rite (which by rubric was to be done entirely at the grave), but retained several of the older Scripture sentences and added to them in order to speak of death as both penalty and promise: during the procession to the grave, the minister could repeat one or more readings from John 11:25–26, Job 19:25–26 (no verse 27), Revelation 14:13, 1 Peter 1:3–5, and 1 Corinthians 15:51–57; after the apostolic benediction and while the sexton was filling in the grave, the minister had the option of selecting from among Genesis 3:19, Revelation 20:6; 21:4, 1 Corinthians 2:9, Revelation 22:14, and Psalm 116:16. By rubric the minister, upon arrival at the graveside, could "exhort those present to reflect on the shortness and uncertainty of human life; and to prepare for death, judgment, and eternity." Those same themes were then addressed in a lengthy prayer, which wedded Scripture not found in either the Prayer Book or Wesley's burial rite to snippets and allusions from those sources, thereby formalizing the style typical of Methodist extemporary prayer—and giving written form to the way the Methodist Episcopal service may, in fact, have been reworked by some ministers:

Almighty and most merciful God, in whose hands are the issues of life and death; and before whose bar we shall all stand, and give an account of the deeds done in the body; we beseech thee to grant unto us, at all times, a salutary conviction of the frailty of life, and our great responsibility to thee, the judge of quick and dead.

In the midst of life we are in death; we come up and are cut down like a flower; we flee as a shadow, and never continue in one stay. Death, judgment and eternity are just before us, and of whom may we seek protection and grace, but of thee, O most merciful God, who hath redeemed us with the most precious blood of Christ, that we might be delivered from the power of sin and the fear of death, and be made heirs of eternal life?

We humbly confess, O righteous Father, that we have sinned, and come short of thy glory. We have been undutiful children; slothful servants; and unfaithful stewards of the manifold mercies of God. Be merciful, O Lord, to our unrighteousness, pardon our sins, and raise us from a death of sin to a life of righteousness, through faith in our Lord Jesus Christ, who hath said: I am the resurrection and the life, he that believeth in me, though he were dead, yet shall he live; and whosoever liveth and believeth in me shall not die eternally.

We beseech thee, Father of all our mercies, and giver of every good and perfect gift, to grant us grace whereby we may serve thee acceptably, with reverence and godly fear, all our days; looking for the blessed hope, and glorious appearing of the great God and our Saviour Jesus Christ, to judge the world in righteousness. For the hour is coming, in which all that are in their graves shall hear the voice of the son of God, and shall come forth; they that have done good, to the resurrection of life, and they that have done evil, to the resurrection of condemnation.

Forbid, O most merciful God, that any of us should taste of the bitter pains of the second death; but grant that when we depart this transitory life, we may die in possession of triumphant faith, and rest in Christ. And, at the general resurrection of the last day, be found acceptable in thy sight, and receive that blessing which thy well beloved Son shall then pronounce to all that love and fear thee; saying, come, ye blessed of my Father, receive the kingdom prepared for you from the beginning of the world.

Almighty God, our heavenly Father, grant that this dispensation of thy righteous providence may be sanctified to the good of all present. May we take due warning, and consider the shortness and uncertainty of human life; the solemnities of death, and the awful realities of eternity; and prepare to meet thee in the judgment.

May the relatives of the deceased not sorrow as those who have no hope, but have grace to submit to thy righteous will, and be fully prepared to say the Lord gave and the Lord hath taken away, blessed be the name of the Lord.[32]

For the preachers and for the Methodist people, the funeral sermon functioned as the core of the religious observances surrounding death, with the Scripture readings and prayers from the rites providing authoritative theological support for the sermon content. The centrality of the sermon is indicated in ministers' diaries and journals by the mention of the Scripture verse that was selected or requested and usually little else about the funeral service itself. Preachers anticipated that funeral sermons would be "solemn," "awful," "warning," and "melting" occasions that would bind the Methodist community together and warm the hearts of unbelievers; disappointment resulted when the congregation was unfeeling, or the preacher failed to move the congregation—the latter deemed a likely consequence if the "paper swords" of written sermon manuscripts were relied upon at funerals as a "substitute for the inspiration of the Holy Ghost."[33] Sermons were expected to convict and convince, to encourage preparation before death ("time swiftly flies, and death draws near"; therefore, "be ye also ready"),[34] and to identify death as the portal to a better place for believers. These emphases are certainly evident in most of the sermons or sermon outlines that date from before the mid-nineteenth century. In the sermon based on 1 Thessalonians 4:13–14 that he preached in 1797 at the funeral of Conduce Gatch, the father of minister Philip Gatch, Bishop Francis Asbury first "observed the pleasing, cheering, and charming manner in which the apostle described the death of the righteous[:] . . . sleep in Jesus; a rest from labour, sorrow, affliction, and pain; happy opening visions of God." Secondly, he spoke to "the hope the pious who are alive have for their pious dead who have had experience, and long continuance in religion, and a comfortable dying in the Lord." For those "who have no hope for themselves nor their dead, how awful their sorrow."[35] Almost thirty years later, when preaching at the funeral of a seven-year-old child, George Coles addressed the "happy removal of the child from the evils of the present life and the snares of a wicked world" and the "certainty of its felicity on the ground of the atonement and on the authority of Jesus Christ (Mark 10)."[36] Coles's subject on that occasion may have been chosen in light of the propensity of Methodists (and others) to believe that the death of a child was a "severe chastisement for the soul's well-being" or a divine reprimand for idolizing one's offspring.[37]

In fulfilling their function as a vehicle for converting unbelievers and edifying the faithful, Methodist funeral sermons would, when warranted, illustrate the gospel message with reference to the Christian character of the deceased. On the occasion of Bishop Richard Whatcoat's death, for example, funeral sermons were preached in various locations with each message utilizing a different Scripture text, "but all leading to shew the excellency of the man, the christian and minister."[38] Funeral sermons of notable persons were reproduced in church periodicals, not only to provide a brief biography of the deceased, but also to further the sermon's evangelical scope. A popular Methodist literary genre of this period, as earlier, comprised edifying studies of the faithful in their final days; editor Davis W. Clark contrasted believers with unbelievers in *Death-Bed Scenes; Or, Dying With and Without Religion: Designed to Illustrate the Truth and Power of Christianity* (1851). The apparent Methodist tendency to "improve" upon the vita for any recipient of the last rite may have been partly behind the decision made in 1830 by the New York City preachers to limit funeral sermons to "aged official members and aged matrons."[39] Such Methodist proclivity was publicly challenged at midcentury when Joseph B. Wakely performed the final office (including a sermon) for William Poole of New York, a notorious individual who had been murdered. Initially generated by essays in *The Churchman*, an organ of the "High-Church party" of the Protestant Episcopal Church, the debate focused upon the content of Wakely's funeral "address" and whether he should have used the church's burial rite for a disreputable person. Wakely published a thirty-four-page apologia in which he defended the Methodist Episcopal practice of burying "the poor and the degraded," and denied that he eulogized Poole, but rather "spoke plainly of the evils and errors of his life, and warned his companions to shun his bad course. . . . I uttered, for the benefit of the living, and not for the 'dull, cold ear' of the dead, the words of Christian consolation."[40] In the name of Christian charity, Methodist ministers were generally willing to provide a decent burial and a funeral sermon for all except one category: suicides.[41]

Methodist ministers in the 1850s and 1860s continued to "read the burial services" and preach funeral sermons that, conforming to Thomas O. Summers's recommendation, employed "acceptable words, hitting words, words profitable for doctrine, for reproof, for correction, [and] for instruction in righteousness."[42] Making official what was already extant practice, the Methodist Episcopal Church, South in 1858 inserted into its burial rite before the sentences at interment a rubric permitting a hymn, a sermon or exhortation, and extemporary prayer. Within that denomination and also within the Methodist Episcopal Church, requests for more scriptural options in the official burial service led to the reintroduction in both rites of readings taken from Psalm 90 and 1 Corinthians 15. The Methodist Episcopal Church in 1868 also printed Psalm 39 (which Wesley had deleted in his revision of the Prayer Book) and preceded it with a rubric indicating that "some other suitable portion of Scripture" could be read "in the house or Church." But more than desires for ritual flexibility and a return to Wesley's (or the Prayer Book's) form may have prompted the restoration of verses from the Pauline chapter. In 1844, George Bush, a professor of Hebrew at New York City University, published *Anastasis: Or, the Doctrine of the Resurrection of the Body, Rationally and Scripturally Considered* in which, by a philosophical principle of the "progressive development of Scriptural truth," he determined that the doctrine of the resurrection of the body was not sanctioned by either reason or revelation, and that resurrection took place at death with the disengagement of an already-present spiritual (and immortal) body. Bush denied both the general resurrection and the general judgment, and insisted, based upon his interpretation of scriptural evidence, that the prevailing sense of resurrection in the New Testament was that of immortality and the entrance into a new sphere of existence and not the resuscitation of physical bodies. Methodists, among others, were swift to denounce Bush's claims put forward in that book and elsewhere as attacks upon the classical Christian (and Wesleyan) view of the immortality of the soul and the resurrection of the body. Calvin Kingsley, a member of the Methodist Episcopal Church and a professor at the church-related Alleghany College, directly refuted Bush's work in *The Resurrection of the Dead: A Vindication of the Literal Resurrection of the Human Body*, published in 1847, as did R. J. Cooke thirty-seven years later in *Outlines of the Doctrine of the Resurrection* (1884). Manuals exegeting denominational doctrine, and in particular official catechisms, reinforced belief in a general resurrection and a last judgment. Lest Free Methodists be tempted to abandon such doctrine, a statement on "Future Reward and Punishment" appeared among their founding Articles of Religion. Between the years of Kingsley's and Cooke's publications, and also afterward, numerous articles and essays by Methodists debated the nature of death itself, the existence of an intermediate state, the meaning of resurrection, and the relationship between body, soul, and spirit. Some Methodists succumbed, if only in part, to the new views: although he held the doctrine of the resurrection of the body to be totally dependent upon revelation, theologian Thomas Ralston was willing to concede that not only Scripture, but reason independent of Christian revelation, could support the doctrine of the immortality of the soul.[43]

Thus, the addition into Methodist burial rites of a committal of the body may not have come only as a response to cultural ambiguities about death and the hereafter, and to liturgical needs, but to address a theological issue as well. The committal already in use in 1840 by the African Methodist Episcopal Church had been borrowed from the Protestant Episcopal burial liturgy, which had removed the long-offensive reference to "sure and certain hope of the resurrection to eternal life" and replaced it with language of the general resurrection that, specifically for those who had died in Christ, would be the occasion of a glorious transformation. The Episcopal text was slightly modified, so rather than have God "take unto himself" the soul of the departed, the soul was more generally "taken":

> Forasmuch as it hath pleased Almighty God, in his wise providence, to take out of this world the soul of our deceased *brother*, we therefore commit *his* body to the ground, earth to earth, ashes to ashes, dust to dust; looking for the general resurrection in the last day, and the life of the world to come, through our Lord Jesus Christ; at whose second coming in glorious majesty to judge the world, the earth and the sea shall give up their dead; and the corruptible bodies of those who sleep in him shall be changed, and made like unto his own glorious body, according to the mighty working whereby he is able to subdue all things unto himself.

This form was adopted by the Methodist Episcopal Church, South (1858), the Methodist Protestant Church (1870), and the Free Methodist Church (by 1875), but the Methodist Episcopal committal approved in 1864 slightly adjusted it, so the text spoke inclusively of "the soul of the departed"; the Wesleyans and the African Methodist Episcopal Zion Church followed the Methodist Episcopal design.

Consolation

By the last three decades of the nineteenth century, Methodists held divergent views of the last things. The Holiness Methodists and other conservatives maintained the belief that souls and bodies would be reunited at the resurrection of the dead, to be followed by the general judgment when the righteous would find bliss, and the wicked everlasting punishment. Because eschatology had received "much heterodox attention" and the "doctrine of the Resurrection [had] fared badly of late," the "signs of the times," they believed, called for a restatement of orthodox doctrine.[44] Among liberal Methodists sensitive to the intellectual and theological discussions encouraged by George Bush and others, less certainty was expressed about the scriptural or rational basis for prior teachings about death and its consequences. Emphasis upon the penal aspect of death began to wane and was replaced by a stronger stress upon hope, the mercy of God, the likelihood of immortality immediately upon death, and a reunion with the beloved departed. Such change in perspective can be found in the work of Methodist

Episcopal theologian John Miley, who downplayed death as punishment and instead accentuated the joys of immortality and the blessedness of heaven.[45] With the beginning of the new century, some Methodist theologians stressed not resurrection but immortality, as did Olin Alfred Curtis, though he did not relinquish the concept of death as penalty.[46] The first half of the twentieth century saw a further replacement of the doctrine of resurrection with a doctrine of immortality. Georgia Harkness, in 1947, claimed that even without "the resurrection experience of the early disciples," the goodness of God would have sufficed to ensure belief in "the personal immortality" of God's otherwise short-lived human creatures. "In the life beyond," she posited, "there will be continuance of the individual soul, fellowship with those we love, a lifting of earthly chains of pain and suffering, a chance to grow in the things of Christ, the glory of God's nearer presence."[47]

The theological shift toward a stress on immortality and hope rather than on judgment may also be traced by examining the subject headings in the official Methodist Episcopal hymnals of the period. The *Methodist Pocket Hymn-Book* (1802) had included twenty-three hymns under the heading "Death and Judgment," but by the time of publication of the 1878 *Hymnal of the Methodist Episcopal Church*, hymns of "Judgment and Retribution" figured only seventeen while hymns on the subject of "Heaven" numbered fifty. In the 1905 *Methodist Hymnal*, six hymns appeared under the heading "Judgment and Retribution," with twenty-five identified under the topic "Heaven." The *Methodist Hymnal* of 1935 relocated "Death" from the table of contents to the topical index (reference to "Judgment" completely disappeared) and replaced it with the heading "The Eternal Life," under which twenty hymns were categorized.

Popular articles and essays particularly in Methodist Episcopal publications reflected the new approach to dying and death—and to life as more than a preparation for death. The older genre of Methodist deathbed literature was criticized as overly preoccupied with the last days, since one was to be judged by the entirety of a life lived rather than by one's piety when confronted by death. Warnings about the terrors of death declined as words of hope proliferated at the prospect of a glorious immortality. Descriptions of the eternal fate for unbelievers lessened as Methodists subscribed to the already-prevalent literature of consolation that depicted heaven as a glorified version of domestic life where relationships would continue and one would be cognizant of earthly affairs.[48] "Heaven is more akin to earth than many Christians think," commented minister Jesse S. Gilbert. He added:

> We will meet with many loved ones. There will be greetings as well as partings. The aged will find heaven a more familiar place in that respect than earth. Then the parting is all over, but the greeting will go on until the last Christian friend we have known and loved on earth, has reached the golden shore. One thought more, and it is this: Many persons are often troubled in spirit, because they do not, in the full flash of life and health, feel as they express it, "willing to die." Why should we wish to die when God wants us to live? When the dying hour comes, dying grace will come. A deathbed state of mind would unfit us not only for life's enjoyments, but also for its toils. When the "last enemy" appears, God will supply strength for the conflict.[49]

Readers of periodicals and journals soon adopted the new vocabulary as their own. Emma Lee Taylor wrote upon the death of her father, John A. Taylor, in 1881:

> Death, death; what does it mean, our precious and beloved father has gone. The angel of the Lord came, and wafted his soul to a more beautiful home about three o'clock this evening. Oh, what peace is his, what rest he now enjoys, from all the pain and suffering; with what pleasure he looked up to a brighter world, prepared for all of God's children. Yes, the hour came at last, and *now* he is *gone*; forever gone from our midst. *No more* will we hear his sweet voice, no more will his prayers ascend to a throne of grace in our behalf, for he has gone to inherit the kingdom prepared for him by our crucified Saviour. *Not a week* has passed since Uncle Bob his brother died. May God in his mercy, and goodness watch over the bereaved ones who are left to mourn their loss, though not without hope, of meeting them again at "The beautiful gate," about which Pa was so fond of hearing us sing.[50]

Accompanying the theological shift on matters eschatological was a change in the practice of funerals among some Methodists. Funereal simplicity as the antithesis to the more customary ostentation was gradually being supplanted by assimilation to culture—or at least the adoption of funeral customs embraced in the wider Protestant ethos. Black garb and the simple wooden coffin were replaced by the appurtenances that veiled the realities of death such as the embalming of the body, beautiful caskets, and floral arrangements, all of which generated complaints in some quarters. The Wesleyan Methodists during this time supplemented their condemnation of mourning apparel in the *Discipline* with another statement protesting against "the extravagant waste of money, and needless expense, merely for display, on funeral occasions." Yet one Methodist argued for funeral reform not only on account of the lavishness, expense, and unnecessary pomp of many funerals, but that the obsequies might have a less gloomy and a more hopeful complexion.[51]

Consolation was now seen as the proper outcome of ministry at the time of death, whether the deceased or the mourners be believers or unbelievers. Whereas in earlier years Methodists were encouraged to take one last look at their beloved before the coffin was lowered into the grave, now an open casket was believed by some to be barbaric and uncivilized (though it still continued to occur at Methodist funerals). Certain writers discouraged public funerals in favor of private rites, since "the more practical and intimate the services, the more effective are they in doing good."[52] Funeral sermons—renamed addresses, meditations, or remarks— were now intended primarily to comfort the bereaved with the gospel of peace rather than eulogize the dead or convert the unbeliever. Eyes were to be dried, not moistened:

> A "funeral sermon" is almost never in order, even in the rural districts to-day. The address should not take more than eight or ten minutes, and the whole service should be concluded in a half hour, as a rule. Any biographical sketch of the deceased that may be desirable should be incorporated into the address, and while proper appreciation is ever in order, overstatement and eulogy are distinctly bad form. If the departed was a saint, that fact will be already widely known. If not, only embarrassment can follow

from an attempt to "whiten a sepulcher." Any effort to stir up the emotions of the company, particularly of the family, is reprehensible. Rather the service should soothe the harrowed feelings of those who mourn by its quiet tenderness. The proper material for an address at a funeral consists of the fundamental doctrine that God is love, and all other doctrines are implied in it.[53]

Showing a complete reversal of earlier Methodist practice, pastoral care specialist Russell L. Dicks in 1948 went so far as to state that "the total purpose of the funeral service is to be helpful to the family; the 'sinners' who attend a funeral are of no concern to the minister at that time."[54] To provide solace for the mourners, brevity became the watchword for the ritual activities associated with death. A few words, carefully chosen from Scripture, poetry, or prose, could, alongside compassionate prayer, soothe and console. The favorite songs or hymns of the deceased might be sung to connect the living and the dead, and to sweeten the memory of one lost.[55] Funeral manuals published in response to the demand for resources distinguished material for different ages, genders, circumstances of life, and causes of death.[56]

Only three Methodist denominations acknowledged the shifts in theology and in practice, not only by their excisions and rephrasings but also by introducing a substantial amount of new material into their official rites for the burial of the dead during the late nineteenth through the first half of the twentieth century. These were the Methodist Protestant Church, the Methodist Episcopal Church, South, and the Methodist Episcopal Church. The others added nothing except for a statement of committal if one had not already been introduced; the Wesleyan Church, in fact, abbreviated its rite, so that in 1892 the authorized text consisted of processional sentences (as received from Wesley), the committal at the grave, an optional reading of Revelation 14:13, and "an appropriate prayer."

The Methodist Protestants, in 1870, eliminated the rubric for the funeral exhortation and modified the sequence at the grave so that a few brief sentences (the first clause of *Media vita* conflated with Job 14:1, and John 5:25, 29) preceded a committal; then followed the first, third (without the quotation from John 11:25–26), fourth (with John 5:25, 29 removed), sixth, and seventh paragraphs taken from the long prayer used in 1830. Although the prayer retained references to future judgment, the paragraph disappeared that delineated rest in Christ at the time of death and also the general resurrection. When the Methodist Protestants revised their rite again in 1892, the graveside liturgy was kept intact as the second part of the rite, with a new first part "arranged for the home" to be adjusted if used in the church. The service began with Scripture sentences,[57] mixing messages of warning and hope, and was followed with Scripture verses to be chosen according to specified categories: young children, sudden death, the aged, the faithful, and "selections which set forth the design and gracious consolations of affliction." An address and extemporary prayer closed that part of the service. In 1924, the opening of the first part of the service was expanded to begin with the reading of John 11:25, 26 and Revelation 14:13, and the offering of two prayers, the first focusing upon human accountability, and the second beseeching God the Father's compassion and comfort in the name of Christ "who is touched with the feeling of our infirmities." While the Methodist Protestant rites showed a growing tendency toward consolation and continued as in the earliest ritual text to offer words of hope, neither the penal character of death nor the threat of final judgment had been entirely eliminated.

The textual modifications made to the Methodist Episcopal Church, South's burial rite at their 1910 General Conference displayed the results of a concerted effort to beautify death and to offer words of comfort. Although requests were put forward to omit the opening sentence from Job 1:21 since it "makes God not only pleased at, but responsible for, every death which occurs,"[58] that sentence was left untouched; rather, Job 19:25–27, with its references to worms destroying the body and seeing God in the flesh at the latter day, was replaced with the promise of a heavenly habitation and the "Apostle's own message on immortality" offered in 2 Corinthians 5:1.[59] Verses suggestive of divine wrath or retribution were removed from Psalm 90 and from a newly added Psalm 39. For instances of a child's death, 2 Samuel 12:16–23 and Mark 10:13–16 were authorized as alternate readings. The committal was adjusted so that "Forasmuch as it hath pleased Almighty God, in his wise providence, to take out of this world the soul of our deceased *brother*" became a more assured "Forasmuch as the spirit of our deceased *brother* hath returned to God who gave it." Yet these changes, significant though they were, paled in comparison to those made by the Methodist Episcopal Church, first in 1916, and again in 1932.

The Methodist Episcopal Church's alteration to the rubric at the outset of the 1916 rite signaled the direction taken "to introduce a little more Christian light and gladness into the gloom of our funeral ritual":[60] therein (and in other rubrics) the neutral term "body" superseded the graphically descriptive (and now offensive) word "corpse." In response to the charge set before the Commission on Revision of Ritual to modify the service "principally through the use of additional Scripture selections, with the purpose of giving fuller expression to the Christian hope and comfort as found in the New Testament," the opening sentences from Job 19 and from the conflation of 1 Timothy 6 and Job 1 were replaced with sentences from 2 Corinthians 5:1 and Revelation 21:22–23.[61] Psalm 39 was dropped in favor of Psalm 23, and as in the Methodist Episcopal Church, South rite, Psalm 90 was purged of references or allusions to God's anger and judgment. Psalm 39:4 did survive as one of the sentences at the grave, substituting for the reading from Job 14:1–2; *Media vita* was severely truncated by the excision of references to God as judge, and a new concluding petition was affixed that God would "grant us everlasting life." Optional lessons from John 14:1–3, 15–20, 25–27 and Revelation 7: 9–17 accompanied the reading from 1 Corinthians 15 (now reduced to verses 41– 49 and 53–58). Thomas Benjamin Neely, in his criticism of the 1916 Ritual Commission's propensity to remove Old Testament references and quotations, made extended comments about the deletion of passages that had been used to precede the departed's remains "since time immemorial," and, particularly about the omission of the "sublime" statement from Job 19:25–27. Although he lauded the inclusion of the new sentences, Neely felt their presence did little to compensate for the "obliteration" of the historic material, a complaint he also registered against his church's adoption of the new opening formulation of the committal used by the Methodist Episcopal Church, South.[62]

The Methodist Episcopal revision of 1916 did not add new prayers to the standard burial rite; the denomination, in 1884, had already inserted a prayer of thanksgiving (according to the form of the Protestant Episcopal Church) that spoke of the "souls of the faithful" being in "joy and felicity." Thanksgiving was not given specifically for the deceased, but for "the good examples of all those thy servants" who had "finished their course in faith."[63] In spite of the apparent generality of this version of the prayer compared to that of the 1662 Prayer Book (to which Wesley objected), caution was still advised in its usage, for the exemplary life of the deceased was seen by some as the only justification for including the prayer at all.[64] An alteration in the text occurred with the revision of 1916: "after they are delivered from the burden of the flesh" was simplified to "after death," coinciding, perhaps, with the greater sense of ease in the material world that was continuing to develop.

A new and independent rite for the burial of a child appeared officially in 1916 after services had been proposed, but not approved, at the 1908 and 1912 General Conferences.[65] The liturgy of 1916 allowed for hymn, prayer, the reading of selections from Scripture (Mark 10:13–16, Psalm 23, Psalm 103:13–18, and Revelation 22:1–5), and at the grave, prayer concluding with the Lord's Prayer and a benediction. The opening prayer (to be said at an unspecified location), in keeping with the concerns of the times, acknowledged the mystery of God, but also asked for comfort and strength that the bereaved might "rejoice in the promise of eternal life" in anticipation of being "united again with our loved ones in thy heavenly and eternal kingdom."

The Methodist Episcopal Church's 1932 revision carried further the intentions of 1916, by altering previous texts and expanding the options available within the two official burial rites; the order for the burial of a child was also brought into line structurally with the normative burial service. Specified Scripture passages multiplied in both rites, and even a brief passage from the apocryphal Wisdom of Solomon claimed a place as one of the opening sentences ("The righteous live forever, and the care of them is with the Most High: with his right hand he shall cover them, and with his arm shall he shield them"). To complement the biblical material in the approved orders, the 1935 *Methodist Hymnal* provided in the section on responsive readings four selections indicated for the funeral service.[66] The number of prayers also increased substantially, some of these apparently originating from Methodist authors, and others borrowed from authorized ecclesiastical books and unofficial worship resources.[67] Several of the prayers were constructed by the interweaving of and elaboration upon scriptural texts already present in the burial office, and the content of the prayers bespoke a faithful optimism: "that [those who sorrow] may be enabled to contemplate the joy of that better home where thou art seen and worshipped as the Light of all whom thou keepest in thine everlasting love" and "lift us above unrighteous anger and mistrust into faith and hope and charity." With the words "forasmuch as the spirit of the departed has entered into the life immortal we therefore commit his body to its resting place, but his spirit we commend to God," an assurance was given about the eternal fate of anyone who received the last rite.

When the Methodist Church was created in 1939, the Methodist Episcopal Church's 1932 revision served as the basis for the new rite. Even so, new Scripture readings (from the Old and New Testaments) replaced some of the older options or were added outright. Only four of the prayers of 1932 were taken over into the revision of 1939; attention was given to expanding the number of prayers in the rite by utilizing material published elsewhere in service books or collections.[68] Although it is unclear which sources were originally used by the revision committee since a particular prayer may be found in a multiplicity of previous books, prayers may be traced to such American resources as the Presbyterian *Book of Common Worship (Revised)* (1932, 1936); the *Book of Common Worship for Use in the Several Communions of the Church of Christ* (1932), produced by Methodist Episcopal bishop Wilbur Thirkield and Oliver Huckel; and James Dalton Morrison's edited *Minister's Service Book, for Pulpit and Parish Use* (1937). Awareness of British publications is evident by the committee's apparent use of John Hunter's *Devotional Services for Public Worship* (9th ed., 1915), W. E. Orchard's *The Order of Divine Service for Public Worship* (1919), *A Free Church Book of Common Prayer and of the Administration of the Sacraments and Other Rites, Ceremonies, and Services of the Christian Church* (1929), and *The Book of Offices* (1936) of the Methodist Church of Great Britain. The understanding of the funeral as an occasion to convey hope, consolation, and the promise of immortality is clear from the content of these prayers, which are, for the most part, universal in scope. Christian faith on the part of the deceased or of the deceased's loved ones is certainly not requisite for the praying of a large portion of the prayers, which thereby provided for pastors a generalized, optimistic service that could be used for all persons who asked for the care of the church.[69] Yet the pain of death was not glossed over, undoubtedly because of attention to developing psychological theories about the resolution of grief. God does "not willingly grieve or afflict the children of men"; nevertheless, death is "part of thy plan for life."

A few modifications to the 1939 text were made when the Methodist Church published its *Book of Worship* in 1945; in both of those years a separate service for the burial of a child followed the normative rite. When revisions were made for the 1965 *Book of Worship*, the child's order was subsumed into the other text, which was then further expanded with Scripture and prayer resources, though textual connections were retained to its predecessors of 1945 (#), 1932 (*), and earlier:

 # Opening sentences [#John 11:25–26; *#Deuteronomy 33:27a;
#Psalm 27:1; Psalm 28:6–7a; *#2 Corinthians 5:1]
Hymn [optional]
*# Prayers [one or more]
   # "O God, the Lord of life. . . ."
   # "Almighty God, our Father, from whom we come. . . ."
   "O God our Father, creator of all mankind. . . ."
   "O Jesus Christ our risen Lord. . . ."

 # Psalms [one or more] [#Psalm 23; #Psalm 27; *#Psalm 90 [selections] ;
   #Psalm 121]
 # Gloria Patri
  Apostles' Creed or another affirmation of faith
*# New Testament lesson [one or more]
     *# John 14:1–7, 15–17, 27
     *# Romans 8:14–18, 28, 31, 35, 37–39
     *# 1 Corinthians 15:20–22, 35–36, 38a, 42–44, 49–50, 53–58
     *# Revelation 21:2–7
     # Revelation 22:1–5
     # Ephesians 3:14–21
*# Hymn or anthem
*# Sermon [in 1932 and 1945 identified as "address"]
*# Prayers [extemporaneous, or one or more of following]
     *# "Eternal God, who committest to us. . . ."
     # "O God, who art the strength of thy saints. . . ."
     *# "Almighty God, the fountain of all life. . . ."
     "Remember thy servant, O Lord. . . ."
     # "Father of spirits, we have joy at this time. . . ."
     # "O Lord and Master, who thyself didst weep. . . ."
     # "O Thou who hast ordered this wondrous world. . . ."
     # "O Lord, we pray thee, give us thy strength. . . ."
     # "Almighty God, who art leading us. . . ." (for a child)
     # "O God, whose most dear Son did take little children into his
       arms. . . ."
     "O God, we pray that thou wilt keep. . . ."
Benediction [Philippians 4:7]

*# Sentences at the grave [#Psalm 124:8; #Psalm 103:13; *#Isaiah 35:4;
   #Psalm 103:7]
*# Committal [one of three to be used]
     *# "Forasmuch as the spirit of the departed has entered into the life
       immortal. . . ."
     # "Forasmuch almighty God hath received unto himself the soul of
       our departed *brother*. . . ."
     *# "Forasmuch as the spirit of the departed hath returned to God
       who gave it. . . ."
*# Revelation 14:13
 # Kyrie eleison
*# The Lord's Prayer [also found after the opening prayer in 1932 and
   1945]
*# Prayer [one or more]
     *# "Almighty God, with whom do live the spirits. . . ."
     *# "O merciful God, the Father. . . ."
     # "O God of infinite compassion. . . ."
Benediction [Hebrews 13:20–21 or *#2 Corinthians 13:14]

The Methodist Church's 1965 rite not only increased the number of optional texts offered, it also showed the growing tendency toward understanding the burial liturgy as a worship service of praise and thanksgiving comparable in form to Sunday morning. The funeral's purpose "as a tribute to the dead" and for "comforting the bereaved" was, for some at least, secondary to "a service of worship in which the faith of the Church in the love and mercy of God is affirmed."[70] As worship, the funeral was to allow the congregation honestly to face death—that of the loved one and their own death—within the context of the "good news concerning the life everlasting."[71] But the rite did not fully address concerns that some members were raising about the denomination's departure from a biblical and Christian understanding of death. The use of the perceived "pagan" term of "immortality" was questioned, with preference given to the nomenclature of "resurrection" and "eternal life."[72] As the result of intentional discussions about eschatological terminology and theology prompted in part by participation in ecumenical conversations, emphasis upon resurrection instead of immortality would be more fully evident in the service produced by the United Methodist Church that succeeded the 1965 rite.

Conformity to Christ

In the latter half of the twentieth century, a funeral presided over by one of Wesley's spiritual descendants might be seen as an evangelistic opportunity to convert the reluctant or the indifferent, but more often it was deemed an occasion to offer words of God's mercy and love while confronting the stark and painful reality of death. To further this purpose, all the Methodist denominations realigned the first part of their authorized burial rites, now held in church or funeral home, to conform more recognizably to a Sunday pattern. Among the Holiness and African-American Methodists, remnants of the 1792 burial rite were still very much in evidence. The Free Methodists approved in 1974 an order of worship to be used in "church or chapel," with the graveside service preserving Wesley's processional sentences, collect, and the apostolic benediction. The rite published in the 1992 Discipline of the African Methodist Episcopal Church was virtually the same as that of 1840;[73] that denomination's 1984 Book of Worship, however, placed the familiar text within the framework of a broader worship structure of prelude, hymns, and choral selections. The African Methodist Episcopal Zion Church kept the historic readings and included for the first time in their 1996 Book of Worship a rubric about the practice of a wake, thereby acknowledging officially what had long been a custom among African-American Methodists and African-American Christians in general.

A substantial shift in Methodist burial rites and the theology behind them took place with the production of the United Methodist Church's "Service of Death and Resurrection," offered as a supplemental text in 1979, officially approved in 1984, and published in the United Methodist Hymnal (1989) and the United Methodist Book of Worship (1992). The ritual text itself, aside from the continuity of some suggested Scripture readings, marked a significant departure from all previous Methodist funeral liturgies both in structure and in content. The rite did, however, provide stated options within the ritual text, as had some other twentieth-century rites, and further resources were supplied within the introductory guide that accompanied the first publication of the text, selections from which were later included in the *Book of Worship*.[74] The service was designed in three parts rather than two: to the service of the word and the graveside service was added, for the first time in any American Methodist rite, Holy Communion, which was strongly encouraged as an integral component of the funeral. A unique eucharistic prayer devised for the occasion was printed that incorporated themes of resurrection, eternal life, and the communion of saints. The shape of the funeral liturgy thus followed the stated denominational pattern for "Word and Table" in its printing of 1979:

Gathering of the People

The Word of Grace
Greeting
Sentences [here if not used earlier with the placing of a pall]
Hymn or Song
Prayer
Pardon [if prayer of confession used]
Psalm 130

Proclamation and Praise

Old Testament Reading
Psalm 23
Epistle Reading
Gospel Reading
Sermon
Naming [reading of a memorial or appropriate statement]
Witness [persons voice thankfulness to God for the life of the deceased]
Hymn

Offering of Life

Apostles' Creed
Prayers
Holy Communion or Prayer of Thanksgiving
The Lord's Prayer
Hymn
Dismissal and Blessing

An Order of Committal

Sentences [first phrase of *Media vita* conflated with Psalm 121:1b; Psalm 124: 8; Romans 8:11b; 1 Corinthians 15:51, 53, 54b–55, 57; and/or Psalm 16: 9, 11]
Prayer
Scripture Readings [suggested: 1 Peter 1:3–9; John 12:23–26]

Commendation [while earth is cast on the coffin]
Committal
Prayers
The Lord's Prayer
Hymn or Song
Dismissal and Blessing

The Lord's Supper in the funeral liturgy was intended to remind those gathered of the presence of the One whose paradigmatic death and resurrection defined the Christian's approach to life and to death. Drawing upon theological and liturgical resources from other Christian communions, the United Methodist funeral task force, guided by principal author Paul Waitman Hoon, opted to locate the funeral in the context of the Easter liturgy, and in baptism as the recapitulation of the Easter event: "The funeral is the completion of the Christian's passover undertaken when the baptizand died unto Christ in Baptism—the rounding out of the full paschal cycle."[75] The penalty of death as a consequence of human sin was thus reaffirmed, and set once again within the atoning and sacramental work of Christ. Death had to be confronted and not avoided: the God "who gave us birth" was supplicated to "help us live as those who are prepared to die" that "we may die as those who go forth to live." Thus the baptismal approach to death, implicit throughout the rite, was expressed overtly in the opening sentences:

Dying, Christ destroyed our death.
Rising, Christ restored our life.
Christ will come again in glory.
As in baptism N. put on Christ,
so in Christ may N. be clothed with glory.
Here and now, dear friends, we are God's children.
What we shall be has not yet been revealed.
But we know that when he appears we shall be like him, for
we shall see him as he is.
Those who have this hope purify themselves as Christ is pure.

In distinction from popular concepts of natural immortality, the rite (and its accompanying introductory essay) stressed resurrection as an act of God that encompassed the gift of new life to the believer, the embrace of each believer at the point of death, and the final transformation of all Christ's followers at his return.[76]

Although the "Service of Death and Resurrection" was intended to counteract what was perceived to be the increased secularization of the American funeral, it was not meant to ignore the real human elements of grief and loss. The revising committee took seriously the latest work in pastoral psychology, and heard reports on customary funeral practices among ethnic and racial United Methodist congregations.[77] Yet the therapeutic was subordinated to the kerygmatic, lest the funeral yield to being a "secular therapy in a Christian idiom instead of Christian reality in a therapeutic idiom."[78]

The "Service of Death and Resurrection," in many respects, embodied both the countercultural posture found particularly in early American Methodism and the desire for cultural adaptation expressed in the late nineteenth and the twentieth centuries. Death was recovered as both penalty and promise, and the sacraments were magnified as a means by which the individual (and the community) conformed to and imitated Christ. By its presumption of baptismal identity for the deceased and for those gathered, the rite appeared to be meant for those whose faith was evident. The celebration of the Eucharist reinforced that claim, though in reality few United Methodist funerals included the Supper. Yet the provision—still under the heading of "Death and Resurrection"—of some alternative prayers and Scripture texts for those "who did not profess the Christian faith" conceded the rite to the trajectory of accommodation. While the pastoral concern to comfort the bereaved was itself legitimate, and hope in God's generosity toward the departed may always be entertained, the kerygmatic truth requires that the summons in the end must be one of conversion if the promises of the Maker and Judge of all are to be authentically represented and offered for acceptance.

9

Devotion and Discipleship

Aᴄᴄᴏʀᴅɪɴɢ ᴛᴏ ᴊᴏʜɴ ᴡᴇsʟᴇʏ, Methodists, like all real Christians, were to be Christians "not in *name* only, but in *heart* and in *life*."[1] True Methodists translated their belief into sanctifying actions: love toward God and neighbor was concretized by regular engagement in spiritual disciplines and charitable deeds. Prayer, be it in the congregation, in the family, or in one's closet, was typically listed as the first "work of piety," among which also figured searching the Scriptures (by hearing, reading, and meditating upon them), reception of the Lord's Supper, fasting or abstinence, and "conversation with the children of God." These "ordinances" were understood to be the instituted and usual means by which God's grace was channeled to the church; and all Methodists, but especially the lay leadership and (after the ordinations of 1784) the ministers, were expected diligently to employ them.[2] "Works of mercy" toward persons of varying conditions, whether they be friend or foreigner, were to be extended to needy bodies and souls: the hungry fed, the naked clothed, the stranger entertained, the infirm and imprisoned visited, and the comforting yet demanding words of the gospel shared with all.[3] Glorification of God and obedience to the law of Christ properly motivated such acts of devotion and discipleship, and resulted in authentic and spiritual worship. For, as Wesley noted by quoting St. Augustine, "*Optimus Dei cultus, imitari quem colis*—It is the best worship or service of God, to imitate him you worship."[4]

Three of these works of piety and mercy in their American Methodist aspects will be the focus of attention here. Family worship or family religion, what Wesley perceived as the "grand desideratum among the Methodists,"[5] was a matter of great concern. So was also the prayer meeting or the gathering of persons for public worship at a time in addition to the Lord's Day; both family worship and the prayer meeting composed essential Methodist "usages" according to backwoods preacher Peter Cartwright.[6] Visitation of the sick was a charitable work expected of all Methodists, but especially the clergy. These practices of devotion and discipleship that truly were the work of the people constitute important ingredients in the mix of American Methodist worship.

Family Worship

Methodists have always regarded the domestic family as a microcosm of the family of God, and a divinely ordained institution for instructing and nurturing religion especially in the rising generation.[7] Every Methodist family ideally was "a sanctuary in which God is continually dwelling,"[8] and the family altar was considered the cornerstone for the development or intensification of personal piety and godly conduct. Public worship, no matter how regularly attended, was by itself deemed insufficient to prevent spiritual lukewarmness. Attention to regular family duty properly reinforced "experimental" religion, and also preserved the family (and hence the church) through the mutual dependence and love required of its members. By domestic prayer the family was bound together in faith, granted security from encroaching worldliness, and provided with an escape from life's trials. The resolution "As for me and my house, we will serve the Lord" (Joshua 24:15) thus became the motto for Methodists, who took seriously what was understood to be the Christian obligation of family worship based upon scriptural paradigms (in the absence of an explicit dominical warrant)—including the pattern of Jesus himself, who sang hymns and prayed with his family, namely, the disciples.[9]

During the late eighteenth century and throughout the nineteenth, the benefits of family worship were lauded, and recommendations put forward on how to promote prayer within the household. Domestic prayer very quickly came to be understood more as a Christian duty to be fulfilled than as a means of grace to be received. Methodist couples just married, as well as the newly converted, were advised immediately to erect a family altar and to persist in daily prayer, preferably at a consistent time in the morning and in the evening. At some homes, family worship took place three times on the Sabbath if attendance at public corporate worship was impossible.[10] The primary responsibility for leading prayers fell to the husband, as God's appointed head of the household, with his wife joining and encouraging him in the sacred work. However, by the end of the nineteenth century, women assumed a greater role as husbands took employment at a distance from the family dwelling. Anyone in the house at the time of prayer was expected to attend. When children were present, the time for worship was to be chosen that best suited alertness and full participation. Because the temporal and spiritual well-being of servants rested with the head of the household, masters were to ensure that they too participated in devotions, either in the house itself or standing outside an open door. Daniel Wise, writing in 1854 about white domestics, went so far as to insist that Protestant servants should be dismissed who did not consent to take part in family worship, but allowed exceptions for Catholics.[11] Visitors in the home were also not to be excluded from worship and were invited to the proceedings in recognition that, in the case of the unconverted, the foundation of an individual's faith might be laid and the seed for future Methodist membership planted.[12] The family altar was usually open to both neighbor and stranger; particularly at the end of the eighteenth century and in the early nineteenth, family prayer could function as a public evangelistic opportunity in conjunction with a quarterly meeting or otherwise:

> At family prayer two or three mourners got under [great] distress of soul. A shout soon broke out & continued till near 11 o'clock. The way it came was as follows— soon as family prayer was over two young women went upstairs to prayer. I sent two others up to them. They presently were so affected that others went up also & then others and joined them till their prayer and cries passed through all the house and all got up in the chamber—the black people also crowded on the stairs to see & hear. Glory to God for these favours![13]

In villages heavily populated by Methodists, a wayfarer passing by in the morning or evening might choose from among the several families heard at prayer.[14] Even though receiving invitations to join another household for prayer, a single individual might rather feel obliged to engage in solitary family worship:

> In Lancaster county, Pennsylvania, a man lived by himself whose name began with M. He was one of the happiest men I saw at a quarterly meeting. Going along the road a man asked me: "Do you see that house across the field?" I said "Yes." "There," said he, "lives M., that you saw so happy at the meeting; he is a mechanic, lives alone, and has family prayer evening and morning. When some asked why he did so, as he had no family, he said he belonged to the household of faith, the family of God. He identified himself with all the praying families, and while hundreds and thousands were worshiping, he would worship too; their prayers all met at the throne of grace, and great blessings came down from heaven and made a heavenly place. He would not be deprived of the privilege and blessing of family prayer. He was often heard by the neighbors praying and praising God, and shouting, 'Glory to God! glory to God!' "[15]

Methodist leaders feared that marriage with an unawakened individual potentially jeopardized the fulfillment of the requisite spiritual duties within the family, and they provided legislation against such unions (which later was repealed at various times by the different Methodist bodies). The conversion of one already-married individual and not the spouse could likewise lead to spiritual complications. Yet accounts abound describing occasions where a believing partner fostered the conversion of the antagonistic or hesitant spouse by insisting upon the practice of family prayer. In one instance, a wife routinely disturbed her husband's leading of family prayer. The husband went to his class leader and had his name removed from the class list, because he believed he had to do "what a member should not do, whip his wife." After his wife again interrupted him, he whipped her soundly. When the woman went to the class leader to complain about her husband's "un-Methodist" behavior, she discovered that his name had been struck from the list. "For the Lord's sake take him again, or he will kill me," she pleaded. Eventually the woman was converted and her husband became an itinerant preacher.[16] In another case, it was a wife who challenged her reluctant husband to lead family prayer when he feared he couldn't pray. One morning she held prayers with the expectation that her husband would hold forth in the evening. When the hour came, he fell to his knees, and cried aloud for mercy and pardon. Now converted, he never again questioned his duty as the spiritual leader of the family.[17]

No formal instructions for the content of family devotions were authorized by any Methodist denomination during the nineteenth century, though there were, nevertheless, common elements that paralleled the substance of the rubrics stip-ulated for public worship from 1792. Of course, prayer, properly offered while kneeling, was a staple of family worship. Extemporaneous prayer was considered evidence of religious conviction and maturity, and was thus encouraged from every family member. Prayer books functioned as a stopgap only until an individual could pray without one; children, it was recommended, were to be given short and simple prayers to memorize and repeat morning and evening until they were capable of extemporizing.[18] Bible reading was *lectio continua* or with lections chosen for the occasion. In the evening worship of some families, children were called upon to read a chapter, with interesting results if a child was fatigued (one sleepy little boy reportedly began Matthew 25, "Then shall the kingdom of heaven by likened unto the ten Virginians who took their lamps and went forth to meet the bridge gang").[19] Afterward, the spiritual and contemporary relevance of the reading might be discussed, or personal testimonies offered. Hymn or psalm singing was inter-woven among the other components, with selections taken from different sources: the official hymnals, some of which designated sections for family devotions and for morning and evening worship; song books unauthorized by the denominations; and the unprinted repertoire memorized at the camp meeting and other venues of worship. Family worship was thus intentionally doxological, catechetical, and evangelical. Although Methodist writers urged a methodical approach to the dis-cipline of family prayer, caution was raised against the "great evil" of formality: a family should not be "scrupulously bound" to any particular form, especially when "the Scripture has left [them] free."[20]

Despite the enthusiasm with which many Methodists approached the duty of family worship, others were apathetic, or enumerated such excuses as inability, timidity, inconvenience, lack of time, and belief in the sufficiency of personal prayer. Because family religion was considered "shamefully wanting" in many places, legislation to provide concrete remedies was enacted in the first American Methodist *Discipline* (Questions 15 and 66, adopted from the Large Minutes) and in subsequent action by the various Methodist denominations. Preachers were to watch over each other and those under their care to ensure a positive answer to the query, "Have you family prayer?" Preachers who lodged in private homes while traveling were to attend family devotions or initiate them if nothing had been planned. Every Methodist leader was expected to visit from house to house and, by word and example, commend the virtues of family worship. Family prayer was serious business: one class leader in Ohio "allowed no family to live without prayer."[21] Persons notably lax in domestic duties might first be given a reproof, and on second offense be brought up on charges, as happened to Jonathan Kidwell of Kentucky, who was informed by his quarterly meeting conference that he must meet with a committee of three to converse "in a friendly manner" on the subject of his negligence.[22] Repeated or intentional delinquency after the first two reprimands might result in dismissal from the class or from the church. From 1864 to 1939 the Methodist Episcopal Church expressly identified the habitual neglect of the means of grace as cause for trial or, if uncorrected, expulsion, although it is unknown how often this ruling was actually carried out.

As late as the 1890s, personal accounts testify to the concerted attention that was given by some pastors to family prayer:

> The most of the time my mother would take the lead in the family worship, and would read the Bible and have family prayer. My earliest recollection is of holy men of God like Bro. McClesky, Bro. John Mashburn and Bro. W. A. Dodge visiting in our home and having family prayer. . . . These mighty warriors for God would come riding up to our home on a horse, as the old-fashioned Methodist circuit riders would do. They would come in the house and my mother and father would call all the children in and there was a small table in the front of the house that contained an old-fashioned Methodist hymnal, a family Bible, and a Methodist discipline. The dear man of God would line off a hymn and sing it in long meter. He quite often would read the general rules of the discipline of the Methodist Church, after which he would read some passage from the Bible and kneel down and have prayer. My mother and father would be weeping many times after he left.[23]

In spite of such continuing diligence, the practice of family worship had nevertheless dwindled over the course of the nineteenth century as the denominations grew in membership: what had been the perceived rule in Methodist family life became an exception. Some parents believed the Sunday school to be a sufficient substitute for instilling Christian disciplines in their young, though church leaders were quick to refute such claims. Calls increased throughout the century and into the next for families to hold prayer regularly, and for pastors to be more assertive in accomplishing their pastoral obligation of promoting domestic piety. Fears that Methodist families—a supposed microcosm of church and nation—were succumbing to worldly amusements and distractions such as card playing, theatergoing, circus attending and dancing drove many of the appeals. By the beginning of the twentieth century, family prayer was identified by proponents as both a Christian responsibility and a means to preserve the institution of the family embattled by growing secularism and irregular work schedules (including the employment of women). The problem was not unique to Methodism, and many Methodists subscribed to the work of the ecumenical and international Family Altar League established in the first decade of the twentieth century to encourage regularized devotion and provide requesting families with resources.[24]

Printed aids specified for family worship did not suddenly appear in the twentieth century. In 1850, Charles F. Deems complemented his apologia for family worship in The Home Altar with stated Scripture lessons and prayers assigned to morning and evening for each day of the week over the course of a month. Since Deems preferred extemporary prayer, bracketed sections in each prayer designated the place for petitions "particularly adapted to the circumstances and exigencies of the family." Practical necessity was not the only justification for printed prayers, according to Deems; the primitive church had used both extemporized and written forms, and Scripture had left the church at liberty to choose which was the most expedient.[25] Thirty-six years later, Aid and Guide to Family Worship was published, edited by layman L. D. Palmer and printed by the Southern Methodist Publishing House, which contained formulated prayers and simple orders of worship designed specifically to prop up domestic leaders until they could improvise on their own; this book was reprinted into the 1920s. Other books followed, but now without disclaimers for written prayers, since forms could be justified by the increasing acceptance and use in Sunday worship of prayer texts and formal orders. The rationale that the reading of prayers was "thoroughly Methodistic" was given in the 1921 publication *"Keep the Home Fires Burning"*, which included, for every day of the week for six months, a Scripture lesson, a brief exposition of the passage, a short prayer, and at the end of each week's presentation, a "Lesson Question" to stimulate conversation.[26] In a significant departure from earlier practice, one person writing in 1928 even advised the use of a book of prayers lest family devotions sink into "ruts and meaningless repetitions."[27]

The first official book with materials specified for family worship was the 1945 *Book of Worship* of the Methodist Church, which continued the custom in earlier resources of providing Scripture selections and prayers for each day of the month (though now reduced to one time per day), but also supplied prayers addressing family needs and other situations, and orders for morning and evening. These worship orders for "a family or other small group" fell under the category of services for occasional use, and introduced new acts of worship such as versicles and responsive readings to the practice of family prayer. No placement was specified for Scripture readings or extemporary prayer within the orders. The extensive helps for families furnished in the 1945 book were not repeated in the 1965 *Book of Worship*; what remained was an order for family or small group use that, as in years past, borrowed elements familiar from Sunday morning, though now these took a more elaborate shape: Scripture sentences or call to worship; prayer; psalm, canticle or other act of praise; Gloria Patri; Scripture lesson; extemporary or written prayers; and a hymn. Even though the Methodist Church's successor, the United Methodist Church, maintained a commitment in the *Discipline* to family life as the forum for the Christian nurturing of its members, an explicit ritual expression of that concern no longer existed; no specified resources were identified for families in the 1992 *Book of Worship*, though persons who desired orders might use the forms for "Daily Praise and Prayer" derived from early Christian models.

Even with the publication of resources throughout the twentieth century, the once-rigorous routine of twice- or thrice-daily family worship had been reduced, in homes that practiced it, to the saying of a table grace, or to a brief reading from a prepared devotional booklet at the dining table or at bedside. Although the admonition to observe family prayer remained in each Methodist *Discipline* produced in the twentieth century, if only in the General Rules, the mechanisms for enforcement were gradually abandoned. The Methodist Episcopal Church, for example, introduced into the 1920 *Discipline* instructions that the number of families who observed family worship was to be reported at every quarterly conference, and that pastors and other leaders were to encourage in each home a regular and systematic program of prayer, Scripture reading and study, and conversation upon "moral and spiritual" subjects (¶61 §2.9; ¶589); sixteen years later, both directions were gone. In 1948, the Methodist Church's *Discipline* contained the recommendation that each family have a worship center in the home (¶2021.1); in the 1956 *Discipline*, the Christian family was defined as one that had daily prayer and grace at meals (¶2021.1). But family worship was not specifically addressed in the polity of the United Methodist Church, although Christian education and formation (especially moral development) in the church and home continued as a legislative priority.

Public Prayer

The relaxation in both the practice and enforcement of devotional piety evident in over two hundred years of Methodist family worship holds true as well for social, public prayer observed outside of the Lord's Day service. In many respects, prayer meetings up to the mid-nineteenth century were like family worship of that period, only on a grander scale and held in various settings, one of which might be a family dwelling. Extemporary prayer, Scripture readings, hymn singing, conversations, and testimonies also characterized these scheduled or spontaneous assemblies. Exhortations were not ordinarily a part of family worship unless a preacher came to call, but they were often a component of common prayer (and sometimes blurred indistinguishably with a prayer) and more frequently heard than a sermon. Shouts, vocalized "amens," and hand clapping punctuated the proceedings which did not require—or need—pastoral direction, though the clergy and other leaders were admonished by the *Discipline* to guarantee that prayer meetings regularly took place. Preachers attending judicatory convocations convened prayer meetings. Saturday night of the quarterly meeting was typically designated the occasion for prayer meeting, with several gatherings occurring simultaneously. Camp meetings had prayer meetings organized by gender, generation, and race, with some mixed groups; racial exclusion increased as the nineteenth century progressed. The enthusiasm begotten by the camp meeting might lead to the emergence of prayer meetings in areas inhabited by persons just returned from the camp and possibly as a consequence inflame an extended revival; conversely, local prayer meetings might give birth to a camp meeting. In urban areas and in adjacent settlements, prayer meetings might be held once or twice weekly, with one of those meetings possibly taking place following a Sunday evening preaching service. The meetings could occur at sunrise or in the evening, and if circumstances required it, late at night:

> Some time in the Night—I judge near the Middle watch—I awaked in raptures of Heaven by the sweet Echo of Singing in the Kitchen among the dear Black people (who my Soul loves). I scarcely ever heard anything to equal it upon earth. I rose up and strove to join them—ah—I felt the miserable weight of oppression intolerable upon my heart—while the proud whites can live in luxury and abomination making a mock of God and his word, the African upholds him by his Swet and labour of his willing hands—and if they serve the Lord God it must be in the dead of night when they ought to be taking rest to their bodys, O blood, blood how aweful it Cryes up before God, against my poor unjust professing Bro—well I must have patience—hope God will work for his own Glory.[28]

If necessary, prayer meetings could also be scheduled in lieu of a preaching service or a Lord's Day gathering. Prayer meetings were thus the heart and soul of the Methodist revival in the young nation.

Gifted leaders able to draw the entire assembly into full participation were believed essential to achieve the goal that persons at prayer meeting should be "refreshed & made glad, converted & sanctified."[29] Women known for the power of their exhortations and prayers led female meetings, as well as general gatherings. Leaders might call upon young girls or boys who had previously given evidence of vital piety, and their impassioned prayers were known sometimes to soften hard hearts.[30] In some areas it was the custom for the leader to solicit all those assembled to offer prayer when inspired, resulting in a symphony of praise and petition.[31] The ideals of democracy undergirded the prayer meeting in its early years and contributed to its success. In turn, the confidence and skills acquired in the church gathering might help a political or professional career.

Other occasions for public prayer also accentuated conversion or growth in holiness. Prayer combined with fasting was stipulated by church leaders routinely in the early years as a corporate act of penitence and supplication, in addition to the private discipline of fasting and prayer that was expected at least on the Friday preceding the local quarterly meeting. Members of all the churches in New York City were called to fasting and prayer on September 20, 1793 "to intreat the Lord to put a stop to the Malignant disorder in the City of Philadelphia," and in response, overflow crowds attended services of prayer and preaching; in 1810, a general fast was appointed for the "African Churches."[32] At the request of Jefferson Davis, many southern Methodists, along with other Christians, observed a day of fasting and prayer for the Southern Army in 1861.[33] While the General Conference of the Methodist Episcopal Church was in session in the year 1864, a fast day was set apart for the nation in "this hour of her peril."[34] The importance Methodists attached to the "public fast" was expressed by the designation of hymns under that heading in certain authorized hymnals published during the nineteenth century, with the theme of the texts principally lamentation for the sin of the nation and God's impending judgment:

> Dread Jehovah! God of nations!
> From thy temple in the skies,
> Hear thy people's supplications;
> Now for their deliv'rance rise.
>
> Lo! with deep contrition turning,
> In thy holy place we bend;
> Hear us, fasting, praying, mourning;
> Hear us, spare us, and defend.[35]

As was the case with domestic worship, the disciplined practices of public prayer and public fasting gradually lost their intensity and popularity. By the 1860s, writers mourned the fervency of former days and urged renewed attention to the prayer meeting, not only for its own sake, but also as a means of preserving the public expression of experiential religion since that practice was increasingly at risk in the larger Methodist denominations as the old institution of the class meeting began to decline. The gradual passing away of the historic mechanism for spiritual accountability among the people meant that new methods for encouraging the regular practice of public (and private) prayer were necessary, such as the Sunday school and missionary societies. The responsibility of spiritual oversight, once shared among a network of leaders, started to fall more singularly to the pastor, whose special training, it was surmised, better equipped him for the task. Leadership for the prayer meeting also came to be placed more firmly into his hands. The Methodist Episcopal Church, South, for example, introduced into its *Discipline* in 1866 a section on social meetings, in which preachers were directed to hold weekly prayer meetings when practicable, or appoint someone in their absence. Members were instructed that it was their duty to attend as frequently as possible, though that charge was dropped four years later. Although lay leadership was still solicited, the virtual turning over of the prayer meeting to the clergy may have ultimately contributed to its demise: the institutionalizing of the people's unfettered expression of worship in part redefined both its purpose and its content.

Attendance at prayer meetings continued to slip, though less so among the Holiness and African American denominations. Concerned that less than one-fifth of its membership came to prayer meetings—ostensibly because the meetings were dull and lifeless on account of "long hymns," "perfunctory prayers," and "want of spirituality"—the Ohio Conference of the Methodist Episcopal Church in 1875 proposed a united effort to cure "wide-spread prayer-meeting paralysis."[36] A frequently stated corrective, generated undoubtedly by fond memories of the practice of former years, was to encourage a brief service, one characterized by simplicity, freedom, variety, spontaneity, general participation, and above all, the "power of the Holy Ghost."[37] Yet despite the familiar worries about formality in worship, scripted helps began to circulate to bolster the beleaguered prayer meeting. Grace Methodist Episcopal Church of Baltimore published in 1892 an eighty-page resource for its own Wednesday evening prayer meeting, with an order of service, the Decalogue with responses, the General Confession from the Prayer Book daily office, and responsive Scripture lessons for each week of the year; these were placed alongside gospel and revival hymns expressive of personal faith. The arrangement of the service, made by the pastor and a layman, shows the growing complexity of urban Methodist Episcopal worship at the turn into the next century, interest in emulating Wesley's services and the Prayer Book, and also a newly accepted posture for prayer:

Doxology "Praise God from whom all blessings. . . ."
Versicles
Prayer (in unison, said standing) ["O Almighty God, who hast bidden us seek that we may find. . . ."]
Hymn
Prayer
Gloria Patri (standing)
Versicle
Scripture lesson (responsive)

Leader's exposition (Ten minutes.)
Remarks by the people. Testimony. Prayer
Announcements. Offertory. Hymn
Prayer (Prayer of St. John Chrysostom)
Doxology
Benediction[38]

Books with resources to infuse new life into the prayer meeting and other services of worship Sunday night or midweek were especially numerous in the first three decades of the twentieth century. Some volumes supplied orders of worship, prayer texts, and lectionaries, or offered a general guide for planning a successful gathering; others furnished meditations or short addresses upon topics related to spiritual growth or contemporary Christian life (particularly social issues) that could be read aloud or inspire an original discourse.[39] The authors of these books did not consider themselves abettors of formalism in worship. Rather, they regarded their work as a contribution toward the greater variety that was believed to be a viable remedy for low attendance and a bland meeting. Variety, some believed, conformed to divine example:

> He who made the world likes variety. We see that everywhere. . . . The fact that God's efforts are never formal, neither in nature or grace, in time or eternity, constitutes one reason why men love God's handiwork, why the "old, old story" as experienced in life and related in testimony is ever new, and why we shall enjoy heaven forever.
>
> If our prayer meetings lack variety must we not in frankness admit that they are less than what God desires them to be, and should we not expect that men should fail in enthusiasm for them; and, on the other hand, if we build them as God builds his universe of nature and grace, shall we not more perfectly please him and more surely enlist and hold the interest of men? This question has but one answer.[40]

The public testimony of faith that had always been at the heart of the prayer meeting was seen by some early twentieth-century writers as, in fact, a possible contributor to absenteeism. The expectation that each week an inspirational witness of personal faith or religious experience would be given evidently led some testifiers to exaggerate or to repeat ad nauseam their account. There were also those dubbed "prayer-meeting killers": persons unable to differentiate between personal comment and faith testimony, and those who monopolized the allotted time. Because of this problem, some congregations opted to restrict testimonies to a separate "experience" meeting. A Scranton, Pennsylvania, church held prayer meetings until 1920 consisting of a short address and extemporary prayer; an experience session followed.[41] Not unexpectedly, the experience meeting could also be the victim of a "killer." One North Carolina congregation discontinued its testimony meetings after an elderly woman detailed her difficulties with her family for an entire hour.[42]

The diminishing drawing power of public prayer outside of Sunday morning could also be explained by other factors internal and external to the church. To apathy and poor preparation on the parts of both clergy and laity, one author in 1910 added:

Lack of interest in truly spiritual things; waning faith, pressure of business and social life; multiplicity of other church services, and of all kinds of social and business engagements; lack of genuine religious training in the home; abandonment of the habit of prayer; growing formality in the churches; the growth of young people's societies, which in their devotional meetings take the place of the prayer meeting for those who attend; the increased attention to Sunday school work, and the absorption to such a large extent of the energies of the church to build up this service; the missionary societies, whose services are so often wholly, and always more or less, prayer services; the increase in the number of church organizations, the work of which leaves little time for interest in anything else.[43]

Herein the institutionalization of the church was listed as a source of the spiritual decay, or at least as a motivating force in a redefinition of spirituality. The business of mission, education, and outreach had, in some places, taken precedence over the discipline of public prayer that had in years past soundly undergirded works of mercy and discipleship. The relaxing in several denominations of social restrictions added to the temptation to abandon public gatherings for prayer. So did the increasing affluence of some Methodists, whose financial wherewithal gave them access to advances in technology, which thereby granted greater ease of travel and communication, and provided diversions through motion pictures, television, and other developing forms of entertainment. The frenetic pace of modern life, along with its many distractions, threatened to kill the practice.

Nevertheless, many Methodist leaders continued to promote the prayer and midweek preaching service, not only because they were compelled to do so by *Discipline*, but also because it "teaches democracy, fosters spiritual life, creates Christian fellowship, perpetuates the family altar, stimulates Bible study, and promotes evangelism."[44] Recognizing that technology could also be used to the advantage of public prayer and not just its detriment, some pastors prepared services intended for radio broadcast: in one community, the pastor designed a service for the unseen congregation with choral singing, hymns, poetry, prayers, and a message "to meet some specific human need."[45] Other creative leaders developed programs that retained components of the prayer meeting, but integrated them with classes, talks, or programs focused upon the questions of their constituency regarding spirituality or modern life. Ecumenically and denominationally designated days or weeks of prayer, such as the World Day of Prayer on the first Friday in Lent promoted in the 1930s by the Federal Council of Churches of Christ in America, generated services of public prayer sometimes shared among congregations. Some pastors reported a resurgence in attendance especially in the years during and after the Second World War and the Korean conflict. Worship suggestions continued to be printed, but only two official Methodist books in the twentieth century contain significant resources: the 1945 *Book of Worship* of the Methodist Church, which included seven orders of service for corporate evening prayer, as well as the services for "a family or other small group"; and the 1992 United Methodist *Book of Worship*, with its orders for "Daily Praise and Prayer" (morning, midday, evening, and night) and a "Midweek Service of Prayer and Testimony," the latter structured very much like the Baltimore church's 1892 service.

In the late twentieth century, there was still the expectation and the demand among some Methodists for organized meetings of public prayer. A United Methodist writing in 1999 asked the same question possibly posed by his grandparents, "Whatever happened to Sunday night services and Wednesday prayer meetings?"[46] since opportunities for public prayer in the older style existed only in a minority of congregations. During the 1990s new forms of public prayer started to emerge, with some of them reminiscent of former practices. Evangelistic "seeker" services of praise and prayer, and midweek alternatives to the "traditional" service on Sunday morning opened church doors for worship on days other than the Lord's Day. Another forum for corporate prayer arose with the multiplication of small groups (some defined by gender) for sharing, study, and support. The small group phenomenon expressed a more broadly based desire within the American culture to find an intimate and mutually accountable community. The recovery of corporate devotions may give the appearance of a return to historic Methodist practices, yet the underlying assumptions were drastically different: public prayer was not understood to be a means of grace, but rather a means for self-fulfillment.

Visitation of the Sick

The spiritual and physical care of the sick was regarded by American Methodists of the first several generations as a work of mercy incumbent upon all Christians—what Bishop Morris of the Methodist Episcopal Church identified in 1852 as a "plain duty of practical religion" and a "charitable work inseparable from true piety."[47] By calling upon the ailing, visible testimony was given of love for God and of obedience to the mandates of the gospel for which one would answer at the day of judgment (e.g., Matthew 25:31–46). Benefits were received by both the sick and the visitor: for the former ideally came relief of body and comfort of soul; and in the case of the latter, visitation could be a means of grace if approached with clarity of purpose.[48] Women were regarded as naturally suited to the tasks of visiting and caring for the sick; female ministry to the infirm would be institutionalized by the office of deaconess in various Methodist branches from the final third of the nineteenth century through the twentieth.

The content of the visit, whether made by a minister, class leader, or church member, was determined by the medical and spiritual condition of the infirm, though brevity was always the watchword. One or more of the basic worship components of reading, prayer, singing, and speaking (here conversation or exhortation) in innumerable combinations could be used. An abbreviated service of Holy Communion also might be celebrated by an elder if requested by the bedridden or the family. In all circumstances the sick person was to be directed to Christ, though the visitor was advised to avoid provoking an emotional state that might aggravate the illness.[49] Yet a certain honesty was required, for the salvation of the individual was believed to be at stake. One minister, in attending an unconverted young man, reportedly offered an "affectionate exhortation," and then, kneeling at bedside, prayed fervently for the safety of his soul. The sickness worsened, and despite the minister's prayers and encouragement, the man breathed his last without uttering words of faith, much to the despair of the minister and the man's family.[50]

Ministers especially were to use the "room of affliction" to move the unconvinced toward belief gently but persuasively. The Methodist Protestants alone among the Methodist denominations formalized this approach by including directions for the visitation of the sick among the occasional services in editions of the *Discipline* published from 1830 to 1877. Their work was not original; the instructions were taken almost verbatim from the chapter "Of the Visitation of the Sick" located in the "Directory for the Worship of God" that had been approved in 1821 by the General Assembly of the Presbyterian Church in the United States:[51]

> If the minister find the sick person to be grossly ignorant, he shall instruct him in the nature of repentance and faith, and the way of acceptance with God, through the mediation and atonement of Jesus Christ.
>
> If the sick person appear to be a stupid, thoughtless and hardened sinner, the minister shall endeavour to awaken his mind; to arouse his conscience; to convince him of the evil and danger of sin, of the curse of the law, and the wrath of God due to sinners; to bring him to an humble and penitential sense of his iniquities; and then to state before him the fulness of the grace and mercy of God, in and through the merits of the Redeemer; the absolute necessity of faith, and repentance, in order to his being interested in the favor of God, and his obtaining everlasting happiness.
>
> If the sick person appear to be broken in spirit with a sense of sin, and apprehensions of the divine displeasure, then it will be proper to administer consolation and encouragement, by setting before him the freeness and richness of the grace of God, and the precious promises of the gospel made to all penitents.
>
> The minister must, in all cases, guard the sick against all ill-grounded persuasions of the mercy of God, without a vital union to Christ; and against unreasonable fears of death, and disponding discouragements; against presumption upon his own goodness and merit, on the one hand, and against despair of the mercy and grace of God in Christ Jesus on the other.
>
> In a word, it is the duty of all ministers and pious persons, when visiting the sick, to pray with and for them; and to administer instruction, conviction, support, consolation, or encouragement, as the case may seem to require. And to improve the occasion to exhort those about them to consider their mortality; to turn to the Lord, and make their peace with him; and in health prepare for sickness, death and judgment.

The removal of these instructions in 1877 came at a time when the approach to sickness—as with dying and death—was changing. The minister might still inquire about the state of the soul at bedside, and even instruct or warn, but now the comfort obtained through the mercy and grace of God acquired the greater stress. Those entrusted with the care of the sick were advised "to administer the consolations of religion in hours of trouble."[52] Deaconesses of the African Methodist Episcopal Church were charged to "use tact in presenting the claims of the Bible" since "too much talk may nauseate and cause the patient to wish you gone."[53] The transition in emphasis is particularly evident from the printed pastoral helps to sickroom visitation that emerged in the last decades of the nineteenth century and proliferated in the twentieth. In the revised edition of his *Minister's Manual and Pocket Ritual* issued in 1902, C. E. Mandeville advised that the sickroom visit be characterized by "real sympathy for the suffering one and for the distressed family," with a short Scripture reading followed by a brief prayer "generally sufficient." If the invalid be an unbeliever or an "avowed infidel," the pastor was not "to set forth any doctrine peculiar to his creed, but faithfully to urge the duty of repentance toward God and faith in the Lord Jesus Christ." For the visitor's convenience, Scripture lessons specified "for the comfort of believers," "for troubled hearts," and "helpful to the unsaved" were printed in full.[54] The *Pastor's Vade Mecum*, first published in 1886, took a different approach and simply suggested fourteen psalms for "Comfort in Sickness" without differentiating who might receive the consoling words. A revised edition of the same book produced in 1929 showed a new tendency by using the heading "Healing in Sickness," under which were printed Old and New Testament lessons as well as prayers soliciting strength and the healing presence of Christ. Visits to the sick were now expected to have therapeutic value, with the sensitive pastor doing all in his power to "create a state of mind favorable to the restoration of health."[55] God's care for the sick— God's suffering with human suffering—was to be set before the ill. Ministers were to be cautious in seeking the Christian profession of the unconverted sick lest the patient be placed under psychological—and hence physical—stress; likewise, pastors were to think twice about offering prayer since damage could possibly result if words were carelessly spoken.[56] The prayers for ministry to the sick provided in the Methodist Church's 1945 *Book of Worship* and in the revision of 1965, the only authorized Methodist books to be produced with such prayers, spoke neither of confession of sin nor the invalid's spiritual condition (and its improvement), but of patient endurance, and God's merciful compassion that could spare, heal, and restore.

The authorization of healing services by the United Methodist Church in 1992 for its *Book of Worship* thus appeared to perpetuate the tendency to accentuate the restorative and consolatory over the confrontative. Yet, taken seriously, the healing service for the sickroom (or for a public gathering), through a formal prayer of confession or an informal conversation, expected that the participant, if possible, would take stock of his or her spiritual state. This recovery of the connection between sickness and weakness of faith, and between physical and spiritual healing, not only brought late twentieth-century practice into line with New Testament models, it also linked Methodists, though somewhat cursorily, with the theological approach taken by their Wesleyan ancestors. The intentional return to early Christian praxis also resulted in the first official Methodist instruction to lay hands on the sick and anoint them with oil, though some pastors throughout the Methodist family had, even in the nineteenth century, already made use of the scriptural custom found in the Gospels and in James 5:14–15, and the practice of laying on of hands had been commended in literature accompanying the 1965 *Book of Worship*.[57]

The Privatization of Devotion and Discipleship

The consequences of the transition of American Methodism from evangelical revival to national denomination, and from religious society to institutional
churches, are perhaps most clearly evident by the slippage in the disciplined practice of the works of piety and the works of mercy that were intended to be performed by all those who called themselves Methodists. Although the mandates for
spiritual disciplines and charitable works were never withdrawn from any Methodist *Discipline*, they over time lost priority of place as the denominations grew,
the character of American life changed, and the emphases for ministry were altered
to meet the challenges of each new age. Related to the increased bureaucratization
of the churches was the transference of worship leadership more definitively to the
clergy, so that what once had been expected of the entire people of God became
the purview of the trained expert. Informal gatherings for prayer, praise, reading,
and conversation became formalized, though not standardized, and improvisatory
prayer was more acceptably replaced by printed forms. With these shifts came a
decrease in the ability of individuals to articulate their personal faith, as well as a
further encouragement toward the privatization of religion—already a risk because
of the emphasis in American society upon the individual—since persons were no
longer required to state openly and be accountable for what they believed. Outward
expressions of the Christian faith in the home, the small group, or the sickroom
became potentially a source of embarrassment and were engaged in with great
hesitation. The services of prayer and acts of discipleship that had been understood
as occasions for worship and channels of grace came to be regarded as personal
options, to be elected if needs warranted it.

The loss of these public expressions of the personal assurance of salvation coincided with or perhaps contributed to a redefinition of conversion. In the early
years, conversion was viewed as a corporate, public, and yet personal process that
was tested and strengthened in the context of a wider community: in the family,
by intensive formation through morning and evening worship; in public prayer, by
prayer, exhortation, and testimony; and in the sickroom, by confession and conversation. But by the end of the nineteenth century, conversion was being conceived as a private, individual, and instantaneous event. Devotion and discipleship,
originally construed primarily as acts of worship, and secondarily as opportunities
for spiritual refinement, were no longer considered critical elements in the conversion process, or as necessary components for continued growth in faith, but
supplements. The privatization of conversion, along with the privatization of devotion and discipleship, was challenged in the late twentieth century by some
Methodist theologians and liturgical scholars, who, following the consensus that
grew out of the liturgical and ecumenical movements, advocated a renewed understanding of the corporate nature of the church.[58] Such a recovery was difficult,
however, on account of the exaltation of the individual that continued to permeate
American life.

A House for Worship

THE PLACES SET APART FOR American Methodist worship, like the liturgies they housed, were shaped by different forces. A denomination's—and the local community's—conception of the nature and purpose of corporate worship, along with the patterns of worship that gave form to that understanding, was usually key to the establishment, construction, or renovation of the area for worship. The other activities of the community, devotional and social, likewise affected the disposition of the space. But demographics also played a part in the configuration of the place for worship, with variations especially noticeable between urban and rural areas. Geography determined the location of the site, the availability of building materials, and the types of structures that could feasibly be built in a particular climate. Native peoples, and long-resident Hispanic and French populations, offered distinct designs and building methods; immigrants who became Methodists brought with them the architectural memories and techniques of their homelands. Economics was also a factor: as some Methodists became more affluent, aesthetic considerations came to be valued in addition to the functional.

Multiple forces thus contributed to the organization of the worship space in any given locale. But once the place had been configured, it in turn influenced how worship would be carried out, by encouraging the perpetuation of a particular style of worship, and by inhibiting or impeding other forms, but occasionally also inviting new expressions. The space for worship itself made theological and liturgical statements about those who gathered therein and the God they worshiped; alterations in design both expressed and motivated shifts in theology and liturgical praxis. In the course of two hundred years perspectives changed on what constituted appropriate spaces for Methodist worship. Nevertheless, every place and building hallowed by prayer and praise was recognized as a symbol of an ever-present God and a testimony to the faith of God's people called Methodists.

Creating a Place for Worship

In the early decades, the Methodist determination to spread scriptural holiness throughout the land meant that the inaccessibility or absence of church buildings and meetinghouses would be no hindrance to their mission. The pragmatic American Methodist preachers, like their "venerable Father," saw only boundless opportunity: "Pure spiritual worship, which emanates from the pious heart, can be offered acceptably in any place; and wherever Christ meets his worshipping saints, there is peace, paradise, and heaven."[1] Sermon, supplication, and song could therefore be rendered in any imaginable venue, and it was this flexibility that permitted expansion, first over the eastern seaboard then westward as preachers followed the wagon train and later the railroad. Methodist worship took place wherever people could gather. Some services were held out-of-doors, with a preacher or exhorter elevated above the crowd by standing upon a log or rock, a chair, or a cart. Boats of all types were put to gospel use. A stand for speakers and simple plank benches for hearers could be built in a shaded area or under a brush arbor if a site was to accommodate frequent assemblies. Worship might be conducted from a second-story window or from a doorway, with the people clustered outside below. If available and commodious, buildings or shelters were always preferred since worship could then be held regardless of weather. In some communities, a single, multipurpose building might be shared by Methodists and their ecclesiastical rivals. But Methodists also did not hesitate to use buildings primarily intended for other than spiritual activities. Private homes or cabins were regularly used when size permitted. Schoolhouses, courthouses, Masonic halls, warehouses, barns, rigging lofts, and abandoned buildings all might be taken over for the purpose of worship. Even the barroom of an Ohio tavern that James Finley judged to look more like "the celebration of a bacchanalian orgie, than a place for the worship of God" was deemed suitable since "the Gospel was to be preached to every creature" and his mission "extended to every place this side of hell."[2]

Methodists also acquired or built their own houses, as they had done soon after the first Methodist immigrants arrived from Britain. In the 1760s, windowless log meetinghouses for worship, with dirt floors, rough-hewn benches and pulpit, and holes sawed in the logs to permit entry of air and light, were erected in rural Maryland by members of the societies founded by Robert Strawbridge. Aided by the financial subscription of Quakers and other non-Methodists, New York City Methodists in 1768 completed a sixty-foot-long by forty-two-foot-wide stone building on John Street. Wesley Chapel was furnished with a simple wood pulpit opposite the central door, backless benches, and a gallery accessible at first only by ladder; a Communion table and a baptismal font were, of course, not permissible prior to 1784. These buildings conformed to the popular wisdom, later approved by Wesley for the 1770 edition of the Large Minutes, that Methodist buildings were to be simple and undecorated, and that there should be no (box) pews or backs to the seats. The log meetinghouses did, however, violate the expectation, also codified in 1770, that special attention be given to suitable light and ventilation. Wesley's enthusiasm for building octagonal preaching houses, first noted in his journal in 1761 and first commended in the 1770 Large Minutes, apparently was never shared in colonial America.³

In adapting the Large Minutes (the 1780 edition) at the founding of the Methodist Episcopal Church, the Americans deleted most of the instructions for building design and arrangement, and settled instead for two points that were subsequently printed in the *Discipline*. The first directed that "all our chapels be built plain and decent, but not more expensively than is absolutely unavoidable" lest the church become dependent on the rich, who consequently might expect to control the community and thus potentially compromise the established discipline and doctrine. The rule was consistent with both the overall Methodist preference for simplicity of lifestyle and the abiding concern for ministry to the poor; and it recognized that the majority of Methodists were, in fact, from the lower economic classes. The phrase "plain and decent" could, however, be variously interpreted, though for most Methodists it indicated what they could barely afford. Some leaders, among them Bishop Asbury, understood it to mean that anything not strictly utilitarian—steeples, bells, cushions, fancy fences—was inappropriate. Buildings that displayed unnecessary decoration, and the preachers in charge of them, were thus roundly criticized. When Asbury noticed that the bell hung on an Augusta, Georgia, church was cracked, he wrote, "may it break! It is the first I ever saw in a house of ours in America; I hope it will be the last."⁴

According to the second policy, men and women, without exception, sat apart in Methodist chapels. The separation of the sexes was a practice believed to harken back to the primitive church, and it had long been a custom of Methodists in Britain and in the colonies. "A general mixture of the sexes in places of divine worship is obviously improper," explained Bishops Asbury and Coke.⁵ To meet the prescribed condition, women and men were assigned to different sections of the building, on the floor and in the galleries. Physical barriers, such as a low wall or a railing stretching from the back to near the front of the space, were sometimes added to prevent the intermingling of the sexes. The construction of separate entrances for men and women in all new buildings was recommended in 1790 to ensure proper decorum.⁶ Although it was not explicitly stipulated in any *Discipline*, seating was often racially segregated as well, with nonwhites in attendance relegated to "separate sittings" usually in a special section of the gallery, or if there was no gallery and space was unavailable on the floor, outside the open windows or doors.⁷ In later years, the entrances once distinguished for genders might be used to separate the races in white-dominated churches. There is no evidence that reversed racial segregation in seating arrangements was practiced among the black denominations.

After the provision was made in 1784 for the celebration of the sacraments, additional furnishings had to be supplied, usually a simple table (though not all houses had one) and, when needed, a bowl or basin. Already by January 1785 a New York congregation had railed in a Communion table in imitation of the then-current Anglican practice.⁸ A Communion or altar rail encircling both table and pulpit eventually came to characterize Methodist interior design; for many Methodists, the rail—the point of encounter with the divine—marked the most sacred spot in the worship space and might itself be called "the altar." However, the pulpit or reading desk as the location for the reading and preaching of God's word remained the focal point of attention, and for that reason it was usually centered in the front of the room and could be elevated upon a small platform. The pulpit could be of a well-crafted wineglass or tub design with an overhanging sounding board, but more often it was a crude wooden box, desk, or table, corresponding to the simple, basic structure in which it was placed—what was sometimes derogatorily referred to as a "Methodist barn." Logs and unfinished lumber were the most frequently used building materials in towns and in remote areas, though a congregation with financial means might substitute stone or brick; on the prairie, mud or sod houses were fabricated. The floors could be paved with planks, but usually they were dirt, sometimes sprinkled with sand. Even so, prayers were said kneeling, with the congregation characteristically turning their backs to the pulpit and resting their folded hands on the benches upon which they had been sitting. Light came from windows, tallow candles in sconces or wooden chandeliers, and lamps that burned whale or lard oil. Few buildings had heating stoves; congregations shivered in the winter months or opted to suspend services until warmer weather. The arrangement of the interior space, which was well suited for heartfelt and body-moving Methodist worship, might also include one or two "Amen corners" set off near the pulpit at right angles to the rest of the assembly, from which the older members or the particularly pious might punctuate the proceedings with single-word or short-phrased outbursts of praise.

The place for Methodist worship was to be austere and functional, with ostentation avoided. This was true (for a time) in the city houses:

> Saint George's Methodist Episcopal church in Fourth street, and the only one at the time in Philadelphia, was without galleries within or railing without, a miserably cold looking place in winter time, when, from the leaky stove pipe, mended with clay, the smoke would frequently issue, and fill all the house. It was then customary with the female worshippers to carry with them small "wooden stoves" for the feet, such as are to be seen used by the women in market. The front door was in the centre; and about 20 feet from the east end, inside, there stood a square thing not unlike a watch box, with the top sawed off, which in that day served as their "pulpit of wood," from whence the Rev. Mr. Willis used to *read* prayers previous to the sermon, from Mr. Wesley's Liturgy, and John Hood (lately living) raised the hymn standing on the floor. Mr. Willis, during service, wore a black silk gown, which gave offence to many, and was finally laid aside.[9]

Such plainness typified the Methodist people themselves, though their "decency" was sometimes questionable. A description of a service held in a Morristown, New Jersey, church in the 1830s illustrates not only separation by sex and the style of Methodist prayer but also the propensity of some men to bring to church unspiritual habits:

> In the evening I went with Mr. Cook and my friend to the Episcopal Methodist Church. It is not large, and has been recently built. The men occupied one side of the place, and the women the other; an unsocial plan, and more likely to suggest evil than to prevent it. We were there before the service commenced. The silence was interrupted disagreeably, by continued spitting, which fell, to a strange ear, like the

drippings from the eaves on a rainy day. They have the custom of turning their back to the minister in singing, that they may face the singers; and they have also the practice, to a great extent, of interlining the prayer with exclamations and prayers of their own. Such as these, for instance, were common:—Amen—Do so, Lord—Lord, thou knowest—Let it be so, Lord—Yes, yes, Lord—Come, come, Lord, &c.[10]

Tobacco chewing in church was evidently a recurring problem. One congregation in the 1840s provided spittoons lest the walls and floors be soiled; another, at the end of the nineteenth century, numbered among its spring cleaning duties the scraping of tobacco remnants from the floor.[11]

Reconfiguring the Inheritance

The requirement for "plain and decent" churches remained in the *Discipline* of several denominations throughout the first half of the nineteenth century. However, increases in Methodist membership and affluence, the regularity of a Sunday service conducted by a resident preacher, and a growing sense of sophistication in some denominations all favored changes in architectural design and in the approaches made to the disposition of space. The costly brick, stone, or wood frame oblong buildings with longitudinally directed worship spaces that were erected in the larger cities had, by midcentury, started to become the models for construction in towns and rural areas of the East and South, and were taken westward with the migrating population. The old log houses were gradually displaced by buildings intended to be both comfortable and pleasing to the eye in order to attract new members (rich and poor) and preserve the old ones. A good house could have "a fine moralizing effect upon a community," and so its exterior was expected to be neat and kept in good repair.[12] Windows were to be positioned in such a way that the preacher or worship leader never disappeared to the observer on account of blinding sunlight or deep shadow. Proper ventilation, permitted by the opening of windows from the top or bottom of the sash, was essential lest the liveliness and health of those gathered be jeopardized. Such an arrangement, noted African Methodist Episcopal bishop Daniel Payne, would keep preachers from effectiveness-limiting respiratory distress and disease, and prevent women and children from experiencing "fits and fainting."[13]

The organization of the space for worship was largely consistent across the Methodist denominations. The rectangular layout of the interior was perpetuated even though the exterior might not be designed as a plain meetinghouse but rather (particularly in the cities) imitate Colonial, Georgian, Greek Revival, or Gothic Revival architectural styles. The earlier plan of a central pulpit or desk raised upon a platform continued as the best arrangement for delivering an evangelical sermon, though now it almost always was located on the short wall opposite the entrance(s). Three chairs might be placed upon an enlarged platform for the minister, the visiting preacher or evangelist, and the song leader—a practical custom later interpreted as representing the Trinity. A Communion table typically was set in front of the pulpit and closely surrounded by the rail, since maximum space was to be accorded to seating. Methodists generally distinguished a table from an altar by the distance the furnishing was placed from the pulpit; an altar would be flush against the pulpit, while the table was moved out to allow the minister to stand behind it. Galleries on one or three walls provided additional seats and could be the location for the still controversial choir. By the 1850s, there was a growing expectation among some that the furnishings and the space were to be crafted with care as evidence of Methodism's progressive spirit and as a tactic to entice the worldly: the building, after all, was not only to be fit as the house of God, it was also the "gate of heaven" for sinners (Genesis 28:17). A LaGrange, Missouri, building had "neatly grained" pulpit and seats, carpeted coverings for the aisles and the platform, a beautiful chandelier and "two handsome pulpit lamps"; Calvary Church, near Richmond, Virginia, boasted a desk "surmounted by a beautiful white marble slab" and a pulpit platform "adorned with a luxurious sofa"; a building at Lebanon, Tennessee, had windows "ornamented with beautiful Venetian blinds."[14] Memberships that could afford it added gaslight and heat.

Greater attention was paid at this time to the location of what was increasingly called a church rather than a meetinghouse or preaching house. Buildings had often been placed on sites away from population centers because of the availability of cheap land, thus requiring that persons venture some distance from their homes for worship. On this matter Methodist Episcopal bishop Thomas Morris quipped, "Under the old dispensation, it was supposed that some difficulty in reaching the place of worship was a necessary sacrifice for the privilege of attending." For the sake of evangelism and growth in membership, Methodists were advised to take well-considered financial risks and bring their churches to the people. "It is far better to pay the full value of a church lot in the proper place," commented Bishop Morris, "than to have one for nothing in the wrong place."[15]

The purchase of prime real estate and the erection of attractive buildings necessitated a level of financial support not immediately available to most Methodist communities. A solution that had been put to use by some New Englanders in the first decade of the nineteenth century was the one utilized by their Congregationalist neighbors: the renting or selling of pews. Up to this time the Methodists had vaunted their offering of free grace to every person who sat in the Methodists' free seats. While traveling in 1808, Jesse Lee observed several churches that had departed from the generally assumed Methodist convention. A Newport, Rhode Island, church not only had large square pews arranged so that "a part of the people sit with their faces, and others with their backs towards the preacher" but also sold the pews and allowed men and women to sit together. The new "large and elegant" house in Boston that sold pews "to the highest bidder" had "an altar round the pulpit, in a half-circle, and . . . long pews of a circular form, to be uniform with the altar." In an unnamed church:

> The people have fixed pews all around the house, and all the rest have no seats, except a few loose boards on blocks. Whilst I was preaching, if a well dressed person came in, the people would jump up in their pews and slam open their doors, and thump on their pews, and beckon with their hands to get the person into their pews. I was quite displeased with their pews, and with their conduct.[16]

As part of a wider doctrinal and disciplinary crisis that threatened the "simplicity and glory of the gospel plan of salvation," controversy erupted as some feared that pews compromised the Methodist economy by privileging the rich, offending or excluding the poor, and overturning the foundational principles of democracy. Thus, by 1816, arguments reached the floor of the Methodist Episcopal Church's General Conference, whereupon a resolution was passed disallowing pews. At their next quadrennial assembly, after votes were taken upon multiple proposals, new advices were added to the *Discipline* (1820) that Methodist houses were to be built "plain and decent, and with free seats"—a stipulation taken over by the Methodist Episcopal Church, South upon their founding—and that, as far as possible, houses already with pews were to be made free.[17] Nonetheless, numerous members of both denominations apparently read the instruction not as law but as a recommendation,[18] and thereby continued the pewing of churches and their selling, though not without ongoing disputes in local congregations and at the meetings of the Annual Conferences and the General Conferences (the South and West being for a while the most resistant to the practice). In concession, the 1852 General Conference added "wherever practicable" to the direction (the Church, South made a similar change in 1870), apparently to stave off the threat of multiple litigations against the preachers who advocated the pew system.[19] The controversy persisted, however, and in 1860, a group of New York Methodists, distressed over the Methodist Episcopal Church's policy on pews—and on slavery as well as other matters— formed the Free Methodist Church, whose name revealed one of their intentions: free seats. Free churches, they believed, maintained the purity of biblical Christianity, facilitated the preaching of the gospel to every individual, and were essential for truly spiritual worship since pews intimated formalism.[20]

The year 1852 also signaled for the Methodist Episcopal Church another departure from what had been Methodist practice regarding arrangements in the worship space. What Jesse Lee noticed in the Rhode Island church had become more widespread: the "promiscuous sittings" whereby men and women, and entire households, sat conjointly in worship. The pew rent system had encouraged such impropriety, since the selling of individual places was impractical. But the custom of free seats had also raised the question why, in the name of democracy, families couldn't worship together. Arguments that removing the barrier between the sexes would create disorder in worship were countered with claims that the new approach would be more beneficial in securing attendance. Besides, to legislate the mode of seating for every congregation inhibited the spirit of freedom bequeathed by Methodism's founder.[21] The removal of the restriction in 1852 (and subsequently by the other denominations that had taken up the rule) did not immediately alter either the practice of separate seating or the architecture that sustained it. When Elizabeth Chapel near Alma, Georgia, was built in 1886, a rail (with pillars attached to support the roof) divided the building and the sexes, and remained until the interior was renovated in the late 1970s, though the arrangement of congregational seating had changed much earlier.[22] Some elderly southern Methodists, reminiscing in the mid-twentieth century about their childhoods and beyond, recalled the separate seatings even though the Methodist Episcopal Church, South had dropped the restriction in 1866. Nannie Belle Coghill remembered that, prior to the remodeling done shortly after World War I, Tabernacle Church in Townsville, North Carolina, had "a strip right down the center of the long pews" that required courting or married couples to sit close on opposite sides of the barrier.[23]

Hundreds of Methodist houses for worship had come to dot the American landscape during the 1840s and 1850s. In the four decades following, the number of new constructions rapidly increased on account of population growth, westward expansion after the Civil War, and the deepening pockets of the larger denominations as they attracted and kept a middle-class constituency. Agencies created within some of the denominations for church extension spurred on building programs in the new western settlements.[24] Many of the new or renovated houses across the country were designed and decorated in a fashion that raised the eyebrows of some, and certainly would have repulsed earlier Methodists. Fernandez Holliday remarked upon this very visible transition evident in Indiana by 1873:

> In church architecture, Methodism has undergone a great change. Our first churches, like the homes of the early settlers, were made of logs. The second editions of our houses of worship were usually plain frame or brick buildings, without steeples or bells. Now the finest and most costly Protestant churches in our chief towns are those owned and occupied by the Methodists; their steeples are as high, and their bells as numerous and as rich toned as any; and it is evident that Methodists are investing more money in church-building than the members of any Church among us. And while the Methodist Church has required no high standard of literary qualification as a condition of admittance into the ministry, it has come to pass that in our principal churches the highest ministerial qualifications are demanded, and that demand is as fully met as in any of our sister Churches. We have also changed our customs in regard to sittings in congregational worship.[25]

In answer to the question whether the construction of such elegant buildings endangered Methodism's spiritual integrity and impaired its commitment to provide resources for the poor, Abel Stevens and others responded that by attracting the wealthy, the means to care for the poor was enhanced. Indeed, Stevens believed that "Methodism should feel itself responsible to minister . . . to the public culture, by the improvement of its church architecture":

> True art should be recognized as one of the noblest handmaids of religion; elevating impressions and associations, through the senses in our temples, may ennoble even divine worship; and imposing monuments of taste, consecrated to piety, are among the highest means of national culture, and the highest proofs of advanced civilization. It is a sacred peculiarity of architectural art that, unlike painting and sculpture, it will not lend itself to vice; its severe and stately beauty disdains effeminate or voluptuous tastes. It is the most sublime, the most religious, of the works of man.
>
> On really utilitarian grounds, then, may we plead for religious art. Yet we may plead for it also on really economical grounds. The most expensive temple is usually the most economical. The Church that builds its edifice in the most eligible locality and in the most attractive style, almost invariably finds its expense the best reimbursed, by its command of the people, their attendance, their intelligence, and their money. A well located, substantial, and commanding temple aids much in giving security to a

Church, and is cheap in this respect. The stability of the religions of the old world, their power over local populations, are owing largely to their grand edifices. Methodism should not despise this power.[26]

Such positive words about architectural elegance and Methodist respectability inspired some church memberships to overstep their financial capabilities. A Grand Rapids, Michigan, congregation, whose first building was constructed for under $1,000, in 1869 completed for $33,000 a second edifice in Gothic Revival style with a dozen small spires (nicknamed the "Church of the Holy Toothpicks"), and despite repeated fund raising still owed $15,000 in 1882.[27]

"Plain and decent" houses still were built in this period on account of economic restrictions, as a protest against those Methodists who were believed to be abandoning their heritage by capitulating both to formality and pride, and because the legislation instructing such remained in the *Discipline*; the episcopal Methodist bodies kept the rule into the twentieth century, with the African Methodist Episcopal Church retaining a version of it ("Let all our churches be built with simplicity and dignity") until the 1980s. The Free Methodists, who at their founding in 1860 assumed simplicity of construction to be the norm and therefore included no instruction in their *Discipline*, added a statement in 1882 (kept until 1955, with some editorial emendations) affirming that their churches were to be "built plain, and decent, without steeples, and not more expensive than is absolutely required for comfort, convenience, and stability, and with all seats free." In spite of cautions about departing from historic Methodism and the *Discipline*, many urban Methodists of the larger denominations gladly adopted for their building exteriors the prominent architectural designs found in the wider culture, even though the Greek Revival "temple" was now sometimes deplored as too pagan, and the Gothic Revival as too Catholic. Gothic interiors, with the long nave and the deep chancel suggesting both hierarchy and formalism, and with the pulpit removed from close proximity to the people, were often dubbed unsuitable for effective Methodist worship. The Romanesque Revival style grew in popularity after the Civil War and was used into the early twentieth century. By the early 1870s, both the Methodist Episcopal Church and the Methodist Episcopal Church, South were looking to use denominationally produced architectural manuals and plans to guide the erection of future buildings: the former established a Department of Architecture in 1875, which, from 1877, annually published catalogs of architectural plans; the latter recommended and published clergyman W. M. Patterson's *Manual of Architecture* (1875) for the use of building committees when it was deemed neither feasible nor desirable for a congregation to hire an architect.[28]

A trend in the design of city church interiors, which was then adopted elsewhere, directly resulted from the emergence of the pulpit princes in the heyday of the urban revival. The pulpit platform was substantially enlarged to hold a choir behind the pulpit or to the side, as well as the preacher, who, to accentuate the gospel message and make eye contact with the hearers, would employ action and motion while preaching. Organ pipes often supplied a backdrop behind both pulpit and choir. Charles Grandison Finney, with his Broadway Tabernacle, built in New York City in 1836, had been one of the first to experiment with the so-called auditorium or theater style, which rejected a long, narrow nave with a central aisle in favor of a square or wide oblong space with radiating aisles. Methodists embraced this plan after the Civil War, and found the rounded and wide Romanesque-style structure particularly compatible with the interior design, though elongated Gothic buildings were also accommodated to it.

In the auditorium arrangement, large windows could be placed at the back and sides to provide illumination. Sunlight was diffused through leaded stained glass depictions of Scripture scenes in the buildings of the affluent, but more commonly by the use of tinted "art glass" or a faux stained glass created by affixing special colored paper with abstract designs to plain windows.[29] Curved or angled open pews in a concentric semicircular arrangement brought preacher and congregation closer together. Affluent congregations might maximize comfort by cushioning the pews or installing individual seats. The main floor could be level or be graded to rise away from the platform so that sight lines were optimized. If there were balconies, they might be shallow, sloping, or in an oval configuration to reduce the distance between the second level and the speaker. Ideally, all seats could be rentable to help recoup construction costs. Under this scheme, the sermon was paramount; the usually small Communion table stood before the pulpit and off the main platform, and if there was a pedestaled baptismal font permanent in the space, it was placed to one side. The national flag might be displayed either on the platform or the floor, continuing the patriotic custom established during the Civil War years in the North. The prominence of the auditorium arrangement in the second half of the nineteenth century led to the use by Methodists of the term "auditorium" to refer to the entirety of the worship space. Designation of the space in this way signaled the expectations for worship itself: worship was highly individualized, with congregations mostly passive auditors to the sermon, the prayers, and the music of organ and choir.

A variation on the auditorium plan placed organ pipes, choir, and pulpit on a platform in a corner diagonal with the entrance. This style, popularized by architect George Washington Kramer of Akron, Ohio, especially during the 1880s and 1890s, fanned the congregation around the pulpit on a sloped floor, thus maximizing both seating and sight lines. Kramer also promoted a "Combination Church" arrangement by which a Sunday school hall or "lecture room" was attached to one side of the worship space but separated from it by sliding doors. When additional space was needed, especially during revivals and funerals, the partition could be opened to supply additional seating. Kramer's concept borrowed from but went beyond the arrangement first proposed by businessman and Sunday school superintendent Lewis Miller for the Sunday school of Akron's First Methodist Episcopal Church, according to which classrooms opened out into a central space with a platform and desk for Sunday school exercises and worship.[30] Denominational concerns about Christian education, and the desire for multifunctional and economical worship space, contributed to the popularity of the so-called Akron plan. At the turn into the twentieth century, Akron and other auditorium plans were widely represented in Methodist buildings across the country.[31]

Regional and local idiosyncrasies in decoration—some purported to be "common features" of Methodist churches—were also in evidence throughout the nineteenth century. One custom was to cut a false door in the wall behind the pulpit as a symbolic entrance for the Holy Spirit and as a reminder that Jesus Christ was the doorway to heaven, though of course this provoked jokes that the door provided a handy escape for any preacher who irked the congregation. When a new building for a Greenville, North Carolina, congregation was in the final stages of construction, it was observed that the door was missing. Following a congregational meeting, where the expense and delay of adding a door were duly noted, the decision was reached that local artists should be hired to paint a door on the rear wall.[32]

Many of the Methodist denominations had, by the end of the nineteenth century, formalized a long-practiced but unwritten set of liturgical services for the laying of a cornerstone and for the dedication or consecration of a building. Wesley's *Sunday Service*, as a revision of the 1662 *Book of Common Prayer*, did not contain such services because none were present in the Prayer Book. Although the English Convocation had endorsed a consecratory rite in 1712 and revised it in 1714, neither form had received the authorizing royal sanction; yet they were used in some English dioceses and became the foundation for the American rite approved by the Protestant Episcopal Church in 1799. In spite of the availability of a service to pass on, Wesley was persuaded that consecratory rites were superstitious innovations, since neither the Bible nor the law of the land recommended them. To Wesley's mind, the act of worship itself was sufficiently consecratory; hence, he was not bothered about holding services in any space, consecrated or not.[33] Nevertheless, the American Methodists from the eighteenth century onward marked the laying of the foundation and the opening of the house with special observances. Bishop Asbury described a service in 1796 that commenced with singing part of Isaac Watts's "The Corner Stone" and then led to prayer; more song and prayer followed after the laying of the stone.[34] A substantial number of hymns for use at these events was, by the 1830s, designated in several official Methodist hymnals. One widely used text spoke to the multiple purposes of the building as God's dwelling place and as house for the gathering of God's people in praise and prayer:

> Behold thy temple, God of grace,
>   The house that we have reared for thee,
> Regard it as thy resting-place,
>   And fill it with thy majesty.

> When from its altar shall arise
>   Joint supplication to thy name,
> Deign to accept the sacrifice,
>   Thyself our answ'ring God proclaim.

> And when from hence the voice of praise
>   Shall lift its triumphs to thy throne,
> Show thy acceptance of our lays,
>   By making all thy glory known.

> When here thy ministers shall stand,
>   To speak what thou shalt bid them say,

Maintain thy cause with thine own hand,
And give thy truth a winning way.

Now, therefore, O our God, arise!
In this thy resting-place appear;
And let thy people's longing eyes
Behold thee fix thy dwelling here.

In addition to hymns and prayer, cornerstone and dedication services usually featured a sermon (with preachers recording the text that was used), a dedicatory prayer, and a collection to reduce the debt on the house. Since dedication services drew numbers of preachers (Methodist and otherwise) and substantial crowds, Communion was sometimes held at the conclusion of the service or at a later hour. In some places, Masonic rites were conflated with local Methodist customs: the cornerstone of the church at Sydney (a western suburb of Richmond, Virginia) was laid according to Masonic ceremonies, with a concluding address by a Methodist pastor; inside the box inserted into the cornerstone was, along with a Bible and a copy of the Methodist Episcopal Church, South Discipline, a copy of the Masonic textbook.[35]

Proposals began to circulate in the 1840s that formal orders for cornerstone laying and building dedication be approved, perhaps as a means of discouraging the indiscriminate blending of churchly and Masonic practices. The General Conference of the African Methodist Episcopal Church commended in 1848 that J. M. Brown, Byrd Parker, and Daniel Payne write two services to be included in that year's Discipline, thereby becoming the first Methodist body to authorize standardized services for the setting apart of church buildings. Both services placed on paper what was already common practice, with the lengthy composed prayers imitating the extemporaneous style. Bishop Payne later testified that the cornerstone service had been copied from the form used by the Evangelical Lutheran Church; the dedication order was inspired by the Lutheran rite and the 1799 Protestant Episcopal Church's service, but a large portion of it was new since the authors "labored more to be scriptural than to be original, believing that in all the service of religion man ought to hide himself beneath the glorious manifestation of the God-head as made in his written word."[36] The order "For Laying Cornerstones of New Churches," which was to be preceded or followed by an appropriate discourse, consisted of a hymn, a prayer (text given), the reading of Scripture (e.g., 1 Kings 5; Psalm 96; Haggai 1:1–10; or 1 Corinthians 3), a stated address on the biblical understandings of "cornerstone," a prayer (text supplied), a rubric regarding the contents of the cornerstone and its placement, and a final declaration. The order "For the Dedication of New or Remodelled Churches" supposed the presence of the bishop, though the service could proceed in his absence under the direction of an elder. The service simultaneously claimed the house for the denomination and marked it as God's domain: an opening rubric instructed that the keys to the building were to be presented to the bishop "in token of the fact that they will ever after submit to the discipline, doctrine and government of the African Methodist Episcopal Church and 'will at all times hereafter permit such ministers and preachers belonging to said church to preach and expound God's holy word therein' "; and a concluding rubric noted that, after dedication, the building was not to be used for "any other purpose than the glory of God." The lengthy dedicatory prayer was the centerpiece of the liturgy:

Procession with responsive reading of Psalm 84 [between the bishop and the other ministers present]

Psalm 122 [chanted by the choir]

Prayer [substantially quoting 1 Kings 8:23–51, by the bishop, kneeling]

Dedicatory Prayer [by the bishop] "And now, O Lord God, Most High, whom the heaven, and heaven of heavens cannot contain, we dedicate this house to thy service: receive it, we humbly beseech thee, receive it unto thyself, and number it among thine earthly sanctuaries; that thine own presence, the presence of thy Son Jesus Christ, and the presence of thy Holy Spirit, may ever fill this house which we have builded and called by thy name; so that whensoever the Gospel is preached in this house, it may descend with all its purity, power, and demonstration upon the hearts of the impenitent, turning them from darkness to light, and from the power of sin and Satan unto God; that its sanctifying influences may be felt in the souls of all believers, lifting their desires, their hopes, and their affections, from earth to heaven, and leading back the wandering sheep of the house of Israel into the fold of eternal life."

[seven more petitions follow, each addressing some aspect of the worship to take place within the house]

Consecratory Hymn [no more than six stanzas]

Sermon

Collection

Hymn

Extemporaneous Prayer

Benediction

The African Methodist Episcopal orders and the Protestant Episcopal rite of 1799 influenced the production of other Methodist services in the nineteenth century, among them those of the Methodist Episcopal Church (1864), the Methodist Episcopal Church, South (1870), and the Methodist Protestant Church (1877). The service introduced into the Wesleyan Church in the twentieth century borrowed verbatim entire prayers from the American Prayer Book. Even with established orders, local congregations felt free to emend the standard text to produce a dedicatory service unique to their situation. When First Methodist Episcopal Church at Holyoke, Massachusetts, was dedicated at 2:00 P.M. on Wednesday, June 25, 1890, the service expanded the conventional order by including the reading of a financial statement and an address after the sermon; another service of hymns, prayer, Scripture, and sermon was held at 7:30 P.M. under the guidance of eight clergy who had not given leadership at the afternoon service.[37]

Raising Architectural Monuments

At the beginning of the twentieth century, the majority of Methodist denominations strove to erect houses of worship exhibiting beauty and artistry, not only for
their own ends as divine gifts but as statements of Methodism's influence as the
most "American" of denominations and as means to successful evangelism with
the economically advantaged and the culturally astute. Romanesque and Renais-
sance exteriors surrounding pulpit-centered, auditorium-style interiors remained
popular well into the 1920s, as the architectural plans reproduced in the Methodist
Episcopal Church, South's *Church Extension Hand Book* attest. But moves that had
started in the last decades of the nineteenth century away from the dominance of
pulpit oratory toward liturgical complexity on Sunday morning—expressed by the
publication of standard orders, and the use of psalmody and other responsive readings—led some Methodists to suggest that the sermon-focused auditorium plan
had outlived its usefulness. The content of preaching also was shifting and with
it the method of delivery: the fiery exhortations seeking to convict lost souls were
heard less often in some quarters than were manuscripted sermons addressing
Christian life and values. Attention turned again to the Gothic style, which Boston architect Ralph Adams Cram and others were promoting as the most sublimely
Christian architectural form. Although the long-naved Gothic longitudinal plan
did not invite congregational interaction as well as the fanned auditorium, the
associations of the Gothic with beauty, mystery, and an "enriched" liturgy made it
attractive. Lucius Clark, writing in a Methodist Episcopal publication in 1912,
declared that with the auditorium plan "the church lost much of that which was
real churchly and became a hall," and by focus upon "the man who stood on the
platform," the congregation became little more than "minor accessories." Use of
the Gothic design was not a reversion to medievalism, claimed Clark, but an
"evolving to the place where the congregation is the unit rather than the priest
of Romanism or the preacher in Protestantism."[38] Halford Luccock was more adamant in his denunciation in 1924 of the "deadly sins" of the auditorium, especially
the Akron, design. In his opinion, "the most uplifting worship" could not be led
from a pulpit in a corner; the display of organ pipes across the front of the space
distracted worship; the "Age of Sliding Doors" should be quickly left behind; and
windows should be functional and not simply decorative: "Now, in the conduct of
worship there abideth three things, art, music, and air. But the greatest of these is
air. Neither Chrysostom nor Henry Ward Beecher is any match for carbon diox-
ide."[39]

The Gothic revival both encouraged and reinforced many of the liberal-mystical
views of worship and theology circulating in the new century, and particularly the
psychological-aesthetic approach to religion and worship promoted by Von Ogden
Vogt and Willard Sperry. According to Vogt, the beauty of the Gothic inspired
the celebration of life that was true worship; its verticality evoked emotion and
mystery, and invited communion with the "infinite unknown."[40] Vogt's utilitarian
approach to worship and his appreciation for the Gothic was appropriated by some
Methodist leaders, among them Elbert Conover, director of the Bureau of Architecture of the Methodist Episcopal Church and later the director of the Interde-

nominational Bureau of Architecture. Because, claimed Conover, "the human personality enters into its most sublime experience" in worship, a service and the environment in which worship was held failed if it did not make "the Divine Presence appreciable" or "inspire or comfort or create humility of mind." The space where true worship was best realized, Conover posited, consisted of an oblong nave bathed in the colors eminating from stained glass. Floors were to be level and pews straight so attention could be focused toward a chancel containing a centered altar (against the back wall) or Communion table (freestanding near the back wall) that was decorated with cross and candles. A lectern was placed on one side of the central aisle, the pulpit on the other, with both located at the juncture of the chancel and the nave, which might be demarcated by a railing and cushions for kneeling (or the railing could surround the altar or table). The choir could sit divided within the chancel or be placed on the side opposite the organ or piano. A baptismal font could be tucked somewhere in the chancel or be placed at the entrance into the nave. Worship leaders were placed in seats at the sides of the chancel lest the appearance be given of worshiping them instead of God.[41]

Led by the advice of Conover and other advocates of the Gothic and the beautiful,[42] hundreds of Methodist buildings, large and moderately sized, were constructed in the Gothic design during the first half of the twentieth century, particularly in the boom years between World War I and the Great Depression, and again after World War II (most noticeably in suburban areas). But even more houses of worship were configured or renovated to conform to the altar-centered or so-called "divided chancel" plan—with the altar at the far end and choir seats on either side in the chancel, and the pulpit and lectern on opposite sides of its entrance—though the arrangement apparently did little to encourage more frequent reception of the Lord's Supper. Interiors were decorated with a rich use of symbols arranged in glass, carved in wood, or embroidered on textiles. The Methodist Episcopal Church was now finally forced to admit that it no longer built houses of worship that were simply "plain and decent," and in 1932 replaced those words with the instruction "Let our church buildings be designed in keeping with the lofty purpose of providing for divine worship, for the administration of the Holy Sacraments and be suited to the ministries of preaching, religious education, and Christian fellowship and service."

Not all were enthusiastic about the emphasis upon the Gothic and the chancel. Claims were made that these architectural forms contributed to the deadening of the spiritual power that had been a hallmark of earlier Methodism, and elevated the liturgical at the expense of the prophetic and the evangelical. In 1931, the minister of First Methodist Episcopal Church of Long Beach, California, queried:

> Is not the flaming evangel rather than the flickering candle Christ's way; the burning heart rather than the burnished bronze of more importance; the glowing countenance rather than the glittering altar Methodism's method of letting the world know that this is the place where God's honor dwelleth?[43]

Because of concerns that the chancel design potentially devalued preaching and the historic Protestant focus upon the word of God, Georgian or Colonial-style buildings with a pulpit-centered configuration were also constructed during this period, usually with a long, narrow nave (still referred to in some plans as the "auditorium"). For the next twenty-five years or so, Methodists from all denominations actively debated the pros and cons of the altar-centered and the pulpit-centered plans—and with them the shift in most of the denominations toward liturgical formalism. The Free Methodists found it necessary in 1955 to alter the statement about buildings in their Discipline when controversy broke out at that year's General Conference over the construction of several buildings with divided chancels.[44] Yet they kept their characteristic restraint and emphasis upon evangelical proclamation in the revised text:

> All our houses of worship must be built plain and neat, and no more expensive than is absolutely required for comfort, convenience, and stability, and with all seats free. Let the architecture and interior arrangements of our churches be planned and constructed to contribute to a distinctively evangelical simplicity and reverence in worship which makes the preaching of the Word central in the service. It is understood that we will build in keeping with prevailing architecture of the surrounding area and with such attractiveness as to commend the gospel to the community.

By the 1950s, the Methodist Church, officially, and representatives from other Methodist bodies, unofficially, had cast their lot with the "divided chancel" arrangement, and with the elongated nave since a square was believed by some to be too closely identified with an auditorium. Attempts were made to squelch the disparities between "preacher-centered" worship and the "sacramental-type" of worship by advocating an all-encompassing "God-centered" worship in which pulpit ("to set forth the word of the Almighty") and table ("to symbolize the presence of eternal God") both had a central position; in this scheme, the lectern, as a "purely incidental" furnishing, was deemed unnecessary.[45] A related issue, one that remained unsettled, was whether Methodists had altars or tables. Some congregations had both, with an "altar" immovably fixed to the back wall upon which accumulated various artifacts (and toward which the pastor might pray when presenting the monetary offerings), and a Communion table set out when necessary for the vessels and the trays of individual cups. For the exterior, the classical styles of earlier years continued to be promoted, but modern designs constructed from new building materials caught the imagination as congregations prepared for the next generations. The plan published in 1955 for a new Methodist church in Lawton, Oklahoma, showed the worship space in the shape of a broad arrow, with the altar at the point, and interior gardens between the diagonal transepts.[46] Although congregations were encouraged by the Methodist Church's Department of Architecture to explore new designs, they were also cautioned against adopting wholeheartedly those forms that did not express or were alien to the realistic functions of worship in the space. A 1962 publication of the department advised that the "church-in-the-round" plan, popular among the "more liturgical denominations," be avoided as a "passing fad." Arranged "to get the maximum number of worshipers as close to the altar as possible, ostensibly to create the effect of the family of God gathered around the altar," the plan was believed to subordinate all other aspects of worship to the sacrament when, in fact, for Methodists the Supper was celebrated only monthly or quarterly.[47]

No single style of architecture, exterior or interior, could be definitively iden-tified as Methodist in the last four decades of the twentieth century—a statement that could be made about Methodist buildings in other, if not all, periods as well. Architectural eclecticism characterized the Methodist family, in part because lov-ingly tended older houses of worship erected by previous generations still welcomed congregations, some with the original interior configuration, others gutted and reoriented in order to conform to the community's new expectations for prayer and praise. Among these, pulpit-centered and chancel arrangements dominated, but Akron and fanned auditorium styles that had survived the campaign against them also were used.

New constructions reflected the diversity of opinions about worship and its pur-poses found among Methodists. Exterior designs ranged from classical to modern; interiors were longitudinal or centralized. At one end of the spectrum, congrega-tions attentive to the ecumenical and liturgical movements fashioned interiors that intentionally acknowledged the setting as both the house of God and the house of the people. While creating areas for people and for movement within the space, parts of the room were set apart for distinct liturgical functions: proclamation of God's word by the reading of Scripture and preaching; celebration of the Lord's Supper at a freestanding altar-table; and Christian initiation through baptism.[48] In some places these three centers were in close proximity, with the baptismal font moved into the space where a lectern might have stood (one desk was regarded as sufficient for the proclamation). In the last decade of the twentieth century, a few United Methodist constructions included a baptistery in the nave that could accommodate adult baptism by immersion and infant baptism by submersion. The United Methodist Church, in its 1992 "Service for the Consecration or Recon-secration of a Church Building," acknowledged the centrality of the space for word and sacraments by including three separate consecrations: for the pulpit ("When your Word is read and preached from this pulpit, purify the lives and lips of those who speak here, that your Word alone may be proclaimed and your Word alone may be heard and obeyed"); the baptismal font ("When we pour the water of baptism, making and renewing our covenant vows, pour out your Spirit and give new birth; wash away sin and clothe your people in righteousness"); and the Lord's table ("When we eat this bread and drink from this cup, refresh all those who partake at this holy table").

At the other end of the spectrum, congregations that had embraced a style of worship focused upon preaching, drama, and music provided by singers and a band were drawn to an "auditorium revival" plan. Worship leaders situated themselves upon an extended platform that dominated the space and had few decorations; simplicity was not so much the issue as was the desire to remove symbols and furnishings that might be meaningless (or threatening) to those in attendance. The people were placed on a sloping floor in individual seats in a semicircle around the stage. The choice of the plan was deliberate: to attract concertgoing young people who would already be familiar with such an arrangement.

Methodist houses of worship constructed during the first hundred years of Meth-odism in America largely conformed to Chicago architect Louis Sullivan's dictum that "form ever follows function." Buildings were designed for evangelistic preaching, with the people's focus oriented to the pulpit, and the preacher's gaze directed toward the congregation, who could be perched on benches on the floor and in the galleries, or on pews fanned around him in an auditorium. The Lord's Supper and Christian baptism, though both important, were not weekly occurrences, so table and font were mostly inconspicuous. Although styles of worship continued to determine arrangement of the worship space even into the late twentieth century, by the late nineteenth century it was clear that the unidirectional principle framed by Sullivan was not the only possibility for Methodists. The architectural design elected for both the exterior and the interior of a given building influenced the shape and the character of worship celebrated in the space. The popularity of the Gothic style and the rising interest of some Methodists in a more formal service of worship allowed for such a change to come about, thereby bearing witness to architect Ludwig Mies van der Rohe's notion that "form is function." The house in which prayer and praise is offered is more than a shelter from the elements; it is an integral part of the worship itself.

Roles in Public Worship

A S HAS BECOME EVIDENT from the previous chapters, American Methodist public worship prior to 1784—from the small class and the extended-family prayer meetings to the watch nights and the larger revival gatherings—was lay led. Yet such a statement, while technically true, requires qualification. Sympathetic Anglican and other clergy presided over sacramental services for those Methodists willing to attend. Until they suspended their actions, the handful of men ordained by presbytery at Fluvanna in 1779 held baptism and Communion services of their own design. This second type of assembly could be more accurately identified as a Methodist service than the first, though it was nonetheless irregular, at least from the standpoint of the Wesley-appointed and American-approved "General Assistant" Francis Asbury. The most noteworthy qualifier to the claim of exclusively lay-led Methodist worship was the leadership exhibited by the "preachers" or "helpers" so defined in the Methodist system. These persons were indisputably laymen (and in England, a few laywomen),[1] who directly or indirectly had received John Wesley's approval for ministry based upon evidence of a divine call and were thus set apart for duties as itinerant preachers and evangelists. According to Wesley, such work did not require ordination, for to his mind the offices of preaching and sacramental administration were separate and distinct, and only the latter required ministerial orders.[2] Wesley's use of lay preachers was contrary to Anglican canon law, which forbade unauthorized preaching, but he justified their employment by positive evidence from the history of the church, as well as by the visible fruits of their labors to seek and save the lost. Under Wesley's supervision the lay preachers in America (as in Britain) were selected, organized, held to particular tasks and standards as specified in the Large Minutes and the "American" Minutes, and deployed into the field. Certain preachers were given oversight of the others. The "assistant," the man who had charge over the societies and preachers within a particular circuit, was responsible, among other things, for ensuring that watch night services and love feasts were regularly held. The special duties given to the preachers differentiated them from the rest of the Methodist flock, particularly since many of them devoted their full energies to the work. They were laity, but they were extraordinary laity—"extraordinary messengers" Wesley called them—and their contributions stoked the fires of the early Methodist revival and effectively spread the gospel even at the close of the twentieth century. Thus any look at the leadership of Methodist worship must include this quintessentially Methodist and unordained group, whose devoted diligence provided Methodist prayer, praise, and preaching even in the remotest parts of the nation, and whose liturgical duties gradually expanded to meet the expectations for their ministry. But to be best understood, their liturgical responsibilities must be placed alongside the presumed roles in worship for clergy and laity.

Ordained Leadership

The General Superintendent or Bishop

Wesley's decision to use the ordination services from the 1662 *Book of Common Prayer* as the liturgical source for the Methodist ordinal carried with it significant implications for delineating the leadership of worship, and for subsequent definitions of ministry and church polity. With the adoption of the *Sunday Service* in 1784, Methodists had rites for the ordaining of deacons, elders, and "superintendants" (so spelled), and they drew up accompanying legislation for the *Discipline* accordingly. Methodists of that and later generations debated the motivations behind Wesley's substitution of "superintendant" for "bishop" and the reasons for his ire when the Americans began to use the nomenclature of bishop from 1787. Questions were also raised about what Wesley meant by the *ordaining* of the "superintendant" (Wesley dropped the term "consecrate" throughout his revision of the Prayer Book's "Form of Ordaining or Consecrating of an Archbishop or Bishop"), especially since he had indicated, following his reading of Peter King's *Account of the Primitive Church*, that bishops and presbyters (elders) were of the same order. A consequence of these discussions was that various approaches to pastoral oversight were selected by the different Methodist denominations. The majority ordained bishops; these same denominations gradually redefined the liturgical occasion as a consecration rather than an ordination beginning with the Methodist Episcopal Church in 1864, though that denomination had been actively discussing the issue at least twelve years earlier. The African Methodist Episcopal Church at first ordained general superintendents, then soon altered the nomenclature throughout the *Discipline* to read "bishop." The Methodist Protestants and the Wesleyan Methodists opted to have a president of conference whose office was conferred by election and not by rite (a distinction the churches that elected and then ordained bishops were required to clarify). The Free Methodists elected but did not ordain general superintendents (who usually also held the office of conference president), and in a controversial move agreed in 1907 to use instead the term "bishop." An attempt to repeal the decision at the next General Conference was unsuccessful. Regardless of title and method of setting apart, only one unique liturgical function was ascribed to the office beyond those normally assigned to the elder: presidency at the rites of ordination and consecration. A slight variation existed in the Free Methodist Church, for technically, responsibilities for ordination fell to the president of conference, who usually was, but was not required to be, the general superintendent (bishop). Because Wesley had not included confirmation in the *Sunday Service*, that exclusive duty of Anglican bishops did not enter into Methodist praxis. When confirmation rites were authorized by the Methodist Church in 1965 and then by the United Methodist Church, local congregations sometimes invited the bishop to participate in the event, but his (and after the election of Marjorie Swank Matthews in 1980, her) involvement was not required.

The Elder

By providing a purely liturgical definition for the elder's duty, the first American *Discipline* reflected the need that had prompted Wesley to ordain and ensure an ongoing supply of sacramental ministers for the Methodist people in North America:

Q. 30. What is the Office of an *Elder?*
A. To administer the Sacraments of Baptism and the Lord's Supper, and to perform all the other Rites prescribed by our Liturgy.

This instruction complemented the elder's task as defined by the words spoken at the imposition of the superintendent's and other elders' hands during the ordination rite, words that Wesley took verbatim from the Prayer Book, omitting only the sentence pertaining to the binding and loosing of sins, and substituting "elder" for "priest":

Receive the Holy Ghost for the Office and Work of an Elder in the Church of God, now committed unto thee by the imposition of our hands. And be thou a faithful Dispenser of the Word of God, and of his holy Sacraments; in the Name of the Father, and of the Son, and of the Holy Ghost. Amen.

Then the Superintendant shall deliver to every one of them, kneeling, the Bible into his hand, saying,

Take thou authority to preach the Word of God, and to administer the holy Sacraments in the Congregation.

The full spectrum of worship leadership was thereby entrusted to the elder, whose liturgical ministries were not limited to a particular place or congregation. The distinguishing characteristic of the elder was the unqualified capacity to baptize, celebrate the Lord's Supper, solemnize matrimony, bury the dead, or perform any service of worship wherever there was need. Constraints, when they were imposed, came from outside the church, as with the restriction of movement placed upon blacks (and thus upon black elders) in some regions during the years prior to the Civil War. An elder might be appointed as the presiding elder of a circuit, and it was then his responsibility to oversee the Methodist great festival that was the quarterly meeting.

Each of the Methodist denominations kept the office of elder, thereby maintaining continuity with Wesley and establishing a connection among the members of the Methodist family. Although with the issuance of the second *Discipline* the elder's job description had started to expand, and the separate denominations over time would delineate the elder's work in their own particular formulations, nevertheless the statement of the elder's liturgical tasks always remained an integral component of the overall definition. The ordination rites as they evolved mentioned explicitly the elder's responsibilities for sacramental ministry and the proclamation of God's Word. Most typically this was done, using Wesley's text or an approximation of it, at the laying on of hands and the delivery of the Bible. With the United Methodist Church's 1980 *Ordinal* and its 1992 successor,[3] these duties were articulated not at the imposition of hands, but at the ordination prayer, and also at the preliminary examination where worship leadership is set out as the first among several obligations: "As an elder in the Church you are called to share in the ministry of Christ and of the whole Church: by preaching and teaching the Word of God and faithfully administering the Sacraments of Baptism and Holy Communion; by leading the people of God in worship and prayer."

The Deacon

The consistency found across the churches regarding the liturgical leadership of the elder was not replicated with the deacon. In fact, the Wesleyan Methodist Church never had deacons. The Methodist Protestant Church's General Conference removed the order in 1874 despite the protest that such deletion was "a great innovation" and opposed to "New Testament precedent and teaching."[4] All the other denominations had, according to what had been received from Wesley, a transitional deacon whose years of service in that office were directly tied to the preparation and experience deemed necessary before ordination as elder. In a bold departure from what it had inherited, the General Conference of the United Methodist Church in 1996 approved the phasing out of the transitional diaconate and the establishment of a permanent order of deacon to stand alongside the order of elder.[5]

Because in the ancient church the deacon was under the care and supervision of the bishop and functioned as his assistant, only the bishop laid hands on the ordinand to the diaconate. This custom was retained in the majority of diaconal ordination rites that developed in the East and West, and found its way into the Methodist rite in 1784 via Anglican praxis.[6] Even so, the first *Discipline* and ordination rite did not define the deacon's liturgical role in relationship to the superintendent or bishop, but rather in terms of the ministry of the elder.

Q. 31. What is the Office of a *Deacon*?

A. To baptize in the Absence of an Elder, to assist the Elder in the Administration of the Lord's Supper, to marry, bury the Dead, and read the Liturgy to the People as prescribed, except what relates to the Administration of the Lord's Supper.

In the examination of the candidate, according to the 1784 rite, the "superintendant" stated:

It appertaineth to the office of a Deacon, to assist the elder in Divine Service, and especially when he ministereth the holy Communion, to help him in the distribution thereof, and to read and expound the holy Scriptures; to instruct the youth, and in the absence of the elder to baptize. And furthermore, it is his office, to search for the sick, poor, and impotent, that they may be visited and relieved.

Descriptions of the deacon's liturgical leadership that referred to the availability and authority of the elder persisted and still could be found in both *Discipline* and ordinal in the late twentieth century. But the deacon was not meant to be simply an understudy to the elder, for like the elder, the deacon was to engage in a traveling ministry in a parish without walls. As the statement in the *Discipline* about the deacon clearly indicated, and as the exigencies of Methodist ministry to those in need of redemption demanded, most deacons led worship in the absence of the elder.

The leadership of general public gatherings for worship, including Sunday and daily services of preaching and prayer, love feasts, watch nights, and revivals, belonged to the deacon's prerogatives. Burial of the dead and funeral sermons comprised part of the work as well. For most of their histories, none of the denominations permitted the deacon, by admission to the order, to celebrate the Lord's Supper, though proposals sometimes were put forward to grant the uniform privilege of eucharistic presidency to the diaconate.[7] The exception was the Free Methodist Church, which, from 1979 onward, listed presidency of Communion as a diaconal duty when an elder was unavailable. Some denominations, such as the Methodist Episcopal Church, South in 1926, made special allowance for deacons in charge of a church or churches to preside at the table, but with the firm understanding that such was an exception and not the rule. The deacon was permitted to conduct weddings as part of the normal functions prescribed in the first and second editions of the *Discipline*, but already by 1787 that decision had been tempered to read "in the absence of the Elder." The change probably was made in recognition of the lack of precedent for the deacon as officiant and to reinforce the historic role of the presbyterate in matters matrimonial, thereby conveying the transitory and subordinate character of the diaconate in relation to the presbyterate. Nevertheless, circumstances required that more authorized ministers than just the elder be available to unite and bless a couple if civil law allowed. Eventually the earlier formulation was restored in most of the denominations: the Methodist Protestants from the outset gave their deacon unqualified responsibilities for the solemnization of matrimony; but the Methodist Episcopal Church, South never removed the limitation.

Numerous approaches, at times different ones in the same denomination, were taken regarding the diaconal role at baptism. Some churches kept the deferential ruling established in the earliest *Discipline* and ordinal that the deacon could baptize only in the absence of the elder. Others applied no restriction or eventually removed it. When the Methodist Church, which permitted the deacon to baptize without qualification, merged in 1968 with the Evangelical United Brethren Church, which had no diaconate, the resulting legislation of the United Methodist Church read that the deacon was not automatically granted the authority to officiate at baptism. Yet in the examination posed within the approved ordination liturgy, the celebration of baptism was listed among the deacon's liturgical roles. Only with the publication of the 1980 *Ordinal* was the inconsistency removed by the stipulation that the deacon ordinarily was to assist the elder at both sacraments. When the permanent diaconate was established in that denomination, the language of assistance was continued.

The roles in worship assigned to the deacon, the elder, and the general superintendent or bishop (or president of conference) generally followed historic precedent, with variations adopted on the basis of practical necessity.[8] Despite being "set apart," the functions of the ordained were not intended to remove them from the liturgical work expected of the whole people of God: to worship in private, in families, and in public; to read, hear, and meditate upon the Scriptures; and to attend regularly the Lord's Supper. Indeed, perhaps the most important liturgical responsibility shared by persons in these offices was that they would intentionally build up and encourage the laity in ways that could result in their more active participation and leadership in worship.

The Roles of the Laity

Every attender at Methodist worship, no matter the time period or the denomination, was counted on to engage heart and voice, mind and body, in prayer and praise. Precisely how this was accomplished depended upon the style of service, the occasion, and the setting in which worship took place. But in each denomination, the lively participation of the congregation was a paramount issue. When possible, Methodists were to worship in their mother tongue. One of the reasons for efforts to preserve the discipline of family worship was that it served as a school for corporate, public worship. The rules established early on about singing and the endless debates about the place of soloists or choirs in worship give evidence of the desire not to compromise the congregation's role. Methods of preaching were advocated that would solicit the attention and interest of those gathered and ideally produce effects. Requests for legislation that uniform patterns or components of worship be practiced across a denomination were put forward with the purpose of facilitating the people's worship no matter which congregation they might attend. While some deplored the formalization of worship for fear of diminishing congregational participation, its advocates believed it assigned a more explicit role to the people through the responsive reading of Scripture (the psalter) and the praying of unison written prayers; in other words, a more formal style invited the people's involvement. Methodist worship, however, could be less the work of the people and more the performance of preacher and choir; and the congregation's passivity might not be considered a hindrance to the prospect of a personal, spiritual response.

Among the laity were those with specific roles related to public worship—roles that had been constituted prior to the establishment of Methodism as an ecclesiastical body, though some were redefined after 1784. Class leaders prayed with their classes and the sick of the community. Exhorters, men and women who by design did not directly interpret Scripture, held forth at prayer meetings with spiritual encouragements and admonitions. Precentors and song leaders lined out and directed congregational singing. Stewards registered marriages and baptisms, collected and arranged for the distribution of alms that had been offered for the poor at the Communion service, and provided bread and drink for the Lord's Supper and the love feast. In the second half of the nineteenth century, some of the churches permitted women to assume the role of steward, which in the African-American churches evolved into the distinctive work of the stewardess, who could easily be recognized since oftentimes she dressed in white for worship. The African Methodist Episcopal Church, which in 1868 approved female stewards, had in its *Discipline* by 1964 an elaborate description of her duties related to the celebration of the sacraments:

> It is the duty of the Stewards to provide the elements for the Communion. This duty traditionally falls to the Stewardess Board, which should also dress the pulpit and altar rail with suitable clean white coverings. It is recommended that the Stewardess Board prepare the bread itself as a service of love and devotion rather than purchase it. Always white and perfectly clean, the linen used for the table may be embellished with white embroidered or crocheted symbols and made very beautiful. The utensils should be kept polished and shining. An appropriate bowl and a number of small linen guest towels should be supplied for use for the ministers in preparation of their hands for service in the communion.
>
> The Stewardess Board shall also make adequate preparation for all baptisms. Where there is not a Baptismal Font, they shall provide a decent basin of water, clean white linen guest towels and such other items as may be required.

The African Methodist Episcopal Zion Church included in its 1996 *Book of Worship* a service for the "Confirmation of Stewardesses," but had no ritual counterpart for the steward. In churches of other Methodist denominations, the role served by the stewardess was placed under the purview of an altar guild or a lay worship committee. New and distinct roles for laity not imagined prior to 1784 also emerged, among them choristers, instrumentalists, lay readers, acolytes, and ushers. Where permitted, lay servers assisted in the distribution of Communion.

Except for the sacraments, weddings, and funerals, any service of worship and prayer could, in principle, be led by the laity. At least this was true for males. Though most denominations in their *Discipline* did not explicitly delimit lay presidency by gender, the female role in practice was much more circumscribed until the middle of the twentieth century, and even then eyebrows still could be raised at the prospect of a laywoman guiding the Sunday morning assembly. With the freedom for lay leadership, Methodists preserved a characteristic from their origins as a religious society and perpetuated the democratic ideals present at the founding of the denomination. The Sunday school superintendent, for example, directed worship "exercises" for the school and was often recognized as the logical replacement for the designated worship leader at the main service when that individual was absent. In the late twentieth century, some congregations deliberately scheduled Sunday morning services that were planned and conducted entirely by the laity. Methodists in their worship leadership, it may be said, embraced a theology of the priesthood of all believers, although such was rarely stated explicitly and in some places only occasionally embodied.

The Leadership of the Extraordinary Laity

The employment of lay preachers and deaconesses was practically expedient for advancing the gospel message—and Methodism—and for overseeing works of piety and mercy. Like all Methodists, these persons could lead worship services of prayer and praise. But because the "extraordinary laity" set apart for specific ministries were distinguished from the general laity but not ordained, their betwixt and between status opened the door to queries about the other liturgical roles permitted to them. For some of the denominations, the controversies that resulted, and the theological ambiguities that emerged as a consequence of decisions taken, remained unresolved at the end of the twentieth century.

The Unordained Preacher

The work of a licensed lay preacher, after 1784, could be a lifelong or short-term vocation, and often served as the point of entry into the ordained orders.[9] Like the deacon and the elder, the lay preacher was appointed by the ecclesiastical superior to a place of service. The ministry of lay preaching was believed to be as legitimate and substantive a ministry as that of elder; a divine call was considered a prerequisite to either endeavor. Charles Giles, reflecting upon his ordination to the diaconate in 1808, noted that his work as a lay preacher was the true manifestation of his ministerial call. Ordination "added no gift or faculty to the soul, nor conferred any intrinsic worth to moral character," for to his thinking it was "only an outward, visible ceremony" recognizing a prior commitment:

> For several years, preceding my ordination, I had been preaching under divine authority, with only a license from the church, and God owned my labours then as evidently as he has done since. Though young and weak, still the gracious Redeemer gave me many seals to my ministry before the hands of the bishop were laid upon me. My high authority to preach the gospel I had received long before, in a direct line from the throne above, by the call and inspiration of the Holy Ghost while under the elm-tree. The sacred credentials which I there received, written by the finger of God on the tablet of my heart, accompanied from time to time with his approval and blessing on my feeble labours, were sufficient to confirm me in the fact, that I was in the *"true succession."*[10]

The seriousness and the dedication with which most lay preachers carried out their call, even under adversity, is demonstrated by the notice that appeared in the August 15, 1800, issue of the *Newbern Gazette* regarding the escape of a slave named Simbo: "He is a Methodist Preacher and can read and write. . . . the most probable method to catch him, will be at Methodist meetings."[11]

From 1784 to the end of the twentieth century, one single liturgical responsibility was consistently—and obviously—assigned to the preacher: to preach. Leadership for prayer and singing could be overtly stated or implied. Prior to the abandonment of Wesley's orders for morning and evening prayer in 1792, certain lay preachers with written permission were allowed to "read the liturgy"; the preachers not receiving that permission evidently led worship as they saw fit. After 1792, no distinctions were made about the type of service that the ordained and the licensed could conduct: both could follow or improvise upon the guidelines and orders for public worship set forth by the respective denominations. Proposals in some denominations to establish liturgical uniformity for Lord's Day worship never addressed the fact that both ordained and unordained presiders would lead those services. The content and shape of the preaching service was thus not dependent upon the ordination status of the leader.

On account of the greater supply of Methodist communities than the number of ordained ministers to serve them, licensed preachers were placed in charge of circuits or stations, and therefore carried responsibilities for local oversight comparable to those borne by the deacon or elder who was given the same assignment. This blurring of identities and overlapping of duties eventually provoked questions why additional roles couldn't be made available to the unordained since, to the people they served, the licensed preacher appeared on most occasions to be no different from the deacon or elder. The subject first broached in a few of the denominations was the feasibility of the unordained solemnizing matrimony. The General Conference of the Methodist Episcopal Church entertained a proposal to that effect in 1856 and would continue to do so each quadrennium until the end of that century and into the next, finally granting the exception in 1904 but only in places where it was permissible by state law. Meanwhile, petitions were also put forward that the unordained so appointed also be allowed to administer baptism, since candidates were sometimes obliged to go to non-Methodist ministers for the sacramental service and as a result "our ministry is somewhat disparaged and our Church suffers loss."[12] Impatient preachers—even those not in charge of a circuit or station—sometimes took matters into their own hands. One minister described without regret the action he had taken when he was a licentiate of the Methodist Episcopal Church, South pastoring in Louisiana:

> There I was, authorized to preach the gospel, to call sinners to repentance, to lead them into the church and the Kingdom of God; and here was one ready and I had no authority to publicly pour a little water on her head as a symbol and a token. And she was ready right then, and if postponed until I got an ordained minister, the nearest one being fifty miles away—which was a long way then—when could it ever be done?
>
> I had to think fast. If it had been under any ordinary circumstances, I might have explained the situation to her, but here were the others present that maybe could never understand what it meant; could not understand why I was authorized to preach, yet could not baptize; and as I planned later to have a revival meeting there and take in a great number more, I just quickly decided to baptize her right then and there and did it; *and never said a word about it.*
>
> Did I do wrong? No! I have never to this day had the slightest compunction about it. If I was ever called of God to preach His gospel, I was called to perform all the functions of a minister, and the laying on my head the hand of a Bishop some years later added nothing to the authority to baptize that I did not already have.[13]

The claim of this man that the warrant to officiate at the sacraments rested upon an inward call was not unique. But most of the arguments for permitting baptism by the unordained preacher in charge centered upon pastoral need and the desire of local congregations to receive the sacraments from their regularly appointed pastor. Some contended that sacramental privileges would have the added benefit of legitimating the ministry of the lay preacher whose duties were largely indistinguishable from those of the ordained. One justification put forward for the practice was that in the history of the church the laity had been allowed to baptize under special circumstances. After lengthy debate, the Methodist Episcopal Church, South, in 1906, authorized the unordained preacher in charge to celebrate baptism in the absence of an elder or bishop, while at the same time rejecting pleas for dispensation to celebrate the Lord's Supper. The Methodist Episcopal Church followed suit and conceded baptism in 1912, as would the Free Methodist Church in 1939. Although in 1914 the Methodist Episcopal Church, South's bishops soundly denounced the action of 1906 as "illogical in its conception" and "confusing in its operation,"[14] the church took the next step in 1926 and allowed the unordained in charge to administer the Supper "with the understanding that no permanent powers of ordination are conferred until granted by the laying on of hands after he shall have met the disciplinary requirements" (*Discipline*, ¶139). This privilege was reluctantly carried over into the Methodist Church in 1939 despite the absence of such an arrangement in the other two uniting bodies. Opponents then and in the ensuing years reminded the denomination that not only was their policy contrary to the practice of most Christian churches (of vital importance given the church's ecumenical interests), it was furthermore at variance with historic Methodism, since Wesley's actions that culminated in the creation of the Methodist Episcopal Church were the result of his insistence that sacramental ministers be ordained. Heeding those voices, certain strictures were applied in the 1944 *Discipline* (¶308), namely that sacramental administration was dependent upon written episcopal consent, and that permission would be revoked should the unordained exercise those privileges outside the bounds of the congregation or congregations where assigned.

Nine years after the merger, the bishops noted in their Episcopal Address at the 1948 General Conference that having any unordained person sanctioned to administer the sacraments "involves us in an unsound and illogical position with respect to the meaning of the sacraments and the purpose of ordination."[15] When the dust settled from that meeting, the approval for celebrating the Supper had been rescinded (at least until the 1952 General Conference); baptism and marriage, with the requisite episcopal authorization, remained as options. Between 1948 and 1952, articles on ordination and the sacraments deluged the Methodist Church's periodicals and newspapers, with no fewer than nine essays on the topic appearing in *The Pastor*. Amusingly, one of the complaints registered against the 1948 change was that the frequency of the Lord's Supper for persons pastored by the unordained would be diminished if permission (or, as some put it, the "right") was not restored—this from churches observing quarterly Communion. The church's general body reconvened in 1952 and received a report from the commission established at the previous Conference to study the ministry, which recommended the continuation of the 1948 policy.[16] However, two reports were brought from the 1952 Conference's General Standing Committee on Ministry, with the majority report advising the restoration of Communion administration, and the minority report preserving the 1948 position.[17] In the end, permission for the unordained to preside at Communion was printed in the *Discipline* (¶308), with an extended list of provisos added, but without the requirement of an episcopal signature. In spite of attempts in 1964 to revoke the permission as a consequence of another study on the ministry, the denomination retained the provision until 1968. The expanded privilege of the unordained was hinted at in the "Office for Licensing Persons to Preach" within the church's *Book of Worship* (1965) by the statement that the candidate was "authorized to preach the gospel in the congregation and to perform such other acts of service in the church as you may be appointed to do."

With the formation of the United Methodist Church, the subject was revisited yet again. For the first eight years of the denomination, unordained preachers appointed to pastoral duties were expressly forbidden to administer the Lord's Supper and baptism. But from 1976 through to the 1996 *Discipline* they were authorized to perform both sacraments, as well as the rites for marriage, burial, confirmation, and the reception of members. Such inconsistency and confusion for more than sixty years in the largest Methodist denomination created tensions at all levels. Contributing to the mix in those years was the sacramental renewal advocated in parts of the church as the result of the rediscovery of early Christian and early Methodist eucharistic praxis. These practical dilemmas and tensions were, however, symptomatic of a wider and more significant problem, namely, a weak ecclesiology that was compounded by the lack of developed theologies of the sacraments and ordination. The other members of the Methodist family were not entirely immune from these problems, for like the larger body, they claimed the double heritage of being both mission society and ecclesiastical institution. The Free Methodist Church followed the option taken by the United Methodist Church and in 1985 permitted the unordained preacher in charge of a church to administer both sacraments. Yet on the matter of sacramental administration, the African-American churches were clear: according to the *Discipline*, ordination was always the prerequisite.

Deaconesses

Inspired by the success of Lutheran pastor Theodore Fliedner at Kaiserswerth, Germany, a few Christian denominations in America began to revive the biblical (Romans 16:1) and early Christian office of woman deacon during the second half of the nineteenth century. Most Methodist denominations by 1920 engaged deaconesses in benevolent work, following the lead set by the Methodist Episcopal Church, which officially recognized the office in 1888 and, prior to that, the recommendation (and evidently the practice in Georgia) of John Wesley.[18] Women had, of course, already been offering their ministry and leadership for decades, though their work generally had not been sanctioned by their judicatories; and sometimes when consent had been given, it was soon revoked.[19] Jarena Lee approached Richard Allen around 1809, when Allen was a deacon of the Methodist Episcopal Church, about preaching the gospel in response to what she perceived was a divine call. Allen did not grant her permission on that occasion ("our Discipline . . . did not call for women preachers"), but eight years later the new Bishop

Allen recognized her abilities and licensed her to exhort but not to preach (though to her mind she did both).[20] Her sisters in the African Methodist Episcopal Church, who likewise were not silenced by the absence of a piece of paper, were eventually granted licenses to preach in 1884. Helenor M. Davison was ordained deacon in 1866 by the North Indiana Conference of the Methodist (Protestant) Church, but the 1871 General Conference disapproved women's ordination, leaving Davison uncertain of her status (though she too continued to preach). Margaret Newton Van Cott, a certified evangelist in the New York Conference, received in 1869 the first preacher's license given to a woman in the Methodist Episcopal Church. Eleven years later the General Conference legislated that women could not be licensed as preachers and kept that policy until 1920.[21]

The Methodist Episcopal Church's certification of deaconess work came as appeals were made for additional help in domestic and foreign missions, urban evangelism, and care for the sick and poor. By approving the diaconessate as a recognized, full-time female vocation, the General Conference strove to meet human need and at the same time conveniently thwarted efforts within the denomination to secure the licensing and ordination of women. Surprisingly, the impetus for endorsement came not from a petition generated by the Rock River Conference in the geographical bounds of which a training school for women had already been established in Chicago in 1885, but from a request sent by the Bengal (India) Conference that deaconesses be provided to administer the sacraments in zenanas to converted women who by cultural code could not receive them from male hands.[22] When the duties of the deaconess were stipulated in the 1888 *Discipline*, neither the sacraments nor worship leadership was explicitly mentioned. There was certainly latitude for the latter, as it was encompassed under the stated tasks to "minister to the poor, visit the sick, pray with the dying, care for the orphans, seek the wandering, comfort the sorrowing, save the sinning, and ever be ready to take up any other duty for which willing hands cannot otherwise be found." The "apostolicity" of, and hence the warrant for, these female endeavors was claimed by the use in the service of consecration (not ordination) of a prayer for the installation of deaconesses intentionally taken from the early Christian church order known as *Apostolic Constitutions*.[23] The prayer was printed in the Methodist Episcopal *Discipline* only from 1896 to 1916; the African Methodist Episcopal Zion Church adopted the formulary and still used it at the end of the twentieth century. Although the Methodist Episcopal Church after 1916 did not use the ancient prayer, and neither did the other denominations with an official rite (e.g., the African Methodist Episcopal Church), they still named notable biblical women in the prayers of the consecratory rite as justification for and examples of the female office.

The ever-pragmatic Methodists never precluded the possibility that the theological and practical training of the deaconess might be put to service for the leadership of worship. Deaconesses who functioned as pastoral assistants had liberty to conduct worship, especially with children and youth, or to hold prayer meetings. Those who were trained musicians prepared choirs for the sanctuary. After obtaining the proper license to preach, a woman might work as a "pastor deaconess," what was virtually a local church pastor usually in the mission field.[24] In 1976, the

United Methodist Church introduced the nongendered office of Diaconal Minister that, like the deaconess, was meant for full-time ministries of service. Numerous types of church work were defined under the rubric of diaconal ministry, including vocations in music ministry. Though more recognized overall for their contributions to nursing, education, visitation, and evangelism, deaconesses (and diaconal ministers) nonetheless played a role in assisting Methodists and others in public prayer and praise.

To Stir Each Other Up

> Lift up your hearts to things above,
>   Ye followers of the Lamb,
> And join with us to praise his love,
>   And glorify his name.
> · · · · · · · · ·
> O let us stir each other up,
>   Our faith by works to approve,
> By holy, purifying hope,
>   And the sweet task of love.[25]

As this hymn by Charles Wesley suggests, all faithful Christians were charged to stir up both believer and stranger in order to elicit the praise and glorification of God. It was anticipated, therefore, that every Methodist would serve as a leader in enabling the worship of others, whether by speaking words of encouragement, providing an opportunity, or making a contribution in the assembly. Different and specific roles were necessary to carry out the public liturgical work that defined Methodists as church. According to the brief statement "Of the Church" handed on by the majority of the denominations as one of the Articles of Religion, church meant the congregation where "the pure Word of God is preached, and the Sacraments duly administered." To corporealize those essential characteristics, American Methodists imitated their father in the faith and looked to means that were both apostolic and evangelical. Occasionally pragmatic considerations caused an odd combination of the two norms. Methodists generally did not seek to reconcile apparent tensions since they were more interested in accomplishing the divine mandate to make disciples than in devising a systematic and cohesive theological rationale for the method undertaken. The strained juxtaposition of the evangelical and the apostolic was most obvious by the decision made in the largest of the denominations to allow sacramental administration by the unordained. A less conflictual decision would have been to ordain any person appointed to serve a local congregation—which was proposed in the largest body, and taken up in some of the others. Even in matters of ecclesiology, Methodists coveted the freedom to move in ways that would best care for the God's people and spread scriptural holiness throughout the land.

American Methodist Worship
Memory and Modernization

EXAMINATION OF THE liturgical texts and practices of an ecclesiastical family, of a denomination within that family, or of a local congregation opens a window onto a particular people's beliefs about God, themselves, and the world. This is so because the liturgical performance ideally summarizes in ritual language and action the spiritual, theological, and ecclesial perspectives of the corporate body in both its denominational and local manifestations. John Reeder, in an essay for the *Methodist Review* of 1896, came to just such a conclusion when he remarked that liturgy "has to do with all those acts of pastor and people which spring from and find expression in the common feelings of devotion" whether through the use of "certain formulas" or through "constructive, and, in a measure, spontaneous" means.[1] Services of worship, of course, link the present generation in various ways with the acknowledged standards of the faith, since the ritual used (whether written or unwritten) serves to "impart and preserve the historic truths of Christianity" and to "witness to doctrinal truths."[2] Thus how and where a people worship, the *ordo* they select for Sunday or occasional services, and what they say (and who says it) speak volumes about their corporate piety and their diachronic and synchronic Christian (and denominational) identity.

An integral connection exists therefore between what a community does in its worship and what that community believes. The history of Christian liturgy demonstrates that how a people prays not only shapes personal and communal belief but sometimes also the formulation of doctrine. Conversely, established doctrine or theological consensus may determine or at least contribute to the content of the liturgy. Among American Methodists, both "directions" in the relationship between liturgy and belief are present. The popular hymns and songs of the camp meeting and revival reinforced old or supplied new theological perspectives on soteriology and the spiritual accountability of the Christian. The rite of Christian initiation approved by the United Methodist Church in 1988, with its hint of baptismal regeneration and its allowance for infant communion, sparked a denomination-wide theological study of baptism and confirmation that led to an officially adopted doctrinal statement in 1996. Going the other direction, shifts in theological (and anthropological) understanding within some of the Methodist churches found expression in liturgical practice, most notably in the textual revisions made over time to the rites for baptism, marriage, and the burial of the dead. One central belief shared by all members of the Methodist family in every period was continually addressed in and by worship: the Christian duty, aided by the power of the Holy Spirit, to fulfill the divine mandate to spread the gospel. The priority of evangelism in worship resulted in a pragmatism that saw different patterns and words used to achieve the goal of making disciples and church members.

Within the system of belief that influences liturgical practice must also be counted the particularities and self-definitions that distinguish a certain ecclesiastical family or denomination from others. One fundamental characteristic of American Methodism in its approach to worship—though it is not alone in this among churches—has been its simultaneously retrospective and prospective orientation. At the 1886 General Conference of the Methodist Episcopal Church, South, the bishops acknowledged Methodism's ecclesial distinctiveness within the broader Christian tradition and implied its propensity to be simultaneously backward- and forward-looking:

> In common with the evangelical bodies of Protestant Christendom we have held those truths which relate to God, to his moral government, to immortality, to eternal retribution, to the sacred authority of the Scriptures, to the sacraments, and the Christian ministry. We have, with them, preached the universality of the fall, the necessity, universality, and fullness of the atonement, the freeness of the will, and the freeness of grace. None of these have been omitted, and yet they do not constitute the characteristic Methodist doctrine. That is to be found in truths which more immediately underlie the Christian experience, by which all that is provisional and relative in God's system of recovering mercy becomes actual and personal. . . .
>
> These doctrines of experience have constituted the charm of our ministry. They give being and form to our Church. The joy and life which they infuse into every part of our body have redeemed it from all sepulchral tradition, and have arrayed it as a company of virgins going forth to meet the Bridegroom.
>
> It is the vitality of this holiness that has brought relief to humanity and glory to the name of our God. Its swiftness, certainty, freeness, and fullness meet the necessities of a dying and guilty world. . . . We therefore exhort you, dear brethren, to hold fast the form of sound words, the established customs, and the clear experience which have come down to us from our fathers.[3]

Thus it may be said that adherence to perceived Wesleyan or Methodist principles and the intention to spread scriptural holiness in a "Methodist" way to each new generation have underlain the constancy and change of Methodist worship from the eighteenth century to the end of the twentieth. Memory and modernization: these concepts will guide an assessment of more than two hundred years of American Methodist worship.

Upholding the "Methodist Tradition"

When in 1784 the American Methodists received the unbound copies of John Wesley's *Sunday Service* and his letter to "Our Brethren in America," they already had in hand the 1780 version of the Large Minutes from Britain and had kept several years' worth of their own "Minutes of Some Conversations between the Preachers in Connexion with the Reverend Mr. John Wesley." All these four guides were then brought to bear in determining the texts and practices to be used for worship in the Methodist Episcopal Church—combined, of course, with what Methodists had already found to be faithful and faith-filled expressions of Christian worship. The *Sunday Service* provided a collection of liturgical texts that gave a standard and printed form to Methodist worship, thereby at the start defining American Methodism as liturgical kin to the Anglican tradition and as a citizen in the church catholic. The letter of September 10 granted Wesley's spiritual offspring "full liberty simply to follow the scriptures and the primitive church," and in the post-Revolutionary context, the notions of freedom and democracy in worship were readily embraced, though they were qualified within the parameters of what was perceived to be biblical and apostolical. The Large Minutes and the American Minutes interspersed worship-related subjects (e.g., appropriate music, and general fasts and thanksgivings) among the other topics of Methodist polity, providing guidelines and rules for practice. Therefore, three authoritative and distinctly different sources for worship coexisted by early 1785: a book with orders of worship; permission from Methodism's "venerable Father" to worship according to scripture-guided conscience and Spirit-inspired piety; and a book of Methodist law and discipline derived from the Large Minutes of 1780 and adapted for American usage.

These three sources established that Methodist worship should not be haphazard, but rather be organized according to certain principles. Although the details changed, most Methodist denominations throughout their respective histories opted to continue what the three sources represented and provided. A section of the *Discipline* was devoted to ritual texts, or independent books were published containing denominationally authorized orders for worship. Legislation was printed in the *Discipline* regarding worship leadership, the house for worship, and worship practices, including the peculiar services and conventions of the Methodists not formalized by liturgical texts. And despite occasional calls within particular churches for liturgical uniformity, especially in regard to the administration of the sacraments, orders of worship were never strictly *mandated* by any Methodist body; a certain degree of flexibility for local custom and pastoral preference was always permitted—and, indeed, assumed. The linking of these three sources has throughout given American Methodism a hybrid approach in defining the basics of its worship, for worship was legitimately to be constituted from a juxtaposition of formal texts (a "form of sound words"), rubrics from a book of law ("established customs"), and popular practices ("clear experience"). Other denominations might combine liturgical texts with canon law or a book of church order. But few placed ritual forms in tandem with an officially articulated concept of freedom in worship—a connection Wesley himself had illustrated by, for instance, inserting a rubric for extempory prayer at the conclusion of his revision of the Anglican Communion service. Methodists are, in a manner of speaking, simultaneously "liturgical" and "free."

Although the three sources have been in place to direct Methodist thinking about worship, reconciling the three has not been easy, especially since liberty in expression may be perceived to stand in direct contradiction to a book of law and to a collection of ritual forms. Many Methodists found holding freedom and form together so troubling that one position—most often that of freedom, encouraged by the American ideals of democracy and individual rights, and by the fear of a Spirit-inhibiting ritualism—was adopted and proclaimed to be *the* Wesleyan paradigm, despite the ongoing presence in the *Discipline* of orders for sacraments and occasional services that still carried the imprint of Wesley's *Sunday Service*. Leaders and the communities they served who took this route—and they were legion— believed they then could elect whether to depart from, abbreviate, or improvise upon the approved texts. On the other hand, those who promoted the value of liturgical forms and advocated few verbal alterations pointed to liturgical texts as a valuable inheritance, and as a means of reinforcing a recognizable denominational identity. The tension between liturgical form and freedom has been a part of Methodism from 1784, and, as such, it may be claimed as a characteristic of Methodist worship praxis. Perhaps the tension was at the root of the custom within some denominations to revise their hymn books and liturgical texts roughly every generation: the regular revamping of service books gave the appearance of not being bound to a single formulation. Unfortunately, the tension has also occasionally been a source of division within denominations and congregations.

There has been a tendency within liturgical studies, inspired in large part by the comparative work of Anton Baumstark, to view the history of a liturgical tradition in evolutionary terms, with movement from austerity to richness, simplicity to elaboration, though as Baumstark noted, a reversal is possible if curtailment of prolixity is warranted.[4] In many respects, this evolutionary picture may be painted for American Methodism. The 1792 Lord's Day rubrics were, after all, expanded and formally structured in the larger denominations by the end of the nineteenth century, with further embellishment in the twentieth. After decades of resistance, the Free Methodists eventually granted a place in worship for choirs and musical instruments. But to come to such a conclusion risks simplifying the complexity of the American Methodist experience and overlooking the three sources that have for generations guided the Methodist denominations. Form and freedom have stood together from the beginning, though at any given time, and in any denomination, one of the pair might be emphasized in practice or in discourse over the other. Therefore, a reversion to an "austere" form of worship may not be a reaction against "richness" per se, but rather, for Methodism, a reassertion of the freedom that had been slighted in favor of form. On the other hand, the reemergence of Wesley's morning prayer in 1867 under the leadership of Thomas O. Summers is a case where a liturgically elaborate form was interjected into an overall climate of liturgical freedom and simplicity. Sometimes the austere and the rich, the free and the formulated, could, in fact, be found side by side. As attested by the announcements and articles published in some denominational weeklies during the late nineteenth century, the same Methodists who extolled the camp meeting and the simple prayer service also had a pronounced preference for Gothic architecture. At the end of the twentieth century, an informal service of word, spontaneous prayer, and unaccompanied song, and a formal service with choral anthems, chanted psalmody, and formulated prayers designed according to the day or season of the Christian year could be observed in a single church at different hours on Sunday morning. Thus, rather than taking a singular, monodirectional course, Methodism has been, in effect, constantly meeting itself.

Methodists were sometimes compelled to state that their worship practice or their theology departed from what they understood to have been presented by Wesley, as did John Emory regarding the subject of baptismal regeneration shortly before he was elected a bishop of the Methodist Episcopal Church. But most often, Methodists sought to identify their worship as "Wesleyan," with the appellation used as a justification whether or not the practice or theological position could actually be traced directly to Wesley and the early Methodists in Britain. To John Wesley has been anachronistically credited the camp meeting, the use of grape juice for Communion, advocacy for women in ministry, and the first performance of "contemporary" worship. The authentication of Methodist practice by being "Wesleyan" has been a significant factor in legitimating the shape of liturgical revision and innovation, and in defining Methodism over and against other ecclesiastical traditions. But as was the case regarding ritual form and liturgical freedom, the "Wesleyan" memory has sometimes been selective.

Similarly, Methodists were inclined to describe what they did in worship as decisively and authentically "Methodist." Or, if church leadership or certain individuals felt that a congregation or denomination had strayed too far from what were construed to be the denomination's defining characteristics, appeals were made to return to "Methodist" practice. Such a fluid, and occasionally contradictory, attribution gives evidence that Methodists recognized their heritage in terms of historic fact, and that they also interpreted their liturgical identity dynamically in light of present circumstances, recent memories, and an idealized or romanticized understanding of their denomination's past. In other words, to be "Methodist" in worship automatically carried with it a variety of meanings at different times and in different locations. That this was so should not be surprising. An ecclesiastical family that put such heavy stock in the work of the Holy Spirit and in the reason and experience of the individual would be expected to understand itself as being remade in each generation, not ex nihilo, but grounded in the events and practices of its past. In effect, Methodist liturgical self-perception was formed by a nonidentical repetition, whereby certain linkages with the past were carried forward, some of which were reinterpreted, while others were intentionally dropped or unwittingly forgotten in response to new definitions of personal and social religion. The liturgical changes sanctioned by a denomination or the style of worship adopted in the local congregation also contributed to this process of retraditioning, and indeed, it could be argued that the liturgy, each time it was revised, constituted the tradition.[5] Each generation's or each community's practices were therefore, in their own eyes, truly Methodist. What had been normative in practice often remained so even when newer liturgical configurations were taken up, not just because of the slowness with which ritual changes oftentimes took hold but because both could be argued to be legitimately "Methodist." For this reason, baptism alone, baptism with an additional rite of membership or confirmation, personal profession, an affirmative response to the Invitation, or simply attendance on Sunday morning could all be deemed "Methodist" prerequisites for admission to Lord's table. The "Methodist tradition," therefore, should not be conceived of as an evolutionary line, running from Wesley to the establishment of the American denominations and on into the future. Rather, the Methodist liturgical tradition should more properly be imagined in spiral form, with various and diverse points of development evenly carrying the weight of "tradition."

The "extraordinary genius for adapting the means at hand to the end desired,"[6] celebrated as a characteristic of Methodism from the beginning, has complemented and contributed to the emergence of a multivalent American Methodist "tradition." But it has meant that a singular and absolute description of Methodist worship for one ritual occasion or event is not possible within one denomination or even within one denomination in a narrowly circumscribed area, though the denominationally authorized services (particularly for the sacraments) lent a particular cast to the worship. Even a standard component regularly found in Methodist worship services, whenever and wherever, could not be ascribed a uniform function or location in the order. A case in point was the use of hymns or songs in Lord's Day worship. Whereas in British Methodism hymns were generally understood to be an integral part of the ordinary, with their placement determinative of the shape of the entire *ordo*, in American Methodism hymns might structure a service (in a so-called hymn sandwich, with hymns at beginning and end, and perhaps somewhere in the middle), serve as transitions or bridges at various points in a service (with or without a thematic or structural connection), amplify another act of worship (e.g., the sermon), or be used simply to stir the emotions (with extended singing at the beginning of a service, or toward the end during an "altar call"). The use of hymns in worship thus may be a "traditional" Methodist enterprise, but how those hymns were used keyed into the set of traditions expected for the liturgical occasion, and the traditions resident in a particular place and time.

Methodists were retrospective in planning and ordering worship, but their attention to the past stood in the service of the present. The denominations aimed to be consistent with, or at least not blatantly to contradict, what was recorded in holy writ, with the Holiness Methodists generally preferring a more literal approach throughout their histories. The churches strove to uphold the apostolic faith, and summarized it in sermon and expressed it in prayer, if not also in formulated liturgical text or creed. They intentionally imitated what was believed to be apostolic practice by the performance of the watch night and the love feast, the use of extemporary prayer, and the holding of services in the open air or in every imaginable building; in later years, orders from the early church served as paradigms for some Methodist praxis, and ancient Christian theological writings informed the content of certain rites (e.g., for the burial of the dead in the United Methodist Church). Methodists looked back to Wesley as evangelist and theologian, to the three sources that he bequeathed to them, and to the revisions or adjustments made to the three sources within the respective denominations. Individual Methodists and Methodist congregations also treasured their own peculiar liturgical memories, thereby honoring and preserving the work of worship done by their fathers and mothers to the glory of God.

But what was remembered of the past had at one time been an innovation of the present. Methodists took seriously their charge to proclaim the gospel and applied almost any available means to achieve that goal. Generations sang of their conviction, expressed poetically by Charles Wesley:

> A charge to keep I have,
>   A God to glorify,
> A never-dying soul to save,
>   And fit it for the sky.

> To serve the present age,
>   My calling to fulfill;
> O may it all my powers engage,
>   To do my Master's will!

Methodist worship, therefore, also needed to be prospective: to be a genuine expression of thanksgiving and petition for Christians of the present age in order to maintain a viable community of faith for the ages soon to come. But concern for the continuing task brought its own tensions, since numerous approaches could be and were taken in response to the question of how to spread scriptural holiness and elicit faithful worship in an ever-changing environment. Members of the Methodist family found different answers based upon their modifying self-definitions and their understanding of what constituted "traditional" Methodist worship.

Creating Faithful Worship for Each Generation

Christian worship, which the bishops of one denomination defined briefly as "the adoration of God, the ascription of supreme worth to God, and the manifestion of reverence in the presence of God,"[7] cannot be carried out in the abstract, but must be given concrete form in a manner that permits for the worshipers an honest and authentic articulation of their faith. The challenge for Methodists, as for other Christians, has been to determine the extent to which worship be allowed to speak in the language and circumstances of each time and place; in other words, to assess to what degree worship may take on popular idioms or mirror the social context. A certain amount of acculturation is inevitable, and some liturgical adjustments may be expected in response to modernization. But there is a difference between acknowledging and addressing in worship the current situation for the sake of effective praise and prayer, and conformity to the times—often with the explicit purpose of attracting a certain type of worshiper. Each of the Methodist denominations employed the two approaches, though at different paces, with a denomination's willingness to embrace the second approach typically coinciding with that church's reevaluation of its relationship with the wider society.

American Methodist worship through roughly the first third of the nineteenth century embodied the intention of the respective Methodist denominations to reform the moral and spiritual character of their members and of the nation as a whole. To enliven religion and convert the unawakened, Methodists used innovative means counter to the practices of the institutionalized Congregational and Episcopal churches, and consistent with the contemporary spirit of democracy and freedom. They peppered their preaching, their prayers, and their polity with the Americanized language of liberty of conscience and personal responsibility before God; the Methodist Protestants went so far as to take the vernacular of mutual rights as an undergirding principle of that denomination. Yet at the same time Methodists preserved certain markers that unmistakably identified them as a people of God distinct from the world where ministry was to occur. Methodists displayed an egalitarianism by allowing the leadership of worship and testimonies to God's goodness to be rendered by laymen, and in a more limited way by laywomen. However, preaching was limited to those recognized with a license, and sacramental presidency was restricted to the ordained ministers. Methodists preached in the open air to all who would hear and insisted upon family prayers in whatever home they lodged, but made the love feast and the Lord's table accessible only by ticket or token. Baptism could occur in the mode of the candidate's (or the parents') choice, yet the reception of baptism was nonnegotiable for anyone who would be a Christian. Funeral sermons were not to be indiscriminately preached; neither were Methodist ministers to unite in marriage a Christian with an unbeliever. The dress of the Methodists was to be simple and unadorned, and their places of meeting plain and decent: they were to be a peculiar people. Methodists may have capitalized upon the popular language and the political agendas of the times to facilitate their work of evangelism—they may have borrowed components of the social medium—but the essential message was decidedly different. Firm delineations were made between the "temporal" and the "spiritual." Even the collection of monies made for the poor during the love feast or the Communion service was handled by the steward, not by the preacher.

By the mid-nineteenth century, a notable change was occurring, one that caught the attention of Philip Schaff in his study of American religious, political, and social life first written in German in 1854. Schaff commented on the rapid growth of Methodism and its "uncommon energy and activity"; he also observed that Methodists were so numerous that in Indiana they controlled the political elections. Whereas Methodism had formerly sought to challenge, confront, and reshape the broader culture, it was now becoming more closely aligned with its environs, which, Schaff predicted, could substantially redefine the denomination:

The Methodists are now beginning to establish colleges and seminaries, to publish scientific periodicals, and to follow the steps of the culture of the age. But it is a question whether they will not thus lose more in their peculiar character and influence with the masses, than they will gain in the more cultivated circles.[8]

Indeed, the peculiar character of Methodism was at risk as Methodists identified themselves more fully as a national church and protector of the nation's moral values, and as the once strict demarcation between temporal and spiritual matters slowly dissolved. These shifts were borne out by the reorganizing and bureaucratizing of denominational structures, particularly manifested in the Methodist Episcopal Church and Methodist Episcopal Church, South in the years after the nation's war, and also by the concerted efforts within some of the churches to woo the middle class and to retain those members who had become affluent. Rules started to relax on attendance, membership, and the "Methodistic" disciplines of Christian life, and many regulations fell by the wayside as the century progressed and spiritual temperatures cooled. The increase in the number of stationed pastors added new dimensions as circuit riding became a treasured memory. The dismounted preachers took up many of the temporal duties formerly relegated to selected resident laity, and began to adopt the institutionalizing tendencies that their forefathers and foremothers had not too long before critiqued. All these factors found liturgical expression in the larger denominations, as new assessments were made of the shape and content of ritual forms, and the aesthetic and practical contributions of architecture and art were weighed in regard to liturgical space. Though not indiscriminate in doing so, the Methodist Episcopal Church was the most willing to adapt its liturgical texts and practices to its new self-understandings, to emerging social and theological issues, and to popular practices from the wider society—all for the sake of constructing meaningful worship. The spirit of Methodism was not characterized just by the spirit of revival and the spirit of liberty, Methodist Episcopal bishop Thomas Morris declared in 1864, but also by the spirits of progress and improvement.[9] Not unexpectedly, the opinion of the Methodist Episcopal constituency was not unanimous in that regard. At the most extreme, fear of the loss of "old school" Methodist peculiarities, and the desire to avoid "dead formalism" and "conformity to the world," contributed to the reluctant separation of Free Methodism from the Methodist Episcopal Church. Perhaps it was no coincidence that as Methodist denominations began to accommodate to the larger society and shed their denominational peculiarities, the general percentage of Methodists among the declared church members in the nation's population began to decline.

In effect, the denominations wanted to have it both ways. To various degrees each denomination sought to "serve the present age"; yet they did not wish to forsake their "tradition," however defined. Members of the Methodist Episcopal Church, for example, cried "worldliness" when at the same time others in their denomination were proposing to "keep up with the times" and to become "interested [in] where the people are."[10] They bemoaned the demise of family prayer and the prayer meeting as their denomination removed (or did not enforce) the mechanisms that had ensured the perpetuation of those peculiarities. At the General Conference of 1900, the bishops of the Methodist Episcopal Church recognized that what could be regarded as progress could also be read as a decline:

That many changes have occurred in the outward forms of Methodism is obvious. Which do they indicate, growth or decay? The class meeting, for instance, is considerably disused: have fellowship and spiritual helpfulness among believers abated, or do they find, in part, other expressions and other instruments? The rigid and minute Church discipline of former years is relaxed: is this a sign of pastoral unfaithfulness, or is it a sign of growing respect for individual liberty and of a better conception of the function of the Church? The plainness of the early Methodist congregations has disappeared: is this simply vanity and worldliness, or is it, in part, the natural and justifiable development of the aesthetic faculty under more prosperous external conditions? The strenuous contention for this or that particular doctrine or usage of Methodism, once common, is now rarely heard: is this indifferentism, or is it, in part, a better discernment of that which is vital to the Christian faith, and, in part, the result of an acceptance by others of the once disputed opinion?

The bishops viewed acculturation and modernization as a type of faithfulness to the gospel, and not a capitulation to secularity.

Whoever in the presence of such conditions hastens to pronounce judgment on the general question of growth or decay is evidently unequal to the task.... There are reasons for both fear and hope, for both congratulation and solemn admonition. But we believe that in the clearer acceptance of Christianity as spirit and not letter, in the growing sense of individual right and responsibility, in the increase of the altruistic feeling, and in the multitude of sincere and earnest souls found in our ministry and in our laity there is evidence that the Church is advancing toward the end of its high calling.[11]

The course of Americanization begun in 1784, and intensified from the middle of the nineteenth century onward by the willingness of a few denominations at first to appropriate the views and customs of the larger society, continued unabated into the twentieth. Even the more wary Holiness and African-American denominations by the end of the century had surrendered numerous peculiarities and accommodated certain "worldly" customs, with the African Methodist Episcopal Church's liturgy (using the official ritual texts as the standard) the least affected by external influences. The language of democracy and freedom so prevalent in Methodism's early years was still spoken, but in the late twentieth century it shaped liturgical decisions in a new way. For some Methodists, the vision of a democratic kingdom of God allowed for no discrimination at the Lord's table— not by race, gender, or age, but also in some churches not by baptismal status. Many Methodist parents felt free to withhold baptism from their offspring to allow the child to make a conscious choice, something that would have been unheard of in Methodist families of the nineteenth century. Engaged couples, both churched and unchurched, were oftentimes permitted to decide upon the shape and content of the nuptial rite officiated by Methodist clergy. The ethos of religious freedom and diversity that pervaded the nation, and the collapsing of denominational loyalties (possibly aided inadvertently by the ecumenical movement), invited a consumerist approach to ordering worship, as local congregations vied to attract attenders with a lively and "friendly" liturgy. At the end of the twentieth century, the once solid line between "temporal" and "spiritual" was virtually invisible.

There were, of course, periods when liturgical progress was measured by looking backward to Wesley or further back to the exercises of the early church. These retrospectives, while perhaps a phase of retraditioning, may also have found reinforcement from broader societal factors. The first reissuance of the *Sunday Service* occurred during reconstruction after the Civil War. At the end of the nineteenth century and the beginning of the twentieth, Wesley's texts in unofficial collections provided resources for liturgical and aesthetic "enrichment" and connected Methodists more directly with their upscale Protestant Episcopal neighbors. The incorporation of material from the *Sunday Service* into the Methodist Episcopal Lord's Day services of 1932 came at a time when organic models of cultural growth and theories of psychological development were being popularized. The social turbulence of the 1960s may have encouraged a "back to the basics" reaction. For the United Methodist Church, this meant revising their official rites to reflect more directly the structures and theological content of Christian liturgy from the first four centuries—a time when the church and the ambient society were not so closely identified. Advocacy of a countercultural Methodism was renewed in the late twentieth century by Methodist writers who called for worship appropriate to the status of the Christian community as "resident aliens" in the world.[12]

The acculturation of Methodist liturgy may have been inevitable. As H. Richard Niebuhr suggested, a posture of separatism may be replaced by a willingness to accommodate if the wider society in which the church resides is judged to have been converted:

> A converted church in a corrupt civilization withdraws to its upper rooms, into monasteries and conventicles; it issues forth from these in the aggressive evangelism of apostles, monks and friars, circuit riders and missionaries; it relaxes its rigorism as it discerns signs of repentance and faith; it enters into inevitable alliance with converted emperors and governors, philosophers and artists, merchants and entrepreneurs, and begins to live at peace in the culture they produce under the stimulus of their faith; when faith loses its force, as generation follows generation, discipline is relaxed, repentance grows formal, corruption enters with idolatry, and the church, tied to the culture which it sponsored, suffers corruption with it. Only a new withdrawal followed by a new aggression can then save the church and restore to it the salt with which to savor society.[13]

Methodism's explicit plan to reform the continent, and its efficiency for a time in doing so, tied it to the nation in a manner it could not have originally anticipated. As nation and denomination grew up together, each contributed to the development and identity of the other. Once the trajectory of Americanization had begun, Methodism relished its status as both prophet and patriot, and strove to keep pace with the increasing complexity of American life under the banner of progress. Even the occasional withdrawal of certain Methodists in reaction to accommodation did not, in the end, halt the movement within those younger groups toward modernization, undoubtedly because of the pressing mission to save souls. Thus, Methodism's evangelicalism and social conscience has always caused it to address—and sometimes take on aspects of—its context in order to proclaim faithfully the perennial gospel.[14]

Worship in the Quintessential American Denomination

Liturgical scholar Robert Taft has posited that "liturgical history . . . does not deal with the past, but with tradition, which is a *genetic vision of the present*, a present conditioned by its understanding of its roots." The purpose of liturgical history is neither to recover nor to imitate the past, "but to *understand liturgy* which, because it has a history, can only be understood in motion."[15] Study of the changes made to Methodist worship, from the practices of the first Methodist immigrant to those at the close of the twentieth century, reveal the tensive and dynamic quality of that worship as it sought to express fully what it meant to be a Methodist Christian living in the United States who prayed that God's kingdom would come to trans- form the world. On the eve of the New Year, Methodists for generations often used the words of Charles Wesley to sing of the restlessness required by the gospel:

> Come, let us anew our journey pursue,
>   Roll round with the year,
> And never stand still till the Master appear!
> His adorable will let us gladly fulfill,
>   And our talents improve
> By the patience of hope and the labor of love.

Methodist worship in the future, as in the past, will surely be shaped by the situations and movements of the nation. Insofar as it retains its own identity, Methodism will continue to play a part in influencing American society, though that society no longer looks to Methodism as it once did and, in fact, more recently prides itself on not elevating any religion, Christian or otherwise, over another. If in addressing society the tendency to adaptation becomes even stronger than it has been, American Methodism risks becoming more American than Methodist. The summons therefore may be, as Niebuhr proposed in the 1930s to the churches at large, for Methodism to become more countercultural and, where needed, more critical in order to "restore to it the salt with which to savor society." By providing occasions for praise, prayer, and proclamation offered in the idioms of the Amer- ican people, but utilizing the vocabulary of the Christian narrative and the peculiar Methodist traditions, and shaped by their syntax, the Methodist churches in the twenty-first century may still or again fulfill the divine purpose for which Meth- odism was raised up.

Notes

Abbreviations

CAJ (NY) *Christian Advocate and Journal* and the *Christian Advocate*, published in New York.

Discipline Inclusive title for the published collection of doctrinal and legislative materials approved by each Methodist denomination (e.g., *Minutes of Several Conversations, General Minutes, Doctrines and Discipline, Constitution and Discipline*.

Discipline with Notes *The Doctrines and Discipline of the Methodist Church in America. With Explanatory Notes, by Thomas Coke and Francis Asbury.* 10th ed. Philadelphia: Printed by Henry Tuckniss, 1798; facsimile ed., Rutland, VT: Academy Books, 1979.

EH *Epworth Herald.*

JGC/MC *Journal of the General Conference of the Methodist Church* for the year indicated.

JGC/MEC *Journal of the General Conference of the Methodist Episcopal Church* for the year indicated. Various publishers.

JGC/MEC (1796–1836) *Journals of the General Conference of the Methodist Episcopal Church, 1796–1836.* New York: Carlton and Phillips, 1855. Year indicated in parentheses.

JGC/MECS *Journal of the General Conference of the Methodist Episcopal Church, South* for the year indicated. Various publishers.

JGC/MECS (1846–1850) *Journals of the General Conference of the Methodist Episcopal Church, South, held 1846 and 1850.* Richmond: Published by John Early for the Methodist Episcopal Church, South, 1851. Year indicated in parentheses.

JJW *The Journal of the Rev. John Wesley, A.M.* Edited by Nehemiah Curnock. 8 vols. London: Epworth Press, 1909–1916.

JLFA   *The Journal and Letters of Francis Asbury*. Edited by Elmer T. Clark. 3 vols. London: Epworth Press, 1958; Nashville: Abingdon Press, 1958.

LJW   *The Letters of the Rev. John Wesley, A.M.* Edited by John Telford. 8 vols. London: Epworth Press, 1931.

LQHR   *London Quarterly and Holborn Review*.

MH   *Methodist History*.

Minutes MC   *Minutes of the Methodist Conferences, Annually Held in America; From 1773 to 1813, Inclusive*. New York: Published by Daniel Hitt and Thomas Ware for the Methodist Connexion in the United States, 1813.

MQR   *Methodist Quarterly Review*. General title given to the multi-titled periodical published by the Methodist Episcopal Church, South. Titles were *Quarterly Review of the Methodist Episcopal Church, South* (1847–1885; 1888–1894); *Southern Methodist Review* (1886–1888); *Methodist Review* (1894–1902; 1906–1924); *Methodist Quarterly Review* (1903–1906; 1925–1930).

MR   *Methodist Review*. General title given to the multi-titled periodical published by the Methodist Episcopal Church. Titles were *Methodist Magazine* (1818–1828); *Methodist Magazine and Quarterly Review* (1830–1840); *Methodist Quarterly Review* (1841–1884); *Methodist Review* (1885–1931).

NCA   *Northwestern Christian Advocate*.

NT Notes   *Explanatory Notes Upon the New Testament*. London: William Bowyer, 1755.

OT Notes   *Explanatory Notes Upon the Old Testament*. 3 vols. Bristol: William Pine, 1765.

Poetical Works   *The Poetical Works of John and Charles Wesley*. Edited by G. Osborn. 13 vols. London: Wesleyan-Methodist Conference Office, 1868–1872.

PWHS   *Proceedings of the Wesley Historical Society*.

WCA   *Western Christian Advocate*.

Works [J]   *The Works of John Wesley*. Edited by Thomas Jackson. 14 vols. London: Wesleyan Conference Office, 1872; reprint, Grand Rapids, MI: Zondervan, [1958–1959].

Works   *The Works of John Wesley*; begun as "The Oxford Edition of The Works of John Wesley," Oxford: Clarendon Press, 1975–1983; continued as "The Bicentennial Edition of The Works of John Wesley," Nashville: Abingdon Press, 1984– .
Vol. 1: *Sermons I*. Edited by Albert C. Outler, 1984.
Vol. 2: *Sermons II*. Edited by Albert C. Outler, 1985.
Vol. 3: *Sermons III*. Edited by Albert C. Outler, 1986.
Vol. 4: *Sermons IV*. Edited by Albert C. Outler, 1987.
Vol. 7: *A Collection of Hymns for the Use of the People Called Methodists*. Edited by Franz Hildebrandt and Oliver A. Beckerlegge, 1983.
Vol. 8: *The Methodist Societies: History, Nature, and Design*. Edited by Rupert E. Davies, 1989.

Vol. 11: *The Appeals to Men of Reason and Religion and Certain Related Open Letters*. Edited by Gerald R. Cragg, 1975.
Vol. 18: *Journal and Diaries I (1735–1738)*. Edited by W. Reginald Ward and Richard P. Heitzenrater, 1988.
Vol. 19: *Journal and Diaries II (1738–1743)*. Edited by W. Reginald Ward and Richard P. Heitzenrater, 1990.
Vol. 20: *Journal and Diaries III (1743–1754)*. Edited by W. Reginald Ward and Richard P. Heitzenrater, 1991.
Vol. 21: *Journal and Diaries IV (1755–1765)*. Edited by W. Reginald Ward and Richard P. Heitzenrater, 1992.
Vol. 22: *Journal and Diaries V (1765–1775)*. Edited by W. Reginald Ward and Richard P. Heitzenrater, 1993.
Vol. 23: *Journal and Diaries VI (1776–1786)*. Edited by W. Reginald Ward and Richard P. Heitzenrater, 1995.
Vol. 25: *Letters I (1721–1739)*. Edited by Frank Baker, 1980.
Vol. 26: *Letters II (1740–1755)*. Edited by Frank Baker, 1982.

1. The Lord's Day: The Shape of Worship

1. Report 19, "The Lord's Day," Committee on State of the Church, General Conference of the Methodist Episcopal Church, *Daily Christian Advocate* 22 (24 May 1932) 605.

2. Letter to "Our Brethren in America," 10 September 1784, *LJW*, 7:238–39.

3. "Ought We to Separate from the Church of England?" (3).2, *Works*, 9:570–71.

4. See Karen B. Westerfield Tucker, "John Wesley's Prayer Book Revision: The Text in Context," *MH* 34 (July 1996) 230–47, esp. 240–42.

5. Ted A. Campbell, *John Wesley and Christian Antiquity: Religious Vision and Cultural Change* (Nashville: Abingdon/Kingswood 1991), esp. 23–53.

6. For Wesley's views on reason, see especially his two essays "Appeal to Men of Reason and Religion," and his sermon "Catholic Spirit."

7. Experience is designated as a corollary with Scripture in Wesley's sermon "On Knowing Christ after the Flesh," and with Scripture and reason in the sermon "The Repentance of Believers." See also Wesley's sermon "Spiritual Worship" and his letter of 25 June 1746 to John Smith.

8. Dated Bristol, 9 September 1784, the statement is found as a preface in most extant copies of *The Sunday Service of the Methodists in North America. With Other Occasional Services* (London: [William Strahan] 1784), though differences in the watermark suggest it may not have been part of the original printing. Because the *Sunday Service* was shipped loose-leaf to avoid the duty required for bound books, the preface may have been bound in at a later date.

9. Ibid.

10. Ezekiel Cooper, 11 June 1788, Journal, Ms., Garrett-Evangelical Theological Seminary Library, Evanston, IL; cf. the "Valedictory Address," Francis Asbury to William McKendree, 5 August 1813, *JLFA*, 3:475–92.

11. For a thorough study of Wesley's revisions of the Lord's Day services and materials (especially the psalter) from the Prayer Book, see William N. Wade, "A History of Public Worship in the Methodist Episcopal Church and Methodist Episcopal Church, South from 1784 to 1905" (Ph.D. diss., University of Notre Dame 1981) 24–77.

12. A brief overview of the revisions is presented in Wesley F. Swift, " 'The Sunday Service of the Methodists,' " *PWHS* 29 (March 1954) 12–20; see also J. Hamby Barton, " 'The Sunday Service of the Methodists' (with a response by Wesley F. Swift)," *PWHS* 32

(March 1960) 97–101; and A. Raymond George, "The 'Sunday Service,'" *PWHS* 40 (February 1976) 102–105.

13. Journal, 4 September 1785 [Sunday], *JLFA*, 1:494; and Richard Whatcoat, 7 February 1790, Journal, Ms., Garrett-Evangelical Theological Seminary Library, Evanston, IL.

14. Thomas Haskins, 23 January 1785, Journal, Ms., Manuscripts Division, Library of Congress, Washington, D.C.

15. Jesse Lee, *A Short History of the Methodists, in the United States of America; Beginning in 1766, and Continued Till 1809* (Baltimore: Magill and Clime 1810) 153. The Council, fashioned by Asbury, proved to be unpopular and controversial, and in 1791 was abandoned in favor of a general conference.

16. Ibid., 190.

17. George Coles, 3 January 1841 [Sunday], Journal, Ms., Drew University Library, Madison, NJ.

18. Leonard Smith, 12 February 1860 [Sunday], Journal, Ts., Archives, Illinois Great Rivers Annual Conference, United Methodist Church, Bloomington, IL.

19. Lee, *A Short History of the Methodists*, 152–53.

20. JGC/MEC *(1824)*, 298–99.

21. JGC/MEC *(1832)*, 394.

22. Alexander McCaine, *Letters on the Organization and Early History of the Methodist Episcopal Church* (Boston: Thomas F. Norris 1850) 35–36.

23. Charles Grandison Finney, *Lectures on Revivals of Religion*, 2d ed. (New York: Leavitt, Lord and Co. 1835). See especially the lecture "Measures to Promote Revivals."

24. B. T. Roberts, "New School Methodism," *The Northern Independent* (July 1857), repr. in Leslie R. Marston, *From Age to Age a Living Witness: A Historical Interpretation of Free Methodism's First Century* (Winona Lake, IN: Light and Life 1960) 573–78; and *The Doctrines and Discipline of the Free Methodist Church, 1862* (Buffalo: B. T. Roberts 1863) iii–vii, 71–72.

25. JGC/MEC, *1892*, 311.

26. JGC/MEC, *1888*, 125–27.

27. Episcopal Address, JGC/MECS, *1934*, 374–75.

28. JGC/MEC, *1932*, 651.

29. JGC/MECS, *1866*, 23, 116–17.

30. Preface, *The Sunday Service of the Methodist Episcopal Church, South*, ed. T. O. Summers (Nashville: A. H. Redford for the M. E. Church, South 1867) 3–5. Summers did not include Wesley's Select Psalms, arguing that Wesley himself was not satisfied with his abridgement ("Forms of Prayer," *MQR* 19 [January 1882] 74).

31. Henry M. Turner, *The Genius and Theory of Methodist Polity, Or, The Machinery of Methodism* (Philadelphia: Publication Department, A. M. E. Church 1885) 235–36. There is no indication that another reprinting was done of the 1784 service, so assumably Summers's version was used.

32. Charles S. Harrower, ed., *Select Psalms Arranged for the Use of the Methodist Episcopal Church by John Wesley, with Other Selections and the Order for the Sacraments and Occasional Services of the Church* (New York: Hunt and Eaton 1891; Cincinnati: Cranston and Stowe 1891).

33. Charles S. Harrower, ed., *The Sunday Service Recommended to the Societies in America by the Rev. John Wesley Edited by Comparison with the Public Book of Prayers and Services of the Wesleyan Church Including Select Psalms with the Order for the Sacraments and Other Occasional Services According to the Use of the Methodist Episcopal Church* (New York: Eaton and Mains 1893; Cincinnati: Jennings and Pye 1893; also New York: Hunt and Eaton 1894; Cincinnati: Cranston and Curts 1894); cf. JGC/MEC, *1892*, 215.

34. *From the Sunday Service of the Methodists in North America prepared by John Wesley, 1784* (Chicago: Jennings and Pye, for the Methodist Episcopal Church 1903). The unknown editor indicates in a note that in this version the "General Thanksgiving" is "restored," apparently unaware that Wesley had originally included it in his *Sunday Service*, though it was not placed in the prayer services.

35. Hugh D. Atchison, "Symposium Concerning Public Worship: A More Adequate Service of Worship in Methodist Episcopal Churches," *MR* 110 (May 1927) 362.

36. Commission on Worship and Music, *Proposed Order of Worship for the Methodist Episcopal Church* (New York: Methodist Book Concern 1930).

37. Von Ogden Vogt, *Modern Worship* (New Haven: Yale University Press 1927) 31–104; and Willard L. Sperry, *Reality in Worship: A Study of Public Worship and Private Religion* (New York: Macmillan 1925) 277–303. Vogt for a time pastored First Unitarian Church in Chicago and lectured at Chicago Theological Seminary; Sperry was dean at what would eventually be Harvard Divinity School. In *Art and Religion* (1921; rev. 1948), Vogt laid the groundwork for his scheme in *Modern Worship*; Sperry claimed to have developed his sequence independently of Vogt. Earl Enyeart Harper in "The Methodist Order of Public Worship" (*MR* 109 [May 1926] 388–90), and J. Hastie Odgers and Edward G. Schutz in *The Technique of Public Worship* ([New York: Methodist Book Concern 1928] 109–10) had already proposed using Vogt's scheme for ordering Methodist worship; cf. "Notes on the Proposed Orders of Worship," in *Proposed Order*, 7–8; and JGC/MEC, *1932*, 296.

38. Nolan Harmon, 10 March 1990, tape-recorded interview by author, Atlanta, GA.

39. *The John Wesley Prayer Book*, commentary by W. Maynard French (Nashville: Parthenon 1956); and Edward C. Hobbs, ed., *The Wesley Orders of Common Prayer*, National Methodist Student Movement (Nashville: Board of Education for the Methodist Church 1957).

40. *Report of the Commission on Worship to the General Conference, The Methodist Church, 1960* (Nashville: Methodist Publishing House 1960) 4, 11–16. The Gloria Patri was placed after the creed in the proposed revision printed in 1960, but was returned to its classical place after the psalm when the service was approved in 1964.

41. For a thorough study of the process by which the United Methodist services were created, see Robert B. Peiffer, "How Contemporary Liturgies Evolve: The Revision of United Methodist Liturgical Texts (1968–1988)" (Ph.D. diss., University of Notre Dame 1992).

42. Samuel A. Seaman, *Annals of New York Methodism, Being a History of the Methodist Episcopal Church in the City of New York, from A.D. 1766 to A.D. 1890* (New York: Hunt and Eaton 1892; Cincinnati: Cranston and Stowe 1892) 470.

43. A. W. Leonard, "The Passing of the Sunday Evening Service," *MR* 93 (May 1911) 436–39.

44. Washington Gladden, *The Christian Pastor and the Working Church* (New York: Charles Scribner's Sons 1924) 121–22. Gladden undoubtedly would have questioned some of the "strategic opportunities" suggested by Wilbur Fletcher Sheridan in *The Sunday-Night Service: A Study in Continuous Evangelism* (Cincinnati: Jennings and Pye 1903; New York: Eaton and Mains 1903).

45. S. Joseph Platt, ed., *A Book of Remembrance: Church Street United Methodist Church (1793–1816?)–1975* (Knoxville: n.p. 1982) 27.

46. For example, the contents of chapter 26 in the 1787 *Discipline* are devoted entirely to the instruction of children.

47. C. C. Goss, *Statistical History of the First Century of American Methodism: With a Summary of the Origin and Present Operations of Other Denominations* (New York: Carlton and Porter 1866) 119. Goss combined the totals for the Regular Baptists (estimated), Congregationalists, Episcopalians, Old School and New School Presbyterians, and the Reformed

Dutch. He also provided the totals for the Methodist Episcopal Church from 1847 to 1865, noting the number of conversions obtained through the Sunday school program.

48. Leonard Smith, 13 June 1869, Journal, Ts.

49. Terry W. Mullins, *Pisgah United Methodist Church: Two Centuries of Faith, 1793–1993* (Acton, MA: Tapestry 1993) 61.

50. "Welfare of Ohio Conference Methodism," in *Ohio Annual Conference of the Methodist Episcopal Church, Held at Portsmouth, Ohio, September 29, 1875* (Cincinnati: Western Methodist Book Concern 1875) 220.

51. For example, "The Children and the Preaching Service," *The Methodist* 21 (5 June 1880) 2; Joseph F. Berry, "Children at Church," *EH* 1 (24 January 1891) 1; and J. Montcalm Brown, "Young People and the Preaching Service," *NCA* 57 (12 May 1909) 26 (602); cf. *JGC/MEC, 1864,* 117; *JGC/MEC, 1872,* 208; and *JGC/MECS, 1878,* 244–45.

52. "A Proposition to Consolidate Sunday Services," *WCA* 76 (3 August 1910) 26–27.

53. Section on "Public Worship" in *The New Cokesbury Hymnal for General Use in Religious Meetings* (Nashville: Cokesbury 1928) unpaginated; cf. Josephine L. Baldwin, *Worship Training for Juniors* (New York: Printed for the Teacher Training Publishing Association by the Methodist Book Concern 1927) 15–25.

54. A. W. Martin, *Worship in the Sunday School: For Workers in Small Schools* (Nashville: Cokesbury 1930) 28–30; and *JGC/MEC, 1932,* 531–32.

55. For example, Alice Anderson Bays, *Worship Programs in the Fine Arts for Young People* (New York: Abingdon-Cokesbury 1940); *Worship Programs for Intermediates* (New York: Abingdon-Cokesbury 1942); *Worship Services for Purposeful Living* (New York: Abingdon-Cokesbury 1949); *Worship Services for Life Planning* (New York: Abingdon-Cokesbury 1953); *Worship Services for Teen-Agers* (New York: Abingdon 1954); *Worship Services for Junior Highs* (New York: Abingdon 1958).

56. United Methodist Conferences that produced worship materials include the Baltimore Conference (Commission on Worship's "Worship Concepts" 1971), the Minnesota Conference (Commission on Worship's "The Worship Manual" 1972), and the Virginia Conference ("Living Acts of Worship" 1972).

2. The Lord's Day: Ordinary and Propers

1. "The Character of a Methodist," §8, *Works*, 9:37.

2. For Wesley's defense of extemporary prayer, see "The Principles of a Methodist Farther Explained," 3.3–4, *Works*, 9:187–88.

3. In an egregious, but all-too-frequent, misreading of historical fact, a writer of local church history notes that "Wesley had frowned on hymn books and written prayers. He had prescribed extemporaneous prayers except Wednesday and Thursday for his followers" (Wyatt Brown, *Early Methodism in Greenville, North Carolina, and a History of the Jarvis Memorial United Methodist Church*, ed. John D. Ebbs [Greenville: Jarvis Memorial United Methodist Church 1978] 83).

4. Notes on Chapter 1, section 12, *Discipline with Notes*, 89.

5. T. O. Summers provides an excursus on the "Use of the Lord's Prayer" in "Forms of Prayer," *MQR* 19 (January 1882) 87–91.

6. The notion of the quadrilateral is refuted in Ted A. Campbell, "The 'Wesleyan Quadrilateral': The Story of a Modern Methodist Myth," *MH* 29 (January 1991) 87–95. Without leveling them to a single plane, Wesley himself alludes to five "norms"—Scripture, Christian antiquity of the first three centuries, the Church of England, reason, and experience—in "Farther Thoughts on Separation from the Church," written in December 1789 and published in the *Arminian Magazine* in 1790. For a fuller account of Wesley's understanding of

Scripture, see Scott J. Jones, *John Wesley's Conception and Use of Scripture* (Nashville: Kingswood 1995).

7. Notes on Chapter 1, section 24, *Discipline with Notes*, 121; cf. Pastoral Address, *JGC/MECS (1846)*, 113.

8. See especially the journal entry for 1 August 1742, *Works*, 19:290.

9. Hans W. Frei, in *The Eclipse of Biblical Narrative: A Study in Eighteenth and Nineteenth Century Hermeneutics* (New Haven: Yale University Press 1974), details the changes in interpretation (and concomitantly worldview) that would have threatened the more literal Methodist understanding.

10. Address of the Bishops, *JGC/MECS (1850)*, 139; cf. Thomas O. Summers, "Signs of the Times," *MQR* 19 (April 1882) 379–80; and C. H. Buchanan, "Worship and Its Abuse," *MQR* 27 (July 1888) 367–69.

11. Report of the Committee on the American Bible Society, *JGC/MECS, 1858*, 480.

12. Review of *Ritual of the Methodist Episcopal Church*, MR 46 (October 1864) 688.

13. Samuel W. Marble, in "Revise the Psalter" (MR 109 [January 1926] 112–17), questioned the appropriateness of several psalms selected for responsive readings in the 1905 hymnal, finding them incompatible with the Methodist Episcopal Church's pronouncements on world peace.

14. Report of the Special Committee on Standards of Doctrine, *JGC/MECS, 1922*, 156.

15. Episcopal Address, *JGC/MECS, 1934*, 360; see also John Poucher, "Methodism as Affected by Recent Biblical Criticism," *MR* 75 (November 1893) 964–65; and "Biblical Criticism and the General Conference," *NCA* 60 (17 April 1912) 488.

16. Memorials of the General Conference, Methodist Episcopal Church, 1912, unpublished materials, United Methodist Archives, Madison, NJ. See also, from the same year, the concern expressed for congregational participation in Scripture reading in Lucius C. Clark, *The Worshiping Congregation* (Cincinnati: Jennings and Graham 1912; New York: Eaton and Mains 1912) 91–95.

17. G. A. Raybold, *Reminiscences of Methodism in New Jersey* (New York: Lane and Scott 1849) 43; also his *Annals of Methodism; Or, Sketches of the Origin and Progress of Methodism in Various Portions of West Jersey; Derived from the Most Authentic Sources* (Philadelphia: T. Stokes 1847) 134. Exaggeration and boasting about preaching prowess are typical of early Methodist lore; see Donald E. Byrne, Jr., *No Foot of Land: Folklore of American Methodist Itinerants*, ATLA Monograph Series, no. 6 (Metuchen, NJ: Scarecrow Press and the American Theological Library Association 1975) 244–55.

18. Isabella Lucy Bird Bishop, *The Aspects of Religion in the United States*, repr. of 1859 edition (New York: Arno 1972) 40; for her discussion on the characteristics of American preaching, see pp. 157–60.

19. Freeborn Garrettson, *Substance of the Semi-Centennial Sermon, Before the New-York Annual Conference, at Its Session, May, 1826* (New York: N. Bangs and J. Emory, for the Methodist Episcopal Church 1827) 33.

20. George Coles, 25 June 1826, Journal, Ms., Drew University Library, Madison, NJ.

21. William C. Doub, 12 February 1832, Journal, Ms., Special Collections Library, Duke University Library, Durham, NC.

22. Thomas Rankin, 30 June 1776 [Sunday], "The Diary of the Revd. Thomas Rankin," Ts., Garrett-Evangelical Theological Seminary Library, Evanston, IL.

23. Maria Dyer Davies, 29 December 1850, 29 August 1852, and 21 April 1853, Diary, Ms., Special Collections Library, Duke University Library, Durham, NC.

24. Neil Postman, *Amusing Ourselves to Death: Public Discourse in the Age of Show Business* (New York: Penguin 1985).

25. Richard Adicks, *A Time to Keep: History of the First United Methodist Church of Oviedo, Florida, 1873–1973* (Oviedo, FL: History Committee, First United Methodist Church 1973) 14.

26. J. A. Phillips, " 'The Holy Catholic Church,' " *MQR* 71 (April 1922) 217–29.

27. See, for example, the entry for 22 January 1785 in the journal of Thomas Coke, cited in the *Arminian Magazine* 1 (June 1789) 293.

28. Edward W. Poitras, "How Korean is the Methodist 'Korean Creed'?", *MH* 36 (October 1997) 3–16.

29. Nineteenth-century accounts indicate that sometimes the tune "Sessions" was appointed for the singing of "Praise God, from Whom All Blessings Flow," and was exported from the United States to Methodist missions in Korea and elsewhere. See L. L. Nash, *Recollections and Observations during a Ministry in the North Carolina Conference, Methodist Episcopal Church, South, of Forty-three Years* (Raleigh, NC: Mutual 1916) 18; and Edward W. Poitras (Pak Tae In), "Ten Thousand Tongues Sing: Worship among Methodists in Korea," in *The Sunday Service of the Methodists: Twentieth-Century Worship in Worldwide Methodism*, ed. Karen B. Westerfield Tucker (Nashville: Kingswood 1996) 205.

30. Henry Boehm described German-English services in *Reminiscences, Historical and Biographical of Sixty-Four Years in the Ministry*, ed. Joseph B. Wakeley (New York: Carlton and Porter 1865) 106–107.

31. For a study of American Methodist influences on worship practices among Methodists in Germany, see Walter F. Klaiber, "Building up the House of God: Sunday Worship in German Methodism," in *The Sunday Service of the Methodists: Twentieth-Century Worship in Worldwide Methodism*, esp. 287–98.

32. Records and History Committee, *Bishop Hill Community Methodist Church* (Marceline, MO: Walsworth 1951) unpaginated; for a brief overview of Swedish Methodist work in Illinois, see C. G. Wallenius and E. D. Olson, *A Short Story of the Swedish Methodism in America*, repr. from vol. 2, *The Swedish Element in America* (Chicago: Swedish-American Biographical Society 1931) 33–44.

33. *A History of the Congregation, 1858–1983. First United Methodist Church. Lindstrom, Minnesota*, ed. 125th Anniversary Committee, Robert Porter, chairperson (Lindstrom, MN: United Methodist Church 1983) 53–54; see "Babies Can Make a Sunday Sermon," *Together* 6 (September 1962) 2. According to the church secretary Carol Schmidt, the annual service is highly anticipated by the congregation (telephone interview by author, 28 January 1998).

34. "The Nature, Design, and General Rules of the United Societies (1743)," *Works*, 9: 70. Most Methodist bodies continued to include the General Rules as part of their constitutive documents.

35. Journal, 20 April 1777, *JLFA*, 1:237; and *JGC/MEC* (1828), 348–51.

36. H. M. Hamill, ed., *Manual of Southern Methodism including Church History, Doctrine, Polity, and Missions* (Nashville: Publishing House Methodist Episcopal Church, South 1914) 125; and Report of the Committee on Sabbath Observance, *JGC/MECS*, 1906, 246.

37. Mary Louise Butler Edwards, *Salem: A Goodly Heritage, 1848–1976; A History of Salem United Methodist Church* (Fayetteville, NC: Salem United Methodist Church 1976) 29–30.

38. The latter, somewhat plausible, theory is proposed by William Wade, "A History of Public Worship in the Methodist Episcopal Church and Methodist Episcopal Church, South from 1784 to 1905" (Ph.D. diss., University of Notre Dame 1981) 45–46. Wesley himself does not give the rationale for the deletion.

39. On Wesley's appreciation of the festival of All Saints', see Geoffrey Wainwright, "Wesley and the Communion of Saints," in *Methodists in Dialogue* (Nashville: Kingswood 1995) 237–49.

40. Thomas Rankin, 25 December 1773 [Saturday], 3 April 1774 [Easter], 25 December 1774 [Sunday], and 26 May 1776 [Whitsunday], "Diary," Ts.

41. Nathan Bangs, *The Life of the Rev. Freeborn Garrettson: Compiled from His Printed and Manuscript Journals, and Other Authentic Documents* (New York: J. Emory and B. Waugh 1832) 122.

42. Ezekiel Cooper, 25 December 1788 and 25 December 1792, Journal, Ms., Garrett-Evangelical Theological Seminary Library, Evanston, IL; cf. Benjamin Lakin, 25 December 1803, Journal, Ms. on microfilm, Washington University Library, St. Louis, MO; and "Letter from Seely Bunn, to the Rev. Dr. Coke, 6 March 1805," *Methodist Magazine* 28 (October 1805) 474.

43. Notes on Chapter 1, section 12, *Discipline with Notes*, 89. William Wade boldly claims that after 1792 the liturgical year was "*totally rejected*," not to be officially recognized until the early twentieth century (pp. 102–103). But he is forced to soften this statement when confronted with Asbury and Coke's commentary and other documentation (p. 215). The evidence makes it clear that a rudimentary liturgical year was maintained, albeit by the observance of a few special days.

44. Thomas A. Morris, *Miscellany: Consisting of Essays, Biographical Sketches, and Notes of Travel* (Cincinnati: L. Swormstedt and J. H. Power 1852) 113. Morris was a bishop of the Methodist Episcopal Church. For another expression of concern regarding the solemn honoring of Christmas, see Raybold, *Reminiscences of Methodism in West Jersey*, 29.

45. Russell E. Richey, *The Methodist Conference in America: A History* (Nashville: Kingswood 1996) 126–31, 202–204.

46. JGC/MECS, 1870, 173; and JGC/MEC, 1872, 355.

47. See, for example, Robert E. Taylor's diary entry for 5 June 1898 (and for 27 May 1900 and 25 June 1905) in Taylor Kinsfolk Association at Tabernacle Church, *The Taylors of Tabernacle: The History of a Family* (Brownsville, TN: Tabernacle Historical Committee 1957) 375, 388, 405. A variation on this practice is described for a Children's Day on 14 June 1885, in which the children, on the day following their exercises of "songs of praise, recitations and dialogue," met at the church to decorate the graves of Sunday school children who had died during the previous year (Mary Katharine Kern, *The Market Street United Methodist Church: Methodism in Winchester, Virginia, from 1772 to 1953* [Stephens City, VA: Commercial Press 1985] 110).

48. For example, eighteen hymns in *Hymns for the Nativity of Our Lord* (1745), seven in *Hymns for Ascension-Day* (1746), sixteen in *Hymns for Our Lord's Resurrection* (1746), and thirty-two in *Hymns of Petition and Thanksgiving for the Promise of the Father* (1746).

49. Joseph F. Berry, "A Christian Festival," EH 2 (19 December 1891) 1. Heather Murray Elkins notes a gradual qualitative shift in the Methodist Episcopal Church from the "honoring" of days to the "observing" of them (" 'On Borrowed Time': The Christian Year in American Methodism, 1784–1960" [Ph.D. diss., Drew University 1991] 68ff).

50. Bostwick Hawley, *A Treatise on the Lenten Season: Including Ascension-Day, Whitsuntide, and Trinity Sunday* (Cincinnati: Walden and Stowe 1882; New York: Phillips and Hunt 1882) 10. Chapters tracing the historical development of Lent, Ash Wednesday, Palm Sunday, Passion Week, Good Friday, Easter, the Forty Days, Ascension, Pentecost, and Trinity also contained suggestions for practice.

51. "Ecclesiastical Feast Days in Protestantism," MR 77 (May 1895) 475–76.

52. Matthew Simpson Hughes, *The Higher Ritualism* (Cincinnati: Jennings and Graham 1904; New York: Eaton and Mains 1904) 47.

53. A virtual explosion of observances is suggested in Marion Lawrance, *Special Days in the Sunday School* (New York: Fleming H. Revell 1916); Lawrance served as general secretary of the International Sunday School Association. This genre of literature continues into the

late twentieth century with books such as *Celebrating Special Days in the Church School Year: Liturgies and Participation Activities for Church School Children* (Colorado Springs: Meriwether Publishing 1981), by Judy Gattis Smith, a United Methodist.

54. Leigh Eric Schmidt, *Consumer Rites: The Buying and Selling of American Holidays* (Princeton, NJ: Princeton University Press 1995) 246–56. Moves were made, as early as the 1908 Methodist Episcopal General Conference, for the churches to recognize Mother's Day.

55. Clark, *The Worshiping Congregation*, 165.

56. For the Methodist days, see JGC/MEC, *1912*, 450; and JGC/MEC, *1916*, 351, 457. On the promotion of Good Friday as a legal holiday, see JGC/MEC, *1928*, 625, 1832; and the JGC/MEC, *1936*, 523–24, 1307.

57. The Methodist constituent bodies were the African Methodist Episcopal Church, the African Methodist Episcopal Zion Church, the Colored (Christian) Methodist Episcopal Church, the Methodist Episcopal Church, the Methodist Episcopal Church, South, and the Methodist Protestant Church.

58. Federal Council of the Churches of Christ in America, *Annual Report, 1935* (New York: Federal Council of the Churches of Christ in America 1935) 53–54.

59. Fred Winslow Adams, "The Altar of Worship," MR 109 (May 1926) 385.

60. Federal Council of the Churches of Christ in America, *Annual Report, 1937* (New York: Federal Council of the Churches of Christ in America 1937) 57–58; and Fred Winslow Adams, *The Christian Year: A Suggestive Guide for the Worship of the Church* (New York: Federal Council of the Churches of Christ in America 1937; rev. 1940). In the revised edition, Adams reduced the number of Sundays that had been designated for Kingdomtide.

61. Other Methodist resources in this period included Thomas Albert Stafford, *Christian Symbolism in the Evangelical Churches* (New York: Abingdon-Cokesbury 1942); Hersey Everett Spence, *Holidays and Holy Days: Plays, Pageants, and Programs for Many Occasions* (Greensboro, NC: Piedmont 1946); and a 1951 book that went through numerous printings, Dessie Ash Arnett, Lenace Robinette Clark, and Betty Isaac Stewart, *Methodist Altars*, rev. ed. (Charleston, WV: Lenace Robinette Clark 1956). Clarence Seidenspinner, in *Great Protestant Festivals* (New York: Henry Schuman 1952), organized his book not according to the liturgical cycles, but following nature's seasons.

62. Douglas R. Cullum, "From Simplicity to Multiplicity: Sunday Worship among Free Methodists," in *The Sunday Service of the Methodists: Twentieth-Century Worship in Worldwide Methodism*, 181–94.

63. George G. Smith, *The Life and Times of George Foster Pierce, D.D., LL.D.* (Sparta, GA: Hancock 1888) 508–509.

64. "Discipline for Mr. Roosevelt," NCA 57 (10 March 1909) 6.

65. Robert T. Handy, *A Christian America: Protestant Hopes and Historical Realities*, 2d ed., rev. (New York: Oxford University Press 1984) 182.

66. Freeborn Garrettson, *Substance of the Semi-Centennial Sermon*, 25–26.

67. "The Order of Public Worship," MR 76 (September 1894) 810.

68. Thomas B. Neely, "The Order of Public Worship," 82 MR (January 1900) 84–85.

69. Episcopal Address, JGC/MECS, *1934*, 375.

70. S. M. Merrill, *A Digest of Methodist Law; Or, Helps in the Administration of the Discipline of the Methodist Episcopal Church*, ed. R. J. Cooke (Cincinnati: Jennings and Graham 1908; New York: Eaton and Mains 1908) 131.

71. Romey P. Marshall, "Liturgical Question Box," *The Pastor* 14 (January 1951) 19; and Ivan Lee Holt, "The Book of Worship and the Book of Law," *The Pastor* 18 (January 1955) 25; cf. Nolan B. Harmon, "Uniform But Unfettered," *The Pastor* 15 (March 1952) 19.

72. Nolan B. Harmon, "Are We Headed Toward Formalism in Worship?" *The Pastor* 19 (March 1956) 4.

73. JGC/MEC, *1868*, 566.

74. Cited from an 1889 newspaper article by William C. Bakes entitled "Mr. Wesley's Sunday Service," which is affixed to the inside back cover of one of Duke University's copies of Wesley's *Sunday Service* of 1784.

75. Part 6, chapter 8, section 2, *The Doctrine and Discipline of the African Methodist Episcopal Church, 1884* (Philadelphia: A. M. E. Book Concern 1885) 376–77; cf. "Ritualistic Tendencies of our Time," MR 81 (May 1899) 467–68.

76. Charles M. Giffin, "More Liturgy or More Life," MR 84 (January 1902) 71–79; response by Ernest Vernon Claypool, "More Liturgy and More Life," MR 84 (May 1902) 462–65.

77. Episcopal Address, JGC/MECS, *1930*, 360.

78. "The Character of a Methodist," §18, *Works*, 9:42.

79. Sermon 77, "Spiritual Worship," §3.4, *Works*, 3:99.

3. The Great Festivals of the Methodists

1. David Lewis, *Recollections of a Superannuate: Or, Sketches of Life, Labor, and Experience in the Methodist Itinerancy*, ed. S. M. Merrill (Cincinnati: Methodist Book Concern 1857) 61.

2. William Cave, *Primitive Christianity* (1672), abridged in John Wesley, *A Christian Library*, 50 vols. (Bristol: E. Farley 1753) 31:219–20. Wesley, whose diary records the reading of Cave in 1732, considered the history essential reading for all Methodists, and so included it, abridged, as part of the *Christian Library*.

3. Wesley borrowed the concept of the band—the oldest basic unit of Methodist organization—from Moravian practice, and it was a collection of bands (and others) in a geographic region that constituted a particular Methodist society. Regulations and behaviors for the bands were defined by Wesley in the "Rules of the Band Societies" (1738) and "Directions Given to the Band Societies" (1744). Soon another small group, the class, developed, the purpose of which was delineated in "The Nature, Design, and General Rules of the United Societies" (1743). At first bands and classes coexisted with the Methodist societies, but by the nineteenth century, the bands were in decline and eventually disappeared. For a brief overview of the economy of the Methodist societies, see the introduction in *Works*, 9:8–15.

4. A letter to the Rev. Mr. Vincent Perronet, vicar of Shoreham in Kent, published as "A Plain Account of the People called Methodists" (1749), 6.5, *Works*, 9:267–68.

5. Frank Baker, *Methodism and the Love-Feast* (London: Epworth 1957) 15.

6. *Poetical Works*, 1:350–51.

7. Joseph Pilmore, *The Journal of Joseph Pilmore*, ed. Frederick E. Maser and Howard T. Maag (Philadelphia: Message Publishing for the Historical Society of the Philadelphia Annual Conference of the United Methodist Church 1969) 40, 45.

8. The 1784 *Discipline* (published in 1785) gave the responsibility of keeping the love feast to the "assistants." In Wesley's usage this designated preachers who had oversight of a circuit (namely, a specified collection of Methodist societies). As understood in 1787, it seems that the duty of the love feast was given specifically to *deacons*. In 1792, it was made clear that responsibilities for a love feast resided with the preacher in charge of the circuit who would usually be an ordained elder, though it could also be a deacon or a lay preacher.

9. Thomas Rankin, 22 May 1774, "The Diary of the Reverend Thomas Rankin," Ts., Garrett-Evangelical Theological Seminary Library, Evanston, IL.

10. Nathan Bangs, A History of the Methodist Episcopal Church, 3d ed., vol. 1 (New York: T. Mason and G. Lane 1840) 249.

11. Emory Stevens Bucke, "American Methodism and the Love Feast," MH 1 (July 1963) 12.

12. Henry M. Turner, The Genius and Theory of Methodist Polity, Or, The Machinery of Methodism (Philadelphia: Publication Department, A. M. E. Church 1885) 210–12.

13. "Love-feasts," CAJ (NY) 23 (7 June 1848) 92.

14. Leonard Smith, 26 June 1859, Journal, Ts., Archives, Illinois Great Rivers Annual Conference, United Methodist Church, Bloomington, IL.

15. Journal of the Reverend Benjamin F. Brooke, 8 January 1861, cited in Mary Katharine Kern, The Market Street United Methodist Church: Methodism in Winchester, Virginia, from 1772 to 1953 (Stephens City, VA: Commercial Press 1985) 50. Kern determined that the last recorded love feast at Market Street Church occurred on 10 July 1896—the same year the congregation experienced their first early morning Christmas service (p. 121).

16. Tobias Spicer, "Love-feasts," CAJ (NY) 13 (23 November 1838) 53. This article was the final installment of a seven-week series on love feasts.

17. Wesley transcribed in his journal "An Extract of the Constitution of the Church of the Moravian Brethren at Herrnhut," which included as number 18 a description of the nightly watch. See Works, 18:297.

18. "A Plain Account of the People called Methodists," 3.1–2, Works, 9:264; and also "A Letter to the Rev. Mr. Baily of Cork" (1750), 2.15, Works, 9:305.

19. Journal, 9 April 1742, Works, 19:258–59.

20. Turner, The Genius and Theory of Methodist Polity, Or, The Machinery of Methodism, 221.

21. Thomas Rankin, 31 July 1776 [Wednesday], 10 November 1776 [for Monday], and 4 August 1777 [Tuesday], "The Diary of the Reverend Thomas Rankin."

22. Journal, 22 November 1787, JLFA, 1:554; and notes on Chapter 1, section 10, Discipline with Notes, 76–77.

23. Ezekiel Cooper, 1 January 1793, Journal, Ms., Garrett-Evangelical Theological Seminary Library, Evanston, IL.

24. Pilmore, 31 December 1770, The Journal of Joseph Pilmore, 70.

25. Centennial History of the First Methodist Episcopal Church, Schenectady, New York, ed. William C. Kitchin, Benjamin H. Ripton, and Fred Winslow Adams (Schenectady, NY: Official Board of First Methodist Episcopal Church 1907) 74.

26. All three of these rituals might be included in a single watch night. See Leonard Smith, 31 December 1867, Journal, Ts.

27. G. A. Raybold, Annals of Methodism; Or, Sketches of the Origin and Progress of Methodism in Various Portions of West Jersey; Derived from the Most Authentic Sources (Philadelphia: T. Stokes 1847) 16.

28. George Coles, 31 December 1829, Journal, Ms., Drew University Library, Madison, NJ.

29. Thomas A. Morris, Miscellany: Consisting of Essays, Biographical Sketches, and Notes of Travel (Cincinnati: L. Swormstedt and J. H. Power 1852) 118–19.

30. For example, Frederick Hunter, "The Origins of Wesley's Covenant Service," LQHR 164 (January 1939) 82; and Frank Baker, "The Beginnings of the Methodist Covenant Service," LQHR 180 (July 1955) 215.

31. For studies detailing the covenant texts of Richard Alleine and Joseph Alleine, see Hunter, "The Origins of Wesley's Covenant Service," 78–82; and Marion A. Jackson, "An

Analysis of the Source of John Wesley's 'Directions for Renewing our Covenant with God,' " *MH* 30 (April 1992) 176–84.

32. The text, inspired by Jeremiah 50:5, was first published in *Short Hymns on Select Passages of the Holy Scriptures* (1762) and is here cited from the reprinting of that text in *Poetical Works*, 10:46. Wesley records in his journal for 12 July 1778 the use of this hymn at a covenant service, during the singing of which "God poured down upon the assembly the Spirit of grace and supplication" (*Works*, 23:99).

33. A comparison of the Lee and Wesley texts, an analysis of the editions of Wesley's *Directions*, and a full history of the development and practice of the covenant service in British Methodism is provided by David Tripp, *The Renewal of the Covenant in the Methodist Tradition* (London: Epworth 1969).

34. Ezekiel Cooper, 1 March 1786 [Wednesday] and 30 June 1786 [Friday], Journal, Ms.

35. Miriam Fletcher, *The Methodist; Or, Incidents and Characters from Life in the Baltimore Conference* (New York: Derby and Jackson 1859) 81.

36. Kern, *The Market Street United Methodist Church: Methodism in Winchester, Virginia, from 1772 to 1953*, 96, 146, 163.

37. H. Hughes Wagner, "Gaiety—and Worship—on New Year's Eve," *The Pastor* 13 (December 1949) 24–25. The Holiness branches of Methodism, which consistently called for their members to avoid such frivolities on New Year's Eve and Day (e.g., "New Year's Visitations," *The Earnest Christian and Golden Rule* 3 [January 1862] 36), persisted in their solemn assemblies.

38. "Watch Night at the Coliseum," *NCA* 57 (6 January 1909) 27.

39. The British Methodist bodies united in 1932 were the Wesleyan Methodists (the largest group), the Primitive Methodists, and the United Methodists (the result of a merger in 1907 joining the Methodist New Connexion, the United Methodist Free Church, and the Bible Christians).

40. The material finally approved for the 1992 book as "Wesley's Covenant Service" was a significant reduction and recasting of United Methodist bishop Ole E. Borgen's 1990 abbreviation and adaptation of Wesley's 1780 *Directions*.

41. Frederick Hunter and Frank Baker, "The Origin of the Methodist Quarterly Meeting," *LQHR* 174 (1949) 28–37.

42. Jesse Lee, *A Short History of the Methodists, in the United States of America; Beginning in 1766 and Continued Till 1809* (Baltimore: Magill and Clime 1810) 42, 131, 145–46; see also George A. Phoebus, *Beams of Light on Early Methodism in America* (New York: Phillips and Hunt 1887; Cranston and Stowe 1887) 94–95.

43. Elizabeth A. Roe, *Recollections of Frontier Life* (Rockford, IL: Gazette Publishing House 1885) 85–87.

44. The Methodist Episcopal Church kept the rule on the quarterly fast until the 1888 *Discipline*; the Methodist Episcopal Church, South retained it until 1934.

45. Sometimes funerals were held and funeral sermons preached at the quarterly meeting, and though this task was not restricted to the ordained, many Methodists preferred a clergyman's words at the marking of the final passage.

46. Lester Ruth, *A Little Heaven Below: Worship at Early Methodist Quarterly Meetings* (Nashville: Kingswood 2000) 120–25. Using the diaries and journals of the early Methodists, as well as official documents, Ruth carefully describes and analyzes the liturgical practices and piety of the quarterly meeting to around 1830.

47. Russell E. Richey, "From Quarterly to Camp Meeting: A Reconsideration of Early American Methodism," *MH* 23 (July 1985) 207.

48. Leigh Eric Schmidt, *Holy Fairs: Scottish Communions and American Revivals in the*

Early Modern Period (Princeton, NJ: Princeton University Press 1989) 50–68; and Robert B. Semple, *A History of the Rise and Progress of the Baptists in Virginia*, rev. by G. W. Beale (Richmond, VA: Pitt and Dickinson 1894) 23–24.

49. Controversies about the date and location of the first camp meeting arise primarily from debates on definitions, but also from geographic and denominational allegiances. See in particular Charles A. Johnson, *The Frontier Camp Meeting: Religion's Harvest Time* (Dallas: Southern Methodist University Press 1955) 25–40; Bernard A. Weisberger, *They Gathered at the River: The Story of the Great Revivalists and Their Impact upon Religion in America* (Boston: Little, Brown, and Co. 1958); Catharine C. Cleveland, *The Great Revival in the West, 1797–1805* (Chicago: University of Chicago Press 1916; repr. Gloucester, MA: Peter Smith 1959); and Kenneth O. Brown, *Holy Ground: A Study of the American Camp Meeting* (New York: Garland 1992) 3–22.

50. Neither this instruction nor any other statement about camp meetings is found in the *Discipline* of either the Methodist Episcopal Church or the Methodist Episcopal Church, South; the practice of camp meetings was a matter of expectation, not legislation; see Lee, *A Short History of the Methodists*, 362.

51. Despite their immediate benefit, the prodigious use of camp meetings may, in the end, have inhibited the development of a strong Methodist ecclesiology. See Russell E. Richey, *Early American Methodism* (Bloomington: Indiana University Press 1991) 79–80.

52. See the study by Ellen Eslinger, *Citizens of Zion: The Social Origins of Camp Meeting Revivalism* (Knoxville: University of Tennessee Press 1999).

53. Letter to Jacob Gruber, 1 September 1811, *JLFA*, 3:453. By the time of Asbury's letter to Gruber, the camp meeting had already been exported to Britain where it was censured by most British Methodists. A faction supporting its use broke off in 1811 to form the Primitive Methodists.

54. See Ellen Weiss, *City in the Woods: The Life and Design of an American Camp Meeting on Martha's Vineyard* (New York: Oxford University Press 1987); and Glenn Uminowicz, "Recreation in a Christian America: Ocean Grove and Asbury Park, New Jersey, in *Hard at Play: Leisure in America, 1840–1940*, ed. Kathryn Grover (Amherst, MA: University of Massachusetts Press 1992; Rochester, NY: Strong Museum 1992) 8–38.

55. William Cooper Howells, "Camp-Meetings in the West Fifty Years Ago," *Lippincott's Magazine* 10 (August 1872) 211.

56. "A Short Account of a Camp-Meeting Held at Cow-Harbour, Long Island, which commenced August 11th, 1818," *MR* 1 (1818) 357.

57. The origins and content of camp meeting hymns and spirituals are discussed in Dickson D. Bruce, Jr., *And They All Sang Hallelujah: Plain-Folk Camp-Meeting Religion, 1800–1845* (Knoxville: University of Tennessee Press 1974) 96–122; and Ellen Jane Lorenz, *Glory, Hallelujah! The Story of the Campmeeting Spiritual* (Nashville: Abingdon 1980).

58. Abel Stevens, *Life and Times of Nathan Bangs* (New York: Carlton and Porter 1863) 183.

59. John Brooks, *The Life and Times of the Rev. John Brooks, in Which Are Contained a History of the Great Revival in Tennessee; with Many Incidents of Thrilling Interest* (Nashville: Nashville Christian Advocate 1848) 27.

60. "A Camp Meeting Incident," *Zion's Herald and Wesleyan Journal* 32 (14 August 1861) 129. On church relations during the nation's war, see William Warren Sweet, *The Methodist Episcopal Church and the Civil War* (Cincinnati: Methodist Book Concern 1912) 47–110.

61. John H. Wigger describes Methodism's contributions to popular Christianity and American society, and its metamorphosis from counterculture to American subculture in

Taking Heaven by Storm: Methodism and the Rise of Popular Christianity in America (New York: Oxford University Press 1998), esp. 173–95.

62. Pastoral Address, *JGC/MEC*, 1880, 433; cf. pp. 181, 212.

63. W. R. Goodwin, "The Old-Time Camp-Meeting," *EH* 1 (9 May 1891) 3; and J. H. Potts, *Pastor and People; Or, Methodism in the Field* (New York: Phillips and Hunt 1879; Cincinnati: Hitchcock and Walden 1879) 162.

64. Program for the 36th Annual Camp Meeting of the Galesburg District, Central Illinois Conference; Gilson Camp Grounds, 18–24 August 1903, Archives, Illinois Great Rivers Annual Conference, United Methodist Church, Bloomington, IL.

65. Cited in Taylor Kinsfolk Association at Tabernacle Church, *The Taylors of Tabernacle: The History of a Family* (Brownsville, TN: Tabernacle Historical Committee 1957) 422.

66. "The Amen Liturgy," in *Annals of Southern Methodism for 1855*, ed. Charles Force Deems (New York: J. G. Gray 1856) 373.

67. J. V. Watson, *Helps to the Promotion of Revivals* (New York: Nelson and Phillips 1856; Cincinnati: Hitchcock and Walden 1856) 17.

68. Kern, *The Market Street United Methodist Church*, 87.

69. William Reddy, "Methodism—Its Peculiarities," *The Earnest Christian and Golden Rule* 14 (July 1867) 17.

70. Journal, 19 July 1761, *Works*, 21:336.

71. Nathan O. Hatch, *The Democratization of American Christianity* (New Haven: Yale University Press 1989) 81–93.

72. Harold Bloom, *The American Religion: The Emergence of the Post-Christian Nation* (New York: Simon and Schuster 1992) 45–75.

4. The Rites of Christian Initiation

1. "Ought We to Separate from the Church of England?" (3).4.8, *Works*, 9:571–72.

2. Letter from Mr. Hall included in Wesley's Journal, 27 December 1745, *Works*, 20:109–10; and Journal, 12 April 1789, *JJW*, 7:486.

3. One of the accusations against Wesley presented to a grand jury in Savannah, Georgia, was that he refused to administer the Lord's Supper to William Gough after it was disclosed Gough had been baptized by a Presbyterian and had refused "rebaptism." See under the journal entries for 16 August to 2 September 1737, *Works*, 18:189–93; also the manuscript voyage journal entry for 18 October 1735, *Works*, 18:313.

4. Journal, 21 October 1738, *The Journal of the Rev. Charles Wesley, M.A.*, vol. 1, ed. Thomas Jackson (London: Mason 1849; repr. London: Wesleyan Methodist Book-Room n.d.) 133; and Journal, 29 September 1749, *Works*, 20:305. As late as 26 December 1785, Wesley noted in his journal that he "baptized a young woman brought up an Anabaptist," though he doesn't indicate whether she had previously received the sacrament.

5. The introduction is included with the printing of the "Treatise on Baptism" in Albert C. Outler, ed., *John Wesley* (New York: Oxford University Press 1964) 318. Though the essay did not originate with John Wesley, the fact that the younger Wesley republished his father's text arguably means that he concurred with its contents, particularly as he did not scruple to make changes in the works he took over from others.

6. Letter to James Clark, 3 July 1756, *LJW*, 3:182; see Frank Baker, *John Wesley and the Church of England* (London: Epworth 1970) 145–49.

7. Letter to Joseph Benson, 19 May 1783, and Letter to John Valton, 6 January 1784, *LJW*, 7:179, 203–204; and Letter to Alexander Suter, 24 November 1787, *LJW*, 8:23.

8. "Serious Thoughts Concerning Godfathers and Godmothers," *Works* [J], 10:508; and "Ought We to Separate from the Church of England?" (3).4.8, *Works*, 9:571.

9. In the infant rite proposed by the Non-Juror Thomas Deacon, one of the parents is the preferred sponsor (*A Compleat Collection of Devotions, both Publick and Private* [London: Printed for the Author 1734] 102). The matter of the sponsors' answers is discussed in John Jones' *Free and Candid Disquisitions Relating to the Church of England, and the Means of Advancing Religion Therein* (London: Printed for A. Millar 1749) 131.

10. Wesley's manuscript notes on the *Apostolic Canons* include a claim that it is his duty "to baptize by immersion" (cited in Baker, *John Wesley and the Church of England*, 40). On threefold immersion, see Diary, 22 February 1736, *Works*, 18:360; see also John Wesley's comments on immersion related to Romans 6:4 and Colossians 2:12 in his *NT Notes*.

11. Journal, 5 May 1736, *Works*, 18:157; cf. Charles Wheatly, *A Rational Illustration of the Book of Common Prayer of the Church of England* (Oxford: Clarendon 1802) 357–59 [chap. 7, sect. 3].

12. In *Baptism in Early Methodism* ([London: Epworth 1970] 154–55), Bernard G. Holland questioned the identification of William Wall as the direct source of Wesley's "Thoughts Upon Infant Baptism," though few writers since then have recognized the legitimacy of his claims. As Holland notes, it is possible that Wesley's "late writer" may have been an individual who had already combined Wall, Watts, and even material of Richard Baxter (from *Plain Scripture Proof of Infants' Churchmembership and Baptism* [1651]), but that document has not yet been found.

13. "Thoughts Upon Infant Baptism" in *The Works of the Rev. John Wesley*, vol. 13 (London: Printed at the Conference Office, Thomas Cordeux 1812) 428–29; cf. *The Works of the Late Reverend and Learned Isaac Watts, D.D.*, vol. 1 (London: Printed for T. and T. Longman et al. 1753) 821; and "Treatise on Baptism," 1.2–5, *Works* [J], 10:188–90.

14. "I baptized seven adults, two of them by immersion" (Journal, 21 March 1759, *Works*, 21:180).

15. J. Hamby Barton, "The Two Versions of the First Edition of John Wesley's 'The Sunday Service of the Methodists in North America,'" *MH* 23 (1985) 153–58.

16. Letter to Walter Churchey, 20 June 1789, *LJW*, 8:144–45.

17. "A Letter to the Reverend Dr. Conyers Middleton," 4 January 1748/49, *Works* [J], 10:9; and Jones, *Free and Candid Disquisitions*, 131. According to his journal, Wesley began reading Jones's book on 15 August 1750. Puritan objections to signation were recorded in an "Admonition to the Parliament" (1572), the "Millenary Petition" (1603), and the "Exceptions against the Book of Common Prayer," section 18 (1661).

18. "Treatise on Baptism," 1.1; 3.1, 3; 4.2, 10; Matthew 3:16, *NT Notes*; and Letter to Gilbert Boyce, 22 May 1750, *LJW*, 3:35–36.

19. "Treatise on Baptism," 4.1–10; cf. "Thoughts Upon Infant Baptism," 1–7.

20. *Poetical Works*, 11:30, #982. The original printing of the text was in the two-volume *Short Hymns on Select Passages of the Holy Scriptures*, 1762. In *Hymns for the Use of the Methodist Episcopal Church* of 1849, the final line has been altered to "Let them in thy glory share."

21. "Treatise on Baptism," 2.3.

22. *Poetical Works*, 7:71–72, #62. The text was first published in 1767 as one of the "Occasional Hymns" in the *Hymns for the Use of Families, and on Various Occasions* and was composed for the baptism of an unidentified girl; later printings of the hymn in America (and in Britain) would substitute masculine pronouns and remove particular verses (for reasons that shall become clear).

23. To trace the full course of the *via salutis* according to Wesley, see Sermon, "The Scripture Way of Salvation," 1.3–4, 6, 8–9; 3.9–10, *Works*, 2:157–60, 166; Sermon, "God's Love to Fallen Man," 2.14, *Works*, 2:434; and "Treatise on Baptism," 2.4; cf. Sermon, "The Means of Grace."

24. "Treatise on Baptism," 2.1, 4. The statement conveying the certainty of salvation for deceased infants, taken from one of the final rubrics in the Prayer Book's rite for the public baptism of infants, was kept in the "Treatise," but omitted from Wesley's 1784 revision of the rite.

25. Sermon, "The New Birth," 4.2, *Works*, 2:197.

26. Wesley quotes from the Catechism in the sermon "The Means of Grace" (2.1, 3, *Works*, 1:381–82) and the sermon "The New Birth" (4.1, *Works*, 2:196–97).

27. See Wesley's sermons "The Marks of the New Birth," "The Great Privilege of Those That Are Born of God," "The New Birth," and "On Sin in Believers."

28. Bernard Holland regards the two new births as, for Wesley, distinct and unrelated moments of regeneration (*Baptism in Early Methodism*, 53–68), while Ole E. Borgen, disagreeing with Holland, sees the two new births as components of a synthetic whole in Wesley (*John Wesley on the Sacraments: A Theological Study* [Nashville: Abingdon 1972] 177–82). See also Robert E. Cushman, "Baptism and the Family of God," in *The Doctrine of the Church*, ed. Dow Kirkpatrick (New York: Abingdon 1964) 83–88.

29. Acts 22:16, *NT Notes*. In *A Farther Appeal to Men of Reason and Religion, Part 1* (2.4, *Works*, 11:111), Wesley acknowledges that the Church of England requires candidates of "riper years" to come to the font with both repentance and faith.

30. Journal, 5 February 1760, *Works*, 21:240.

31. "Come, Father, Son, and Holy Ghost, Honour the means ordained by thee!", *Works*, 7:646–47, #464. A succession of American Methodist hymnals included this hymn, though with not all of the stanzas, and some stanzas received editorial modifications: in several books, "effectuate now the sacred sign" becomes a less instant "effectual make the sacred sign."

32. Acts 10:47, *NT Notes*; cf. Sermon, "The New Birth," 4.2, *Works*, 2:197; and Journal, 8 November 1774, *Works*, 22:436.

33. Nevertheless, numerous American (and British) Methodists have insisted that Wesley did not believe in baptismal regeneration. See, for example, the commentaries on infant and adult rites in Nolan Harmon, *The Rites and Ritual of Episcopal Methodism, with Particular Reference to the Rituals of the Methodist Episcopal Church and the Methodist Episcopal Church, South, Respectively* (Nashville: Publishing House of the Methodist Episcopal Church, South 1926).

34. On the former position, see A. Raymond George, "The People Called Methodists—4. The Means of Grace," in *A History of the Methodist Church in Great Britain*, vol. 1, ed. Rupert Davies and Gordon Rupp (London: Epworth 1965) 269; on the latter, see Holland, *Baptism in Early Methodism*, 135.

35. WCA 4 (26 May 1837) 19. This publication (also in 19 May 1837) of Philip Gatch's manuscript copy of the *Minutes* for the Conferences of 1773–1779 seems to be the first reproduction of the material. Gatch's record is the only one to give the full account of the sacramental controversy, since ostensibly the information was purged from the official *Minutes*; cf. Journal, 29 June 1815, *JLFA*, 2:783.

36. Journal, 17 January 1776, *JLFA*, 1:176; cf. Nathan Bangs, *The Life of the Rev. Freeborn Garrettson: Compiled from His Printed and Manuscript Journals, and Other Authentic Documents* (New York: J. Emory and B. Waugh 1832) 102, 144–45.

37. Ezekiel Cooper, 6 July 1788, Journal, Ms., Garrett-Evangelical Theological Seminary Library, Evanston, IL; cf. 27 July 1788, Journal.

38. Journal, 15 December 1797, *JLFA*, 2:143.

39. Thomas Ware recorded that he baptized the child of a poor man who was unable to pay "the accustomed fee of fifty cents" to his Reformed Dutch pastor (Thomas Ware, *Sketches of the Life and Travels of Rev. Thomas Ware* [New York: T. Mason and G. Lane 1839] 192–93).

40. The Methodist Episcopal Church, South kept the restriction about payment in the section "On Baptism" until 1858, when it was dropped entirely. The Methodist Episcopal Church retained the rubric at various locations in the *Discipline* until it was lost with the 1939 merger.

41. Notes on Chapter 1, section 22, *Discipline with Notes*, 118.

42. Stith Mead, *A General Selection of the Newest and Most Admired Hymns and Spiritual Songs Now in Use* (Richmond, VA: Printed by Seaton Grantland 1807) 98–99, #66. William Warren Sweet lists Mead's book as one of the three most popular songsters during the period 1805–1843 (*Religion in the Development of American Culture: 1765–1840* [New York: Charles Scribner's Sons 1952] 155). A notice on the cover page indicates that the profits from the sale of the work were to be used to decrease the debt on the Lynchburg meetinghouse.

43. The *Collection*, a doctrinal anthology that went through at least fifteen editions with different publishers during the nineteenth century, separated the "doctrine" from the "discipline" that until 1812 had been combined in one volume. The tracts were removed to provide a *Discipline* that was "small and cheap." For a brief history of the *Collection* and its contents, see Frank Baker, *From Wesley to Asbury: Studies in Early American Methodism* (Durham, NC: Duke University Press 1976) 176–80.

44. George Brown, *Recollections of Itinerant Life: Including Early Reminiscences*, 4th ed. (Cincinnati: R. W. Carroll 1868) 340. Detailed linguistic analysis of the various Greek terms related to "baptism" and, regarding infant baptism, *oikos* and *oikia*—"household"—may be found, for example, in Freeborn G. Hibbard, *Christian Baptism: In Two Parts* (New York: G. Lane and P. P. Sandford 1841; repr. New York: Carlton and Phillips 1853) Part 2, 11–106; and Thomas O. Summers, *Baptism: A Treatise on the Nature, Perpetuity, Subjects, Administrator, Mode, and Use of the Initiating Ordinance of the Christian Church* (Richmond: John Early 1853) 78–123, 220–40.

45. George Coles, 4 November 1832, Journal, Ms., Drew University Library, Madison, NJ.

46. Gayle Carlton Felton, *This Gift of Water: The Practice and Theology of Baptism among Methodists in America* (Nashville: Abingdon 1992) 65–66, 88.

47. See, for example, Henry Slicer, *An Appeal to the Candid of All Denominations: In Which the Obligation, Subjects, and Mode of Baptism Are Discussed*, 3d ed. (New York: G. Lane and P. P. Sandford 1842) 99–167; Orceneth Fisher, *The Christian Sacraments: Or, A Scriptural Exhibition of the Nature, Design, Mode, and Subjects of Christian Baptism*, 2d ed. (San Francisco: Whitton, Towne and Co. 1858) 12–80, and *History of Immersion, as a Religious Rite*, 2d ed. (San Francisco: Whitton, Towne and Co. 1858); John Levington, *Scripture Baptism Defended, and Anabaptist Notions Proved to be Anti-Scriptural Novelties* (Chicago: Poe and Hitchcock 1866) 19–37; and Daniel D. Whedon, "The Double Baptism," in *Essays, Reviews, and Discourses*, ed. J. S. Whedon and D. A. Whedon (New York: Phillips and Hunt 1887; Cincinnati: Cranston and Stowe 1887) 216–48.

48. J. H. Potts, *Pastor and People; Or, Methodism in the Field* (New York: Phillips and Hunt 1879; Cincinnati: Hitchcock and Walden 1879) 124–25.

49. For example, JGC/MEC, 1868, 218; JGC/MEC, 1880, 222; JGC/MEC, 1884, 325; and JGC/MECS, 1886, 133–34.

50. References to trine immersion practiced through the fourth century are made, without comment, in James A. Clement's *An Exposition of the Pretentions of Baptists to Antiquity; As Viewed from Scripture and History* (Nashville: Published for the Author 1881) 156–58.

51. Henry M. Turner, *The Genius and Theory of Methodist Polity, Or, The Machinery of Methodism* (Philadelphia: Publication Department, A. M. E. Church 1885) 220; and JGC/MEC, 1908, 485.

52. Pastoral Address, JGC/MEC, *1840*, 160; and *Centennial History of the First Methodist Episcopal Church, Schenectady, New York*, ed. William C. Kitchin, Benjamin H. Ripton, and Fred Winslow Adams (Schenectady, NY: Official Board of First Methodist Episcopal Church 1907) 78.

53. "Welfare of Ohio Conference Methodism," in *Ohio Annual Conference of the Methodist Episcopal Church, Held at Portsmouth, Ohio, September 29, 1875* (Cincinnati: Western Methodist Book Concern 1875) 223–24.

54. For example, Leonidas Rosser, *Baptism: Its Nature, Obligation, Mode, Subjects, and Benefits* (Richmond: Published by the Author 1853) 405–414; Samuel Gregg, *Infant Church Membership: Or, The Spiritual and Permanent Character of the Abrahamic Covenant* (Cincinnati: Swormstedt and Poe 1854) 360–70; and G. H. Hayes, *Children in Christ; Or, The Relation of Children to the Atonement, the Ground of Their Right to Christian Baptism* (Cincinnati: Elm Street Printing 1884) 201–39.

55. For example, Ware, *Sketches of the Life and Travels of Rev. Thomas Ware*, 158; and Josephus Anderson, *Our Church: A Manual for Members and Probationers of the Methodist Episcopal Church, South*, ed. Thomas O. Summers (Nashville: Southern Methodist Publishing House 1860) 98–99.

56. Rosser, *Baptism*, 386.

57. This, for example, was the position espoused by John Miley in his influential *Systematic Theology*, vol. 2, Library of Biblical and Theological Literature, ed. George R. Crooks and John F. Hurst, vol. 6 (New York: Hunt and Eaton 1894; Cincinnati: Cranston and Curts 1894) 409.

58. Fisher, *History of Immersion*, 145–71, 183–84.

59. Summers, *Baptism*, 74, 77.

60. Rosser, *Baptism*, 379–80.

61. JGC/MEC, *1872*, 272–73; and JGC/MEC, *1876*, 94.

62. So insisted Bishop Stephen M. Merrill in *A Digest of Methodist Law; Or, Helps in the Administration of the Discipline of the Methodist Episcopal Church*, rev. ed. (Cincinnati: Jennings and Graham 1904; New York: Eaton and Mains 1904) 141–43, 281.

63. Every *Discipline* of the Methodist Protestant Church, from its inception, included rubrics in the baptismal rites that imply the normativity of baptism in the church building with the congregation present.

64. For Hibbard's contributions to baptismal theology and to the baptismal rites, see Charles R. Hohenstein, "The Revisions of the Rites of Baptism in the Methodist Episcopal Church, 1784–1939" (Ph.D. diss., University of Notre Dame 1990) 118–21.

65. *Report of the Commission on Worship to the General Conference of the Methodist Church, 1960* (Nashville: Methodist Publishing House 1960) 18–19.

66. Richard Watson, *Theological Institutes: Or, A View of the Evidences, Doctrines, Morals, and Institutions of Christianity*, ed. Thomas O. Summers (Nashville: Publishing House of the Methodist Episcopal Church, South 1903) 700–703.

67. J. R. Graves, *The Great Iron Wheel; Or, Republicanism Backwards and Christianity Reversed*, 7th ed. (Nashville: Graves, Marks, and Rutland 1855; New York: Sheldon, Lamport, and Co. 1855) 419–27; and Slicer, *An Appeal to the Candid of All Denominations*, 9, 111. In his critical response to Graves, William G. Brownlow remarkably does not comment directly on the accusations of Methodist advocacy of baptismal regeneration (*The Great Iron Wheel Examined; Or, Its False Spokes Extracted* [Nashville: Published for the Author 1856]).

68. Hibbard, *Christian Baptism*, Part 1, 277–78, 328.

69. A. A. Jimeson, *Notes on the Twenty-Five Articles of Religion as Received and Taught by Methodists in the United States*, 3d ed. (Cincinnati: Applegate, Pounsford, and Co. 1868) 257, 284.

70. Summers, *Baptism*, 124–25. Yet elsewhere, Summers, in defining sacraments, posits that sacraments are "an instrument to convey the grace which it represents . . . he who worthily receives baptism, receives with it and by it the sanctifying grace which it signifies" (*Systematic Theology: A Complete Body of Wesleyan Arminian Divinity*, vol. 2, rev. John J. Tigert [Nashville: Publishing House of the Methodist Episcopal Church, South 1888] 295).

71. Rosser, *Baptism*, 21; see *JGC/MEC*, 1856, 292–93.

72. William Capers, *Catechism for the Use of the Methodist Missions, and Infant Classes in Sunday-Schools*, Part First, rev. T. O. Summers (Nashville: Southern Methodist Publishing House 1861) 15.

73. The Methodist Episcopal Church, which in 1864 dropped the reference to sanctifying water from the opening prayer only, included this hymn in their 1878 hymnal under the revealing title "Rites inefficacious." The second reference to sanctifying water in the prayer for the candidates survived until 1916 when the entire prayer was deleted.

74. Summers, *Baptism*, 154.

75. On the importance of covenant theology, particularly for southern Methodism, see E. Brooks Holifield, *The Gentleman Theologians: American Theology in Southern Culture, 1795–1860* (Durham: Duke University Press 1978) 155–85.

76. H. Shelton Smith, *Changing Conceptions of Original Sin: A Study in American Theology since 1750* (New York: Charles Scribner's Sons 1955) 164–66.

77. Address of the Bishops, *JGC/MEC*, 1860, 318.

78. For comments on the significance and meaning of the 1864 formulations, see R. J. Cooke, *History of the Ritual of the Methodist Episcopal Church; With a Commentary on Its Offices*, 3d ed. (Cincinnati: Jennings and Pye 1900; New York: Eaton and Mains 1900) 192–222. Hohenstein, in "The Revisions of the Rites of Baptism in the Methodist Episcopal Church, 1784–1939," details the alterations made for the 1864, and for the later 1916 and 1932 revisions.

79. By the end of the nineteenth century, the opening prayer had been reworded to imply that regeneration had occurred prior to baptism, thus casting a different meaning upon the opening address.

80. Robert E. Chiles, *Theological Transition in American Methodism: 1790–1935* (New York: Abingdon 1965) 65. For the conservative response, see, for example, George W. Wilson, *Methodist Theology vs. Methodist Theologians: A Review of Several Methodist Writers* (Cincinnati: Jennings and Pye 1904).

81. "Baptism and Regeneration," *The Methodist* 18 (27 October 1877) 675.

82. Thomas O. Summers, "The Ritual," *MQR* 19 (April 1882) 357; and James A. Burrow, "That Methodist Creed," *MQR* 58 (July 1909) 532.

83. Thomas B. Neely, *The Revised Ritual of 1916* (Philadelphia: E. A. Yeakel, Agent; Methodist Episcopal Book Store 1920) 102. Neely, an expert on denominational polity, also objected to the process by which the new ritual was approved: on account of extended debate at the General Conference, the matter was referred to the bishops, who then printed the revision without the informed approval of the entire body of denominational representatives; and because alterations in the ritual effectively created a new doctrinal standard, the denomination's first restrictive rule was violated since constitutional protocols had not been followed.

84. *JGC/MC*, 1960, 192.

85. Robert W. Goodloe, *The Sacraments in Methodism* (Nashville: Methodist Publishing House 1953) 106, 113, 116–17; and Elmer L. Harvey, "Do We Have Infant Baptism?" *The Pastor* 11 (January 1948) 35.

86. *Report of the Commission on Worship to the General Conference of the Methodist Church*, 1960, 19–20.

87. An alternate text, drawn from the former Methodist and Evangelical United Brethren traditions, is provided in the 1992 book as well. For a detailed history of the development of the United Methodist rite, see Robert B. Peiffer, "How Contemporary Liturgies Evolve: The Revision of United Methodist Liturgical Texts (1968–1988)" (Ph.D. diss., University of Notre Dame 1992), esp. 271–91. For a discussion of the changes in baptismal theology by the principal author of the United Methodist baptismal rites, see Laurence Hull Stookey, *Baptism: Christ's Act in the Church* (Nashville: Abingdon 1982), esp. 133–74.

88. See, for example, Ted A. Campbell, "Baptism and New Birth: Evangelical Theology and the United Methodist 'Baptismal Covenant I,' " *Quarterly Review* 10 (1990) 34–45; and Charles R. Hohenstein, "New Birth Through Water and the Spirit: A Reply to Ted A. Campbell," *Quarterly Review* 11 (1991) 103–112.

89. *By Water and the Spirit: A United Methodist Understanding of Baptism* (Nashville: Discipleship Resources 1996) 12.

90. Nathan Bangs, *An Original Church of Christ: Or, A Scriptural Vindication of the Orders and Powers of the Ministry of the Methodist Episcopal Church*, 2d ed., rev. (New York: T. Mason and G. Lane 1837) 322. Bangs's comment appears in a chapter where he refutes the Protestant Episcopal Church's claim of practicing "scriptural" confirmation.

91. The Methodist Episcopal Church, South dropped the specified six-month period of probation in 1866; the Methodist Episcopal Church did so in 1908.

92. Graves, *The Great Iron Wheel*, 352; and the *Autobiography of Peter Cartwright* (repr. Nashville: Abingdon 1984) 304.

93. See chapter 5, pp. 143–48.

94. T. F. R. Mercein, "The Relation of Baptized Infants to the Church," *MR* 37 (January 1855) 101–102.

95. "Introduction of Children into the Church," *MQR* 15 (January 1861) 81–84; cf. "Introduction of Children into the Church," *MQR* 14 (October 1860) 505–15.

96. Thomas O. Summers, *Commentary on the Ritual of the Methodist Episcopal Church, South* (Nashville: A. H. Redford for the M. E. Church, South 1873) 55.

97. "The Wesleyan Condition of Church Membership—Its Modifications," *MR* 65 (July 1883) 491–513. Inquiries raised about the constitutionality of the ritual question at the 1920 General Conference of the Methodist Episcopal Church were meticulously addressed by Bishop Thomas B. Neely in *The Only Condition* (Philadelphia: E. A. Yeakel 1920). The question was altered in 1924 to a less sectarian—and less elaborated—"Do you receive and profess the Christian Faith as contained in the New Testament of our Lord Jesus Christ?"

98. For the different viewpoints, see Felton, *This Gift of Water*, 127–31. However, all four of these factors were often accentuated as essentials in the guidebooks for probationers and new members. See, for example, S. Olin Garrison, *Probationer's Hand-Book: Religious, Historical, Doctrinal, Disciplinary, and Practical*, rev. ed. (New York: Eaton and Mains 1883; Cincinnati: Jennings and Pye 1883); and J. E. Godbey, *The Methodist Church Member's Manual: A Hand Book for Every Methodist* (St. Louis: South-Western Methodist Publishers 1886).

99. B. T. Roberts, "Church Membership Qualifications," *The Earnest Christian* 2 (September 1861) 262.

100. L. F. Sensabaugh, "Membership in the Christian Church," *MQR* 78 (July 1929) 401–405.

101. *Report of the Commission on Worship to the General Conference of the Methodist Church*, 1960, 26–27.

102. "United Methodist Church [USA]," in *Churches Respond to BEM*, vol. 2, ed. Max Thurian, Faith and Order Paper 132 (Geneva: World Council of Churches 1986) 179–80.

By "modes," the bishops here appear to mean entire patterns of practice, not simply the method for the application of the water.

5. The Lord's Supper

1. See *The Unpublished Poetry of Charles Wesley,* vol. 3: *Hymns and Poems for Church and World,* ed. S. T. Kimbrough, Jr., and Oliver A. Beckerlegge (Nashville: Kingswood 1992) 81–101.

2. Wesley's sermon "The Duty of Constant Communion," published in 1787, was an abridgment of an extract Wesley made in 1732 of Non-Juror Robert Nelson's *The Great Duty of Frequenting the Christian Sacrifice.* The sermon was prefaced with a note "To the Reader" in which Wesley claims that his opinions expressed therein had not changed in fifty-five years (*Works,* 3:428). See also *NT Notes* for Matthew 6:11 and Acts 2:46; and the unpublished "On a Weekly Sacrament" by Charles Wesley, printed in John C. Bowmer, *The Sacrament of the Lord's Supper in Early Methodism* (London: Dacre 1951) 225–32. Cf. the final rubrics in the Communion rites of William Whiston (*The Liturgy of the Church of England, Reduc'd Nearer to the Primitive Standard,* 1713) and the Non-Juror Thomas Deacon (*A Compleat Collection of Devotions,* 1734), which would have been familiar to Wesley and which carry an identical instruction: that "all the faithful are to frequent [the Eucharist] constantly."

3. Preface to the Journal, and Journal, 24 May 1738, *Works,* 18:127, 244.

4. "Directions Given to the Band Societies, 25 December 1744," 3.1, *Works,* 9:79.

5. Letter to "Our Brethren in America," 10 September 1784, *LJW,* 7:238–39.

6. See Jesse Lee, *A Short History of the Methodists, in the United States of America; Beginning in 1766, and Continued Till 1809* (Baltimore: Magill and Clime 1810) 41, 47; *Minutes MC* (1773), 5.

7. See the note dated 9 September 1784 that was included as a preface in many copies of the *Sunday Service.*

8. See the reply to Question 77, *A Roman Catechism, Faithfully Drawn Out of the Allowed Writings of the Church of Rome. With a Reply Thereto, Works [J],* 10:124. Wesley also struck from the General Confession the phrase "the burthen of them [our misdoings] is intolerable" (see Sermon, "The Means of Grace," 3.11, *Works,* 1:389; and Sermon, "Sermon on the Mount, II," 3.17, *Works,* 1:507).

9. From 1784 to 1939, the Methodist Episcopal Church would instruct in the *Discipline* that while kneeling was preferred, persons could also legitimately receive the sacrament while standing or sitting. The preachers meeting at Fluvanna (1779) had likewise determined that the mode of reception was purely a matter of conscience.

10. For example, William Whiston in *The Liturgy of the Church of England, Reduc'd Nearer to the Primitive Standard* (1713), and the 1764 Scottish Communion rite.

11. On this subject, Bishop Nolan Harmon remarked: "I recall once when meeting with the Commission on Unity of the Protestant Episcopal Church to talk about working out intercommunion, we found our Episcopal compeers astonished to learn that we Methodists had kept the Church of England's office for the solemnization of the Lord's Supper, whilst they had followed the Scottish Liturgy in the service they have. 'Is it possible,' one of these brethren asked, 'that you have kept the Church of England's office as it has always been?' 'Yes,' I took pleasure in replying, 'it is a case where the illegitimate daughter is more like the Queen, her mother, than is the Princess of the blood royal!'" (Nolan B. Harmon, "John Wesley's 'Sunday Service' and its American Revisions," *Proceedings of the Wesley Historical Society* 39 [June 1974] 143).

12. The *Pocket Hymn Book* appears to be a conflation by American editors of two sources, John Wesley's *A Pocket Hymn Book for the Use of Christians of All Denominations* (1785) and Robert Spence of York's *A Pocket Hymn-Book, Designed as a Constant Companion for the Pious* (1785), but the designation of "sacramental" is unique to this collection. The earliest known copy is from 1786 (New York: Printed by W. Ross) and is identified as the fifth edition, which suggests an earlier printing, possibly 1785. See Carlton R. Young, *Companion to the United Methodist Hymnal* (Nashville: Abingdon 1993) 98–105.

13. An example of usage may be evident from the contents of a manuscript sermon outline book by Philip Gatch, possibly dating from the 1770s, that includes fifteen hymns copied by hand from the Wesleys' collection; see Lester Ruth, *A Little Heaven Below: Worship at Early Methodist Quarterly Meetings* (Nashville: Kingswood 2000) 140 n. 146. The classic study of the Communion hymns is J. Ernest Rattenbury, *The Eucharistic Hymns of John and Charles Wesley* (London: Epworth 1948).

14. From the hymn "Jesu, at whose supreme command" in *Hymns on the Lord's Supper* (Bristol: Printed by Felix Farley 1745) #30, and in *A Pocket Hymn Book, Designed as a Constant Companion for the Pious* (New York: Printed by W. Ross 1786) 221. The other eight Communion hymns in the "sacramental" section of the 1786 *Pocket Hymn Book* were "In that sad memorable night" (*HLS* #1; *PHB*, p. 217); "Let all who truly bear" (*HLS* #4; *PHB*, p. 218); "Who is this that comes from far" (*HLS* #17; *PHB*, p. 222); "Rock of Israel, cleft for me" (*HLS* #27; *PHB*, p. 219); "Author of our salvation, thee" (*HLS* #28; *PHB*, p. 220); "O Thou, who this mysterious bread" (*HLS* #29; *PHB*, p. 221); "Jesu, dear redeeming Lord" (*HLS* #33; *PHB*, p. 223); "Jesu, we thus obey" (*HLS* #81; *PHB*, p. 223). Snippets from these hymns will be quoted in the text without direct attribution; longer portions of hymns will be cited in the text with the *HLS* number.

15. From the hymn "Happy the souls to Jesus join'd," *HLS* #96; *PHB*, p. 123, in the section "Rejoicing."

16. From the hymm "God of all-redeeming grace," *HLS* #193; *PHB* p. 81, in the section "Petition."

17. The 1784 *Discipline* (1785, Question 44.2); and *Discipline* 1787 (Section 20); and Ezekiel Cooper, 11 May 1788, Journal, Ms., Garrett-Evangelical Theological Seminary Library, Evanston, IL.

18. Ezekiel Cooper, 28 June 1789, Journal, Ms.

19. Methodist preacher Richard Boardman served Communion during a Maryland quarterly meeting in 1772 (*JLFA*, 1:60), as did Philip Gatch at a quarterly meeting north of the James River (Virginia) in 1779 (Nelson Reed, 31 July 1779, Journal, Ts., Methodist Historical Society, Baltimore, MD). Thomas Rankin, in a diary entry dated 31 October 1775, noted that for the "quarter day for Alexandria circuit" the sacrament was given by "Mr. Griffiths, the clergyman" to "as many as choosed to receive it" ("The Diary of the Revd. Thomas Rankin," Ts., Garrett-Evangelical Theological Seminary Library, Evanston, IL.

20. Thomas Ware, *Sketches of the Life and Travels of Rev. Thomas Ware* (New York: T. Mason and G. Lane 1839) 115. The 1784 *Discipline* (1785, Question 33) and that published in 1786 (Question 32) noted that "No *Helper*, or even *Deacon*, shall on any pretense, at any time whatsoever, administer the Lord's Supper." The spirit of this rule would continue, for roughly a century, in later editions of the *Discipline*.

21. William Wade sees the 1792 changes as a significant break with Methodist praxis since 1784 (which he considers to have been a weekly Eucharist) and fingers Bishop Asbury as the source of apparent waning interest in the sacrament ("A History of Public Worship in the Methodist Episcopal Church and Methodist Episcopal Church, South from 1784 to 1905" [Ph.D. diss., University of Notre Dame 1981] 115–206). In fact, there is no evidence

that pastoral circumstances in these early years ever allowed American Methodists to develop a pattern of weekly Communion in a given congregation or society.

22. *WCA* 4 (26 May 1837) 19.

23. Wesley was known to have abbreviated the Prayer Book's eucharistic liturgy when "straitened for time" (see "Some Remarks on Mr. Hill's 'Review of all the Doctrines Taught by Mr. John Wesley,' " *Works [J]*, 10:411). On the other hand, the value he set on the Prayer of Consecration is demonstrated by his instruction, already noted, that the prayer be repeated in its entirety if more bread or wine were needed for Communion.

24. Freeborn Garrettson, *Substance of the Semi-Centennial Sermon, Before the New-York Annual Conference, at Its Session, May, 1826* (New York: N. Bangs and J. Emory, for the Methodist Episcopal Church 1827) 26; cf. Notes on Article 22, *Discipline with Notes*, 27; and *JGC/MEC (1824)*, 298: "In the administration of the ordinances some use the form in the Discipline, some mutilate it, and others wholly neglect it."

25. Such is the description given in James B. Finley, *Autobiography of James B. Finley; Or, Pioneer Life in the West*, ed. W. P. Strickland (Cincinnati: Printed at the Methodist Book Concern for the Author 1856) 401. The hymn sung on that occasion was "Glory to God on high, Our peace is made with Heaven," a hymn found in the sacrament section of several early nineteenth-century Methodist Episcopal hymnals. It was not unknown for some elders to reduce the Prayer of Consecration itself to the Words of Institution—a move totally out of line with Wesley.

26. "[Constitution] and Proposed Plan for the New Denomination to be called United Societies of the People commonly called Methodists, late in connection with the Methodist Episcopal Church," Ms., 1801, in the "Book of Antiquities," St. George's United Methodist Church Archives, Philadelphia, PA.

27. Phrases from the Prayer of Humble Access, the Prayer of Consecration, and the Post-Communion Prayer are spliced into the text in the first three paragraphs.

28. *HLS* #16. The hymn text displays familiarity with *Apostolic Constitutions*, book 8.12.39, and the invocation there of the Spirit as the "witness" of Christ's sufferings. See Geoffrey Wainwright, " 'Our Elder Brethren Join': The Wesleys' *Hymns on the Lord's Supper* and the Patristic Revival in England," *Proceedings of the Charles Wesley Society* 1 (1994) 27.

29. Benjamin Lakin, 9 October 1809, Journal, Ms. on microfilm, Washington University Library, St. Louis, MO.

30. For example, *Journals of the Rev. Thomas Morrell*, ed. Michael J. McKay (Rutland, VT: Academy Books, for the Historical Society, Northern New Jersey Conference, United Methodist Church 1984) 32; Charles Giles, *Pioneer: A Narrative of the Nativity, Experience, Travels, and Ministerial Labours of Rev. Charles Giles* (New York: G. Lane and P. P. Sandford 1844) 259–60; and George Coles, 11 April 1820, Journal, Ms., Drew University Library, Madison, NJ.

31. *Life and Observations of Rev. E. F. Newell* (Worcester: C. W. Ainsworth 1847) 158.

32. Adam Clarke, *A Discourse on the Nature and Design of the Eucharist, or Sacrament of the Lord's Supper* (New York: G. Lane and P. P. Sandford 1842) 89, 98–99, 134, 142. The British Methodist Clarke first published his study in 1808 (which appeared in an American edition in 1812), and revised it in 1814.

33. "O Thou eternal Victim" (*HLS* #5) was included in an abbreviated version in *A Selection of Hymns, from Various Authors, Designed as a Supplement to the Methodist Pocket Hymn-Book* (New York: John Wilson and Daniel Hitt 1808) and appeared throughout the first half of the nineteenth century in hymn books of several Methodist denominations either in the abbreviated form or with the full text (as in *A Collection of Hymns for the Use of the Methodist Episcopal Church* [New York: N. Bangs and T. Mason 1821]) given here.

34. Charles Wesley's hymn "Victim Divine, thy grace we claim" (*HLS* #116) was one of two hymns (#123) from the section "The Holy Eucharist as it implies a sacrifice" in the *Hymns on the Lord's Supper* introduced into American Methodist hymnals during the years 1847 to 1889.

35. Richard Watson, *Theological Institutes: Or, A View of the Evidences, Doctrines, Morals, and Institutions of Christianity*, ed. Thomas O. Summers (Nashville: Publishing House of the Methodist Episcopal Church, South 1903) 734.

36. Methodists denied that the rite produced any physical change in the elements, but some concluded that setting them apart for sacred purposes required that they be respected: just prior to the distribution at a Communion service in 1834, James Gilruth "felt [himself] in an awkward situation" having spilled a portion of the wine. "But instantly reflecting that it was accidental I calmed My Mind & proceeded with the service as tho nothing had happened" ("The Journal of James Gilruth, 1834–1835 [2 November 1834]," in *Religion on the American Frontier, 1783–1840*, vol. 4: *The Methodists*, ed. William Warren Sweet [Chicago: University of Chicago Press 1946] 406).

37. From the hymn "Glory to God on high," by English Independent Joseph Hart, found in the 1808 *Selection of Hymns* and other early Methodist Episcopal hymnals; see note 25.

38. "Acts of Faith," *The Life Experience and Gospel Labors of the Rt. Rev. Richard Allen* (repr. Nashville: Abingdon 1960) 42–43.

39. Pastoral Address, *JGC/MEC, 1856*, 301.

40. J. G., "The Sacrament," *CAJ (NY)* 37 (20 February 1862) 59.

41. Orceneth Fisher addressed this topic as the fortieth question in his *Sacramental Catechism. Part Second. The Lord's Supper: Or, A Scriptural View of the Nature, Design, Perpetuity & Subjects of the Holy Communion of the Church of Christ* (San Francisco: Whitton, Towne, and Co. 1858).

42. Josephus Anderson, *Our Church: A Manual for Members and Probationers of the Methodist Episcopal Church, South*, ed. Thomas O. Summers (Nashville: Southern Methodist Publishing House 1860) 221.

43. Although the Methodist Protestants kept their legislation only until 1877, the Methodist Episcopal Church retained theirs until 1939.

44. Samuel Luckey, *The Lord's Supper* (New York: Phillips and Hunt 1859; Cincinnati: Walden and Stowe 1859) 34–54.

45. Ibid., 180.

46. Thomas O. Summers, *Commentary on the Ritual of the Methodist Episcopal Church, South* (Nashville: A. H. Redford for the M. E. Church, South 1873) 23.

47. Such, at least, was the interpretation given by R. J. Cooke in *History of the Ritual of the Methodist Episcopal Church; With a Commentary on Its Offices*, 3d ed. (Cincinnati: Jennings and Pye 1900; New York: Eaton and Mains 1900) 255. Another Methodist, a member of the faculty at Drew Theological Seminary, would describe this "dislocation" (which he attributed to Wesley) as "a most inappropriate position" (J. A. Faulkner, "Where Did We Get Our Lord's Supper Service?" *MR* 93 [November 1911] 886).

48. The Gloria in excelsis was altered in 1864, but restored to its original form in 1868.

49. J. C. Havemeyer, "The Communion Service," *The Methodist* 22 (9 April 1881) 4.

50. *JGC/MEC, 1932, 275.*

51. Ibid., 275, 1515–16. Methodists knew much of the literature of the day, including, apparently, a proposed eucharistic rite produced by German Lutheran Rudolf Otto (*Religious Essays*, trans. Brian Lunn [London: Oxford University Press 1931] 53–67). Two years after the revision, Methodist New Testament scholar Clarence Tucker Craig would observe that his denomination, on the subject of the Lord's Supper, had "become conscious of our barren

services and unpsychological orders of worship" (*We Have an Altar* [New York: Abingdon 1934] 57).

52. For example, "The Ritual for the Pews," *CAJ (NY)* 39 (8 December 1864) 388; and, closer to the actual revision, James Albert Bebee, *The Pastoral Office* (New York: Methodist Book Concern 1923) 107; and J. Hastie Odgers and Edward G. Schutz, *The Technique of Public Worship* (New York: Methodist Book Concern 1928) 227–29. The Commandments, in litany form, were supplied in the reproduction of material from the 1784 *Sunday Service* (including an outline of the Communion rite) in Charles S. Harrower's *Select Psalms Arranged for the Use of the Methodist Episcopal Church by John Wesley, with Other Selections and the Order for the Sacraments and Occasional Services of the Church* (New York: Hunt and Eaton 1891; Cincinnati: Cranston and Stowe 1891), his *The Sunday Service Recommended to the Societies in America by the Rev. John Wesley Edited by Comparison with the Public Book of Prayers and Services of the Wesleyan Church Including Select Psalms with the Order for the Sacraments and Other Occasional Services According to the Use of the Methodist Episcopal Church* (New York: Eaton and Mains 1893; Cincinnati: Jennings and Pye 1893; also New York: Hunt and Eaton 1894; Cincinnati: Cranston and Curts 1894), and in the 1905 *Methodist Hymnal.*

53. The Summary of the Law was found in the 1718 eucharistic liturgy of the Non-Jurors, which would have been familiar to Wesley and to the compilers of the 1789 American *Book of Common Prayer.* Harrower included it in *Select Psalms* following the Decalogue.

54. Jeremy Taylor's revision of the eucharistic rite in his *Collection of Offices* (1658) used the Beatitudes in this location, as did the authors of the so-called "Liturgy of Comprehension" (1689), who were familiar with Taylor's work. The litany response of the 1689 Beatitudes is similar to the Methodist refrain; yet the source for the Methodists probably was an early twentieth-century Presbyterian liturgical book, perhaps the 1906 *Book of Common Worship* of the Presbyterian Church in the United States of America.

55. John W. Suter, ed., *Devotional Offices for General Use* (New York and London: Century 1928) Foreword, 85–86. Suter abridged this material from an "Act of Faith" provided in both daily offices contained in *A New Prayer Book* (London: Oxford University Press 1923), which was a collection of liturgical proposals drafted for a revision of the 1662 Prayer Book but that were never approved.

56. JGC/MEC, 1932, 1515.

57. For example, E. B. Chappell, *The Church and Its Sacraments* (Nashville: Publishing House of the Methodist Episcopal Church, South 1928) 99–105. Chappell's book was required reading for the Church, South's course of study program for pastors.

58. Proper prefaces were included for Christmas, Epiphany, Easter, and Whitsunday. Harrower, in his *Sunday Service* (1894), had reprinted Wesley's proper prefaces for Christmas, Easter, Ascension, Whitsunday, and the Feast of Trinity.

59. See, for example, Paul S. Sanders, "The Heart of the Liturgy," *The Pastor* 17 (March 1954) 20–22; for what probably was the more general Methodist view, see Robert W. Goodloe, *The Sacraments in Methodism* (Nashville: Methodist Publishing House 1953) 50–53.

60. Romey P. Marshall, "A Proposed Order for Holy Communion," *The Pastor* 15 (April 1952) 13–16. Among the new components included were a prayer for the whole state of Christ's Church, an epiclesis upon the elements, and the use of the Agnus Dei. Sources Marshall admitted to using were, in addition to the 1945 Methodist ritual, the 1549 Prayer Book, W. S. Porter's *The English Eucharist,* and Mar Eshai Shimum's *The Liturgy of the Church of the East.*

61. JGC/MC, 1960, 190–92.

62. *Report of the Commission on Worship to the General Conference of the Methodist Church,* 1960 (Nashville: Methodist Publishing House 1960) 32–33.

63. The contents of the brief form were stipulated by rubric as the substance of the service at the Communion of the sick.

64. Massey Shepherd to Lawrence Snow, 15 March 1964, Order of St. Luke Collection, Drew University Library, Madison, NJ.

65. The component parts of the historic Antiochene anaphora, in sequence, are: introductory dialogue, preface (of praise and thanks), Sanctus, continuation of the thanksgiving, institution narrative, anamnesis, oblation, epiclesis, diptychs or intercessions, and the concluding doxology.

66. The United Methodist Church, *The Book of Services* (Nashville: United Methodist Publishing House 1985) 8–9.

67. Texts of the manuscript drafts are found as appendix A in Robert B. Peiffer, "How Contemporary Liturgies Evolve: The Revision of United Methodist Liturgical Texts (1968–1988)" (Ph.D. diss., University of Notre Dame 1992) 320–75.

68. The principal author of the 1972 text, James F. White, summarizes the process of producing the United Methodist rite in "United Methodist Eucharistic Prayers: 1965–1985," in *New Eucharistic Prayers: An Ecumenical Study of Their Development and Structure*, ed. Frank C. Senn (New York: Paulist 1987) 80–95. For a fuller description, see Peiffer, "How Contemporary Liturgies Evolve."

69. The 1972 "Great Thanksgiving" included the novel sentence "When we eat this bread and drink this cup, we experience anew the presence of the Lord Jesus Christ." This was an interesting attempt to convey in contemporary and perhaps characteristically Methodist language the sense of the biblical anamnesis. It was, however, abandoned in the revision approved in 1984 for fear that it was too subjective. See James F. White, "Response to the Berakah Award: Making Changes in United Methodist Euchology," *Worship* 57 (July 1983) 343–44.

70. The structure of the Ante-Communion prior to the Invitation is as follows: Greeting (Scripture sentences), Hymn, Opening Prayer (the Collect for Purity), the Lord's Prayer, an Act of Praise (Gloria in excelsis), Scripture lessons (interspersed with a Psalm, hymn, or anthem), Sermon, Response to the Word (a hymn, creed, act of Christian discipleship, etc.), and a Pastoral Prayer or a responsive Prayer for the Whole State of Christ's Church.

71. The pattern of the new order of service, as printed in the African Methodist Episcopal Church's *Book of Worship* (1984), is as follows: Salutation, Hymn of Praise, Prayer of Purification (Collect for Purity), Collect, Anthem, Old Testament Lesson, New Testament Lesson, Gloria Patri, Announcements, Choral Selection, Prayer of Intercession, Choral Response, Hymn of Preparation, Sermon, Invitation to Christian Discipleship, Affirmation of Faith (Apostles' Creed), Offertory, Presentation of the Offering (1 Chronicles 29:14), the Peace, General Confession (older form, altered), Prayer of Pardon (older form, slightly altered), Great Thanksgiving (introductory dialogue, Common Preface enlarged, Sanctus), Consecration (older form, altered), Lord's Prayer, Prayer of Humble Access (older form, altered), Communion of the Ministers, Invitation (older form, slightly altered), Communion of the People, Prayer of Thanksgiving, Hymn of Fellowship, Nunc Dimittis, and Benediction.

72. Journal, 27–28 June 1740, *Works*, 19:158–59; cf. Letter to John Simpson, 28 November 1774, *LJW*, 6:124.

73. Journal, 22–26 June 1740, *Works*, 19:153–58; "An Answer to the Rev. Mr. Church's Remarks on the Rev. Mr. John Wesley's Last Journal" (1745), 2.1–2, 3.3, *Works*, 9:82–85, 112; and Letter to Richard Tompson, 25 July 1755, *Works*, 26:575; cf. Sermon, "The Means of Grace," *Works*, 1:378–97.

74. Letter from the Revd. Ralph Erskine, 31 January 1741, *Works*, 26:48.

75. According to John Bennet's Minutes of Conference (1747), two answers were given to the question "How shall we keep off unwary [unworthy] communicants?": "by being exactly careful whom we admit into the Society"; and "by giving notes to none but those who come to us on the days appointed in each quarter" (*John Bennet's Copy of the Minutes of the Conferences of 1744, 1745, 1747 and 1748; with Wesley's Copy of those for 1746*, Publications of the Wesley Historical Society, no. 1 [London: Charles H. Kelly 1896] 49).

76. This legislation requiring examination and tokens had previously been rescinded by the Methodist Episcopal Church in 1848, and by the Methodist Episcopal Church, South in 1854.

77. Finley, *Autobiography*, 401–402; cf. *Life and Observations of Rev. E. F. Newell*, 39–40.

78. Jonas Oramel Peck, *The Revival and the Pastor* (New York: Eaton and Mains 1894; Cincinnati: Jennings and Pye 1894) 259–63.

79. Giles, *Pioneer*, 241; and Alfred Brunson, *A Western Pioneer: Or, Incidents of the Life and Times of Rev. Alfred Brunson, A. M., D. D.*, vol. 1 (Cincinnati: Walden and Stowe 1880; New York: Phillips and Hunt 1880) 58–59; cf. Fisher, *Sacramental Catechism. Part Second. The Lord's Supper*, Questions 53–54.

80. Legislation from 1792 associated the Friday fast with the quarterly meeting as a whole and not specifically with the sacrament, though some Methodists apparently linked the fast to the sacrament; see Minton Thrift, *Memoir of the Rev. Jesse Lee. With Extracts from His Journals* (New York: N. Bangs and T. Mason 1823) 207 [12 December 1794]. A failed proposal to the 1876 General Conference of the Methodist Episcopal Church had sought a direct connection between the fast and the sacrament (JGC/MEC 1876, 139).

81. Freeborn G. Hibbard (*Christian Baptism: In Two Parts* [New York: G. Lane and P. P. Sandford 1841; repr. New York: Carlton and Phillips 1853] Part 2, 184–89) insisted that, as a church ordinance, the Lord's table was open only to church members. Similar views were held by Orceneth Fisher (*Sacramental Catechism. Part Second. The Lord's Supper*, Questions 42–44); Daniel Whedon ("The Lord's Supper Only to the Lord's People"; a Review of N. Burwash's *The Relation of Children to the Fall, the Atonement, and the Church*, MR 65 [October 1883] 760); Henry M. Turner (*The Genius and Theory of Methodist Polity, Or, The Machinery of Methodism* [Philadelphia: Publication Department, A. M. E. Church 1885] 224, 275); and S. Olin Garrison (*Probationer's Hand-Book: Religious, Historical, Doctrinal, Disciplinary, and Practical*, rev. ed. [New York: Eaton and Mains 1883; Cincinnati: Jennings and Pye 1883] 22–23). Thomas O. Summers allowed for limited exceptions to baptism (*Systematic Theology: A Complete Body of Wesleyan Arminian Divinity*, vol. 2, rev. John J. Tigert [Nashville: Publishing House of the Methodist Episcopal Church, South 1888] 409–10). See also *Life and Observations of Rev. E. F. Newell*, 69–70.

82. Leonidas Rosser, *Open Communion* (Richmond, VA: Published by the Author 1858) 42–59.

83. JGC/MEC, 1852, 25; cf. JGC/MEC, 1868, 107–108, 165–66.

84. Bostwick Hawley, *Manual of Methodism; Or, The Doctrines, General Rules, and Usages of the Methodist Episcopal Church, with Scripture Proofs and Explanations* (New York: Carlton and Lanahan 1869; Cincinnati: Hitchcock and Walden 1869) 159. James Porter, in arguing that baptism was not a prerequisite to the Supper, nevertheless granted that baptism prior to Communion was "a prudent arrangement" (*A Compendium of Methodism: Embracing the History and Present Condition of Its Various Branches in all Countries*, 15th ed. [New York: Carlton and Porter 1851] 290–91).

85. J. R. Graves, *The Great Iron Wheel; Or, Republicanism Backwards and Christianity Reversed*, 7th ed. (Nashville: Graves, Marks, and Rutland 1855; New York: Sheldon, Lamport and Co. 1855) 369; *The Graves-Ditzler: Or, Great Carrollton Debate, on the Mode of Baptism, the Lord's Supper, Infant Baptism, Believers' Baptism, Church of Christ, Final Perseverance of*

Saints, between J. R. Graves, LL.D., and Jacob Ditzler, DD. (Memphis, TN: Southern Baptist Publication Society 1876) 817, also 807–907; and Rosser, *Open Communion*, 22–42. Graves the Baptist delighted in citing against the Methodists one of their own, F. G. Hibbard, who had vehemently argued for a baptismal prerequisite (see note 81 above).

86. Garrettson, *Substance of the Semi-Centennial Sermon*, 32.

87. Wesley admitted children to the table after instruction and personal interview (*Journal*, 29 May 1737; and *Journal*, October 2 1784). Summers (in *Systematic Theology*, 2:410) stated that "the Lord's supper requires repentance, faith, obedience—a ratification of the threefold vow of baptism—and a discerning of the Lord's body and blood, of which infants are incapable; hence the folly, not to say the profanity, of giving infants the sacred symbols." Along this line, it was proposed that Communion serve for older children as "the symbol of their confirmation" and "the beginning of their full membership" ("Introduction of Children into the Church," *MQR* 14 [October 1860] 512).

88. Benjamin Lakin, Sermon 3 (On Baptism), in *Religion on the American Frontier, 1783–1840*, 4:728.

89. Leonidas Rosser, *Baptism: Its Nature, Obligation, Mode, Subjects, and Benefits* (Richmond, VA: Published by the Author 1853) 388–90. This was likewise the opinion of Henry Slicer, who also found infant Communion to be "an innovation, the result of superstition" (*An Appeal to the Candid of All Denominations: In Which the Obligation, Subjects, and Mode of Baptism Are Discussed*, 3d ed. [New York: G. Lane and P. P. Sandford 1842] 51–54).

90. Hibbard, *Christian Baptism*, Part 1, 281.

91. Leonard Smith, 26 July 1867, Journal, Ts., Archives, Illinois Great Rivers Annual Conference, United Methodist Church, Bloomington, IL.

92. Rosser, *Open Communion*, 40–41; see also the *Autobiography of Peter Cartwright* (repr. Nashville: Abingdon 1984) 81–82.

93. William G. Brownlow, *The Great Iron Wheel Examined; Or, Its False Spokes Extracted* (Nashville: Published for the Author 1856) 178; also Rosser, *Open Communion*, 170–79; and Z. A. Parker, *The People's Hand-Book or Immersion, Infant Baptism, Close Communion, and Plan of Salvation; Or, Justification by Water versus Justification by Faith*, rev. ed. (Nashville: Publishing House of the Methodist Episcopal Church, South 1893) 116–34. The ecclesiological assumptions begged by these writers were not addressed.

94. For example, Graves, *The Great Iron Wheel*, 470–99.

95. T. Spicer, "Love-Feasts," *CAJ* (NY) 13 (23 November 1838) 1.

96. *The [Duke] Memorial Church Messenger* 1 (July 1916) 171.

97. Henry C. Sheldon, *System of Christian Doctrine* (Cincinnati: Jennings and Graham 1903; New York: Eaton and Mains 1903) 531.

98. Gilbert T. Rowe, *The Meaning of Methodism: A Study in Christian Religion* (Nashville: Cokesbury 1926) 28.

99. Leonard Smith's journal entry for 2 May 1869 seems to indicate that Wesley's sermon was read during an afternoon or evening (P.M.) celebration of the sacrament.

100. William Jessop, various entries for 1790–1791, Journal, Ms., St. George's United Methodist Church Archives, Philadelphia, PA; Ezekiel Cooper, 14 October 1792, Journal, Ms.; and Samuel A. Seaman, *Annals of New York Methodism, Being a History of the Methodist Episcopal Church in the City of New York, from A.D. 1766 to A.D. 1890* (New York: Hunt and Eaton 1892; Cincinnati: Cranston and Stowe 1892) 479. A comparable pattern is recorded for Philadelphia in William Colbert's journal of 1805 ("A Journal of the Travels of William Colbert Methodist Preacher Thro' Parts of Maryland, Pennsylvania, New York, Delaware, and Virginia in 1790 to 1838," Ts., 5:86–139, United Methodist Archives, Madison, NJ), and as late as the 1830s according to published preaching appointments for the several Baltimore stations and for Cincinnati.

101. Seaman, *Annals of New York Methodism*, 480–81. Ezekiel Cooper's biographer, George A. Phoebus, claims that by 1795 a pattern had been established of holding Communion on the first Sunday of the month at the "old church" in the morning, the "new church" in the afternoon, and following the general society meeting in the evening, but this cannot be substantiated (*Beams of Light on Early Methodism in America* [New York: Phillips and Hunt 1887; Cincinnati: Cranston and Stowe 1887] 197–98).

102. Clarke, *A Discourse on the Nature and Design of the Eucharist, or Sacrament of the Lord's Supper*, 131.

103. Porter, *A Compendium of Methodism*, 292.

104. JGC/MEC, *1844*, 31; and S.T.K., "The Lord's Supper," *CAJ (NY)* 37 (6 March 1862) 74; see also chapter 11, pp. 261, 266–67.

105. JGC/MEC, *1888*, 199; and see note 43.

106. Thomas O. Summers, Review of *The Lord's Supper* by Rev. Samuel Luckey, *MQR* 13 (October 1859) 608; see also JGC/MECS, *1866*, 118, and JGC/MECS, *1870*, 203.

107. Buckhorn Charge (Buckhorn, Morrellville, Fishhook churches), Waverly District, Illinois Conference, "The Complete Quarterly Conference Record Book Embracing a Record of Four Years; Questions Arranged According to the Revisions Made in the Discipline by the General Conference of 1922, Methodist Episcopal Church, South" for the years 1922–1926, and "The Complete Quarterly Conference Record Book Embracing a Record of Four Years; Questions Arranged According to the Revisions Made in the Discipline by the General Conference of 1934, Methodist Episcopal Church, South" for the years 1936–1939, Archives, Illinois Great Rivers Annual Conference, United Methodist Church, Bloomington, IL.

108. W. P. Strickland, *The Genius and Mission of Methodism; Embracing What Is Peculiar in Doctrine, Government, Modes of Worship, etc.* (Boston: Charles H. Peirce 1851) 98. See also Clarke, *A Discourse on the Nature and Design of the Eucharist*, 79. Strickland here is not referring to the comixing of water and wine as practiced in some Christian churches. R. J. Cooke, in commenting on the Methodist Episcopal rite in 1900, notes that Methodists should not add water to the cup, even though the custom is found in Christian antiquity (*History of the Ritual of the Methodist Episcopal Church*, 240).

109. JGC/MEC, *1860*, 395; JGC/MEC, *1864*, 265; and Methodist Episcopal Church *Discipline 1864*, appendix, xvii.

110. Summers, *Systematic Theology*, 2:413. On the use of unleavened bread, see Fisher, *Sacramental Catechism. Part Second. The Lord's Supper*, Question 32; JGC/MEC, *1892*, 214; and S. M. Merrill, *A Digest of Methodist Law; Or, Helps in the Administration of the Discipline of the Methodist Episcopal Church*, rev. ed. (Cincinnati: Jennings and Graham 1904; New York: Eaton and Mains 1904) 148.

111. Methodist Protestant L. P. Driskell recalled the "old-fashioned" method of Communion: bread without seasoning and blackberry wine (*Victory Out of Defeat* [Sanford, FL: n.p. 1950] 50–51).

112. The 1784 *Discipline* (1785), Questions 23, 61, 66, 69. The *Discipline* of 1791 that first introduced the "Directions Given to the Band Societies" included therein the prohibition "to taste no spirituous liquor, no dram of any kind, unless prescribed by a physician."

113. Field's book (New York: Phillips and Hunt 1883; Cincinnati: Walden and Stowe 1883) comprised a series of essays that had previously appeared in *MR* 64 (1882) to which was added new material. For other controversial literature, see Betty A. O'Brien, "The Lord's Supper: Fruit of the Vine or Cup of Devils," *MH* 31 (July 1993) 205–23.

114. Leonard Smith, 10 August 1862, Journal, Ts.

115. See, for example, Luther W. Peck, "Nott's Lectures on Temperance," *MR* 40 (July 1858) 450.

116. *JGC/MEC*, 1872, 384.

117. "Unfermented Wine," *WCA* 41 (27 May 1874) 161.

118. William Chazanof, *Welch's Grape Juice: From Corporation to Co-operative* (Syracuse, NY: Syracuse University Press 1977) 1–19.

119. For the intervening years, see Methodist Episcopal *Discipline* 1876, ¶484 ("General Conference recommends the use of pure, unfermented juice of the grape on Sacramental occasions"); 1880, ¶494 ("Let none but the pure, unfermented juice of the grape be used in administering the Lord's Supper, whenever practicable"); and 1884, ¶183 §5 ("see that the Stewards provide unfermented wine . . . whenever practicable"). In 1916, the "whenever practicable" was dropped.

120. Summers, *Systematic Theology*, 2:415; see also "The Two-Wine Theory," *MQR* 40 (November-December 1894) 280–82.

121. M. O. Terry, "The Poisoned Chalice," *The Physicians and Surgeons' Investigator* 8 (15 June 1887) 165.

122. Mildred Morse McEwen, *First United Methodist Church, Charlotte, North Carolina* (Charlotte, NC: First United Methodist Church 1983) 48–49.

123. Individual cups were introduced in 1905 to the congregations of First Methodist Episcopal Church, Schenectady, and Elm Park Methodist Episcopal Church, Scranton; the latter had been using Welch's product since 1874. In 1911, Richmond's Centenary Methodist Episcopal Church, South adopted the individual cups (*Centennial History of the First Methodist Episcopal Church, Schenectady, New York*, ed. William C. Kitchin, Benjamin H. Ripton, and Fred Winslow Adams [Schenectady, NY: Official Board of First Methodist Episcopal Church 1907] 103; Henry Reed Van Deusen, *Elm Park Historical Sketches* [Scranton, PA: Board of Elm Park Methodist Church 1955] 40; and Floyd S. Bennett, *Methodist Church on Shockoe Hill: A History of Centenary Methodist Church, Richmond, Virginia* [Richmond, VA: n.p. 1962] 120).

124. J. M. Buckley, "The Common Cup or Individual Cups," *CAJ (NY)* 73 (1 September 1898) 1407. Over the course of several years, editor Buckley wrote numerous columns summarizing the historic practice of the church, setting out the current debate and articulating his own views. See, for example, from *CAJ (NY)* 70 (1895), his eight-part series: 24 January, 49–50; 31 January, 66; 7 February, 81–82; 14 February, 97–98; 21 February, 114–15; 28 February, 130–31; 7 March, 146–47; and 14 March, 161–62. Betty A. O'Brien summarizes Buckley's contribution to the debate in "The Lord's Supper: Traditional Cup of Unity or Innovative Cups of Individuality," *MH* 32 (January 1994) 81–95.

125. Joseph Pullman, "The Individual Cup and the Common Cup," *CAJ (NY)* 73 (6 October 1898) 1613. For other essays promoting the individual cup, see E. W. Ryan, "Individual Communion Cups," *CAJ (NY)* 70 (21 March 1895) 180; W. C. Holliday, "The Common Cup, or Individual Cups?" *CAJ (NY)* 70 (21 March 1895) 180–81; and Joseph Pullman, "The Law of the Church Concerning the Individual Cup—A Reply," *CAJ (NY)* 76 (30 May 1901) 851–52.

126. James Albert Beebe, *The Pastoral Office: An Introduction to the Work of a Pastor* (New York: Methodist Book Concern 1923) 109.

127. Romey P. Marshall, "Liturgical Question Box," *The Pastor* 14 (September 1950) 26. For the theological and liturgical implications of intinction, see Robert F. Taft, "Communion via Intinction," *Studia Liturgica* 26 (1996) 225–36.

128. Romey P. Marshall, "Liturgical Question Box," *The Pastor* 13 (September 1949) 27; and Edward Laird Mills, "Frequency of Communion," *The Pastor* 19 (September 1955) 1.

129. See Marian Y. Adell, "Mystery—Body Lost, Body Found: The Decline, Loss, and Recovery of the Body of Christ in Methodist Worship" (Ph.D. diss., Drew University 1994), esp. 67–134.

130. The 1905 hymnal did include two hymns from the *Hymns on the Lord's Supper*, but the eucharistic associations are not identified: *HLS* #157 is in the section "Entire Consecration and Perfect Love" (#373); and the first stanza of *HLS* #155 is numbered among the doxologies (#726). A fourth eucharistic hymn (*HLS* #96) was included in the 1965 hymnal, though it was located in the section "Reformation and All Saints" (#535).

6. The Music of Methodist Worship

1. The 1737 *Collection*, which may rightly be considered the first American—and Methodist—hymn book, contributed to Wesley's ecclesiastical (and hence legal) problems in the Georgia colony because it was another example of his deviation from the practices of the Established Church: here he had introduced "into the church and service at the altar, compositions of Psalms and Hymns not inspected or authorized by any proper judicature" (Ms. Journal, 22 August 1737, *Works*, 18:555).

2. *Minutes MC* (1784), 47.

3. *Works*, 7:73–78. Wesley outlined the essentials of his understanding of the *via salutis* in his 1741 sermon "Hypocrisy at Oxford": "sorrow on account of sin; humiliation under the hand of God; hatred to sin; confession of sin; ardent supplication of the divine mercy; the love of God; ceasing from sin; firm purpose of new obedience; restitution of ill-gotten goods; forgiving our neighbour his transgressions against us; works of beneficence, or almsgiving" (*Works*, 4:397).

4. The preface to the Wesleys' *Hymns and Sacred Poems* of 1739 includes the remark that "The gospel of Christ knows of no religion, but social; no holiness but social holiness" (*Works [J]*, 14:321).

5. Among the verse by John Wesley himself were some original hymns and some translations from the German. Significant numbers of hymn texts were also included by William Cowper (Anglican), Philip Doddridge (Independent), Joseph Hart (Independent), Thomas Olivers (Methodist), and Anne Steele (Baptist).

6. Notes on Chapter 1, section 25, *Discipline with Notes*, 124.

7. Journal, 9–10 August 1768, *Works*, 22:152; see also Wesley's journal for 20 September 1757, 22 October 1768, 19 March 1778, and 8 April 1787.

8. Although Wesley expressed a restrained appreciation for the organ in Anglican worship (see Wesley's journal for 7 April 1751, 29 August 1762, and 29 March 1782), a few months before his death he wrote in a letter to Joseph Taylor that he did not object to an organ in a Methodist chapel as long as "it be played upon no more." In the same letter he demanded "that there be no more chanting in our chappel if ever they expect or desire to see me in it" ("An Unpublished Wesley Letter" [21 August 1790], *PWHS* 39 [June 1974] 144).

9. The Methodist Episcopal Church, South would take up the entire contents of "Of the Spirit and Truth of Singing," but abbreviated them in 1854. The Methodist Protestants apparently never introduced such regulations into their *Discipline*.

10. Singing schools first arose in New England in the early eighteenth century and were originally designed to improve congregational singing, but instead created a caste of trained vocalists. For those interesting in reading music, the school also became a significant social institution. Tune books compiled for the singing schools preserve some of the earliest original tunes written by American composers to accompany metrical psalms and hymns for both congregational and private gatherings. Notated folk hymns—by the early nineteenth century sometimes put into shape notes to simplify the reading of music—were introduced into tune books in the 1810s, as, for example, John Wyeth's *Repository of Sacred Music, Part Second* (1813).

11. Jesse Lee, *A Short History of the Methodists, in the United States of America; Beginning in 1766, and Continued Till 1809* (Baltimore: Magill and Clime 1910) 190. A fugue tune is one where "in at least one phrase, two or more voice parts enter non-simultaneously, with rests preceding at least one entry, in such a way as to produce overlap of text" (Nicholas Temperley and Charles G. Manns, *Fuging Tunes in the Eighteenth Century* [Detroit: Information Coordinators 1983] x).

12. See John Wesley, "Thoughts on the Power of Music" [1779], *Works*, 7:766–69.

13. Ezekiel Cooper, 3 July 1785, Journal, Ms., Garrett-Evangelical Theological Seminary Library, Evanston, IL.

14. Two tune books issued by the Wesleys, with melody only in a variety of meters, were *A Collection of Tunes, Set to Music, As They Are Commonly Sung at the Foundery* (1742) and *Select Hymns with Tunes Annext: Designed Chiefly for the Use of the People Called Methodists* (1761); the tune section of the latter work was referred to as *Sacred Melody* and included in the preface the "Directions for Singing," of which one instruction was to sing the tunes without alteration. With the 1770 edition of *Select Hymns*, the florid anthem tune "Cheshunt" was added, evidently as a concession to popular demand. A third tune book, *Sacred Harmony, or A Choice Collection of Psalm and Hymn Tunes in Two or Three Parts for the Voice, Harpsichord & Organ* (1780), showed an even greater accommodation to popular forms by the inclusion of a bass line along with the melody. Tune names from *Sacred Harmony* were associated with particular hymn texts in the fifth edition of the *Collection of Hymns for the Use of the People Called Methodists* (1786). The melodies for these tune books, some of which came from previously published sources, were drawn from metrical psalm tunes, German chorales, folk tunes, Italian opera, Handel's oratorios, and original compositions by local musicians. Tunes in the popular style of the theater also came from the hand of Methodist composer John F. Lampe, who published twenty-four of them to accompany Charles Wesley's *Hymns on the Great Festivals and Other Occasions* (1746). See Nelson F. Adams, "The Musical Sources for John Wesley's Tune-Books; The Genealogy of 148 Tunes" (S.M.D. diss., Union Theological Seminary 1973).

15. Evans's tune books were *David's Companion* (1808), *David's Companion, Or, The Methodist Standard* (1811, 1817), which was aligned with the "Large Hymn Book," and *Wesleyan Selection, Being a Supplement to David's Companion* (1820).

16. So concludes J. Roland Braithwaite in his introduction to a recent edition of Richard Allen's 1801 *A Collection of Hymns and Spiritual Songs* (Philadelphia: Mother Bethel African Methodist Episcopal Church 1987) xlvi. Further information on the "old way" is given in Nicholas Temperley, "The Old Way of Singing: Its Origins and Development," *Journal of the American Musicological Society* 34 (1981) 532–39. For accounts describing the lining of hymns in Methodist worship during this period, see George Brown, *Recollections of Itinerant Life; Including Early Reminiscences*, 4th ed. (Cincinnati: R. W. Carroll 1868) 64; and Samuel A. Seaman, *Annals of New York Methodism, Being a History of the Methodist Episcopal Church in the City of New York, from A.D. 1766 to A.D. 1890* (New York: Hunt and Eaton 1892; Cincinnati: Cranston and Stowe 1892) 471.

17. "The Journal of James Gilruth, 1834–1835 [29 August 1834]," in *Religion on the American Frontier, 1783–1840*, vol. 4: *The Methodists*, ed. William Warren Sweet (Chicago: University of Chicago Press 1946) 393.

18. George Coles, 19 January 1830, Journal, Ms., Drew University Library, Madison, NJ; see also Brown, *Recollections of Itinerant Life*, 95–97.

19. The African Methodist Episcopal Church kept the guideline in principle, although not in the exact form, until the end of the twentieth century. On the use of choirs, see Daniel A. Payne, *History of the African Methodist Episcopal Church*, ed. C. S. Smith (Nash-

ville: Publishing House of the A. M. E. Sunday-School Union 1891; repr. New York: Johnson Reprint Corporation 1968) 452–59.

20. "The Journal of James Gilruth, 1834–1835 [18 March 1835]," in *Religion on the American Frontier, 1783–1840*, 4:428.

21. The hymnal figured among the books required in the Methodist Episcopal Church, South for the ministerial Course of Study. Regarding the method for examination on the hymn book, it was proposed that consideration be given to the book's arrangement: "parts, sections, sub-sections, consecutive order of the hymns; as they are all arranged in philosophical order, with headings suggestive of the particular subjects, and specially framed to assist in selection for particular purposes and occasions" ("The Hymn-Book," MQR 14 [July 1860] 466).

22. The remaining headings, in order, are as follows: Justification by Faith, Prayer and Intercession, Prayer and Watchfulness, Christian Warfare, Christian Zeal, Trusting in Grace and Providence, Rejoicing and Praise, Christian Fellowship, Christian Perfection, Prospect of Heaven, Formal Religion, Backsliding, The Church, Baptism, Lord's Supper, Love Feast, Family Worship, Holy Scriptures, Pastoral, Spread of the Gospel, Dedication, Birth Day, Thanksgiving, Nativity, New Year's, The Sabbath, Sabbath Schools, Children and Youth, Missions, Anti-Slavery, Temperance, Seamen, Peace, Afflictions, Ministers in Sickness and Death, Death and Funeral, Resurrection, Second Advent, General Judgment, Miscellaneous, and Doxologies.

23. JGC/MEC, 1864, 46; and JGC/MEC, 1868, 58–59, 500–501.

24. Some books with texts and tunes, considered supplementary to the authorized hymnals and tune books, had appeared before the 1850s: e.g., *The Wesleyan Psalmist; Or, Songs of Canaan*, compiled by M. L. Scudder of the New England Conference and first published by Methodist Episcopal agents in 1842, printed tunes harmonized in two and three parts along with hymn texts.

25. "On Singing in Public Worship," CAJ (NY) 22 (13 October 1847) 161; Andrew Wheeler, "The Meaning of Our Music," CAJ (NY) 40 (7 September 1865) 281. For a study of tune preferences, see Terry L. Baldridge, "Evolving Tastes in Hymntunes of the Methodist Episcopal Church in the Nineteenth Century" (Ph.D. diss., University of Kansas 1982); and for an inventory of the most frequently used tunes, see Fred Kimball Graham, " 'With One Heart and One Voice': A Core Repertory of Hymn Tunes Published for Use in the Methodist Episcopal Church in the United States, 1808–1878" (Ph.D. diss., Drew University 1991) 55–148.

26. Leonard Smith, 9 December 1867, Journal, Ts., Archives, Illinois Great Rivers Annual Conference, United Methodist Church, Bloomington, IL.

27. George G. Smith, *The Life and Times of George Foster Pierce, D.D., LL.D.* (Sparta, GA: Hancock 1888) 537. On "promiscuous sittings," see later chapter 10, p. 245.

28. W. P. Strickland, *The Genius and Mission of Methodism; Embracing What Is Peculiar in Doctrine, Government, Modes of Worship, etc.* (Boston: Charles H. Peirce 1851) 107.

29. "Methodist Psalmody," CAJ (NY) 32 (26 February 1857) 34; cf. Bostwick Hawley, "Church Music," MR 49 (October 1867) 514.

30. JGC/MEC, 1840, 73; cf. JGC/MEC, 1848, 36; Pastoral Address, JGC/MEC, 1852, 160; JGC/MEC, 1868, 115.

31. JGC/MECS (1846), 116 and JGC/MECS, 1874, 571, also p. 457; cf. JGC/MECS, 1858, 439.

32. See, for example, Helen M. Waggoner, *For Worship and For Service: 1931–1963* (Indianapolis, IN: North Methodist Church 1963) 17; and John Theodore Oakey, "History of the Methodist Protestant Church of Lynchburg, Virginia, 1828–1939," in *A History of the*

First United Methodist Church of Lynchburg, Virginia, 1828–1988, with Genealogical Index and Descriptions of the Church Archives, ed. James Siddons (Bowie, MD: Heritage Books 1992) 12.

33. Twelve other objections to choirs were identified in D. F. Newton, "Church Music," *The Earnest Christian and Golden Rule* 3 (May 1862) 138–41.

34. Thomas O. Summers, "The Organ," *MQR* 19 (April 1882) 358–67.

35. The vocalion, "constructed upon the principles of the human voice," was advertised in Methodist periodicals; see, for example, *EH* 2 (7 November 1891) 12.

36. Wyatt Brown, *Early Methodism in Greenville, North Carolina, and a History of the Jarvis Memorial United Methodist Church*, ed. John D. Ebbs (Greenville, NC: Jarvis Memorial United Methodist Church 1978) 63–64.

37. The 1955 Free Methodist *Discipline* sets out in four statements under paragraph 93 the expectations about music, including a provision about instruments in worship, from which can be inferred the volatility of the subject: "The use of instrumental music is left to the decision of the local church or other ecclesiastical unit conducting worship, but change of policy shall require a majority vote and may not be considered twice in the same conference year." The changes in Free Methodist policy on this matter are chronicled in Leslie R. Marston, *From Age to Age a Living Witness: A Historical Interpretation of Free Methodism's First Century* (Winona Lake, IN: Light and Life 1960) 343–44.

38. F. D. Hemenway, "How Shall We Improve Our Congregational Singing?" *Zion's Herald* 55 (3 January 1878) 1; cf. the Bishops' Address, *JGC/MECS*, 1902, 24.

39. Henry M. Turner, *The Genius and Theory of Methodist Polity, Or, The Machinery of Methodism* (Philadelphia: Publication Department, A. M. E. Church 1885) 217.

40. Daniel Curry, "Reading the Hymns," *MR* 67 (January 1885) 108–110.

41. For criticism of jazz as church music, see, for example the *Journal of the One-Hundredth Session of the North Carolina Annual Conference of the Methodist Protestant Church*, 1925 (n.p.: C. W. Bates 1925) 43, 79; cf. Alleen Moon, *Worship; One of the Program Manuals of the Young People's Division* (Nashville: Publishing House of the Methodist Episcopal Church, South 1932) 27.

42. For the contributions of women and women's issues to gospel song, see June Hadden Hobbs, *"I Sing for I Cannot Be Silent": The Feminization of American Hymnody, 1870–1920* (Pittsburgh: University of Pittsburgh Press 1997).

43. "To testify to the world the essential unity of the two great branches of Episcopal Methodism," the 1905 *Methodist Hymnal* had been a joint production of the Methodist Episcopal Church and the Methodist Episcopal Church, South.

44. Cf. Address "The New Methodist Hymnal" by commission member John W. Langdale, *JGC/MEC*, 1936, 1254–59.

45. The Wesleyan Church was formed in 1968 by the union of the Wesleyan Methodist Connection and the Pilgrim Holiness Church.

7. The Solemnization of Christian Marriage

1. John Wesley, *Thoughts on Marriage and a Single Life* (Bristol: Printed by Felix Farley 1743) 3–9.

2. These issues were addressed in *Thoughts on Marriage and a Single Life*, in Wesley's revision of that work found in *Thoughts on a Single Life* (London: Printed and sold at the Foundery 1765) 5–7, 10–11, and in "A Thought upon Marriage," *Arminian Magazine* 8 (September 1785) 533–35.

3. Elizabeth Connor, *Methodist Trail Blazer: Philip Gatch, 1751–1834; His Life in Maryland, Virginia and Ohio* (Rutland, VT: Academy Books 1970) 86.

4. Ezekiel Cooper, 22 January 1792, Journal, Ms., Garrett-Evangelical Theological Seminary Library, Evanston, IL. In his journal for 5 January 1790, Asbury bemoaned the injury caused by the marriage of young people to unbelievers (*JLFA*, 1:619).

5. Generally, by law, parental consent was no longer necessary at age twenty-one for males and at either eighteen or twenty-one for females. See George Elliott Howard, *A History of Matrimonial Institutions*, vol. 2 (Chicago: University of Chicago Press 1904; repr. New York: Humanities Press 1964) 396–97, 429–33, 472–73.

6. Letter from Robert Lindsay to Edward Dromgoole, 18 May 1784, Ms., Southern Historical Collection, University of North Carolina Library, Chapel Hill, NC.

7. Robert Emory, in *History of the Discipline of the Methodist Episcopal Church* ([New York: Lane and Scott 1851] 188), is incorrect in stating that this change first occurred in the 1789 *Discipline*.

8. For these and other details of Wesley's revision of the 1662 marriage rite, see Karen B. Westerfield Tucker, " 'Till Death Us Do Part': The Rites of Marriage and Burial Prepared by John Wesley and Their Development in the Methodist Episcopal Church, 1784–1939" (Ph.D. diss., University of Notre Dame 1992) 103–69.

9. John 2:2, *NT Notes*.

10. Sermon, "On Friendship with the World," 25, *Works*, 3:138.

11. The 1789 Prayer Book revision went further than that of the American Methodists, for all material after the first blessing (accompanying the procession to the Lord's table in the 1662 Prayer Book) was deleted. The Methodists even kept the prayer "O God, who by thy mighty power" that included the much-debated "sacramental" reference to marriage as an "excellent mystery."

12. See Wesley's *Advice to the People Called Methodist with Regard to Dress* (1760, 1780), and the sermons "On Dress" and "The Danger of Increasing Riches."

13. See 1792 *Discipline*, Section 9; also Jesse Lee, *A Short History of the Methodists, in the United States of America; Beginning in 1766, and Continued Till 1809* (Baltimore: Magill and Clime 1810) 185; and Nathan Bangs, *A History of the Methodist Episcopal Church*, 3d ed., vol. 1 (New York: T. Mason and G. Lane 1840) 348–49.

14. For example, Daniel Wise's *Bridal Greetings: A Marriage Gift, in Which the Mutual Duties of Husband and Wife Are Familiarly Illustrated and Enforced* (New York: Carlton and Phillips 1854) and *The Young Lady's Counsellor: Or, Outlines and Illustrations of the Sphere, the Duties, and the Dangers of Young Women* (New York: Carlton and Lanahan 1869; Cincinnati: Hitchcock and Walden 1869); R. Donkersley's *Facts about Wives and Mothers* (New York: Carlton and Lanahan 1869; Cincinnati: Hitchcock and Walden 1869); and the subtle or direct marriage advice found in the *Ladies' Repository*.

15. *The Journals of the Rev. Thomas Morrell*, ed. Michael J. McKay (Rutland, VT: Academy Books, for the Historical Society, Northern New Jersey Conference, United Methodist Church 1984) 40; cf. W. D. W. Schureman, "Thoughts on Marriage" in *The Semi-Centenary and the Retrospection of the African Methodist Episcopal Church*, ed. Daniel Alexander Payne (Baltimore: Sherwood 1866; repr. Freeport, NY: Books for Libraries Press 1972) 120.

16. S. W. Cope, "Marriage and the Home," *MQR* 37 (July 1893) 262.

17. Diary entry of Robert E. Taylor for 16 January 1879, cited in Taylor Kinsfolk Association at Tabernacle Church, *The Taylors of Tabernacle: The History of a Family* (Brownsville, TN: Tabernacle Historical Committee 1957) 271.

18. Cited from *The Methodist Pocket Hymn-Book. Revised and Improved. Designed as a Constant Companion for the Pious of All Denominations*, 34th ed. (New-York: Published by Ezekiel Cooper and John Wilson 1807) #317.

19. The official Methodist Protestant rite used from 1830 to 1870 followed the pattern of brief introduction, final publication of the banns, exhortation, declaration of intention and consent, prayer, "Those whom God hath joined," and pronouncement of marriage. In 1870, a truncated version of the 1792 opening exhortation began the service; the Methodist Protestant statement on mutuality was entirely removed, but no "active" marriage vow was introduced. The woman's promise to obey was retained until 1892.

20. Petitions suggesting the switch of "man" to "husband" were put forward periodically at sessions of the Methodist Episcopal Church, South's General Conference from 1854 until the change was made in 1914.

21. Review of *Ritual of the Methodist Episcopal Church*, MR 46 (October 1864) 687.

22. "The Change in Our Marriage Ceremony," *CAJ (NY)* 43 (20 February 1868) 58.

23. JGC/MEC, 1868, 184.

24. Summers also asserted that "the woman is first asked if she will obey and serve her husband as submission on her part is necessary to conjugal fellowship." He substantiated his claim by reference to Scripture: Genesis 3:16; 1 Corinthians 14:34; Ephesians 5:22–24; Colossians 3:18; Titus 2:4,5; and 1 Peter 3:1–6. See Thomas O. Summers, *Commentary on the Ritual of the Methodist Episcopal Church, South* (Nashville: A. H. Redford for the M. E. Church, South 1873) 60.

25. Nolan Harmon noted prophetically that although the Methodist Episcopal Church, South retained the obedience language at the time of publication for his 1926 study on Methodist rites, the words were "often omitted by the Southern ministry" and that undoubtedly they would be "discarded in time" (*The Rites and Ritual of Episcopal Methodism, with Particular Reference to the Rituals of the Methodist Episcopal Church and the Methodist Episcopal Church, South, Respectively* [Nashville: Publishing House of the Methodist Episcopal Church, South 1926] 266). The Methodist Episcopal Church, South may have eliminated "obey" and "serve" from the question of consent (the words had already been deleted from the marriage vow—which itself had been deleted in 1854 and restored in 1910) after witnessing the debates on the topic that ensued from the General Convention of the Protestant Episcopal Church; the Episcopalians altered their marriage rite in the revision of 1928.

26. The form of the Lord's Prayer was amended in 1864 with the addition of the doxological conclusion; resolutions presented in following years to restore the prayer to the "language of Jesus as given in St. Matthew, vi, 9–13" were unmet (JGC/MEC, 1868, 138; and JGC/MEC, 1876, 234).

27. "Rebecca was not faithful when she terribly imposed upon her husband Isaac, made her son Jacob lie to him in word and deed, made Esau a murderer in heart, broke up her home, and drove both of her sons into exile" (H. J. Zelley, "Form of Marriage," *CAJ (NY)* 67 [5 May 1892] 293). The revision of the rite proposed in 1912 eliminated the reference to Isaac and Rebecca with the rationale that though the biblical pair were "good people," "we do not know that in all respects they ought to be especially commended in our marriage service" (General Conference of the Methodist Episcopal Church, *Daily Christian Advocate* [24 May 1912] 604–605; and [30 May 1912] 795).

28. Thomas B. Neely, who had many causes for complaint regarding the 1916 revision, found in the deletion of the reference to Isaac and Rebecca an example of one of his greatest criticisms: the widespread excision of Old Testament references from the entire Ritual of the Methodist Episcopal Church (*The Revised Ritual of 1916* [Philadelphia: E. A. Yeakel, Agent; Methodist Episcopal Book Store 1920] 55, 97).

29. Margaret Deland, a popular writer during the early twentieth century, believed female selfishness was the cause of the demise of the family. She wrote: "The individualist believes

that happiness is the purpose of marriage,—whereas happiness is only an incident of marriage. The purpose of marriage is the protection of the family idea. Happiness and marriage may go together . . . But if the incident of happiness is lost, duty remains! the obligation of contract remains; marriage remains . . . Marriage is civilization's method of remaining civilized" ("The Change in the Feminine Ideal," *The Atlantic Monthly* 105 [March 1910] 296; cf. "Shall We Have a New Code of Marriage?" WCA 72 [24 January 1906] 4).

30. *The Standard Catechism of the Methodist Episcopal Church and the Methodist Episcopal Church, South* (Cincinnati: Jennings and Graham 1905) 16; and S. M. Merrill, *A Digest of Methodist Law; Or, Helps in the Administration of the Discipline of the Methodist Episcopal Church,* ed. R. J. Cooke (Cincinnati: Jennings and Graham 1908; New York: Eaton and Mains 1908) 149.

31. General Conference of the Methodist Episcopal Church, *Daily Christian Advocate* (9 May 1916) 137 and (10 May 1916) 153.

32. Nolan B. Harmon claimed that several persons preparing the rite to be approved in 1939 objected to the "dreadful day of judgment" language in the historic charge to the couple (10 March 1990, tape-recorded interview by author, Atlanta, GA).

33. Even with the familial emphases, the sacred character of the wedding remained a paramount issue, as attested by criticism of the growing popularity of a burlesque of the marriage ceremony sometimes performed as a church fund raiser—the "mock" wedding. See, for example, Paul F. Wohlgemuth, "The 'Mock' Wedding Practice," *The Pastor* 15 (December 1951) 16–17; and Frank R. Greer, "Some Things Are Sacred," *The Pastor* 15 (February 1952) 28.

34. James Albert Beebe, *The Pastoral Office: An Introduction to the Work of a Pastor* (New York: Methodist Book Concern 1923) 110. Spenser B. Meeser, in 1927, also condemned the laxity of clergy and the state in contributing to "hasty," "secret," and "easy" marriages, and consequently, to divorce. An appropriate remedy, Meeser believed, was the reinstatement of the banns or some public announcement of intention to marry as well as premarital conversations on the moral implications of marriage ("Divorce and Remarriage," MR 110 [November 1927] 854–57). Concerns such as these had existed for some time; a comparable complaint was made about New York ministers who knew little or nothing about the couples they married ("New York Correspondence," *Nashville Christian Advocate* 21 [24 September 1857] 2).

35. The statement was continued in the Methodist marriage rites published in the *Book of Worship* of 1945 and that of 1965, and was introduced into the African Methodist Episcopal Church's practice through its optional text first issued in 1960.

36. JGC/MEC *(1796),* 28; the approved text was first printed in 1798 in *Discipline with Notes* (p. 157) with the accompanying note (N.B.) as part of the commentary. The original accompanying note (N.B.) approved in 1796 was not published beyond the 1798 *Discipline.*

37. G. A. Raybold, *Reminiscences of Methodism in West Jersey* (New York: Lane and Scott 1849) 27–28.

38. JGC/MEC *(1808),* 95; cf. JGC/MEC *(1800),* 43.

39. See, for example, S. Olin Garrison, *Probationer's Hand-book: Religious, Historical, Doctrinal, Disciplinary, and Practical,* rev. ed. (New York: Eaton and Mains 1896; Cincinnati: Jennings and Pye 1896) 71–72.

40. Thomas A. Morris, *Miscellany: Consisting of Essays, Biographical Sketches, and Notes of Travel* (Cincinnati: L. Swormstedt and J. H. Power 1852) 57–66.

41. Daniel P. Kidder, ed., *The Minister's Study, and Scenes Connected with It* (New York: Lane and Scott 1849) 16–17.

42. Neither the Methodist Protestants nor the Wesleyans included a provision for parental consent in their first or any *Discipline;* the Methodist Episcopal Church, South

dropped it in 1866, and so it was not transmitted to the Colored (Christian) Methodist Episcopal Church.

43. Carl N. Degler, *At Odds: Women and the Family in America from the Revolution to the Present* (New York: Oxford University Press 1980) 10–12.

44. "A Chapter on Marriages," *The Methodist* 16 (16 October 1875) 658; cf. Benjamin Lakin, 26 December 1802, Journal, Ms. on microfilm, Washington University Library, St. Louis, MO.

45. A Ritual published in 1864 bears the handwritten entry, "who giveth," following the questions of consent. This entry was probably made before 1916; the volume was acquired by the library of the Garrett Biblical Institute (now Garrett-Evangelical Seminary) in 1915 from the estate of the Reverend William Goodfellow. A comparable insertion with the question handwritten in full is found in an 1870 edition of the Methodist Protestant *Constitution and Discipline*, although its approximate dating cannot be ascertained.

46. Summers, *Commentary on the Ritual*, 61. Regarding the ritual of the Methodist Episcopal Church, South (which never officially printed the giving away in the text), Harmon concluded that since the woman is "tacitly, if not verbally" given away, "it is perhaps wise to insert this old form here, making it optional" (Harmon, *The Rites and Ritual of Episcopal Methodism*, 266).

47. Bishops' Address, JGC/MECS, *1886*, 29.

48. For a commentary on dancing, see Josephus Anderson, *Our Church: A Manual for Members and Probationers of the Methodist Episcopal Church, South*, ed. Thomas O. Summers (Nashville: Southern Methodist Publishing House 1860) 278–93.

49. For example, Benjamin Lakin, 9 February 1814, Journal, Ms.; see also the *Autobiography of Peter Cartwright* (repr. Nashville: Abingdon 1984) 36.

50. Entry for 17 February 1835, "The Journal of James Gilruth, 1834–1835," in *Religion on the American Frontier, 1783–1840*, vol. 4: *The Methodists*, ed. William Warren Sweet (Chicago: University of Chicago Press 1946) 424.

51. Catherine Livingston Garrettson, 30 June 1793, Diary, Ms., United Methodist Archives, Madison, NJ. The unspecified "Covenant Hymn" likely refers to the Charles Wesley text "Come, let us use the grace divine."

52. John B. Matthias, Memoirs, Ms., United Methodist Archives, Madison, NJ.

53. *Life and Observations of Rev. E. F. Newell* (Worcester: C. W. Ainsworth 1847) 139–40.

54. George Brown, *Recollections of Itinerant Life: Including Early Reminiscences*, 4th ed. (Cincinnati: R. W. Carroll 1868) 86–87.

55. J. R. Graves, *The Great Iron Wheel; Or, Republicanism Backwards and Christianity Reversed*, 7th ed. (Nashville: Graves, Marks, and Rutland 1855; New York: Sheldon, Lamport, and Co. 1855) 336–39.

56. In 1879, J. H. Potts included in *Pastor and People; Or, Methodism in the Field* matters related to dress under the heading of "obsolete customs" ([New York: Phillips and Hunt 1879; Cincinnati: Hitchcock and Walden 1879] 183–185). Yet still the regulations for dress were published in 1896 in Garrison's *Probationer's Hand-book*, between the rules related to tobacco and amusements (p. 73).

57. Charles A. Thiel, 25 February 1903, Diary, Ms., United Methodist Archives, Madison, NJ. In 1903, Thiel, a deacon in the Northern German Conference, was stationed in North Dakota.

58. See the comments in "Sunday Marriages," *CAJ (NY)* 47 (25 January 1872) 30.

59. Such is the rationale given by Paul W. Hoon, "The Order for the Service of Marriage," in *Companion to the Book of Worship*, ed. William F. Dunkle, Jr. and Joseph D. Quillian, Jr. (Nashville: Abingdon 1970) 77.

60. J. Bernard Dryfield, "Wedding Music and the Marriage Service," *The Pastor* 18 (May 1955) 29.

61. A. Atwood, "The Golden Wedding," *CAJ (NY)* 37 (30 October 1862) 346.

62. "Golden Anniversary," *WCA* 72 (14 February 1906) 20.

8. Methodist Funerals

1. James J. Farrell, *Inventing the American Way of Death, 1830–1920* (Philadelphia: Temple University Press 1980) 44–98.

2. Philippe Ariès, *Western Attitudes toward Death: From the Middle Ages to the Present*, trans. Patricia M. Ranum (Baltimore: Johns Hopkins University Press 1974) 55.

3. Charles O. Jackson, "Death Shall Have No Dominion: The Passing of the World of the Dead in America," in *Death and Dying: Views from Many Cultures*, ed. Richard A. Kalish (Farmingdale, NY: Baywood 1980) 48–49.

4. Vanderlyn R. Pine makes two significant observations about the development of the funeral industry and the church's role at burial: "An important reason for his [the undertaker's] rise to prominence was the church's unwillingness or inability to maintain authority over all aspects of the burial process" and "since the church did not encourage the development of special rooms for the care of the dead, funeral directors found an additional reason to develop facilities to house such activities" (*Caretaker of the Dead: The American Funeral Director* [New York: Irvington 1975] 16, 18).

5. A reprint of guidelines from 1917 is found in Frank A. Heywood, "The Etiquette of Mourning Up-to-Date," *American Funeral Director* 96 (1973) 42–43.

6. Letter to Charles Wesley, 28 June 1755, *Works*, 26:565; and Letter to Joseph Benson, 19 May 1783, *LJW*, 7:179. See, for example, Joseph Pilmore, 17 December 1772, *The Journal of Joseph Pilmore*, ed. Frederick E. Maser and Howard T. Maag (Philadelphia: Message Publishing for the Historical Society of the Philadelphia Annual Conference of the United Methodist Church 1969) 170; and Journal, 9 February 1780, *JLFA*, 1:335.

7. Nathan Bangs claimed that the Methodist preachers did not perform the burial rite prior to 1784, yet Asbury's journal records several entries in which he "read the burial service." See Nathan Bangs, *The Life of the Rev. Freeborn Garrettson: Compiled from His Printed and Manuscript Journals, and Other Authentic Documents* (New York: J. Emory and B. Waugh 1832) 125; and Journal for 26 January 1780, 17 February 1780, 12 December 1780, and 23/24 May 1783, *JLFA*, 1:332, 336, 393, 441.

8. *Minutes MC* (1777), 15. Methodists in Great Britain later established a similar policy, which was recorded in their Minutes of 1786.

9. Notes on Chapter 1, section 22, *Discipline with Notes*, 118. As was also true with baptism and marriage, the stipulation (explicit or implicit) that ministers should not make a charge for burial remained with the denominations, with each eventually dropping the restriction against receiving a monetary gift.

10. Sermon, " 'Awake, Thou That Sleepest,' " 1.8–9, *Works*, 1:145; Sermon, "Justification by Faith," 1.4–9, *Works*, 1:184–87; and Wesley's response to the Unitarian John Taylor in "The Doctrine of Original Sin, according to Scripture, Reason, and Experience," *Works [J]*, 5:192–464.

11. Sermon, "Death and Deliverance," 4, *Works*, 4:207. See also Sermon, "The Way to the Kingdom," 1.10, *Works*, 1:223; and Sermon, "The Spirit of Bondage and Adoption," 3.4, *Works*, 1:262. See also the Charles Wesley hymn "Ah, lovely appearance of death!"

12. Sermon, "Death and Deliverance," 4, *Works*, 4:208. See also Sermon, "The Trouble and Rest of Good Men," 2.4–6, *Works*, 3:539–41.

13. Sermon, "On Love," 3.5, *Works*, 4:386–87.

14. Job 26:5, *OT Notes;* Luke 23:43, *NT Notes;* Sermon, "The Important Question," 2.4–5, *Works,* 3:186–87; Sermon, "Dives and Lazarus," 1.3–5, *Works,* 4:7–9; Sermon, "On the Discoveries of Faith," 8–9, *Works,* 4:32–33; Sermon, "On Faith," 4–6, 10–11, *Works,* 4: 189–92, 195–97.

15. "Popery Calmly Considered," 2.5–6, *Works [J],* 10:144–45; cf. Letter to George Blackall, 25 February 1783, *LJW,* 7:168.

16. *Works,* 7:140. John Wesley's position, exemplary of an "Eastern Orthodox view," stood counter to the popular Anglican position that, according to Clarence Bence, had developed from an interpretation of the Pauline desire to be "present with the Lord" as referring immediately to heaven itself. Bence may be correct when he surmises that conformity to biblical chronology may be the motivating factor for Wesley's delineation of the intermediate state. See "John Wesley's Teleological Hermeneutic" (Ph.D. diss., Emory University 1981) 188; also Albert Outler's note 24 in Sermon, "Dives and Lazarus," *Works,* 4: 9.

17. Romans 1:4 and Matthew 27:52–53, *NT Notes.* See also a letter to the Moravian Church recorded in Wesley's journal for 3 September 1741 (*Works,* 19:222).

18. *Works,* 7:149–50; cf. Hymn nos. 53–55, 57–64, *Works,* 7:146–61.

19. Letter to Mrs. Martha Hall, 17 November 1742, *Works,* 26:90–91; cf. Sermon, "On Mourning for the Dead," *Works,* 4:237–43.

20. Letter to Miss March, 5 July 1768, *LJW,* 5:96; Letter to Hannah Ball, 23 May 1773, *LJW,* 6:27; Letter to Christopher Hopper, 16 March 1777, *LJW,* 6:259; and Journal, 23 January 1781, *JJW,* 6:303.

21. Luke 16:22, *NT Notes.* Comparing Scottish funerals with those of England, Wesley wrote: "The English does honour to human nature, and even to the poor remains, that were once a temple of the Holy Ghost! But when I see in Scotland a coffin put into the earth, and covered up without a word spoken it reminds me of what was spoken concerning Jehoiakim, 'He shall be buried with the burial of an ass' " (Journal, 20 May 1774, *JJW,* 6: 20).

22. John C. Bowmer refuted the contention made by W. H. Holden (in *John Wesley in Company with High Churchmen,* 2d rev. ed. [London: Church Press 1870] 112) that early Methodist funerals were eucharistic, citing the absence of concrete data. However, the practice of administering the sacrament to the sick and dying was seen by Bowmer as a regular and significant aspect of Methodist pastoral ministry (*The Sacrament of the Lord's Supper in Early Methodism* [Westminster: Dacre 1951] 143–46).

23. For additional explanations about these and other alterations made by Wesley, see Karen B. Westerfield Tucker, " 'Till Death Us Do Part': The Rites of Marriage and Burial Prepared by John Wesley and Their Development in the Methodist Episcopal Church, 1784–1939" (Ph.D. diss., University of Notre Dame 1992) 185–239.

24. "Ought We to Separate from the Church of England?" (3.8), *Works,* 9:572.

25. John Dowden's suggestion, that the last six lines of Coverdale's poem exhibit close affinity with the version of *Media vita* in the 1549 Prayer Book, has been generally accepted. See *The Workmanship of the Prayer Book in Its Literary and Liturgical Aspects* (London: Methuen 1899) 162–64, 233–34.

26. See, for example, Sermon, " 'Awake, Thou That Sleepest,' " 1.9, *Works,* 1:145; and Job 14:10, *OT Notes.*

27. For example, Journal, 21 August 1785 and 26 January 1790, *JLFA,* 1:493, 622; and Richard Whatcoat, 25 December 1790, Journal, Ms., Garrett-Evangelical Theological Seminary Library, Evanston, IL.

28. *Minutes MC* (1809), 444; cf. Journal, 16 March 1790, *JLFA,* 1:628.

29. *Nashville Christian Advocate* 21 (17 June 1858) 1.

30. *Centennial History of the First Methodist Episcopal Church, Schenectady, New York,* ed. William C. Kitchin, Benjamin H. Ripton, and Fred Winslow Adams (Schenectady, NY: Official Board of First Methodist Episcopal Church 1907) 57–58.

31. William Colbert, 19 December 1805, "A Journal of the Travels of William Colbert, Methodist Preacher, Thro' Parts of Maryland, Pennsylvania, New York, Delaware, and Virginia in 1790 to 1838," Ts., 5:129, United Methodist Archives, Madison, NJ. The hymn "A solemn march we make" was included in Richard Allen's *A Collection of Hymns & Spiritual Songs* (1801).

32. References may be found in the prayer to 2 Corinthians 5:10, *Media vita,* Job 14:1, 1 Peter 1:19, Titus 3:7, Romans 5:25, John 11:25, James 1:17, Titus 2:13, John 5:25, 29, Revelation 2:11; 20:6, Matthew 25:34, 1 Thessalonians 4:13, and Job 1:21.

33. *Life and Observations of Rev. E. F. Newell* (Worcester: C. W. Ainsworth 1847) 159.

34. "Death," *The Methodist Protestant* 4 (20 January 1838) 236.

35. Journal, 29 October 1797, *JLFA,* 2:137. In 1788, a comparable theme had been taken up by James Meacham in a sermon taken from the burial rite's reading of Revelation 14: 13 and developed under four points: "show the certainty of death"; "what is implied in being in the Lord"; "how they are blessed and why they are called blessed"; and "the blessed as consequence of dying in the Lord" (22 August 1788, Journal, Ms., Special Collections Library, Duke University Library, Durham, NC).

36. George Coles, 30 March 1826, Journal, Drew University Library, Madison, NJ.

37. Maria Dyer Davies, 2 March 1853, Diary, Ms., Special Collections Library, Duke University Library, Durham, NC; and, for example, *The Journals of the Rev. Thomas Morrell,* ed. Michael J. McKay (Rutland, VT: Academy Books, for the Historical Society, Northern New Jersey Conference, United Methodist Church 1984) 46.

38. *Minutes MC* (1807), 389.

39. Samuel A. Seaman, *Annals of New York Methodism, Being a History of the Methodist Episcopal Church in the City of New York, from A.D. 1766 to A.D. 1890* (New York: Hunt and Eaton 1892; Cincinnati: Cranston and Stowe 1892) 477.

40. Joseph B. Wakely, *The Ethics of Funerals: A Vindication of the Methodist Episcopal Church and of the Rev. J. B. Wakely against the Slanders of the New-York Churchman with Regard to the Funeral of William Poole* (New York: Printed 200 Mulberry-Street, and for sale by the Principal Booksellers 1855) 20.

41. See, for example, Joseph Travis, *Autobiography of the Rev. Joseph Travis, A.M.,* ed. Thomas O. Summers (Nashville: E. Stevenson and F. A. Owen, Agents, for the Methodist Episcopal Church, South 1856) 93. Wesley had deleted the rubric from the 1662 burial rite prohibiting use of the service for suicides, yet in the first half of the nineteeenth century, some Methodist ministers regarded those who took their own life as unworthy of Christian burial.

42. Thomas O. Summers, "The Pastoral Office," *MQR* 15 (July 1861) 446.

43. Thomas N. Ralston, *Elements of Divinity* (Louisville, KY: Published by E. Stevenson for the Methodist Episcopal Church, South 1851) 444–47.

44. Thomas O. Summers, "Signs of the Times," *MQR* 19 (April 1882) 380–81, and see also his *Systematic Theology: A Complete Body of Wesleyan Arminian Divinity,* vol. 1, rev. John J. Tigert (Nashville: Publishing House of the Methodist Episcopal Church, South 1888) 331–84; cf. Amos Binney and Daniel Steele, *Binney's Theological Compend Improved, Containing a Synopsis of the Evidences, Doctrines, Morals, and Institutions of Christianity* (Cincinnati: Curts and Jennings 1875; New York: Eaton and Mains 1875) 135–47; and Daniel D. Whedon, "The Resurrection," in *Essays, Reviews, and Discourses,* ed. J. S. Whedon and D. A. Whedon (New York: Phillips and Hunt 1887; Cincinnati: Cranston and Stowe 1887) 328–41.

45. John Miley, *Systematic Theology*, vol. 2, Library of Biblical and Theological Literature, ed. George R. Crooks and John F. Hurst, vol. 6 (New York: Hunt and Eaton 1894; Cincinnati: Cranston and Curts 1894) 93–96, 428–29, 474–75.

46. Olin Alfred Curtis, *The Christian Faith: Personally Given in a System of Doctrine* (New York: Methodist Book Concern 1905) 287–88, 291, 296–99, 453–54.

47. Georgia Harkness, *Understanding the Christian Faith* (New York: Abingdon-Cokesbury 1947) 141–44.

48. See Ann Douglas, "Heaven Our Home: Consolation Literature in the Northern United States, 1830–1880," *American Quarterly* 26 (December 1974) 496–515.

49. Jesse S. Gilbert, "The Fear of Death," *The Methodist* 22 (6 August 1881) 4.

50. Cited in Taylor Kinsfolk Association at Tabernacle Church, *The Taylors of Tabernacle: The History of a Family* (Brownsville, TN: Tabernacle Historical Committee 1957) 304.

51. "Funeral Reform," *The Methodist* 16 (20 February 1875) 121.

52. For example, J. H. Potts, *Pastor and People; Or, Methodism in the Field* (New York: Phillips and Hunt 1879; Cincinnati: Hitchcock and Walden 1879) 179–80.

53. James Albert Beebe, *The Pastoral Office: An Introduction to the Work of a Pastor* (New York: Methodist Book Concern 1923) 112. For a detailed excursus on the expected roles of undertaker, minister, the bereaved, and friends at a funeral in the first decade of the twentieth century, see Joseph N. Greene, *The Funeral: Its Conduct and Properties* (Cincinnati: Jennings and Graham 1905; New York: Eaton and Mains 1905).

54. Russell L. Dicks, "Questions of the Month," *The Pastor* 11 (February 1948) 20.

55. In recounting his grandmother's funeral, Charles Thiel of North Dakota noted that his "text was Rev. 14:13. The spirit helped me to deliver a short fitting sermon. We sang some songs which Grandma always loved to hear and were dismissed quietly" (Charles A. Thiel, 11 February 1903, Diary, Ms., United Methodist Archives, Madison, NJ).

56. For examples by Methodist authors and publishers, some of which also included sample funeral addresses, see W. C. Knapp, *Funeral Services: Being a Collection and Arrangement of the Scriptures Suitable for Funerals, with Appropriate Hymns and Tunes* (Peoria: Franks 1874); C. E. Mandeville, *Minister's Manual and Pocket Ritual: A Ready Help in Time of Need for the Sick-Room, Funerals, etc., Together with Full Ritual for Marriage, Baptism, the Lord's Supper, etc.*, rev. ed. (Cincinnati: Jennings and Graham 1904; New York: Eaton and Mains 1904); Jesse Halsey, *A Living Hope: Suggestions for Funeral Services* (New York: Abingdon-Cokesbury 1932); William H. Leach, ed., *The Cokesbury Funeral Manual* (Nashville: Cokesbury 1932); Earl Daniels, *The Funeral Message: Its Preparation and Significance* (Nashville: Cokesbury 1937); and Nolan B. Harmon, ed., *The Pastor's Ideal Funeral Manual* (New York: Abingdon 1942).

57. Job 14:1–2; Psalm 103:13–18; Psalm 90:1–9; 2 Corinthians 5:10; John 5:25–29.

58. James A. Burrow, "That Methodist Creed," *MQR* 58 (July 1909) 532.

59. Nolan Harmon, *The Rites and Ritual of Episcopal Methodism, with Particular Reference to the Rituals of the Methodist Episcopal Church and the Methodist Episcopal Church, South, Respectively* (Nashville: Publishing House of the Methodist Episcopal Church, South 1926) 300.

60. John Alfred Faulkner, "Our Somber Burial Service," *MR* 93 (September 1911) 790.

61. JGC/MEC, 1916, 1335; cf. General Conference of the Methodist Episcopal Church, *Daily Christian Advocate* (10 May 1916) 150. In the proposed revision produced in 1908 (JGC/MEC, 1908, 978–82), the conflated sentence from 1 Timothy 6 and Job 1 was retained; the only text to be deleted was Job 19:25–27, which was replaced with the reading from 2 Corinthians 5:1—the revision taken in 1910 by the Methodist Episcopal Church, South. The revision suggested at the 1912 General Conference deleted both Job references

and the citation from 1 Timothy 6, and replaced them with 2 Corinthians 5:1 and John 14:1–3 (*Daily Christian Advocate* [24 May 1912] 605 and [30 May 1912] 795).

62. Thomas Benjamin Neely, *The Revised Ritual of 1916* (Philadelphia: E. A. Yeakel, Agent; Methodist Episcopal Book Store 1920) 55–59.

63. Questions may have been raised among some Methodists whether the prayer of thanksgiving constituted a prayer for the dead. An article that appeared in a Methodist Episcopal publication in 1927 defended prayers for the dead (and cited the prayer of thanksgiving from the burial rite as an example) on the basis of the biblical witness and apostolic tradition. Prayers *"for* the saints, but not *to* them" were deemed appropriate and spiritually edifying ("Prayer for the Dead," *MR* 110 [July 1927] 629–31).

64. Richard J. Cooke, *History of the Ritual of the Methodist Episcopal Church; With a Commentary on Its Offices*, 3d ed. (Cincinnati: Jennings and Pye 1900; New York: Eaton and Mains 1900) 277. Cooke commended the prayer for its ability to comfort, for "[e]ven at the mouth of the remorseless grave the Church of God proclaims the doctrine of immortality" (ibid.).

65. JGC/MEC, 1908, 983–84; and General Conference of the Methodist Episcopal Church, *Daily Christian Advocate* (24 May 1912) 605–607 and (30 May 1912) 796.

66. The readings included a conflation of Psalm 23 and John 10:7–11, 14–16, 27–30; Psalm 118:14–26, 28; Psalm 16:1–3, 5–11; and a conflation of Revelation 21:1–7 and Revelation 22:1–5, 12–14.

67. For example, among the prayers from the burial rite for a child, one prayer, "O Loving Father, comfortingly look upon us in our sorrow," has some affinity with a prayer provided in the Presbyterian *Book of Common Worship (Revised)* (Philadelphia: Presbyterian Board of Christian Education 1932) and may come from the committee that prepared this book, or from a common source. The 1928 Protestant Episcopal service "At the Burial of a Child" may have influenced the Methodist Episcopal revision of 1932: both rites contain an opening sentence from Isaiah 40:11, lessons from Psalm 23, Psalm 121, and Matthew 18, and an opening sentence at the grave from John 16:22.

68. According to Nolan Harmon's recollections, the revision committee was charged to submit for review prayers printed in other books; original compositions generally were not to be used (10 March 1990, tape-recorded interview by author, Atlanta, GA).

69. In 1923, James Beebe approved the church's burial of all persons, identifying it as the pastor's "spiritual service" (*The Pastoral Office*, 111).

70. "The Christian Funeral" in "Standards," Commission on Worship and the Fine Arts, New York Annual Conference, The Methodist Church, June 1965, Order of St. Luke Collection, Drew University Library, Madison, NJ.

71. "A Manual for the Funeral" (Nashville: Abingdon 1962) 1; and "An Approach to a Christian Funeral" (n.p.: Commission on Worship of the Northern New Jersey Conference of the Methodist Church 1967).

72. See, for example, William M. Wilder, "Resurrection or Immortality?" *The Pastor* 16 (May 1953) 13; and Howard L. Stimmel, "Communicating the Christian Hope," *The Pastor* 18 (March 1955) 7–8.

73. In the burial rite of the 1940 African Methodist Episcopal *Discipline*, a line was accidently dropped from *Media vita* at a page break, and the omission was perpetuated in the publication of the ritual text for the next twenty years; *Media vita* was returned to its original form in 1960.

74. *A Service of Death and Resurrection: The Ministry of the Church at Death*, Supplemental Worship Resources 7 (Nashville: Abingdon 1979) 73–91. Optional prayers and readings were provided for the general service, and for a child or youth, an untimely or tragic death, and for the non-Christian or unchurched.

75. Paul Waitman Hoon, "Theology, Death, and the Funeral Liturgy," *Union Seminary Quarterly Review* 31 (Spring 1976) 169; cf. [Paul Waitman Hoon], "The Ministry of the Church at Death," in *A Service of Death and Resurrection*, 12–13.

76. "The Ministry of the Church at Death," 12–16.

77. The task force was supplied with a series of papers by group member and pastoral counselor Edgar N. Jackson on bereavement and grief, and on children (youth) and death; L. L. Haynes, Jr., another member and pastor of an African-American congregation in Baton Rouge, contributed an essay on "The Black Funeral Service." These papers are now on file at the United Methodist Archives, Madison, NJ.

78. Hoon, "Theology, Death, and the Funeral Liturgy," 172.

9. Devotion and Discipleship

1. "The Character of a Methodist," §17, *Works*, 9:41.

2. "General Rules of the United Societies," §6, *Works*, 9:73; Sermon, "The Means of Grace," *Works*, 1:378–97; Sermon, "The Scripture Way of Salvation," 3.9, *Works*, 2:166; and Sermon, "On Working Out Our Own Salvation," 2.4, *Works*, 3:205–206. Also Question 48 in the so-called Large Minutes, transferred into Methodist Episcopal legislation as Question 66 in the first *Discipline*.

3. "General Rules of the United Societies," §5, *Works*, 9:72; "The Character of a Methodist," §16, *Works*, 9:41; and Sermon, "The Scripture Way of Salvation," 3.10, *Works*, 2:166.

4. Sermon, "Sermon on the Mount, 9," §6, *Works*, 1:635; Augustine, *De civitate Dei*, 8.17.

5. Journal, 16 November 1766, *Works*, 22:68.

6. *Autobiography of Peter Cartwright* (repr. Nashville: Abingdon 1984) 334–35.

7. Two especially helpful studies on the Christian (and Methodist) family in the nineteenth century are Colleen McDannell, *The Christian Home in Victorian America, 1840–1900* (Bloomington: Indiana University Press 1986); and A. Gregory Schneider, *The Way of the Cross Leads Home: The Domestication of American Methodism* (Bloomington: Indiana University Press 1993).

8. "Pastoral Address," *JGC/MEC, 1860,* 466.

9. Jacob Moore, "An Essay on the Obligation of Family Worship," MR 9 (July 1826) 257.

10. Joseph Travis, *Autobiography of the Rev. Joseph Travis, A.M.*, ed. Thomas O. Summers (Nashville: E. Stevenson and F. A. Owen, Agents, for the Methodist Episcopal Church, South 1856) 16.

11. Daniel Wise, *Bridal Greetings: A Marriage Gift, in Which the Mutual Duties of Husband and Wife Are Familiarly Illustrated and Enforced* (New York: Carlton and Phillips 1854) 151–54.

12. See, for example, the story of John Maris, benefactor of Arch Street Methodist Episcopal Church in Philadelphia, recounted in L. L. Nash, *Recollections and Observations during a Ministry in the North Carolina Conference, Methodist Episcopal Church, South, of Forty-Three Years* (Raleigh, NC: Mutual 1916) 57–59.

13. Ezekiel Cooper, 28 December 1790, Journal, Ms., Garrett-Evangelical Theological Seminary Library, Evanston, IL. Punctuation added. What Cooper described may represent an early manifestation of the episcopal suggestion eight years later that "every family in our connection had occasionally a prayer-meeting at stated times for the benefit of their neighbours" (Note on Section 10, question 2, answer 11, *Discipline with Notes*, 82); for later

evidence of this practice, see Robert Boyd, *Personal Memoirs: Together with a Discussion upon the Hardship and Sufferings of Itinerant Life* (Cincinnati: Methodist Book Concern 1868) 28.

14. Elizabeth A. Roe, *Recollections of Frontier Life* (Rockford, IL: Gazette Publishing House 1885) 106.

15. W. P. Strickland, *The Life of Jacob Gruber* (New York: Carlton and Porter 1860) 69–70.

16. Ibid., 70–71.

17. David Sullins, *Recollections of an Old Man: Seventy Years in Dixie, 1827–1897* (Bristol, TN: King 1910) 25–26. Sullins remembered from his student days (1847–1850) at Methodist-related Emory and Henry College that the college "family" held prayers morning and evening (p. 83).

18. Thomas A. Morris, *Miscellany: Consisting of Essays, Biographical Sketches, and Notes of Travel* (Cincinnati: L. Swormstedt and J. H. Power 1852) 37.

19. George T. Ashley, *Reminiscences of a Circuit Rider* (Hollywood, CA: Published by the Author 1941) 112.

20. "John Newton's Letter on Family Worship," *Methodist Protestant* 4 (28 April 1838) 348.

21. James B. Finley, *Autobiography of Rev. James B. Finley, or Pioneer Life in the West*, ed. W. P. Strickland (Cincinnati: Printed at the Methodist Book Concern for the Author 1856) 259.

22. Quarterly Meeting of the Madison Circuit, 15 August 1812, Minutes, Ms., Archives, Louisville Annual Conference, United Methodist Church, Kentucky Wesleyan College, Owensboro, KY.

23. L. P. Driskell, *Victory Out of Defeat* (Sanford, FL: n.p. 1950) 17–18.

24. Frank Hayes, "The Family Altar League: Its Purposes and Progress," WCA 76 (24 August 1910) 12–13.

25. Charles F. Deems, *The Home Altar: An Appeal in Behalf of Family Worship; with Prayers and Hymns, and Calendar of Lessons from Scripture for Family Use* (New York: M. W. Dodd 1850) vi–vii. Deems provided two courses of prayers for morning and evening of every day of the week (one course borrowed or adapted from the 1662 *Book of Common Prayer*), a two-year daily lectionary, extra Scripture readings for Sunday mornings throughout the month, and selected hymns and doxologies. He also suggested orders of worship to be used Sunday mornings and evenings. For Sunday morning: selected readings from the Old and New Testaments; the Decalogue; a hymn; the prayer for the day; the Lord's Prayer; and the apostolic benediction. Sunday evening was structurally similar, though a psalm could be added to the Sunday evening lesson stipulated in the lectionary. Although not as extensive a *worship* resource as Deems's book, Ohio minister C. R. Lovell nonetheless provided in his *Methodist Family Manual* (Cincinnati: H. S. and J. Applegate 1852) a system for Bible study and Scripture readings assigned by topic.

26. *"Keep the Home Fires Burning": Readings, Explanations, and Prayers for the Use of Daily Bible Reading and Prayer League and Family Worship League* (Nashville: Publishing House of the Methodist Episcopal Church, South [1921]) 7. Resources for family worship were designated within two larger collections of services and prayers by Methodist Episcopal editors: Wilbur P. Thirkield, ed., *Service and Prayers for Church and Home* (New York: Methodist Book Concern 1918) 117–69; and Wilbur P. Thirkield and Oliver Huckel, eds., *Book of Common Worship* (New York: E. P. Dutton 1932, 1936) 289–323.

27. O. E. Goddard, *The Methodist Evangel* (Nashville: Board of Missions of the Methodist Episcopal Church, South 1928) 160.

28. 15 August 1789, "A Journal and Travel of James Meacham; Part 1. May 19 to Aug.

31, 1789," *Historical Papers*, ed. William K. Boyd, Trinity College Historical Society and the North Carolina Conference Historical Society, series 9, no. 5 (1912) 88.

29. Leonard Smith, 13 September 1867, Journal, Ts., Archives, Illinois Great Rivers Annual Conference, United Methodist Church, Bloomington, IL.

30. See, for example, William Keith, *The Experience of William Keith. Together with Some Observations Conclusive of Divine Influence on the Mind of Man* (Utica: Printed by Asahel Seward 1806) 15.

31. Finley, *Autobiography*, 286.

32. *The Journals of the Rev. Thomas Morrell*, ed. Michael J. McKay (Rutland, VT: Academy Books, for the Historical Society, Northern New Jersey Conference, United Methodist Church 1984) 22; and Journal, 10 January 1810, *JLFA*, 2:628; cf. *Minutes MC* (1782), 37; (1783), 42; and (1795), 162–63.

33. Taylor Kinsfolk Association at Tabernacle Church, *The Taylors of Tabernacle: The History of a Family* (Brownsville, TN: Tabernacle Historical Committee 1957) 177.

34. JGC/MEC, 1864, 22–23.

35. Cited as #1019 in *Hymns for the Use of the Methodist Episcopal Church* (1849). Six hymns are included under the subheading "Public Fasts" within the general heading "Miscellaneous."

36. "Welfare of Ohio Conference Methodism," in *Ohio Annual Conference of the Methodist Episcopal Church, Held at Portsmouth, Ohio, September 29, 1875* (Cincinnati: Western Methodist Book Concern 1875) 221.

37. See, for example, J. S. Gilbert, "The Prayer Meeting," *The Methodist* 16 (18 September 1875) 594; J. H. Potts, *Pastor and People; Or, Methodism in the Field* (New York: Phillips and Hunt 1879; Cincinnati: Hitchcock and Walden 1879) 167–72; and G. O. King, "Hints on the Conduct of a Prayer-Meeting," *EH* 2 (29 August 1891) 202.

38. *Prayer-Meeting Annual for the Year 1892, Arranged for the Wednesday-Evening Service of Grace Methodist Episcopal Church, by the Pastor, Rev. Richard Harcourt, D. D., and Mr. Joseph Hindes* (Baltimore: Methodist Episcopal Book Depository 1892).

39. See, for example, Wilbur Fletcher Sheridan, *The Sunday-Night Service: A Study in Continuous Evangelism* (Cincinnati: Jennings and Pye 1903; New York: Eaton and Mains 1903); Norman E. Richardson, ed., *Present-Day Prayer-Meeting Helps: For Laymen and Minister* (New York: Eaton and Mains 1910; Cincinnati: Jennings and Graham 1910); J. George Haller, *The Redemption of the Prayer-Meeting* (Cincinnati: Jennings and Graham 1911; New York: Eaton and Mains 1911; and Nashville: Smith and Lamar 1911); Halford E. Luccock and Warren F. Cook, *The Mid-Week Service* (New York: Methodist Book Concern 1916); Robert Elmer Smith, *Midweek Messages* (New York: Abingdon 1925); and Robert Seneca Smith, *The Art of Group Worship* (New York: Abingdon 1938).

40. William T. Ward, *Variety in the Prayer Meeting: A Manual for Leaders* (New York: Methodist Book Concern 1915) 7.

41. Henry Reed Van Deusen, *Elm Park Historical Sketches* (Scranton, PA: Board of Elm Park Methodist Church 1955) 42.

42. Wyatt Brown, *Early Methodism in Greenville, North Carolina, and a History of the Jarvis Memorial United Methodist Church*, ed. John D. Ebbs (Greenville, NC: Jarvis Memorial United Methodist Church 1978) 118–19.

43. William W. King, "The Redemption of the Prayer Meeting," MR 92 (November 1910) 964–65.

44. Edmund E. Prescott, *The New Midweek Service* (Nashville: Cokesbury 1929) 14–16.

45. Wilson O. Weldon, "Broadcasting the Midweek Service," *The Pastor* 12 (October 1948) 27.

46. Michael Shaw, "Whatever Happened to Sunday Night Services and Wednesday Prayer Meetings?" *North Carolina Christian Advocate* 144 (12 January 1999) 3.

47. Morris, *Miscellany*, 109.

48. See, for example, John Wesley's Sermon "On the Visitation of the Sick"; and Morris, *Miscellany*, 110.

49. "On Pastoral Visiting," MR 20 (October 1838) 378–79.

50. Daniel P. Kidder, ed., *The Minister's Study, and Scenes Connected with It* (New York: Lane and Scott 1849) 35–38.

51. No rationale has been found for this explicit borrowing from the Presbyterians. One Methodist Protestant historian generally noted the courtesies that had been extended by the Presbyterians to emerging Methodist Protestantism, and the respect the new denomination accorded the older body (John Paris, *History of the Methodist Protestant Church* [Baltimore: Printed by Sherwood 1849] 313–14).

52. Abraham Grant, *Deaconess Manual of the African Methodist Episcopal Church* (n.p.: African Methodist Episcopal Church 1902) 28.

53. "The Ministry of Public Prayer," MR 79 (September 1897) 805.

54. C. E. Mandeville, *Minister's Manual and Pocket Ritual: A Ready Help in Time of Need for the Sick-Room, Funerals, etc., Together with Full Ritual for Marriage, Baptism, the Lord's Supper, etc.*, rev. ed. (Cincinnati: Jennings and Graham 1902; New York: Eaton and Mains 1902) 9–24.

55. James Albert Beebe, *The Pastoral Office: An Introduction to the Work of a Pastor* (New York: Methodist Book Concern 1923) 284.

56. "Ten Commandments for Pastors Visiting the Sick," *The Pastor* 13 (October 1949) 16; and "Questions of the Month," *The Pastor* 15 (January 1952) 15; cf. Richard C. Cabot, "Spiritual Ministrations to the Sick," *Religion in Life* 4 (Winter 1935) 32–44; Russell L. Dicks, "The Clergyman in the Sickroom," *Religion in Life* 8 (Spring 1939) 244–47; and Edmond H. Babbitt, *The Pastor's Pocket Manual for Hospital and Sickroom* (New York: Abingdon-Cokesbury 1949).

57. M. Lawrence Snow, "Uses of 'The Book of Worship' in the Home and with Small Groups," in *Companion to the Book of Worship*, ed. William F. Dunkle, Jr. and Joseph D. Quillian, Jr. (Nashville: Abingdon 1970) 189.

58. John R. K. Fenwick and Bryan D. Spinks, *Worship in Transition: The Liturgical Movement in the Twentieth Century* (New York: Continuum 1995) 5–7. For American Methodist writers, see, for example, Paul Waitman Hoon, *The Integrity of Worship: Ecumenical and Pastoral Studies in Liturgical Theology* (Nashville: Abingdon 1971), esp. 102–14; and Don E. Saliers, *Worship as Theology: Foretaste of Glory Divine* (Nashville: Abingdon 1994), esp. 25–31.

10. A House for Worship

1. Charles Giles, *Pioneer: A Narrative of the Nativity, Experience, Travels, and Ministerial Labours of Rev. Charles Giles* (New York: G. Lane and P. P. Sandford 1844) 138.

2. James B. Finley, *Autobiography of James B. Finley; Or, Pioneer Life in the West*, ed. W. P. Strickland (Cincinnati: Printed at the Methodist Book Concern for the Author 1856) 229.

3. Between 1761 and 1776, fourteen octagons for Methodist worship were built in England and Scotland. Records show no such octagonal buildings in eighteenth-century North America. See Karen B. Westerfield Tucker, " 'Plain and Decent': Octagonal Space and Methodist Worship," *Studia Liturgica* 24 (1994) 129–42.

4. Journal, 16 November 1806, *JLFA*, 2:521.

5. Notes on Chapter 3, section 1, *Discipline with Notes*, 177.

6. *Minutes; Taken at a Council of the Bishop and Delegated Elders of the Methodist Episcopal Church: Held at Baltimore, in the State of Maryland, December 1, 1790* (Baltimore: Printed by W. Goddard and J. Angell 1790) 7.

7. In 1846, the General Conference of the Methodist Episcopal Church, South approved the recommendation of the Committee on Missions (not printed in the *Discipline*) that preachers should "induce our coloured friends to attend public worship at the churches with the whites" and that separate sittings be provided "as our practice usually has been" (*JGC/MECS* [*1846*], 66).

8. See the entry for 22 January 1785 in the journal of Thomas Coke, cited in the *Arminian Magazine* 1 (June 1789) 293.

9. John F. Watson, *Annals of Philadelphia, Being a Collection of Memoirs, Anecdotes, & Incidents of the City and Its Inhabitants* (Philadelphia: E. L. Carey and A. Hart 1830; New York: G. and C. Carvill 1830) 397.

10. Andrew Reed and James Matheson, *Narrative of the Visit to the American Churches, by the Deputation from the Congregational Union of England and Wales*, vol. 1 (New York: Harper and Brothers 1835) 48.

11. Floyd S. Bennett, *Methodist Church on Shockoe Hill: A History of Centenary Methodist Church, Richmond, Virginia* (Richmond, VA: n.p. 1962) 36; and Hersey Everett Spence, *McBride: A Mother in Methodism* (Durham, NC: Seeman 1957) 7.

12. "Plan of a Comfortable Church" in *Annals of Southern Methodism for 1855*, ed. Charles F. Deems (New York: J. A. Gray 1856) 374.

13. *Bishop Payne's First Annual Address to the Philadelphia Annual Conference of the A. M. E. Church. May 16, 1853.* (Philadelphia: C. Sherman 1853) 5.

14. *Annals of Southern Methodism for 1857*, ed. Charles F. Deems (Nashville: J. B. M'Ferrin 1858) 108, 110, 133.

15. Thomas A. Morris, *Miscellany: Consisting of Essays, Biographical Sketches, and Notes of Travel* (Cincinnati: L. Swormstedt and J. H. Power 1852) 19.

16. Leroy M. Lee, *The Life and Times of the Rev. Jesse Lee* (Charleston, SC: John Early 1848) 451–52 (on the last episode, cf. James 2:1–7).

17. *JGC/MEC* (*1816*), 155–58; and *JGC/MEC* (*1820*), 199–200, 208–11.

18. In a sustained argument, J. S. Inskip (*Methodism Explained and Defended* [Cincinnati: Applegate 1856] 63–110) set forth the view that the provision delineating free seats, as well as the disciplinary directions and services for the administration of the sacraments and the burial of the dead, were advisory and not mandatory.

19. *Autobiography of Peter Cartwright* (repr. Nashville: Abingdon 1984) 312–13.

20. B. T. Roberts, "Free Churches," *The Earnest Christian and Golden Rule* 3 (May 1862) 133–36.

21. For example, W. P. Strickland, *The Genius and Mission of Methodism; Embracing What Is Peculiar in Doctrine, Government, Modes of Worship, etc.* (Boston: Charles H. Peirce 1851) 110–21.

22. Virginia Gust Byers, *Elizabeth Chapel . . . A Place to Worship* (1986) unpaginated.

23. Michael G. Cartwright, ed., *History of Tabernacle United Methodist Church* (1984) 129.

24. For a survey of church extension programs in the Methodist Episcopal Church and Methodist Episcopal Church, South, see Paul Neff Garber, *The Methodist Meeting House* (New York: Board of Missions and Church Extension, Methodist Church 1941) 44–121.

25. Fernandez C. Holliday, *Indiana Methodism: Being an Account of the Introduction, Progress, and Present Position of Methodism in the State* (Cincinnati: Hitchcock and Walden 1873) 157.

26. Abel Stevens, *The Centenary of American Methodism: A Sketch of Its History, Theology, Practical System, and Success* (New York: Carlton and Porter 1865) 233–36; and "Methodist Church-Building," *The Methodist* 12 (4 February 1871) 36.

27. James D. Bratt and Christopher H. Meehan, *Gathered at the River: Grand Rapids, Michigan, and Its People of Faith* (Grand Rapids: Grand Rapids Area Council for the Humanities 1993) 29.

28. JGC/MECS, 1874, 515–16.

29. The paper imitations of stained glass were advertised in the section for the Board of Church Extension within successive volumes of the *Manual of the Methodist Episcopal Church: A Quarterly Magazine of Information Concerning the Benevolent and Publishing Interests of the Church*, published from 1880 to 1888. Sample patterns were sometimes included as part of the notice, which indicated that samples and price lists were available from the Methodist Episcopal Church's chief architect, Benjamin Price, through the denomination's Board of Church Extension office in Philadelphia.

30. Kenneth E. Rowe, "Redesigning Methodist Churches: Auditorium-Style Sanctuaries and Akron-Plan Sunday Schools in Romanesque Costume, 1875–1925," in *Connectionalism: Ecclesiology, Mission, and Identity*, United Methodism and American Culture, vol. 1, ed. Russell E. Richey, Dennis M. Campbell, and William B. Lawrence (Nashville: Abingdon 1997) 117–34.

31. For example, see the plans included in the section for the Board of Church Extension in the *Manual of the Methodist Episcopal Church*; also *Catalogue of Architectural Plans for Churches and Parsonages* (Philadelphia: Board of Church Extension, Methodist Episcopal Church 1885, 1889).

32. Wyatt Brown, *Early Methodism in Greenville, North Carolina, and a History of the Jarvis Memorial United Methodist Church*, ed. John D. Ebbs (Greenville, NC: Jarvis Memorial United Methodist Church 1978) 18–19, 51–53.

33. See Journal, 20 August 1764, *Works*, 21:486; and "Thoughts on the Consecration of Churches and Burial-Grounds" (1788), *Works*, 9:531–33.

34. Journal, 9 August 1796, JLFA, 2:93.

35. *Annals of Southern Methodism for 1856*, ed. Charles F. Deems (Nashville: Stevenson and Owen 1857) 84–85.

36. Daniel Alexander Payne, *History of the African Methodist Episcopal Church*, ed. C. S. Smith (Nashville: Publishing House of the A. M. E. Sunday-School Union 1891; repr. New York: Johnson Reprint Corporation 1968) 222–23.

37. "Programme for the Dedication of the First Methodist Episcopal Church, Holyoke, Massachusetts," United Methodist Archives, Madison, NJ.

38. Lucius C. Clark, *The Worshiping Congregation* (Cincinnati: Jennings and Graham 1912; New York: Eaton and Mains 1912) 118–19. Clark also contended that Sunday school ought not be held in the worship space lest "reverence for both place and service of worship" be lessened (p. 120).

39. Halford E. Luccock, "The Seven Deadly Sins of Church Architects," *CAJ (NY)* 99 (3 April 1924) 417–18.

40. Von Ogden Vogt, *Art & Religion* (New Haven: Yale University Press 1921) 187–89; and *Modern Worship* (New Haven: Yale University Press 1927) 3–28. For the contributions of Vogt and Cram to the second Gothic revival, see James F. White, "Theology and Architecture in America: A Study of Three Leaders," in *A Miscellany of American Christianity:*

Essays in Honor of H. Shelton Smith, ed. Stuart C. Henry (Durham: Duke University Press 1963) 371–90.

41. Elbert M. Conover, *Building the House of God* (New York: Methodist Book Concern 1928) 33–36, 100–116; also *The Church Building Guide* (New York: Interdenominational Bureau of Architecture 1946); and *The Church Builder* (New York: Interdenominational Bureau of Architecture 1948).

42. See, for example, William S. Mitchell, "Glorifying God in Architecture," *MR* 110 (March 1927) 263–67; J. Hastie Odgers and Edward G. Schutz, *The Technique of Public Worship* (New York: Methodist Book Concern 1928) 43–72; Henry Nelson Wieman, "Beauty and God in Public Worship," *MQR* 77 (April 1928) 179–92; Burnell L. Schubel, "The Nature of Worship," *MQR* 78 (January 1929) 76–86; Ralph D. Harper, "Worship as an Aesthetic Experience," *MR* 113 (November 1930) 896–901; Thomas Albert Stafford, *Christian Symbolism in the Evangelical Churches* (New York: Abingdon-Cokesbury 1942); and William H. Leach, *Protestant Church Building* (New York: Abingdon-Cokesbury 1948).

43. Fred Winslow Adams and R. N. Merrill, "Is the Present Trend Toward Gothic Architecture and a More Elaborate Ritual a Real Advance?" *MR* 114 (March 1931) 205.

44. Leslie R. Marston, *From Age to Age a Living Witness: A Historical Interpretation of Free Methodism's First Century* (Winona Lake, IN: Light and Life 1960) 350.

45. Clarence Seidenspinner, "It Is Time We Considered a Sound Church Architecture," *The Pastor* 18 (April 1955) 28–29; see also Romey P. Marshall, "Gothic Architecture or Gothic Thinking?" *The Pastor* 13 (January 1950) 21–22; and John Robert Van Pelt, "Pulpit or Altar?" *The Pastor* 14 (June 1951) 4–5.

46. J. J. Stowe, Jr., "A Building for the Future," *The Pastor* 19 (December 1955) 28–29.

47. Methodist Church, *Sanctuary Planning* (Philadelphia: Department of Architecture, Methodist Church 1962) 40–42.

48. See, for example, James F. White and Susan J. White, *Church Architecture: Building and Renovating for Christian Worship* (Nashville: Abingdon 1988).

11. *Roles in Public Worship*

1. See Paul W. Chilcote, *She Offered Them Christ: The Legacy of Women Preachers in Early Methodism* (Nashville: Abingdon 1993).

2. Letter to Nicholas Norton, 3 September 1756, *LJW*, 3:186–87; and Letter to William Thompson, 21 February 1787, *LJW*, 7:372. See also A. B. Lawson, *John Wesley and the Christian Ministry: The Sources and Development of His Opinions and Practice* (London: SPCK 1963).

3. For a study of the development of the 1980 *Ordinal*, including a history of the revisions in the ordination rites of the United Methodist Church's Methodist ancestors, see John D. Grabner, "A Commentary on the Rites of *An Ordinal, The United Methodist Church*" (Ph.D. diss., University of Notre Dame 1983).

4. *Journal of the Eleventh General Conference of the Methodist Protestant Church Held in Lynchburg, Va., May, 1874* (Baltimore: William J. C. Dulany 1874) 17. However, by 1925, one explanation given for the absence of deacons in the denomination was that "the New Testament recognizes but one order in the ministry, that of elder, deacons not being ministers of the Word" (Thomas Hamilton Lewis, *Handbook of the Methodist Protestant Church* [n.p.: Thomas H. Lewis 1925] 39).

5. For the debates on the change, see General Conference of the United Methodist Church, *Daily Christian Advocate* 3 (26 April 1996) 693–710.

6. See the explanation given in notes on Section 7, *Discipline with Notes*, 57.

7. See, for example, JGC/MEC, 1872, 204.

8. The issues of conference membership and of itinerancy added complications to the matter of roles that will not be addressed here.

9. The designations "licensed preacher" and "lay preacher" found in early Methodism are used throughout this section even though variant terms and new descriptors were used in the denominations at different periods.

10. Charles Giles, Pioneer: A Narrative of the Nativity, Experience, Travels, and Ministerial Labours of Rev. Charles Giles (New York: G. Lane and P. P. Sandford 1844) 155–57; cf. Nathan Bangs, An Original Church of Christ: Or, A Scriptural Vindication of the Orders and Powers of the Ministry of the Methodist Episcopal Church, 2d ed., rev. (New York: T. Mason and G. Lane 1837) 245–49.

11. "Eighteenth Century Slave Advertisements," Journal of Negro History 1 (April 1916) 205.

12. JGC/MEC, 1884, 94.

13. George T. Ashley, Reminiscences of a Circuit Rider (Hollywood, CA: Published by the Author 1941) 59–60.

14. Bishops' Address, JGC/MECS, 1914, 58.

15. JGC/MC, 1948, 174; cf. pp. 670–71.

16. JGC/MC, 1952, 1655–59. The commission recognized that one facet of this complicated issue was the unwillingness of some unordained pastors to pursue the educational requirements for ordination when they could already be accorded the privileges of sacramental administration.

17. For the reports and debates, see JGC/MC, 1952, 537–45, 550–55, 1268–73. That the decision in 1952 had to do both with sacramental theology and with ecclesiology may be signaled by the two individuals who brought the Standing Committee's reports: Robert W. Goodloe for the majority and Oscar Thomas Olson for the minority.

18. Wesley's "appointing Deaconesses" while in Georgia was used as evidence to support the charge that he was a Roman Catholic. See Patrick Tailfer, Hugh Anderson, David Douglas, et al., True and Historical Narrative of the Colony of Georgia (Charles-Town, SC: Printed by P. Timothy, for the Authors 1741) 42.

19. For accounts of pioneering preaching women, see Hilah F. Thomas and Rosemary Skinner Keller, eds., Women in New Worlds: Historical Perspectives on the Wesleyan Tradition, vol. 1 (Nashville: Abingdon 1981); and Rosemary Skinner Keller, Louise L. Queen, and Hilah F. Thomas, eds., Women in New Worlds, vol. 2 (Nashville: Abingdon 1982).

20. Jarena Lee, Religious Experiences and Journal of Mrs. Jarena Lee: Giving an Account of Her Call to Preach the Gospel (Philadelphia: 1836; repr. Nashville: A. M. E. C. Sunday School Union 1991) 12–22.

21. In its final Discipline (1938, ¶722), the Methodist Episcopal Church, South carried the legislation that "Our Church does not recognize women as preachers, with authority to occupy the pulpit, to read the Holy Scriptures, and to preach, as ministers of the Lord Jesus Christ."

22. So noted Lucy Rider Meyer in Deaconesses: Biblical, Early Church, European, American, 2d ed. (Chicago: Message 1889) 63. Neither the Journal of the 1888 General Conference nor the Daily Christian Advocate for that gathering gives the detailed information on the petition provided by Meyer.

23. Meyer, Deaconesses, 24–25.

24. J. M. Thoburn, The Deaconess and Her Vocation (New York: Hunt and Eaton 1893; Cincinnati: Cranston and Curts 1893) 23, 82, 112–17; and Stella Wyatt Brummitt, Looking Backward, Thinking Forward: The Jubilee History of the Woman's Home Missionary Society of

the Methodist Episcopal Church (Cincinnati: The Woman's Home Missionary Society 1930) 45. See Laceye Cammarano Warner, "Methodist Episcopal and Wesleyan Deaconess Work in the Late Nineteenth and Early Twentieth Centuries: A Paradigm for Evangelism" (Ph.D. diss., University of Bristol 2000).

25. Hymn #558 in *The Methodist Hymnal* (1905), the joint hymnal of the Methodist Episcopal Church and the Methodist Episcopal Church, South.

12. American Methodist Worship

1. John L. Reeder, "Liturgical Developments of New Testament Times," MR 78 (November 1896) 927.

2. Matthew Simpson Hughes, *The Higher Ritualism* (Cincinnati: Jennings and Graham 1904; New York: Eaton and Mains 1904) 48.

3. Bishops' Address, *JGC/MECS, 1886,* 16–17.

4. Anton Baumstark, *Comparative Liturgy*, rev. Bernard Botte, trans. F. L. Cross (Westminster, MD: Newman Press 1958) 19–23.

5. See Geoffrey Wainwright, "Tradition as a Liturgical Act," in his *Worship with One Accord: Where Liturgy and Ecumenism Embrace* (New York: Oxford University Press 1997) 45–64.

6. Charles Edwin Schofield, *We Methodists* (New York: Methodist Publishing House 1939) 20.

7. Episcopal Address, *JGC/MECS, 1930,* 360.

8. Philip Schaff, *America: A Sketch of the Political, Social, and Religious Character of the United States in North America* (New York: Scribner 1855) 167–68.

9. Sermon by Bishop Morris, *JGC/MEC, 1864,* 281–91.

10. F. A. Cone, "About Ourselves and Our Times," NCA 60 (24 January 1912) 98.

11. Episcopal Address, *JGC/MEC, 1900,* 59–60.

12. See, for example, James F. White, "Worship and Culture: Mirror or Beacon?" *Theological Studies* 35 (1974) 288–301, revised in *Christian Worship in North America* (Collegeville, MN: Liturgical Press 1997) 59–74; Thomas C. Oden, *Pastoral Theology* (San Francisco: Harper and Row 1983); William H. Willimon, *The Service of God* (Nashville: Abingdon 1983); Stanley Hauerwas and William H. Willimon, *Resident Aliens* (Nashville: Abingdon 1989); and Don E. Saliers, *Worship as Theology* (Nashville: Abingdon 1994). For a slightly different approach on the same issue, see James H. Cone, "Sanctification, Liberation, and Black Worship," *Theology Today* 35 (1978–1979) 139–52.

13. H. Richard Niebuhr, "Toward the Independence of the Church," in *The Church against the World*, ed. H. Richard Niebuhr, Wilhelm Pauck, and Francis P. Miller (Chicago: Willett, Clark, and Co. 1935) 123–24.

14. For studies at the end of the twentieth century on "United Methodism and American Culture," see the multivolume series edited by Russell E. Richey, William B. Lawrence, and Dennis M. Campbell.

15. Robert Taft, "The Structural Analysis of Liturgical Units: An Essay in Methodology," in his *Beyond East & West: Problems in Liturgical Understanding* (Washington, D.C.: Pastoral Press 1984) 153–54.

Index